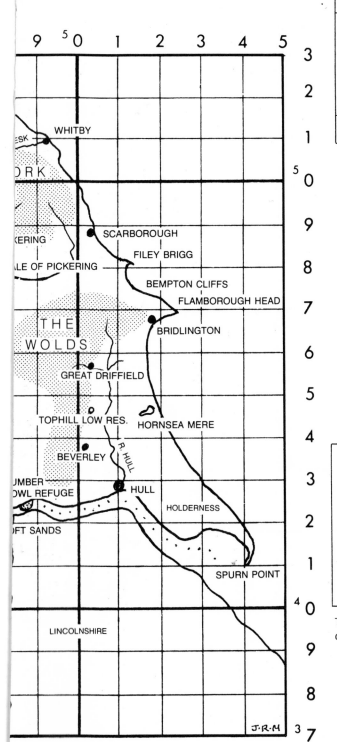

9 ⁵0 1 2 3 4 5

3
2
1
5 0
9
8
7
6
5
4
3
2
1
⁴0
9
8
3 7

WHITBY

ESK

ORK

KERING

SCARBOROUGH

FILEY BRIGG

ALE OF PICKERING

BEMPTON CLIFFS

FLAMBOROUGH HEAD

THE
WOLDS

BRIDLINGTON

GREAT DRIFFIELD

TOPHILL LOW RES.

HORNSEA MERE

BEVERLEY

R. HULL

UMBER
OWL REFUGE

HULL

HOLDERNESS

OFT SANDS

SPURN POINT

LINCOLNSHIRE

J·R·M

NY
35

NZ
45

SD
34

SE
44

TA
54

SK
43

The six 100-km square Ordnance
Survey map numbers covering
Yorkshire

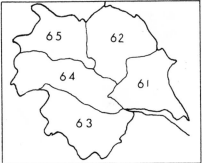

65

62

64

61

63

The five Watsonian vice-county
divisions of Yorkshire

The Bird

YORKSF

The Birds of YORKSHIRE

John R. Mather

An account of their historical and
present status and distribution

CROOM HELM
London · Sydney · Dover, New Hampshire

© 1986 John R. Mather
Croom Helm Ltd, Provident House, Burrell Row,
Beckenham, Kent BR3 1AT, England
Croom Helm Australia Pty Ltd, Suite 4, Sixth Floor,
64-76 Kippax Street,
Surry Hills, NSW 2010, Australia

British Library Cataloguing in Publication Data

Mather, John R.
  The birds of Yorkshire
    1. Birds—England—Yorkshire
  I. Title
  598.29428′1   QL690.G7

  ISBN 0-7099-3510-2

Croom Helm, 51 Washington Street, Dover,
New Hampshire, 03820, USA

Library of Congress Cataloging-in-Publication Data

Mather, John R.
  The birds of Yorkshire.

  Bibliography: p.
  Includes indexes.
    1. Birds—England—Yorkshire—History.   I. Title.
  QL690.G7M23 1985   598.29428′1   85-17065
  ISBN 0-7099-3510-2

Typeset in 'October' by Leaper & Gard Ltd, Bristol, England
Printed in Great Britain by
Butler & Tanner Ltd, Frome and London

Contents

List of Black and White Plates

1. Thomas Hudson Nelson, author of *The Birds of Yorkshire* which was published in 1907
2. Ralph Chislett, one of Yorkshire's most celebrated ornithologists
3. The plateau of the lofty Ingleborough
4. Pen-y-ghent
5. Stocks Reservoir
6. Great Wegber Scar
7. Upper Ryedale
8. Summer Lodge Tarn
9. Semerwater
10. Dallowgill Moor
11. The River Wharfe
12. Langstrothdale Chase
13. Kilnsey Crag
14. Kilnsey Crag
15. Upper Wharfedale
16. Dallowgill Moor
17. Gouthwaite Reservoir
18. Gouthwaite Reservoir
19. The River Strid
20. Cropton Forest
21. A view looking northeast towards Bransdale
22. A view near the head of Bransdale
23. A view looking south along the Hambleton Hills near Sutton Bank
24. The old bridge over the River Derwent near the Ferry Boat Inn
25. The floods in full spate on the Lower Derwent
26. D. Waudby and the author at Wheldrake Ings
27. The Plain of York
28. Skipwith Common
29. Typical scrubland on Thorne Moors
30. A drain on Thorne Moors
31. A view looking southwest over Kilnsea Clays to the Spurn lighthouse
32. A view looking east over Whitby, down the River Esk
33. A view looking north over Scarborough
34. The famous Castle Hill Cliff at Scarborough
35. A view looking east along the eroded boulder-clay cliff of the Carr Naze to Filey Brigg
36. Looking north from Filey Brigg during a 'northeaster'
37. The Dotterel Inn at Reighton
38. The impressive chalk cliffs at Bempton

80. Herring Gulls nesting on the roof of the Rowntree building in the centre of Scarborough
81. First-winter Iceland Gull (upper) and an adult Glaucous Gull in Scarborough Harbour, January 1983
82. Immature Great Black-backed Gull with aberrant head markings which frequented Lingerfield Tip, near Knaresborough, from 31st March until at least 14th April 1967
83. A group of gulls at Scalby Mills, Scarborough, in March 1976
84. Ross's Gull which frequented Scalby Mills, near Scarborough, from 22nd to 28th April 1976
85. Ross's Gull which occurred at Filey Brigg from 17th to 20th February 1983
86. Adult White-winged Black Tern at Broomhill Flash on 19th June 1975
87. Yellow-billed Cuckoo caught at Spurn Bird Observatory on 27th October 1978
88. Yellow-billed Cuckoo found at Armthorpe, near Doncaster, on 14th November 1981
89. Barn Owl
90. Long-eared Owl incubating on the old nest of a Carrion Crow in a hawthorn thicket
91. Short-eared Owl brooding its young
92. Tengmalm's Owl which stayed at Spurn Point from at least 6th March 1983 until being last seen on 27th
93. The 1983 Spurn Tengmalm's Owl having been caught and ringed on 7th March
94. Nightjar on its nest in Cropton Forest on the North York Moors
95. Swift with abnormal plumage caught at Knaresborough Ringing Station on 22nd June 1975
96. The first Yorkshire record of Olive-backed Pipit, at Spurn Bird Observatory in 1981
97. Olive-backed Pipit caught and ringed at Flamborough Head on 27th September 1984
98. Grey Wagtail, a bird of the fast-flowing streams and rivers of the Pennines and North York Moors
99. Dipper, one of the characteristic birds of the upland streams in the west and north of the county
100. Thrush Nightingale seen alive in Locke Park , Redcar, on 16th May 1967 and found dead there next day
101. First-year male Red-spotted Bluethroat, caught at Knaresborough Ringing Station on 18th September 1971
102. Siberian Stonechat at Flamborough Head in October 1981
103. Wheatear, a common breeding bird over much of the high ground in the west and north of the county
104. A cock Ring Ouzel at its nest on a Yorkshire heather moor
105. Blyth's Reed Warbler caught at Spurn Point on 28th May 1984
106. Booted Warbler, caught and ringed at Spurn Bird Observatory, where it remained from 5th to 7th September 1981
107. Icterine Warbler caught at Flamborough Head in August 1982
108. Desert Warbler, the first record for Yorkshire and only the second for the British Isles, at Spurn Bird Observatory from 20th to 24th October 1975
109. The Spurn Desert Warbler, having been caught and ringed on 20th October 1975
110. Pallas's Warbler caught at Flamborough Head in October 1982
111. Radde's Warbler which stayed at Spurn Bird Observatory from 14th to 16th October 1978

112. B.R. Spence holding the 1978 Radde's Warbler for a party of birdwatchers who were fortunate enough to be visiting the observatory
113. A male Red-backed Shrike caught at Spurn on 25th May 1984 showing a white wing patch, found only in the eastern populations
114. Serin caught at Spurn Bird Observatory on 7th November 1982
115. Parrot Crossbill trapped at Spurn Bird Observatory on 11th October 1982
116. Two Parrot Crossbill skins
117. Song Sparrow caught and ringed at Spurn Bird Observatory on 18th May 1964
118. White-throated Sparrow, caught and ringed at Spurn Bird Observatory on 12th May 1983
119. Rustic Bunting which stayed at Flamborough Head from 21st to 23rd May 1978 and was caught and ringed

To Bunty . . .
without whose infinite patience and understanding my
ornithological lifestyle during the past 35 years would
have been much the poorer.

Acknowledgements

This undertaking was made easier by the help given in various ways by several people. I am particularly grateful to A.J. Wallis of Scalby, who prepared a card index of all the species contained in the Yorkshire Naturalists' Union Annual Ornithological Reports from 1940 to 1982 by cutting out and pasting each species comment onto cards, thus facilitating much easier reference then would otherwise have been possible. He also read the complete manuscript and made many useful suggestions based on his vast knowledge of the county.

Miss A. Mettam of Harrogate extracted all the references to Yorkshire birds contained in *The Naturalist*, and shared the task with A.J. Wallis of extracting the more important ringing recoveries from *British Birds* and the *Ringing and Migration* reports of the British Trust for Ornithology. I must also thank her for the loan of the machine on which I typed the complete manuscript of this book. Martin Hodgson of Harrogate drew the breeding distribution maps.

I must give very special thanks to R.G. Hawley, M.Whorley and D.I.M. Wallace for their line drawings, which greatly enhance the character of the work, and to the latter for the delightful dust-jacket design. The work of D.I.M. Wallace is well known to many people but that of Ray Hawley and Mark Whorley less so, and I am therefore pleased that theirs will now be seen by a wider audience. I am also most grateful to the following, who very kindly agreed to contribute special chapters: R.H. Appleby, J.S. Armitage, J. Cudworth, J.E. Dale, A. Gilpin, B.S. Pashby, R.J. Rhodes, C.G. Varty, A.F.G. Walker, A.J. Wallis and D.R.J. Watkins.

I must also thank the following people who have very kindly sent photographs of birds and habitats which form a necessary part of the book: G.V. Adkin, G.E. Alderson, J. Armitage, J.S. Armitage, K. Atkin, D.Brown, H.O. Bunce, N. Carling, T.M. Clegg, D.M. Cottridge, J. Cudworth, P.A. Doherty, Doncaster Museum and Arts Service, P.J. Dunn, A. Gilpin, I. Glaves, P. Harrison, J.W. Hartley, N.W. Harwood, P.A. Lassey, R. Leslie, C. Massingham, G. Neal, B.S. Pashby, A.G. Phillips, J.A. Pollentine, J. Seeviour, B. Shorrock, E.S. Skinner, A.J. Wallis, D.R.J. Watkins, S.J. Weston and G.K. Yeates. Thanks must also go to M. Densley for the loan of the photograph of the Temminck's Stint by G.A. Newby; to Mrs S. Garland for permission to use the photographs by her father W.E. Higham; and to M.F. Brown, a professional photographer and friend who accompanied me on several field trips to take habitat photographs under my direction and who also photographed the specimens in my laboratory.

Many others helped in various ways, particularly J. Cudworth, J.E. Dale, G.T. Foggitt, P.J. Stead, P.T. Treloar and the Yorkshire Naturalists' Union vice-county recorders, some of whom have answered many queries and without whose dedication over the years the Annual Reports of the union, which have formed the major source of reference since 1952, would not have been available. Some are sadly no longer with us and some have retired from office, but credit must go to all who have acted in this time-consuming capacity over the years since the inception of the vice-county recording system in 1953, as follows:

West Riding	R. Chislett (1953-59).
York District	E.W. Taylor (1953-59).
Vice-county 61	H.O. Bunce (1953-74), D.E. Murray (1975-76), W.F. Curtis (1977-84).
Vice-county 62	R.M. Garnett (1953), A.J. Wallis (1954-66), R.H. Appleby (1967-84).
Vice-county 63	J. Cudworth (1960-67), C. Bower (1968-69), R.J. Rhodes (1970-73), J.E. Dale (1974-80), D. Herringshaw (1981-84).
Vice-county 64	A.F.G. Walker (1960-61), J.R. Mather (1962-78), P. Singleton (1979-84).
Vice-county 65	J.P. Utley (1953-59), R. Chislett (1960-63), P.J. Stead (1964-72), C.J. Waller (1972), B. Shorrock (1973-82), R. Temple (1983-84).

Finally, I must thank the staff of Croom Helm Limited for their friendly advice and assistance, and in particular David Christie, who has been an invaluable contact during the final preparation of this book.

Introduction

The Birds of Yorkshire, published in 1907, was a large and detailed two-volume work by T.H. Nelson. In 1952, R. Chislett published *Yorkshire Birds*, a much shorter treatise and written in a very different style. During the intervening 45 years, field ornithology changed but little and not until the last decade of that period was there a significant increase in the number of active observers in the county. The attractions of the recently established bird observatory at Spurn Point and the emerging pursuit of sea-watching, which was to change completely our knowledge of the status of some seabirds and their movements, brought more people to the ranks, and the number of contributors to the Annual Reports of the Yorkshire Naturalists' Union Ornithological Section increased annually to reach the very high figure of today.

Nelson listed 325 species, not including Capercaillie which, although he published the details without square brackets, he declined to admit to the list. Chislett published details of 320 species, the discrepancy being accounted for by the exclusion of racial forms which were given specific rank in Nelson's time (i.e. Iceland and Greenland Falcons, Hooded Crow and the redpolls), and he omitted, presumably through oversight, the American Bittern.

The total list of fully acceptable species recorded within the county now stands at 404, not including Great Black-headed Gull, Brünnich's Guillemot, Bald Eagle, Siberian Meadow Bunting and Red-headed Bunting, all of which have been rejected for various reasons. The occurrence of seven other species not included in the total of accepted records, Least Bittern, Hooded Merganser, Swallow-tailed Kite, Golden Pheasant, Demoiselle Crane, Ring-necked Parakeet and Blue-tailed Bee-eater, all of which have some claim to a place on the county list, are discussed in detail in the systematic list, as are the rejected records referred to above.

Breeding species listed by the two previous authors were 123 and 134 respectively. Today there are 138, not including Marsh and Montagu's Harriers, Quail and Common Tern, all of which may do so from time to time. Species now breeding regularly in the county which were only regular passage migrants or winter visitors in Chislett's time are Shag, Wigeon, Goosander, Common Gull, Fieldfare and Siskin, although the Common Gull and Fieldfare are represented by very few pairs and do not breed in every year. The Collared Dove, which did not enter the county list until 1959, is now common almost everywhere.

Breeding species lost to Yorkshire since 1952, although some had a very precarious foothold at that time, are Spotted Crake, Corncrake, Red-backed Shrike and Woodlark, but it is not impossible that the first two of these may breed in some years.

The majority of species making up the 84 additions to the Yorkshire list since 1952 have been recorded as a result of sea-watching and trapping with mist-nets at both coastal and inland localities, coupled with the tremendous increase in active field observers during the last 35 years. Spurn Bird Observatory has added many of the new birds, this being due almost certainly to the presence of a full-time warden. That some of the recently recorded passerines passed unnoticed in Nelson's time is certain. The presence of wardens at other sites and regular watching in one particular locality by small groups of people have also provided new and sometimes unexpected records. The list of additions seems endless and one wonders when new species will cease to be recorded.

I have not started each species chapter with a brief status summary, because it is often impossible to define such in a clear-cut way. Rather, I have included a fuller paragraph within the chapter, giving the true and often complex situation.

The decision to adhere to the old and established Yorkshire boundaries has been applauded in many quarters. I have always felt that the decision of most county report editors to adopt the new administrative boundaries so readily was a mistake, although realising that in some areas there seemed to be little alternative. The whole of the British Isles is divided into vice-counties of roughly the same size, devised originally to facilitate botanical recording by H.C. Watson in 1873. Yorkshire has five such areas, vice-counties 61 to 65, and these have been used as administrative units by the Yorkshire Naturalists' Union Ornithological Section since 1953. These vice-counties are stable, but the new administrative counties could so easily change again at the whim of politicians. It is difficult to accept the present break-up of this ancient county; those people living in Kilnsea are just as much a part of Yorkshire as are those within sight of the Tees or in the industrial conurbations of the southwest.

I have purposely avoided the use of histograms, believing that words are better and more appreciated by the many people interested in birds simply for the pleasure they give and who do not regard them as tools for the pseudo-scientist. Nor have I presumed that readers possess either Nelson or Chislett and have included all the important historical records published in those works.

During the present century, and particularly during the last 50 years, there have been many changes in the Yorkshire countryside; much land has been lost under the plough, for new roads and for industrial and housing development. Once removed, habitats that have taken hundreds of years and more to develop are gone for ever and attempts on the part of some planners to create compensatory areas, often with completely misguided ideas about what is required, are seldom successful and are totally inadequate substitutes.

On the positive side, the creation of new reservoirs and gravel-pits has provided very suitable habitat for both migratory and breeding birds and such areas have been very well monitored over the years, the information gained often being used to back up attempts to have them made into reserves. The sharing of human interests at large sheets of water is inevitable in these overcrowded times, but it can work well if planned with care. Anglers, divers and sailing enthusiasts are usually members of organised clubs whose interests are wholly directed to a particular sheet of water where they are able to ensure a foothold by paying large sums of money. Naturalists often lose out in this respect by virtue of the nature of their hobby, which does not require a headquarters on site to establish their interest. Such organisation and investment will probably have to come if sites of less than county or national importance are to be preserved for birds. At the present time, only when sites are taken over by county trusts or the Royal Society for the Protection of Birds is their future secure for both birds and those who watch them.

The planting of large areas of heather moorland with conifers by the Forestry Commission and others has taken away a specialised man-made habitat and created another with perhaps more interest for birdwatchers. The young forests are favoured by breeding Short-eared Owls, harriers, Black Grouse and Whinchats, and the more mature stands are being colonised by Siskins and Crossbills with Sparrowhawks and Woodpigeons finding a new and suitable niche. Although lamented by some naturalists, the change is not that bad.

Increasing human pressure on the countryside and the ease of access to hitherto inaccessible regions will have a deleterious effect on some bird species and we can do little to alleviate it. Some species seem to cope well with human intrusion into their domain, but others are quite unable to tolerate it. In spite of all these seemingly insurmountable problems the number of breeding species in the county is increasing, and it is not being overly optimistic to believe that we are living in an age far better for birds than did our predecessors. Only time will tell.

John R. Mather
Knaresborough
1st March 1985

Thomas Hudson Nelson (1856-1916)

Author of *The Birds of Yorkshire* (1907)

Nelson was born on 12th February 1856 at Bishop Auckland in County Durham. His father, Ralph Nelson, was also born there and died at the age of 83, having been a leading citizen and magistrate. His mother died when he was only ten years old; he was the second of three sons. The headmaster at the Bishop Auckland King James's Grammar School was known as Mr Edward Keruen Limoclan, but he was actually the French Marquis de Keruen Limoclan who had been compelled to leave France during the War of 1870, and Nelson spoke of him with admiration, stating that he was 'the cleverest and one of the most perfect gentlemen he had ever known'. Nelson became head boy at the school and was urged by the head to take Holy Orders, but declined, although he remained a devout churchman. He took up Law as a profession, but before he came of age illness overtook him and left a weakened heart, which forced him to abandon a professional career and dictated that he should lead the life of a semi-invalid.

He married in 1898 and had one son, who died at a very early age. His two brothers also died when they were very young and his early life was thus traumatic. His doctors ordered that he must live a much easier life, suggesting that he moved to somewhere on more level ground, and so he chose to live in Redcar, where he pursued his studies of birdlife.

In writing Nelson's obituary in *British Birds* (1917, pp. 205-9), A.E. Pease said:

'Although his name may not be placed among the first of our scientific ornithologists or field naturalists he has left an imperishable one amongst lovers of nature in Yorkshire and a memory ineffacable in the hearts of his friends. The range of his mind and tastes was too great to allow him to specialise or to become engrossed in the purely technical side of the science he loved. The whole field of nature was embraced by his passion, not merely were the birds, their lives and their haunts his study, but he delighted in the folk-lore and legends, in the superstitions and in old or quaint allusions, indeed he loved every accessory of his chief pursuit. ...'

The local fishermen and boys were regular callers at his home with any new or strange bird or beast, and he would welcome everyone 'down to the poorest working lad'. An old fisherman told of how, in the early days, Nelson always slept with a string tied to his foot, the other end of the string hanging out of the window so that the fishermen could wake him at dawn when they returned home if there was 'anything particular about'.

Like his father, Nelson was a magistrate. He also took a great interest in the Redcar Lifeboat and crew, and the latter group preceded his body to the grave. He died on 5th November 1916 at the age of 60 and the opening remarks of his obituary read as follows:

'Within sight and sound of the sea, on a November afternoon we laid to rest, at Redcar, all that was mortal of Thomas Hudson Nelson. No man loved this neighbourhood better, no man knew it so well ... there is more reason to rejoice over his life than to lament that he was not spared to become old. ...'

The publication of *The Birds of Yorkshire* in 1907 was monument enough for this great man and, on degree day at the University of Leeds on 3rd July 1915, The Duke of Devonshire, as Chancellor, conferred on him the degree of Master of Science *honoris causa*, in recognition of his labours in connection with Yorkshire natural history and especially his work on *The Birds of Yorkshire*.

The two-volume work was reviewed in *British Birds* (vol. 1, 1907-08, pp. 194-6) and did not avoid criticism. Perhaps the most surprising was the following comment:

'These volumes are crowded with illustrations, excellent of their kind, but nine-tenths are entirely unsuited to the needs of a work such as this. We find innumerable photographs of the nests of every common bird, but we look almost in vain for illustrations of bird-haunts, of which Yorkshire can boast so many of such varied character. We cannot lay to the charge of the author[s] the absurdity of these illustrations, for they are certainly well aware of the requirements of a county avifauna in this respect, and *we can only regret that it was found necessary for a committee out of sympathy with the subject, to meddle with what was an ornithologist's affair. ...*' (The italics are mine.)

Ralph Chislett (1883-1964)

Author of *Yorkshire Birds* (1952)

Ralph Chislett was born at Rotherham on 2nd June 1883 and trained as a chartered accountant, a profession he practised in that town until his retirement in 1945. He joined the Yorkshire Naturalists' Union in the early 1900s, and was later to become a very successful bird-photographer. He made several trips to the more remote parts of northern Britain and Europe and perhaps did his best work in Lapland.

He was associated with the Zoology Photographic Club for nearly 50 years, was its secretary from 1931 to 1946 and later became its president. In 1932 he published *Northward Ho! For Birds*, in which he described some of his experiences on photographic trips to northern Britain and Lapland. He abandoned photography before he retired and during the late 1940s concentrated his efforts on establishing the Spurn Bird Observatory, having secured a lease on the peninsula from the War Department. His part in the formation of this important observatory cannot be praised too highly.

He was actively involved in the ornithological affairs of the Yorkshire Naturalists' Union until his death in 1964; he edited the Annual Report of the Ornithological Section from 1940 to 1959, when he handed over to a committee of recorders. He was, for many years, the father of Yorkshire ornithology and his unstinting devotion to this pursuit, and the publication of his *Yorkshire Birds* in 1952, led to an honorary degree of Master of Science being conferred on him at the University of Leeds in 1963. *Yorkshire Birds* was reviewed by E.M. Nicholson in *British Birds* (1953, pp. 266-7).

He was at times a stern character and applied strict disciplines to the Annual Bird Reports for which he was responsible, although he would accept records from some observers at face value, and condemn those from others without real cause if he did not know them well. I met him in 1955 and had the pleasure of serving under his chairmanship on the Reports Committee of the Yorkshire Naturalists' Union Ornithological Section during the early 1960s.

His obituary in *British Birds* (1964, pp. 219-20 and plate 35), written by his close friend John Armitage, concluded with the following:

'He was at once a devastating critic and an extraordinarily generous counsellor to whom nothing was too much trouble, whether friend or stranger was involved, if he thought its cause worthwhile. Those meeting him for the first time were often shaken by his forthright manner, but underneath was a warm heart and a strong sense of justice. ...'

He was certainly all those things and never again will there emerge a character to dominate the Yorkshire scene as he did for so many years.

The Yorkshire Environment

Writing in their *Geology of Yorkshire* (1924), Kendall and Wroot said of the 6,000 square miles (15,540 km²) that constitute the largest county in the British Isles: 'Scarcely anywhere in the world is an equal area which presents to the student of the past history of the Earth so full and comprehensive a range of the geological formations and phenomena, and presents them also in a manner so clearly inviting and so amply rewarding investigation'. The folding of the earth's crust which created the Pennine Chain, part of which forms the western boundary of the county, is 'of antiquity far exceeding the great mountain ranges of the world'.

Yorkshire can certainly boast more varied and beautiful scenery and a wider variety of avian habitat than any other English county, and the latter fact is obviously reflected in the large number of species recorded within its boundaries. The value of each particular area or habitat will be evident from the records of species which follow in the systematic list, and I have therefore mentioned only the most important or typical species in this summary of the county's regions.

The Pennines

From the highest Pennine peak in the county, Mickle Fell (2,591 feet/790 m) in the northwest, the barren uplands continue southwards in an almost unbroken range of heather-clad moorland to the boundaries of Lancashire and Derbyshire, west of Sheffield. Only through the valley created by the River Aire as it flows eastwards from its source near Malham is there a cross-country corridor. Artificial waters along this river, as it is traced eastwards through Skipton, Keighley and Leeds, past Fairburn Ings to its confluence with the River Ouse just west of Goole, provide a chain of resting and feeding places for the many birds, notably waterfowl and waders, which pass across the country from coast to coast in both directions according to the season. The wide Ribble Valley, which continues southwestwards from the vicinity of Settle, takes over from the Aire Gap and channels migrating birds into Lancashire and its coastal mudflats and estuaries or beyond. Lying to the north of the River Ribble, in the great Forest of Bowland, is Stocks Reservoir, one of the largest sheets of water in the county and an important stopping-off place for migrants.

South of the Aire Gap, the Pennines, composed mostly of millstone grits and coal measures, are lower and softer in character than the part which lies to the north, where all the 36 peaks in excess of 2,000 feet (610 m) are situated. In the southern part is the most densely populated area of Yorkshire, home of the mills and factories of the Industrial Revolution, bordered in the north by Leeds, Bradford and Keighley, and southwards through Halifax, Dewsbury, Wakefield, Huddersfield, Barnsley and, finally, Sheffield. In spite of the vast built-up areas along the eastern foothills, the heights on the western borders are wild and open moorlands where Merlins breed and Twites have their county stronghold. The proliferation of moorland reservoirs in this southern region of the Pennines — and there are well over 100, most of which have been created this century — attract many passing ducks and waders to feed and rest during their trans-Pennine migrations. Many are well watched by birdwatchers, and records from Blackmoorfoot, Wintersett, Ardsley, Redmires, Newmillerdam, Langsett and others figure prominently in the records of the Yorkshire Naturalists' Union Ornithological Section.

North of the Aire Gap, the Pennines take on a different character with an elevated plateau of Carboniferous limestone, capped in parts with millstone grit creating a more rugged appearance. Five great valleys have been cut back into this northern section of the range, each with its river, the most northerly of which is the River Tees. This makes its own way to the sea and forms the county boundary for almost half of its course from Cauldron Snout to South Gare, the southern point of Teesmouth. The other four rivers, the Swale, Ure, Nidd and Wharfe, all join the River Ouse at different points southwards in the Vale of York. There are several reservoirs in the upper reaches of four of the five, or on tributaries to them. The newest of these is Cow Green on the upper reaches of the Tees just to the north of Mickle Fell, while to the southeast of the Fell are two tributaries, the Lune and the Balder, both of which have been dammed to create the large series of reservoirs of Selset and Grassholme in Lunedale and Balderhead, Blackton and Hury in Balderdale. Leighton and Roundhill Reservoirs are on tributaries of the Ure; Gouthwaite, Scar House and Angram have been built in Upper Nidderdale, but the most notable is the chain of four waters, Lindley, Fewston, Swinsty and Thruscross along the Washburn Valley, a tributary of the Wharfe on its east side, and with high Chelker Reservoir near Skipton on the west side, the outlet from which also drains into the Wharfe.

Some of the finest grouse moors in Britain are to be found on the watersheds of these five major valleys. Golden Plovers, Curlews and Dunlins all make their summer home here and along with Ring Ouzels and Meadow Pipits are species which typify the bleak Yorkshire moors.

Descending down the rivers into the foothill country, the valleys become wider, with pastureland and scattered deciduous trees. The slopes are often covered with hanging deciduous woodlands where Redstarts, Pied Flycatchers, Wood Warblers and Nuthatches are regular breeding species. Dippers and Grey Wagtails follow the rivers and breed along their banks until the rivers reach the plains.

The North York Moors

The North York Moors lie in the northeast of the county and are fringed on the north by the Cleveland Hills and on the west by the Hambleton Hills. The eastern boundary is formed by the rugged coastline between Loftus and Scarborough, while the southern boundary runs along the northern edge of the flatlands of the Vale of Pickering, into which flow most of the rivers draining this upland area. The whole area comprises the North York Moors National Park and covers about 1,000 square miles (2,590 km²), including the largest area of unbroken heatherland in England.

The rock beneath consists almost entirely of Jurassic limestones, sandstones, shales and clays, cut into high relief by erosion. The northern edge rises above the valley of the Tees and the western edge above the Vale of Mowbray, both with steep and abrupt escarpments, some of which are covered by a series of hanging woodlands. Most of the upland regions, which reach a height of 1,200 feet (366 m) in some parts, are heather-clad and are the home of Red Grouse, Curlew and a few Golden Plover, as well as Ring Ouzels and Meadow Pipits. Large areas are covered with conifers, most of which have been planted within the last 40 years. Especially in the southeastern part, the extensive forests of Allerston, Dalby, Wykeham, Cropton and Staindale dominate the landscape. Many other areas are now administered by the Forestry Commission, but whether more heatherland will disappear under spruce is open to speculation. A growing number of pairs of Sparrowhawks and great hordes of Woodpigeons frequent these relatively barren stands of timber, particularly along the forest edges, while Chaffinches, Goldcrests and Coal Tits can be found throughout. In recent years Siskins have colonised. Crossbills breed in some areas, and the forest edges and isolated clearings have proved to be the best places in Yorkshire for breeding Nightjars. The uplands provide hunting grounds for a few Rough-legged Buzzards during the winter months.

Running in the main from north to south are several valleys, some of which, notably Rosedale, Farndale, Bransdale, Newtondale and — somewhat farther west — Bilsdale, are well timbered with deciduous trees. Through Newtondale, perhaps the most famous, runs the Pickering to Whitby railway line and the valley was once the hunting ground of the Norman and Plantagenet kings. Until as late as the thirteenth century 'droves of Wild Boars' were common there.

The Hambleton Hills are famous for the steep 'one-in-four' road at Sutton Bank where the impressive Whitestone Cliff juts out and overlooks the vale below. Lying to the south of the Hambletons, between Easingwold and Malton, are the Howardian Hills, a relatively low range with woodland and agricultural land on their summits.

The Yorkshire Wolds

The chalk Wolds sweep in a broad belt from Reighton in the north to Hessle on the River Humber, and, according to Kendall and Wroot in their *Geology of Yorkshire*, 'their scenery and surface are unlike anything else in England'. The chalk rises sharply, forming a bold escarpment overlooking the Vale of Pickering along the northern edge and dominating the Vale of York along the western edge. Most of the Wolds are under the plough and the thin soil is scattered with bits of chalk, yet it is perhaps the best land in Britain for growing barley. There is little woodland of any size and the area is very open and relatively poor for birds.

The Great Bustard and the Stone-curlew bred here in good numbers before the barren sheepwalks were enclosed and cultivated; it was once possible to walk for 30 miles (48 km) without encountering a fence. The Great Bustard was exterminated during the 1830s, but the Stone-curlew lingered on for another 100 years before it was finally driven out of its breeding haunts.

The Vales of Mowbray, Pickering and York

The Vale of Mowbray, which runs northwards from York to the county boundary near Darlington, is flanked on the west by the high Pennines and on the east by the Cleveland and Hambleton Hills. It is heavily cultivated, with some stands of large timber, but is perhaps the least interesting part of the county. Several rivers meander along this wide valley. The Swale, rising in the Pennines, enters from the west, while opposite, springing from the Clevelands, is the River Wiske, which, after flowing northwards until within 2 miles (3.2 km) of the River Tees, is deflected by massed drift and turns abruptly southwards to join the Swale. After picking up the Cod Beck near Topcliffe, this then joins the River Ure near the ancient town of

Aldborough, once the most important Roman centre in Britain, to become the River Ouse.

The Vale of Pickering runs eastwards from the Howardian Hills to Filey. The wide valley floor is rich in alluvium, evidence of a once great lake around which ancient beasts roamed in a climate much warmer than today. It is heavily farmed. Much of the pasture is remnant carrland with *Juncus* rush and was once subject to extensive flooding in the winter months, but modern drainage has greatly reduced any standing water except during very heavy falls of rain. The River Derwent, which rises only 3 miles (4.8 km) from the sea on Fylingdales Moor in the North York Moors, flows southwards through Langdale End and Hackness and was prevented from turning east down the course of the Scalby Cut at Mowthorpe after the last Ice Age left a glacial moraine in its way. At the end of the Ice Age the meltwater formed into the huge Hackness Lake, which forced its way through the steep-sided Forge Valley, a valley probably created in no more than two decades, and in the process laid down a deep bed of sand and gravel between Seamer and Wykeham. At East Ayton today, much of the Derwent's water disappears underground into a huge artesian well which supplies Scarborough with its water supply. Much reduced in size, the river meanders across the Vale of Pickering to Ganton where it is joined by the River Hertford, which has its source from springs rising to the surface at Muston, no more than 2 miles from the sea. This river is also blocked from its natural outlet to the sea by a glacial moraine of boulder-clay and in consequence flows westwards, draining the eastern end of the Vale, or carrs as the flatlands are known locally. From Ganton the River Derwent continues southwest through Malton, escaping from the Vale of Pickering through the Kirkham Gap, flowing southwards through Stamford Bridge to join the Ouse just east of Howden.

Water meadows of great antiquity line the Derwent's path along the lower reaches from Wheldrake to Bubwith and the winter floods, so much a feature of this region over the centuries, attract hordes of ducks and large numbers of Bewick's Swans. The Yorkshire Wildlife Trust now has administrative regard for the ings at Wheldrake, and controlled flooding during the spring is starting to attract several species of ducks and waders which stay to breed. Other parts of this area have also been saved, at least for the present, as an important refuge for wintering wildfowl by the decision in November 1984 not to permit a pumped drainage scheme on North Duffield Carr.

The vast Plain of York stretches from the Pennine foothills to the Wolds, extending to Selby and Goole in the south, eventually giving way to the lowland carrs about Doncaster. Encircling the City of York it is a patchwork of intensively cultivated and relatively flat land. Areas of ancient birch still exist on the commons of Strensall, Skipwith and Allerthorpe, although the latter has, in recent years, been largely spoilt by the planting of conifers over much of its area. To the west of the city is Askham Bog, the last remaining example of a post-glacial swamp; the protection of this led to the formation of the Yorkshire Wildlife Trust and the area became its first reserve.

Holderness

The low and flat land of Holderness lies at the foot of an ancient sea-cliff of chalk, which, though mainly buried beneath glacial accumulations, can be traced from Sewerby through Great Driffield, Beverley, Cottingham and Hessle. East of this line, down to the unique promontory at Spurn, the land is composed wholly of glacial sands, clays and gravels and is little above sea-level.

It is intensively cultivated, with arable land predominating. The Barn Owl is, perhaps, commoner here than anywhere else in Yorkshire. There are some isolated stands of timber, but mature woodland is scarce. Hornsea Mere is the largest fresh-water lake in Yorkshire, and is a natural formation although less than a mile from the sea. In consequence it attracts large numbers of ducks and passing waders, as well as some species of seabirds. Gatherings of Swifts during early May can be dramatic and the numbers of Little Gulls enjoying the fresh water in late summer can be high. Red-legged Partridges are numerous on the arable land and Collared Doves, having gained their first county foothold in this region, are still very common. Rough ground as at Cowden and elsewhere is frequented during the autumn and winter months by occasional Hen Harriers, Short-eared Owls and Great Grey Shrikes.

Tophill Low Reservoir, near Beverley, has proved an important site for waders and waterfowl during the migration seasons and is now well watched by several observers.

The southern carrlands

Continuing southwestwards over the River Ouse into the low-lying flat country near Doncaster, the remnants of once extensive heath and carrland drained during the early part of the seventeenth century can still be seen at Hatfield and Thorne Moors. These are important areas for both breeding and wintering species, and it is here that the few pairs of Nightingales to nest in Yorkshire have their most northerly station in Britain. Nightjars and a few pairs of Long-eared Owls also find the habitat to their liking. During the autumn migration period, the drains and marshy areas attract many waders and ducks, and the wide expanse of heathland is hunted over by Merlins and harriers at the appropriate season.

Most of the Yorkshire duck-decoys were situated in this region, but adequate documentation concerning most of them is lacking. After extensive research into the history and ultimate fate of at least six major ones, M. Limbert published his very full and detailed findings in *The Naturalist* (1978, pp. 95-103, and 1982, pp. 69-71).

The once extensive marshland had largely disappeared before the start of the present century, and the need for more land to be cultivated during the two world wars reduced the remaining wet pastureland still further. An increase in agricultural development, and latterly peat extraction, continues to put pressure on this important area in spite of much opposition from those caring naturalists who are mindful of its natural values.

The Humber Estuary

Where the Rivers Ouse and Trent meet, the two become the River Humber, which flows through a widening tidal estuary for some 36 miles (58 km) to the sea between Spurn Point on the north bank and Grimsby and Cleethorpes on the Lincolnshire side. Being tidal, the river is bounded by wide expanses of mud important to large concentrations of waders, which have been counted over recent years as part of the 'Birds of Estuaries Enquiry' organised by the British Trust for Ornithology.

The wide expanse of mud which forms the Kilnsea and Skeffling Clays and also Sunk Island Sands is an important feeding area for Brent Geese and very many ducks and waders, embraced as it is by the long curving finger of the Spurn promontory to the east and the large bulge of land from Patrington to Stone Creek in the west. Continuing upstream past the busy port of Hull, the shallower river provides large areas of tidal mud at Whitton Sands and Broomfleet Island, the centre of the Humber Wildfowl Refuge set up to protect large numbers of Pink-footed Geese which used the area for roosting. In the 1960s concentrations of 6,000 birds were recorded, but today the numbers are much reduced, no doubt owing to changed farming practices on the Wolds. The ploughing and re-seeding of stubble immediately following harvesting has robbed the birds of much of their winter food supply.

On the south side of the River Ouse at its junction with the River Trent lies Blacktoft Sands, a vast expanse of reedbeds, home for many hundreds of Bearded Tits and an occasional pair of Marsh Harriers. Managed as a reserve by the Royal Society for the Protection of Birds, the future of this important habitat is now secure.

The coast

From Teesmouth southwards to the mouth of the Humber lies a coastline as varied in character as the people of Yorkshire. The extensive Tees marshes, over which Nelson roamed at the end of the nineteenth century, have suffered much in recent years through reclamation for industrialisation. When Chislett published his *Yorkshire Birds* in 1952, Middlesbrough had already increased in size and the development on what was once famous saltmarsh had caused a dramatic change in the land-use and driven out the birdlife. Today, there are just a few places left where migrating waders and waterfowl find food and shelter, and some of these are under threat. The South Gare breakwater is a favourite place from which to watch passing seabirds, and it also acts as host for many migrant passerines.

Moving southeastwards past the Redcar sandhills, so often referred to by Nelson, the coast rises steadily to the promontory of the 'Birdflight Goit' at Saltburn, then higher to the great cliffs at Boulby, once the home of Choughs. Southwards through Staithes and Runswick Bay to the old fishing town of Whitby, thence onward past Robin Hood's Bay to Scarborough, dominated by the Castle Hill, the coast is much indented with small bays, some of which provide shelter for waders and sea-ducks.

The finger of Filey Brigg, pointing towards the Flamborough Headland, is a special place for birdwatchers and the large sheltered bay attracts many seabirds. From Reighton Gap at the south end of the bay, the cliffs begin to rise to the impressive chalk heights of Speeton, Buckton and Bempton, long famous for the seabirds which nest in their thousands. Here is the only colony of Gannets in England and also the only one on the British mainland.

Sticking out into the North Sea for some 6 miles (9.6 km) is Flamborough Head, with its eroded cliffs providing caves and gullies where Shags have their only Yorkshire breeding location. The headland is an important point from which to watch passing seabirds and is the most obvious point of landfall to migrant passerines as they come in over the North Sea in autumn, when large numbers and a wide variety of species may occur.

The cliffs along the south side of the headland lose height steadily until they reach the busy fishing town of Bridlington, south of which the broad sweep of Bridlington Bay is fringed by a wide sandy beach backed by low boulder-clay cliffs. The beach is an important feeding place for Sanderlings and Ringed Plovers as well as hordes of gulls, which also frequent the harbour at Bridlington, often feeding and bathing at Fraisthorpe where the Auburn Beck flows over the shingle and sand. Beyond Fraisthorpe the low cliffs stretch southwards in an almost unbroken line to Hornsea, Withernsea and finally Kilnsea Cliff, where they give way to the sand dunes of the Spurn Peninsula. Erosion has claimed much of the soft boulder-clay along this part of the coast, and as much as 100 yards (91 m) or more has gone into the sea in some parts during the present century.

The Spurn Peninsula, famous throughout the British Isles as a focal point for migrating birds and home of the Spurn Bird Observatory, is unique, acting as it does as a funnel down which thousands of passerines and other species pass every spring and autumn. The promontory itself is an unstable spit of sand and shingle formed by eroded material from the coast of Holderness. It has shifted its location over the centuries as the tides have torn at the seaward side and forced aggregate towards the tip, occasionally breaking through completely, only to start the process of building and depositing at a new location either seaward or landward, creating a time-lapsed waving finger.

The Development of Ornithology in Yorkshire

Contributed by A.J. Wallis

Two-hundred-and-fifty-eight species was the sum total which Thomas Allis was able to include in his *Report on the Birds of Yorkshire* which was presented to the meeting of the British Association held in York in 1844. This report was never published, but the manuscript is still held by the Yorkshire Museum in York.

In September 1861, naturalists in Heckmondwike met to found a naturalists' society, and the meeting was supported by some 60 naturalists from the Huddersfield, Holmfirth and Wakefield Societies. After, presumably, the business of forming the Heckmondwike Society was completed, a proposal was put forward that the four societies would benefit from combined and organised meetings and outings, and from this proposal the West Riding Consolidated Naturalist Society came into being. It remained as such for 15 years, and in 1877 societies from farther afield were invited to join with the aim of making it a county-wide organisa-tion, and the name was changed to Yorkshire Naturalists' Union. Since those early beginnings the union has played a major role in the development of ornithology in the county, and today there are 44 affiliated societies.

The second publication to list all the bird species seen in the county came in 1881, when W. Dennison Roebuck and W. Eagle Clarke published for the Yorkshire Naturalists' Union *The Vertebrate Fauna of Yorkshire*; Eagle Clarke had responsibility for the section on birds, and he named 307 species. W. Eagle Clarke is best remembered today for his classic two volumes *Studies in Migration*, published in 1912 after he had left Yorkshire and moved to Edinburgh. Neverthe-less, his contribution to Yorkshire should not be hidden by this, perhaps greater achievement. Born in Leeds, he played a significant part in recording Yorkshire ornithology for he was joint editor with W. Dennison Roebuck of *The Naturalist*, the journal of the Yorkshire Naturalists' Union, from 1884 to 1888, and a special testimonial was presented to him at the Union Annual General Meeting in Sheffield on 16th November 1888, the year he moved to the Royal Scottish Museum, Edinburgh. His studies of migration were fostered while in Yorkshire for in the pre-face of his major opus he acknowledges 'In the year 1880 it was my good fortune to become the intimate friend of John Cordeaux, who first inspired me with an interest in bird-migration that has never waned.' In 1906 the union further honoured him by appointing him president for that year.

John Cordeaux lived on the south side of the Humber, but was in his day the accepted authority on birds of the Humber District, covering both sides of the river. In 1872 he wrote his book on the *Birds of the Humber District*.

It was clearly the intention of the union to have prepared a fuller history of the birds seen in the county, and Eagle Clarke began this, in instalments. When he left Yorkshire the union invited T.H. Nelson to complete this work, and handed him for this purpose the whole of the manuscripts and lists in the possession of Messrs Eagle Clarke and Roebuck. Nelson finished his task in 1907 with the publication, in two volumes, of *The Birds of Yorkshire, A Historical Account of the Avifauna of the County*. In this work Nelson lists 325 species.

It was not until 1952 that the next full and historical account of the county's birds appeared, when Ralph Chislett published as a private venture his *Yorkshire Birds*. In this book he lists 320 species and mentions 35 subspecies and recognised races.

Other events which all added to the development of ornithology in the county had been taking place in between the above publications, and one of the earliest concerned bird protection. In the 1860s the seabird breeding colonies on the Flamborough and Bempton Cliffs came under extreme pressure from shooting, which began with the collecting of Kittiwakes for the millinery trade, but developed into senseless slaughter, the birds being used solely for target practice. The slaughter was so great that the men who climbed the cliffs to harvest the Guillemot eggs had to cease their activities because of the lack of birds, and therefore eggs. This shooting activity also concerned Reverend Henry Frederick Barnes-Lawrence, then Vicar of Bridlington. He obtained the support of Reverend F.O. Morris, Rector of Nunburnholme, and several other influential people within the county. The Association for the Protection of Sea Birds was formed and had such public approval that Christopher Sykes, MP for the East Riding of Yorkshire, presented the Sea Birds Preservation Act before the House of Commons on 26th February 1869. So rapid was the passage of the Bill through the Commons and the Lords that it received Royal Assent by 24th June 1869.

In 1969 E.M. Nicholson suggested that the centenary of this important event should be marked in some way by the union, and in consequence I was asked to arrange with the owner of the pleasure steamer *Coronia*, which sailed out of Scarborough, for a special excursion for birdwatchers to sail and look at the Bempton Cliffs from the sea. It was an enthusiastic gathering of some 150 birdwatchers from all parts of the county who enjoyed the trip. The day was fine, the sea calm, and the only problem came as we approached Bempton. It was the first time the Captain had taken the ship close in to the cliffs, and not knowing the depth of water available he would not approach as close as we would have liked.

Writing in 1961 on *A Century of Ornithology in Yorkshire*, Ralph Chislett says:

'In considering ornithologically the hundred years of the Union's existence several matters call for comment, notably the changes from the times of private collecting of specimens to those of recording occurrences with detailed notes written at the time, and of securing quick confirmation of the facts if possible, and expert concurrence later. In the earlier years records often included the word "obtained"; thus W.J. Clarke on Christmas Day in 1888 received a Black Redstart that had been "obtained" at Cayton Bay.'

It was not surprising therefore that the union set up a Wild Birds and Eggs Protection Committee (now shortened to Bird Protection Committee) as early as 1891, only two years after the national Society for the Protection of Birds (now the RSPB) had been formed. This committee was to attract long and loyal service from several union members, and Chislett, reporting on the committee's formation, mentions: 'One collector accepted membership with expressed determination never again to take an egg in Yorkshire; a bargain I believe he honoured.' The longest period of service to bird protection in the county was by Dr E.W. Taylor, who joined the union in 1911 and in the same year began an uninterrupted 61 years working for the Protection Committee, serving the last 24 years as its chairman.

The committee worked, very much, quietly and without a lot of fuss but, while it is known that many successes were achieved, it had to admit that it was not possible to save the Stone-curlew from being exterminated from its last breeding site in Yorkshire, just to the north of Thornton-le-Dale. Egg thieves were undoubtedly what took this fine bird off the list of Yorkshire breeding species, for one collector is known to have exhibited, with pride, a whole series of Stone-curlew's eggs, all of which were taken in the county.

It was not until after the Second World War that conservation by the purchase or leasing of land with the sole purpose of creating Nature Reserves had any impact. In the early 1940s parts of Askham Bog, just outside York, were put on the market; and in 1944 Sir Francis Terry and Mr Arnold Rowntree joined forces to buy the area, knowing of its supreme interest to naturalists of varying disciplines. In 1946 the Yorkshire Naturalists' Trust was founded, becoming the second county conservation trust in the country and receiving as a gift Askham Bog from the above two benefactors. The trust now administers 49 reserves, of which six, and perhaps some others, are of significance to the ornithologists: Spurn, Denaby Ings, Potteric Carr, Wheldrake Ings, Bretton Lakes and Wath Ings.

In June 1957 Fairburn Ings, a very significant wetland area created by mining subsidence and flanking the River Aire, was declared a nature reserve by the West Riding County Council under the National Parks and Access to the Countryside Act 1949. The management and control of the area has since been transferred to the RSPB, who also administer three other reserves in the county, Bempton Cliffs, Hornsea Mere and Blacktoft Sands, all prime sites and of high ornithological importance.

Recording birds seen in Yorkshire was in the early part of this century very fragmented, with reports from independent areas being printed in *The Naturalist* at seemingly irregular intervals, each submitted by correspondents who reported on an area surrounding their home ground. This continued until 1940, when a Committee for Ornithology was set up with R.M. Garnett as its chairman and Ralph Chislett as secretary. Four recorders were appointed: H.B. Booth (West Riding), W.J. Clarke (North Riding), C.W. Mason (East Riding) and E.W. Taylor (York District). These four collected records from their areas and submitted them to Ralph Chislett, who edited the first Annual Report covering the whole county for that year. In that first report, which was published in the April 1941 issue of *The Naturalist*, the species seen were reported on separately for each of the four areas covered by the four recorders. The second report, for 1941, was produced with all areas combined into the one list. It was not until the report for 1942 that a list of contributors is given, and in that year 65 names are listed. By comparison, in 1980 the list of contributors included 286 names, and in addition many birdwatchers contributed records but are not mentioned individually because their records became amalgamated in the summaries of both the Spurn and local society reports. It is likely that over 1,000 people are now actively birdwatching in Yorkshire.

Of the above-named recorders H.B. Booth served for one year, after which Ralph Chislett took over the recordership for the West Riding on top of his other duties, and continued to collect the records from this area until 1959. In 1942 C.W. Mason resigned and was replaced by G.H. Ainsworth and John Lord, the latter serving until 1948 when he left Yorkshire. In 1944 W.J. Clarke handed over his duties as recorder to R.M. Garnett, and in 1948 the North Riding was split into two areas, east and west, R.M. Garnett retaining the eastern half and J.P. Utley taking responsibility for the west. G.H. Ainsworth relinquished his duties in 1955, and his place was taken by H.O. Bunce, and in 1953 R.M. Garnett left the county and A.J. Wallis became the recorder for the North Riding (East).

In 1959 it became clear that the effort, maintained since 1940, for Ralph Chislett, now of advancing age, to continue to produce the annual Ornithological Report was more than he could sustain. In addition to being editor of the report from the inception of the Ornithological Section in 1940 and recorder for the West Riding from 1941, offices he held until 1959, he was the section secretary from 1940 to

1953 and chairman from 1956 to 1963, the year before he died in February 1964. He was also instrumental in the founding and setting up of the Spurn Bird Observatory, which will be referred to later, and in 1952 he published his last book, *Yorkshire Birds*, which he compiled and wrote single-handed. His achievements on behalf of Yorkshire birds, and his work for the Yorkshire Naturalists' Union are unsurpassed. He joined the union in 1919; was elected president in 1939; and was made an honorary member at the Annual General Meeting held in Ilkley on 3rd December 1960. It is little wonder that today memory of him is kept alive by the Chislett Memorial Lecture given by a prominent birdwatcher of the day, in Leeds, in March of each year.

So, in 1960, a Reports Committee was set up as an executive committee responsible to the General Committee of the Ornithological Section of the union, and this committee remains responsible for the production of the Ornithological Report. On its inception a change was made from recorders in the Ridings to the accepted union recording policy of using the Watsonian vice-county system, Yorkshire being divided into five areas, VCs 61-65. The first recorders for the new committee were H.O. Bunce (VC 61), A.J. Wallis (VC 62), J. Cudworth (VC 63), A.F.G. Walker (VC 64), and R. Chislett (VC 65), it also being arranged that each recorder in turn should have the responsibility for compiling the report. The recorderships have all changed over the years. In VC 61 H.O. Bunce held office until 1974 and was followed for two years by D.E. Murray, while W.F. Curtis has held this position for the last seven years. A.J. Wallis handed over VC 62 to R.H. Appleby in 1970, when the committee was expanded and Wallis took over the secretarial work. In VC 63 J. Cudworth served for seven years, was replaced by C. Bower for two years, followed by R.J. Rhodes for four years; J.E. Dale took over in 1975, being replaced by D. Herringshaw in 1982. J.R. Mather took responsibility for VC 64 in 1962, and served in this capacity until 1978, when S.P. Singleton became recorder. On R. Chislett's death early in 1964, P.J. Stead accepted responsibility for VC 65, even though he did not reside in the vice-county; he held this position until he moved south in 1972, and from 1973 B. Shorrock looked after this very unpopulated area faithfully, though at the time of writing he has relinquished the task and has been succeeded by R. Temple.

The rotation system for writing the Report hit traumatic difficulties in 1965, which held up publication of Reports from that year up to 1969. In 1970 J.R. Mather became the editor and produced the reports for 1970 to 1979 inclusive, passing this duty to J.E. Dale with the 1980 report. Delays in production have beleaguered the committee for many years. The causes are various, but the growing number of local societies and the rapid growth in the hobby of birdwatching, and in consequence the explosion in the volume of individual records to be processed, have always been the main stumbling blocks to establishing a fixed and regular timetable which will ensure a full and comprehensive report being published at regular annual intervals.

In addition to the development of the recording systems, other changes have all added to and aided a fuller and more comprehensive picture of the occurrence of birds within the county boundary, whether resident species, passage migrants or the rare vagrant. Observatories and the sophistication of ringing from a casual pastime of the lone birdwatcher in the 1930s to an advanced and co-operative science with the advent of the Heligoland trap and more particularly the mist-net have made a tremendous impact.

The importance of the Spurn Peninsula as a site for observing visible migration has been known at least since the days when Eagle Clarke began his study of migration. Ralph Chislett made regular visits there during the 1930s and it was, perhaps, the intrusion of the Second World War which delayed yet helped the setting up of the Spurn Bird Observatory. At the beginning of the war the peninsula was taken over by the War Department, and at the end of hostilities, in late 1945, Ralph Chislett was able to obtain a lease for the Warren Cottage from that government department. With the help of G.H. Ainsworth, John Lord and R.M. Garnett, Chislett set up the Spurn Bird Observatory, the third to be formed in the present chain of observatories and the first to be sited on the mainland of Britain. The observatory grew in popularity, and there has been a tremendous growth in its observer visits as the years have passed. It seems difficult to imagine that in 1946 I was able to spend a full week at Spurn, living in the Warren Cottage, without seeing another bird-watcher during the whole of my stay. In 1960 the peninsula was put on the market and was purchased by the Yorkshire Naturalists' Trust, largely because the union was not in the position to hold property within its framework. Spurn became the third reserve owned and administered by the trust, and the peninsula has from that time had a resident warden, always a person with primarily ornithological interests. Many have been the faithful supporters of Spurn, and R.F. Dickens, B.S. Pashby, Lt Col. H.G. Brownlow and G.R. Edwards come readily to mind, but the most faithful and longest-serving member of the Observatory Committee after Chislett's 18 years must be John Cudworth, who took over as chairman in 1964, a position he still holds.

While the observatory maintains records of all birds seen on or passing along the Spurn Peninsula, ringing remains one of the major activities. How this has grown can be seen from the ringing progress tables. During the two years from November 1945 to October 1947, 926 birds of 48 species were ringed. In the one year of 1982 the comparative figures were 4,661 of 80 species, yet 1982 was well below the average of 6,230 birds ringed annually during the 28 years from 1955. In two years, 1967 and 1973, over 10,000 birds were caught and ringed in each of the 12-month periods; the Blackbird topped the species totals in both years, with 2,190 and 2,458 birds respectively.

In 1955 a ringing station with a completely different background came into being. In that year John R. Mather set up a Heligoland trap on a 4-acre site on the banks of the River Nidd, and on the outskirts of Knaresborough. The nearby land was being worked for the extraction of sand and gravel, and the company responsible provided the facilities for this venture to go forward. This it did, with the creation of the Knaresborough Ringing Station and Nature Reserve. In 1964 the owners entered into a lease with the group and in 1966, when the gravel extraction became uneconomic, Mather was able to purchase the four acres and thus ensure the security of the ringing station, which has become well known for its monitoring of the passage of warblers during late July and August.

Since the 1950s birdwatchers in the county, along with others in all parts of the country, have discovered the benefits of spending many hours of continuous watching from vantage points along the coast. Sea-watching has become a major attraction, often bringing exciting rewards. Amateur ornithologists living in the county have also, over the last 30 years, supported in a full and proper manner the various national enquiries organised by the British Trust for Ornithology, and there are four regional representatives of the BTO to assist in organising this work within Yorkshire.

It would be monotonous to list in precise detail the formation of the numerous ornithological or bird-study societies or groups which have given a base for the ever-growing number of people who have discovered the joys and fascination of the hobby of birdwatching during the past 20 years or so. From a somewhat odd and suspicious activity up to the end of the last century, and often the pastime of ministers of religion, ours is now a fascinating and enjoyable hobby for the many, and offers a lucrative living to an ever-growing band of authors, artists, publishers, photographers and film producers.

What is certain is that there will always be more to learn about the birds of

Yorkshire, and if we can remember that birdwatching is, for the majority at least, a hobby, and a hobby which creates friendships that transcend the divides of class or occupation, of religion or political opinion, then the enjoyment of birdwatching and the study of avian behaviour can continue to grow in the county.

The growth of interest shown in the last 20 years is reflected in the current compilation of *The Birds of Yorkshire*, which is able to list 404 species. The existence of more watchers, better informed and more skilful in identification, is reflected in this total.

September 1984

Bird Protection in Yorkshire

Contributed by Clive Varty

A notable feature of Yorkshire ornithology, which goes back some 120 or so years, is the long and commendable tradition of directly protecting birds in the county and a continuous active involvement in the cause of bird protection. In fact, the origins of our present national protection framework are so deeply rooted in the county of Yorkshire that it seems entirely appropriate to include here a chapter dealing briefly with its early history and subsequent development in the region.

Undoubtedly, one of the very earliest naturalists to make an impact on the Yorkshire ornithological scene, and especially so in this particular connection, was the remarkable Charles Waterton (1782-1865) of Walton Hall, near Wakefield. Waterton spent many of his early years in Georgetown, Demerara, and first came to prominence in 1825 with the publication of his renowned *Wanderings in South America*, in which he describes his exploratory journeys into the tropical forests of the interior, as well as many new and fascinating aspects of the wildlife of the region.

As a field naturalist, Charles Waterton was an astute, perceptive and somewhat fearless observer, and he rather despised what he termed the 'closet naturalists' who seldom ventured beyond the walls of their museums and dissecting rooms. Nevertheless, he was himself a highly skilled taxidermist, as can be confirmed by reference to the fine collection of his skins in the Waterton Room at Wakefield Museum.

It was, however, his vision and his early pioneering conservation work for which Waterton should now best be remembered, for in this he was unquestionably years ahead of his time. On returning to England, he established in Walton Park what was probably the first consciously created bird sanctuary in Britain. He gave strict orders that no shot was to be fired in the grounds, no dogs must be permitted to roam in the woods, and no boats were allowed on the lake from Michaelmas to May Day, so as to provide the waterfowl with complete freedom from disturbance. Protection was even accorded to raptors, owls and crows, which he believed were essential to maintaining a correct balance in the natural order — a most remarkable appreciation at that time. Waterton even built a special nesting site for Barn Owls on the ruined watergate, and his journal records that he 'threatened to strangle the keeper if he ever molested either the old birds or their young'. He made similar nesting provision for other species, including the construction of an artificial bank for Sand Martins, with pipes placed in the retaining wall as nesting places. He dug out a stream to attract and encourage Grey Herons and eventually could boast a heronry consisting of between 60 and 70 nests each year. Extensive tree planting was carried out, particularly of yew and holly as roosting cover for birds, and his major undertaking was to surround the whole of the 260-acre (105-ha) estate with a substantial wall for the purpose of excluding poachers.

In our eyes now, Charles Waterton certainly appears a most remarkable man, though — perhaps not unnaturally, especially in view of certain other mild idio-syncrasies in his behaviour and spartan lifestyle — he was often regarded as being something of an eccentric by many people at that time. Nevertheless, he undoubtedly had a profound effect on general attitudes to wildlife, and it was this changing climate of opinion which led to the protection work which began in Yorkshire only four years after his death.

Other significant developments had also been taking place at about this time. The first half of the nineteenth century had witnessed a quite astonishing upsurge of interest in natural history and related sciences, and this had been accompanied by the same robust enthusiasm and vitality which characterised so many facets of Victorian society. In consequence, numerous natural history and local scientific societies were established and flourished in that exciting era; and, as elsewhere in the country, several of the Yorkshire societies soon recognised the benefits to be gained from some form of organised contact with each other, both for the purpose of exchanging information and to establish systems of regional recording.

It was in the 1860s, at a time when egg collecting and the shooting of wild birds were at their peaks, that Yorkshire naturalists were instrumental in promoting the very first act of legislation which protected birds for other than sporting purposes. The focus of this historical event was the large seabird colonies on the cliffs at Bempton and Flamborough. Here, from the 1830s, could be witnessed the com-bined elements of commercial exploitation, appalling cruelty and sheer ignorance. Steamships from Bridlington regularly took large parties of shooters beneath the cliffs, and sounded their sirens, which caused all the birds to take to the air. They then faced an intense barrage of shot! Charles Waterton had been appalled by all this senseless destruction and also by the fate of the young birds left to starve on the nest ledges, which he had described in his book *Essays on Natural History*, published in 1838. Thousands of Kittiwakes and terns were also shot annually in Bridlington Bay, and their wings and feathers sent to London to supply the demands of the millinery trade.

These atrocious activities continued for many years, but in 1868 Professor Alfred Newton, a founder member of the British Ornithologists' Union and the then editor of *The Ibis*, drew widespread attention to this mass slaughter in his address to the British Association. The resulting publicity, together with the unjust accusation in the national press that it was almost entirely the fault of the local people, prompted the Reverend H.F. Barnes-Lawrence, Vicar of the Priory Church of Bridlington, to call a meeting of the clergy and naturalists of the county to consider ways of stop-ping the Bempton shootings. In this he was vigorously supported by another clergyman, the Reverend Francis Orpen Morris, who was Vicar of Nunburnholme in the East Riding. Morris had already made a major contribution to the expanding popular interest in natural history, having produced in easily available monthly parts his *Natural History of British Birds* (1850-57), *A Natural History of Nests and Eggs of British Birds* (1851-53), and also *A Natural History of British Butterflies* (1852-53). This had been an incredible output in so relatively brief a period, and it established him as a prominent and influential naturalist.

The result of this historic meeting was the formation of the East Riding Asso-ciation for the Protection of Sea Birds, which very soon had the support of many influential men, including the two major landowners at Bempton and Flamborough, the Archbishop of York and several Yorkshire members of parliament. The asso-ciation realised their aims the following year when the MP for the East Riding, Christopher Sykes of Sledmere House, introduced a Bill into Parliament which was supported by many scientific organisations. The historic Sea Birds Preservation Act became law in June 1869, and provided protection for 35 species by a close season running from 1st April to 1st August. The eggs, though, were specifically excluded from the Act at the request of the local 'climmers' (or climbers), who for generations had traditionally harvested the eggs and whose trade had been badly affected by the more recent shootings. These hardy men had a long tradition of working certain sections of the cliffs on a rotational basis so as to ensure a continuous supply of eggs, which were sold for food on the markets of the West Riding and even as far afield as London. This was the livelihood of several local families, and, although the practice continued up to the end of the Second World War, it subsequently declined and was stopped finally in 1954 with the introduction of the Protection of Birds Act.

The Sea Birds Preservation Act was the forerunner of several Acts of Parliament, giving wider degrees of protection, which soon followed, and these were all later revised under the Wild Birds Protection Act which received the Royal Assent in 1880. With the 1869 Act on the statute book, however, the society formed by Barnes-Lawrence seems to have died a natural death. It was another 20 years before the group of ladies in London formed the Society for the Protection of Birds (the forerunner of the RSPB) for the purpose of campaigning against the then extensive plumage trade. It was also at this same time that another new protection organisation came into being in Yorkshire.

At the Yorkshire Naturalists' Union Annual General Meeting in Scarborough in 1891, it was resolved to form a special committee 'for the purpose of co-operating with the one appointed at the last meeting of the British Association to consider proposals for legislative protection of wild birds and eggs'. This marks the beginning of the YNU Yorkshire Wild Birds and Eggs Protection Committee, which, some years later, was shortened to the Wild Birds Protection Act Committee. In 1954 it was changed to the Protection of Birds Act Committee to correspond with the title of the major new legislation passed in that year, and then in 1979 the word Act was deleted and it became simply the Protection of Birds Committee.

This specialist committee has been in continuous existence now for 93 years, almost the same time as the RSPB, and during this time has played a prominent role in the history and development of bird protection in Yorkshire. Little appears to have been recorded of its activities in the initial years, which were clearly a period of evolving a pattern and initiating new schemes, but one of its very early achievements was to persuade the East Riding County Council to apply a protection order on Spurn Point in 1895, under the provisions of the Wild Birds Protection Act, because of its importance for breeding seabirds. The early bird-protection legislation did not afford automatic protection to all species everywhere, but rather gave local authorities the powers to apply protection orders in their areas, to draw up their own list of protected species and to designate certain areas as deserving special protection. Unfortunately, this often led to considerable variation from one county to another, even between different districts, and, despite sustained pressures from the protection lobby, this rather confused state of affairs continued for many years.

The East Riding County Council certainly took an early lead in these matters, for it also applied to the Home Secretary in 1904 for 'an order prohibiting during the whole year, the shooting or killing, or attempting to shoot or kill seabirds on or from the pier at Bridlington, or from the sands or seashore, or any part of the sea within an imaginary line from Flamborough South Landing to Barmston Drain'. The result of this application was the declaration of a Bird Sanctuary Order over quite extensive an area, and which remained in force up to 1960, when it was considered to be no longer necessary under current protection legislation. Another effective achievement by the protection committee in those early years was to prevail on various local authorities to impose a ban on Sunday shooting, and this eventually operated over major sections of the whole county.

By 1906 the committee had become much more firmly established, and an increased complement of 17 members drawn from various parts of Yorkshire provided a wider representation and coverage in its activities. In that year precise records commence, and these have been carefully maintained ever since. In 1907 it was decided to embark upon more direct and active measures to protect some of the rarer and more vulnerable breeding species; members dug deeply into their own pockets and a subscription fund was opened to pay the wages of their own warden at Spurn, whose particular duty was the protection of the nesting colony of some 200 pairs of Little Terns. Representatives from various natural history societies attended a special meeting held that year in Leeds, and they all agreed to provide financial assistance.

Additional temporary wardens were also employed to watch over other sensitive sites, and several bounty schemes were introduced whereby farmers and gamekeepers were financially rewarded for allowing isolated pairs of rare breeding birds to nest successfully on their land, and for preventing the activities of egg collectors. The species which benefited from such measures included Little Tern, Great Crested Grebe (which was then quite a scarce bird owing to persecution for its head feathers), Peregrine, Merlin, Raven, Buzzard, Stone-curlew (of which several pairs then nested on the Wolds), and Montagu's Harrier. Species-protection schemes have constantly remained one of the principal activities of the committee over the years, and since the 1960s the list has been extended to include such new breeding species as Marsh and Hen Harriers, Goshawk and Bearded Tit.

In 1914, the committee tried an experiment which would definitely be frowned upon today. Several pairs of Bearded Tits were purchased from Holland (the species was then virtually extinct in Britain), and released at Hornsea Mere in an attempt to get them established. Although some did in fact nest for a couple of years, the birds eventually disappeared, but of course the species has recently established itself in the county entirely under its own power. In the same year, the committee purchased a network of perches for erection on the Spurn lighthouse for the benefit of the migrant birds which were attracted to the light. Active co-operation with the RSPB stems from that time, and thenceforth numerous cases concerning illegal shooting, various forms of persecution, use of pole traps and egg collecting regularly feature in the records; this close liaison between both organisations has been fully maintained ever since. At one time the committee had to initiate its own court proceedings on infringements against the protection laws, and included a solicitor among its membership for this precise purpose.

Education, too, has always been an important objective, and during 1907 and 1908 numbers of posters were produced for display at prominent and sensitive sites around the county. In 1924, it was proposed that members should offer their services as lecturers and appropriate slide illustrations for their use were provided by those who were bird-photographers. These lectures helped to raise necessary funds and also increased public awareness of the committee's work, which is the reason for their being continued right through to the present time. Circulars for the purpose of discouraging children from collecting eggs were distributed to schools throughout the county, and numerous letters and articles featured in the local press. At one time the annual report of the committee appeared in the *Yorkshire Post*, and all this early publicity made bird protection a widely appreciated issue.

In 1914, the committee again became directly involved in legislative matters when W.H. St Quintin of Scampston Hall near Malton (he was chairman from 1906 to 1932) presented submissions in person to an important Royal Commission inquiry on bird protection. Similar representations and comments have been made since that time, particularly prior to the introduction of the Protection of Birds Act in 1954, and more recently during the consultative stages of the Wildlife and Countryside Act. The use of local authority protection orders on certain species was also continued. As a result of very sustained pressure, the West Riding County Council instigated a protection order in 1919 on the Green Plover (or Lapwing), and this was soon followed by similar provisions in the North and East Ridings. Prior to that time, huge numbers of their eggs were collected annually for sale on the London markets. In 1922, when the first Fulmars started to nest at Bempton, the species was added to the East Riding Special Schedule for Protection, and the same applied to the Gannet when the first breeding attempt occurred in 1937.

Reference to the past records and minute books reveals not only much of considerable ornithological interest, but also provides a fascinating insight into the type of people who have been so actively involved in bird protection in Yorkshire over the years. Something of the order of 95 different individuals are referred to in the files. In the Edwardian period, the majority of the committee were prominent and highly respected naturalists who contributed substantially to the early ornithological records — names like Riley Fortune, who was also a pioneer bird-photographer, Henry B. Booth, W. Dennison Roebuck, Jasper Atkinson, E.W. Wade, Thomas H. Nelson, W.J. Clarke, Leonard Gaunt, Thomas Bunker and S.H. Smith. The name of Henry Eeles Dresser, a very distinguished ornithologist of international repute, features on the list of early members up to the time of his death in 1915. He was born at Thirsk in 1838, and had travelled extensively throughout Europe, Russia and North America. He published a number of erudite monographs, and his magnificently illustrated *History of the Birds of Europe and the Western Palaearctic*, published in eight handsome volumes (1875-81), was the acknowledged 'handbook' of the day.

Ralph Chislett joined the protection committee in 1921, and remained a member up to the time of his death in 1964. The longest-serving member, however, was Dr Edward Wilfred Taylor, who joined the committee in 1911 and served continuously through to 1972: an incredible period of 61 years, the last 24 of which as chairman. In the 1930s R.M. Garnett and W.F. Medlicott became actively involved, and were later largely responsible, together with C.E.A. Burnham and H.O. Bunce, for the measures to protect the breeding Montagu's Harriers. William Bennett also appeared on the protection scene at that time, and in the late 1940s he organised a group of regular volunteers from among the Leeds Birdwatchers' Club and others, even getting them enrolled as Special Police Constables, to warden the washlands of the lower Aire Valley against extensive illegal shooting.

Since the Second World War, a number of other notable Yorkshire ornithologists have been active members of the protection committee: G.H. Ainsworth who, together with Ralph Chislett, founded the Spurn Bird Observatory, A.J. Wallis, V.S. Crapnell, J. Cudworth, A.H.B. Lee, A.F.G. Walker, C. Wilson (one-time chairman of RSPB Council), J.R. Govett, R. Crossley and R.F. Dickens, to mention but a few.

There have been many changes since bird protection as such first began. Right up to the Second World War very few organisations concerned with wildlife protection even existed, and bird protection in Yorkshire had been virtually in the sole hands of the YNU Protection Committee. Since the late 1940s the whole nature conservation movement has expanded dramatically, with support coming from a wide variety of associated and kindred organisations as more and more of the populace have become concerned with environmental and countryside conservation generally. The Yorkshire Wildlife Trust and the RSPB are now protecting several of the county ornithological sites of regional, national and international importance, with nature reserves established at Spurn Point, Bempton Cliffs, Hornsea Mere, Wheldrake Ings, Blacktoft Sands, Fairburn Ings, Potteric Carr and many more smaller sites. The Humber Wildfowl Refuge was the first of such to be established, and is more fully described elsewhere in this book.

The Nature Conservancy Council, the statutory government agency responsible for nature conservation, maintains a strong and active presence throughout the region, as does the RSPB through its structure of regional offices and staff. The Yorkshire Wildlife Trust, the second oldest in the county nature-conservation-trust movement, deals with a whole range of conservation issues in addition to owning or leasing nearly 50 nature reserves, and has responsibility for many more management agreement sites. The 44 active local natural history societies located throughout the county, which are now federated to the Yorkshire Naturalists' Union, undertake much of the important recording work, and they provide many of the essential data that are always required to substantiate or support the majority of nature conservation issues.

There is nowadays considerable co-operation between all the various organisations which may at any time be involved in conservation or protection matters, including the county and district planning authorities, the Yorkshire Dales and the North Yorkshire Moors National Park Committees and staff, and many others in the voluntary sector. Regrettably, though, the pressure on the countryside, and on wildlife in particular, is now more intense than ever owing to fundamental changes which have destroyed, or altered, or reduced much of the more natural types of habitat; and it seems particularly ironic that, despite more than 100 years of protection legislation, the various threats to wild birds still exist, and this is especially so in the case of the rarer and more sensitive species. Active species-protection measures therefore still have to be maintained by the YNU Protection of Birds Committee, the RSPB and the Yorkshire Wildlife Trust, with considerable help provided by other organisations, various landowners, local societies and individual birdwatchers.

Yorkshire has a long history of active involvement in the affairs of bird protection, and through the combined efforts of the several organisations and the many people involved, this fine and worthy tradition is still being maintained.

February 1984

Yorkshire Bird-Photographers

Yorkshire has produced so many good bird-photographers that it is appropriate to include some details in the present work, and I have accordingly asked Arthur Gilpin to contribute the following chapter. He was naturally reluctant to include himself, but, as one of the best and most successful exponents of the art, he certainly deserves acknowledgement. He has been actively involved in bird-photography for over 50 years and is still an enthusiast, sharing hides with G.V. Adkin as recently as 1983. He has travelled widely in Britain, and has been to Hawk Mountain in Pennsylvania and to South Africa in pursuit of his hobby.

A past president and secretary of the Zoological Photographic Club, Arthur Gilpin has also been the Secretary of the Association of British Nature Photographers. He is a founder and a life member of the Royal Naval Birdwatching Society and was involved in the formation of the Leeds Birdwatchers' Club. By his example as a photographer and from the offices that he has held, he has exerted a considerable influence on British bird-photography, and the University of Leeds presented him with an honorary degree of Master of Science for his work in that field.

Some of his work and that of G.K. Yeates, W.E. Higham, G.V. Adkin and J. Armitage appears elsewhere in this book.

Contributed by Arthur Gilpin

From the earliest days of bird-photography there have been Yorkshiremen among its leading exponents. The Kearton brothers, born at Thwaite in Swaledale, were the first of these and their pioneering work was the foundation upon which British bird-photography was built. In their own time they were famous and now, 80 years later, theirs is the only name that most people associate with those early days. The only formal education that Richard and Cherry received was at the tiny village school at Muker in Swaledale; even so, when assisting at a grouse shoot, Richard so impressed one of the sportsmen that he was offered a job at Cassells the publishers. He was in his twenties at the time and did not enjoy his early days in London. Writing of that period, he said 'We were struggling with a Yorkshireman's independence and fourteen shillings a week, to maintain ourselves in London.'

He prospered, and on 11th April 1895, after finding the attractively sited nest of a Song Thrush near his Enfield home, asked Cherry to photograph it with his recently acquired camera. So good was the result that the brothers decided to combine photography with their interest in natural history. Realising that, if they wished to portray birds at the nest, a hiding place would be necessary, they had hides made in the shapes of an ox, sheep, tree stump and large rock. Experience taught them that such modelling was unnecessarily complicated and that a small tent, if properly introduced, would do as well.

Their results were extremely good, and for technique and artistry the best of their work can be compared with the best monochrome pictures taken today. Early this century, Cherry saw the possibilities of cine-photography and, after making some films of British birds, he went to East Africa to photograph big game. Again in the lead, his films of African Wildlife were the first of their kind to be shown in British cinemas. On 4th August 1914 — the day the First World War commenced — Richard was on the Bass Rock photographing Gannets. With him was his friend and contemporary, Jasper Atkinson of Leeds.

Joining the Zoological Photographic Club in the 1930s, I came to know Atkinson well. He was thin, in his seventies, and I was greatly impressed with his kindness and character. Originally a shooting man, he gave this up when he started taking bird-photographs and said 'I could not photograph grouse in spring and shoot them in August!' A bachelor and a cricket enthusiast, he believed in playing the game for the game's sake, and detested any form of faking. Some of his finest bird-photography was done in 1912, when he was with a group photographing Peregrines at a site on one of the Scilly Isles, where he obtained pictures of the birds at their eyrie. When, in 1924, he visited Öland in the Baltic with Mr and Mrs Ralph Chislett, he added Black-tailed Godwit and Turnstone to his 'bag'.

Riley Fortune, who lived in Harrogate, was contemporaneous with the photographers already mentioned. He was a prolific worker and about 140 of his photographs, mainly of nests and eggs, were published in Nelson's *The Birds of Yorkshire* (1907). Like some other early bird-photographers, Fortune photographed captive as well as wild birds and much of his work appeared in journals and magazines. Unfortunately, his careless attitude to darkroom techniques prevented some of his work reaching the highest standard of his period.

Two Yorkshire bird-photographers whose work was outstanding in the first half of this century were Ralph Chislett and Tom Fowler. The name of the first-mentioned is 'writ in letters large' in the annals of the Yorkshire Naturalists' Union, and his services to that body have been given recognition elsewhere in this book. It is, however, worthy of note that not long after the last war he gave up his photography to allow himself more time for field ornithology in the country, and in addition to extensive journeys in search of birds in Britain he also visited Öland and Swedish Lapland. His book *Northward Ho! For Birds* tells the story of his travels and adventures. He set himself a high standard as a photographer, and his work in both field and darkroom was of exceptional quality.

The interest of his contemporary and friend, Tom Fowler, was in British birds and he did not photograph abroad. He was particularly interested in those that nested in trees, and on estates around his native Barnsley he took pictures of Rooks, Sparrowhawks, Long-eared Owls and many others at the nest. Although his work was of the highest quality, little of it was published. He did not like the editorial practice of reproducing only the picture of the bird and its immediate surroundings, feeling that an injustice was done to the original composition, and did not seek publication. When Fowler retired he moved to Suffolk and there, before he died, did some original work in photographing Shelducks at their nests in holes in pollarded oaks.

W.W. Nicholas of Hessle was in the same age group as the two last-mentioned photographers, but he came to bird-photography later in life. Much of his material was found on trips to the Scottish Highlands and Islands, and he also visited Northern Ireland. In addition, he took photographs of the species around his East Riding home. He preferred to photograph birds serially, starting with a portrait of the nest and eggs, and ending it with pictures of the young ready to leave the nest. Herons, Black-throated Divers and Sparrowhawks received this treatment. It is probable that, of all his photographs, the best remembered will be those of Choughs nesting in a Northern Ireland cliff crevice.

Each generation of bird-photographers overlaps the previous one, and H.R. Lowes, whose mentor was Tom Fowler, had already become a talented exponent of the hobby in the 1920s. For some 40 years I had the privilege of being his partner. His work in the field, his taste in choosing what and what not to photograph, and his ability to make prints of outstanding quality earned him the admiration of his fellow bird-photographers. As he shared Fowler's views on the cropping of prints by editors, he too did not seek publication. He enjoyed building hides in trees and photographed many species that nested there. Photographs of a Goshawk in Jutland have probably given him the greatest satisfaction. In the early 1970s, the increasing restrictions on bird-photography prompted him to call it a day and he discontinued his hobby. He now lives in Harrogate, and the attractive appearance of his garden is indicative of the time that he devotes to it. He continues to enjoy the birds, flowers and butterflies seen on his walks.

Coming to bird-photography at about the same time as Harold Lowes was G.K. Yeates, who now lives at High Birstwith. Born in Leeds, he soon became widely known, for he wrote, and illustrated with his excellent photographs, many very readable books about his birding expeditions. The early volumes were about British birds and they were followed by accounts of his adventures in the Rhône Delta and in Iceland. Whether of a common bird or of a rarity, his photographs were noted for their artistic quality and technical excellence. He was a keen wildfowler, and it is therefore not surprising that he particularly enjoyed photographing the Pink-footed Goose in Iceland. Another favourite was that magnificent bird, the Great Northern Diver. His visits to the Camargue yielded pratincoles, Flamingos and Bee-eaters.

Born in Wakefield in 1909, A.M. Stone was interested in the creatures of the countryside from boyhood; while still in his teens, he photographed Lapwings that were nesting near to his home. His hobby was, however, interrupted by the studies needed to prepare him for his entry into the ministry of the church. When ordained and appointed to a country parish, he again found time to pursue his hobby. His photographs were characterised by their critical definition and clarity. Most of his work was done around the vicarages in which he lived, although he took some fine photographs of Scottish birds. Upon retirement he settled in Wales, where he died a few years ago.

Two York photographers whose work should have been more widely known were F. Jefferson and W. Farnsworth. Both made first-class lantern slides and lectured within the county, but to the best of my knowledge they had little contact with other bird-photographers. Fred Jefferson worked among the Wood Warblers, Pied Flycatchers, Nuthatches and Dippers of Duncombe Park. William Farnsworth did much of his bird-photography around the village of Haxby, where he lived, and also produced some very fine prints of captive mammals photographed in natural-looking surroundings.

Arthur Butler, who lived for a time near York, was born at Mexborough. Like most bird-photographers, he cannot remember a time when he was not interested in birds. Although most of his photography has been done in Britain, he had worked also in Trinidad and Tobago, where he had a special interest in humming-birds. As can be expected of a keen member of several photographic societies and a frequent exhibitor, his technique is of the best and he is particularly keen on good definition. Needless to say, his work is appreciated not only by his colleagues but by all those interested in good photography. Now retired, he has left Yorkshire and is photographing birds in the Welsh borders and on expeditions for special species.

George R. Edwards and Vernon S. Crapnell, two bird-photographers who were working in the Halifax area in the third decade of this century, concentrated on cine-photography. One of the great events of their early days was finding the first nest of a Temminck's Stint recorded in Britain. When eventually Edwards turned professional, Crapnell continued to photograph birds on his own, making prints in addition to films. Edwards began his worldwide travels: he became cine-photographer for the RSPB, made films of Sir Vivian Fuchs's expeditions to the Antarctic, then, working for Anglia Television, he photographed birds in many exotic places; a great deal of his work has been seen on the small screen. Although now living outside the county, he is still a familiar figure on his frequent visits to Spurn.

Soon after the last war, A. Faulkner Taylor and Harold A. Hems, both from the Sheffield area, teamed up to do bird-photography and were very successful. Unfortunately, owing to sickness in his family, Taylor had a comparatively short career in nature-photography, but in that limited time he produced many fine prints and films. Hems continued, and, although birds were his main interest, few if any nature-photographers have done work of equal quality on small, wild mammals. Now living on the Norfolk coast, in a house with a large garden in which he has photographed many species, he has also produced many fine pictures of rarities that have occurred in the surrounding area. A series of his photographs of Brent Geese was used in *British Birds*. When the material for making colour prints became available, he was quick to take advantage and most of his work is now done in that medium.

The present generation of bird-photographers has been quick to take advantage of the comparative ease with which one can travel to distant countries. Many from Yorkshire have taken pictures in faraway places. Vernon Adkin, whose home is at Sutton-in-Craven, has been on four photographic expeditions to Kenya and has also visited the American Everglades. In addition, he has done a considerable amount of work in Yorkshire's dales and in Scotland. Birds of prey feature in his large collection of photographs, and those of Peregrine, Merlin and Hen Harrier please him no less than the pictures of birds that he has taken abroad. Like so many present-day bird-photographers, he works extensively in colour and the standard of both his prints and transparencies is a high one.

Living, and taking photographs, in much the same area as did the late W.W. Nicholas, Michael Holliday of Cottingham is producing fine colour prints of its birds in addition to those that he has photographed in other parts of Britain. When working at the nest, he chooses photogenic sites and aims at good composition. He finds his enjoyment in making pictures, and to him pictorial sites are of more importance than the rarity of the species. His photographic trips to Scotland and Wales have been for species that do not breed near his home, rather than for uncommon birds. Having been trained as a photographer, he uses large-format negatives in his search for perfection.

Barry Nattress and Roger Hainsworth, both of whom live near Leeds, partner each other not only in photographing birds but also in taking pictures of other types of wild creatures. They are interested in photographing bird parasites as well as their hosts, and their prints and transparencies are of a wide range of subjects. Knowledgeable naturalists, they enjoy their time in the countryside, even when it is not possible to take photographs. They have used their cameras on birds, other creatures and plants in many parts of Britain, and they do not look upon photography as seasonal but take pictures throughout the year.

A Yorkshireman, living in York, Derrick Bonsall also photographs many forms of wildlife in addition to birds, and has produced some very fine colour pictures of butterflies. Like many others who are interested in birds, he has found that northern Scotland has an irresistible appeal. There, amid its moors and within sight of the mountains, he has photographed such attractive species as Red-throated Diver, Greenshank and Merlin.

There are more Yorkshire bird-photographers now than ever before, and many are doing good work. To any that I have missed, either from lack of memory or space, I tender my apologies. I cannot, however, end this narrative without mention of three bird-photographers who, while not Yorkshire-born, have spent major parts of their lives in the county. Walter E. Higham was a Lancastrian associated with the cotton industry. He had periods when his health was not good, and that may have been the reason for his move to Harrogate on the drier side of the Pennines. He was of the same generation as Ralph Chislett and Tom Fowler. Making long spring stays in his favourite parts of Norfolk and Scotland, he made detailed plans well in advance. Abroad, he took bird-photographs in Hungary and the Camargue. His cine-films and still pictures were among the best of his period and he was truly professional. From Broadland he had photographs of Bittern, Water Rail and the now extremely rare Montagu's Harrier. His impressive series of photographs of Golden Eagles was the result of years of preparation and many journeys to Scotland. Ill health brought his photographic career to a premature end, and he moved to the Channel Islands where, a few years later, he died.

Another Lancastrian, John Armitage moved to Leeds to take the post of Keeper of Biology at the City Museum. For many years before that he had been a professional lecturer, giving his accounts of the wildlife of places that in those days few people had visited. He gathered material in Spain, Morocco, Finland and the West Indies. His camera was a small and rather simple one that had previously belonged to his friend T.A. Coward, but he produced many fine pictures with it. Beautifully hand-coloured and covering a wide variety of subjects, his lantern slides are legendary. Born in the early days of this century, he gave up his photography some years ago, but he is still using his slides for lectures and lessons on many forms of natural history.

Morley Hedley was not a Yorkshireman and it is a coincidence that his first name was the same as that of the town in which he spent much of his life. He had a country cottage near Helmsley for some years, and after that one at Masham, where he and his family enjoyed their weekends and holiday periods, during which he took excellent photographs of the small birds in the countryside around. By the time he retired, he was a widower and went to live on Islay, although he kept a *pied-à-terre* near Leeds, to which he returned each year at Christmas. While on Islay, the photographs that he took of small parties of flying Barnacle and Greenland White-fronted Geese were in a class of their own. Morley died on the island he loved, early in the present decade.

December 1984

Some Sites of Special Interest

There are several sites in Yorkshire that have become well known to birdwatchers through the dedicated efforts of certain people who have carried out observations over long periods of time at their favourite localities. Bird-ringing, especially, has tended to anchor observers in one particular place and three such sites are included in this section. Spurn Bird Observatory, Filey Brigg and the Humber Wildfowl Refuge are also well known and brief histories of these and other, inland, sites are included.

I have invited those people who have been instrumental in setting up these establishments, or who are actively involved in the continued running of them, to contribute the following chapters. There are many other sewage-farms, reservoirs and gravel-pits which are watched regularly by groups of people and it would be impossible to give accounts of them all. The important records from such places are included in the systematic list of species.

Spurn Bird Observatory
Contributed by J. Cudworth

There was a good deal of interest in the birds of Spurn and the nearby parts of Holderness during the second half of the nineteenth and the early years of the present century, an interest that stemmed from the first visit of J. Cordeaux to Spurn in July 1868. He visited the peninsula regularly over the next 30 years from his home in north Lincolnshire and, as importantly, tried to collect information on birds in the area in a systematic way for publication in *The Naturalist* and *The Zoologist*. In the 1880s he frequently accompanied his friend, W. Eagle Clarke, on his trips to Spurn and it was almost certainly the work of these two that prompted others to visit the area: some were members of the Yorkshire Naturalists' Union, some came from farther afield. Notable among the latter were H.F. Witherby, C.B. Ticehurst and T.A. Coward. Two local shooters, the brothers George Edwin Clubley and Craggs Clubley of Kilnsea, should also be mentioned; George Edwin is remembered for his bagging the Macqueen's (Houbara) Bustard in 1896 when it had eluded the guns of the visiting ornithologists. That period, still the age of collecting, a necessary evil which gave a firm foundation to our present knowledge of birds, came to an end in 1912 when J.K. Stanford spent two weeks in September at Spurn. He was fortunate enough to get some easterly weather and obtained a Blyth's Reed Warbler — we had to wait 72 years for the second.

There followed almost 20 years when little was heard about birds at Spurn. The YNU kept a contact with the area through its Bird Protection Committee which, in most years, employed a watcher to look after the breeding Little Terns and Ringed Plovers. But, apart from the annual reports on the breeding successes, there were few other records published. It can only be assumed that few people interested in birds visited Spurn at that time.

Then, in 1929, H.O. Bunce and L. Smith began to visit the area regularly, mainly at weekends from March to September. Their main interest was in photographing birds at the nest and they admit to probably missing unusual migrants through inexperience. They did, however, record the sometimes day-long movements of Swifts in June and early July, Shelducks heading out east in July, and days when Wheatears 'flickered' everywhere and there were large numbers of Redstarts and Willow Warblers. In 1934 G.R. Edwards, V.S. Crapnell and several other Halifax members began a series of short and almost annual visits. On these, at least at first, they concentrated on the birds of the coast and the mudflats, so unfamiliar to inland watchers at that time. In the late 1930s other people, including R. Chislett, R.M. Garnett, G.H. Ainsworth and J. Lord, also visited Spurn and a communal log for observations was instituted in 1938. This included a roll-call of species, the beginnings of a recording system which has become standard at bird observatories. Soon these visitors began to think of the peninsula as a suitable place for setting up a bird observatory, to be run on similar lines to those already established on the Isle of May and on Skokholm. They also saw Warren Cottage at the north end of the peninsula as an ideal headquarters for such an observatory; R.M. Garnett suggested that its garden would be just the site for a Heligoland trap. R. Chislett approached the War Department Northern Command and was promised the tenancy of the cottage when it became vacant. Any further plans had to be shelved when war was declared in September 1939; the last visit to the peninsula in that year was in late August. During the war years permission was granted for occasional day visits, mainly by G.H. Ainsworth, from autumn 1943, so there was some continuity even at that time.

The original idea of R. Chislett was to get a lease of Warren Cottage for himself and a few ornithological friends to carry on and develop the kind of observations begun in 1938. H.B. Booth had suggested that the YNU should be involved if a lease were obtained. The intervening war years probably allowed the germ of this idea to grow, because when, late in 1945, the War Department Lands Department offered the lease of Warren Cottage the bird observatory was set up under the auspices of the YNU, and not as a private venture. It was the third to be established in Britain and the first on the mainland. R. Chislett, G.H. Ainsworth, J. Lord and R.M. Garnett formed the first committee to administer the observatory.

Initially, the coverage was during the main migration seasons, with an attempt made to have the observatory manned at least in May, September and October. In the early 1950s, successful trapping of Snow Buntings in the winter encouraged coverage at that time of year, albeit only at the weekends. This was followed by similar visits during the late spring and summer. An interest in birds throughout the year was fostered, though the main migration seasons were still the prime periods. Then, in 1959, there was an important move: the Yorkshire Naturalists' Trust (now the Yorkshire Wildlife Trust) became the owner of the peninsula, and a full-time warden was appointed in 1960. He is the employee of the trust, but helps the observatory as and when his other duties allow. The observatory has been fortunate in that the first warden, P.J. Mountford, was an ornithologist, as is B.R. Spence, the warden since 1964. This has meant that there has been some sort of coverage almost daily since 1960. One person cannot, however, do full justice to the various observatory activities, but at least he can record the main feature of any day, whether it be, for example, visible passage along the peninsula, a movement of seabirds or ducks offshore or numbers of grounded migrants present, and can try to concentrate on that aspect as time permits.

The four activities which contribute to the study of birds at Spurn are the ringing of birds, the counts of visible migration, sea-watching, and the walkabout to check on the numbers of grounded birds. Ringing was the main activity during the early years, probably because of its novelty as a tool in the study of birds, and it is still an important part of the work of the observatory. At first, most birds were caught in Heligoland traps, with some in small automatic traps. Over the years there have been eight Heligoland traps at Spurn, the one built near Warren Cottage in October 1945 having been operated ever since. The choice of its siting was certainly a wise one. It has been consistently successful and has turned up several 'firsts' for Spurn or even for the county, most already in the holding area of the trap when found. In 1949, a second Heligoland was built on the Point dunes. This promised to be another excellent choice of site, judged by the results of the first autumn, but in early October 1950 the Army authorities decided to bulldoze the sand dunes to afford better sighting for the coastal batteries. Most of the material was rescued from the trap and used to re-build it in the 'wire-dump'. This trap, still in operation, has proved to be an important one in an open site. Newcomers to Spurn obviously wonder about the name 'wire-dump'; this area, in the southern half of the small saltmarsh at Chalk Bank, was so called because the Army had dumped piles of barbed wire after clearing various wartime entanglements. In the 1950s these piles, acting as artificial shrubberies as good as heaps of brushwood, attracted chats, warblers and flycatchers. Gradually, the wire corroded, and now there are no visible signs of it. After being relatively obsolete for several years, the trap has come into its own again with the development of tape-lures, enabling Meadow Pipits to be caught in large numbers in September and October. A double-ended Heligoland trap was built at Chalk Bank in 1951, about 400 yards (365 m) north of the wire-dump. This had soon to be converted into two traps because of the inherent difficulty of using one holding area with two entrances! In 1964 the southern half was abandoned, and in 1972 it was decided to dismantle the rest. The area was attracting fewer birds and the cost of repairing traps was constantly rising. This phase of trap building came to an end in 1956 with Chalk Bank East, a small Heligoland on the east side of the peninsula. This was lost to coastal erosion when one tide swept a whole dune away in early March 1963.

Soon after the Yorkshire Naturalists' Trust became the owner of the peninsula, it was decided to build another Heligoland at the Point, this time on the east side of the Point camp, an area hitherto closed to observations because of the military presence. This trap showed how useful a Heligoland can be during the large Blackbird arrival on 5th November 1961, when it would have been unwise to have used mist-nets; it also caught large numbers of Fieldfares in the late autumns of 1965 and 1966, but was abandoned in 1977 because of the threat of coastal erosion. The last Heligoland to be built and still in use was again at the Point. Known as the Hollow trap, it was completed in 1966 on the south side of the open area of short turf known as the 'parade ground'. The only other permanent trap is the House trap at the Warren, built in early autumn 1974.

The use of mist-nets (since 1958) has shown how many warblers may be on the peninsula on any one day (such as the 63 Blackcaps caught on 8th October 1974). It has also enabled skulking species to be caught, no matter where on the peninsula, and this is sometimes necessary to confirm identification; and it has sometimes revealed the presence of species otherwise unsuspected, the best example of which is the River Warbler in 1981, not seen before capture nor after release. 'Flick-netting', originally developed for catching Swifts, was adapted for sampling the hirundines that migrate along the peninsula. Again, coastal erosion has stopped this activity through the loss of the dunes north of the 'narrow neck'. A more recent addition to catching techniques has been the 'dazzle-netting' of waders on the Humber shore.

In 1968, part of one of the derelict buildings at the Point was converted into a ringing laboratory in preparation for the British Trust for Ornithology Ringing Course in October that year, and in every October since. Better facilities for ringing were provided at the Warren in 1971, when half of one of the derelict buildings there was also made into a laboratory.

The idea of lengthy observations from one place really stemmed from 1951 with the visit from S. Ulfstrand from southern Sweden, where this practice had been developed at Falsterbo. The narrow neck was found to be the ideal spot for counting migrants passing along the peninsula; incoming and outgoing migrants, many crossing at this most easterly point, could also be seen, as well as birds over the sea and the Humber. In 1961 the observers were given a base, and a welcome shelter and windbreak, when part of an old Army hut was moved on to the site. In the early days such watches tended to be for only an hour or so, more or less just sampling what was taking place; nowadays, they are likely to be for the minimum of three hours, may continue for as long as any movement lasts, and are part of the daily routine, given that there are the necessary observers present.

Sea-watching was pioneered in the late 1940s and the early 1950s by G.R. Edwards. Like the watches for visible migration, those for 'ocean-gazing', as sea-watching used to be called, were fairly short at first; there was no question of watching for hour after hour to get some idea of totals for the day. Gradually, the willingness to stay all day if necessary, so long as birds were moving, developed. This was helped in 1965 by the provision of a sea-watching hut, kindly made and erected by a Barnsley group, led by D.J. Standring. This facility put sea-watching on a firm footing as all attention was focused on the sea; observations could be carried out in otherwise impossible weather conditions. The hut has had a chequered career, being now in its fourth position because of the ever-present threat of coastal erosion. The frequency with which it has had to be moved serves as a good indicator of the amount of erosion that has occurred over the last 20 years.

Then, finally, there is the walkabout to check on birds present. Ideally, the whole area should be covered, and this can sometimes be combined with driving the Heligoland traps to record where birds are, so that fairly accurate numbers can be arrived at at log time. This includes, of course, looking at the birds on the Humber mudflats; experience of the habits and preferences of different species has indicated the best times and places to do this.

The four activities are helping to build up an accurate picture of birds at Spurn. They are showing not only the main migration seasons of many species, but also how long the actual seasons can be. Some species once thought to be unusual are now known to be regular migrants and others to occur in larger numbers than suspected at one time. What migrants may occur at Spurn depends completely on the weather situation at any time, particularly on the wind direction. Given the appropriate conditions, diurnal migrants will pass through, seabirds, ducks and waders will move offshore, or nocturnal migrants will be grounded.

The peninsula as a whole has not changed much over the years, except that it is more overgrown and with a reduced variety of habitats, and that the area around the Warren at the base of the peninsula has suffered not only from loss of habitat but also from loss of land. Not only are there fewer places to attract and hold migrants but there are fewer alternative places for them when they are disturbed. Such disturbance by day visitors has greatly increased during the last 20 years. For the observatory itself there is the long-term worry that even its accommodation may be lost to the continuing threat from the sea.

February 1985

Knaresborough Ringing Station
Contributed by D.R.J. Watkins

Since its formation in the early 1950s, the members of Knaresborough Ringing Station have, up to the end of 1984, recorded 182 different species of birds within the recording area and have ringed more than 100,000 — no small achievement for a 4-acre (1.6-ha) site and a small dedicated group of people.

The actual ringing station is a small rectangular piece of land lying within a large loop of the River Nidd just southeast of Knaresborough. To the east stretches the flat farmland of the Plain of York, and west of the town the foothills of the Pennines rise through mixed woodland and farmland to the heather moors.

John R. Mather first became interested in the area in 1945 when, as a teenager, he birdwatched along the river's edge and in the adjacent sewage-farm. During the following years he spent a great deal of time in the area, and in 1953, on receiving his ringing permit, concentrated all his efforts there. J.A.S. Borrett, a ringer and bird-photographer from York, became a regular companion during the 1950s and P.J. Murton, a serving RAF Officer, was actively involved during the 1960s, as was Major 'Tigger' Worrin.

About this time, the Farnley Sand and Gravel Company re-opened an old sand-pit on the adjacent land and began to work extensively for gravel. The resulting slurry pools soon attracted a wide range of birds; waders and ducks were frequent visitors, especially at the weekends when pumping operations ceased and the water level dropped to reveal large areas of mud on which the birds fed. In 1955, with the co-operation of the quarry owners and the help and encouragement of R.F. Dickens, the first Heligoland trap was built in an unused corner of the quarry by the side of the river. These were still pioneering days for bird-ringers and liaison with other groups, particularly the Wharfedale Naturalists' Society and the Harrogate ringers A.F.G. Walker and Miss M.R. Sanderson, brought mutual benefits and new techniques. Starlings were one of the main species to be caught and ringed, and much work was done on ageing and sexing by J.R. Mather, R. Evison and G.R. Wilkinson, the last a very active member until his death in 1973.

Gravel extraction ceased in 1959 and the land began to mature vegetatively, with Lapwings and Redshanks now breeding and Teals and Snipe becoming frequent visitors to the overgrown pools, where they were caught in grain-baited traps. With the emergence of *Juncus*, gorse and willows, Reed Buntings and Sedge Warblers were quick to colonise, along with Linnets and an occasional pair of Whinchats.

At the end of 1965, bulldozers started to level off the whole site as they prepared for its return to grassland. The owners offered the area for sale, but not before contacting J.R.M. to offer him the option to purchase an area centered on the Heligoland trap. Four acres were bought and this permanency meant that a second Heligoland trap could be built. A new ringing hut was erected, having been donated by G.V. Adkin. A second shed, donated by Miss Joan Fairhurst in 1968, became the common room and provided the opportunity for overnight stays.

Sadly, the disappearance of the lagoons radically reduced the number of different species visiting the area and efforts were, in consequence, levelled at the 4-acre site. A study of Starling breeding behaviour was started in 1968 by D.M. Burn, then a student at Leeds University, which led to post-graduate research into Hippoboscid flies, parasitic on birds. For the next eight years, all birds caught between spring and autumn were examined and the flies collected. Several new host species were recorded and a great deal of information was documented.

Bird-ringing has always been the most important aspect of the station's work, and the grand total of over 100,000 birds ringed reflects the time and effort allocated to this pursuit. Although most of the birds have been ringed within the boundaries of the station, there have been occasions when members have ventured forth locally. The founder members still gain much pleasure relating to the younger personnel the dangers of ringing at heronries and rookeries. Later, there were large flocks of finches on autumn harvest fields; Sand Martins at their colonies at dawn on cool summer mornings; and Swallow roosts on clear, crisp September evenings. The sewage-farm, next to the station, has proved a productive ringing site where wagtails, pipits and Moorhens were, and are still, caught, along with hirundines and Swifts over the filter beds. Since ringing began, much emphasis has been placed on warblers and, as the annual pattern and frequency of netting has remained much the same over the years, changes in populations have been well monitored. The most spectacular example was when the Whitethroat population crashed dramatically in 1969 and only eight birds were caught after a record 234 in 1968. A decrease in the number of common small birds ringed has been apparent over the past ten years or so, this probably being linked to considerable development for both industrial and housing schemes on the nearby land.

Notable among the birds caught and ringed were the first Yorkshire inland record of Bluethroat in September 1971 and two Wrynecks caught within two days of each other in the autumn of 1976. Also recorded have been two Yellow-browed Warblers, an Icterine Warbler, the first county Savi's Warbler in May 1969 and a Great Reed Warbler in May 1984. Several other interesting species have been seen flying overhead from the observation tower, including Leach's Petrel, Fulmar, Purple Heron, Night Heron, Eider, scoters, several waders, Arctic Skuas, Honey Buzzard, Osprey, Goshawk, Red-footed Falcon and several Hobbies.

Nestboxes are an important aspect of the work and over 100 are situated in and around the ringing station. Species using the boxes annually are Kestrels, Tawny Owls, Stock Doves, Starlings, Great and Blue Tits and Tree Sparrows.

The area needs to be constantly maintained and the vegetation is rigidly controlled to provide the best habitat for breeding and passing birds. In recent years, much work has been done to encourage butterflies by creating meadow areas, and ponds have been created for damselflies and dragonflies. Moths have been caught regularly for many years and beetles, flies, spiders, caddis-flies, fungi, plants and mammals have all been studied by experts in their respective fields, aided by ringing station members. All the details are published annually in a report and the amount of information collected over the years is quite impressive, demonstrating the value of intensive study on a small area of land.

Through the kind auspices of Terry Eggleshaw of Burley, we have recently constructed a new building for our headquarters and hope to install a warden in the near future.

January 1985

Adwick-le-Street Ringing Station
Contributed by R.J. Rhodes

For more than 25 years, members of the Doncaster and District Ornithological Society have been ringing birds in the Doncaster district, and for 13 of those years at Adwick-le-Street Sewage-farm.

By 1962, after experimenting with mist-nets in a number of different habitats, most of the 14 society ringers then holding permits (the number was to peak at 22 in 1964/65) had obtained their own nets, and Adwick-le-Street Sewage-farm, with its combination of habitat variety and the large concentrations of feeding birds, was chosen as the most suitable site at which to set up a ringing station. Following permission granted by the Adwick Urban District Council for work to commence, a grant from the DDOS, supplemented by contributions from members, raised sufficient funds to purchase a ringing hut and the necessary equipment. On 29th July 1962, the first entry was made in the logbook, and in 1963 the venture was recognised by the Ringing Committee of the British Trust for Ornithology.

The sewage-farm lies approximately 4 miles (6.4km) northwest of Doncaster and is surrounded by arable land, pasture, ditches and hedgerows. From the opening date, the station was manned chiefly at weekends by a rota of registered ringers using their own nets and assisted by volunteers. Initially, seed-baited traps and clap-nets were operated in addition to the nets, but these were phased out as netting techniques improved. From the outset, most of the permanent trapping sites were created by cutting lanes and gaps through the bushes and by cutting ground vegetation. A stream favoured by many birds as a regular flight-line and feeding area was bridged to enable a net to be erected from bank to bank, and many interesting birds were caught, including Water Rail, Kingfisher and Grey Wagtail. A large patch of reeds in one of the settling beds attracted many roosting birds; among these were hirundines in August and September and Pied Wagtails from late October, many of which were caught and ringed.

During the 13 years to the end of 1975, 10,709 birds of 72 different species were ringed: thrushes, warblers, finches and buntings being in the majority. The largest annual total of birds ringed was 1,465, in 1963, the 1,000 mark being exceeded in only four further years, with the lowest total of 116 birds in 1973, which reflected the steady decrease in the number of days on which the station was being manned.

Throughout the 13 years of the station's existence, the ringing work was combined with intensive observations. Daily counts were made of all species seen, and the list included Garganey, Buzzard, Merlin, Little Stint, Curlew Sandpiper, Kittiwake and Great Grey Shrike. The first overwintering Chiffchaffs for the area were recorded in 1965, and birds showing characters of the following races were identified in the hand: Northern Great Spotted Woodpecker, Northern Willow Warbler, White Wagtail and Mealy Redpoll. A great deal of information was collected on visible migration, post-breeding and winter flocking, and autumn and winter roosts. In 1963, and subsequently, work was carried out on the study of bird ectoparasites by H.E. Beaumont and details have been published in local, county and national reports.

Modernisation of the sewage-works in the 1970s and a marked reduction in the number of active local ringers led to the cessation of activities, and by 1975 it was felt that the small number of birds being ringed annually did not warrant the considerable administrative work involved. At a specially convened meeting of the ringers and the executive committee of the DDOS, it was decided to close down the station. The ringing hut was sold, but a few individual ringers continued to trap there and some do so at the present time.

To list the names of all the people who devoted their time and energy to the project would be impossible. Some were dedicated to its success from the start, others came out of curiosity and became converts. As in every major undertaking, however, a few stand out for special mention: R.A. Marshall, W.G. Dye, B.M. Baxter, H.E. Beaumont, T. Grant (who was the first of several excellent secretaries) and finally J.B. Hague, whose contributions to the overall effort were immeasurable.

October 1984

Wintersett Reservoirs, Near Wakefield
Contributed by J.S. Armitage

This area lies midway between Barnsley and Leeds, is immediately adjacent to the village of Ryhill and comprises two reservoirs, one called Wintersett and the other Cold Hiendley. The overall area has had a long association with birds, as the Walton Hall Estate, where Charles Waterton employed wildlife conservation policies in the nineteenth century, lies a mile or so to the north. The reservoirs were built much later, to act as feeders for the Barnsley Canal, remnants of which can still be seen on the western boundary of Cold Hiendley Reservoir.

From the late 1940s to the late 1950s the reservoirs were watched frequently, though by very few people, but records such as Green-winged Teal and Sabine's Gull were particularly noteworthy. At the end of that period, the reservoirs were partially drained to relieve the weight of water from deep-mining workings being carried out beneath. This heralded the beginning of several good years of bird-watching, particularly as far as waders were concerned. A gradual build-up of water levels was allowed and the next few years, until the mid 1970s, were a period of much active birdwatching in the area.

The peak of activity which followed arose through two distinct incidents. The first was the major threat of opencast coal-mining affecting the reservoir, deposits of coal being quite clearly seen outcropping on the eastern banks of Wintersett Reservoir itself; and the second was the occurrence of two Bearded Tits in November 1973, one of which had been ringed at Minsmere in Suffolk. At that time, a small group of people consisting of J.S. Armitage, D. Faulkner, F. Mitchell, A. Porter and P. Smith had begun to visit the reservoirs on a very regular basis. A couple of meetings led the group to conclude that if good birds such as Bearded Tits and many others could keep turning up then the site warranted much more than cursory attention. It was decided that some form of inland bird observatory should be created in order to collect data which could be used to prepare a case for conservation in the event of threats from opencast mining. Thus, the Wintersett Ringing Station was formed, organised by a group that, over the years, has had various people assisting in its operation but one which is still active with considerable success.

The first few years after the inception of the ringing station proved to be an exciting period. The discovery of the actual amount of passage through the site at various seasons; the fluctuations in the winter gull roost of sometimes in excess of 10,000 birds, with a rewarding increase in sightings of Glaucous and Iceland Gulls as observations grew; and the charting of the ever-changing duck populations throughout the winter months all proved, as did many other aspects, to be absorbing fields of study in themselves. Ringing took over as a full-time occupation during certain periods, with the volume of migrant passerines, in autumn in particular, passing all initial expectations. Special circumstances sometimes arose, such as the occasion when an uncut field of cereals near the reservoirs yielded almost 1,500 birds for ringing in the first two months of that particular year, including several hundred Tree Sparrows. Another instance involved Lesser Redpolls, when in one spring their numbers often rose above 100, with a large flock being regularly present in the nearby afforested area of Haw Park; the chance location of a drinking pool provided an opportunity to ring over 600 Redpolls in a few weeks, which illustrated the amount of passage and change within the feeding flock during that particular period.

As with any well-watched area, the list of birds grew — and so did the numbers ringed — in response to increased effort, with the annual total ringed in one year exceeding 5,000 birds. Particular highlights were the ringing of a Barred Warbler and of a Siberian Stonechat, but equally attractive was the opportunity to process large numbers of warblers during the autumn.

Sadly, the situation has altered, with increased pressure from angling and various construction works causing changes in the habitat and amount of cover around the reservoirs. The threat of opencast mining, while not receding completely, has not directly affected the reservoirs, although an extremely large site has been developed to the north of them. A tremendous amount of information about the area has now been collected, and this will obviously be of use should a threat to its future ever arise. With more than 160 species being seen in most years, the value of the locality to birds, particularly to migrants, is self-evident. Despite changes, the area remains an exceptionally good site for birds and one hopes that its existence will not be threatened in future years.

November 1984

Blackmoorfoot Reservoir
Contributed by J.E. Dale

Blackmoorfoot Reservoir is situated 3 ½ miles (5.6 km) southwest of Huddersfield at an elevation of 833 feet (254 m) above sea-level. The four banks are each approximately 700 yards (640 m) in length; the greatest depth when full is 40 feet (12 m), and the gently shelving western side provides, in times of water shortage, a considerable area of shore which forms good feeding habitat for many species. Plantations of deciduous woodland fringe the west and east banks and also the western half of the south bank. That on the west provides valuable shelter from prevailing winds for birds on the shore and on the water.

A hide was built on the west bank in 1959 by members of the Huddersfield Naturalists', Antiquarian and Photographic Society, and replaced in 1970 by a new one constructed by members of the Huddersfield Birdwatchers' Club. Records of observations have been kept since 1956, and annual coverage since 1971 has been well in excess of 300 days.

Since 1956, a total of 181 species has been recorded in the reservoir area, including all the usual species of waterfowl, three species of divers and five of grebes, as well as nearly 30 species of waders, including Stone-curlew, Buff-breasted Sandpiper and Grey Phalarope. More unusual visitors to the area include Fulmar, Osprey, Pallas's Warbler and Firecrest. A gull roost first attracted attention in 1961, and subsequently proved to be of outstanding interest. Since 1971, regular counts have been carried out which have indicated both seasonal and long-term changes for the five common species. Seven other species have been observed, including Glaucous and Iceland fairly regularly, and Ring-billed on three occasions.

Bird-ringing has been undertaken regularly since 1972, particularly of Willow Warblers in the summer and finches in the autumn, the latter having provided Twite recoveries of national importance. Situated high above the Colne Valley, the area is most suitable for recording visible migration, an activity that has yet to be fully exploited.

An excellent summary of the birds of Blackmoorfoot Reservoir was produced by P. Bray for the years 1959 to 1973.

Many people from the Huddersfield Birdwatchers' Club are now involved in the activities at the reservoir, of which gull-watching is perhaps the most rewarding.

September 1984

Filey Brigg
Contributed by R.H. Appleby

Filey Brigg is a small but conspicuous promontory composed of the calcareous grit of the Corallion series pointing a finger in a more or less southeasterly direction from the higher boulder-clay cliffs of the Carr Naze towards Flamborough Head.

A superb sandy beach has accumulated in the shelter of the Brigg and this stretches away past Primrose Valley to Reighton, where it gives way to stones and boulders, and eventually to the dramatic cliffs of Speeton and Bempton. The complex system of rocky pools and ledges coupled with the relatively shallow sandy bay makes the area one of the most important feeding areas for seabirds and waders along the Yorkshire coast. The 'sportsmen' naturalists of the mid to late 1800s were responsible for many bird records. The earliest were referred to in 1844 by T. Allis when he wrote about Purple Sandpipers observed by A. Strickland; and in *The Birds of Yorkshire* by T.H. Nelson, who recorded a male Steller's Eider shot there in 1845 and several other interesting records up to 1903. Chislett made further references in *Yorkshire Birds*, as did A.J. Wallis in his *Natural History of the Scarborough District* in 1956. Richard Vaughan published many excellent photographs taken at the Brigg in *Birds of the Yorkshire Coast* in 1974.

I was first introduced to the area by A.J. Wallis in 1952, and, with M.H. Ness, made several visits around that time; I also wrote my first notes after a visit on 31st August in that year, the highlight of which was a Velvet Scoter. Having to rely on public transport, as we did in those early days, prompted us to camp overnight on the clifftop on several occasions during the next few years. After an absence while on National Service during the years 1955-57, regular visits were resumed and it became obvious that the general area had great potential as a major birdwatching station. In 1960 a logbook was started, and 194 species had been recorded up to 1975. As news of the birds to be seen there filtered around the county, many other birdwatchers came to see such species as Shore Larks, Lapland Buntings and possibly a Red-necked or Slavonian Grebe, as well as the many passing seabirds. Many of the autumn and winter observations of seabird movements were made possible by the availability of an existing tea hut, which the lessee allowed us to use as a shelter during inclement weather.

During the years 1952 to 1970, pressures on the area were few. Indeed, in the early years it was a wild and lonely place and I often spent whole days there alone. One of the main problems was shooting, and there were many instances of waders being killed on the rocks. The ultimate tragedy occurred in late October 1967, and an entry in my diary reads as follows:

> '28th October 1967. A warm, sunny morning with a force 2 s.w. wind and good visibility. At 0920 hrs. a Lapland Bunting flew up the Brigg and several small flocks of Redwings, Fieldfares and Starlings came in off the sea. Walking to the end of the Brigg, 57 Common Terns and 3 Arctic Terns were found shot dead. All had obviously been shot at point blank range whilst roosting, some shot having passed right through. At 1400 hrs. another Grey Phalarope for the Brigg. ...'

A leader article in the *Yorkshire Post* read 'Make Brigg nature reserve call after Terns slaughtered' and attempts were subsequently made in 1968-69 to persuade the Filey Council and the Home Office to declare it as such. These efforts met with an encouraging response and the area was eventually granted sanctuary.

During the late 1950s, the northern clifftop fields underwent a dramatic change owing to a new style of farming practice, and what were six fields bordered by hawthorn hedges became two. The loss of hedgerows was to be regretted.

During the early 1970s, the commercial development of some of the Church Farm fields adjacent to Arndale and southwards to Ravine Hill began, with the laying of a metalled footpath alongside the stream running down Arndale (or Horndale as it was formerly known). This sheltered gully, which runs from the beach to the clifftop, is a favourite resting and feeding place for passage migrants, and the footpath made access much easier for both visitors and birdwatchers. The clifftop area was to become the new Filey Country and Caravan Park, with a golf course, football field, picnic and parking areas for both cars and caravans, complete with a shop and ablutions. Again there was a loss of some excellent hedgerows, but this was compensated for at the time by the planting of hundreds of trees and shrubs bordering the area and in the envisaged flowerbeds between car-parking bays. Because of the exposed situation, many of these plants failed or became stunted in growth. There was no doubt that this was to be the ultimate pressure on the Brigg area, and it became a far more accessible place; one could now drive a car almost to the Carr Naze pond.

To someone who had visited and watched birds at Filey for so many years, this development was somewhat devastating and this, coupled with pressures at work, led me to spend more time closer to Scarborough and I made my last regular visit on 27th September 1975. The temptation to reflect upon the rarities seen over the years is great, but these are dealt with elsewhere in this book.

Due to government re-organisation, Filey was taken under the umbrella of Scarborough Council, and in late 1975 plans were formulated by some of the regular observers to start a Filey Brigg Ornithological Group. The lease of tenancy of the tea hut expired at this time and, as nobody wanted to renew it, F.J. Thompson and 12 others persuaded the Scarborough Council to lease it to them as an observation hut for birdwatching. This approach brought some financial help from the Countryside Commission, and members of the new group were able to convert the building into a headquarters. The group began to record all species found within a defined area around the Brigg, and produced their first annual report, for the year 1977. More birdwatchers and better coverage have provided many interesting records, particularly of seabird movements. The group, with a membership of around 23 people, is supported entirely by the proceeds from the sale of reports and by donations from visitors. It is also encouraged and supported in its aims by the Filey Town Council, who erected a notice board depicting some of the birds likely to be seen in the area, together with a brief outline of the activities of the group.

Bird-ringing started with a trial run in 1977, when 127 birds were trapped in a total of five days. Regular ringing has been carried out in Arndale and the adjacent scrub since 1983, and some waders have been caught on the Brigg. Over 1,000 birds have now been ringed, and the area continues to be an important site for both passerine and seabird observations.

Having had such a long association with the Brigg, it is pleasing to have been invited to contribute this chapter and most encouraging to know that observations are continuing, and the information being published by the new group. I should like to take this opportunity of thanking them, and in particular P.J. Dunn for providing details of the group's formation and activities.

December 1984

The Humber Wildfowl Refuge
Contributed by B.S. Pashby

The Humber Wildfowl Refuge covers 3,200 acres (1,300 ha) of tidal mudflats, chiefly Whitton Sand, in the upper Humber, plus the frontage of Broomfleet Island. It was created by order under Section 3 of the Protection of Birds Act 1954, and extended in 1963, and it forms an important part of the Humber Flats and Marshes Site of Special Scientific Interest designated in 1975.

The idea of a wildfowl sanctuary in the area arose in the early 1950s, when local wildfowling circles became concerned at the irresponsible activities of a small minority of shooters who were violating the roosting site of the Pink-footed Geese. Some of those involved were actually 'digging in' on the flats, completely disregarding the accepted code of conduct in the wildfowling world. Frank Mason, a Hull teacher and wildfowler, and, quite independently, W.E. ('Judge') Johnson, a farmer and north Lincolnshire wildfowler and vice-president of the Wildfowlers' Association of Great Britain and Ireland (WAGBI), had similar ideas for protecting the Pinkfeet roost and together they proceeded to translate these into action. Appeals for support from local naturalists and help from the then Nature Conservancy resulted in a meeting in 1954 of Yorkshire and Lincolnshire naturalists and wildfowlers with E.M. Nicholson, then director-general of the Nature Conservancy. This, no doubt, was the meeting referred to by Ralph Chislett in the Yorkshire Naturalists' Union Ornithological Report for 1954, under the heading 'Grey Geese'.

Section 3 of the 1954 Protection of Birds Act included legislation for the establishment of bird sanctuaries, and Nicholson, with this in mind, called a meeting of all interested parties in the Humber area to discuss details of a refuge for wildfowl. This meeting was held in January 1955 in the offices of the then Humber Conservancy Board, who, as agents for the Crown Estates, were in the position of landowners. As a result, Nicholson was able to go ahead with his own ideas, the most important of which was that such a refuge should be under the management of a local committee of equal numbers of wildfowlers and naturalists, with the Nature Conservancy providing the services of a warden. He called a third meeting in September 1955, at which he took the Chair until the election of Trevor Field, a local wildfowler and Justice, to that office, following which the first meeting of the Humber Wildfowl Refuge Committee was held and Frank Mason appointed secretary. Some well-known names were present at these early meetings: Ralph Chislett, E.W. Taylor, E.B. Burstall, R.K. Cornwallis, G. Atkinson-Willes and J.K. Stanford, to mention but a few. The friendly relationship established between wildfowler and naturalist came as something of a surprise to many and is best summed up by quoting Max Nicholson himself: '... will find it a pleasure to meet your members again and recall the discomfiture of the Press when we broke it to them that we had decided not to quarrel after all!'. It had been agreed that the chairmanship of the committee should alternate each year, with a wildfowler being followed by a naturalist and so on. That it was 23 years before a change of chairman took place shows the high regard in which the rest of the committee held Mr Field.

It is extremely ironic that the Pink-footed Goose, to whose welfare all this effort was directed, began to take advantage of changes in Scottish agriculture. Widespread conversion of pasture to arable in Scotland meant that the geese did not have to fly down so far as the Humber for adequate food supplies. Their numbers began to fall off from the 15,000 mark and eventually, in the 1970s, a peak of 3,000 was the norm; but then, in 1975, a disastrous poisoning incident occurred and in subsequent years only 1,000 Pinkfeet has been the maximum recorded. As well as the drastic reduction in numbers, their feeding methods have changed: instead of a regular morning flight to the stubble fields on the Wolds, modern agricultural harvesting followed rapidly by straw-burning and re-ploughing has meant feeding flights in most directions, to take whatever is available wherever it may be. In fact, the only forecast that can now be made is that flights to the southern hinterland will greatly outnumber those to the north.

Another significant change has been the gradual replacement of the original Broomfleet saltmarsh (principally silt and sea aster) with a marsh dominated by *Agrostis stolonifera* and *Puccinellia maritima*, the first of these a direct result of sheep-grazing commenced in 1965. The second of these grasses is a favourite food of the Wigeon and is the reason for the vastly increased number of Wigeons wintering at the refuge. The roosting flock of up to 5,000 Mallards is one of the largest in Britain, and the recent re-emergence of the 'Island' at the western end of Whitton Sand has meant an ideal habitat for Teals and up to 5,000 Golden Plovers. These figures show that the refuge is a site of international importance for wildfowl. The tidal reedbeds on the north shore provide a habitat for species other than wildfowl. Here, Reed and Sedge Warblers breed, D.B. Cutts having carried out a ringing programme for many years under the BTO *Acrocephalus* inquiry. During early August, in most years, the beds are the site of a large Sand Martin roost and later a Swallow roost of considerable size. In winter occasional Bearded Tits are seen, no doubt wanderers from the Blacktoft Sands reserve. It was in front of these reedbeds, in 1965, that the Marsh Harriers bred among the debris of the previous year's sea aster.

The changes already mentioned occurred in the main during the 1960s, and it was in 1965 that further steps were taken to provide a solution to a problem which had evolved through the increase in the use of private transport and better road systems. These had led to an increase in visiting shooters from afar and a consequent 'free-for-all' situation in which the 'cowboys' thrived. The committee, with the co-operation of the Humber Conservancy Board, set about establishing a system of controlled shooting in which only permit-holders were allowed to shoot on the fringes of the refuge. The committee was granted the lease of the foreshore shooting rights, the local landowners between Brough and Crabley Creek agreed to allow the committee to restrict the right of access over their greenshore to armed wildfowlers, and as a result relative peace and order was restored. This eventually led to extremely heavy pressure at the Faxfleet end of the refuge, and in 1969 the committee leased the foreshore shooting rights there from the newly created British Transport Docks Board. One of the problems here was the close proximity of several Faxfleet residents to the shore, and the agreement here was as much to improve the lot of these people as anything else. As a result, no shooting is permitted on Sundays there. Recently, steps have been taken to establish a similar scheme on the south shore of the refuge. Although not yet finalised, a start is to be made in the autumn of 1983.

There have been about six different wardens since the establishment of the refuge, but none made his mark more than Arthur Chapman. A retired police sergeant, his knowledge of the practical side of the law was a great advantage. His meticulous attention to detail in all aspects of his duties and, above all, his work in the field of public relations were invaluable. No reserve of this nature can function without the goodwill of those living and working close by. Arthur commenced his duties in 1969, at a time when the policing nature of the warden's work was beginning to consume less time, and he made relations with local people his main concern. The south shore villagers heard him lecture on the refuge, which, to them, had previously been only a name. His devotion to duty can be illustrated with a short extract from his weekly worksheet during the severe weather of December 1981:

'... 17th Dec. Faxfleet Hall shore hard as concrete with an even depth of 8"-10" snow. Short-eared Owl hunting along plumb edge. ... Island Farm to Observation Post — found milk-container in lunch bag frozen solid — calor gas and water container similarly affected. Returned to Island Farm for refreshment. Later crossed fields to floodbank, found saltings frozen solid and snow-covered — the whole area completely deserted.'

The award of the British Empire Medal in 1981, for services to wildfowl conservation, was a just recognition of 13 years work well done, and his retirement just over a year later was marked with a function attended by at least 30 of the local residents from both shores. A presentation was made to him of a picture of 'Pink-feet on Kirkconnell Marsh' by Donald Watson. This was a result of donations from constituent bodies represented on the committee, as well as private contributions. Arthur Chapman is now a member of the Refuge Committee, representing one of the local wildfowling clubs.

From an administrative aspect, it is perhaps as well that changes in personnel on the committee at officer level have been minimal compared with those of the organisations supporting the concept of the refuge. The Humber Conservancy Board became the British Transport Docks Board, and later Associated British Ports. The old North Region of the Nature Conservancy handled refuge affairs from Grange-over-Sands until re-organisation improved matters with the creation of the North East Region in Newcastle, with its sub-office at York, the name now being the Nature Conservancy Council. The Wildfowlers' Association of Great Britain and Ireland (WAGBI) is now the British Association for Shooting and Conservation (BASC). As against this, Trevor Field's chairmanship lasted 23 years and he was succeeded by Derek Cutts, who came to the committee in place of Henry Bunce. The office of secretary has, similarly, been held by two individuals: Frank Mason, who retired after 14 years' service, and the writer (the union's second representative on the committee), who is due to retire from office in 1983, also after 14 years.

What began as an experiment in wildfowl conservation (the Humber Refuge was the first of its kind) was followed by others, all more or less identical in operation, and all over the world. Its continued success has relied on co-operation between apparently conflicting interests, but with one object in view. Only if this spirit remains will it continue.

August 1983

Systematic List

The birds included in this section fall into three main categories. These are the historical records published by Nelson and by Chislett, which must be taken at face value unless there is evidence to justify a query; the birds accepted as proven by the Ornithological Committee of the Yorkshire Naturalists' Union, and, where applicable, by the *British Birds* Rarities Committee since 1958, up to the end of 1984; and finally those records which for various reasons have not yet been submitted to the latter committee although all have been examined and accepted by the Yorkshire committee. In this category are most of the records of rare birds seen at Flamborough Head since 1978 and it should be noted that the fact is not stated in every case under the records concerned.

Where the YNU committee has had occasion to accept fully a record subsequently rejected by the *British Birds* Rarities Committee, this has been published and the situation stated. Knowledge of an observer's ability and attitude are often more important than the written description when considering the claim for a rare bird, and the two elements should always be viewed with the same importance. It would be quite wrong not to publish such records and their inclusion will ensure that they are not lost, or overlooked, by future researchers in the event of re-appraisal by the *British Birds* Rarities Committee.

The order and nomenclature follow that of K.H. Voous, *List of Recent Holarctic Bird Species* (1973 and 1977).

The breeding distribution maps

The breeding distribution maps are based mainly on the results of a survey, carried out during the period 1968-72, organised by the British Trust for Ornithology and the Irish Wildbird Conservancy, and presented in *The Atlas of Breeding Birds in Britain and Ireland* compiled by J.T.R. Sharrock and published by T. and A.D. Poyser in 1976. They have been brought up to date where possible, but no census work on the scale of the BTO survey has been undertaken in the county since that time.

The fieldwork was based on units of 10-km squares and the maps show a much more complete density than is really the case for some species. A large dot indicates that the species was proved to breed in that particular square, although one pair would qualify for the same size dot as 100 pairs within another square, but whatever its shortcomings in this respect the method shows the actual breeding distribution very well. Any such variation in relative abundance is usually dictated by the availability of preferred habitat in any one square. A small dot indicates that the species was, or has since been seen, in suitable habitat during the summer in circumstances indicating probable breeding but without actual proof being obtained. The third category used in *The Atlas*, that of possible breeding only and indicated by a smaller dot, has been omitted or upgraded. There is clearly a case for breeding surveys within the county based on smaller units of 1-km squares.

Red-throated Diver
Gavia stellata

When Nelson wrote in 1907 'Winter visitant, common, and regular in appearance; immature birds sometimes remain off the coast all the year round, occurs on inland waters, but not numerously', he unwittingly forecast the situation for the next 75 years, for his summary applies today.

His comments were in the main of a general nature, and included a statement that 'it is never altogether absent from the neighbourhood of the coastline ...'. Only a handful of actual occurrences were cited one of which concerned a bird he obtained on 28th March 1875, 'in full nuptial garb'. He illustrated the species' appetite in the case of one, killed at Teesmouth in December 1901, which disgorged eight sand-eels, three of which were 8 inches (20 cm) in length. He also recorded a pure white bird, with pale yellow legs, feet and bill, which was shot at Spurn and went to the collection of J. Whitaker.

Chislett (1952) said that there had been no recent record to equal that of Nelson, who, on 20th September 1883, saw at least 50 at sea flying to the southeast in advance of an approaching storm. We now know that the sight of large numbers of passing Redthroats, especially during January to March, is quite usual. On 25th February 1957, 160 passed north off Hornsea in two hours. On 26th December 1959, a concentrated movement at Spurn was witnessed by C. Winn, R.C. Parkinson and J.S. Armitage, when 250 birds flew north including 223 passing the 'Narrow Neck' in eight minutes; the next day, 155 flew north between 14.00 hours and 15.15 hours. In 1960, 303 flew south at Spurn between 08.00 hours and 08.45 hours on 2nd March and G.R. Bennett counted 240 flying north off Hornsea on 6th February. Up to 400 birds were at Spurn during early January 1964, and the species was 'numerous' off Fraisthorpe on 5th January and again on 26th.

An all-day movement occurred at Filey on 30th January 1965, when R.H. Appleby counted 306 birds flying south; and, on 6th March in the same year, 300 were at Spurn. A total of 279 birds flew north at Hornsea in half-an-hour on 28th January 1968, and 185 flew north off Scarborough on 23rd January 1977, when a further 20 birds were in the South Bay, while 162 flew north there on 26th. Many other coastal localities had counts of up to 50 or 60 birds during this period in early 1977 and a second movement occurred in late February and March, with 78 in Filey Bay on 13th February, 322 at Spurn on 5th March — when up to 70 were together on the sea at times — and 72 off Withernsea on 8th March.

The same pattern emerged in 1978, with 304 off Filey and 278 off Scarborough on 14th January. A northerly passage took place at Spurn during late March, with 125 on 25th and 128 as late as 8th April. At Filey on 7th January, 245 flew south, and 196 flew north there on 13th January, when 130 were seen off Flamborough. On 25th February, 168 flew north at Filey and 105 did likewise at Flamborough. In 1979, 304 were counted at Spurn on 31st December.

Large numbers occurred in 1981 and, after several counts of 100 to 200 birds off Flamborough and the Holderness coast during January and February, much off-shore movement was witnessed during March and early April. S.M. Lister counted 567 flying south off Withernsea in two hours on 8th April, on which day 363 flew south off Flamborough. An obvious movement occurred at Spurn Point on 22nd March, when 420 flew north, and again on 5th and 6th April, when 220 and 275 respectively flew north.

Such is the situation today, established as a result of concentrated sea-watching from the favoured watchpoints, and the annual pattern differs little, except for fluctuating numbers. The autumn vanguard can be seen passing as early as mid July, but the first main arrival is not usually until a month later.

Robin Hood's Bay was proved to be a gathering area for migrating divers in the late 1960s. C.J. Feare watched it regularly during that period while he was studying at the Wellcome Marine Laboratory; a build-up in January 1967 peaked at 100 at the mouth end, and similar concentrations still occur, mainly in March as the species moves northwards.

Movements to the north and the south during December and January, and perhaps later ones, may be associated with feeding flights. Birds are usually on the move during the early part of the day and those flying north could be moving only short distances to the favoured feeding places, having drifted south with the tide during the night.

The species turns up regularly at inland waters and the occurrences during the last 30 years are too numerous to list. A Redthroat may be seen on any inland sheet of water during the period September to May, and such events are not always linked to coastal activity or to severe weather.

Black-throated Diver
Gavia arctica

Nelson listed several instances of this species' appearance in the county and said that 'immature specimens have been reported from most stations on the coastline at irregular intervals, and it was especially abundant in 1876'. Inland occurrences were more numerous than those of the Great Northern Diver, which was, he said, a reversal of the coastal situation, where the latter was commoner. He cited seven inland occurrences of the Blackthroat.

Chislett listed six inland records and could record only 12 for the coast. Since the appearance of *Yorkshire Birds*, more birdwatchers have produced more records and, since 1952, the species has been an annual visitor to the coast in small numbers. Of the many divers which sometimes pass, many are undoubtedly Redthroats, but some Blackthroats will go by unidentified; I doubt, though, if the number missed is very many. Experienced sea-watchers can now identify this species more readily than formerly, but not until the mid 1970s did the numbers recorded increase significantly.

In 1956 there were six birds at five localities, and in 1963 it was recorded singly at Spurn on six dates and also at Hull, Goole and Hornsea. There were seven records in 1964, involving eight birds at five localities along the coast, and five records in 1972.

In 1976, there were more recorded than ever before, with birds identified on many dates during January to May and from August to the end of the year. Spurn, Hornsea, Withernsea, Flamborough, Filey, Scarborough and Burniston all had the species, and at the year's end from one to four were seen on 63 dates, mainly during October and November. Five off Flamborough on 14th November was the maximum seen at any one place. One was picked up alive by Gordon Follows at Coatham Marsh on 14th February. Towards the end of the year Blackthroats occurred inland: one at Fairburn Ings on 28th October, which stayed until 3rd November when it was seen to be ailing and had hauled out onto the bank; one at Tophill Low Reservoir on 29th October, which stayed until 15th November; and two at Hay-a-Park Gravel-pit, Knaresborough, on 29th October, which stayed until 21st when R. Evison saw them fly off and circle the area, gaining height before leaving to the east.

The newly discovered trend of frequency was maintained in 1977 and subsequently. D.I.M. Wallace saw eight off Flamborough on 29th January 1978 and a small spring passage was seen there, with three on 29th April, two on 1st May and three on 23rd May; single birds in full summer plumage were off Flamborough on 17th and 18th June in that year. Farther north, at Burniston, M. Francis counted 16 flying north on 18th January and an unprecedented 39 birds on 26th, when a further nine were sitting on the sea. The species was also numerous during the autumn, when birds were recorded from most coastal watchpoints, including seven off Mappleton on 24th September. P.A. Lassey and H.J. Whitehead saw nine flying into Bridlington Bay on 20th May 1979, in which year Blackthroats were again numerous along the coast and included one at Flamborough in full breeding dress on 21st July, another on 4th August and a third, similarly garbed, at Filey on 14th August.

In 1956, when there were six coastal records, there were also several inland: one was on the River Hull at Dunswell on 1st February; a dying bird was taken to H.O. Bunce by a wildfowler in the same month; two were on the River Ouse near York on 25th February; one at Fairburn Ings from 26th to 28th February; one on Lake Gormire on 31st March and 1st April; one on Castle Howard Lake on 8th April; and there were single sightings at Hornsea Mere on 1st, 15th and 22nd January, 25th February, and 3rd, 4th and 22nd April. The species has occurred inland in 13 of the years since 1956 and has done so annually since 1976, when the numbers have reflected the coastal frequency. In 1979 single individuals occurred at six waters, with two birds at another site and one in full breeding plumage at Bolton-on-Swale Gravel-pits on 18th May. A badly oiled specimen was found dead by John Martin at Ardsley Reservoir on 27th January 1981 and this he presented to me for my collection.

Of regular occurrence along the coast in varying numbers, mainly from September through to April with a few birds during the summer months, occurring occasionally and mainly singly on inland waters, summarises the status of this diver today.

Great Northern Diver
Gavia immer

In Willughby's *Ornithology,* under the title of 'Gesner's Greatest Douker', appears the following: 'Mr. Johnson (of Brignall, near Greta Bridge), in his papers sent us, writes that he hath seen a bird of this kind, without any spots on its back or wings, but yet thinks it not to differ specifically but accidentally.' What a name, that, Gesner's Greatest Douker!

There are more records at the present time than formerly, no doubt owing to increased observer activity, and the species is now seen annually on the coast and has occurred inland in 25 of the 32 years since Chislett published *Yorkshire Birds* in 1952. Chislett said of a bird at Wintersett Reservoir on 26th January 1947 that it was still in winter plumage on 13th April. One assumes that he implied an expectation of the acquisition of breeding plumage by the latter date, but this need not be the case. Many birds, both on our coastline and on inland waters, are juveniles showing scalloped backs and such birds do not acquire black-and-white-spotted summer plumage until they reach their second spring, some 20 months after being born. Their first-summer plumage is similar to the adult's winter dress.

Some birds arrive off the Yorkshire coast in complete summer plumage, or acquire it while in the area before leaving for their northern breeding grounds. One example was at Spurn in August 1967, another was at Hornsea on 19th July 1973, and such birds were seen at Flamborough on 11th June and 8th July 1978.

Groups of this species are rare: six were at South Gare on 29th November 1970, and seven were on the sea off Hornsea on 5th February 1971. Such assemblies are loosely scattered and do not really constitute flocks.

As with the Black-throated Diver, the number of Great Northerns recorded has increased since the mid 1970s. The watchers at Flamborough Head counted a total of 22 birds between September 1976 and March 1977 and, from September 1976 to the end of that year, 25 birds were seen on 23 dates at Scarborough, Filey, Hornsea and Spurn. Three flew north off Flamborough on 14th May 1977, and D.I.M. Wallace saw four flying south there on 20th November. A juvenile was found dying on a small pond at Withernsea on 21st November 1977 by S.M. Lister, who took it to Howard Frost for care, but it died on 23rd. I skinned the specimen, a male, and found it to have cankerous growths in its throat. The autumn of 1979 produced more Great Northern Divers than usual, at least 23 individuals being involved.

Two birds stayed at Thrybergh Reservoir from 4th December 1960 to 26th February 1961, when one left, the other remaining until 4th April. Such stays are unusual and most occurrences at inland waters are of brief duration, a few days at the most. Of the 30 inland records during my review period, all but two have been in an apparently healthy and free-flying condition. Of those two, one was found oiled at Wintersett Reservoir on 31st December 1956 and the other was grounded at Huddersfield on 4th September 1969. Some have been seen in flight between waters, and one which was shot on Silsden Moor on 7th November 1965 is now in Keighley Museum.

Nelson particularised his 12 inland records and Chislett listed his 14 from the coast and eight from inland waters. Included in the latter's list was a record of five on Thornton Reservoir on 21st December 1921, a very unusual number for an inland locality. I do not propose to give details of the birds which have been seen inland during my review period; suffice to say that the sight of an 'immer goose' on any large sheet of inland water from September to May need not occasion any surprise.

Except for the numerical increase illustrated above, the Great Northern Diver remains as assessed by Nelson, 'winter visitant, regular but not common on the coast, also occasionally inland though rarely'.

White-billed Diver

Gavia adamsii

In John Cordeaux's *List of British Birds belonging to the Humber District*, published in 1899, there is reference to a White-billed Diver having been shot from Filey Brigg in January 1897 which went to Mr Brown, the local taxidermist, in whose shop Cordeaux inspected it. Nelson merely reported the occurrence, stating that he had been unable to obtain any further information about the specimen. The editors of *The Handbook* regarded the record as uncertain, but Chislett defended it on the grounds that 'Cordeaux was an excellent naturalist and a careful recorder', a defence which Bannerman, in 1959 in *The Birds of the British Isles*, accepted. There have been many 'excellent naturalists', both in Cordeaux's time and since, who have made mistaken identifications and in view of the problems associated with this species at that time, and even until very recently, coupled with the fact that there are no supporting details of the bird available, I cannot accept the record.

The first authenticated Yorkshire example occurred between 29th February and 2nd March 1916, when W.J. Clarke watched a bird in Scarborough Harbour at close range and noted all the salient features. It was assuming summer plumage and the details published at the time leave no room for doubt. This was the fourth record for Britain (*The Naturalist*, 1916, pp. 217-19).

It was to be 34 years before the species was recorded again in Yorkshire, when two occurred in 1952. The first was an oiled bird picked up on Scarborough south beach on 30th January by Eric Sigston and sent to A.J. Wallis for identification. Unfortunately, owing to the badly oiled state of the plumage, only the head was preserved. It has the most classic bill shape of any winter-plumaged *adamsii* I have examined, and Wallis kindly donated the specimen to my collection (*The Naturalist*, 1952, pp. 105-6). The second occurred at Sandsend, near Whitby, on 10th February. It was oiled, and died shortly after being taken to A.B. Walker, who arranged for it to be made into a cabinet skin for the Whitby Museum. Prepared at the Hancock Museum and sent to the British Museum for confirmation, the skin is now lost, but fortunately the occurrence was well documented and the specimen photographed. It was an adult female assuming summer plumage and was the ninth British record (*British Birds*, 1952, pp. 421-4).

The fourth record for the county came from Hedon Haven on the upper Humber when a bird was found oiled and dying on 18th February 1953. It was an adult assuming summer plumage and was the thirteenth British record (*British Birds*, 1953, pp. 214-15).

The next, again oiled and dying, was found at Saltwick Nab, near Whitby, and taken to A.B. Walker. Another adult assuming summer plumage, it was preserved as a mount and is now in the Whitby Museum, where I have examined it. It is unfortunately in a bad state of preservation, having been attacked by insects, and the head is badly moth-eaten. This was the seventeenth record for Britain.

The sixth Yorkshire bird was the most controversial of all White-billed Diver records. It was an adult female found dead at Tunstall on 18th March 1962 by B.S. Pashby and preserved as a cabinet skin by A.H. Rider. It was submitted to the *British Birds* Rarities Committee, who in turn sought an independent opinion. After much correspondence, the bird was finally pronounced to be a Great Northern Diver, but no reasons were stated for having arrived at this erroneous conclusion. A note on this supposed aberrant Great Northern Diver was published by Pashby in *The Naturalist* (1963, p. 30). I saw the specimen at the autumn meeting of the Yorkshire Naturalists' Union Ornithological Section in 1962 and was confident that it was in fact *adamsii*. The apparent wrong identification by the authority of the time prompted me, in collaboration with David M. Burn, to look into the problems surrounding the separation of these two species, the results of which research appeared in *British Birds* (1974). Having been eventually accepted by the *British Birds* Rarities Committee, this became the 22nd British record.

The seventh example was seen swimming close inshore at Robin Hood's Bay on 15th February 1966 by C.J. Feare and was watched from the windows of the Wellcome Marine Laboratory of the University of Leeds, which abuts the sea at high tide. It was seen to be oiled on one side, and the next morning had come ashore and was found alive on the beach. It was in a very weak condition and was photographed just before it died. I received the corpse through the post two days later and the skin is preserved in my collection. It was an adult female assuming summer plumage and was the 26th record for Britain.

The next came from Filey beach on 1st March 1969, when R.H. Appleby found a dead bird on the tideline. This was yet another adult female assuming summer plumage and was badly oiled on the breast and flank. It was the 30th British record and is preserved as a cabinet skin in my collection.

On 8th December 1973, a dead bird was picked up on the beach at Hornsea by R.R. Lowe and taken to D.T. Ireland, the RSPB warden at Hornsea Mere. The decomposing corpse was finally sent to me via Tony Taylor of the Newcastle University Seabird Research Unit, to whom it had been taken by Ireland. I am greatly indebted to Taylor for making the specimen available after first realising that it was possibly *adamsii*. It was in juvenile plumage and only the second such to be found in British waters. It was not oiled. This ninth county record was the 39th for Britain.

Full details of all the above records are published in a paper 'The White-billed Diver in Britain' in *British Birds* (1974, pp. 257-96), and in *The Naturalist* (1975, pp. 15-18).

At 10.00 hours on the morning of 3rd January 1982, M. Williams was birdwatching along the Marine Drive at Scarborough when he saw a large diver in the North Bay. It showed a white bill and he identified it as this species before going to phone R.H. Appleby, having asked two nearby anglers to keep an eye on it while he was away. When the two observers returned, the diver was only 20 yards from the wall and they were able to examine it closely for the next three hours before it flew off to the south. The bill was not unusually large and the bird was therefore most likely a female; it also exhibited some white spots on the back, indicating that it was an adult.

Later in the year, on 9th October 1982, while watching at Flamborough Head, P.A. Lassey and A. Grieve saw a very large diver flying north at 08.15 hours. It was fairly close and, as it passed them at just above eye level, they noted its massive head and bill, the former being very pale and the latter being described as pale yellowish-white with no trace of dark coloration along the culmen ridge, a diagnostic feature of this species. Another was seen similarly on 10th December 1983 by D.G. Hobson and P.A. Lassey.

A few other large divers, thought to be White-billed, have been seen off Flamborough Head in recent years, usually during periods of northeasterly gales, and that more occur than are recorded is inevitable. January to March would appear to be the most likely period for a Yorkshire *adamsii* to occur.

Pied-billed Grebe
Podilymbus podiceps

On 9th June 1965, Major 'Tigger' Worrin saw a grebe on Beaverdyke Reservoir, 3 miles (4.8 km) west of Harrogate. He knew from the brief and unsatisfactory views that it was something unusual and returned the next day, when, after taking notes, he phoned me, as a result of which I visited the area that evening with R.C. Parkinson. The bird was out on the open water and swam past us at a range of about 80 yards to the cover at the end of the reservoir.

We were able to see the large white bill crossed by a black vertical band, the black throat and otherwise mainly uniform brown plumage. It was clearly a Pied-billed Grebe, and with Parkinson I made detailed notes and sketches before returning to Worrin's house to consult the literature.

The bird stayed until 24th November, after which date the reservoir was frozen over. During its stay it was seen by a great many people from all over Britain, but when I invited James Ferguson-Lees to come up to Yorkshire to see this great rarity in mid June it was characteristically nowhere to be seen. Miss Joan Fairhurst made excellent tape recordings of its calls and song, which were answered with enthusiam when played back to it from the water's edge. It was perfectly at home at the edge of the aquatic vegetation and seemed to be holding territory, chasing off Coots and Mallards when they approached too closely. It was in peak condition when first seen and had doubtless been in British waters for some time, probably on the coast, having come inland to find its perfect habitat for the breeding season. There cannot have been many more frustrated birds in Britain that year, the nearest female being probably 3,000 miles (4,800 km) away in North America.

By the end of August, the bill and white eye-ring were beginning to lose their brightness, and on 22nd October the breeding plumage had moulted out and the bird was in almost complete winter dress. Soon after this, the black band across the bill had completely disappeared. It was often seen to catch and eat small fish and frogs, which were abundant in the reservoir.

Parkinson photographed the bird in June and the picture, together with a full detailed account of the grebe's stay, were published in *British Birds* (1967, pp. 290-5).

This was only the second record in Britain of this North American grebe, the first having been at Blagdon Lake, Somerset, in December 1963. Another, or the same, was at Chew Valley Lake, near Blagdon, in August 1965 and subsequently.

Yorkshire was treated to a second Pied-billed Grebe in 1977, when Tony and Jean Denison of York saw one at Gouthwaite Reservoir on 23rd April. This bird stayed until 15th May and attracted the usual attentions of birdwatchers from far and near.

Little Grebe
Tachybaptus ruficollis

Mention was made of this small, familiar grebe as a Yorkshire bird as early as 1791. It is resident and common, breeding on most waters, ranging from small ponds to large reservoirs and slow-moving stretches of some rivers. Any such piece of water with suitable cover along its edge from sea-level to the upland tarns may hold a pair or two during the summer months.

The long frosts and snow of early 1947 severely affected the Little Grebe, and Chislett reported a marked reduction in the subsequent breeding population. He noted this particularly at Fairburn Flash, as it was then known, and at Gouthwaite Reservoir. Recovery did not appear to be complete at these waters in 1949 or in 1950.

The breeding season can be very protracted and eggs have been found from April through to early September, replacement layings for lost eggs or young no doubt accounting for the late clutches. At Fairburn Ings in 1955, six pairs had nests in close proximity on 22nd June when seven other pairs already had chicks.

A drastic reduction in breeding numbers followed the long and severe winter of 1962/63 and some small populations were wiped out or much reduced, although it was reported to be as common as usual in the Doncaster area. Without specific monitoring it is often difficult to be sure of the exact situation, and subjective impressions often belie the truth.

In recent years, breeding pairs have been counted where possible in some areas, and in 1970 12 waters in vice-county 63 (the old West Riding, South) held 35 pairs. In 1971 there were 40 pairs at 14 waters, and in 1972 36 pairs at 18 waters. In 1976, 50 young were reared at Denaby Ings and there were 58 other pairs elsewhere in vice-county 63, many of which failed to breed successfully owing to fluctuating water levels. In 1980, however, 66 pairs bred at 29 waters, 41 of which reared at least 100 young.

Little Grebes build and anchor their nests in a variety of places: among branches hanging in the water or, more traditionally, among rushes or reeds and often on floating debris such as planks of wood, especially in gravel-pits, where such sites are often the only ones available. In 1955, I saw a nest built on the bottom of a submerged five-gallon drum, one inch (2.5cm) of which was sticking above the surface of the water. The site was completely exposed, some 6 feet (1.8m) from the bare gravelly bank.

Post-breeding concentrations are often large. In 1955, there were 68 birds at Fairburn Ings on 18th September and 50 at Bottomboat on the same date, with 95 at Swillington Ings during the month. Numbers have remained fairly constant since the 1950s; Fairburn Ings usually has the largest gatherings, as in 1965 when there were 57 birds on 18th September and 60 on 29th, with 63 there on 18th September 1978. Some Little Grebes spend the winter on rivers, the lower reaches of the Nidd around Knaresborough holding several, as do many other streams, often with small backwaters in otherwise fast-flowing stretches. Individuals occur in most years during the autumn on the Spurn Canal and some are often seen on the sea. Whether these are of Yorkshire origin or travellers from over the sea is not known for certain. In 1973, birds were on the canal almost daily during August to October, with eight on 24th September. On 26th March 1923 one was killed at the Flamborough lighthouse (*The Naturalist*, 1923, p. 212), and on 8th November 1905 Nelson saw a party of seven on the sea off Redcar.

The species has attracted several local names, apart from the familiar Dabchick, and Nelson listed the following: Didapper, Dipper, Small Ducker (Allen MS. 1791), Tom Pudding (North and West Ridings), Dipper Duck (central Ryedale), Tom Puffin or Tom Poofin (North and East Ridings) and Peep-o-day (East Cottingwith). In 1949, an old Knaresborough lady gave me a case containing two stuffed 'Poofs' which were actually Little Grebes.

Common resident on most suitable waters, some large post-breeding concentrations occurring during the autumn, when birds may also be found on rivers and along the coast, summarises the Dabchick's status in Yorkshire.

Great Crested Grebe
Podiceps cristatus

Nelson wrote 'Notwithstanding the persecution to which it was being subjected, this singular looking and beautiful bird is still resident in Yorkshire though very local and few in numbers being restricted to sheets of inland waters where it is protected from molestation, and where it finds the seclusion necessary for its nidification, one of which is Hornsea Mere in Holderness; in 1888 no fewer than six nests were observed there.'

By 1931, when the British Trust for Ornithology organised a national survey of breeding Great Crested Grebes, there had obviously been a considerable recovery. H.B. Booth undertook to survey Yorkshire (*The Naturalist*, 1933, pp. 87-92) and reported 65 pairs of these birds on 24 waters. The spring and summer of 1931 were very wet and conditions for breeding grebes were good, few being stranded by falling water levels, a common cause of failure in dry summers.

Some sheets of water are not static in the nature of their condition and suitability for nesting. Excessive disturbance by the public, advancing vegetation and the reverse when some private lakes are drained and cleared, all contribute to the fluctuating fortunes for grebes. In more recent times, the appearance of gravel-pits has provided many suitable breeding sites, once these have matured with emergent vegetation.

Chislett said that fewer pairs bred in the county during the period 1946-49 than in 1931. During 1949, 90 individuals (not pairs) were counted on Yorkshire waters in May and June, and in 1951 up to 100 birds were recorded. Quite a number of waters were apparently no longer available to grebes, having become untenable since about 1939.

When, with increasing subsidence during the early 1900s, Fairburn Flash was forming, Great Crested Grebes soon colonised it and Chislett wrote: 'As the area of this subsidence-formed water grew, hedgerows and bushes became flooded until only the tops of hedgerows stood out, and it became possible to see grebes sitting on nests in the tops of dead thorns and other bushes. . . .' Three pairs bred in 1921, increasing thereafter up to 1928, when A. Whitaker, investigating only part of the flooded area, counted 16 nests and estimated that there were probably 20-25 pairs. During the 1931 survey, Booth's figure for the ings was 15 pairs with broods on the water and another pair incubating. The numbers decreased after this, but Bill Bennett counted ten breeding pairs in 1949.

Although Hornsea Mere is the traditional Yorkshire breeding water, it has never held very many pairs and only single figures have bred there until the 1970s, when 12 pairs did so in 1979. Fourteen pairs were present in 1980, but only seven young resulted.

Over the county as a whole, the number of breeding pairs began to increase in the early 1950s, no doubt aided by the appearance of gravel-pits, particularly in the West Riding. In 1952 50 pairs were counted, and in 1953 50 pairs were present at 20 waters and reared 52 young. In 1955, 60 pairs at 23 waters reared 62 young; half of these were at Fairburn Ings. In 1970, 35 pairs bred but only 25 were successful. There was a marked increase in 1971, when 55 pairs nested in the county. Between 60 and 70 pairs bred in 1972 and 1973. The increase has continued, and in 1980 at least 113 pairs nested in Yorkshire, including 14 pairs at Hornsea Mere. Most were concentrated in the West Riding — in vice-counties 63 and 64, with 46 and 49 pairs respectively. The first breeding record in the Scarborough area occurred at Seamer Road Mere in 1982.

In winter, most grebes leave the smaller breeding waters and congregate on larger sheets or along the coast. A traditional coastal wintering area is in the broad sweep of Bridlington Bay, where concentrations of birds can be seen off Barmston or Fraisthorpe: for example, 100 were there in late February 1957; 74 on 6th January 1960; 80 on 18th February 1975; 68 on 22nd December 1975; 60 on 6th January 1978; exceptional numbers in 1980, when 140 were counted on 1st January, 137 on 27th January, declining to 30 by 16th February, with 72 at the year's end on 27th December; and 160 on 4th March 1983. Numbers here are probably affected by the severity of the weather, often being highest when inland waters are frozen over.

To summarise, there is no doubt that the Great Crested Grebe has increased as a

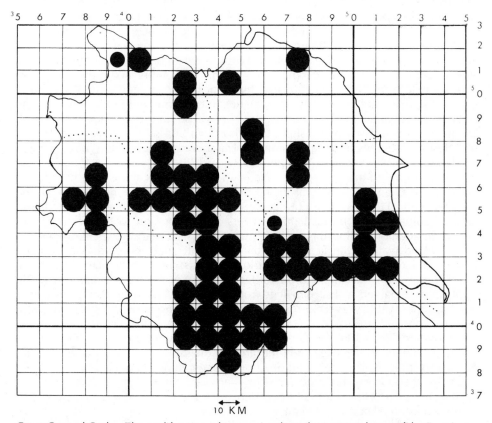

Great Crested Grebe. The proliferation of reservoirs along the eastern slopes of the Pennines and the subsidence flashes along the Aire Valley are well shown by the breeding distribution of this species.

breeding species since 1907, when Nelson published *The Birds of Yorkshire*. The availability of gravel-pits as suitable nesting sites has clearly contributed to that recovery, if such it was, in more recent years.

Red-necked Grebe
Podiceps grisegena

Thomas Allis in 1844 mentioned this species as being obtained near Doncaster every winter. He also noted individuals being taken at Barnsley; at Worsborough Reservoir in 1830; 'many' shot or taken near Huddersfield; the species being 'rare' near Leeds; one at Ripponden in 1800; and said that it was occasionally met with near York and was rare at Hebden Bridge. He concluded with the statement that it was occasionally found in winter in Bridlington Bay but was by no means common. This suggests that more occurred inland than on the coast, which could never have been the case and indicates that only those that were shot or killed ever came to the notice of the early naturalists, birds along the coastline going unnoticed.

Nelson's quoted records give a much more accurate picture of its status. He said of it: '... winter visitant to the coastline from September to March, of very irregular occurrence, in some years being altogether absent, whilst in very severe seasons it has been observed in considerable numbers. Such was the case in 1891 when "it appeared in such surprising numbers as to excite the attention of ornithologists on the whole length of the seaboard".' On 19th January, Nelson was at sea off Redcar and obtained three birds, seeing at least 12 more which he could not pursue owing to cold snow showers and darkness coming on. Two other boatmen, who were about a mile from Nelson's craft, told him that they had seen at least 20 more. During the following week, the weather became stormy and fishermen reported 'astonishing quantities of grebes at sea between Huntcliffe and Teesmouth'. Twenty-eight specimens were shot at Scarborough and seven at Filey, and it was reported as unusually abundant about the Flamborough Headland (*The Zoologist*, 1891, pp. 193-253; and *The Naturalist*, 1891, p. 123).

Nelson surmised that the appearance of so many grebes at this time was due to their having been forced out of their Continental quarters by the severity of the weather there. He was quite correct, of course, and the same severe conditions during February 1979 brought many divers and grebes on to the east coast of Britain. In addition to the many coastal records in that year, the species occurred on 15 inland waters with at least 18 different individuals involved. Most arrived during late January and some stayed for long periods, one at Newington Flash from 21st February until 4th June and one at Denaby Ings from 26th February until 12th April. One remained at Fairburn Ings from 16th March to 16th April, and some birds at other waters stayed for up to two weeks. Along the coastline, birds were present from January to May and were scattered along the whole length from Teesmouth to Spurn. On 20th February five were at South Gare, two at Redcar and one on Coatham Marsh; Filey had four birds on the same date, after two from 17th. At least six individuals were found dead on the cost during February.

Red-necked Grebes have occurred in every year but two since 1940, the year for which the first Ornithological Report covering the whole county was published by the Yorkshire Naturalists' Union.

There would appear to have been no change in the species' status during the last 75 years except for a numerical increase, doubtless resulting from the more expert and intensive watching at the coastal vantage points and inland waters.

Slavonian Grebe
Podiceps auritus

The Slavonian Grebe, like the last species, is an autumn and winter visitor to Yorkshire, occasional birds lingering into the spring when they may be in full breeding dress. Since Chislett's time, the increase in birdwatching activity along the coast and elsewhere has inevitably led to an increase in sightings of this small black and white grebe, and during the past ten years there have never been fewer than ten records annually.

Nelson knew the bird well during his time at Redcar; in 1901, he procured one in a channel at the Teesmouth which had been feeding on sprats, one fish hanging out of its bill when the bird was brought ashore. Several were killed in the Tees Estuary during the winters of 1874/75 and 1896/97, when it was also reported as more numerous than usual off Scarborough. Two, out of four birds present, were shot at Sunk Island in the Humber in 1912 (*The Naturalist*, 1913, p. 77). On 10th March 1940, after a period of severe weather, two were on Hornsea Mere and three were picked up dead on Bridlington beach. On 29th November 1954, at Gouthwaite Reservoir, a Slavonian Grebe was heard to whinny; by imitating its call, A.F.G. Walker called it up to a range of 15 yards, where it swam backwards and forwards, calling furiously.

One was picked up in the centre of Bradford on 27th February 1955 which went eventually to the Cartwright Hall Museum. On 19th October 1958, at Spurn, Mr A. Bird brought in a Slavonian Grebe which had been caught in a ditch between the Bluebell and the Crown and Anchor. It was uninjured and, after being ringed, was released on the sea. A photograph appears in the Spurn Bird Observatory album.

During early 1975, the species was affected by the cold weather on the adjacent Continent and more than usual were seen off the Yorkshire coast. Birds were recorded at Easington Lagoons, Hornsea Mere, Flamborough, Filey and Scarborough during January and February. One was found dead at Easington on 31st January and another was picked up alive in a field at Roos on 29th, when it was taken to Hornsea and released on the sea. One was at Flamborough on 10th March and one at Hornsea Mere on 8th and 18th April, with two in Scarborough South Bay on 2nd April. Individuals were also seen inland during the period: at Broomhead Reservoir on 2nd January; Farnley Reservoir, Bramley, on 22nd January; and Wheldrake Ings on 25th February.

Slavonian Grebes are sometimes seen in Yorkshire in full breeding dress. G.H. Ainsworth saw one at Cherry Cobb Sands on 28th April 1940; one was observed by D.J. Standring and P.B. Wordsworth at Wintersett Reservoir from 18th to 20th April 1971; W.F. Curtis saw one off Atwick on 31st May 1972, another on 28th August in the same year, and one on 19th August 1977; one was on Scaling Dam on 8th August 1975; and R.G. Hawley watched one on Hornsea Mere between 28th April and 2nd May 1978. The gravel-pits at Bolton-on-Swale have attracted full-plumaged Slavonian Grebes in three recent years. G.D. Moore recorded single birds from 13th to 17th April 1974, on 11th September 1977 and on 9th September 1979: could this be the same bird?

Two early birds were seen by J. Fenton at Stocks Reservoir on 7th August 1955.

An oiled bird, found alive on the beach at Hinderwell, between Whitby and Saltburn, on 7th April 1963, had been ringed at Vologda in the USSR on 21st July 1962.

Sheltered bays and harbours anywhere along our coastline and any inland sheet of water may attract this species, usually singly and mainly between January and March, but in any month from August to May.

Black-necked Grebe
Podiceps nigricollis

The first recorded occurrence of this species in Yorkshire was in *The Zoologist* (1845, p. 1182), where J. Hogg remarked that one was reported to have been taken at the Teesmouth in January 1823. Nelson listed 22 records up to 1905. He said that 'though it has been captured in spring and summer when in full breeding plumage, there is no evidence that the "eared grebe" has ever bred in Yorkshire'.

It has bred since, and no doubt did so before, albeit in very small numbers. Riley Fortune located a pair which stayed for two weeks at Fewston Reservoir in May 1919. In 1928, nests were found at Fairburn Ings on 25th and 30th May and on 18th June, with one, two and four eggs respectively, by C.E. Rhodes of Stapleton, who reported the finds to A. Whitaker. On 14th July, these two egg collectors visited the locality together and found a fourth nest containing a chipping egg and shells of eggs that had already hatched. Whitaker watched one adult through his binoculars in the thick cover. One of the eggs taken that day from the nest built among floating willow branches is now in the City of Sheffield Museum, and I have to thank Derek Whiteley for this information. Whitaker corresponded later with Chislett and wrote 'unfortunately, the bird appears to have failed to establish itself'. Little wonder!

Between 1928 and 1942, Chislett records only nine occurrences from seven waters between early August and March, including one in Scarborough Harbour on 30th January 1939 (*The Naturalist*, 1940, p. 15). Breeding occurred in 1942 and the late A.G. Parsons in a letter to John Cudworth in 1982 wrote:

'Unfortunately I lost some notes in a fire in 1967 but I can help you over the Black-necked Grebe nesting. In August 1942, I observed a convoy of three or four stripey necked grebes led and followed by obvious adult Black-necked Grebes. They were on the smallish flash bordered by the dirt tip track on the opposite side to good old Bob Goodall's cottage. I wrote to R.C. but made no claim as I did not know where they had their nest as a medley of ducklings, Moorhens, Coots and Dabchicks as well as Great Crested Grebes was present. The following year, George Edwards found three occupied nests at the same flash, which Chislett and I also saw'.

It was on 25th May 1943 that G.R. Edwards, that excellent naturalist, saw two adult Black-necked Grebes at this site, and on 17th June he found a sitting bird there. On 20th June, there were five pairs with eggs; on 26th June two males were seen and birds were sitting on the only two visible nests, growing vegetation having hidden the others. With V.S. Crapnell and H. Foster, Edwards saw two sets of chicks (two and three) on 12th July, and both pairs were feeding young on 17th July, when a fifth adult was present. Two unescorted well-grown young were present on 7th August and two adults some distance away showed no apparent interest in them. No adults were seen after this date, but the young survived and were still present on 18th September. Edwards invited Chislett to view these breeding grebes and, on 26th June, they watched two females climb back onto their nests. Edwards described the 'dirt tip' track as a cinder track known as Astley Lane, and the small flash may well have been known as Astley Pond. A few years after the breeding of the grebes, probably in the early 1950s, this flash was filled in and the nearby cottages pulled down, and the whole area is now completely changed owing to the activities of the National Coal Board. In the same year, on 29th July, Edwards saw another adult grebe in breeding plumage, swimming with a Common Scoter on Whiteholme Reservoir. In 1944, five pairs were on the main ing at Swillington on 3rd May, again seen by Edwards, and on 5th July nine adults were counted and one occupied nest together with three platforms which were almost certainly in use. Chislett reported (*Yorkshire Birds*) that only one young was reared, after floods had destroyed four nests and the second attempts were similarly unsuccessful. An adult and a juvenile were present on 12th September and odd birds up to late October. In 1945, after two on 21st January, seven birds were noted in breeding plumage on several dates in March and on 8th April. Two were seen on 25th July and singles on 26th August and 16th September, but no breeding was proved. A party of 17 grebes at Swillington Ings on 7th October 1945, claimed as Black-necked by several observers including V.S. Crapnell, H. Foster and W. Bennett, is a remarkable and unprecedented occurrence. Breeding was proved at Fairburn Ings on 18th May 1946, when A.G. Parsons saw a bird sitting on a nest and its mate swimming nearby. A week later, this attempt to breed was thwarted by an egg-raiding party and the birds left the area shortly afterwards. In the same year, Ken Dawson saw two adults with eight well-grown young on a water known to him at the time as Methley Ings. This was no doubt what is now known as Mickletown Flash, but the western end is now filled in and so the area known to Dawson has long disappeared. Two adults and two young seen on Whiteholme Reservoir on 22nd August 1948 had probably come from a nearby breeding water. The species was present at Swillington Ings on several dates in late April and early May 1949 and two were there on 4th and 20th August, without any breeding having been proved during the interim. Birds occurred sporadically at Swillington during the early 1950s, but again breeding was never proved. On 11th June 1955, two birds in breeding dress were seen at Wath Ings by T.M. Clegg and C.E. Burton, and a pair attempted to breed there in 1983. The species tried to breed in 1956, but two nests containing four and five eggs were abandoned after the site, at Brotherton Ing, was drained by the Central Electricity Authority. There were no further attempts to nest until 1982, when a pair hatched two young at a flash in the south of the county, where breeding also occurred in 1983 and 1984 under the watchful eye of local volunteer wardens and (in 1982) with help from the Royal Society for the Protection of Birds.

There are a surprising number of records of both old and young birds during the period July to October. Such occurred in almost every year up to 1966 and have done so in most years since 1975. In 1980, there were two at Wintersett Reservoir on 18th April, one at Fairburn Ings from 25th April to 20th May and two at Southfield Reservoir on 12th May, all in breeding plumage. It could well be that this grebe is breeding unnoticed at some secluded water, or may do so at any time if unmolested.

The species occurs regularly in Yorkshire on inland waters and less so along the coast, and has been recorded in every year since 1942. Hornsea Mere is a favoured locality and it has been seen there in eleven out of the last 20 years. A bird which flew north at Spurn Point on 18th November 1975 was the first record for the peninsula. Records usually involve only one or two individuals and larger gatherings are rare. A party of eight seen by D. Gosney and D. Herringshaw at Agden Reservoir on 13th October 1973 was an interesting and unusual number. Black-necked Grebes can be seen in any month of the year, but mainly from July to April, birds in breeding plumage being not uncommon.

Black-browed Albatross
Diomedea melanophris

A Black-browed Albatross was recorded off Spurn Point between 4th and 7th November 1965. It was seen once each day and flew north on each occasion. Among those who saw it were John Cudworth, B.R. Spence and C. Winn, whose detailed notes ensured this oceanic straggler a place on the county list.

In 1967, an adult was seen off Filey Brigg by C.J. Feare and J.E. Wall and a year later, on 13th October 1968, at the same locality, P.T. Treloar, M.L. Denton and others watched an immature bird flying north.

On 24th April 1969, an adult was seen off Hornsea by W.F. Curtis, an experienced pelagic traveller who knows the albatrosses better than most from his frequent visits to the southern oceans.

It is possible that the adult sightings refer to the same individual, which may well have been the bird which frequented the Bass Rock area in the Firth of Forth from May to August 1967 and from February to July 1968 and subsequently. For full details of this bird see *British Birds*, 1968, pp. 22-7, which includes some excellent photographs taken by G.V. Adkin of Keighley.

In addition to the above birds, which were all specifically identified as Black-browed Albatrosses, there have been three other authentic but unspecified records off the Yorkshire coast. On 10th November 1963, John Cudworth watched an albatross off Spurn which he could not identify with certainty. On 15th September 1966, one flew across Robin Hood's Bay which C.J. Feare could only say was an 'albatross', and later in the year, on 27th October, what was probably the same bird was seen off Spurn Point; again, its precise identity was not established.

In the Yorkshire Naturalists' Union Ornithological Report for 1954, Chislett recorded, in square brackets, the sighting of two albatrosses, viewed at 300 yards' (270m) range off the Spurn Narrow Neck by H.G. Brownlow and J.D. Craggs, which they described as having long, tapering and curved black wings with long thick necks. Dr Craggs said that the range was too great for the species of albatross to be distinguished, but, at 300 yards, the views must have been excellent and any modern sea-watcher would give a lot to see an albatross at that range. I share Chislett's inferred doubts.

Fulmar
Fulmarus glacialis

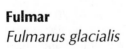

The Fulmar is well known to anyone who visits the Yorkshire coast during the summer months: it can be seen as a breeding bird on almost any high cliff from

Saltburn southwards to Flamborough. It has not yet established itself on the lower boulder-clay cliffs south of the Flamborough headland, but birds have been prospecting for some years and one was seen to land at Mappleton on 22nd April 1971, after surveying a 200-yard (180-m) stretch for 15 minutes.

In Nelson's time, the Fulmar was 'a coastal visitant in autumn and winter'. It did not establish itself as a breeding species until 1922, when, on 26th May, two eggs were seen at Bempton; in June of that year, the climbers reported that they had taken four eggs since 26th May, and that there were 15-20 pairs present. In the same year, birds were also seen about the Castle Cliffs at Scarborough and at Whitby.

In May 1923, H.B. Booth was 'simply astounded' at the numbers present along the Yorkshire cliffs, and Fulmars were now frequenting the stretch between Robin Hood's Bay and Whitby. By 1924, the species had spread south of Scarborough to Gristhorpe and Speeton, where it bred in considerable numbers. In 1926, E.W. Wade reported that Fulmars were ousting Herring Gulls from ledges north of Filey. In 1927, the species bred sparingly all along the cliffs from Flamborough north to Saltburn. A period of apparent stability followed until, in 1937, C.W. Mason estimated about 200 pairs on the Bempton Cliffs. W.J. Clarke reported 40-50 birds along the Scarborough Cliffs on 19th January 1940, and G.H. Ainsworth counted six birds sitting on ledges between Dane's Dyke and Sewerby at Whitsuntide.

The breeding ledges are usually deserted during September, and some birds return towards the end of November or in December. One landed on a nest site at Flamborough on 5th October 1971 and another did so on 1st October 1973, the only two records of birds so landing in October at that time.

In 1964, A.J. Williams counted 767 occupied sites (not definite breeding birds) between Flamborough Fog Station and Speeton Red Cliff Hole, a distance of about 5 miles (8 km), between 7th and 13th June. D.I. Fotherby counted at least 68 occupied sites at Ravenscar on 10th June 1968.

In 1973, S.C. Madge, the RSPB warden for Bempton Cliffs, counted 312 chicks on about 3 miles (4.8 km) of cliff from Red Cliff Hole to Close Nooks, and a count of the entire chalk cliff from the Flamborough Fog Station southwards to Sewerby showed a total of 350 pairs. There were 832 occupied nest sites at Bempton in June 1983. In 1974, H.O. Bunce reported that at least 500 chicks were produced between Speeton and Sewerby. In that same year, 52 sites were occupied on Scarborough Castle Hill and 46 at Cloughton Wyke.

During the summer of 1956, three Fulmars were present in Stoupe Brow Quarry, about a mile inland near Ravenscar, where six pairs were seen in 1963 and again in 1969. In 1974, R.H. Appleby counted 22 birds on ledges there on 7th July, ten pairs were present in 1975 and eight pairs in 1977, since when the site has been used annually. At Hasty Bank on the North Cleveland Scarp, about 8 miles (12.8 km) from the sea, two sites were occupied in 1963 and seven birds were there in 1971, when an egg was seen; two birds were present in 1975, and a forester said that they had been regular visitors for the past 15 years. Fulmars still frequent this site and there were six there on 28th June 1980. Peter Hutchinson of Brandsby saw two birds on ledges and four others flying around a peak on Clay Bank, near Broughton, about 12 miles (19.2 km) from the sea, in June 1975. Miss A.L. Cooper watched one prospecting a westward-facing cliff at Sutton Bank, 25 miles (40 km) from the sea, on 25th May 1963 and H.O. Bunce saw one sitting on a ledge there in April 1984. D. Summers-Smith saw three circling Roseberry Topping on 24th June 1972.

Since 1956, large numbers of Fulmars have been proved to be present off the Yorkshire coast and sea-watchers sometimes record very large movements. On 16th September 1959, 187 flew north at Spurn in one-and-a-half hours in the evening. This is the period when birds are deserting the breeding cliffs, and other

September moves have included 120 flying north in 80 minutes off Scarborough on 3rd September 1965 and 704 off Spurn on 5th September 1970.

Birds pass in large numbers at other times of the year and there have been records of 150 flying north in 25 minutes at Filey on 24th April 1960; 300 north at Spurn on 20th April 1965; 360 at Spurn on 26th April 1970; and 400 north off Hornsea on 4th May 1971. On 12th June 1961, 200 passed Spurn Point.

Some winter movements occur, usually coinciding with strong winds from the north or northeast: for example, 254 flew south off Filey in two hours on 10th December 1960; 120 passed on 21st November 1970; and 184 flew north there on 18th November 1972, when 300 more were sitting on the sea. Intensive watching at Flamborough Head by D.I.M. Wallace, P.A. Lassey and others from the mid 1970s has produced some very large counts of passing Fulmars. In 1975, Wallace saw 500 flying north in three hours on 31st August, D.E. Murray counted 400 passing north in three hours on 14th September, and R.H. Appleby witnessed 960 flying north in one-and-a-half hours on 13th December, an unprecedented number at that time.

Watchers at Spurn Point often see large movements of Fulmars, as on 27th August 1976 when 750 birds flew past. On the following day, 770 flew north off Hornsea and 191 did so off Filey in two hours. Later in the year, on 10th September, P.A. Lassey counted no fewer than 1,000 Fulmars flying north off Flamborough. This figure was to be eclipsed in 1977, when, on 17th September, Lassey and Miss Irene Smith counted 4,500 flying north in seven hours; 680 flew past Spurn on the same day. Wallace saw 1,650 off Flamborough in one-and-a-half hours on 31st December 1977. It is curious that none was seen at Spurn during December of that year, indicating the fact that the birds are not passing along the coast from farther south, but are indulging in great circular movements which bring them near the coast at places such as Flamborough. In 1978, very large numbers were seen off the headland: 1,290 flew north on 30th January; 2,000 were actually counted flying south on 30th April, and many others were known to have passed; 1,450 flew north on 12th June and 3,765 on 26th November, with 2,250 on 17th December. Watchers at Filey Brigg witnessed the same movements, and added 3,000 flying north on 1st August. In 1979, large numbers were also seen and the maximum counts at Flamborough were 1,470 flying north on 29th January; 1,900 flying south on 3rd February; 2,005 on 26th September; 2,500 on 15th November; 2,840 on 16th December; 6,120 flying north on 18th December; and 8,500 which flew north on 20th December. Counts at Flamborough since 1980 have often reached up to 2,000, and were far exceeded in 1982 by 6,200 on 7th December and 7,200 on 11th December, and by a phenomenal 19,300 on 8th February 1983.

All the above figures illustrate the maxima only, and smaller numbers may be seen passing from any coastal watchpoint during the same periods and at other times.

'Blue' Fulmars occur occasionally and can from time to time be found washed up on the beaches along with normal birds. I have two in my collection which came from Bridlington beach on 1st December 1969 with bills measuring 39mm and 40mm respectively (thus not differing from our Yorkshire breeders in this respect). Another was found dead on a Holderness beach in February 1963. There are several sight records of dark-phase birds: five were in the Tees Bay in mid August 1962, during a sprat wreck which attracted many Fulmars; one flew past Hornsea on 21st March 1964; one was present at the Dane's Dyke breeding colony on 3rd May 1964; and, on 8th January 1972, many passing Fulmars at Filey included a dark one. In recent years, the large numbers seen passing off our coastline have included many 'blues'. The largest counts were made in 1978, when P.A. Lassey saw 41 such birds off Flamborough on 30th April and H.J. Whitehead saw

25 off Filey on 27th April. On 17th December of that year, Lassey and Wallace saw several very dark birds and 'hundreds' of intermediates off Flamborough. In 1979, these dark-form birds were seen again, with maximum counts of ten at Flamborough on 14th March and 88 on 16th.

In February 1962, following a period of gales, an unprecedented 'wreck' of Fulmars occurred along the east coast of England and 835 dead birds were found. B.S. Pashby organised a complete check of the Holderness beaches from Spurn northwards to Sewerby, a distance of some 40 miles (64km), and most of the 334 Yorkshire corpses were found there. Bodies were collected over the period from late January to the end of March. Those birds that were examined in detail were all below normal weight, had no fat reserves and showed wastage of the breast muscle tissue, suggestive of prolonged starvation. For full details of this wreck, see *British Birds*, 1969, pp. 97-109. Several 'dark-phase' birds were included, and P.J. Boylan of the Hull Museum identified at least two small and dark birds, with bill lengths of only 34mm, as belonging to the Baffin Island race *Fulmarus glacialis minor* (*The Naturalist*, 1967, pp. 109-13).

On 28th December 1981, I found a dead Fulmar on the beach at Bridlington which was a 'blue' of the intermediate type, but had unfortunately been badly mutilated and the head was missing. I was able to salvage one wing, which measured only 316mm, placing the specimen well within the range of *minor* from the northwest Atlantic. In mid January 1982, I received a phone call from Howard Frost of Withernsea saying that a 'blue' Fulmar had been taken to him for care. It was oiled and had been found on the beach on 6th January. It had died next day and he had buried it, but, on learning of my interest in Fulmars, he dug it up again some days after its internment and sent it to me through the post. It was a male with a wing measurement of 325mm and a bill length of 35.5mm and was also referable to *Fulmarus glacialis minor*. The specimen is in my collection (see Plate 56).

Degrees of darkness vary in these so-called 'blue' Fulmars, but most are pale blue-grey on the head and underparts, instead of pure white as in the normal and common form. On 16th August 1969, H.O. Bunce saw a fully feathered juvenile on a ledge at Sewerby which was deep blue-grey all over.

Nelson was unable to record any Fulmar occurrences inland but a few were cited by Chislett in *Yorkshire Birds*. R.M. Garnett saw single birds passing over Thornton-le-Dale on 23rd April and 27th May 1941, and also on 4th May 1942 when two flew over, being mobbed by Rooks. The record of 'a dozen' over the River Aire, near Bingley, on 3rd December 1945, and published by Chislett, which 'glided around precisely as [the observer] had seen them at Scarborough' is perhaps a doubtful one in the absence of more details. T. Bagenall identified two Fulmars on the edge of a steep valley on Great Whernside on 14th July 1946 and stated that there were eight other similar birds in the distance (*British Birds*, 1947, p. 89).

Since the publication of *Yorkshire Birds*, there have been about 30 undoubted records well inland, as well as several up to a few miles from the sea. The majority of these have occurred since 1970, with four birds in May, seven in June, three in July, one in August and four in September.

Nelson recorded a Fulmar, caught on a fish hook at Filey on 26th October 1868, which was found to have swallowed a Redwing.

The Fulmar's status has changed yet again since Chislett amended Nelson's summary. 'Casual visitor in autumn and winter, rather rare inshore, but in some seasons plentiful on the fishing grounds. Has been occasionally met with in summer' is how Nelson wrote of it. Chislett said that it was 'still casual as a visitant in autumn, but no longer so in winter for birds may begin to assemble on the cliffs in December, and early February is considered late for them. The species is now thoroughly well established as a breeder on most of the Yorkshire cliffs.'

Today, it cannot be termed 'casual' at any season, for large offshore movements can be witnessed in almost any month, though mainly during autumn and winter; and it is certainly more numerous and widespread as a breeding bird than in 1952. The low boulder-clay cliffs of Holderness, where occasional birds have been seen to prospect and land, offer few suitable breeding sites for Fulmars, but colonisation may come eventually.

Capped Petrel
Pterodroma hasitata

On 16th December 1984, I. Forsyth, R. Lyon, D.E. Murray and P.M. Scanlan were walking along the beach at Barmston, near Bridlington, when they found a dead and bedraggled black and white shearwater which they examined only briefly. Subsequent reference to the literature aroused suspicions that it may have been one of the rarer species and in consequence, on 19th, P.M. Scanlan cycled from Beverley to Barmston and relocated the specimen on the tideline. On returning with the corpse, he and I. Forsyth examined it closely and identified it as a Capped Petrel. After being photographed, the corpse was taken to W.F. Curtis at Atwick for confirmation and I was invited to examine it there later the same evening.

The bird had apparently been dead for about three weeks and, although the wings and body plumage were in relatively good condition, the head was badly decomposed and it was not possible to prepare a complete cabinet skin. The tail was missing, but the wings, feet and skull complete with the bill sheath were preserved after further photographs had been taken by D. Milnes and J. Cudworth (see plate 57).

The bird was a juvenile female with measurements as follows: wing 310mm; tarsus 40mm; bill (from feathers) 35mm; ovary 10 × 4mm.

The Capped Petrel is a rare bird with a limited breeding distribution in the West Indies, where it nests in crevices and among tree roots on the high mountains of Hispaniola and probably some other islands. Until recently, it was thought to be in danger of extinction, but breeding colonies have now been rediscovered and several birds are regularly seen by birdwatchers off Cape Hatteras and elsewhere along the eastern seaboard of North America. This is an exciting addition to the Yorkshire list of birds, and it is indeed fortunate that the corpse was still on the tideline when looked for three days after its initial discovery. I am most grateful to I. Forsyth and P.M. Scanlan, to whom all credit must go for identifying the specimen and for making it available for preservation. This is only the second record for the Palearctic region, the first being found alive on a heath near Swaffham, Norfolk, in March or April 1850 (*The Zoologist*, 1852, pp. 3691-8).

Bulwer's Petrel
Bulweria bulwerii

In *The Birds of Yorkshire*, Nelson tells in great detail of the first European example of this oceanic species. The bird in question was found dead by the River Ure at Tanfield, near Ripon, on 8th May 1837 and was formerly in the collection of Capt.

Dalton of Slenningford, near Ripon. The specimen was eventually lost, but as a result of enquiries made by W. Eagle Clarke, then the curator of the Museum of the Phil. and Lit. Society in Leeds, and Mr James Carter, a local naturalist from Masham, it was located at Ripon, having been bought at a sale by a Mr Jacobs, the head-master of the Ripon Choir School. As usual in those early days, the case was not fully labelled and the specimen could not immediately be associated with the Tanfield record. James Carter took it upon himself to enquire of all the surviving members of the Dalton family and eventually contacted Mr George Clarke, a son-in-law of Capt. Dalton, who fortunately remembered the bird very well, having seen it 'scores of times'. Clarke produced an old manuscript note he had made in the margin of a copy of *Bewick* to the effect that this bird was found dead on the bridge at Tanfield and had been given to his father-in-law, who had had it pre-served by John Stubbs of Ripon. He also remembered Capt. Dalton having several times refused the offer of 20 guineas for the specimen, which had been put away in a lumber room and wholly forgotten.

Such was the evidence published by Nelson, and the specimen is now in the York Museum — and presumably the one in a case with the Scalby bird, for this rare petrel, which breeds no nearer than the Atlantic islands, was to occur in Yorkshire again. On 28th February 1908, A.W. Linfoot found a dead specimen washed up on the beach at Scalby Mills, near Scarborough. This example also went to the York Museum, where I saw it in September 1984 (see *The Naturalist*, 1922, p. 128).

These are the only two Bulwer's Petrels ever to have been recorded in Great Britain; there is one record from Ireland and another from the Mediterranean.

Cory's Shearwater
Calonectris diomedea

On 1st October 1960, a Cory's Shearwater was sent down to the Spurn Bird Obser-vatory by the Hull RSPCA, having landed some days earlier on a ship bound for Hull. The exact position of the ship at the time was unknown and attempts to ascertain this were unsuccessful. In the absence of such details, the bird cannot therefore be counted as an undoubted Yorkshire specimen. It appeared healthy and, although very slightly oil-stained on the breast, flew off strongly after I had ringed it. It was considered to belong to the North Atlantic race *C.d.borealis*.

There have been several records since then, most occurring from the mid 1970s when sea-watchers intensified their efforts at Flamborough, Spurn and Filey. The first of these came from Spurn on 10th July 1965, when G.R. Edwards, that expert sea-watcher of the period, observed two birds. In the same year, on 19th September, Edwards, together with J.R. Collman and D.J. Standring, saw three more there.

A Cory's was seen by R.H. Appleby flying north off the Scarborough Marine Drive at 09.50 hours on 14th August 1968, during a seabird movement including many Manx Shearwaters and skuas. D.I. Fotherby watched a Cory's feeding among a dense pack of Kittiwakes close inshore at Scalby Mills, near Scarborough, on 6th September 1971; it eventually flew out to sea for about 100 yards and settled on the water before being flushed by a fishing boat, when it flew close inshore again before finally flying off to the south. Fotherby also saw two flying south off Filey Brigg on 8th September in the same year. One flew south at Spurn Point on 25th August 1973, and two did likewise on 16th August 1975.

In 1976, there were more records than ever before, and most were seen off Flamborough Head by P.A. Lassey, D.I.M. Wallace and others. The first occurred on 21st August, when three were seen, followed by two birds on 28th, four on 29th, one on 30th, one on 3rd September and another on 19th. The last bird was feeding with gulls among the trawlers. R.H. Appleby saw single birds passing north off Scarborough Marine Drive on 28th and 30th August, and M. Francis had one off Burniston on the latter date. Six Cory's Shearwaters flew south at Spurn on 2nd September.

There were eight records in 1977. S.M. Lister saw one flying south off Withernsea on 17th June and singles flew north at Flamborough on 11th, 19th and 26th June. One was seen at Filey on 7th August, one at Flamborough on 12th, one off Hornsea on 16th, one at Spurn on 30th, and two singles flying north off Hornsea on 18th September.

During 1978, 1979 and 1980, there were several records, continuing the trend started in 1976. On 25th June 1978, H.J. Whitehead and A. Botterill saw one flying north off Filey. On 28th August, N.A. Bell and P. Higson watched one flying north at Spurn, where three were seen on 17th September by A. Hately, D. Kirton and G. Warrilow. Singles flew north at Flamborough on 16th, 22nd and 29th July, and on 12th August.

1979 produced a good series of records, including the only spring one for Yorkshire when P.A. Lassey and Miss Irene Smith watched a Cory's as it flew north at Flamborough on 13th April. A.W. Wallis and S.G. Wilson saw eight birds flying south at Grimston on 17th August, and one flew north off Flamborough on 14th September.

In 1980, one flew south at Spurn on 10th August, being watched by J.C. Lidgate and D. Smith, and two were seen flying north at Flamborough Head on 9th August by P.A. Lassey.

In 1981, single Cory's Shearwaters were seen at Spurn on 11th June and 16th August, at Filey on 9th and 22nd August, and at Flamborough on 15th August. One was seen at Spurn on 10th July 1982, while single birds flew north at Flamborough on 10th and 25th July and 16th August, with three birds on 22nd September in that year.

In 1983, there were single birds at Flamborough on 28th July, 2nd August and 2nd, 4th and 5th September, and at Filey on 24th September. One flew south during a large movement of Manx Shearwaters off the Marine Drive, Scarborough, on 3rd August 1984, and P.A. Lassey and others saw single birds flying north off Flamborough on 30th July, 1st August, 12th August and 4th October 1984.

Cory's Shearwaters occur regularly in British waters, usually off western Ireland and Cornwall. The known wintering grounds are off South Africa, and the British records occur mainly in the autumn during the period of post-breeding dispersal. Intensified sea-watching during recent years has doubtless led to more birds being seen than formerly, but it is strange that the species was never encountered in Nelson's time.

Great Shearwater
Puffinus gravis

In the mid-nineteenth century, the bird we now know as the Sooty Shearwater was thought to be the immature form of the Great Shearwater, and several early Yorkshire records of this latter species were almost certainly Sooties. This Nelson was able to prove by his investigations into the two species, and under Sooty Shearwater he lists seven collected specimens and 'others seen' which were undoubted Sooties, but claimed originally as Great Shearwaters. He cites 16 under Great Shearwater, but precedes the list with the warning that 'it must be borne in mind that in considering it, the instances are not all authenticated, some specimens not being available for examination and the reader is requested to peruse the history of the next species [Sooty Shearwater]'.

Of those that were available, some were certainly referable to the species under review, and Nelson had one in his collection which was obtained off Scarborough in the autumn of 1904. Chislett examined a specimen which was formerly in the Hull Museum until it was bombed during the 1939-45 war. The others occurred up to 1898 and came from Robin Hood's Bay, Scarborough, Flamborough and Bridlington, except for one 'taken' in Leeds on 6th October 1854 and purchased by the Leeds Philosophical Society about which Nelson gives no further details.

In the annotations to his personal copy of *The Birds of Yorkshire*, Nelson recorded one shot off Flamborough Head on 20th November 1908 by S. Barkly of Bridlington which was sent to Nelson and which was only the second Barkly had known in 25 years. This specimen, and the one from Scarborough in 1904 (see above), are now in the Dorman Museum, Middlesbrough.

There were no other records until 1948, when, on 3rd October at Spurn Point, G.R. Edwards and A. Mitchell saw two large shearwaters which they described as 'brown above, white below, had white cheeks and were as large as Gannets'. The last point is obviously an exaggeration, otherwise these really were 'great' shearwaters.

Chislett gave details under this species as follows:

'J.R. Govett noted a large bird on the water forty yards from the cliffs at North Landing, Flamborough, on 4th September 1949, and that it had whitish sides and breast, was brown above with a dark cap and white chin, and had a fairly long petrel like bill. The bird then flew low over the water rising steadily to cliff top level and passed the observer northwards. The flight was described as being typical "shearwater" but steady and gliding, the neck was white nearly right round and the brown formed a broken collar effect. The underparts were white, to whitish buff with grey flecking on the under tail coverts.'

Chislett went on to say 'the description fits no other species', but I consider the bird may well have been a Pomarine Skua and, in any case, find the record unacceptable even as a *probable* Great Shearwater.

In 1952, in the Yorkshire Naturalists' Union Ornithological Report, Chislett recorded a very large shearwater with dark cap and back, and white underparts, which flew past Spurn in the evening of 10th August. It alighted on, and rose from, the sea several times and once plunged from about 10 feet (3m), sending up a shower of spray. There is nothing in those notes to preclude Cory's Shearwater. In the following year, he cited another occurrence, the details of which were published as: 'on 18th August ... at Spurn ... a large shearwater wheeled twice during its southward movement showing a warm brown back and wings in contrast with white body and underparts and whitish underwings. ...' This bird, too, is far from proven and may well have been a Cory's.

On 20th September 1959, D.G. Bell saw a shearwater off the South Gare at Teesmouth which conformed to the Great Shearwater. It followed a ship into the river, then veered north, gliding rather higher above the waves than Manx Shearwaters.

On 31st October 1967, C.J. Feare recorded one in Robin Hood's Bay which flew southeast, and R.H. Appleby had one flying north off the Scarborough Marine Drive on 14th August 1968.

It was 1973 before another Great Shearwater was seen in Yorkshire, when, as with the last species, regular sea-watching produced a series of records, and it has occurred in every year since 1975. W.F. Curtis watched two fly south off Hornsea on 3rd September 1973, and S.C. Madge saw another off Flamborough on 30th September. Singles were seen at three places in 1975: at Filey on 23rd August, Flamborough on 31st August and Bempton on 14th September. The latter flew north during a northerly gale.

As with Cory's Shearwater, 1976 produced more Great Shearwaters than ever before. The regular watchers at Flamborough Head were rewarded with 19 individuals which they were able to identify positively and ten more which were too distant for certainty. Two occurred on 20th August, two on 28th, seven on 29th and one on 30th, four on 2nd September and three on 3rd. All were flying north. W.F. Curtis saw one flying north off Hornsea on 28th August, on which date R.H. Appleby saw one pass close inshore off the Scarborough Marine Drive, where, with D.J. Britton, he saw three more on 29th.

There were only four birds in 1977 and all occurred singly at Flamborough, on 19th and 28th August and 3rd and 18th September; all were seen by P.A. Lassey. The many hours of concentrated sea-watching at Flamborough Head by Lassey, Wallace, Miss Irene Smith and others were amply rewarded in 1978, when 32 Great Shearwaters were seen between 6th August and 20th September, no fewer than 13 occurring on the latter date. All flew north. The only other record in that year was of one flying south at Filey on 24th September.

In 1979, off Hornsea, two birds were seen flying north at 07.30 hours, two flew north at 07.45 hours and one at 08.30 hours. It would be interesting to know if the same two individuals were involved, and were indulging in a circular movement off the Holderness coast, as none was seen elsewhere.

In 1980, singles flew north off Flamborough Head on 9th and 31st August and were seen by Lassey and A.M. Allport. One flew south, close inshore, at Filey on 22nd August.

One flew north off Flamborough on 22nd August 1981, and another flew south on 31st August. In 1983, there were single birds at Flamborough on 6th and 28th August and 12th September, with two on 15th August, and one flew north there on 7th August 1984. On 20th October 1984, one flew south at Filey Brigg which was seen by P.J. Dunn, M. Feather and others.

Large numbers of this shearwater occur in the Western Approaches each autumn, and over 5,000 were seen in two days in September 1965 off Cape Clear in southwestern Ireland. There are many records off Cornwall and western Ireland, but relatively few penetrate the North Sea. The species is known to breed only in the Tristan da Cunha island group in the South Atlantic.

Sooty Shearwater
Puffinus griseus

The first record of this species in Yorkshire and Britain concerns a bird shot near the mouth of the Tees on a stormy day in mid August 1828 by G. Marwood of Busby Hall in Cleveland. It was originally recorded as a Great Shearwater, as were several early specimens of this species, and published by Nelson along with 42 other Sooty Shearwaters, six of which had been erroneously recorded as *P. gravis*. All occurred from August to December at the regularly worked places such as Teesmouth, Whitby, Scarborough, Flamborough and Bridlington.

Matthew Bailey of Flamborough told Nelson that in several autumns he had seen scores of Sooty Shearwaters, and even 'hundreds' in flocks, off Flamborough Head in a single day. On one day in the autumn of 1887, he secured three in the course of a few minutes, and, if he had wished, could have killed a score. In the same year, several specimens were brought into Flamborough and Filey. In the autumns of 1895 and 1904, the species was again abundant off Flamborough and Bridlington, where several examples were captured, and from 20 to 30 others were reported by fishermen and boatmen. On 17th September 1883, off the Cleveland coast, Nelson shot one on the water which he thought was a Pomarine Skua until he handled it.

Chislett added only three other records of birds obtained, in the autumns of 1908, 1910 and 1912. I have a mounted specimen which was shot off Flamborough in October 1914.

When sea-watching became a popular pursuit in the 1950s, records of several species of seabird became more numerous and their recorded status changed dramatically in some cases. This is certainly true of the Sooty Shearwater. On 21st November 1951, G.R. Edwards saw two flying south at Spurn, and the species has been recorded in every year since, the main months of occurrence being August, September and October.

Numbers vary greatly; in some years only odd birds are seen, but occasionally large numbers pass. The first such large number was on 26th September 1958, when 34 flew north at Spurn. In 1959, during the period 13th to 17th September, there were daily counts of 12, 10, 20, 43 and 26. In 1962, 30 birds were counted at the same place on 27th August, and 24 were seen off Flamborough on 19th October in the same year. On 2nd September 1965, 27 were seen off Spurn and 61 off Scarborough. In 1972, there were 39 off Hornsea on 17th September, and at Spurn there were 27, 94 and 24 on 23rd, 24th and 25th September respectively. A large movement was recorded on 30th September 1973, when 74 were counted off Spurn and during a two-hour watch at Flamborough S.C. Madge saw 70 birds. Such movements can now be expected during this period in most years.

In 1975, the numbers of Sooties hitherto recorded were eclipsed by a tremendous movement on 24th September, when 240 were counted flying north off Spurn and R.H. Appleby saw 30 off Scarborough on the same day. In the Yorkshire Naturalists' Union Ornithological Report for that year, I commented 'Times have changed since Chislett wrote in *Yorkshire Birds*; those who would see this species should put to sea off the Yorkshire coast, preferably in the evening.'

In 1976, after small numbers had been seen during late July and August, a large movement occurred on 28th August: 192 were seen at Spurn, 71 at Hornsea, 219 at Flamborough and 141 at Scarborough; all flew north, with a force five to seven southeasterly wind blowing at the time. On 2nd September, a second movement took place which was to overshadow the first: watchers at Spurn counted 200 birds, and 548 passed Flamborough Head in eight hours. At Flamborough a further 352 were seen on 5th September, 304 on 10th, 39 on 11th, then smaller numbers until one bird on 25th and a few single birds in October.

During the autumn of 1977, similar movements occurred but smaller numbers were involved. In 1978, birds were recorded on every day during August and, after a moderate passage during the early part of the month, 173 were seen off Spurn on 25th and 222 on 26th. Farther north, off Flamborough, 197 were counted on 25th and an incredible 1,003 on 26th, when 456 were also seen off Filey Brigg. The movements continued into September, when there were counts at Flamborough of 456 on 2nd, 551 on 19th and 320 on 20th. Large numbers continued to pass into October, with 316 at Spurn, 216 at Hornsea and 430 at Flamborough, all on 1st, with smaller numbers being seen at other watchpoints along the coast. Movement continued well into the month, and, on 17th, 168 were seen off Scarborough in four-and-a-half hours. A few were still passing into December, with one at Flamborough and three at Filey on 28th. This was certainly the best autumn on record for Sooty Shearwaters off the Yorkshire coast, and the numbers were spectacular by any standards. Most were seen during periods of strong to gale-force winds from the north to northeast.

The largest count in 1979 was 585 at Flamborough on 22nd September. Relatively few were seen in the years 1980 to 1982, but 622 flew north at Flamborough on 13th August 1983.

When reading Chislett's *Yorkshire Birds,* it is difficult to understand the paucity of records compared with the 1970s. Even allowing for the more sophisticated techniques and capabilities of the sea-watchers, the gunners of old never reported such numbers as may be seen in almost every year now. The main months of occurrence are August to October, with small numbers passing from June and up to December. Very few have been recorded outside these months, single birds at Filey on 17th January 1970, Flamborough on 20th March 1977, Scarborough on 28th January 1978, Filey on 23rd April 1978 and Flamborough on 13th May 1979 being the only ones.

The Sooty Shearwater breeds in Australasia and in southern South America, migrating northwards into the Atlantic and Pacific Oceans. Good numbers penetrate the North Sea, the majority probably doing so when gales force them eastwards and then down into the North Sea from their preferred areas to the west.

Manx Shearwater
Puffinus puffinus

The Manx Shearwater was known to be a visitor to Yorkshire waters in Nelson's time and before, but not a very common one. In 1844, T. Allis wrote 'A. Strickland says it is seldom found on the east coast, but occasionally met with, generally in the autumn.' Later in the mid-nineteenth century W.W. Boulton considered it rare off Flamborough, and was surprised when he met with eight specimens at Filey. In 1876, however, Nelson stated that it was common off the East Riding and Cleveland coasts, when several were obtained near Bridlington, a flock of ten was at Teesmouth on 7th July, and fishermen at Redcar and Staithes reported it as numerous there. It was similarly plentiful in 1885, 1887 and 1904.

In 1952, when Chislett produced *Yorkshire Birds,* he could only say of the coastal occurrences 'recorded at Spurn in each of the four years 1947 to 1950', and cited 13 actual dates within that period, with two on 30th September 1947 as the only figure given, apart from 'a number' off Teesmouth on 9th and 20th August 1950.

As with the other shearwaters, concentrated sea-watching has produced many more records and the species is now known to occur annually off our coast in varying numbers, mainly during July, August and September with the peak numbers during July and early August. On 30th August 1959, I persuaded the stalwart Scarborough boatman 'Blondie' Wood to take D.M. Burn, R.C. Parkinson and myself out to sea in a force six northeasterly. Just outside the harbour mouth, the coble was lifted on a wave and crashed down into the next trough, the impact splitting the fuel tank, which was hastily mended with tied rags. When 3 miles (4.8km) offshore, we were rewarded by finding ourselves in the flight path of a movement of 'Manxies'. We counted 80 as they passed the boat, sometimes at only a few feet range, when it was possible to see their tube-noses and their shining black eyes. Many others must have passed unseen in the deep wave troughs. Such trips can be very rewarding in the autumn.

At Flamborough, on 2nd August 1964, H.O. Bunce counted 235, and on 30th 325 passed; all were flying north. Farther south at Atwick, on 3rd August, G.R. Bennett counted 622 flying north and another 560 were sitting on the sea in four rafts. Smaller numbers seen farther north at Filey Brigg on the same day were flying south, and the concentration may have been due to an unusually rich food supply in Bridlington Bay. At Spurn, on 8th July 1967, 106 flew south. R.H. Appleby counted 441 flying south at Filey on 20th July 1969, in which year 131 were off Scarborough on 24th August, and 150 were counted at Spurn on 12th July 1970.

On 1st August 1978, one of the largest movements was recorded: 751 flew north off Filey Brigg in 12 hours, 557 flew north off Burniston between 09.30 and 11.30 hours, and 1,514 flew north off the Scarborough Marine Drive between 07.30 and 20.15 hours. Watchers at Spurn Point did not witness this movement, perhaps indicating that the birds approached the coast to the north of the peninsula before turning and flying north. A further indication of this 'circular' movement was on 1st October 1978, when 365 birds flew north off Hornsea but only 73 passed Flamborough and only 56 were seen at Spurn.

On 18th August 1979, 86 flew south at Grimston, 305 birds passed Flamborough, 406 flew south off Filey Brigg, and 726 flew south off Scarborough with a further 240 birds sitting on the sea in three rafts. The passage continued throughout August, with 259 at Flamborough and 273 at Filey on 25th and 191 at the former and 591 at the latter on 28th, all of which were flying north. In September, Flamborough had 566 on 15th, 463 on 21st and 790 on 22nd. These latter movements were not witnessed off Filey but Spurn had 175 on 22nd, indicating that the birds turned out to sea at Flamborough and were not visible from Filey. On 31st August 1982, 839 birds were seen off Spurn, 725 of which flew north, and on 3rd August 1984 750 flew south off the Marine Drive, Scarborough, in three flocks between 11.50 and 12.30 hours.

In Nelson's period, the communicated and recorded instances of inland birds were 'so voluminous that a recapitulation of them would prove tedious and is unnecessary'. Chislett cited eight inland records and there have been several individuals since, two of which came into my possession. One was found in the centre of Knottingley on 18th September 1965 and the other collided with a combine harvester at Driffield on 14th September 1966. Both were birds of the year, the former still retaining juvenile down at the tips of its belly feathers. Another was found in 1966, at Doncaster on 21st September, and one was found in a field at Edenthorpe, near Doncaster, on 12th September 1970 and released at Southfield Reservoir. Two were found in 1974, one at Eggborough on 11th September and one at Potteric Carr on 16th September, both of which were in an exhausted condition. One was found near Castleford on 12th September 1977 and later released at Bempton. One was seen up the river at Blacktoft Sands on 31st August 1977. A bird was at Wath Ings on 5th October 1978, in which year one was seen flying around the Trent/Ouse confluence on 15th September. In 1980, three were found inland: one was picked up dead at Thorpe Salvin on 18th September, another was found dying at Crofton on the same day, and one at Lund on 19th was released at Carlton Marsh on 26th.

The Balearic Shearwater *Puffinus puffinus mauretanicus* occurs occasionally. Nelson cited 11 examples under the 'Levantine Shearwater'. This Mediterranean subspecies was subsequently divided into two races and all those British specimens available for examination have proved to be of the western 'Balearic' form. The first known example was in Nelson's collection and was taken at Redcar in the autumn of 1877. I have seen this specimen at the Dorman Museum, Middlesbrough, where it is in case number 59 with another specimen, a male, which was shot near Bridlington in the autumn of 1904. Of the other ten, six were obtained in 'autumn' and one in February, the others being undated. The February bird is interesting in that there is only one other record of a February Manx in Yorkshire. It was procured near the Castle foot at Scarborough on 4th February 1899, taken to W.J. Clarke, and forwarded by him to Dr R. Bowdler Sharpe, who identified it (*The Zoologist*, 1900, p. 521). Seven were handled by W.J. Clarke in September of the years 1907 and 1908, four of which were later available for examination and proved to be *mauretanicus*. One was shot from a boat off Scarborough on 3rd September 1912 and recorded by W.J. Clarke in *The Naturalist* (1912, p. 301).

During the last decade there has been an increasing number of Manx Shearwaters attributed to this race, usually accompanying the large numbers of the nominate race now shown to occur annually. Odd ones, or very small numbers, appeared in most years up to the mid 1970s, after when an increasing number has been seen annually. Ten birds occurred in 1977 and 22 in 1978, including six at Flamborough on 28th August and five on 11th September. The race was recorded 'regularly' in 1979 off Flamborough and Filey, with six at the former locality on 14th September; and 19 birds were identified in 1980, 18 in 1981, ten in 1982 and 16 in 1983.

During the long sea-watches from Flamborough Head by P.A. Lassey, D.I.M. Wallace and others, a few shearwaters have been seen which showed characters of the Levantine Shearwater *P.p. yelkouan* from the eastern Mediterranean. Single birds were so ascribed on 28th August and 11th September 1977; 1st May, 9th, 15th and 21st July and 19th September 1978; 2nd and 24th June and 22nd September 1979; 31st August, 16th October (two birds) and 7th December 1980; and 4th June 1983. This subspecies is still not officially admitted to the British list, and it will no doubt require a dead specimen to confirm its presence in our waters. Very few shearwaters are found dead on the beaches and the chances of finding a bird of this race are thus remote.

As with other seabirds, the timing of peak movement of Manx Shearwaters along our coastline usually coincides with northwesterly to northeasterly winds of some strength when the sea is running well and 'white horses' are showing on the wave tops. At any time during the period April to October, mainly during July to September, especially if these weather conditions prevail, the sea-watcher can expect to see this species anywhere off the coast from the Tees to the Humber.

Little Shearwater
Puffinus assimilis

This small shearwater had not been encountered in Yorkshire waters until 1976, when the dedicated sea-watching team of P.A. Lassey, Miss Irene Smith and D.I.M. Wallace saw one off Flamborough Head on 21st August. The bird was described in detail and its very characteristic fluttering flight action was clearly noted by all three observers, who were of course very familiar with the flight of the larger Manx Shearwater. This addition to the county avifauna was not unexpected in view of the remarkable increase in shearwater numbers recorded during the 1970s, due in no small way to the efforts of the above-named observers.

The many hours spent on the Flamborough Head clifftop, counting the passing seabirds, were to provide rewards in the following year when three individual Little Shearwaters were seen. Wallace saw the first on 11th June and the second on 26th June. Lassey and Miss Smith noted the third on 27th August and ascribed it to the race *baroli*, which has white undertail-coverts and breeds in the Madeiran and Canary Islands.

In 1978, on 21st July, Wallace again saw and described in detail the first of seven Little Shearwaters in that year. This was followed by another flying north on 31st August which was seen by N.A. Bousted, A. Grieve and S. Rooke. On 3rd September, Lassey and Wallace, together with R.E. Stokes, saw two more, and on 1st October a further three were seen. This series of records, coming so soon after the first county record in 1976, is quite remarkable.

The following records have been accepted by the Yorkshire Naturalists' Union Records Committee, but have not yet been submitted to the *British Birds* Rarities Committee.

On 3rd June 1979, Wallace watched one flying north, again at Flamborough, and another flew north there on 29th September, which Andrew Lassey and Miss Smith considered to be of the race *baroli*. The year 1980 was to produce yet another record when, on 31st August, A.M. Allport and P.A. Lassey saw one flying north at Flamborough. Single birds seen by Allport, Lassey and Wallace, again at Flamborough Head, on 26th September and 22nd October 1981, on 9th October 1982 and on 23rd and 24th September 1984 indicate that the species may now be looked for annually.

This very interesting addition to the Yorkshire list of birds may well have occurred in Nelson's time, but the chances of the collectors procuring a specimen would have been slight. That modern optical aids and knowledge allow us to appreciate the subtleties which permit the identification of species such as this during routine sea-watches is to be welcomed. Others will occur as the years pass, as it is possible that more Little Shearwaters are visiting the North Sea now than formerly, but it is equally likely that the species has been merely overlooked in the past.

Wilson's Petrel
Oceanites oceanicus

The only Yorkshire claim to this oceanic species rests on the record of one which was shot (Clarke and Roebuck), or killed or found dead (Nelson), on 13th November 1874 at Southowram, Halifax. The specimen was in the possession of C. Ward of Wray, near Lancaster, to whom it was taken in the flesh when quite fresh.

There are only about ten records of this Antarctic petrel in the British Isles and only three this century.

Storm Petrel
Hydrobates pelagicus

Thomas Allis wrote in his report of 1844: 'J. Heppenstall informs me that one was found swimming in the river in a populous part of Sheffield; it flew up and settled on a house, where it was shot.' The colourful writings of the early naturalists are lacking in today's publications, which are so matter-of-fact, and to read Nelson's opening remarks on this species is most entertaining:

> 'This little wanderer is an autumn or winter visitant, not uncommon in some years, but, being essentially a rover of the deep sea, it is not often observed close to land, unless in wild or stormy weather, when it is compelled to fly before the gale and seek refuge from the storms which rage with terrible frequency on our eastern seaboard.'

According to Arthur Strickland, considerable flights occurred before 1844, and in October and November 1867 a number of these petrels appeared in Bridlington Bay, where eight or nine were killed; 'they exhibited no fear of the presence of man, and one was knocked down by a short gaff'.

Nelson mentions 1877 and 1880 as years when it occurred on the coast at Redcar, Spurn and other stations. On 14th October 1881, one was blown against a bathing van and captured alive. Nelson kept this bird for some days, when it readily fed on oil which it took from the surface of water in a saucer, skimming to and fro like a swallow.

Five or six were found dead or exhausted on the Redcar sands during the great hurricane from the north-northeast on 18th November 1893. Nelson saw one at sea on 23rd September 1883, and two were seen off Spurn on 20th August 1889 as they were fluttering and beating for food near the boat as the fishermen hauled their crab pots.

Several struck the Spurn Light on 14th October 1881 and also on 16th/17th November 1898, while on the night of 11th November 1906 no fewer than five petrels were thus killed there. In the annotations to his personal copy of *The Birds of Yorkshire*, Nelson wrote that a Mr C.D. Bacon had seen large numbers, 5 miles (8 km) off Teesmouth in June 1908.

Today, the Storm Petrel is never encountered in the numbers that seem to have been regular in the nineteenth century. Even with intensified watching along the coast during the last 20 years, anything other than one or two birds in a year is exceptional.

Chislett could cite only four coastal records, three of which were in October and one in November. One had been caught on a fishing boat off Scarborough on 4th November 1926; one was found alive on Scarborough Pier on 30th October 1937; one had been caught at sea off Whitby on 23rd October 1930; and the fourth was caught at the Spurn Light on 28th October 1938.

Since 1952, Storm Petrels have occurred in all but seven years. In most years just one or two are reported, but in 1960 there were three coastal records involving single birds on 16th September, 26th September and 18th November and another found on a road at Sutton-in-Craven. In 1966, two landed on a trawler off Scarborough on 11th October and another was picked up in Scarborough on 19th November. Seven flying north off Spurn on 29th October 1974 is the only occasion when such numbers have been seen; one was off Hornsea on the same day.

Many of the coastal records, and those inland to the east of the Pennines, involve birds which have been found in towns and harbours, having been storm driven. If found alive, they often fly off when released onto the sea.

Chislett mentions five single Storm Petrels between 1907 and 1952 picked up inland at Barnsley, Sheffield, Greenfield, Fewston and Riddlesden. Since then, these birds have been found inland on seven further occasions. On 16th October 1974, one was brought in by a cat at Heslington, York, and was presented for my collection by Dr J.H. Lawton and Mrs A. Dennison. In 1975, one was found dead at Sutton-on-Forest which went to the York Museum. One was at Scammonden Dam on 17th September 1977, while another, found injured near Brighouse on 14th August 1979, had been ringed on Skokholm Island in 1978. A Storm Petrel was found in Sheffield on 23rd October 1979, and another was found dead near Holme Moss on 18th October 1981. One at Pugneys Gravel-pit on 19th November 1982 was killed by a predator on 20th, and one was found dead at Settle on 21st October 1983.

A bird was found in Knaresborough in 1813, and Nelson said 'it has also occurred in the recesses of the West Riding dales, and on the moorlands of the north and north-west, though the instances of these occurrences are too numerous to be given in detail'. Such a statement may refer to a 'wreck' or 'wrecks', which may have occurred more often in those days and which nearly always drive birds inland from the west rather than from the east. In October 1952, there was a major wreck of Leach's Petrels (see that species) which probably included a few 'Stormies', as Chislett recorded one picked up near Bolton Abbey on 11th November.

A Storm Petrel was seen on the River Ure at Masham in 1880. That the species should turn up at Knaresborough and Masham will be intriguing to those who realise the inference.

The specimen from which Bewick drew his figure of this species was sent to him by Capt. Dalton, who had found it dead at Tanfield (Bewick, *British Birds*, first ed., ii, pp. 249-51). It is not a little disturbing that the first British record of the rare Bulwer's Petrel was also found dead at Tanfield, and was at one time in the collection of Capt. Dalton's son.

A Storm Petrel found dead at Brighouse on 14th August 1979 had been ringed on Skokholm on 30th August 1968.

Leach's Petrel
Oceanodroma leucorhoa

What has been written about the Storm Petrel applies in general terms to this species. Nelson wrote of it: 'Casual visitant on the coast in winter, of rather rare occurrence; after severe gales it is sometimes found in inland localities.' In 1952, Chislett said that Nelson's assessment still stood, and, with only slight amendment concerning numbers seen (owing to the increase in sea-watching), it remains so today.

There are several accounts of 'wrecks', when petrels are storm driven and are forced onto the shore and farther inland, and Nelson referred to such during the great hurricane of 1893, when several were caught on the beach and six were picked up at Redcar (see also Storm Petrel). More Leach's Petrels than Storm Petrels have been found inland, and the largest wreck occurred in 1952. After a series of severe gales across the country in mid and late October, large numbers were driven ashore and inland. No fewer than 27 were found in Yorkshire between 12th and 31st October. Most of these were found either dead or dying and only three were seen in flight, singles at Stocks Reservoir on 19th and 30th October and at Stone Creek on the Humber on 31st October. There were seven records from the coast, including one at Spurn which was sitting on the mud along the peninsula and two which were fluttering over the spartina grass in the estuary, apparently seeking food. Many birds must have perished unseen.

Since that time, Leach's Petrels have been seen in all but two years. Only during the last few years, with the increased awareness of sea movements, have birds passing along the coast outnumbered those found dead or stranded inland. Most records involve single birds, but P.A. Lassey and D.I.M. Wallace watched six Leach's fly north into a northerly gale off Flamborough on 1st October 1978, on which day one was found dead in Barnsley (see below). Four flew south at Spurn on 22nd September 1979.

Leach's Petrels do still occur regularly inland and the more interesting records in recent years are listed below. One was seen flying over the river near Settle on 4th October 1970 before flying off to the north, and what was presumably the same bird was found dead at Horton-in-Ribblesdale quarry, 6 miles (9.6 km) to the north, on 6th October. Brian Shorrock, the local birdwatcher, sent the corpse to me for preservation. It proved to be a young male in poor condition, with no body-fat reserves, and had obviously died of starvation. One flew over the River Wharfe at Pool on 7th November 1971, on which date one was seen at Spurn. On 5th September 1972, a bird was watched by P. Smith at Wintersett Reservoir for 50 minutes as it flew around and rested on the water. P. Singleton watched one at Eccup Reservoir on 3rd December 1975. One was picked up on Broomhead Moor on 24th April 1977; it died later and is preserved in the Sheffield City Museum. A Leach's Petrel flew into Fairburn Ings on 28th September 1978 and was watched by C. Winn, S.C. Madge and others; it stayed until 30th. One flew across the M1 motorway near Wakefield on the latter date — could this have been the Fairburn bird? — and one was found dead at Barnsley on 1st October. On 25th September 1982, a Leach's Petrel was seen over Knaresborough Ringing Station by R. Evison and P.T. Treloar; it was being mobbed by crows, but eventually passed close to the observers, low over the ground, avoiding the attentions of the crows, and flicked down into the river course. Inland petrels are often attacked by corvids, as near Halifax on 21st October 1957 when Dr I.G. Brown watched four Rooks attacking one. One was seen by K. Moir at Ramsgill in Nidderdale on 10th October 1982, and a Leach's Petrel picked up alive on the beach at Spurn Point on 16th October 1982 had its right wing completely missing and recently severed.

Three specimens in the Nelson collection at the Dorman Museum in Middlesbrough were collected respectively at Redcar in 1896, at Teesmouth in 1903 and on Cowpen Marsh on 21st September 1914.

Gannet
Sula bassana

The noble Gannet is unique among Yorkshire breeding birds, for it nests nowhere else on the British mainland. The story of its colonisation of Bempton Cliffs has been well documented, especially since the early 1950s when that well-known and expert ornithologist, H.O. Bunce, started to study the small colony in detail. His careful research throughout the next 20 years and during much of the 1970s, when he was assisted by Miss Joan Fairhurst, has made an invaluable contribution to the history of this important gannetry.

The first known attempt by a Gannet to nest on the precipitous cliffs at Bempton was in 1924, when a pair frequented the site known as 'Black Shelf' throughout the season. In 1925, a nest was built but no further details were forthcoming. Gannets continued to frequent the site, and an occasional nest was built annually, but it was not until 1937 that W.J. Clarke was able to record that an egg had been laid in a nest built on 'Jubilee Corner', a site so called because it had been first climbed in Queen Victoria's Jubilee Year.

Chislett said that the cliffs were high and precipitous, that bulges frequently hid ledges from view and that only the 'eggers' climbed there, and 'for or against the claim for the 1937 egg to be the first laid by a Gannet in Yorkshire, [he] would not risk a stiver'.

Gannets were reported to be present on the cliffs during the 1939-45 war years, but there were no real details until 1944, when four birds were seen, although there was no nest at the original site. In 1945, J.H. Barrett watched two birds fly repeatedly into the cliffs at one place, staying for periods of from five to ten minutes, and in 1946 he again watched a bird fly onto the cliff. J.R. Artley, one of the climbers at Bempton, stated that he had seen no Gannets in 1945! In 1947, four birds were noted from 12th April onwards and three were on the old nesting ledge on 17th June, but a climber, J. Petty, said that he did not think the species bred. In 1948, four Gannets were again present and A.J. Wallis was told by the climbers that there were three nests on 29th May, one of which held an egg. One of the nests was visible from the clifftop and J.R. Artley reported that two young had been reared. It was thus 24 years from the first known attendance by the species on the cliffs before young were definitely reared. Eggs were no doubt taken by the climbers during the intervening period.

During the ensuing ten years, the small colony did not increase and annual fortunes fluctuated. No more than four young were reared annually until 1959, when five were produced. It was in 1960 when things started to happen; eight nests were built and six young were reared from seven eggs. Henry Bunce continued to watch the colony closely and there was a steady annual increase until, in 1970, 24 sites were occupied and 18 chicks were reared to full size and presumably fledged. The steady increase continued, and in 1971 Bunce and Miss Fairhurst reported that 21 young had fledged from 33 nests and that one of a pair at a new nest site, which was unsuccessful, had been colour-ringed as a chick on the Bass Rock in either 1961 or 1966, probably the latter. This was the first indication of the origin of the Bempton breeders.

The first birds to return to the colony in 1972 were on their ledges on 9th February. There were 43 nests that year and 32 young were presumed to have flown, final desertion of the cliffs taking place between 11th and 15th October. In 1973, 14 Gannets were on ledges as early as 25th January and, on 29th July, 150 to 200 were present at or around the cliffs, including breeding and non-breeding adults and visitors; 42 chicks were raised from 52 known eggs, and 55 sites were occupied. All the breeding adults deserted the colony by 28th September and the last chick fledged on 8th October, having been unattended during the interim. The colour-ringed bird, first noted in 1971, bred successfully. Nine birds were back on the cliffs as early as 31st December in 1974, and a very successful breeding season followed: by 15th February 1975 50 birds were present, and 104 eggs were eventually produced, 35 of which were from birds breeding for the first time; 83 chicks hatched and 76 fledged. In addition, there were 11 unused nests. The maximum number of non-breeding birds on ledges was 80, whereas there had been 120 during the summer of 1974. A few remained at their sites until mid October, but all had departed by the end of the month.

An annual increase in the number of breeding pairs followed, and in 1976 89 young fledged from 97 chicks hatched from 109 eggs. In 1977, the number of nests had reached 169, which received 136 eggs from which 121 chicks hatched; 112 of these fledged. Of the nine chicks lost, five were tethered to the nest material with strands of nylon cord, an all too frequent hazard for seabirds at the present time. The 1978 breeding season produced 160 eggs, of which 153 hatched, and 145 young eventually flew. In addition to these, Miss Joan Fairhurst estimated that a further 20 pairs may have nested on sites not visible from the clifftop.

The warden for The Royal Society for the Protection of Birds, who checked the colony in 1979, reported that about one-third of all the nests were visible from the clifftop and calculated that about 200 pairs reared 200 young. A spectacular increase to 280 pairs in 1980, with at least 250 young being reared, is most encouraging and the future of this unique and spectacular gannetry is secure under the watchful eye of the RSPB who have controlled access to much of the clifftop since 1970. Counts from the clifftop in 1981 and 1982 revealed 312 and 375 pairs respectively, with an increase to 542 nests in 1983. A pale leucistic bird was in the colony during the summer of 1978.

The movements of Gannets along the Yorkshire coastline are variable, both seasonally and numerically. They may be seen in any month, the largest numbers passing during July to September when both adults and juveniles are moving south, although during periods of strong winds from the northern quarter the movement may be to the north as birds seek some shelter in the lee of the shore or seek to correct some temporary displacement. A good example occurred on 17th September 1977 when, during a very large movement including Sooty Shearwaters and Fulmars, Gannets were flying north in large numbers: 650 were seen off Spurn, 640 off Hornsea, 2,000 off Flamborough and 433 off Filey Brigg.

Autumn passage is usually to the south and numbers vary from a few birds daily to several hundreds. Flamborough Head has produced the largest counts in the last few years, owing to the intensified watching by Lassey, Wallace and others. In 1978, 1,400 flew south there on 26th August while in 1979 the peaks were 3,200 on 22nd September and 1,100 on 30th; even higher numbers occurred in 1982, when 2,460 were seen on 31st August, 4,200 on 5th September and 2,400 on 6th September. On 30th August 1978, watchers at Filey Brigg counted 1,134 birds, with 1,060 passing off Spurn Point on the same day; 1,018 birds seen off Hornsea on 1st October were all flying north.

Spring movements are never so spectacular, and the most seen passing at that season in recent years was 329 flying north at Flamborough on 27th April 1979.

Gannets often occur inland, and can turn up almost anywhere from the remote moorlands to the busy town centres. Juveniles making their first long flights are often involved, and mostly during periods of adverse weather, with which they have not learned to cope. September is the main month for such an event. At this time, young birds are often seen well up the Humber Estuary. The instances of inland occurrences are far too numerous to list in detail, but some indication of their frequency and season will be evident from the details during the last 20 years. During this period there have been two birds in February, four in March, three in April, three in June, one in July, 13 in September, five in October and three in November. Immatures have predominated, but adults do occur and may do so in both calm and stormy weather.

In addition to the colour-ringed bird breeding at Bempton, there have been a few other recoveries in Yorkshire of Gannets ringed on the Bass Rock. A juvenile ringed on the nest on the island of Grassholm off Wales on 1st August 1937 was recovered off Scarborough on 21st July 1939. Another juvenile ringed on Hermaness in the Shetland Islands was found alive at Bank Newton, near Gargrave, on 13th August 1974.

A juvenile, washed up dead at Spurn on 1st October 1975, was sent to me for preservation. It had swallowed a piece of wood, 8½ inches (21.5 cm) long and painted pale blue on one side. It had presumably mistaken this for a fish, but it is difficult to understand why the mistake was not realised at the onset of swallowing. Perhaps the proximity of other Gannets induced a degree of panic, and greed reduced the normal power of discrimination. Stuck to the oily wood were eight specimens of parasitic roundworms no doubt killed by the oil, a quantity of which was in the Gannet's stomach.

Cormorant
Phalacrocorax carbo

As a breeding bird, the Cormorant has but a scattered distribution along our coast-line where suitable cliffs provide adequate ledges and sufficient privacy from disturbance. At some traditional sites, however, the species has suffered much at the hand of man over the years.

The most northerly colony is on the Hunt Cliff, a few miles south of Saltburn, where Nelson knew Cormorants had nested at some time prior to 1907, although at that time the site was not occupied. The building of the Whitby-to-Saltburn railway was blamed for the disturbance of the birds, which moved to the next colony southwards on the cliffs below Boulby. According to P.J. Stead in his review of the *Birds of Teesmouth* published in 1964, the Hunt Cliff site was recolonised some time during the first quarter of this century, and, with an annual fluctuation in the number of breeding pairs, is still thriving today. Chislett mentions that C. Nelson estimated 35 pairs in 1949, while Stead says that in 1961 'about 20 pairs now breed there' and mentions 24 nests in 1964. Later, 21 nests were seen in 1973 and 25 in 1978.

The traditional site on the cliffs near Boulby had a particularly rough passage in 1867, when some youths lowered a lighted tar barrel down the cliff, at night, onto the nesting ledges, which, quite understandably, caused the birds to desert the site for a while. The Cormorants apparently established themselves on Kettle Ness, but further persecution there was probably responsible for the traditional site on the Boulby Cliffs being recolonised and where a few pairs were breeding up to 1900. In 1948 and 1952 the count showed 30-40 pairs. By 1969 it appears that the site was again deserted, since it is not referred to in the 'Operation Seafarer' counts of 1969-70, which formed the basis for *The Seabirds of Britain and Ireland* published in 1974 (Cramp *et al.*). Nelson tells how, in the nineteenth century, when Boulby Cliffs, and presumably Hunt Cliff, were occupied by nesting birds, long strings of up to 30 Cormorants were often seen passing Redcar in the early morning on their way to fish in the Tees Estuary.

The Cormorants which established a colony on Kettle Ness, where Nelson saw about 30 pairs nesting in 1880, also suffered persecution, for in 1887 many were shot while on their nests, and the opening of the railway which ran near the clifftop around the edge of the ness finally caused the birds to desert the site. The same applies to the colony which Nelson refers to when he wrote 'The bulk of the Kettleness Cormorants have evidently gone still further south, and about thirty to forty pairs now nest near the Whitby High Lights, two miles from that town.' He even includes a drawing of the cliff and two photographs of young birds at this site. The colony cannot have survived for long, as Chislett makes no mention of it, and this site too is not included in the list of colonies counted for 'Operation Seafarer' in 1969-70.

The next long-established colony to the south is at Ravenscar, the birds nesting on the ledges of Blea Wyke Point. This is undoubtedly the colony Nelson mentions as being at Peak, to the north of Scarborough, where he states that some 50 pairs nested 'before the railway was opened, but they decreased afterwards'. It is very unlikely that the railway was the cause of any decline at this colony, as the site is nowhere near the line of the railway and is particularly difficult to get to. Nevertheless, Nelson goes on to say: 'Several years ago a Scarborough man shot eighteen out of twenty nesting birds with a rifle; the following year none was noted, but a few pairs have since returned.' The colony is still in existence at the time of writing, and counts of the pairs breeding and mentioned in the records may be listed as follows: A.J. Wallis reported 24 pairs in 1949; 28 occupied nests were seen on 20th July 1966; on 20th July 1969, 31 nests were counted for 'Operation Seafarer' by A.J. Wallis, R.H. Appleby and C.R. Clarke; and on 26th July 1975 Mrs Joan Webb counted 30 pairs on the ledges, many of which were feeding young (at the same time Mrs Webb noted 35 birds on a reef of rocks just below the nesting cliff at low tide, and many more were on the sea).

South of Ravenscar, the next cliffs which provide potentially suitable sites for Cormorants to nest are from Cayton Bay southwards to Filey Brigg. Referring to the stretch of coast from Scarborough to Filey, Nelson says: 'Between Scarborough and Filey several pairs find nesting places; Mr. Thomas Carter in 1884 observed

Cormorants there, and was told by a fisherman that he had seen a nest and three eggs at Scout Nab (*The Zoologist*, 1884, p. 446). I am informed by Mr. J. Fountain of Filey that he had a clutch of five eggs brought to him in the year 1902; in 1906 there were eight nests.' It seems certain that 'Scout Nab' is the name given by the local fishermen to the cliff between Gristhorpe Bay and Filey Brigg where a colony of Cormorants has nested throughout the present century. This colony is very difficult to see clearly from the clifftop, and to look up at it from the shore requires a difficult walk along a boulder-strewn beach from the north. In order to obtain accurate counts a boat is needed, which probably explains the sporadic counts noted in the literature until recent times. The site was occupied in 1926 when T.N. Roberts wrote his paper on *The Birds of the Scarborough District*, but this author does not mention the size of the colony. A.J. Wallis counted 45 pairs in 1946, and the next count was in 1969 for 'Operation Seafarer', when only 14 nests were recorded. In 1976 S.M. Lister counted 19 occupied nests, and there were 23 nests in 1977 and 16 in 1978. On 23rd June 1979, H.J. Whitehead checked this colony and found 25 nests with 74 birds on the ledges; on 28th August 1979, 95 birds were on the sea offshore at this point. Twelve pairs bred there in 1980.

The earliest reference to the Cormorant in Yorkshire was made by Pennant, who, on his journey to Scotland in 1769, visited Flamborough on 3rd July and remarked of the birds there: 'Multitudes were swimming about, others swarmed in the air and almost stunned us with the variety of their croaks and screams; I observed among them Corvorants.' (*A Tour in Scotland*, 1771, p. 15).

Nelson continues his comments on the species by saying, with reference to Flamborough, 'The Cormorant used to be a familiar object near the Headland until the "sixties", but there again senseless persecution has banished it as a nesting species.' He then lists several sites where the species did nest and ends by saying 'the Bempton climbers say that some four or five birds frequent a certain portion of the cliffs, but there is no proof of their nesting there now'.

Five years earlier than Nelson, E.W. Wade said in his paper on the *Birds of the Bempton Cliffs*, read to the Hull Scientific and Field Naturalists' Club on 19th February 1902, 'The Cormorant frequently perches on the rocks, but has no breeding place nearer than the Whitby District and the wreck of the "Beaconsfield" at Aldborough' (see below for further reference to this latter site). Sam Leng, one of the Bempton climbers, makes no mention of the species in his booklet *Experiences and Reminiscences of a Cliff Climber*, written some time before 1935, the year in which he died. Chislett in 1952 says 'About Bempton and Flamborough proved nesting of one or two pairs has occurred spasmodically, but is suspected more frequently.'

In June 1964, A.J. Williams and D. Kermode made a census of the seabird colony at Flamborough (*The Seabird Bulletin*, no. 6, Oct. 1968). For Cormorant they include the statement that 'However, in the last decade there has been a marked decline, and the only pair seen during the census was near the Gannet site at Bempton.' They also suggest that the decline appears to correlate with the increase in the Shag, but the very limited success of this latter species during, at least, the present century does not support this theory.

Two more recent Flamborough records are of interest. Firstly, S.C. Madge, while he was warden for the Royal Society for the Protection of Birds, reported birds sitting on ledges in 1975 above the portion of cliff known as 'Blacksmith's Shop'; he considered that breeding would eventually take place there. Secondly, a pair nested at Flamborough in 1980.

The Cormorant is well known as being very intolerant of even the slightest interference by humans at its nesting sites. The activities of the famous 'climmers' of Bempton, during the 250 or so years when they plundered the cliffs for the eggs of the Guillemot, may have been the main controlling factor in preventing the species from establishing itself as a breeding bird among all the others which nest there so successfully. The climbing stopped just 30 years ago, but this is not too long a period for a sensitive species like the Cormorant to adjust to the changed circumstances. The Yorkshire breeding population is now limited to three long-established colonies.

Along the Holderness coast there is no suitable place for Cormorants to breed, but in 1887 an event occurred which offered an unexpected and unusual nesting site for at least one pair over a period of some 13 years. In 1887, a ship called 'The Earl of Beaconsfield' went ashore near Aldborough and the species used the projecting mast for roosting. In 1893, one pair reared young in a nest built on the 'crosstrees' of the main mast, and 16 birds were roosting there on 31st August 1900, when nestlings were seen.

Anglers on both fresh and salt water have never been fond of the Cormorant, and it was this largely unjustified image that prompted their slaughter during the late nineteenth and early twentieth centuries. Even today, some are shot in the supposed interests of angling. On 9th June 1971, F.J. Thompson of Scarborough found two birds hanging on a gibbet at Hackness Lake; and I have an adult female in my collection that was shot at Scarborough in May 1970.

Southerly movement offshore takes place each autumn, and from July to October — and often to the year-end — birds may be seen flying steadily along the coastline. Watchers at Spurn have recorded these movements for many years, and in 1977 more birds than usual passed: 44 on 1st October were followed by 93 on 2nd and 51 on 3rd; these numbers were exceptional, the average daily maximum being usually below 20. Birds concentrate at feeding places during the winter months and large numbers frequent the Teesmouth, where 94 were counted by S.C. Norman on 12th April 1970; 40 were there in July and August with 101 on 13th September and 120 on 19th September. Dennis Summers-Smith saw 185 there on 26th February 1977 and such concentrations occur annually. A roost at the ore terminal on the River Tees held 65 birds on 14th December 1975 and 57 on 14th March 1976.

In October 1974, numbers in Filey Bay were exceptional and Ron Appleby and G. Carr counted 100 on 11th October and 40 on 12th. Shags were numerous at this time too. A count of 80 Cormorants at Flamborough Head on 18th November 1977 was the highest number in that year, while in 1978 140 were counted by P.A. Lassey as they flew north (61 flew south also) on 29th July and 105 flew south on 19th September.

The long-established roost of Cormorants at Hornsea Mere has been well counted over the years. Chislett recorded 50 birds there in 1953, and in February of that year Miss E. Crackles noted one individual showing characters of the southern white-headed race (see below). On 3rd April, five such birds were present and were seen by several observers including H.O. Bunce. This roost thrives today and birds may be seen in any month, the peak numbers being present during mid winter when up to 60 are usually to be seen.

White-headed birds, known colloquially as Southern Cormorants (*P.c. sinensis*), are seen not infrequently in Yorkshire, both on the coast and inland. A few have occurred at Spurn during March and April in the last few years, when single birds have been seen elsewhere along the coastline. On 30th March 1956, at Bempton, G.R. Bennett watched a party of 15, six of which had white heads. At Gouthwaite Reservoir, between 2nd January and 15th April 1960, from one to six Cormorants were present. They often rose to great heights and circled before flying off, but regularly came back to the water. On 4th April, a new bird arrived which had a magnificent 'silver' head. Another, showing the same characters, was at Wath Ings on 19th March 1979.

In 1976, a remarkable movement occurred inland during mid April. Five flew west over Redmires Dam on 11th; one with a white head flew over Swillington Ings on 17th; three were at Gouthwaite Reservoir and four at Blackmoorfoot Reservoir on 18th; four were at Hay-a-Park Gravel-pits, eight flew over Blacktoft Sands, ten flew over Wintersett Reservoir and a party of 23 flew over Fewston Reservoir, all on 19th; five were at Fairburn Ings on 20th and 13 were at Sandsfield Gravel-pit on 24th. A few other waters held single birds during this period. Although birds may occur at inland waters in all months, and in varying numbers, mainly during the winter, movements on this scale are rare. G.E. Alderson of Leyburn reports that a large sheet of water at Ellerton-on-Swale regularly attracts Cormorants. Nine were there on 7th March 1978 and 15 were present on 10th February 1981.

In 1971, several birds seen flying north to the winter cliff roost at Flamborough Head were wearing metal rings on their left legs. No Cormorants are ringed in Yorkshire and these birds were doubtless from colonies farther north, probably the Farne Islands, from where a few ringed individuals found dead on Yorkshire beaches have originated. Chislett mentions a bird ringed at Mochrum, Wigtownshire, in July 1937 which was found on the Humberside at Skeffling on 28th November of the same year. He wondered whether it had crossed Yorkshire, or had crossed into the Firth of Forth before coming south to the Humber. Either route is equally likely.

While counting Cormorants at the colony at Ravenscar on 20th July 1969, C.R. Clark, R.H. Appleby and A.J. Wallis saw a pure white bird on one of the ledges. Seen through binoculars, it was clearly a young bird, though as big as its normal-plumaged parents standing beside it. Two days later, the three watchers visited the site again and inspected the bird through a telescope. It was difficult for them to establish whether or not it was a true albino and, although there was a definite pink hue to the eye area when closed, the eyes appeared dark when open. The bill was pale and almost colourless, the gular pouch was yellow, though paler than in the adults, and the whole plumage was creamy-white. Because of the height of the nest, which was 150 feet (46 m) above the observers, the legs and feet were not seen clearly. For full details, see *The Naturalist*, 912, p. 4. That the bird was never seen again is interesting and may suggest that it did not survive. The absence of pigment would make the plumage structurally weak, and excessive waterlogging would have been a problem. Such birds, often claimed as 'albino', are more usually exhibiting plumage which merely had reduced pigment, giving rise to a creamy or buff coloration. These birds have normal eye colour and the condition is known as leucism.

In 1907, Nelson summed up the Cormorant's status as 'Resident, breeding on the cliffs between Whitby and Scarborough, and near Filey; formerly nested in several other localities. The majority retire southward in winter.' This assessment requires little amendment today save for the fact that the only three established breeding colonies are at Hunt Cliff, Ravenscar and Gristhorpe Cliffs, and that we now recognise it as a regular visitor to inland waters in small numbers, the lack of observers during the early part of the century being no doubt responsible for the paucity of such records that came to the attention of Nelson.

Shag
Phalacrocorax aristotelis

When Pennant visited Flamborough Head on his journey to Sutherland in 1769, he noted Shags in small flocks. Thomas Allis wrote in 1844, quoting Strickland, that the

Shag used to breed at Flamborough some years previously in considerable numbers but 'now seems to be quite banished from there'.

Odd pairs visited the cliffs in Nelson's time and 'would doubtless breed if unmolested'. Two birds arrived there in 1892 but were promptly acquired by fishermen, and the species was rare enough at the time for Nelson to list the only four occurrences known to him during his time at Redcar. His assessment of the Shag's status was that it was a bird of passage on the coast on its way to and from its breeding stations farther north, and that it used to nest at Flamborough. Chislett reaffirmed that assessment and added that, in recent years, one or two birds had been seen at Flamborough entering the caves at the base of the cliffs, and that these might have been confirmed as Shags and not Cormorants had the opportunity for careful inspection been offered. Shags they would surely have been. A Shag was observed at Flamborough on 19th May 1949 and, on 29th June, an adult and an immature were seen. These were joined by others, until eight adults and 20 immatures were present. Chislett said that the species may have bred there or thereabouts. It would appear almost certain that they had been breeding there, perhaps for some years.

H.O. Bunce and K. Fenton watched Flamborough regularly in 1953, and birds were seen to enter caves and the 'bill-fencing' display was noted. On 18th July 25 birds consisted of 15 adults, seven immatures and three juveniles. One of the egg climbers claimed to have found eggs in 1953. Breeding was certainly taking place during this period, but definite proof was lacking. On 10th September 1955, 17 adults and 31 immatures were seen by Bunce, the latter including some juveniles still being fed by the adults. In 1957, a nest was finally seen from the clifftop, and in 1958 three were seen. In the following year there were seven nests with young, and counts of 77 birds on 3rd August and 90 on 13th September indicated the strength of the colony.

On 8th August 1971, a breeding adult was seen to be wearing a colour ring; it proved to have been marked on the Farne Islands in 1967. This was the first proof of the origin of the Yorkshire breeding Shags, and another bird found dead at Flamborough in July had been ringed on the Farnes in 1962. Several ringed Shags have now been found dead along our coastline, the origins of which have been the Bass Rock, the Isle of May and the Farne Islands.

H.O. Bunce reported an increase in the breeding population in 1972, especially on the Bempton stretch of the cliffs. Large roosts were recorded by S.C. Madge, then the Bempton warden, in 1974; also in that year, 72 were on Scale Nab and 51 on Cat Nab on 21st August and 93 were at Flamborough on 12th August. In 1977, S. Rooke, the new RSPB warden at Bempton, counted 135 Shags on the sea at the foot of the cliffs in mid September. Large numbers were counted in that year at Flamborough: 120 on 17th September, 130 on 30th September, 260 on 8th October, 155 on 16th October, 345 flying south on 22nd October and 150 on 18th November. No fewer than 537 were counted there on 27th September 1982 and 634 on 30th October 1983. These numbers were quite exceptional and in part indicative of the success of the breeding colony. In 1979, it was estimated that about 12 pairs nested on the headland at Flamborough and about 15 pairs at Bempton. Thus the Shag is now a regular breeding bird along the chalk cliffs at Flamborough and Bempton and large numbers can be seen there during the autumn.

Movements along the coast away from the breeding area occur annually during the spring and autumn, mainly the latter. A large flock of 60 birds flew south at Spurn on 3rd March 1962, an unusual direction at that time of year. In the same year, B.S. Pashby counted three parties of Shags, totalling 130 birds, flying south off Holmpton on 11th March. In the afternoon of 21st November 1965 129 birds flew south off Spurn, and on 18th November 1975 234 passed south there.

Anywhere from the South Gare to Spurn, in the non-breeding season, Shags may be seen in small numbers, especially in severe weather when they often seek shelter in the harbours of Bridlington, Scarborough and Whitby where they rest on the stone steps and timbers of the piers. D.J. Britton saw 21 in the harbour at Whitby on 30th January 1972, and a flotilla of 56 Shags was seen in the South Bay, Scarborough, on 24th January 1984.

Inland, Shags are not rare, but erratic in their appearance. They may occur, usually singly, in most months, by far the largest number being seen during the period September to January, October being the peak month of occurrence. Of 53 birds seen inland during the last 30 years, 38 have been during that period. May is the next most likely time to see an inland Shag and there have been four records during that month, including four flying over Wintersett Reservoir with two Cormorants on 4th May 1980.

On 2nd November 1952, a Shag walked into a workshop near the river at Wakefield and promptly died. A bird found alive in a quarry at Grassington on 11th August 1971 was taken to the house of Miss Susie Brooks, where it died next day; it was a two-year-old female in heavy moult and extremely thin.

It would appear that the status of this intriguing species has come full circle and that it is once again a regular and relatively common breeding bird along the base of the Flamborough and Bempton cliffs, as it seems to have been in the early nineteenth century.

White Pelican
Pelecanus onocrotalus

Excellent views were obtained of a sub-adult bird on the Humber shore at Welton Water on 16th July 1975. It was watched at length by R.H. Appleby, S.C. Madge, D.E. Murray and D.I.M. Wallace. The latter sketched it and I am grateful to him for his drawing, which is reproduced above. The bird was in perfect plumage and was not confiding, readily taking wing and flying farther out onto the mud when approached too closely. That it was a White Pelican there is no doubt; whence it came can only be conjectured. Captive origin, even if recent, does not always show in the behaviour of such wanderers, and the likelihood of this Yorkshire example being an escaped bird is high.

The species breeds no nearer than Greece and the northern shores of the Black Sea, and wanderers to western Europe are extremely rare.

Bittern
Botaurus stellaris

The Bittern figures often in the history of Yorkshire birds and must at one time have been well distributed as a breeding species in the carrlands and large reedbeds. Nelson cites a reference to the great banquet given at Cawood in honour of the enthroning of George Nevell as Archbishop of York in 1466 at which 'In Bittors, c.c. iiii' were provided among the delicacies. They were also served at Earl Percy's table at the Castles of Wressill and Lekinfield in 1512 at a price of '12d. a pece so they be good'. It was a popular item on the lavish menus of the period, and in 1526 and 1530 Sir John Neville included them in his daughters' wedding feasts. In 1528, we find that '10 bytters' cost 13s.4d.

Some 300 years later, in 1844, Thomas Allis reported that it had been met with a few times near Sheffield, that he heard no mention of it from near Halifax and that it was very rare near Huddersfield. In 1831, a Mr Reid of Doncaster had 25 specimens brought to him, and Arthur Strickland observed that in the winter of 1831 a singular flight visited this country, and he collected a list of upwards of 60 that had been killed in Yorkshire.

Nelson quoted a Charles Hatfield, who said that the Bittern began to desert the carrs about 1750. After that time, its decline seems to have accelerated and, in 1907, Nelson wrote that it was no longer resident in the county.

There was some evidence of immigration in the early days: one was 'taken' on the rocks near Saltburn in November 1868, one was killed on the shore near Whitby in December 1890 and one was killed at the Spurn lighthouse on 21st November 1905. A bird ringed in the Netherlands on 14th January 1967 was shot at Robin Hood's Bay on 22nd December 1969.

Most of the records in the twentieth century have been during the winter months. Of 32 recorded during the period 1906 to 1930, 30 were in the winter, one in May and one in September. Chislett cited 15 records between 1940 and 1950. Since that time, the Bittern has occurred annually with a maximum of eight records in any one year, mainly from the south and east of the county. Hornsea Mere and Fairburn Ings are the favoured localities, and the majority of sightings have been between late August and April. Single birds occurred at six places during January and February 1982, including one found dead at Millfield Flash on 2nd February.

A bird was calling near Goole in the summer of 1954 and one was booming in central Yorkshire during the summer of 1959, in which year one was at Fairburn Ings on 6th August. One was near Wilton in vice-county 62 on 7th June 1972.

In 1979, during the very cold period, there were many Bitterns recorded throughout Britain. Many were weak through starvation and the influx was evidenced in Yorkshire. At Hornsea Mere, R.G. Hawley, the warden for the Royal Society for the Protection of Birds, reported Bitterns regularly from 9th January to 10th March. During this period, one was found dead and two were watched eating small mammals in grassland and taking small invertebrates in ice-free drains. For full details of the influx into Britain, see *British Birds*, 1981, pp. 1-10.

Nelson's summary, written in 1907, of 'Winter visitant of uncommon occurrence, sometimes numerous in severe seasons' more or less applies today. That a few birds occur late in the spring and early in the autumn, with occasional ones during the summer, suggests that an odd pair may one day breed if undisturbed.

American Bittern
Botaurus lentiginosus

In *The Birds of Yorkshire*, Nelson mentions two claims for this bird's inclusion in the county list. One was obtained at Kells Springs, near Slingsby, about 1873 by Robert Hicks of York and identified by James Brigham. It was afterwards exhibited at a meeting of the York Naturalists' Club and the specimen went to Sir Vauncey Crewe's collection at Calke Abbey, Derby.

On 27th October 1882, a female was killed by the Hon. W. Dawnay at Harlsey Hall, near Northallerton. Its gizzard contained the remains of field mice. The specimen was examined by John Harrison of Wilstrop and recorded by James Backhouse in *The Zoologist* (1883, pp. 128 and 180) and by W. Eagle Clarke in *The Naturalist* (1884, p. 177).

Chislett omitted this species from *Yorkshire Birds* without giving reasons and I presume he merely overlooked it. The editors of *The Handbook* admitted the two Yorkshire claims and I can find no reason to do otherwise.

Least Bittern
Ixobrychus exilis

In *The Birds of Yorkshire*, Nelson said that a Little Bittern had been obtained near York in the autumn of 1852 and that the specimen had been acquired by Joseph Duff of Bishop Auckland. It went eventually to Nelson's collection and was in his possession when his book was published in 1907. When he died in 1916, his widow presented the collection of stuffed birds to the Dorman Museum in Middlesbrough, where they are on show at the present time. The bird in question is housed in case number 116, but is in fact a specimen of the American Least Bittern *Ixobrychus exilis*. I saw the bird some years ago and wondered about its identity. I checked the collection again on 21st August 1984 with P.J. Stead and identified it as *exilis*. It is strange that Nelson did not suspect that it was something different, as it is very small and has the sides of the breast a rich chestnut colour and the pale wing patch edged on the major coverts with a chestnut bar. Having now been correctly identified, the question remains as to its eligibility to rank as a Yorkshire record, and indeed the first and only record for the British Isles. There is no doubt that the bird in question is the one which was in Nelson's collection and the one referred to as being obtained near York in 1852. It is unlikely that any fraud was attached to the record as it has never been claimed as anything other than a Little Bittern. Any attempt to pass off an imported specimen as a Yorkshire bird would surely have been coupled with the correct identification as Least Bittern and an attendant demand for more remuneration for such an extreme rarity. I consider that the specimen was shot near York as claimed and misidentified as a Little Bittern, and that the species has, perhaps, as good a claim for a place on the British list as several other rarities.

Little Bittern
Ixobrychus minutus

Thomas Allis referred to the Little Bittern in his report to the British Association meeting at York in 1844, saying that one was shot at Birdsall, near Malton, 'about two years ago'; one was shot at Thorpe, near Bridlington, and a third bird was shot near Doncaster.

One was procured at Redcar on 26th September 1852. Another, reported as being taken about the same time near York, was in fact an example of the Least Bittern, details of which are published under that species. In August 1863, a Little Bittern was shot at Scarborough Mere whilst it perched in a tree at Black House.

W.W. Boulton of Beverley stated that one was killed at Cottingham several years prior to 1880; the specimen was bought by Thomas Boynton of Bridlington on Boulton's death. One was taken about 1870 at Collta in the Rivelin Valley. One was at Cold Hiendley (Wintersett) Reservoir, near Wakefield, on 25th August 1872; this went to the collection of Mr Talbot, who recorded it in his *Birds of Wakefield*. An adult was recorded by F. Boyes at Easington on 25th May 1874. The Whitby Museum had a specimen captured in 1877 at Ruswarp Dam by T. Fletcher. A mature female was procured at Scalby Beck, Scarborough, on 25th February 1879 by Mr Wood of Huddersfield. On 23rd September 1881, a male was caught alive on the Dutch River bank near Goole and was in the collection of W. Eagle Clarke. W. Walton reported a bird to Nelson which had occurred at Mickleton in Teesdale in 1885. One was shot at Sandal, near Wakefield, in 1892. G. Steels of Pocklington had one brought to him for preservation which had been killed within 2 miles (3.2 km) of that town during very hard weather in 1895. G. Heaton picked up the remains of one about 2 miles south of Scarborough on 7th January 1902; it had been partly eaten, but enough remained to enable the identification.

Nelson also mentions four others for which his information was incomplete: one captured alive at Hunslet, near Leeds, and one at Harewood Bridge, both prior to 1881; one in the collection of C.C. Oxley of Redcar and probably taken near that locality; and one on the River Hull near Watton Beck 'some years ago'.

While Nelson was also able to cite 16 authentic records in *The Birds of Yorkshire*, Chislett could add no more during the 45 years which elapsed up to the appearance of *Yorkshire Birds* in 1952. The species has occurred fairly regularly in the British Isles in recent years, and there have been about 140 records since 1958.

Since the publication of *Yorkshire Birds*, there have been records in five subsequent years. One shot at Marley Sewage-farm on 27th September 1957 fell into the river and was retrieved later; it was inspected by D.F. Walker, R.F. Dickens and A.W.A. Swaine, who preserved it, an immature female. I saw the mounted specimen at the annual dinner in March 1967 of the Wharfedale Naturalists' Society where it was exhibited by Walker, who gave the after-dinner address entitled 'Once Bitten'.

On 24th August 1967, good views were had of a male at Catcliffe Flash, near Sheffield, by C. Jacklin. Two others occurred in Britain in that same year, one in Sussex in July and one in Norfolk in September.

In 1976, two occurred in Yorkshire. An adult male was watched by J. Hewitt, N. Addy and J.M. Turton on 17th July at Wath Ings and another adult male was at Millfield Flash, adjacent to the M1 motorway near Wakefield, during the last week of September, when it was watched by R.L. Brook, J.E. Dale and others. It was caught and ringed by J.S. Armitage on 30th September (see plate 58). G.R. Bennett and R.G. Hawley watched a male at Hornsea Mere between 29th May and 11th June 1977.

It was to be seven years before this small secretive heron was seen again in Yorkshire, an event which was to culminate in the first confirmed breeding record for the British Isles. On 11th June 1984, P.R. Lambe was crossing over Low Ellers viaduct when he noticed a number of Black-headed Gulls mobbing something in the reeds on Low Ellers Carr, which forms part of a larger complex known as Potteric Carr Nature Reserve. At first he could see only a small pointed bill darting up at the gulls when they came too close. The gulls eventually flew off, and 20 minutes later a Little Bittern flew out of the reeds and was pursued by the gulls in the area. Having satisfied himself of the identity of the bird, Lambe contacted S. Boyes and they watched it together later the same evening. It was a male, and was seen by many observers during the next few days. On 15th June, a female was seen and, because of the possibility of breeding, a close watch was kept on the area by several local birdwatchers. The birds did in fact breed, and three fledged juveniles were seen during early August; two of these left the site on 10th August and the other, smaller, bird on 11th.

Very full details of the incident were supplied by the two finders and by A.M. Allport. I am very grateful to these three observers, and also to their colleagues who were instrumental in aiding the success of this rare species by their diligence in wardening the site.

Night Heron
Nycticorax nycticorax

Nelson mentioned four records of this species, the first of which was an immature male shot on Cottingham Common in 1837 by Martin, Mr Ringrose's gamekeeper, which came into the possession of W.W. Boulton of Beverley, from whom it was purchased by Sir Henry Boynton. Another was killed on 21st May 1855 on a pond at Birdsall, near Malton, by the keeper of Mr H. Willoughby, and the specimen went into the latter's collection. One was captured near Whitby in the autumn of 1861 and went to Edward Corner of Esk Hall. The fourth was procured at Kirkby Misperton, near Malton, in May 1870. The specimen went to Mr Tindall's collection, which was bequeathed to the Scarborough Museum.

Chislett's *Yorkshire Birds* added two more. An immature female was shot on Ruswarp Carrs on 26th October 1911, a mile from the site of the 1861 record (see

The Naturalist, 1911, p. 428, and *British Birds*, V, p. 203, for full details). Mr R. Scrope of Yarm described to Chislett a bird which spent a week in his grounds up to 13th May 1951. The details published were quite satisfactory. It spent most of the daytime perched in trees and became active to feed in the evenings.

There have been eight records subsequently. On 11th November 1956, at Fairburn Ings, C. Winn and W.C. Wakefield watched a bird about the size of a Raven flying towards them at dusk about 20 feet (6 m) over the water; it eventually passed at 15 yards' range. 'Stocky bodied', 'of compact form', 'wings relatively broad and rounded, heron like bill carried horizontally and feet projecting about an inch beyond the short tail' were details noted at the time. The bird uttered a single guttural note at intervals of between five and 18 seconds as it circled the marsh for several minutes before flying off in the direction of Brotherton Ing. Chislett square-bracketed the record in the Yorkshire Naturalists' Union Ornithological Report for 1956, having started his paragraph by saying 'fading light prevented examination of plumage details of a large bird . . .'. The above notes are more than adequate for a Night Heron seen by two very competent observers, especially those relating to the bird's behaviour, which is so typical of the species as it leaves its daytime roost to forage at dusk.

On 14th January 1959, an immature bird spent most of the day in a weeping willow tree at Ramsgill in Upper Nidderdale. It was watched at close range by D.G. Leonard, D.W. Swindells and Mrs M. Brooke-Taylor. Although placed in square brackets by Chislett, the observers were in no doubt as to its identity and, knowing them, I am confident that the record is a good one.

While watching for diurnal migrants at Knaresborough Ringing Station on 7th October 1967, I saw a fairly large bird flying towards me from the west. It was banking and veering as it flew into a strong easterly wind and was making slow progress. I noticed the broad, rounded wings, long bill, and legs projecting just beyond the tail as it passed me and gained height to fly over some electricity cables. It was a second-year bird with the uniform underparts coloured buffish.

On the evening of 2nd September 1977, while R.G. Hawley was setting a moth trap in the reeds at the Wassand end of Hornsea Mere, he heard the familiar harsh call of a Night Heron and saw it circling the reeds, being mobbed by three Carrion Crows from a nearby corvid roost.

One was seen by P. Dove at Wheldrake Ings on 30th May 1978, and an adult was seen at Graves Park Lakes, near Sheffield, by R.P. Blagden and D. Herringshaw from 3rd to 9th July 1978.

On 19th September 1979, at 06.30 hours, an immature Night Heron was flushed by N.P. Senior from the top of the Warren Trap at Spurn; it eventually flew off to the north. What was very likely the same bird was seen at Flamborough Head on 23rd and 24th September by J.E. Dale and several others.

A juvenile was at Stokesley from 16th September to 31st October 1982. It was watched by C. Craig, J.B. Dunnet and many others and photographed by P.J. Dunn.

An immature Night Heron spent two hours in the trees in Redcar Lane Cemetery, Redcar, on 8th October 1983, where it was watched by T.G. Dewdney and several others.

Green-backed Heron
Butorides striatus

On 27th November 1982, G. and C. Featherstone. A.G. Ross and D. Bickerton went to Stone Creek on the Humber to look for a Great White Egret that had been seen there during the previous week. They stopped on a small bridge over the drainage ditch and were watching a Short-eared Owl when a medium-sized dark bird flew from under the bridge and along the ditch before landing some 50 yards (46 m) distant. The four observers kept it under observation for the next 45 minutes and took detailed notes.

It was a Green-backed Heron, the first for Yorkshire and only the second to be seen in the British Isles, the first having been shot in Cornwall in October 1889 (see plate 59). It remained in the area until 6th December, having been watched by hundreds of people from all over the country during the interim. When the finders arrived at the site on the morning of 28th November, they were surprised to find dozens of birdwatchers already looking for this extreme rarity which breeds in North and South America, with many other subspecies throughout much of the rest of the world. The bird was well photographed during its stay and two pictures taken by P.A. Doherty appeared in *British Birds*, 1983, plates 40 and 41.

Squacco Heron
Ardeola ralloides

Three examples of this small heron from the south and east of Europe have occurred in Yorkshire.

The first was mentioned by Thomas Allis in his 1844 report in which he stated: 'Arthur Strickland says a specimen of this bird was killed some years ago in the low grounds below Askern, near Pontefract and is now in my collection.' In the Yorkshire Museum at York is a case containing two stuffed Squacco Herons, one from Pontefract being no doubt the one from Strickland's collection which went to that museum, and the other from Rudston. No mention is made of a specimen from the latter locality in Nelson's *The Birds of Yorkshire* and I can find no trace of such a record, so have not included it in the total here.

The second was picked up alive on 26th February 1902 by Thomas Lakin, a farmer of Bielby Field, Everingham, in the East Riding, and was preserved by George Steels of Pocklington, who communicated the details to Nelson. The specimen was in the possession of the finder.

One was present at a small farm pond near Easington from 30th May to at least 16th June 1979. It was seen by H.M. Frost and B.R. Spence and was photographed by the former.

The species has become very scarce as a visitor to the British Isles in recent years. Of the 120 or so birds recorded, the great majority were before 1914 and only about 20 have occurred since 1958.

Cattle Egret
Bubulcus ibis

The first and only Cattle Egret to have been recorded in Yorkshire was seen by a Mr Ellerby on 5th April 1981 in Duncombe Park, near Helmsley, where it stayed until 7th. It was seen by many observers as it fed in typical fashion among cattle and several photographers recorded its presence, including P.J. Dunn and R. Leslie. A photograph by the former appears on plate 60. It had probably been in the area since 29th March.

This almost cosmopolitan species which breeds mainly in the tropics has been known to visit the British Isles on some 34 occasions; the nearest breeding colonies are in the south of France.

Little Egret
Egretta garzetta

The mystical information connected with some early records of rare birds is most intriguing. Nelson inspected a case containing a Little Egret in the museum at Chester which was labelled 'Shot March 1826, near Paull, Humberside, Yorkshire.' The writing was all in the same hand and, so far as could be ascertained, written all at one time. J.H. Gurney apparently suggested (see *The Zoologist*, 1901, p. 107) that the word Yorkshire had been added later and considered the specimen to be one sold at Southampton in 1826 and probably shot at that place. One wonders who was kidding whom in those early days! Whether the word Yorkshire was added later or not seems to me to be irrelevant. Paull, Humberside, is certainly not near Southampton.

The second Yorkshire specimen was mentioned by Gould in his *Birds of Great Britain* (vol. iv) and concerns a bird which was killed by a labourer with a stick at Aike Carr, near Beverley, about 1840 and taken to J. Hall of Scorborough, near Beverley, wrapped in a pocket handkerchief and covered with black mud and blood. It was sent to Mr Reid of Doncaster, who 'restored it in a marvellous manner'.

That one which occurred at Hayburn Wyke, near Scarborough, on 4th January 1881, was proved to be an imported bird illustrates that the 'escape' problem was present then as it is now.

Since 1840, five Little Egrets have been recorded in Yorkshire in an apparently wild state. The first was watched by I. Boustead, B. Jones and W. Norman at Coatham Marsh, Redcar, on 27th May 1967.

The second was at Hollym Carrs, near Patrington, on 23rd December 1969,

98

when a decomposing corpse was found by A.W. Wallis. It had been dead for some time, probably since September or October, a period during which ten others occurred in the British Isles. The remains were sent to me for inspection and preservation and the wings and legs together with several bones are in my collection.

The third occurred at Seamer Gravel-pit, near Scarborough, on 27th May 1973 and stayed all day. It was watched by R.H. Appleby, W.A. Clarke and B. Cockerill, and what was presumably the same bird had moved south to Hornsea Mere by 30th May, when it was seen by C.J. Bibby, J. Day, D.T. Ireland and several others.

The fourth was seen at Seamer Gravel-pit on 12th and 13th June 1982 by Dr C. Brown and M.D. Simmonds.

The fifth was present at Queen Mary's Dubbs, near Ripon, on the evening of 4th May 1984. While C. Slator, T. Scott and S. Worwood were watching an Osprey through their binoculars, a large white bird appeared in the same field of view which they recognised as a Little Egret. It eventually landed in a dead elm tree about a mile (1.6 km) away, where they caught up with it by car and were able to see its yellow feet and the full plumes of breeding dress.

There are now over 340 records of Little Egrets in the British Isles, mostly since 1940, and there have been up to 12 annually in recent years with a few over-wintering in the southern counties.

Great White Egret
Egretta alba

Four occurrences of the Great White Heron, as it was then known, are cited in Nelson's *The Birds of Yorkshire*, three of which are nationally accepted. The fourth, obtained at New Hall, near Barnsley, in 1821 by J.S. Townend, was formerly in the possession of Sir Joseph Radcliffe. This specimen was considered doubtful in Harting's *Handbook* (second ed., p. 440) and so I cannot possibly do other than omit it from the Yorkshire list. If doubt existed at that time, the chances of such being well founded must be very high.

The accepted instances are as follows. One stayed at Hornsea Mere for several weeks in 1825 and was eventually caught. The specimen was originally in the Strickland collection, which is now in the York Museum. The second bird was in full summer plumage and was killed in 1843 by John Norris on the River Hull at Aike, near Beverley, and sold to J. Hall of Scorborough. On his death, it was purchased for the Yorkshire Museum. In the summer of 1868, A.S. Hutchinson of Derby, said to be a naturalist of great experience, saw a Great White Heron perched on a fir tree at Clay Wheel Dam, near Wadsley Bridge; he watched it at close quarters for nearly half-an-hour and had no doubt whatsoever as to its identity. I suppose he could have been right.

It was to be 106 years before this rare heron, which breeds regularly no nearer than the Balkans and Austria, made another appearance in the county. In 1974, one was present at Scaling Dam from 28th May until 6th June and was seen by many people during its stay, including R.H. Appleby and D.G. Bell. In the same year, on 1st June, one came in at Spurn from the east-northeast, turned south and flew over the Humber.

On 15th July 1979, Mr and Mrs A.R. Elliott watched one as it fed in the River Esk near Whitby, where it waded in the shallow water for some time before eventually flying off downstream.

There are only 28 records of this rare heron in the British Isles and it is perhaps remarkable that Yorkshire should have yet another, when one frequented drainage ditches at Stone Creek from 13th to 30th November 1982. It gave excellent views to many observers, including K. Rotherham, I. Forsyth and M. Coverdale, who supplied detailed notes to the Yorkshire Naturalists' Union Records Committee. This bird was undoubtedly responsible for attracting watchers to the area, who in turn located the even rarer Green-backed Heron on 27th November.

Grey Heron
Ardea cinerea

Grey Herons have featured along with the Bittern, but more prominently, in the feasts of old. In the accounts of Selby Abbey for the years 1431 and 1432, an entry reads: 'Paid to a certain servant at Fryston bringing two Herons to the Lord Abbot, 20d.' (Morrell's *'Selby'*, 1867, p. 101).

At the great banquet given at Cawood in 1466 by Earl Warwick in honour of his brother George Nevell becoming the Archbishop of York, 'Heronshaws iiiic' were included. In the Earl of Northumberland's Household Book in 1512, at his Castles of Wressill and Lekinfield, near Beverley, the price of 'Heronsewys' was fixed at 12d. Many other menus of the period included the heron.

In the spacious days of falconry, when the Grey Heron was a favourite quarry, heronries were maintained and encouraged wherever they occurred, both for sport and for the young which were taken for the table. With the cessation of falconry and the attendant encouragement of the Grey Heron, which included management of the favoured woodlands, the species was persecuted in the supposed interests of angling during the nineteenth century and it suffered greatly from tree felling. Chislett's words are very apt: 'Whether the Heron does any real harm to anglers on balance is very doubtful, if we remember the great variety of its food and its penchant for eels that destroy such quantities of trout fry and ova. Anglers who call for the destruction of Herons show both lack of sportsmanship and of regard for tradition in the English countryside, of which the Heron is the most picturesque zoological feature extant.' (*Yorkshire Birds* 1952). It is very difficult to question those sentiments.

Nelson listed nine main heronries which had been deserted by the middle of the nineteenth century. He could cite only seven which were in existence in 1906, although he gave details of seven more which no longer existed. Some of these had been large, such as the colony at Sutton-on-Derwent where 100 pairs bred up to about 1860 and then fewer until final desertion about 1880. Moreby Park, near York, which still had five pairs in 1950, held 50 nests in 1884. The ancient heronry in Harewood Park held up to 30 nests in 1866, but in 1884 a terrific gale blew down many of the trees and disturbed them. From that date the numbers decreased, and in 1902 there were only seven nests, in a different part of the wood. The species continued to breed here until 1962, when the very hard winter and severe gales were probable factors contributing to their demise.

Although Grey Herons had bred in small numbers at Hornsea Mere for many years, the main colony at the Wassand end of the mere was established about 1880 and contained 18 nests in 1905. These increased to 37 by 1921 and numbers remained in excess of 20 until 1952, in which year there were 29. After 1958, when there were 22 nests, the numbers declined dramatically, with the last two nests recorded in 1969.

T.R. Birkhead reviewed the Yorkshire breeding situation for the years 1970 to 1975 and showed that 175 pairs were nesting at ten sites. For full details of the study, see *The Naturalist*, 1971, pp. 117-21, and 1976, pp. 129-32. Up to 250 pairs had bred during the late 1960s. The largest heronry was at Healaugh, near Tadcaster, with 40 nests in 1975 after 52 in 1974. This colony is a well-established one and, following eight pairs in 1922, there were 37 in 1936. The colony declined after the severe frost in 1947 and there were only 12 pairs in that year.

Kirby Fleetham had 34 nests in 1975 after 42 in 1974. This colony is a continuation of the old one at Kiplin Hall, established around 1915. There were 22 nests in 1938, which had declined to two by 1951. The colony was refounded in 1967, when 13 nests were located, whereafter numbers increased slightly and 16 pairs nested in 1980.

The ancient heronry at Gargrave has through various pressures been forced on several occasions to shift its location. It existed at Flasby, near Gargrave, until 1865, when tree felling caused the birds to move to Eshton Hall about a mile away. There were 20 pairs in 1881 and 17 in 1905. Chislett reported 24 nests in 1952 at Gargrave. Numbers fell to seven in 1958, after timber felling again forced them to move to a new site at Coniston Cold. After ten nests in 1966, this colony built up to a record 53 pairs in 1971 and is still flourishing today. A heronry at Kirkdale contained 26 nests on 21st April 1981.

There are now several small heronries in widely scattered parts of the county, in addition to the traditional sites. Two pairs at Bretton Park in 1981 had increased to about ten pairs by 1984. Eight pairs nested on the lower Derwent in 1980, with eleven pairs in 1982; and small colonies, sometimes of only two or three pairs, and occasionally only one single pair, have been successful in Wentworth Park, Newby Hall, Upper Nidderdale, Hellifield, Richmond, Clapham, Mowthorpe, Ellerburn and near Sheffield. Twenty pairs bred at Sleightholmedale in 1979, and up to 12 pairs have nested in North Holme Wood at Crathorne, near Yarm, during recent years.

Each spring and autumn, Grey Herons are seen along the coast and coming in over the sea, especially at the Spurn Peninsula, in circumstances which indicate visitations from the Continent and confirmation of such immigration comes from ringing recoveries. Six birds ringed as nestlings in Sweden, Norway and Denmark have been recovered in Yorkshire during the autumn and winter months, and two Yorkshire-ringed youngsters were found respectively in Leicestershire in June and on the Isle of Bute in April.

The Grey Heron is a voracious feeder and in 1962, at Bog Wood, near Whixley, while Nigel Carling and I were ringing nestlings in the small colony there, one regurgitated a whole water vole. In 1948, R.F. Dickens examined a pellet from Swinsty Reservoir which contained the remains of two beetles and vole fur. In 1952, pupils at Ashville College, Harrogate, saw a Grey Heron put its head down a rabbit hole while other herons were standing outside other holes. Dead rabbits with their innards pulled out lay around.

This long-legged and seemedly ungainly species is perfectly at home among the thin branches of the treetops where it chooses to build its nest, and it can also swim when the need arises. At Swillington Ings, on 1st June 1946, Ken Dawson saw one alight in deep water and swim to the shallows.

On 11th April 1958, at Farnley Lake, D.B. Isles saw a heron with salmon-pink bill and legs.

Nelson's summary of the Grey Heron's status — 'Resident, common but local. An influx of migrants from the Continent in autumn and winter.' — still applies today. There is no part of the county where it is not possible to disturb a solitary Grey Heron from a ditch, river, pond or the edge of any large sheet of water at almost any season.

Purple Heron
Ardea purpurea

Thomas Allis, in 1844, mentioned the first Yorkshire specimen, which was shot near Flamborough in 1833 by a Mr Pike and went to the collection of A. Strickland. The bird was in young plumage and I have examined what is thought to be the specimen in the Yorkshire Museum.

One occurred in some old fishponds at Lowthorpe in the spring of 1847 and was mentioned by the Reverend F.O. Morris in *The Zoologist*, 1849, p. 2591. The specimen was acquired by Mr St Quintin and placed in Lowthorpe Lodge. An undated male example was procured at Temple Thorpe, near Leeds. A specimen which went to the Whitby Museum was shot at Ruswarp Dam in the summer of 1860 by Joshua Barry and stuffed by J. Kitching.

Nelson inspected a male in the collection of Sir Henry Boynton at Burton Agnes. It was shot in July 1862 by W. Wellman, the gamekeeper at Hornsea Mere. W. Eagle Clarke examined a dead mature male which had been killed on 19th April 1888 on the margin of Farnley Lake near Otley. The bird was first seen flying in from the direction of Harewood and the keeper shot it in mistake for a '[Grey] Heron'. The specimen was in the possession of the Reverend F. Fawkes of Rothwell (see *The Naturalist*, 1888, p. 330).

No other records were received until 1966, when, on the morning of 3rd May, R.J. Rhodes was watching a large expanse of floodwater from the top of the Eau Beck banking at Almholme, near Doncaster, and saw a heron fly in from the east. When it was at about 200 yards' (180m) range, his binoculars revealed the dark plumage and a shape quite unlike that of the Grey Heron. As it swung over the water, several gulls lifted to harry it, when it dropped to about 50 feet (15m) and circled around for fully 15 minutes as if looking for a suitable spot to land. It eventually gained height again and headed due west and out of sight. It was an immature, and one of seven Purple Herons that occurred in the British Isles during April and May that year. See *The Naturalist*, 1967, p. 50, for full details.

In 1970, this species occurred again, at Adel Dam, near Leeds, on 20th June. It was an adult and was watched from the hide by Colin and Joyce Massingham, P. Larner and Miss M. Rollinson. There were records of 25 Purple Herons in the British Isles in 1970, the most ever in a single year.

On 17th July 1971, P.T. Treloar and C. Winn watched an adult at Fairburn Ings as it circled the area before flying off to the east. There were 15 other occurrences in Britain in the same year, 12 of which were during the period March to June.

At Hornsea Mere, in 1972, an immature bird was present from 26th August to 4th October. It spent most of the days at the mere and on some evenings flew to a small pond in the grounds of Hornsea Pottery, where it settled on the roof of a floating duck house. When it first arrived, the bird was very alert and suspicious of people, gradually becoming more relaxed, when it would walk down the sloping roof of the duck house and spend the night on the platform. During its long stay it was seen by many people, including C. Carter, whose garden adjoined the pond, W.F. Curtis, D.T. Ireland, and H.T. James to whom I am grateful for supplying the above information regarding its behaviour.

An immature bird was seen by P.A. Lassey and Miss Irene Smith at Flamborough Head on 10th October 1975. In the following year, P.J. Smith, G.J. Speight and others watched one at Wintersett Reservoir on 26th September as it flew in from the northeast. Three were recorded in 1977. The first was seen at Fairburn Ings on 17th May by B. Tucker and B. Watson. The second was at Tophill Low Reservoir on 22nd May and was well seen by Peter Dove, that well-known local farmer and birdwatcher. The third was near Selside in Upper Ribblesdale on 26th June and reported by F.J. Roberts, who spent much time birdwatching in that area during the 1970s.

T. Hobson watched a bird fly north at Filey Brigg on 2nd August 1979, and P.A. Lassey was rewarded with an immature bird at Flamborough Head on 24th August 1980.

One was seen by F.A. Whitford, T.M. England and F. Nendick at Seamer Road Mere on 14th May 1981. A juvenile, seen at Wheldrake Ings by T.M. Clegg, B. Bates and T. Barker on 4th January 1981, was found dead on 21st February. The Yorkshire Naturalists' Union Records Committee examined a colour slide of the bird in flight which clearly showed a Purple Heron, but the *British Birds* Rarities Committee declined to accept the record on the evidence supplied.

In 1982, an adult was seen by P.H. Mason on 4th May between Thorpe Marsh Power Station and Barnby Dun, where it stayed for only five minutes before leaving to the northeast, and T.A. Ede saw another at Southfield Reservoir on 26th August.

On 3rd June 1984, several members of Knaresborough Ringing Station saw a Purple Heron as it flew steadily northwards, and on 25th I saw what was undoubtedly the same bird as it flew into Staveley Lagoon, about 4 miles (6.4 km) to the north of Knaresborough.

The Purple Heron has become a much more regular visitor to the British Isles during the past 20 years, and the trend has been well illustrated in Yorkshire.

Black Stork
Ciconia nigra

Three examples of this very rare visitor to the British Isles have been recorded in Yorkshire. The first was mentioned by S.L. Mosley in his *List of Huddersfield Birds* as having occurred in Bretton Park in March 1836.

The second was recorded by Morris in his *British Birds* (iv, p. 163) on the authority of his brother, Beverley R. Morris. It concerns a specimen captured by a Mr Wake on Market Weighton Common about 29th October 1852. The specimen was purchased by the York Philosophical Society and is now in the Yorkshire Museum, where I have inspected it.

Not until 1976 did the species make another appearance in the county, when an immature was at Broughton, near Stokesley, between 11th and 21st June. It was seen by many people, including D.J. Britton and J.E. Dale.

White Stork
Ciconia ciconia

Nelson listed 12 records of this wanderer from southwestern and central Europe. The first was mentioned in Fothergill's *Orn. Brit.* (1798) and concerns the occurrence of one at Howden during the severe winter of that year.

One was obtained near Bawtry about 1825 and mentioned by T. Allis in 1844. In 1831 one was shot in Bretton Park, where it had been feeding in shallow water. Allis also referred to a stork seen on the seashore at Skipsea and acquired by A. Strickland. The Reverend F.O. Morris, in *The Zoologist* (1846, p. 1501), reported a sight record at Wansford, near Driffield. A male, taken on 18th May 1848 near Riccal on the land belonging to Lord Wenlock, went to D. Graham of York for preservation; the specimen was acquired by Sir William Milner, whose collection went eventually to the Leeds Museum.

One was killed about 1855 on a tall fir tree in the village of Great Ayton in Cleveland and went to the museum of the Friends School there. One was obtained at Barmston, near Bridlington, on 18th September 1856 by John Harland; the specimen went to the collection of E. Tindall and subsequently to the Scarborough Museum.

A White Stork was seen flying around Easington Church on 25th September 1869. It was shot at and its leg broken, and was finally killed near Withernsea by a Mr Crawford and preserved by P. Loten of Easington. The specimen went to the Hull Museum. In the collection of Sir Henry Boynton at Burton Agnes was a female captured at Carnaby on 11th May 1878 by H.P. Robinson. One was found floating dead in the sea off Peasholm, Scarborough, on 8th April 1888. It was too far decomposed for preservation, but the skull was preserved and went to the Museum of the York Philosophical Society. Nelson's last record concerned a bird shot off a chimney by T. Ake at Mappleton, near Hornsea. The bird weighed 8 lb (3.6 kg) and had eaten two water voles. No date is given.

Chislett could report only one other occurrence, a bird that appeared at Great Ayton on 27th October 1938 and stayed throughout November. It had been noticed at nearby North Ormesby several days earlier and a photograph taken by a Mr Williamson appeared in the *Yorkshire Post* on 9th November. R.M. Garnett saw it on 4th November, when it was feeding on earthworms in a wet pasture close to Great Ayton. The bird was a juvenile showing pink legs and brown flight feathers (see *The Naturalist* for December 1938).

Eleven other White Storks have been reliably recorded in Yorkshire during the 30 years since Chislett published *Yorkshire Birds*. In late April 1960, one was seen on the farm of Mrs A. Sleightholme at Hawsker. P.J. Stead saw the lady and another local farmer who had also observed it and was satisfied from their comments that it was identified correctly. The bird was present for two weeks.

An adult and an immature were reported near Gisburn on 15th September 1974 by R. Freethy. On 31st May 1975, D. Hirst saw one attending grazing cattle at

Aketon, near Castleford; on 1st June, it was perched on a telegraph pole, where it was photographed. One flew over Blacktoft Sands on 26th May 1976. There were three records in 1977: one at Dunford, near Penistone in vice-county 63, on 27th and 28th March was seen by A. Archer, C. Bower and D.J. Standring; the second was at Spurn Point on 27th March and was watched by C.E. Andrassy and N. Jackson; and the third was seen flying south over Whitestones Point, Whitby, by I. Edgar on 16th April. One was seen by M. Charnock near Greenfield in the Saddleworth area of vice-county 63 on 7th April 1978.

A White Stork was seen at Hornsea Mere on 1st October 1983, and what was presumably the same bird was at Fairburn Ings on 3rd and at Laycock, near Keighley, on 6th. A bird seen at Bishopdale, near Aysgarth, on 20th May 1984 was no doubt the one that stayed in the area of Bell Busk, near Gargrave, from June to the year's end. It frequented fields adjacent to a trout farm and was often given fish by the owners.

Glossy Ibis
Plegadis falcinellus

Five records of this exotic bird were detailed by Nelson up to 1902 and Chislett was able to add 15 others, 14 of which occurred in 1909.

One occurred at Easington in the autumn of 1850 and passed into the collection of Cuthbert Watson. Canon J.C. Atkinson of Danby, writing on 29th May 1880, said that 'An Ibis was seen near the Liverton and Moorsholme vicinity in Cleveland, for some days, about twenty years ago; one day I took my gun, but the bird flew away'. Quite wise of it.

An immature example in Admiral Mitford's collection was captured at Filey in 1863 and is noted in Roberts' Scarborough list. Near Selby, a mature bird was reported at Brayton Bridge in the last week of May 1874 which went to the collection of J. Jackson of Cawood. The fifth record was of a male, obtained on 17th November 1902 at Ackworth.

In 1909, a remarkable influx took place and no fewer than 14 Glossy Ibises were recorded in Yorkshire. Chislett listed the occurrences as follows: one killed at Ulrome during the second week of October; one seen at Hornsea on 15th October by E. Kempsey; one shot and two others seen at Hunmanby on 15th October, and reported in *The Field* by the Reverend E. Mitford; one shot at Ruswarp, near Whitby, on 20th October by T. Stephenson; two shot at Lambwath on 19th October and reported by E.W. Wade; one shot at the same place on 10th November, when another escaped, both birds being in immature plumage; one seen at Beverley, and reported in *The Field* on 13th November; and, finally, two shot at Burton Constable by G. Bolam, the date of which occurrence is not available. One purchased from a game dealer in Doncaster by the Reverend H.H. Corbett on 27th October had been shot at Misson, near Bawtry, and is therefore a Nottinghamshire record. For full details of this influx see *British Birds*, 3, pp. 229 and 308, and also *The Naturalist*, 1909, pp. 441-8; 1910, p. 28; 1911, p. 116; and 1913, p. 59.

One was shot and another seen at Carlton, near Aldburgh, on 18th October 1912. It was reported by E.W. Wade in *The Naturalist*, 1913, p. 115.

There has been no such spate of records since, the species having become extremely unusual as a visitor to the British Isles with only about 24 records in the last 25 years. In Yorkshire, there have been three records since the foregoing. On

13th August 1973, B.R. Spence, B. Banson and A. Butler saw one flying south, low over the Warren Cottage at Spurn, while on 22nd August in the same year, at Wath Ings, G. Needham had excellent views of one as it circled and eventually landed; it is possible that the same bird was involved. One which flew down Hornsea Mere on 15th May 1976 was seen by H. Laidlaw.

Although the Glossy Ibis is common along the eastern seaboard of North America, the European population has declined alarmingly during the present century. It breeds no nearer to Britain than Yugoslavia, where in 1869 there were 4,500 breeding pairs. This figure was reduced to 600 by 1931 and there are now probably fewer than 100 pairs.

Spoonbill
Platalea leucorodia

In the 'Northumberland Household Book', begun in 1512, at Earl Percy's Castles of Wressill and Lekinfield, the list of birds to be supplied for 'My Lordes owne Mees' includes 'Sholardes' at 6d. each. At the request of T.H. Nelson to substantiate this obsolete name for the Spoonbill, J.E. Harting investigated a case contained in the old Law Reports of Henry VIII's reign, with the result that it was found that 'Shovelards', at that time (1523), bred in company with herons in the trees of Fulham Palace grounds. Nelson concludes that the bird may also have nested in Yorkshire at that time. Spoonbills were said to have formerly bred in Leconfield Park, near Beverley, as communicated to Nelson by F. Boyes, who had the information from an old sportsman.

In 1844, Thomas Allis wrote that a Spoonbill had been shot at Masham, and that, in July 1833, one was killed at Staincross but from the state of its wings was thought to have escaped from confinement. One, shot in the Tees Marshes and reported in *The Zoologist*, 1845, p. 1172, may have been on the Durham side, although there is nothing to suggest this (Nelson).

Six others are included in Nelson's *The Birds of Yorkshire*. One was procured at Horbury Mill Dam in 1850 (Talbot's *Birds of Wakefield*, p. 26), and an adult female from Wilberfoss, near York, on 2nd August 1851 went to the Leeds Museum (*The Zoologist*, 1851, p. 3278). An adult male, killed in 1865 at Hornby Decoy by the gamekeeper to the Duke of Leeds, is now in the York Museum (*The Zoologist*, 1868, p. 1135). One was killed at Reeth in 1867 (*The Zoologist*, 1884, p. 138; and *The Naturalist*, 1892, p. 320), and another shot at Masham in 1877 (note the Masham bird mentioned by Allis in 1844). A Spoonbill captured at Thorpe fishponds, near Bridlington, was in Thomas Boynton's collection, formerly the Bessingby Collection, but no more details were available to Nelson.

Chislett could add only five more records, including a party of ten, up to 1952. The first was seen by S. Duncan on the north shore of the Humber on 15th August 1909. An immature bird was found dead on the beach at Saltwick, near Whitby, on 3rd July 1924 by F. Snowden. In 1951, Mr and Mrs Green and B. Pickering saw ten Spoonbills flying south over the Spurn Warren Cottage at 21.10 hours on 24th May.

G.H. Ainsworth, H.G. Brownlow, R.M. Garnett and Ralph Chislett watched an immature at Spurn on 15th July 1951 as it consorted with Great Black-backed Gulls on the Humber mud; it was still present on 25th July. Alan Baldridge saw one in the Tees Estuary on 19th April 1951.

Since 1951, Spoonbills have occurred in 21 of the 30 years to 1981. Fairburn Ings has had its fair share, with one on 10th May 1954, one on 6th June 1959, three on 28th August 1963, single birds on 25th May 1965, 30th June 1966, 9th and 10th April 1969, 14th May 1970, 2nd August 1975, 22nd July and 1st to 3rd August 1976, and three different individuals on consecutive dates in April 1975. See *The Naturalist*, 1976, p. 35, for details of the 1975 birds.

Watchers at Spurn Point recorded Spoonbills in 1957, 1960, 1968, 1970 and 1972, with three records in 1960 and two in 1970. There were three different birds in 1981 and two on 4th June 1982.

Hornsea Mere has inevitably attracted this species. Single birds occurred there on 27th May 1958, 14th May 1961, 24th June 1967, 13th May 1974, 13th July 1975 and from 23rd May to 6th June 1976, with additional single records in 1976 on 19th June and 18th and 31st July.

Spoonbills have been seen along the Humber in several years, some of which would no doubt have ended up over the Spurn Peninsula as they continued their journeys. One was at Welwick Saltings on 29th April 1956, one at Skeffling on 11th September 1971 and one at Patrington on 30th May 1972, while one flew down-river at Blacktoft Sands on 25th June 1975.

No fewer than nine Spoonbills were seen in Yorkshire during 1975. The first three were at Fairburn Ings, as mentioned above, followed by one at Rivelin Dam, Sheffield, on 6th and 7th June and what was presumably the same bird near Penistone from 7th to 12th June. Apart from these and others noted above, one flew over Scarborough Harbour on 20th July and one was at Wath Ings on 2nd August. This latter bird was carrying a colour ring and proved to have been ringed as a nestling in Holland in 1952.

Others were recorded at South Gare on 14th July 1963, Wintersett Reservoir on 18th May 1968, Settle Sewage-farm on 4th and 5th August 1968, Bolton-on-Swale Gravel-pit on 17th July 1973, Broomhill Flash on 27th and 28th May 1974, Potteric Carr on 17th June 1976 and at Staveley Lagoon two days later, Tophill Low Reservoir on 9th May 1979, and at Wath Ings on 3rd June 1979.

Two Spoonbills came in over the sea at Flamborough on 1st October 1978, one of which continued flying south while the other landed on the headland, where it remained for the afternoon. One came in similarly at Bempton on 14th June 1980 and continued flying southeastwards.

In 1981, an adult was at Spurn on 16th and 17th May; one was at Welwick on 17th May, probably the same bird; another flew over Spurn on 5th June, and one flew south there on 7th June. An adult at Whitton Sands on 25th June flew across the river to Blacktoft Sands, where it was seen with an immature bird on 25th. An immature was at Wintersett Reservoir on the late date of 2nd December.

1982 also produced a flush of Spoonbill records. Two flew south at Filey Brigg on 3rd June, two were on the Humber mud at Spurn on 4th June, and two adults were at Blacktoft Sands from 4th to 7th June. The same two birds were probably involved in these three records. The two adults at Blacktoft were carrying sticks and were displaying. An adult flew west along the Humber shore at Skeffling on 19th October, and one was inland at Worsborough Reservoir on 20th October. A young bird ringed in Holland on 5th July 1982 was seen at Blacktoft Sands on 20th and 21st October.

An adult was at Blacktoft Sands from 14th to 16th April 1983, when it moved to Spurn and was seen on 16th and 17th April. Another adult appeared on 21st April at Blacktoft Sands, where it stayed until 23rd; an immature was at Flamborough on

27th and 28th April; an adult was at Fairburn Ings on 30th April and another, or the same, was at Broomhill Flash on 1st and 2nd May; and an immature was near Scarborough on 26th July. One was seen at Barmston on 17th November 1984 by P. Hill, P. Scott and D. Walsh.

'Casual visitant from the Continent; of rare occurrence' is how Nelson summarised the Spoonbill's status in Yorkshire. It is no longer casual and, with a sizeable breeding population in Holland, which has doubtless been responsible for the increased number of Yorkshire records in recent years, the species can now be termed almost annual. Further evidence of immigration from Holland came in 1982 when a Spoonbill, the ring number of which was read in the field at Blacktoft Sands on 20th October, proved to have been ringed as a nestling at Callantsoog in the Netherlands on 5th July 1982. That the species will breed in the county at some time in the near future is not unlikely.

Mute Swan
Cygnus olor

The ancient accounts of Selby Abbey in 1431-32 and the details of the marriage feast of the daughter of Sir John Neville of Chevet, near Wakefield, in 1526 included swans in the 'good things provided'. In the household accounts of the Cliffords in Whitaker's 'Craven', second edition 1812, p. 321, there is mention of a swanherd with his coat and badge costing 23s. 10d.

In 1844, Thomas Allis wrote: 'Mute Swan — I have obtained a specimen of this bird from near Sutton-on-Derwent, the favourite locality of Ferus, it was nevertheless most probably an escaped bird from some gentleman's enclosure, or may have been the next species, of the existence of which I was not then aware.' There were problems even in those days.

As Chislett stated in 1952, the Mute Swan can be seen in a feral state on almost any sheet of water, excepting the high moorland tarns, from the tidal rivers to the smallest village pond. Its favourite haunts today are Hornsea Mere and Fairburn Ings, where large numbers assemble to moult and spend the winter months in addition to those which stay to breed. Numbers at these waters start to build up during June and usually reach their peak in late July. The flocks at Fairburn Ings first made their appearance in the 1950s, and now regularly number up to 150 birds. Larger gatherings have been noted, as on 18th August 1959 when 180 were counted and in July and August 1960 when there were 216. Hornsea Mere attracts slightly fewer, although over 100 birds are regularly present, with peak counts of 145 during July and August 1972 and 155 in July 1975.

A few Mute Swans are sometimes seen along the coast and occasionally small parties are seen over the sea, as on 1st August 1960 when R.H. Appleby saw seven flying south at Filey Brigg and on 13th July 1978 when Mrs Joan Webb saw ten flying in from over the sea at Scarborough. Such birds are no doubt en route to Hornsea Mere. On 13th July 1968, five flew in from the sea at Spurn Point and continued up the Humber Estuary. Severe weather often drives occasional Mute Swans to the coast, where they seek food in sheltered bays or harbours, and I have several times seen them in the harbour at Bridlington. Two birds on the sea off Flamborough Head on 21st January 1979 had doubtless been forced off some inland water by the severity of the winter.

In 1958, at Gouthwaite Reservoir, A.F.G. Walker saw the cob of a pair kill five Mallard ducklings and swallow three of them. *The Handbook of British Birds* states 'young waterfowl killed at times by drowning but not eaten'.

A swan ringed in Cambridge on 31st May 1960 was retrapped at Hornsea Mere on 6th September 1960, having travelled 120 miles (192 km), and another ringed at Hornsea Mere on 3rd September 1960 was recaught in Cambridge on 6th October 1960. A colour-ringed bird seen at Broomhill Flash on 30th January 1966 by H.E. Beaumont proved to have been marked at Tamworth in Staffordshire in 1961, and two birds at Fairburn Ings in August 1978 had been ringed at Tamworth in February that year. An immature ringed at Fairburn Ings on 29th December 1961 was at Holme-next-the-Sea in Norfolk on 9th March 1963. Such ringing recoveries indicate that there is some movement into and out of the county, but the majority of our Mute Swans are quite sedentary.

Bewick's Swan
Cygnus columbianus

Nelson summarised the occurrence of the Bewick's Swan as 'Winter visitant, less frequent than the Whooper, though not uncommon in severe weather.' Chislett reiterated this assessment in 1952 and the same applies today, some 30 years on. The first reference to this species as a Yorkshire bird was made by Thomas Allis, who wrote in 1844 that 'F.O. Morris reported one shot near Bawtry some years ago' and that it was occasionally obtained near York.

The main herds of Bewick's Swans usually come to Yorkshire from their summer home on the Arctic tundras during November to January. Small numbers may be encountered on almost any water, sometimes for only a few hours or less, as they stop off to rest before moving on to their favourite winter quarters. In 1956, severe weather in Friesland caused the wintering Bewick's to pull out and they came over to England in large numbers. Birds started to appear in the county during early February, when five were seen on the iced-over Thrybergh Reservoir by R.J. Rhodes and 14 more at Bottomboat by K. Senior. This latter flock built up to 26 birds by 12th February and these remained until 18th March. Fairburn Ings attracted up to 20 birds, which C. Winn counted on 3rd March. There were 14 at Gouthwaite Reservoir on 7th February, and A.F.G. Walker saw a further 18 arrive on 9th with much bugling as the two herds met and mingled. These birds left on 21st February, when they were seen flying up the Nidd Valley. During the first four months of 1956, Bewick's Swans occurred at 21 other waters, including Hoyle Mill Dam, Bubwith Ings, Worsborough Reservoir, the Dearne Valley and Hornsea Mere.

In early 1964, a very large movement occurred. Flocks of up to 18 were recorded at ten waters up to 23rd February, mainly during January, followed by 31 at Fairburn Ings on 27th February. These were the forerunners of a spectacular spring passage which continued throughout March. There were two features of the movement: large herds resting for short periods or seen passing over, and small groups of up to five birds staying for up to three weeks. The larger herds were 66 at Ringstone Edge Reservoir on 2nd March; 75 at Spurn Point from 2nd to 4th March; 28 birds down on the mud and a further 75 flying east-southeast over the Humber Wildfowl Refuge on 3rd; 55 at Woodhouse Mill on 14th; 46 flying east at Harewood on 22nd; 44 at Knotford Nook Gravel-pit on 23rd; 40 flying southeast at Spurn Point on 25th; and 59 on the Lower Derwent floods on 25th, where smaller numbers had been present since early March. Some birds lingered and 19 were still on the Lower Derwent on 3rd April, one was at Wath Ings on 4th, two at Crabley

Creek from 11th to 25th, and 16 flying over Healaugh on 18th. Nothing similar has happened since.

The floodwaters along the valley of the Lower Derwent became a favourite haunt for wintering Bewick's Swans from the late 1950s. Up to 30 birds were present during February and March 1960, and in the following year H.O. Bunce, Miss M.R. Sanderson and A.F.G. Walker counted 200 in late February, the highest total ever recorded in Yorkshire at that time. In 1965, extensive flooding along the valley attracted 47 birds on 5th December, which increased to 123 by 28th. Numbers were higher in 1966, with 153 on 3rd January, 206 on 30th, 278 on 13th February and 228 on 20th. In 1967, 174 birds were counted on 15th January, and the peak numbers in 1969 were 158 on 23rd March and 235 on 26th December.

The Lower Derwent continued to attract the county's largest herds throughout the 1970s. In 1972, the numbers increased from ten birds on 15th January to 188 by 29th and 229 on 5th February. Between 165 and 220 remained up to 14th whereafter 250 were counted on 24th and 251, including 23 juveniles, were present on 27th. After this date, the numbers declined slowly as the birds left for their northern breeding grounds, and all had gone by 28th March when H.O. Bunce and his colleagues searched the whole area. This is still Yorkshire's stronghold for the species, and in 1980 the January peak count was 196 birds, with 187 present in February, including only 11 juveniles. At the end of the year, 169 were seen on 21st December and 263 on 31st, the highest count since 1966.

Most Bewick's Swans have left Yorkshire by early April, but a few linger until the month end or into early May. A. Credland reported five birds at Patrington Haven from 3rd to 23rd April 1960, and he saw two immatures there on 13th May 1961. Two immature Bewick's were at Bubwith Ings on the Lower Derwent on 5th May 1980. Some late birds are apparently ailing, as was one at Fairburn Ings on 30th April 1955. On 29th May 1956, single birds were at Fairburn Ings and Bottomboat, the latter being obviously sick. One stayed at Fairburn Ings from 6th April to 6th May 1974.

Early arrivals in the autumn have been on 26th October 1960, when D.R. Seaward watched five birds flying low over the dunes at Redcar; on 25th October 1962, when two were on Hornsea Mere; on 29th October 1962, when seven were at Hemsworth; and on 20th October 1968, when a party of 30 flew southeast over Blackmoorfoot Reservoir.

Thus, from late October to the end of April, Bewick's Swans can be seen in Yorkshire, their numbers varying with the season, on any suitable stretch of water or in transit to and fro.

On 30th October 1976, Mrs Joan Webb found a dead Bewick's Swan in Peasholm Park, Scarborough. The corpse was sent to me for preservation and proved to be an adult female which had been shot. There were two pellet holes near the right eye and a piece of shot was lodged in the nasal region. The bird was extremely thin and I presumed it to have been shot before crossing the North Sea. The shot wounds were not fresh and the bird had obviously survived the wounds for some time before succumbing after its long journey.

A female ringed at Slimbridge in Gloucestershire on 23rd December 1969 was found dead at Gransmoor, near Driffield, on 30th December 1976.

An apparently healthy first-year bird spent the whole summer of 1960 at Fairburn Ings. It first appeared on 1st May and remained until 20th November, by which time winter arrivals of both Whooper and Bewick's Swans were taking place (*The Naturalist*, 1961, p. 50).

Whooper Swan
Cygnus cygnus

Nelson cited the earliest reference to the Whooper Swan in Yorkshire as mentioned in Fothergill's *British Ornithology* (1799, p. 10), where it is stated that 'one or two were shot in the winter of 1798 near York'.

In 1844, Thomas Allis wrote:

'Shot near Doncaster in hard winters; rare near Sheffield; ... occasionally met with near Leeds, also on the moors near Huddersfield; about Sutton-on-Derwent they are, in severe winters, occasionally abundant. I have heard of a flock of fifty being seen there. I have had a dozen through my hands in a single season and have known of upwards of twenty in a week exposed for sale in York.'

In the years 1829, 1838 and 1865, the species was very numerous in the Humber Estuary and as many as 100 were offered for sale one market day in York. In the winter of 1880, an immense herd flew northwest past the Teesmouth. When the leading birds arrived at Greatham shore, the rearmost portion of the herd was still at the Yorkshire side of the estuary and it was computed at a rough calculation that the flight must have consisted of at least 1,000 birds (Nelson 1906). This is a remarkable record, and, even allowing for some exaggeration, there must have been many more swans than have since been recorded in the county.

Today, Whooper Swans occur in small numbers at most suitable stretches of water, which must be open and deep. Birds start to arrive from mid October in most years, the main influx occurring during mid November with a second, smaller, arrival sometimes taking place in December. Numbers rarely approach those of the Bewick's Swan, and the largest herds in recent years have been 35 on the Lower Derwent floods on 27th November 1960 and again on 12th February 1961. There were 35 on Tan Hill Reservoir, near Sedbergh, from 2nd November to 20th December 1961. In November 1963, more than usual visited the area and a second arrival followed in December. On 15th December, 32 birds were at Broomhill and 29 were at Fairburn Ings. On 26th, 21 were at Wintersett Reservoir and 32 at Fairburn, and 23 flew into Scarhill Reservoir on 29th. Many other waters had smaller herds during this period.

Since the mid 1970s, the most popular water for Whooper Swans has undoubtedly been Fairburn Ings, and nowhere else have numbers exceeded 30 to 40 birds during the last 20 years. The ings first attracted large numbers in 1967, when 52 were counted by C. Winn on 8th January. In 1970, 76 birds were standing on the ice on 4th January, having arrived in small parties from the east during the day. In 1975, there were 53 present in January and again during December, with that number again in December 1976 and including only one juvenile, perhaps indicative of a poor breeding season in their summer haunts in Iceland and northern Europe. The maximum number present in 1981 was 106 on 13th December, 62 were counted on 31st January 1982 and 112 on 22nd January 1984.

There was a marked passage during February 1977, when Fairburn Ings attracted the largest herds, with 50 on 10th and 65 on 13th, many other waters throughout the county holding smaller numbers for varying periods during this time. Semerwater and the flooded areas around Settle are also favoured, and good numbers of Whoopers may be seen there in almost every year.

Most birds have left Yorkshire for their breeding grounds by mid April, but a few linger on. Seven flew northwest over Illingworth, near Halifax, on 23rd April 1978. Occasional birds spend the summer months in Yorkshire, some of which are known or thought to be injured or ailing, as was one at Wheldrake Ings in 1978. Two birds at Gouthwaite Reservoir on 15th June 1968 may have been late migrants. A single Whooper stayed at Treeton Dyke Reservoir during the summer of 1971 and in each year to 1975. One stayed with Canada Geese on the Lower Derwent floods throughout the summer of 1976. One summered at Fairburn Ings in 1972 and 1974, and one did so in 1978. A bird spent the summers of 1972, 1973 and 1974 at Wellbeck Sand Quarry.

While en route to Spurn Bird Observatory in 1955, C. Winn stopped his 'Sunbeam' motor cycle to pick up a dead Whooper Swan from beside the road. It had collided with overhead wires and, as it was quite fresh, a desire to test its culinary merits prompted him to strap it to his motor cycle. He plucked it in the Warren Cottage, much to the consternation of two elderly ladies present, and later cooked it.

Nelson said of this large impressive swan 'Winter visitor, irregular in numbers, which vary with the season. In severe weather large flocks occur.' Chislett saw no reason to change that assessment some 45 years on, and with perhaps a slight reduction in the total numbers visiting the county, and the fact that an occasional bird may stay throughout the summer months, the same applies today.

The ring number of a Whooper Swan at Broomhill Reservoir was read through binoculars on 18th January 1981. It had been ringed at Myvatn in Iceland on 25th July 1980.

Bean Goose
Anser fabalis

Early references to this species were erroneously mixed up with the Pink-footed Goose and in 1844 Allis, quoting Strickland, said 'This is one of the few species that do not seem to have diminished in numbers in late years, and from the immense flocks that now frequent the Wolds near here we might suppose they have increased of late by the introduction of clover crops which they principally feed on.' John Cordeaux repeated the error in his *Birds of the Humber District* (1872) and the chapters for the Bean Goose and the Pink-footed Goose would have suited admirably if juxtaposed. Clarke and Roebuck (1881) resolved its status correctly and said of the Bean Goose 'Winter visitor to the coast, but rare ...', but they repeated the erroneous fact that 'immense flocks formerly visited the Wolds during the day time, returning to the coast at dusk'. Nelson set the record straight in 1907. Chislett published the two species together under *Anser fabalis* in 1952, as at that time some authorities considered them to be merely races of the same species. They are now officially regarded as two distinct species and the status of each in the county is well understood.

The Bean Goose is scarce in Yorkshire, although some undoubtedly go unrecorded in skeins of 'grey geese' seen passing overhead. The low-lying carrs and marshy areas of the East Riding and occasionally the Humber Estuary were places cited by Nelson as favoured haunts along with the floodlands of the Lower Derwent. In Hatfield's *Historical Notes of Doncaster* (1866), this goose is stated to have been common on the Doncaster carrs, but there was confusion between this and the next species at that time.

Chislett could list only five occurrences of this elusive goose during the 45 years since Nelson published *The Birds of Yorkshire*. One was shot from a party of six at Stone Creek on the Humber on 6th December 1924; one was shot near Pickering in December 1934; a dead bird was found on the beach at Scarborough on 6th March 1940; and another was shot near Scarborough on 25th December 1938. C.F. Proctor reported that a few birds visited the Humber Estuary during the autumn of 1943.

There have been more records during the past 30 years, mainly concerning single birds or small parties, but an occasional larger flock has been seen. One was found dead on the Hessle foreshore on 15th January 1950. P.J. Stead reported the occurrence on 27th February 1955 of a party of 19 geese seen near Eston Nab, which were considered to be the same flock that numbered 20 birds in December 1954 before one was shot by J. Beasley at Greatham Creek, on the Durham side of the Tees Estuary, in late December and which proved to be a Bean Goose. G.R. Bennett found one dead on Bridlington beach on 27th January 1963, and I found another dead one there in February 1968. A.F.G. Walker watched one in Ripley Park on 11th January 1964, and another at Leighton Reservoir from 28th October to 2nd November 1966 which was located on the first date by E.E. Jackson.

Single Bean Geese often associate with other geese — as did one, with three Pink-footed Geese, near Scarborough for four days in January 1973, and one with Canada Geese by the River Ure, near Ripon, on 22nd and 23rd December 1974 and again during January 1975. One was consorting with Pink-footed Geese at Gouthwaite Reservoir on 2nd February 1975.

In 1976, more Bean Geese than usual were reported. The first was at Hornsea Mere on 28th October, followed by two at Kilnsea on 30th. Four were seen at Cromer Point, near Scarborough, on 2nd November and one was seen at Weighton Lock on 25th December, on which date a flock of 15 was at Blacktoft Sands before flying down the Humber. The species continued to be seen during the early part of 1977: one was on the Humber Wildfowl Refuge on 30th January, two were at Fraisthorpe on 19th February, and single birds were at Scarborough on 20th February and at Hornsea the next day; six appeared at Hornsea Mere on 26th February and stayed throughout the following day, and a lone bird frequented this area between 1st and 23rd March. The last of that winter's Bean Geese was at Scalby on 16th April, watched by M. Francis as it flew in from the northeast. Away from the coast, only one bird was seen, which frequented the area of Masham Gravel-pits and Leighton Reservoir during January and early February.

A solitary Bean Goose was at Hornsea Mere from 31st December 1977 until 6th January 1978 and another, or the same, appeared on 12th February and 4th March. M. Francis watched eight birds on stubble at Burniston on 12th February 1978, and five were at Bolton-on-Swale Gravel-pits from 15th January to 19th February. One was on Studley Park Lake on the unlikely date of 8th June and at Gouthwaite Reservoir on 12th. What was no doubt the same individual was in the Masham area from 20th July to 30th September. A single bird near Ripon on 12th December and three at Blacktoft Sands on 30th complete the picture for 1978.

There were even more Been Geese in 1979. P.A. Lassey saw two at Flamborough on 2nd January and I saw two at Fraisthorpe, with 37 White-fronted Geese, on 25th. There were eight at Swinefleet Common on 28th and four at

Cherry Cobb on 29th. On 23rd and 24th February 17 were near Kilnsea, and six more flew north at Spurn on the latter date. A party of 18, no doubt the Kilnsea flock, flew into Hornsea Mere, with 34 Whitefronts, on 25th February and stayed throughout the next day. March produced good numbers, starting with a flock of 18 at Barmston on 1st and 35 near Skeffling on the morning of 5th, 25 of which stayed during the afternoon; 16 were still in the Kilnsea/Skeffling area on 10th March, on which date H.J. Whitehead saw five birds at Muston. A lone bird was with 33 Greylag Geese and a Whitefront at Great Langton on 25th March, while two were at Hornsea on 1st April, with one bird on several dates at the month end. At the end of the year, four flew over Barrow Haven on 19th November and watchers on the observation tower at Knaresborough Ringing Station on 30th December saw two Beans flying with three Whitefronts.

Numbers were smaller in 1980, but from one to three birds occurred at six widely scattered places up to 30th May, when one was at Seamer Gravel-pit. Records of one bird at Welton Water on 8th August, Whitton Sands on 9th August and 30th October, and at Hornsea Mere from 1st to 9th November no doubt refer to the same individual. On 17th February 1982, 15 flew into Wheldrake Ings from the north, 11 of which departed shortly afterwards, the others remaining all day.

Although relatively scarce, the Bean Goose has been recorded more frequently during the last few years than formerly and it can now be termed an annual visitor in small numbers, chiefly along the coastal areas.

Pink-footed Goose
Anser brachyrhynchus

The historical tangle between this bird and the Bean Goose which I have illustrated under the latter species is most intriguing. Nelson said that '... the vast flocks of migratory Grey Geese which each winter come to this country with unfailing regularity, and were such a feature in the landscape of certain districts of our Eastern Seaboard were believed to be Bean Geese ... and were stated to be so in all works on ornithology'.

On 8th January 1839, a Mr Bartlett exhibited at the evening meeting of the Zoological Society several specimens of wild geese which he believed to be new to British ornithology, and which he proposed to call the 'Pink-footed Goose' from the colour of their legs and feet. He pointed out the characteristics of the species and where it differed from other members of the genus, and remarked that 'although resembling the Bean Goose much in appearance, in the formation of its sternum it was more like the White-fronted Goose' (Nelson 1907). Nelson pointed out that, although the Pink-footed Goose had been clearly established as a British bird, and specimens had from time to time been procured in various parts of the county, it seems never to have been suspected that the large flocks of wild geese frequenting Yorkshire were other than Bean Geese.

Today, as in 1952 when Chislett repeated Nelson's assessment of its status, the Pink-footed Goose remains 'the common Wild Goose of the county, abundant in East Yorkshire where it makes its winter home'.

Birds start arriving on the Humber Estuary from their breeding grounds in Iceland during September, the first arrival dates varying with the year. In 1915, some birds had arrived on the Wolds by 21st August, and on 5th August 1948 that keen and careful watcher H.O. Bunce saw three large skeins fly in over Easington.

These geese spend most of the daytime in the upper Humber Estuary on what is now the Humber Wildfowl Refuge, and fly out at dusk to feed on the stubbles of the Wolds or over the river into Lincolnshire. From September into December, skeins of wild geese, which are invariably of this species, may be seen crossing Yorkshire in almost any direction. In the early part of the period they are heading mainly for the Humber Estuary, but thereafter may pass on to other areas of the country.

In the Yorkshire Naturalists' Union Ornithological Report for 1959, Chislett published numbers of Pink-footed Geese which were most spectacular. Birds started to arrive in the Humber Wildfowl Refuge area on 14th September, when 14 were seen, building up to 5,000 by 28th; from 6th to 16th October 1,500 were estimated, after which there was a dramatic increase to 10,000 from 21st and a second influx on 27th, when no fewer than 20,000 were estimated, and these numbers were present until 7th November. Most of the British population of Pink-feet must have stopped off in Yorkshire that year. In the report for 1961, Chislett said that the numbers reported in the previous three autumns must have been greatly exaggerated by the warden, although he did not indicate why he thought so. The bird-photographer and goose-watcher Morley Hedley estimated 15,000 geese present on 3rd November in 1959, so there were obviously many more than usual.

During the late 1960s and the 1970s, peak numbers on the Humber Wildfowl Refuge varied from 1,000 to 2,000, the majority of which often stayed for only a few days, leaving a resident wintering population of only a few hundreds. Arthur Chapman, the refuge warden, and B.S. Pashby have kept careful records of the comings and goings of the geese over the years and have been responsible for producing the figures for the Annual Reports of the Yorkshire Naturalists' Union. In 1969, 4,030 geese were present on 1st February, with 4,120 the following day. In the autumn of that year, 4,900 were counted on 2nd October which decreased to 800 by 29th December and to only 37 by 31st, suggesting that the geese often use the Upper Humber as a stopping-off place before moving on to other wintering areas.

In 1970, the first geese were heard overhead on 16th September and 17 were down on the refuge the next day, the flock increasing to 2,600 by 21st October and 2,220 by 26th. The numbers dropped to 170 by 15th December, followed by a sudden increase to 2,826 on 20th December. Only 280 remained on 24th and 180 on 26th. This pattern of arrival, build-up and dispersal, often with a second influx, is a regular feature.

On 31st December 1974, after a two-month period during which the daily number of geese seen on the Humber Wildfowl Refuge never exceeded 280, Arthur Chapman was surprised to note that 1,180 birds had arrived. Clear moonlit periods prompted these to make overnight feeding forays, which was evident on 5th January 1975, when, before dawn, the refuge was devoid of geese. Later that day, Chapman watched the birds commuting from and to an area on the Lincolnshire side of the River Humber which he calculated was near the village of Coleby, about 3 miles (4.8 m) south of the refuge. On 6th January, Mr B. Crossland of the Adlingfleet and District Wildfowlers and Conservationists found 27 dead and dying Pink-footed Geese on the Alkborough Flats shore. He immediately informed the Ministry of Agriculture, Fisheries and Food in Brigg and the RSPCA at Scunthorpe. Mr G. Black, field officer of the former, and Inspector Russell of the latter visited the scene shortly afterwards. At about the same time, 12 dead geese were recovered from the north shore of the refuge near Faxfleet. These were seen by Chapman, who noticed grains of wheat in their bills and, in some cases, an emission of yellowish-brown fluid. He informed Mr P. Moody of the MAFF in Beverley. On 8th January, following the recovery of several more carcases on the south shore, four specimens from there and four from the north shore were sent to the MAFF laboratory at Tolworth in Surrey and three others to the Monks Wood Experimental Station. Dead geese were actually found on a newly sown cornfield in the Coleby area and it was established that 21 had died on 6th/7th January on a field sown with winter wheat dressed with carbophenothian, known commercially as Trithion. The chemical analyses at both Tolworth and Monks Wood were very similar; the geese had died through eating grain dressed with Trithion. It was considered likely that 1,000 geese may have died during the incident.

The reason for this most unfortunate disaster was the very wet weather during the autumn of 1974, which not only delayed the harvest, but made autumn sowing of winter wheat impossible. It was not until late December that this was done in some areas, and even then the ground was so wet that the grain had to be 'drop-sown' and disc-harrowed. In addition, the feed of the drill was adjusted to allow an extra 20 per cent deposit of grain. In consequence, a plentiful supply of dressed wheat was lying on, or just below, the surface on 3rd/4th January 1975. Had it been possible to sow this grain in the autumn, it would have been well below the surface at a time when the geese would have been feeding on the autumn stubble fields. No matter what the reason for this catastrophic incident, the fact that the potential danger is there at all is lamentable. The full details were written up by B.S. Pashby in *The Naturalist*, 1976, pp. 15-18.

In the following autumn and during the next two years, numbers at the refuge were somewhat lower than usual. The peak count in 1975 was 1,080 on 7th October, but in early 1976 numbers never exceeded 350 during January and 430 during February. On 24th February 1976 160 geese arrived, but they departed to the northwest two days later. The autumn peak was 700 on 20th October.

Numbers in 1977 were still relatively low, with counts of 540 on 13th October and 600 on 1st December. Blacktoft Sands had 640 Pinkfeet on 28th November. The figures for 1978 were 520 on 2nd February; 111 on 20th September, increasing to 400 by 12th October and 582 by 24th October; with 650 at Blacktoft Sands on 28th October.

Rather more occurred in 1979, and during February there were 743 on 8th and 1,170 on 24th. During the first week of March, between 500 and 600 were present before the birds dispersed. The autumn figures were 510 on 22nd September, 300-800 during October, with 600 through to December.

An obvious increase was noted in 1980, when 1,200 were counted on 13th January and 1,000 during early February, 1,430 on 8th February and 440 on 24th February. The autumn peak was 650 on 29th November. The 1981 figures were 1,440 on 22nd January and 1,630 on 24th January, and, in the autumn, 900 on 18th October and 1,060 on 24th October.

Two Pinkfeet ringed in Yorkshire in October 1952 were later recovered in Iceland, one in May 1953 and the other in May 1954. A third bird, ringed in October 1953, was found dead in Denmark on 6th December 1953.

To summarise, the Pink-footed Goose arrives in the Upper Humber from late August and builds up on the Humber Wildfowl Refuge during the next few weeks, many birds often moving out to other quarters after a short period; those that remain feed mainly on the Wolds and depart during March and early April. Large skeins may be seen crossing over any part of the county, mainly during the early autumn and spring while en route to and from their favoured winter haunts. Occasionally, small parties may drop into stubbles or pastures to feed as they make their way across the county, such stops usually being of short duration. A party of 33 fed on pasture at Ellerton-on-Swale on 20th March 1976 and 52 did likewise on 7th March 1978, perhaps indicating that geese from the Humber use the valley of the River Ure through Wensleydale as a migration route.

White-fronted Goose
Anser albifrons

Nelson mentioned only a handful of occurrences of this goose and said of it 'Winter visitant of uncommon occurrence'. Most of his records were from coastal localities and involved only very small numbers. During his time at Redcar, Nelson met with the species only once. East Cottingwith Ings were cited as a favoured place and two were shot there in 1903/04.

More have been identified during more recent times, and Chislett (1952) said that 'more have been definitely identified than either Nelson, or the lack of records in the 1940's would lead us to expect'. During early to mid January 1947, 20 birds frequented Leven Carr, and K. Dawson saw 17 flying southwest over Leeds on 22nd March in the same year. Chislett mentioned a further eight records of one to five individuals during the period from 1907 to 1952 when he published his *Yorkshire Birds*. Since then, the White-fronted Goose has been recorded far more regularly.

In the Yorkshire Naturalists' Union Ornithological Report for 1952, it was reported that a 'Dr. A. Mackenzie states that up to 70 White-fronts are usually on the Upper Humber sands in January and February with the Pink-feet.' They may well have been on one or two occasions, but the term 'usually' does not apply now, if it ever did. Intensive monitoring of the Pink-footed Goose populations on the Humber Wildfowl Refuge in recent years by Chapman and Pashby has not revealed any Whitefronts associating with them.

On 4th October 1958, ten Whitefronts were seen by Chislett and friends on the Humber mud at Spurn, and on 11th October 1959 31 were seen at Scaling Dam by D.G. Bell and others. The flooded land along the Lower Derwent Valley attracted two Whitefronts on 12th March 1960 and ten on 20th March. Six were there on 27th December 1965 and again on 4th January 1966. On 10th February 1968, 15 were on the Humber mud at Spurn, departing at dusk when they headed upriver.

During the 1970s and 1980s, the species has occurred more numerously than previously and flocks in excess of ten birds have been recorded fairly often. On 19th November 1970 13 flew into Hornsea Mere, and on 9th December 1971 41 were seen flying over Norton in vice-county 63. In January 1972, there was an obvious influx when five adults flew southeast at Spurn on 1st; 14 were on the Humber mud on 3rd and 4th; two appeared at Gouthwaite Reservoir on 8th; four were at Seamer Gravel-pit on 13th; three were at Lockwood Beck Reservoir on 16th; one was at Scalby on 18th; six were at Hornsea Mere on 21st; 11 were at Scarborough on 23rd; and 13 were on the Humber Wildfowl Refuge on 23rd and 27th, with 11 there on 30th, on which date 14 were near Lissett. Such widespread occurrences are unusual.

A large skein of 40 Whitefronts flew northwest over Thorpe Moors on 30th December 1974, and 60 which flew over Knaresborough, calling, on 6th January 1977 my colleague P.T. Treloar watched from his garden. On 10th November in the same year, P.J. Carlton heard calls from a large party of geese flying over Hampsthwaite in Nidderdale in the dark which he considered to be this species from their calls. On 7th January 1979 a party of 23 was in the Humber Estuary, and on 25th I watched a flock of 37, which contained only one juvenile, as they grazed near Fraisthorpe. This same party, which included two Bean Geese, was seen at Hornsea Mere on 31st January. Also in 1979, Sunk Island Sands attracted 22 birds on 5th February and 34 appeared at Hornsea Mere during the last week of that month.

During the last decade, Whitefronts have occurred at several other Yorkshire localities in small numbers or singly, often in association with Canada Geese. Four which flew into Hornsea Mere on 22nd December 1978 and stayed until 26th February 1979 were wearing spiral plastic colour rings and had doubtless come from a private collection.

Our White-fronted Geese are usually of the pink-billed European race which breeds on the Arctic tundras, but the orange-billed and darker-plumaged Greenland race occurs from time to time in small numbers. Eight such were at Hornsea Mere on 19th November 1970, and a single example at Harewood Lake on 23rd October 1978 was seen subsequently at Eccup Reservoir, Knotford Nook Gravel-pit and Lindley Reservoir on various dates to 7th May 1979. Three Greenlanders were at Farnham Gravel-pits and Staveley Lagoon on 6th January 1980 and at Givendale, near Ripon, from 13th January to 23rd March.

In 1982, there were several records of one to three birds during the early months from the Hornsea and Barmston areas, with occasional individuals inland at Fairburn Ings, Swillington Ings and the Lower Derwent floods, but with nine at Durker, near Wakefield, from 13th to 21st February. At the end of the year, seven appeared at Gouthwaite Reservoir on 5th November and one at Nosterfield Gravel-pit on the same day was joined by five more on 12th, all six remaining until the year end. Four flew west over Fairburn Ings on 14th November. In December, 12 in a field west of Filey on 4th were joined by a further 19 on 5th. A flock of between 16 and 20 Whitefronts fed at Hornsea Mere on several dates between 14th and 24th December.

This attractive goose is now a regular visitor to Yorkshire during the autumn and winter months, in numbers varying annually.

Lesser White-fronted Goose
Anser erythropus

Nelson referred to a male example in the collection formed by Sir Henry Boynton of Burton Agnes which, according to the catalogue, was 'taken near York several years ago'. Chislett adds another mentioned by John Cordeaux which was in the Humber area about 1874.

It was to be over 100 years before the species made an appearance again in Yorkshire, when an adult joined the Canada Goose flock at Fairburn Ings on 15th May 1976. S.C. Madge, then the RSPB warden at the ings, watched the bird along with many other people until 18th, when it departed. What was presumably the same one was reported from Adel Dam, Leeds, on 19th May and again on 4th June, and at Harewood Lake around the same period. A Lesser Whitefront that frequented the lake at York University for several days in May and one at Wheldrake Ings on 30th May could well have been the same one. That this bird had a genuine wild origin is most doubtful.

In the following year, one stayed at Hornsea Mere from 24th April to 10th May. An adult joined the Canada Geese at Fairburn Ings on 24th May and stayed until 26th. This latter bird was no doubt the 1976 bird paying a return visit, and all the records in 1976 and 1977 could well refer to the same individual. A record of one in Derbyshire in June 1976 and one in Cheshire from late June 1976 into 1977 doubtless refer also to this same wandering bird. On 1st May 1984, T.A. Ede watched an adult with Greylags at Broomfleet Ponds.

The species is not scarce in private wildfowl collections and several are bred. If these are not pinioned they remain free to present us with speculative excitement and clerical confusion. As I write, a pinioned pair of these small beautiful geese is grazing on my lawn.

It is, I suppose, doubtful whether this species has ever occurred in Yorkshire in a wild state. Nowadays, one or two birds which are considered to be genuine wanderers from northern Europe, where they breed on the tundras, occur in Britain almost every year. They usually arrive with the flocks of White-fronted Geese on the grazing grounds at Slimbridge in Gloucestershire and depart with them in the spring. The true origin of lone wanderers such as occurred in Yorkshire in 1976 and 1977 must remain a mystery.

Greylag Goose
Anser anser

Much has been written about the Greylag Goose in Yorkshire, for here, in the carrlands of the southern part of the county, the species used to nest. In his *Historical Notices of Doncaster*, Hatfield wrote that 'the Greylag formerly visited the decoy at Potteric Carr in immense multitudes'. That the species was common and an indigenous breeder up to the eighteenth century can be in no doubt, but by 1844 Thomas Allis could cite only occasional occurrences.

Nelson could not add significantly to the number of records and, in mentioning the skeins of grey geese which pass over various parts of the county, said that it was impossible to be certain of their identity without examining specimens. He mentions a Greylag shot at Redcar on 25th February 1891, and he inspected one which had been shot at Teesmouth on 25th October 1909. Chislett listed the species in only five years up to 1952. W.J. Clarke recorded one shot at Scarborough in January 1922, and John Lord and G.H. Ainsworth saw one at Hornsea Mere on 20th January 1946, in which year one was at Spurn on 5th May. The Reverend K. Ilderton saw one with Canada Geese at Ripley Park Lake on 22nd November 1946. R.M. Garnett saw three flying over Pickering Marishes on 17th January 1947, and G.K. Yeates, the well-known bird-photographer, who knows the species well both on its breeding grounds and in its winter quarters, identified a skein of 65 Greylags flying over Otley at 6th January 1948. On 22nd January in the latter year, Lord Bolton recorded five in a grass field by the River Ure near Wensley. On 24th September 1949, 12 were on Harewood Park Lake.

During the 1950s, however, several skeins were reported. These included eight at Spurn on 7th December 1950; 45 over Briscoe Moor on 18th October 1951; 36 flying up Gouthwaite Reservoir on 30th December 1952; 38 over Beamsley Beacon on 25th April 1954; 25 over Roseberry Topping on 4th November 1958; and 47 over Roundhay, Leeds, on 21st December 1958.

In the Yorkshire Naturalists' Union Ornithological Report for 1959, Chislett mentioned that three birds seen at Spurn by G.R. Edwards on 4th August might have been accounted for by the report that wildfowlers in the eastern counties were rearing and releasing Greylags. In 1964, several escaped from East Park, Hull, and were probably the birds seen at Hornsea Mere and Cherry Cobb Sands during May to July. By 1970, a feral population at Hornsea Mere had become firmly established and there were 90 birds there on 11th November. Since that time, between 30 and 70 Greylags have frequented the mere; in 1976, seven pairs bred successfully and reared 30 goslings. Odd individuals were attracted to Castle Howard Lake from the late 1960s and the flock numbered 60 birds on 8th December 1974. At the time of writing there is a small breeding population there. Small numbers are also breeding at East Park Lake in Hull, Rise Park and Burton Constable, and scattered pairs breed along the Lower Derwent Valley.

In autumn and winter when the flocks congregate, some quite large numbers occur. On 15th January 1970, 165 were in East Park, Hull, and the Hornsea Mere flock peaked at 115 on 18th October that year, with 190 on 9th October 1978 and 210 on 15th September 1979. Bolton-on-Swale Gravel-pits attracted Greylags from the mid 1970s and 41 were there from January to March 1977 and subsequently, with 62 on 31st December 1980. The species may also breed in Londesborough Park, near Market Weighton, where 140 birds were assembled on 26th August 1980.

Any suitable water in the eastern part of Yorkshire may attract Greylags, and some may settle to breed. Doubtless the trend will spread to other parts of the county. In 1979, a pair hatched goslings on a small pond near Ripon, and in 1980 a pair probably bred near Wensley.

Skeins of Greylags may now be seen anywhere in Yorkshire at almost any time of the year. Small numbers often spend the summer with Canada Geese at various waters. In 1973, one Greylag Goose which was moulting with the Canada Goose flock at Swinton Park, Masham, was caught by A.F.G. Walker and his team and proved to have been previously ringed as an eight-week-old gosling at Canterbury in Kent in 1968, thus giving an indication of the likely origin of such isolated birds. Separating genuine wild visitors from the large feral population is now nigh impossible, and each skein must be assessed in context. Some truly wild birds will undoubtedly occur, but the real situation will remain clouded by man's desire to improve his lot.

Snow Goose
Anser caerulescens

Nelson cited three examples of this North American goose near Beverley on 16th January 1891, seen by Henry Sharp, a practical wildfowler. Sharp said that the birds were only about 200 yards (180m) distant, and a note published in *The Field* (24th January 1891) prompted the editor to suggest that they could have been Gannets! Sharp replied (7th February 1891) and asserted his claim. Three adult Gannets in a field at Beverley in January would be at least as unusual as three Snow Geese.

Chislett could not add to this record up to 1952, but several have occurred since. Some have been obvious escapes from captivity; others have shown no signs of such confinement, but this is often not apparent in birds known to have been recently captive.

On 16th January 1955, four white geese with black wingtips flew over Ilton, which lies between Masham and the Leighton/Roundhill Reservoirs, and on 19th five such geese flew over the same place. The sightings were reported by P. Young, a naturalist/gamekeeper from Ilton, but no further details are given by Chislett. A white goose with about half of the wing black passed northwest over Aldborough on 15th December 1959. It was seen by H. Fisher, stated to be an observant wildfowler, whose reliability was vouched for by G. Bird, the Hornsea naturalist.

On 12th June 1961, an unringed Snow Goose joined two Canada Geese at Lockwood Beck Reservoir and stayed to moult with them, remaining in the area until the year end. D.G. Bell observed that its primaries had been shed by 27th June. A Snow Goose and two Canada Geese flying past the North Gare Breakwater on 27th December were no doubt the same trio, and a Snow Goose at Scaling Dam on 9th January 1962, seen by P.J. Stead, was very likely the same one. J. Murray saw two white Snow Geese flying over Stokesley on 11th February 1963 and one was seen over Ilton, again by P. Young, on 23rd December 1968. On 19th November 1970, W.F. Curtis watched three white-phase birds fly into Hornsea Mere with 13 White-fronted Geese.

In 1971, a white-phase Snow Goose appeared at Farnham Gravel-pit on 17th June and, together with R.Evison and J.L.C. Gandy, I watched it during the following few months. It joined the small flock of resident Canada Geese and moulted with them, being flightless by 28th June, and was subsequently caught and ringed by A.F.G. Walker. After the moult, it moved about the area and was seen on several dates during August and September, visiting Ripley Park Lake in August and Harewood Park Lake in October.

On 24th June, also in 1971, a flock of nine appeared in a field near Whitby Abbey and stayed for a few hours before moving on. Five were white-phase birds and the other four were blue-phase. They were very confiding and showed no fear of the local people who went to see them, nor of a photographer who approached very close to record their picture which appeared in the *Whitby Gazette*. Later in the same day, eight Snow Geese, four white and four blue. were seen flying north off Whitburn, County Durham, obviously the same party having lost one of its number. The origin of this flock is intriguing.

R.L. Brook saw a single bird at Bretton Park Lake on 11th April 1972. One at Harewood Park Lake for most of 1972 also visited Adel Dam and Golden Acre Park, and was seen flying with Canada Geese on 7th June over Knaresborough, then Harrogate and later at Gouthwaite Reservoir. It was assumed to be the bird which moulted at Farnham Gravel-pit in 1971, but, when it was caught at Harewood during the summer, it was found to be without a ring and therefore a different bird. It remained in the general area until June 1973.

One was at Hedon on 11th January and 1st February 1975 and was seen at Spurn on 23rd March. One at Hornsea Mere with the mixed goose herd from 12th June to the year end was very likely also this same individual.

Two Snow Geese spent the morning of 12th May 1975 feeding on the saltmarsh at Blacktoft Sands. They were unringed and wary, but recent escapes can adjust to wild living very quickly. Since 1976, up to three blue-phase birds have frequented Gouthwaite Reservoir, Harewood Park Lake and the surrounding waters and have moved about with the Canada Goose flocks.

In 1978, single white-phase birds were at Fairburn Ings on 10th September, Blacktoft Sands on 3rd November, Knaresborough Ringing Station on 4th November and in the Gorple area on 5th November. In 1980, two flew south at Spurn on 14th May and north again next day.

It is probable that a few Snow Geese from the New World visit Yorkshire from time to time, but a more likely origin of some of the more recent records is the feral breeding population on the Island of Mull in the Hebrides which was established by the late Niall Rankin. In 1978, I asked Miss Ann Mettam to check the situation while visiting the island and she kindly spoke to Lady Rankin and inspected the flock, which comprised 33 white-phase, 16 blue-phase and seven goslings.

The Snow Goose is a common bird in waterfowl collections and at least 30 were being offered for sale near Thirsk in the spring of 1982. All were pinioned but any subsequent goslings left full-winged could add to the existing confusion.

Canada Goose
Branta canadensis

This North American goose was first introduced into England in the seventeenth century, but Nelson considered that it did not qualify for admission to the Yorkshire list and relegated a short statement to square brackets, together with the Egyptian Goose, saying that they 'have occurred in Yorkshire, but, as these species have been introduced, and are semi-domesticated, it is impossible to discriminate between "escapes" and feral birds'.

The species was, however, breeding freely in Yorkshire long before it was accepted and included in *The Handbook of British Birds* in 1938, and was to become very well established as a Yorkshire breeding species. It has been the object of special study during recent years by the Canada Goose Study Group of Yorkshire, and I have invited A.F.G. Walker of Harrogate, the group's mainstay since its inception in 1970, to write the following chapter, to which he readily agreed and for which I am extremely grateful.

Contributed by A.F.G. Walker

Chislett's account of the status of the Canada Goose in 1952 summarised what was known of its distribution and a little about movements within the county. Quoting a report of a flock being seen to fly from Ripley to Harewood as confirmation that central Yorkshire haunts were interconnected, he concluded with a prophetic forecast that birds might travel farther; subsequent studies have confirmed this view.

By 1950, the Canada Goose was known to be breeding at many lakes and reservoirs in the county and flocks of just over 100 were occasionally reported. More precise knowledge of the species' status, both nationally and within the county, was obtained in 1953 by Blurton-Jones for the British Trust for Ornithology, when his census placed the county's population in the order of 500 birds within the context of a British population of about 3,500. Further national and county censuses revealed that by 1969 the Yorkshire population was about 1,500 (when the British population had increased to approximately 10,500) and that by 1979 the county population had increased to around 2,600.

The reason for such a large increase in just over two decades is worth examining. In the 1950s, in response to complaints from a number of landowners in England, a substantial programme was undertaken of transplanting birds from localities where they were judged to be too numerous to areas where they were more welcome. This geographical redistribution was one of the most important factors resulting in the substantial increase in numbers of Canada Geese nationally. A less important factor, but one of some regional relevance in Yorkshire, from the late 1950s onwards was the creation of the network of flooded gravel-pits in the lower and middle reaches of the Nidd and Ure Valleys, supplementing the number of already existing lakes in country parks.

To study the Yorkshire population more intensively and systematically, the Canada Goose Study Group of Yorkshire was formed in 1970 and much of the information in this account is based on the group's work. By 1983, 6,900 Canada Geese had been ringed, of which 1,167 had been recovered shot, or found dead, some of which latter group would have died as a result of gunshot wounds. These recovery data have shed considerable light on the movement of the species, both within the county and beyond.

As a breeding species, the Canada Goose in Britain favours inland waters which, ideally, lie close to reasonable grazing and provide islands for nesting. These conditions obtain in various country parks such as Ripley, Studley, Swinton, Allerton and Bretton. In the absence of an island, birds usually nest in open sites at the water's edge where the sitting bird commands good all-round views. Less commonly, nests are sited in beds of *Typha*, *Juncus* or sedge. Away from cover, nests are usually sited by a conspicuous landmark such as a rock, tree or fallen timber. A unique feature of part of the Yorkshire population is its adaptation to moorland nesting, recorded by Garnett in 1980 (see below). Many reservoirs nowadays attract odd breeding pairs, but, as only a few have islands, the geese have to take their chance with shore sites, which are often subject to predation. Competition for island sites can be so intense that nests may be only a few metres apart. Though colour ringing has shown that many Canada Geese breed in their second year, it is often the third year before most succeed. On low ground clutches are usually complete by the end of March or early April, but several days later at higher altitude. The average clutch size is normally five to seven and incubation by the female, with the male on guard, lasts about 28 days. The first goslings are normally seen in Yorkshire in late April or early May, the nest site having been deserted within a few hours of hatching, and both parents look after the brood. The gander can be particularly aggressive in defence and once, at Ripley, a gander drove off a well-grown lamb by flying at the animal, alighting on its back and pecking vigorously at the fleece until the lamb dashed away. Gosling mortality is very low, particularly in the average English spring, the observed number in a brood often remaining unchanged from hatching to fledging. Unlike surface-feeding ducklings largely dependent on insect food, goslings graze grasses and other vegetation at a very early age and this food supply is rarely scarce at the time of the hatch.

As the population increased in the two decades from 1960, so the numbers at waters with hitherto only small colonies also expanded. For example, the flock at Castle Howard, near Malton, increased from 75 in 1968 to 230 in 1977, and a parallel increase occurred at Hornsea Mere where the flock of 36 in 1968 had reached 140 ten years later. South of Leeds, a long-standing stronghold is Bretton Park, where the flock of moulting adults and goslings was in the order of 120 in 1953, had reached 200 in 1969, but levelled out at around 160 in the 1970s. In the Doncaster area, the largest flock recorded was one of 90 flying over Wath Ings in October 1967. The Fairburn Ings Nature Reserve began to attract increasing numbers during the 1970s and towards the end of that decade up to 140 were regularly seen. It is fair to say, however, that central Yorkshire (north of Leeds) is still the major stronghold for the species in the county.

To summarise the distribution in Yorkshire, it is apparent that there are probably nine more or less discrete main flocks: central Yorkshire, Castle Howard, Hornsea Mere/Hull, York/Lower Derwent Valley, Bretton Park/Fairburn Ings, Whitemoor/ Oxenhope Reservoirs, and Winterburn/Barden/Grimwith Reservoirs; in the northwest, Stocks Reservoir may be linked with the Lune Valley flock, while in south Yorkshire birds occurring around Doncaster may represent the northern limit of the north Nottinghamshire population. Movement of individuals between these flocks is either non-existent (i.e. not proven) or only slight.

Opinions concerning the extent of damage done to crops by Canada Geese vary. The most persistent is the grazing of grass in the early spring; claims regarding the effects have often been shown to be exaggerated, though there is little doubt that where large numbers of geese occur considerable quantities of grass are consumed, to the disadvantage of grazing stock. Various forms of control measure are practised. On most sporting estates the opportunity is taken to kill geese in the shooting season, though with varying degrees of success. Nevertheless, the fact that some 70 per cent of the mortality is directly due to shooting demonstrates the effect of this activity on the population. Some estates also exercise control by removing eggs.

During the 1950s and 1960s there were several reports of Canada Geese nesting on moorland, mostly adjacent to Gouthwaite Reservoir in Upper Nidderdale, but it was not until a study was undertaken by M.G.H. Garnett during the period 1976-79 (see *Bird Study*, 1980, pp. 219-26) that the true extent of moorland nesting in this part of north Yorkshire was established. A substantial though scattered breeding colony was located on Dallow Moor, Nidderdale, consisting of 60-80 pairs, up to 45 of which bred successfully. It was also established that, surprisingly, most of the geese remained on the moor with their goslings to moult, leaving in August. Moorland clutches were found to be smaller, on average, than lowland clutches, probably owing to the higher proportion of inexperienced young birds which can attempt nesting on high ground, where there is less competition for nest sites. The Dallow Moor colony lies in the wetter areas of mixed heather and *Juncus* between 280 and 350m (920-1,150 feet) above sea-level, but nests have been located above Angram Reservoir at the head of Nidderdale at almost 460m (1,590 feet) above sea-level. The colony on Dallow Moor began to establish itself between 1965 and 1970 and high-ground breeding has now been recorded on several Yorkshire moors, a practice unique in Britain.

A feature of most lakes and reservoirs favoured by the species in the summer is the existence of non-breeding flocks, and these can sometimes be in excess of 100 birds. The breeders and goslings tend to keep away from the non-breeders in the first few weeks after the hatch, but often the two groups amalgamate by July, when the adults are flightless, although parents remain intolerant of strange geese approaching their broods. Such amalgamations have occasionally exceeded 200 birds at Harewood Park and Gouthwaite Reservoir.

By early August geese from all the high-ground sites begin to move to the low ground, the movement from the Pennine reservoirs eastwards to gravel-pits and lakes adjoining the Nidd and Ure being particularly well marked. By late August/early September the high-ground waters are deserted, and autumn flocks of up to 500 or 600 concentrate at lowland waters to exploit the new stubbles.

Ploughing of the stubbles later in the autumn forces the geese to return to grass as their principal food and, with the approach of winter, flocks tend to be smaller, though there are one or two major exceptions. Harewood Park often holds flocks of up to 500 Canada Geese during the winter, and this flock frequently moves to riverside fields adjoining the Wharfe near Weeton, concentrating there particularly in severe winters when lakes and reservoirs are frozen. The most important wintering area in central Yorkshire lies along the riverside fields of the Ure downstream from Ripon, at Givendale, where counts of over 900 have occasionally been made, usually in January or February. A third major wintering area lies farther up Wensleydale in the vicinity of Masham, but smaller flocks in winter continue to circulate around lakes and gravel-pits on the low ground, movements being influenced by such factors as available food supply, severity or mildness of the season and, until the end of January, shooting pressure. Reservoirs in the Pennine foothills may also be visited during the winter months, again this being largely dependent on the mildness of the season. Gouthwaite Reservoir, however, is seldom deserted for long, and January often sees a determined return. By February, in mild winters, geese have returned to most major breeding stations on low ground, and in March they push back to high-ground waters and, towards the month end, to the moor-land sites.

Apart from moorland breeding, Yorkshire Canada Geese had, until recently, another unique trait — migrating to Inverness-shire — although this movement has now spread to some of the Midland populations. In common with all wildfowl, full-grown geese moult their flight feathers more or less simultaneously in mid summer, and are flightless for nearly a month until the new feathers are grown. The flightless state renders the goose vulnerable to predators, and from mid June to late July Canada Geese assemble on suitable larger waters to moult together in safety. Rounding-up and ringing of the flightless geese has been undertaken in Yorkshire since 1956, and on a substantial scale since 1970 by the study group. It was, how-ever, largely the small-scale round-ups at Ripley Park in the early 1960s that led to the discovery of a moult migration to the Beauly Firth in Inverness-shire (*Wildfowl*, 21, pp. 99-104), and it is now known that a significant proportion (usually about a quarter or one-fifth) of the Yorkshire population migrates annually to the Scottish moulting area. The development of the migration is fascinating to trace. In July 1963, 39 of a flock of 153 flightless Canada Geese were caught by Roy Dennis on the Beauly Firth; two of these had been ringed at Ripley, near Harrogate, some 415 km (260 miles) south-southeast. A further catch in 1964 included three more Ripley birds, and numbers of geese ringed on the Beauly Firth began to be recovered in Yorkshire, mostly close to Harrogate. These results stimulated more intensive ringing in Yorkshire and on the Beauly Firth; six more round-ups on the Beauly Firth took place between 1968 and 1980, latterly a joint operation by the Yorkshire group and the Highland Ringing Group. It was established that the first Canada Geese were seen on the Beauly Firth in 1947; there were just over 300 by 1969; but by the end of the 1970s nearly 1,000 Canada Geese were moulting on the Firth. During the same period, the Yorkshire population virtually matched the growth rate of the Beauly moulting flock. At first the migration appeared to involve only Yorkshire birds, and of the 142 retraps in the catch in 1969 only geese ringed in Yorkshire and Beauly Firth were involved, but in 1973 there were 16 from Derbyshire and two from Nottinghamshire. By 1980 the proportion of Yorkshire birds in the retrap totals was 54 per cent compared with 64 per cent in 1978, while the proportion from the Midlands had increased to 30 per cent compared with 24 per cent in 1978. (It should be noted that the increase in the proportion of Midland birds no doubt reflected the substantial ringing programme in that region in recent years.)

Almost all lowland Yorkshire breeding sites 'export' geese to the Beauly Firth each summer but, by comparison, very few geese ringed at high-ground sites in the county such as Angram and Scar House Reservoirs appear on the Beauly Firth. The one exception to this generalisation concerns the Dallow Moor population, which had 15 of the limited number of goslings ringed in 1978 and 1979 retrapped in the 1980 Scottish catch. As would be expected, first-year birds (non-breeders) are always in the majority on the Beauly Firth, having had to survive only one shooting season; second-year birds are the next most numerous, presumably geese which have failed to establish themselves as successful breeders. While in a minority, mature birds regularly migrate to Scotland and these are assumed to have lost their clutches. The move to the Beauly Firth takes place from late May, with the bulk of the birds migrating in the first half of June. A few Beauly Firth-ringed birds have been seen back in Yorkshire by 17th August, but the main return occurs between the last ten days of August and the first ten days or so of September.

From 1974 to 1979, all goslings caught by the group in Yorkshire were marked with coloured darvic rings, each individually lettered and/or numbered, as well as with a British Trust for Ornithology metal ring. The colour rings are readable in the field with the aid of a telescope at ranges of up to 400m and the results of the extensive study from 1974 to 1982, involving over 30,000 observations of colour-ringed birds, are on record. The resulting information, aided by computerised analysis, has shed considerable light on the composition of flocks and the movement of individual birds at different times of the year, but such detail is outside the scope of this account.

Apart from the study of the involvement of Yorkshire Canada Geese in the Beauly Firth migration, ringing has shown that Yorkshire birds may also move considerable distances. There have been seven recoveries in Wales, six in Shropshire, two in Worcestershire, one in Herefordshire, and a few birds have also moved into Cheshire and Lancashire. Most of these originated from the more westerly ringing points in Yorkshire. A clear link has also been identified between Harewood Park and the West Midlands, nine Harewood-ringed birds having been found breeding subsequently in the West Midlands.

The most bizarre and unexpected movement occurred in 1979. In July 1978, a full-grown goose was marked on the Beauly Firth with a BTO ring, number 5086436, and colour ring black OW. Seen on a gravel-pit near Knaresborough in October, it appeared at Gouthwaite in November and by January 1979 had joined the main wintering flock at Givendale, near Ripon, where it remained until 13th April 1979. Seven weeks later, on 13th June, and 3,900km (2,420 miles) east-northeast, it was shot just north of the Arctic Circle in western Siberia, the colour ring being returned to the Ringing Office. This recovery is the first of a British-ringed Canada Goose in Russia. Clearly, the bird was of Yorkshire origin, and the only explanation for the extraordinary movement seems that it might have joined up with a party of Bean Geese, which occasionally pass through Yorkshire on their return migration to Russia. Ralph Chislett's forecast that Canada Geese might travel farther than between Ripley and Harewood was prophetic indeed.

Barnacle Goose
Branta leucopsis

Nelson cited Willughby's *Ornithology* (1678, pp. 359-60), as the earliest reference to the species in Yorkshire, wherein it is stated that Mr Jessop sent a specimen 'out of Yorkshire'. In Ray's correspondence is the letter accompanying the bird: 'Broomhall, 25th November 1668. Mr. Jessop to Mr. Ray. Sir, ... I have procured the skin of a great bird, which he that gave it me called a Scarfe; but I believe it will prove a Bernicle. The description of it I sent to Mr. Willughby ... I am, etc., Fra. Jessop.'

In 1844, Thomas Allis said that it was frequently shot near Doncaster in severe weather; taken occasionally near Huddersfield on the Marsden, Slaithwaite, Neltham and Holmfirth Moors; occasionally met with near York; and rare near Leeds, but one shot at Rigton in 1837. This surely cannot have been the case and confusion with the Canada Goose, which was breeding ferally at that time, is likely. Such confusion was not unknown as recently as 1950 (see below). Allis also quoted Strickland, who said that 'it may at times be found on the seashore during severe winter weather, on the extensive mud flats of the Humber during low tides'. That sounds more like it!

Nelson summarised its status as 'Winter visitant of irregular occurrence on the coast; has occasionally been observed inland.' Three were shot on the Humber on Christmas Day in 1875, and in 1871 a Mr L. West saw one at Brough in the upper estuary. Mr Bailey, the taxidermist from Flamborough, told Nelson that he had only two or three specimens to preserve. Nelson mentioned a few coastal sites where the species had occurred and quoted J. Hogg (*The Zoologist*, 1845, p. 1178): 'occasionally killed on the Tees, but a rare bird'. Morris recorded one procured from a flock of nine on Coatham Marsh on 1st October 1853. George Mussell informed Nelson that 50 years previously it was by no means uncommon; about the year 1857, 14 were killed at one shot on the Teesmouth, and the professional fowlers obtained from four to ten birds in a day.

Nelson recorded the species only twice during his time in the northeast. The first record involved a flock of 11 which flew past him at Coatham Sands on 28th September 1883. The second was of a winged female that he purchased from a fisherman on 1st October that year, and which lived in a walled garden for 19 years: during that early part of its captivity 'it formed an attachment for a Sheld-Duck, and, in its latter years, had for its master a tame Raven, which kept it in complete subjection'. Both the goose and the Raven can be seen in the Nelson collection at the Dorman Museum, Middlesbrough, the former in case number 144.

In 1952, Chislett could add very few records to the handful listed by Nelson, although he published two that undoubtedly referred to the Canada Goose. He wrote: 'During the early part of 1924, up to the beginning of March, Fairburn water was visited several times by parties of geese varying in numbers from ten to forty which W.G. Bramley reported as Barnacles (*The Naturalist*, 1925, p. 23). Mr. Bramley (now a well known mycologist), who was very young in 1924, wishes it to be stated that the identification was unconfirmed.' The second record was published thus: 'During the winter of 1949-50, Mr. K. Wheater informed me that a flock of about fifty geese with white faces and black necks, that he considered to be of this species, paid several short visits to the Harewood Park Lake.' Perhaps Chislett was too kind to his correspondents.

A Barnacle Goose was shot on the Humber, near Ferriby, in early February 1947, and two were seen by H.O. Bunce in a field near Easington on 29th October 1949.

During the last 30 years, Barnacle Geese have occurred in small numbers at many Yorkshire localities, both along the coast and inland, often singly and some-times staying throughout the year. Captive origin of many of these individuals is probable, and it is known that the species is being allowed to breed and to rear unpinioned young in some collections. Some records of single birds and small parties, particularly those along the coast, will probably, however, refer to wild geese, and some larger flocks certainly do, but as with other species of geese and ducks the escape problem will always confuse the true situation.

On 21st February 1965, at Filey, R.H. Appleby watched five Barnacles flying north over the sea, and four came in from the east with Whitefronts on 30th October. Later in the year, 14 birds were at Filey on 6th November; six were on stubble at Flamborough on 7th November; and four flew south at Filey on 20th November.

More Barnacle Geese than ever before were recorded in the county in 1970. W.F. Curtis saw 21 at Hornsea Mere on 8th January; one was on a clifftop field at Filey on 28th February; and four were at Muston for several days from 1st March on the land of J. Temple. More birds arrived in October, with seven on the Humber Wildfowl Refuge on 7th and nine on Hury Reservoir on 13th; 14 were seen coming over the sea at Skipsea on 19th, when eight flew north at Redcar and S.C. Norman saw 12 on the lagoon at South Gare. The Humber Refuge had a party of 14 birds on 22nd October, no doubt the ones seen coming in at Skipsea on 19th, and 20 had assembled by 29th. Smaller numbers, from one to four, were recorded during the same period, from Gouthwaite Reservoir, Fairburn Ings, Tophill Low Reservoir,

Scaling Dam and Leighton Reservoir. In 1971, 18 flew north at Hornsea Mere on 19th January.

On 26th April 1972, Yorkshire's largest ever flock of Barnacle Geese occurred when 90 came in from the north and landed on the Humber mud at Spurn, where they remained for a short while before departing unseen. On 20th April 1974, 33 flew down the Humber at Spurn, turned around the point, and continued north off-shore. In the same year, five were on the Humber mud on 5th May before leaving to the north. On 30th October 1976, ten birds were at Spurn and 14 at Easington, the latter flock staying in the Kilnsea area until 5th November.

Five birds which appeared at Hornsea Mere on 6th May 1974 and stayed throughout 1975 and up to May 1976 were apparently of feral origin. They were often absent for short periods and obviously accounted for occasional records else-where along the coast. On 3rd October 1977, I watched five fly south at Filey and land on the end of the brigg; they looked quite wild in that context, but were probably the Hornsea regulars.

In 1980, some large parties were observed inland, including nine at Wheldrake Ings on 4th January and five on 20th; 16 flying over Blackmoorfoot Reservoir on 2nd April and 15 over Fairburn Ings on the same day were very likely the same birds. On 12th October 1980, there were nine at Gouthwaite Reservoir, four at Fewston Reservoir and nine at Stocks Reservoir. Included in the latter flock was a colour-ringed goose which had been marked on Spitsbergen in July 1977 (see also below), proving that genuine wild immigrants do visit inland localities. In addition, there were five birds at Thrybergh Reservoir from 13th to 22nd October and two at Leighton Reservoir and Masham Gravel-pit on 28th October. Sightings along the coast during the month included 12 at Spurn on 12th; six near Barmston from 10th to 12th and 15 there on 15th; and two at Hornsea Mere from 21st October to 2nd November, one of which had been colour-ringed on Spitsbergen in July 1977, with an additional 18 which arrived on 3rd December and stayed during most of the winter.

During a heavy period of sleet on 25th April 1981, the members of Knaresborough Ringing Station watched a skein of 21 Barnacle Geese flying very high to the northwest. A large flock at Castle Howard Lake during the winter months in 1982 peaked at 51 on 7th March and 53 on 18th December. These birds doubtless originated from a flock of about 60 free-flying Barnacle Geese at Flamingo Park Zoo which disperse in the winter and return in the spring, when a few pairs breed in the park.

In addition to the two records of Spitsbergen-ringed birds mentioned above, there have been four others reported in Yorkshire. A female ringed on Spitsbergen in July 1977 and another female ringed at Caerlaverock in Dumfriesshire on 12th October 1978 were reported as having been found dead at Middleham, near Leyburn, at the end of March 1981. These must surely have been shot. The other two, both ringed on Spitsbergen, one in July 1977 and the other in July 1981, were reported respectively from Langdale, Melsonby, on 23rd September 1978 (shot) and from Broomhill Flash on 13th April 1982 (ring read through binoculars).

It is now clear that immigrant Barnacle Geese visit Yorkshire each year, and appear at inland waters as well as along the coast. The populations of this northern goose have increased in recent years and the birds visiting Yorkshire could be either from the Spitsbergen population (of this we now have proof) which winters mainly in the Solway area, or from the Novaya Zemlya population, which spends the winter in western Europe, principally in the Netherlands.

Brent Goose
Branta bernicla

In Willughby's *Ornithology*, 1678, p. 361, under the name of 'Rat or Road Goose — *Brentus fortasse*', is found the earliest known reference to the Brent Goose in Yorkshire. Here it is stated that 'Mr. Johnson, who showed us this bird at Brignall, in Yorkshire, thus describes it ... [here follows an account of the Brent Goose]. It is a very heedless fowl, (contrary to the nature of other Geese), so that if a pack of them come into the Tees, it is seldom one escapes away, for though they be often shot at, yet they only fly a little, and suffer the Gunner to come openly upon them.'

One old fowler, whom Nelson often saw at work in the Tees Estuary, shot 65 Brents in 1869. The 'immense' flocks which frequented the Tees and Humber Estuaries at the beginning of the nineteenth century no longer occur, but both localities still attract the species. The drastic reduction in the Brent's main food plant, *Zostera marina*, the eel-grass, caused by disease, had a bad effect on the European populations and only in comparatively recent times has the species been on the increase.

Birds started revisiting the Humber Estuary at Spurn in small numbers during the 1960s, and a regular flock became established during the 1970s, when up to 70 birds were present in some years and up to 110 in the spring of 1979. More Brents than usual visited the area in 1980, and on 13th January 176 were present, with 260 on 3rd and 4th November, and slightly fewer remaining to the following March. The peak count in 1982 was 290 on 30th October, but on 5th November 147 flew south at Flamborough and 518 did so at Spurn.

Most birds are of the dark-bellied race *Branta bernicla bernicla*, which breeds in northern Europe, but occasional birds of the pale-bellied form *Branta bernicla hrota* from the Greenland area sometimes occur. Up to eight of the latter have frequented the Humber Estuary and the adjacent coastal areas during the winters of 1978 to 1980.

In 1978, one of the geese was seen to be wearing lettered colour rings and was found to have been marked in Lincolnshire in March 1974. It had been reported subsequently in north Germany in December 1974, in Essex from December 1974 to April 1975, and in north Germany again during April and May of the years 1975, 1976 and 1977. It was seen at Spurn during January and February and from 30th October to 8th December 1979. A second ringed individual was seen on 24th and 27th March 1979 which had been ringed in Norfolk in 1974 and been subsequently sighted some 80 times since then, in Norfolk and at Fohr in West Germany. A third colour-ringed bird appeared in late March 1979, and this had been ringed in May 1977 at Terschelling in the Netherlands. A fourth was seen in October which had been marked in December 1976 on Foulness Island, Essex, and which had been seen at Morbihan, north France, in December 1976.

In contrast to the attraction of the Humber Estuary for this goose, numbers in the Tees Estuary are few and the Yorkshire side is not favoured. It would seem that the winter flock on the Humber Estuary at Spurn is now well established and increasing, and that it occasionally provides other coastal areas with small numbers during the period October to April.

Red-breasted Goose
Branta ruficollis

Chislett appears to have misread Nelson's comments under this species and mentions 'one bird captured alive and another shot in the neighborhood of Wycliffe-on-Tees in 1776'. What Nelson actually said was that Marmaduke Tunstall of Wycliffe-on-Tees wrote: 'Have a beautiful specimen of this scarce species shot in the severe frost in 1776 near London.' Tunstall then goes on to say that he has heard of but two more in England; 'one was taken alive in this neighborhood [Wycliffe] and is still living'. The bird was apparently kept on a pond with other waterfowl and thrived for some time.

Since that early record, which is hardly convincing as regards the true origin of the bird, there have been two other occurrences in Yorkshire of this small goose, which breeds in northern Russia and Siberia and of which only about 30 apparently wild birds have been recorded in the British Isles. On 1st October 1978, B. Caffrey, J. Cudworth and C. Massingham had excellent views of a Red-breasted Goose as it alighted on the Humber mud at Spurn; it stayed only briefly before taking wing and circling the area and then flying off to the east. One appeared at Barmston on 4th March 1984, when it was seen by M.J. Macdonald; it stayed for a short while before moving to Hornsea Mere, where it was last seen on 18th March.

The species occasionally winters in Holland in very small numbers, and could well turn up again on the east coast in the company of Brent Geese.

Egyptian Goose
Alopochen aegyptiacus

This introduced African species was becoming established in private collections during the eighteenth century, but the feral status in recent times was poorly documented until its admission to the British list in 1971. Nelson mentioned it only briefly along with the Canada Goose, when he said that it had occurred in Yorkshire in a semi-domesticated state and that it was impossible to discriminate between escapes and feral birds. The same applies today, but there is now an established breeding population in East Anglia and feral wanderers are in consequence more likely now than formerly.

Chislett omitted the species from his *Yorkshire Birds* in 1952. He did, however, include the Bar-headed Goose *Anser indicus*, never a candidate for naturalisation.

In 1957, an Egyptian Goose was at Bretton Park Lake on 23rd March which J.C.S. Ellis assumed to be an escaped bird. During the 1970s, more have been apparent in Yorkshire and these could well be the result of a spread from the East Anglian breeding population. A pair was by the River Ure, near Ripon, on 13th July 1974, and what was presumably the same duo flew over Knaresborough Ringing Station the next day. C.E. Andrassy saw one at Stanley Sewage-farm from 3rd to 10th April 1977, and J. Hewitt watched what was no doubt the same one fly into Wath Ings on 17th April. A party of four, considered to be a pair and their two young, was at Fairburn Ings and at Newton on 12th and 13th February 1977, and one lone bird was there from 11th to 15th April. Two birds were on flooded land at Halsham, near Withernsea, on 19th May 1978, and at Hornsea Mere on 21st May and again from 31st October to 5th November. D.I.M. Wallace saw a pair at Sutton-on-Derwent on 24th March 1979. Four, including one juvenile, flew over Wath Ings on 6th August 1979. One was in the Ribble Valley at Settle on 14th January and 2nd February, and two flew into Staveley Lagoon on 18th April. An Egyptian Goose flew over Wath Ings on 9th July 1980, and one was at Castle Howard Lake on 27th July 1980 with two there in November 1982. One visited several waters in the Thrybergh, Broomhill and Wath areas during March 1983, with two birds at the latter on 26th June, and one was at Eccup Reservoir on 4th January 1984.

The species will eventually breed in Yorkshire if it has not done so already. An introduced pair at the ICI works at Wilton, near Redcar, laid four eggs in 1983 but did not hatch them.

Ruddy Shelduck
Tadorna ferruginea

There is a reference to this eastern species in the *Handbook of Yorkshire Vertebrata* (Clarke and Roebuck 1881, p. 55), where it is stated that one was killed 'some years ago' at Cottingwith. The specimen was seen by H.B. Hewetson. Nelson considered that the circumstances connected with the record were so dubious that no reliance could be placed on it.

Chislett published a record in square brackets, a common practice at the time for dealing with uncertain records or those of dubious origin. It concerned a drake shot at Sunk Island on 21st June 1909, reported by E.W. Wade, which proved to have been pinioned.

The Ruddy Shelduck is now scarce, even in its nearest breeding grounds in eastern Europe and Morocco, and the chances of a wild bird wandering to Yorkshire are very slight. There are, however, a good many in captivity in Britain and the spate of records during the last few years will doubtless be associated with escaped free-flying birds.

A female spent much of 14th November 1965 on the Humber mud at Spurn. The bird was wary and thought to be of wild origin, but such is impossible to determine. It was seen again on 20th and 21st November. One was at Studley Park Lake on 15th August 1967 and on two subsequent dates, and another, or the same, was at Eccup Reservoir on 21st August. On 28th December 1969, one was seen at Drax. The origin of five birds flying south at Spurn on 23rd July 1972 can only be conjectured, but captive or feral origin would be almost certain. Two years later, on 15th August 1974, P.J. Carlton saw five Ruddy Shelducks flying southeast over Lindley Reservoir; could these have been the same five? A pair flew along the River Trent near Blacktoft Sands on 15th September in the same year.

In 1975, a drake frequented the Blacktoft/Whitton Sands area from 4th June into August, and a pair was present there from 13th to 22nd September. Associating with them was a South African Shelduck *Tadorna cana*, which perhaps gives confirmation of their captive origin. One or two birds have been in the Upper Humber area during the past few years, and up to three were at Whitton from 13th August to 9th October 1978 which consisted of a pair and one immature. It was rumoured by a local farmer that the pair had nested near a barn where he worked, but further details were not forthcoming. It is quite possible that such breeding could take place, given the right conditions of seclusion and available feeding grounds.

In 1978, a lone bird was at Fairburn Ings from 28th June to 17th July and a drake appeared at Bretton park on 22nd July. D.B. Cutts reported that two drakes in the vicinity of Broomfleet Island and Faxfleet during April 1979 were eventually killed by a passing train. One flew up Wharfedale, near Carthick Wood, on 4th March 1980 and one was at Bretton Park on 7th July, perhaps the same bird as in 1978. One was at Catfoss on 2nd May 1981; a pair was at Wheldrake Ings from 17th to 26th August 1982; and two birds were at Pugneys Gravel-pit on 27th August 1982.

There are, it would seem, several feral Ruddy Shelducks roaming Yorkshire and, as mentioned above, breeding could take place and perpetuate their presence.

Further examples of the South African or Cape Shelduck were at Wheldrake Ings on 1st and 2nd October 1977 and at Whitton Sands on 8th July 1979.

Shelduck
Tadorna tadorna

The Reverend John Graves seems to have been the first person to mention the Shelduck in connection with Yorkshire, when, in his *History of Cleveland* in 1808, he listed it among the resident birds. Nelson assessed its status as 'Resident in limited numbers, its breeding quarters being confined to the Humber and Teesmouth districts. Large flocks of migrants observed in spring and autumn. Occasionally occurs inland.'

There has been little change since then, except for the fact that a few pairs are now breeding at inland localities and the species does so more regularly in the upper reaches of the Humber. When Nelson wrote *The Birds of Yorkshire* in 1907, he said 'It is with great satisfaction that I am able to claim this handsome duck as still resident in the county, though in but limited numbers ...' He also said that it was subject to much persecution at Spurn, and was also unintentionally snared in rabbit burrows, the results of which almost banished it as a breeding species. Owing to subsequent protection, the bird fared better and became re-established. In Nelson's time it used to make use of the burrows on the sandhills between Redcar and the Teesmouth, on what was to become the Cleveland Golf Club course. A pair nested near the junction of the Trent and the Ouse in 1900.

In 1942, G.H. Ainsworth reported breeding at Kelsey Hill; another pair was seen with six young in a field near a Hull suburb on 26th June, and a pair nested under a gorse bush at Sunk Island. A few other pairs bred in this general area in other years around this time. At Swillington Ings, three birds were present from February 1949, and on 11th May M.F.M. Meiklejohn reported two pairs there. K. Dawson and B. Speake saw a pair during the early part of 1950 at the same place. Only one bird was seen during May, but on 4th June the pair was seen with 12 ducklings. This brood had been reduced to six by 2nd July, and five young eventually flew. A pair was present here into June 1954, and eight young were produced in 1955. A pair bred successfully again in 1957 and hatched six ducklings.

The ensnaring of Shelducks at the entrance to rabbit burrows mentioned by Nelson was still happening in the 1950s. In 1953, two were so trapped on successive days on Hollym Carrs. The burrow held eight eggs, which were hatched under a hen; the young eventually flew. Another got into a farmer's rabbit snare at Spurn and was later ringed and released.

On 20th June 1956, two adults led 13 ducklings over the mud at Cherry Cobb Sands, and on 25th July Henry Bunce saw an adult with 34 juveniles. Two adults were in charge of 25 ducklings at Reads Island on 10th July in the same year. In 1965, T. Dickinson reported 18 broods brought down the Market Weighton Canal during June and July, through the lock gate and into the estuary. Two pairs bred near Lisset in 1973, when one pair had three young at a gravel-pit, 5 miles (8 km) inland near Brandesburton. More Shelducks were breeding inland in 1974, when there were two or three pairs along the Lower Derwent and single pairs at Brandesburton, Saltmarsh Delph, Howdendyke Island and Asselby, and H.O. Bunce said that there was now a definite tendency to breed away from the Humber.

In 1975, the Lower Derwent Valley had no fewer than seven pairs with some young birds during April and May. There was also a pair with six young at Sandsfield Gravel-pit on 12th June, seen by S.M. Lister and D.E. Murray. B.S. Pashby had many records of breeding in the Welton Water area during the 1950s and 1960s, and they still nest there today. A pair with 11 ducklings was seen at Wheldrake Ings on the Lower Derwent on 31st May 1976, and another pair with nine young was there on 3rd July. In 1979, the species was well established along the Lower Derwent, with a pair on every ing from Bubwith to Wheldrake; in 1983, there were ten pairs on this stretch. A pair reared two young on York University Lake in 1977, and they bred again in the following year. Young have been reared at Bolton-on-Swale Gravel-pits since 1979, and a pair nested successfully near Settle in 1980 and subsequently. A pair bred at Nosterfield Gravel-pit, near Masham, and reared young in 1983 and 1984.

I am informed by N. Carter of Halifax that in 1982 a pair arrived at Whiteholme Reservoir and nested in a small adjacent rocky valley. The adults were later seen on Warland Reservoir, about one mile away, with seven young, having taken them over the open moorland. Only one young survived to fledge in mid August. This is the first breeding record for the area and is interesting in that Whiteholme Reservoir is at an elevation of 1,250 feet (380 m) above sea-level.

Since the appointment of a warden for the Royal Society for the Protection of Birds at Blacktoft Sands in 1974, the breeding population in the area has been well monitored. In that year, about 20 pairs bred and on 27th June 65 young were 'crèched'. Similar numbers bred in the following two years, and 114 young were assembled there on 23rd July 1976. In 1977, about 20 pairs bred but high tides in June flooded many nests and only 25 young were seen in July.

Breeding along the sea coast is sporadic except at the estuaries of the Tees and Humber, and even there the numbers are small. Most of those in the Tees Estuary are on the Durham side. A pair on the Yorkshire side in 1967 was the only one reported in that decade: seven young were hatched, one of which was swallowed by a grey seal. No breeding has been reported on the Yorkshire side for several years now, but it is probable that a few do so annually. Nesting along the Spurn Peninsula is also a rare event. During the late 1960s, a few pairs prospected but were never proved to breed. In 1972, a pair was seen around the Warren area, but did not stay. The only proof of successful nesting in recent years came in 1977, when a bird with eight small young was seen swimming offshore on 27th June.

Numbers of migrating Shelducks on the Tees and Humber Estuaries can be spectacular, especially at the former. In early July, the majority of birds move eastwards on their traditional moult migration, which takes them to the Waddenzee area in Germany. Here Shelducks from all over western Europe congregate to undergo their moult, leaving their crèched young in the care of a few adults, which moult as the young grow on the breeding grounds. This moult migration, not known in Nelson's time, was written up in detail by R.A.H. Coombes in the *Ibis*, 1956, pp. 405-18. He mentioned birds flying eastwards from Morecambe Bay towards Ingleborough and the Aire Gap and, as we know today, Shelducks are regularly seen at inland waters both during the main late summer exodus and during the birds' return in the autumn. The majority of records come from waters along the Aire Valley, and these undoubtedly refer to birds making the crossing to and from the west coast. Shelducks can be seen leaving eastwards over the sea at Spurn Point, and on 9th July 1966 a flock of 45 was watched as it gained height and flew eastwards. During the period 22nd to 25th July 1965, parties totalling respectively 152, 127, 184 and 84 were watched as they flew eastwards out to sea, mainly during the evenings. On 23rd July 1967, 321 flew out in four hours. Such movements occur every year and the passage stretches over the period June to August, the majority passing in late July and early August.

During 1978 and 1979, Mark Tasker studied the Shelducks along the north bank of the Humber and discovered a small flock of moulting birds on Foulholme Sands. On 31st July 1978, a flock of 161 Shelducks was seen clearly enough to note that the birds had very short primary feathers or none at all. As the majority of Shelducks do not start leaving the Humber for their moulting grounds across the North Sea until late July, this early moulting assembly was doubtless made up of failed breeders or of immatures in their second year. More Shelducks have recently been found undergoing their moult in British estuaries, and this new trend could markedly alter the present status of the species in the Humber Estuary. For full details see *Bird Study*, 29, pp. 164-6.

During the past ten years or so, birds have been counted regularly along the Humber shore and some interesting figures are to hand. These 'estuary counts' as they became known were organised by D.B. Cutts on behalf of the British Trust for Ornithology as part of their 'Birds of Estuaries Enquiry'. Volunteers covered the north shore of the Humber, from Spurn Point to Goole, in an attempt to count the numbers of different species using the area for feeding and resting. On 10th October 1971 there were 1,124 Shelducks present, and on 13th April 1975 1,057 were counted. Anywhere along this stretch of estuary, Shelducks can be seen in good numbers, varying with the season. Some high counts have been 633 on the Humber Wildfowl Refuge on 13th October 1972 and 638 on 26th October 1978, at which times the moulted birds are gathering again after their return from the Continent. In 1978 large numbers were in the estuary, and on 8th July D.I.M. Wallace counted 770 adults and 70 juveniles, most of which, except for the juveniles, would be preparing to move out to moult. On the same date in 1979, he counted 980 adults and 60 juveniles at the same place. On 5th November 1978, 700 on the sands there would have been returning birds, assembling before dispersal to their winter quarters. After a build-up of returning birds in September, the Humber Wildfowl Refuge held 880 Shelducks on 11th October 1979, with 800 on 13th and 20th October and 584 on 1st November, after which date the numbers dwindled to leave about 150 during December. A gathering of 400 birds in full wing moult along the Humber shore in late July 1978 would include adults which had stayed to tend the broods of young. Very large numbers congregate in the Tees Estuary, but most birds are on the Durham side at Seal Sands, where there were 3,000 during January 1968.

Shelducks may occur at inland waters in any month, but most frequently and numerously during the late summer, when birds are crossing the country from west to east, and during mid winter, when they are moving to different feeding areas. Numbers are usually in single figures, but occasionally larger flocks are seen. A party of 32 flew west over Fairburn Ings on 3rd January 1976, and 38 were there on 4th September 1971. In 1972, 19 were at Chelker Reservoir on 23rd December and 18 flew northwest over Wintersett Reservoir on 31st December. Chelker attracted 26 birds on 1st January 1973, and there were 19 at Semerwater on the same date. Thirty-nine were at Whiteholme Reservoir on 27th July 1976, 23 at Wath Ings on 15th December 1976, and 25 flew west over Wintersett Reservoir on 9th December 1978. In 1979, an unprecedented party of 153 flew east over

Whiteholme Reservoir on 23rd July, while 20 were at Knotford Nook Gravel-pit on 13th December of that year. In 1980, Fairburn Ings had 26 on 26th June and 24 on 1st November, and there were 20 at Eccup Reservoir on 30th August. Any inland water in any part of the county may have Shelducks passing overhead or dropping in to rest, often for only brief periods before they move on. Watchers at reservoirs and flashes adjacent to the Aire Valley are the most likely to encounter such sights.

Shelducks are thus common in Yorkshire, especially along the Humber and Tees Estuaries, the former attracting large numbers, especially during the summer when birds engaged in their moult migration assemble there, and again in the autumn, when the birds return and gather before dispersing to their winter quarters. Indeed occurrences are frequent during this cross-country migration period when dispersing juveniles are also involved, and in the winter, when birds are wandering to new feeding grounds, many no doubt crossing to the west coast. As a breeding bird the Shelduck is confined mainly to the Upper Humber and its environs, but is increasing as a nester at inland locations in the southeastern part of the county and is spreading to areas much farther inland, such as Whiteholme Reservoir, Nosterfield Gravel-pit, Bolton-on-Swale Gravel-pit and near Settle.

Mandarin
Aix galericulata

This native of the Far East has been naturalised as a feral breeding bird in Britain for many years now, and in 1952 it was estimated that no fewer than 500 were flying free, mainly in the southeast. It is a very common species in wildfowl collections, and even in backyards, kept with chickens, it breeds successfully. Young birds, which are often reared under broody hens, are sometimes left unpinioned and escape. It is, in consequence, often impossible to determine whether a bird is of recent captive origin or a wandering feral individual which may have been hatched in the wild. Pinioned Mandarins were introduced into Swinton Park in 1954 and a pair nested in the following year, rearing one female duckling. The free-flying female nested in a hole in an old beech tree in 1956, and on 2nd July appeared on the lake with four ducklings. During the incubation period, the bird left its nesting hole shortly before the ornamental fowl were fed and joined them to feed, before returning to incubate. The hole was so deep in the tree that Ralph Chislett could not reach down into it.

A female was seen at High Royd on 26th December 1958 by Roy Crossley and friends. During the last few years, Mandarins have become more frequent, and in 1972 M. Limbert watched a drake at Chellow Dene on 30th January and J.E. Dale saw one at Bretton Park from 16th November to 31st December. A full-winged drake was reported by Dr John Lawton at York University Lake from 3rd May 1975 to the year end. D.E. Murray saw single drakes at Tophill Low Reservoir in April and at Weel from 19th to 22nd May 1976. A female was at the former locality on 19th April 1980.

A drake on the River Nidd near Pateley Bridge on 20th April 1975 was stated, by Gordon Follows, to be from a nearby private collection, but it was not pinioned and therefore a potential recruit to the feral ranks. An immature at Throxenby Mere, near Scarborough, from 19th July to 15th August 1978 was watched by M. Francis on several dates, and a drake was on Peasholm Park Lake, Scarborough, on 7th October. One flew into Harewood Park Lake on 5th November 1978. Two drakes, seen by Gordon Follows along a beck at Sleightholmedale, near

Kirkbymoorside, from 29th April to 7th May 1979, were still present on 17th February 1980, one remaining to 5th May. Lone drakes were at Harewood Park Lake on 24th January 1982 and at Fairburn Ings on 24th and 25th April 1982. A drake which was in eclipse plumage when first seen at Hay-a-Park Gravel-pit, Knaresborough, on 12th September 1982 remained until early 1983 and was seen by several people. A pair was at Cleasby Gravel-pit on 25th September 1982, and single birds occurred at nine waters in 1983.

Whether any of these birds are wanderers from the feral populations elsewhere in the country or hatched from feral stocks in Yorkshire is impossible to say. The preponderance of reported drakes is interesting and could mean that some females are going unnoticed on account of their duller plumage. That the Mandarin is now part of the Yorkshire scene as a feral wanderer or occasional breeder is in no doubt.

Wigeon
Anas penelope

The Wigeon was mentioned in connection with Yorkshire as long ago as the sixteenth century, when it figured in the 'Northumberland Household Book' which dated from 1512 at the Earl Percy's Castles of Wressill and Lekinfield; among the birds to be provided for 'My Lordes owne Mees' were 'Wegions', the price of which was '1d Ob [1½d.] the pece except my Lordes comaundment be otherwyze'. Nelson summarised its status as 'Winter visitant, common', and so it remains today with the addition of a small breeding population.

Breeding was a very rare event in Yorkshire during Nelson's time and he could cite only two localities. One was at Fen Bog, near Whitby, where 'it bred regularly' around 1881 and where a female was shot off 11 eggs and examined by a Mr J. Kitching. One of Nelson's correspondents, a Mr Thomas Raine, wrote, in a letter dated 25th February 1902, that on 1st May 1897 he saw a Wigeon fly from a patch of heather on Skipwith Common, and he described the nest with 12 eggs. Nelson thought the evidence doubtful and, in the absence of any further details, I would agree. In 1901, a Mr A. Wood informed Nelson that a pair bred at Malham Tarn and that he saw both old and young birds on the lake.

Chislett knew of only two other instances of breeding, at a 'small moorland tarn in the North Riding'. The first was in 1939 when a dead female Wigeon was found lying near a nest containing broken eggshells and down, which was that of a Wigeon. On 15th June 1940, at the same place, a female was flushed from long grass and a small duckling found; a second female was flushed a few yards from the first and two ducklings were found. The drakes were flying around the area and the incident was published in *British Birds*, August 1940, by C.S. Graham and S.P. Hewitt.

No further breeding records were forthcoming until 1954, when the Yorkshire Naturalists' Union Ornithological Report for that year stated that the species had bred in the northwest and in the centre of the county. The site referred to as the northwest was in fact Fish Lake, near Mickle Fell, where in 1953 K. Baldridge and J. Lumby saw a pair of Wigeons in June and, on 3rd of that month in 1954, Baldridge saw a female Wigeon and found a young duckling, which he handled. Breeding occurred again in 1955, when on 7th May a duck was flushed from six eggs which were later to be smashed by sheep. On 7th June 1956, the duck at this site was killed by a Peregrine.

Baldridge considers that the spread of breeding Wigeons which was to follow in this extreme northwestern spur of Yorkshire, above the old Roman road across Bowes Moor, originated at Fish Lake, which today is overgrown and marshy with little open water. When P.J. Stead became the YNU Ornithological Recorder for that part of the county in 1964, he spent much time in the area checking the breeding Wigeons. On 8th June 1965, he found three broods of six, four and three young on a small tarn surrounded by marshy ground about half-a-mile (0.8km) north of the old Bowes Moor Inn. Three ducks were flying around, croaking, as he watched. Wigeons probably nested at this site in 1958, and certainly did so in 1960. In 1966, there were three broods, again at the Bowes site, on 6th June, this time consisting of four, four and one young. A duck also had young at Fish Lake, and Stead found a new breeding site at Castle Lough, Lartington, where there were four broods of five, eight, three and two ducklings. The species had presumably been breeding at Castle Lough for some years previously, the likelihood of four successful broods being produced in the first year of colonisation being remote.

During the years 1967 to 1972, Stead continued to keep a close watch at the Bowes site and he took me to see it in 1968. In 1971 there were no fewer than 20 pairs there, which had produced at least 40 young. The most spectacular increase was in 1970, when the breeding pairs rose from nine (in 1969) to 18, which hatched 76 ducklings. The species is still breeding in this area, and in 1981 there were at least seven broods at three places: in Lunedale, in Baldersdale (Blackton Reservoir) and at the Bowes Moor site.

The site referred to in the YNU Report for 1954 as 'the centre of the county' was in fact Fairburn Ings, where J.K. Fenton saw a female with two young on 12th June. In 1955, E.S. Skinner located a duckling at Grimwith Reservoir, where a pair of adults had been present in May. On 7th July 1973, M.V. Bell found a pair with four ducklings at this site, and two pairs were present during May and June 1974 but no young were seen. In 1975, Miss Susie Brooks saw a pair and five ducklings. There was a female with four young present on 21st July 1976, and a brood of six young in 1978. Extensive alterations to this remote moorland reservoir began in 1976 and my good friend Terence Eggleshaw of Burley, who was responsible for some of the construction work, informed me that after 1978 there was much disturbance at the site and the water had to be drained while work was in progress, making it totally unsuitable for continued breeding by this sensitive species, although a pair nested again in 1983 when the water level was raised.

Odd individuals or pairs may linger well into the summer at some lowland waters, but, as yet, breeding has been proved at only one site. It is likely to occur only if the water is quiet enough to suit the species' special needs. The multi-use of lowland lakes and reservoirs, and the inevitable excessive disturbance, will prevent the Wigeon from attempting to breed away from the secluded moorland tarns and upland reservoirs which are its only Yorkshire breeding grounds.

In Nelson's time, there appear to have been more Wigeons than there are now, even allowing for exaggeration or misidentification of mixed flocks. He said that it was very frequently observed passing along the shore on the Cleveland coast to the northwest, on migration, and at times came within range of the fowlers stationed on the scarrs and sandhills, who took toll of their numbers. 'In some seasons, when favourable winds from the east or north-east prevail at the time of the full moon, immense flights are seen.' Nelson records that he had seen them passing incessantly from early morning until noon, in flocks numbering several hundred birds. Such was apparently the case in the first week of November 1878, on 1st October 1887, on 13th and 14th October 1894, and on 29th and 30th October 1901. He also recorded it as abundant in the Tees and Humber Estuaries in the winter of 1864/65. In January of that winter, Nelson was 'priveleged to examine' a punt gunner's game book showing that he had killed 23 'Whews' at one discharge of his big gun.

Chislett published records of 200 Wigeons off Bridlington on 27th September 1948 and a build-up at Spurn in that year from 17 on 28th August to 450 on 11th October. Many others had passed into the upper reaches of the Humber 'where large numbers congregate especially in severe weather when inland waters are frozen'. The largest number he could record was 700 birds, at Swillington Ings in February 1948.

During the last ten years or so, this species has been recorded in very large numbers in the southeastern part of the county, traditionally a stronghold for wintering Wigeons. Favourite places are the Humber Wildfowl Refuge and the flooded land along the Lower Derwent. The former attracts very large numbers, and in 1973 there were peak counts of 1,000 on 24th January, 2,600 on 21st October and 2,700 during December, with an isolated influx on 22nd December when 4,300 arrived. The refuge warden, Arthur Chapman, made careful counts of the waterfowl on this reserve and in 1978 he recorded spectacular numbers. An assembly numbering 4,800 on 7th January increased to 6,500 by 19th February. At the end

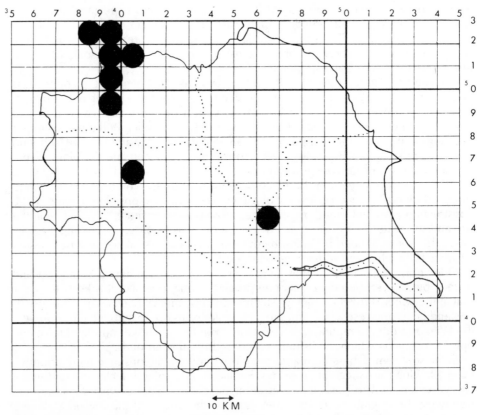

10 KM

Wigeon. A small breeding population persists on the moorland tarns and mosses in the extreme northwest; a few pairs also breed at Grimwith Reservoir and in the Lower Derwent Valley.

of the year, there were 5,000 on 10th December and 5,900 on 29th. There was an immense gathering of 8,000 birds on 4th February 1979. The flock gradually reduced as birds moved out, but 7,100 were still there on 8th February, 1,630 remaining during early March. Numbers in 1980 were also large and D.B. Cutts and the warden counted 7,800 on 13th January and 9,600 on 15th. At the year end, 3,200 had assembled by 1st November, with 4,400 on 16th November and 6,200 on 3rd December.

The Lower Derwent Valley has been attractive to the Wigeon for many years and during the late 1950s and early 1960s, when the area was regularly watched by H.O. Bunce, Miss M.R. Sanderson, A.F.G. Walker and others, up to 5,000 were seen almost annually during the winter months. In 1970, there were 3,000 on 1st February, 4,000 on 8th, 4,500 on 14th and 5,500 on 15th. Numbers in 1974 were also very high, and on 15th February M.V. Bell counted 5,000 birds, 2,000 of which remained during March, and that number was again present at the year end in December. Similar numbers were there in 1978, with peak counts of 2,000 in January, 4,000 in February, 2,800 in March and 2,000 in April. The peak numbers in 1982 were 6,500 in January, 4,400 in February and 3,898 in March. This locality must be one of the most attractive inland areas for Wigeons in the north of England, and certainly in Yorkshire. There is no finer sight than to watch flocks of Wigeons flying and wheeling overhead in a mêlée of movement on a bright, clear winter's day.

Some other inland feeding areas are traditional and smaller numbers have been regular visitors to Gouthwaite Reservoir, Stocks Reservoir, the flooded lands around Settle, Scaling Dam, Malham Tarn, and latterly at Bolton-on-Swale Gravel-pits where there have been flocks of up to 600 birds since 1976. Wigeons may appear almost anywhere inland, but away from the favourite feeding areas numbers are usually small or the visits of a transitory nature.

Waters in the southeastern part of the county attract the species during times of passage and in the winter, when severe weather sometimes forces the birds to move around. Such places as Tophill Low Reservoir often attract good numbers, and in recent years there have been flocks of 250 there on 9th February 1975, 440 on 24th January 1977 and 460 on 18th February 1977. The floodland at Lambwath, near Aldborough, is favourable for the Wigeon and W.F. Curtis counted 750 there on 3rd January 1977. D.I.M. Wallace saw 360 birds near the River Hull at Hempholme on 15th January 1977.

The major water for this grazing duck in this part of Yorkshire is undoubtedly Hornsea Mere, where numbers are often very large. During the early 1960s, when G.R. Bennett regularly counted the birds on the mere, he recorded 800 on 20th February 1960 and 900 on 18th February 1961.

During October 1963, there was a noticeable influx into the county: 650 were at the Humber Wildfowl Refuge on 8th, 1,030 at Hornsea Mere on 12th, and 290 at Spurn and 800 at Teesmouth on 26th. Hornsea Mere was being watched by W.F. Curtis in the late 1960s and 1970s and he saw 3,000 there between 12th and 19th February 1967. On 1st January 1970, 1,850 were seen as they flew in from the southeast, and 1,400 were seen coming in the next day. Between 500 and 900 have occurred here almost annually since then, between October and March.

Coastal passage occurs in every year and watchers on the Spurn Peninsula record southerly movement during the period late August to early November, which movement often coincides with the build-up of birds in the Upper Humber. Flocks are frequently only small, but occasionally some large numbers pass. On 19th October 1967 420 flew south, and 282 did likewise on 5th November, on which date 809 flew south at South Gare. In 1972, 648 flew south on 16th December and 533 on 31st, and 468 flew south on 1st November 1976.

In 1977, 17th September was a good day for sea-watching, with several species of seabirds and ducks in evidence. Watchers at four places — Hornsea, Filey, Burniston and Ravenscar — counted 158, 114, 365 and 194 Wigeons respectively flying north. The large number of 1,150 seen by S.M. Lister flying north off Hornsea during the day on 19th December 1976 has not been exceeded.

This highly migratory duck comes to Yorkshire in large numbers during the autumn from its breeding grounds farther north in Britain, Iceland and northern Europe. It departs in the spring, leaving a small breeding population in the northwest of the county. One shot near Selby on 14th February 1948 had been ringed in Iceland on 29th July 1947, and one shot at Sutton-on-Derwent in January 1974 had been ringed at Murmansk in the USSR on 17th July 1971.

The vernacular name for the species in Nelson's time and since, especially among wildfowlers, is the Whewer or Whew, so labelled because of its whistling call.

American Wigeon
Anas americana

Sir Ralph Payne-Gallway of Thirkelby Park, Thirsk, wrote in *The Field* (March 1895):

> 'On 26th February, Mr. R. Lee, taxidermist, of Thirsk, obtained in Leeds an adult female American Wigeon. It was hanging up for sale with several common Wigeon in the shop of Mr. Murray, gamedealer, who had just received it with other birds from the coast. I saw the bird when quite fresh, and it had pellets of shot in it with which it had been lately killed. It proved on dissection to be a female, though it has the green eyestripe and speckled neck and forehead of the male, but the crown is dark and there is a good deal of chestnut on the flanks and a little on the breast.'

Payne-Gallway acquired the bird for his collection.

Nelson, who recorded this occurrence in *The Birds of Yorkshire*, concluded by saying that the specimen, probably a young male, was exhibited at the Zoological Society's meeting on 2nd April 1895 and was figured in Lilford's work on *British Birds*, vol. 7, plate 42. It is indeed a young male and I have inspected the mounted specimen, which is now in the City of Leeds Museum.

Since that ancient record, there have been four other occurrences of this Nearctic species in Yorkshire. The first was a young drake which S.C. Madge and others watched at Fairburn Ings from 24th July to 12th August 1976. Later in the same year, on 23rd September, D.I.M. Wallace saw an immature bird on Whitton Sands in the Upper Humber. It is not impossible that both these records referred to the same individual. That after a gap of 81 years there should be two records within two months perhaps reflects the more efficient field techniques and expertise of today, compared with the time when one had to rely on the gunner's 'bag' for an interesting specimen.

In 1977, a female was seen at Fairburn Ings on 17th September, again by S.C. Madge, the RSPB warden.

The latest occurrence was in 1982, when a young male frequented Broomhill Flash in the south of the county and was watched by N.W. Addy, J. Hewitt and others during its stay, from 5th March to 7th April.

There are now over 130 records of this North American duck in the British Isles, most of them being during the last 25 years.

Gadwall
Anas strepera

In Denny's *Leeds Catalogue* of 1840, it is stated that one occurred at Swillington, near Leeds.

The species was not well recorded during Nelson's time, indeed it was rare, and he said that it was but a casual visitor in winter, and went on to list only 13 records involving 22 individuals. Most of these were single birds or pairs 'obtained' in various parts of the county, mainly in the southeast, but included a party of four females seen near York on 15th December 1880, one of which was killed, the incident being reported in *The Field* (15th January 1881). Three others, obtained by a punt shooter at Teesmouth in October 1896, were examined by Nelson at the premises of George Mussell, the taxidermist, of Middlesbrough. Between 1912 and 1952 when Chislett wrote *Yorkshire Birds*, Gadwalls were being reported with increasing frequency and records during the summer months were regular after 1940. A. Gilpin saw five birds at Swillington Ings on 16th August 1941, and G.R. Edwards reported a pair there from 20th June 1943 into August. H.O. Bunce watched six at Stone Creek on 16th September 1945, and a pair stayed at Hornsea Mere during the summer of 1946. By 1953 the species was also appearing regularly at Fairburn Ings, and three were seen at Stocks Reservoir in November that year.

The first recorded breeding occurred in 1954, when a brood of nine young was seen on 18th July at Bottomboat, near Wakefield, an excellent area which eventually disappeared under tipped slag. By 1955, records of Gadwall were becoming numerous and the species was being seen in every month of the year. In 1959, Chislett said that 'the increasing frequencies of Gadwall continue'. In that year, 22 were at Hornsea Mere on 1st February and, in the autumn, 11 were there on 19th September and 48 on 31st October and 8th November, which had increased to 56 by 25th December. In 1958, C. Winn saw 17 at Fairburn Ings on 30th August and others occurred at Wintersett Reservoir, Bottomboat, Swillington Ings, Mickletown Flash, Stanley Floods and Hornsea Mere, with single birds at three other waters.

A pair nested at Fairburn Ings in 1959 and the continuing increase prompted Chislett, in the Yorkshire Naturalists' Union Report for 1960, to say: 'The increasing frequencies of Gadwalls mentioned last year has again continued, making it impossible to include all the records sent in.'

G.R. Bennett reported 56 Gadwalls at Hornsea Mere on 3rd January 1960, 60 on 23rd January and 15 on 5th March. From that time, Gadwalls could be seen almost anywhere in the county at almost any season, often only single birds or small parties, but at the favoured waters — Hornsea Mere, Fairburn Ings and Swillington Ings — they were continually present in numbers which built up each autumn.

In 1962, it was reported that about 900 Gadwalls had been released by wildfowlers in the Lake District and some of the subsequent spread may have been due to these introductions.

During the mid 1960s, Hornsea Mere was attracting gatherings of up to 50 birds each autumn, and in 1970 there were 60 on 11th September, 80 during October with 120 on 28th, and up to 100 in November. There were more at the mere in 1972 than ever before or since. During June up to 30 were present, with a steady increase thereafter to 50 in August up to 26th, when 128 were counted, 150 on 10th September, 275 on 23rd September, 250 on 7th October and up to 120 during December. Since tht time numbers have remained relatively high, but have fluctuated annually. In 1980, the maximum numbers were 90 in early October, 160 on 14th October and 110 during November and December. The highest count in 1983 was 225 on 5th November. In 1967, some females present from August to November were wearing red wing tags which had been attached at Loch Leven, in Kinross-shire, giving some indication of the origin of our autumn visitors. A female ringed at Slimbridge on 29th September 1954 was shot near Wakefield on 20th November 1962.

Numbers at Fairburn Ings during the 1970s were smaller than at Hornsea Mere, but followed the same pattern of autumn build-up, which peaked at around 30 to 60 birds annually.

The open floodwaters along the Lower Derwent Valley have never attracted many Gadwalls, which prefer well-vegetated edges and secluded bays.

Breeding has occurred in Yorkshire in most years since 1965, and was suspected during the previous years. B.S. Pashby saw a brood of seven at Hornsea Mere in August 1965, and single pairs bred there in 1967, 1968, and 1971 when D.T. Ireland, the RSPB warden, reported three young. A pair had five ducklings on Scampston Lake on 4th June 1974 which were seen by H.O. Bunce and Dr J.H. Lawton. Single pairs nested at Fairburn Ings in 1974, 1975 and 1976, when there were broods of seven, seven and nine young respectively. A pair had ten ducklings at Wintersett Reservoir in 1977, a pair bred there again in 1978 and three pairs bred in 1979. Breeding also occurred at Mickletown Ings in 1978, 1979 and 1980, and at Newmillerdam in the last two of those years. The first breeding at Tophill Low Reservoir was recorded in 1979, with two pairs in 1980 and three in 1982. In 1980, a pair was successful at Fairburn Ings and a pair attempted to nest at Blacktoft Sands but failed. Two pairs nested at a small overgrown pond near Market Weighton in 1983.

In 1977, the South Yorkshire Wildfowlers Association introduced two pairs onto Newmillerdam, one of which hatched four young. Gadwalls are being reared in captivity by several wildfowl associations and some were released in the county in 1964, and no doubt subsequently.

There has quite clearly been a definite increase in the number of Gadwalls visiting Yorkshire since 1950, and the species can now be seen at any water along the coast during the non-breeding season, often for only short periods as it migrates through the area. At the main waters, outlined above, some birds stay to breed and this trend is increasing. The species is most numerous during the autumn, when birds from farther north visit us for the winter. That introduced birds, now living in a totally feral state, have contributed to the increase there is no doubt.

On 29th October 1982, 45 flew south at Spurn, an exceptional number for such coastal movement.

Teal
Anas crecca

This small duck was evidently popular for the pot as long ago as 1393, when it figured in the ordinances as to the price of victuals at York in the sixteenth year of Richard II, when the value of a Teal was 1d.

At the great banquet given at Cawood in 1466, in honour of the Archbishop of York, 4,000 Mallards and Teals were included in the list of provisions. At the marriage feast of Sir John Neville's daughter at Chevet, near Wakefield, in 1526, 30 dozen Mallards and Teals were priced at £3.11.8d. In 1560, the price of a Teal, fixed by law, was 2d, thus having doubled in 200 years!

It seems to have been very abundant on the Doncaster carrs, for in Hatfield's *Historical Notices of Doncaster* (1866) it is stated that 32 pairs of duck and Teal were killed at one shot by a fowler named Hill at Hatfield Levels in the winter of 1892/93. Between 1856 and 1864, 211 Teals were taken in the nets at Hornby Decoy. Nelson examined the diaries of an old punt gunner at Teesmouth, and the highest number of Teals killed in one day was 23 in September 1863.

This small dabbling duck breeds on most moorland tarns in the Pennines about the western part of the county, in the hills of the northeast, among the lowland carrlands and in some coastal areas. When R.J. Rhodes wrote *The Birds of the Doncaster District* in 1967, he considered that breeding Teals in that area had decreased since Chislett (1952) wrote that it 'breeds in fair numbers in the south of the county, on and about the Hatfield and Thorne Levels'. Rhodes was able to record only odd pairs with young during the five years prior to 1967, at Hatfield Moor, Almholme, Blaxton Gravel-pits, Potteric Carr and Sandbeck Park. In 1979, however, breeding was reported from eight lowland localities in this area, including 12 pairs on Hatfield Moors where there were 11 broods in 1980.

Locker Tarn, above Carperby in Wensleydale, is a favourite moorland breeding site and Teals with young were always in evidence during July when, during the 1960s, I visited the tarn regularly to ring the Black-headed Gull chicks.

A.F.G. Walker counted 12 broods totalling 49 ducklings at Gouthwaite Reservoir on 25th June 1973, and eight broods totalling 40 ducklings on 17th June 1974. In 1977, there were 66 young in 11 broods on 11th June, some of which would have been brought down onto the water from nests on the surrounding moorland.

In the Pennine areas of the southwest in vice-county 63, the broods of Teals were counted regularly during the early 1970s. In 1973, breeding was reported at seven sites, and in 1974 26 pairs were proved to breed at eight localities, with 22 pairs at 15 localities in 1975.

Nelson mentioned Skipwith Common, where breeding still occurs. The Lower Derwent Valley now has its breeding Teals, and in 1979 broods were seen at Aughton and Wheldrake Ings.

Each autumn, very large flocks of Teal gather on suitable sheets of water, their numbers augmented by birds from overseas. Individuals have been recovered in Yorkshire which have been ringed in places as far apart and distant as Russia, Iceland and Holland, and also from other parts of Britain, the most interesting being an adult ringed at Murmansk in the USSR on 6th August 1964 and shot at Thirsk in the following October. Conversely, Teals ringed as young in Yorkshire leave their natal ground in the autumn. Out of five young birds ringed by R.F. Dickens on Malham Moor on 29th June 1952, four had been recovered before the year end.

One was at Bewholme in the East Riding in August; one at Bootle, Cumberland, in October; one in County Cork in August; and one in County Antrim in November. There are many other such recoveries.

During the last 30 years, various artificial waters, principally gravel-pits and sewage-farms, have at certain periods during their development, stabilisation, and in many cases their eventual run-down been attractive to Teals. Swillington Ings was a good water during the 1950s, and on 9th November 1952 1,000 Teals were estimated to be present. R.F. Dickens counted 1,000 at Knostrop Sewage-farm on 22nd January 1956, and in more recent years Potteric Carr has held between 500 and 700 during the winter months. Any reservoir or flash with extensive vegetation along its margins and some exposed muddy shores will attract large numbers during the autumn and winter months. Gouthwaite Reservoir has long been a favourite feeding place for the species and concentrations of up to 500 birds can be found there during the autumn in most years. Fairburn Ings, with its large areas of open water and its acres of reedy margins, is excellent for Teal and attracts upwards of 500 birds every year, with 1,000 in November 1969 and 800 on 3rd January 1971 as maximum counts.

Hornsea Mere must rank as one of the most important waters for feeding Teals. Being close to the coast, it attracts many hundreds of migrating birds each autumn, many of which stay throughout the winter months. Peak counts up to 1970, after which time the Royal Society for the Protection of Birds installed a permanent warden, were 920 on 3rd January 1959, 1,700 on 21st January 1962 and 700 on 24th January 1970. In 1971, D.T. Ireland and W.F. Curtis counted 1,200 Teals on 10th January which had increased to 1,600 by 19th January, after which numbers fell to 750 by 2nd February and 430 by 13th February. The next Warden, R.G. Hawley, counted 1,400 on 26th October 1974.

The flooded land along the valley of the Lower Derwent attracts thousands of waterfowl, among them many Teals. During the 1960s, the ducks at this locality were regularly counted by H.O. Bunce, A.F.G. Walker, Miss M.R. Sanderson and others. Their records emphasised the importance of this unique habitat as a feeding area for waterfowl. On 22nd February 1959, Walker counted 1,500 of this species, and on 21st February 1960 Bunce counted 1,050. The annual peak count is usually 1,000 birds, but there have been higher numbers occasionally, as during early February 1962 when 3,000 Teals were present and during February and early March 1970 when 3,000 were again counted as birds assembled on their migration to the breeding grounds. Peak numbers in 1982 were 4,500 in January and 4,000 in February.

The reaches of the Upper Humber at Broomfleet, where the Humber Wildfowl Refuge is situated, attract more Teal than anywhere else in the county, especially during periods of peak migration. On 3rd September 1955, 1,600 were there, and on 6th 2,750 were at Whitton Sands. A count of Teals between Brough and Broomfleet on 24th September 1955 showed a total of 3,500, with 3,000 present on 3rd October. Many of these would eventually pass on to other parts of Yorkshire and elsewhere. These very large totals are exceptional, but in every year there are high counts of around 1,000 Teals in this region. Numbers were high in the autumn of 1980, and 1,400 had assembled on the refuge by 25th September. Counts on 11th and 23rd November gave totals of 1,330 and 1,750 respectively, and 1,750 were at Blacktoft Sands on 5th October. Migrant and wintering Teals are scattered all along the north shore of the Humber, with concentrations in the upper reaches as illustrated above.

Migration along the east coast is evident in every year. On 2nd April 1956, a passage of ducks moving eastwards at Spurn included 34 Teals. During the morning of 2nd November 1958, 154 flew south at Spurn Point, and in 1967 351 flew south over the sea on three days in late September. The highest daily number seen moving at Spurn was 779 which flew south on 19th November 1972, but up to 100 in a day is commonplace during September to November with 200 to 500 passing on some days.

Nelson said that 'though it is to be feared that, both as a resident and also as an immigrant, this species is decreasing in numbers, there can be no doubt it was extremely numerous in former times . . .'. It is certainly numerous today and it is not easy to be convinced of the reality inferred in such ancient statements. There would no doubt have been more birds about the relatively undisturbed carrlands than there are now, but overall it would be interesting to know how the present totals compare with those 'in former times' as spoken of by Nelson.

The North American race of the Teal, known colloquially as the Green-winged Teal *Anas crecca carolinensis*, occurs frequently in the British Isles. In *The Zoologist*, 1852, p. 3472, it is stated that a Mr John Evans received a dead example of this race which was killed at Scarborough in November 1851. Chislett listed one which K. Brown saw among a flock of 100 common Teals at Swillington Ings on 15th January 1950; the vertical white stripe on the side of the breast which distinguishes this race from our native bird was clearly seen (*British Birds*, 1950, p. 190). John Cudworth saw one at Wintersett Reservoir on 20th March 1951 which was later seen by P.E. Davis and G.R. Edwards (*The Naturalist*, 1951, p. 138). On 19th February 1960, at Eccup Reservoir, G.R. Naylor watched a drake among a party of 13 Teals. A drake appeared at Gouthwaite Reservoir on 8th March 1969 which I watched with A.F.G. Walker. What was presumably the same bird re-appeared on 14th May 1970 and stayed until 21st June. It came back each spring up to 1973 and usually stayed from February to April. A drake was seen by W.F. Curtis at Hornsea Mere on 8th March 1969. One was at Wheldrake Ings from 1st to 4th November 1981. Tophill Low Reservoir attracted a drake on 2nd May and on 2nd and 11th October 1982, in which year one was at Wheldrake Ings on 1st and 7th November with two birds on 8th. Four occurred in 1983, the first being at Long Preston on 8th and 9th March, followed by one at Blacktoft Sands on 23rd and 24th June, one at Fairburn Ings on 27th October and another at Wheldrake Ings on 17th December.

Only the distinctive drake Green-winged is separable from our Teal, but females will obviously occur with their partners.

Mallard
Anas platyrhynchos

The 'Wild Duck' is one of the most familiar wildfowl today, as it was many centuries ago. To give some indication of its past status, from both a numerical and a culinary point of view, I can do no better than quote Nelson's first paragraph on the Mallard from *The Birds of Yorkshire*.

'Historically, the connection of this bird with Yorkshire is of great antiquity, for we find that, in the ordinance issued by Royal Proclamation as to the price of food in the City of York in the year 1393, 16th Richard II, the Wild Duck was put down at 4d.; the same sum was fixed as the value of a "Mallerde" at Hull in 1560; at the great banquet at Cawood, in 1466, four thousand Mallards and Teals were provided; it figures in the Northumberland Household Book (1512), the price being placed at 2d.; and again at the marriage feast of Sir John Neville's daughter at Chevet, near Wakefield in 1526, when thirty dozen Mallards and

Teals were priced at £3.11.8d.; while of its former abundance on the Carrs of Doncaster we find evidence in Hatfield's *Historical Notices of Doncaster*, where we are informed that, in the winter of 1692/93, no fewer than thirty-two pairs of Duck and Teal were killed on Hatfield Levels, in a single shot, by a fowler named Hill.'

The largest migration known for many years at the time of Nelson (1907) occurred on 30th October 1900, during an easterly gale. In the winter of 1903/04 Mallards were exceptionally numerous about Christmas, as, owing to the disastrous effects of the wet autumn, the corn and bean crops were scattered on the ground, and great numbers of duck resorted to the stubbles to feed, where they supplied excellent sport for the flight shooters.

It is very difficult to believe two incidents quoted in *The Birds of Yorkshire*. The first concerns a flock of Mallards which was resting on the water near the shore at Redcar when a heavy wave fell among them, stunning several and washing them ashore, where they were caught in a dazed condition next morning. The second event happened about 1850, when, so an old fisherman told Nelson, nearly 100 ducks were similarly captured after an incident presumed to be of the same nature. Some exaggeration and misinterpretation of other natural phenomena are often the reasons for such unlikely tales.

In recent times, the Mallard is a common bird on any water in almost every corner of the county, especially in autumn when immigrants swell the ranks. Some places are favoured more than others; the reservoirs at Leighton and Eccup, subsidence flashes at Swillington and Fairburn (the former now becoming less suitable), and Hornsea Mere and the floodwaters along the Lower Derwent Valley are high on the list of preferred waters. The Humber Wildfowl Refuge also attracts very large numbers. Populations at any one of these places and in the estuaries of the Tees and Humber can be as high as 4,000 or more during the non-breeding season.

Larger numbers than usual occurred in 1965, and at the end of that year 5,000 were on the Humber Refuge in early December; 4,000 were on Hornsea Mere, 1,200 were on the Lower Derwent and 2,350 were on Leighton Reservoir, all on 12th December; with up to 2,000 at Spurn on 16th, 1,340 at Eccup Reservoir on 25th and 1,000 at Fairburn on 28th. These large numbers remained into 1966, and Fairburn Ings held 4,650 on 2nd January, 4,000 on 16th January and 2,200 on 26th February, while 5,000 were on the Humber Refuge in January with up to 3,000 there in February. This large influx was reflected at most other waters throughout the county. Evidence of the origins of these autumn immigrants has been provided by ringing recoveries, which show them to come from Scandinavia and western Europe. A juvenile ringed at Sevilla, Spain, on 15th June 1964, and shot at Womersley, near Doncaster, on 29th January 1968, is a most interesting recovery.

Numbers begin to disperse during February as birds depart to their breeding grounds, leaving the Yorkshire Mallards to scatter over the county and take summer residence in habitats as varied as the edges of our larger reservoirs to damp hollows among agriculture. The females will choose to lay their eggs in a wide variety of places, the most usual being on the ground near water and concealed among vegetation, but often they will lay in old tree stumps where these have broken off and a flat platform is available. In 1941, E.W. Taylor reported a duck on eggs in an old crow's nest, 30 feet (9m) up a tree in Shire Oaks Wood, Tadcaster, and in 1955 one was similarly sited in an oak tree at Leighton Reservoir.

Public park ducks can be either pure resident Mallards that have become tame and confiding, or a mixture of farmyard stock showing patches of white, especially about the head. These 'man-made' variants are many and varied, and range from pure white to pure black.

146

Nelson mentioned two cases of hybridisation with Pintail, an example of which from Moreby, near York, was exhibited at a meeting of the York Naturalists' Club on 5th December 1849. W.H. St. Quintin shot another from a flock of wild Mallards, which was reported in *The Field* on 17th November 1900. The late E.W. Taylor gave me the skin of a large Mallard-type drake which had been shot in the company of Mallards at Ryedale, Helmsley, in 1968 and preserved by Adam Gordon. It proved on examination to be the result of a cross between a Muscovy and a Mallard, but whether the latter was of pure wild origin is doubtful.

Nelson's assessment of the Mallard's status — 'Resident, local, abundant. Immense flights of migrants arrive in autumn, and become distributed over the county.' — needs little, if any, amendment today.

Black Duck
Anas rubripes

On the afternoon of 20th December 1978, S.C. Madge and Miss P. S. Allen noticed a very dark duck standing on the ice at Fairburn Ings with about 200 other ducks, mainly Mallards. They watched it for an hour at ranges down to 120 yards (110m) and took detailed notes of its plumage. Aberrant Mallards are numerous and this possibility was considered, but the plumage conformed exactly to that of the American Black Duck. The record was accepted as the seventh for Great Britain and Ireland, and full details were published in *The Naturalist*, 1980, p. 154. It was the first occurrence in northern Britain, and the first inland record of this Nearctic counterpart of the Mallard which breeds commonly in eastern North America and migrates down the Atlantic seaboard to spend the winter as far south as the Gulf of Mexico. That others have come to Britain in the past and gone unnoticed or been overlooked as variant Mallards is likely. For instance, on 25th December 1960, an almost black female was seen on Scaling Dam and reported under the commoner species.

There are only 13 records for Great Britain, mostly during the last 20 years. Some of these have taken up residence in the south, and hybridisation with Mallard is recorded.

Pintail
Anas acuta

John Cordeaux, in his *Birds of the Humber District* (1872), stated that 'this beautiful and elegant species is not uncommon in the Humber', and went on to report the Ashby Decoy record book which showed a total of 278 Pintails taken in 35 years, 54 of which were in the winter of 1834/35 with a very large bag of 74 birds in the winter of 1839/40.

Nelson wrote:

'Half a century ago, the Pintail was a numerous species in the Tees where, as Geo. Mussell tells me, it was greatly sought after by the professional gunners, who would not trouble with other fowl if they could get the pintail, and, as it was most plentiful in May, and no restrictions were at that time placed upon shooting, great numbers of this delicious duck were procured and brought into market.'

He went on to say that 'it is now, however, by no means abundant, occurring as a visitant, sparingly on the coast from October onwards to spring'.

It would appear to be more numerous now than in Nelson's time, and has certainly become more numerous since the 1950s. When H.O. Bunce and A.F.G. Walker began watching the floodwaters along the Lower Derwent Valley from the mid 1950s, Pintails were proved to be occurring there in good numbers. A count of 36 birds on 24th March 1957 was considered normal at that time but, in 1958, the Annual Report of the Yorkshire Naturalists' Union stated that the Lower Derwent floods showed unusual numbers: from 44 on 22nd February to 59 on 23rd April, 300 having been seen there on 20th April, the largest number ever recorded inland in the county at the time.

In contrast, there were very few in 1959, but a pattern of continuing frequency developed in the 1960s. On 25th March 1963, 100 birds were counted, and in every year to the present time between 50 and 100 Pintails have spent the winter months there. At no other inland locality is the species so regular or numerous. Hornsea Mere is the only other fresh water to attract large numbers, with 125 in November 1978 being the highest count.

Pintails gather while on migration, along with other species of waterfowl, in the Upper Humber; Arthur Chapman counted 154 at the Wildfowl Refuge on 21st October 1973 and 100 were gathered there in October 1974. On 8th December 1974, B.S. Pashby counted 400 birds on Cherry Cobb Sands, a quite exceptional number. On 8th February 1976 and on 7th January 1978, 100 birds were seen there.

Along the north shore of the Humber, from Spurn to Goole, 300 Pintails were counted on 18th December 1977, most of which were in the area of Stone Creek. This duck is regularly seen passing westwards up the Humber in autumn, and in 1980 there were counts of 67 on 8th September, 53 on 15th, 75 on 17th, 80 on 23rd, 61 on 28th, and 125 on 4th October. Some of these birds would undoubtedly pass through Fairburn Ings and other waters along the Aire Valley on the journey to their winter quarters.

Smaller numbers of Pintails can be seen anywhere in the county from late summer through to the spring, and flocks can be seen flying along the coast at times of passage. A bird shot at Sunk Island in the Humber on 28th November 1966 had been ringed on Mahee Island, County Down, on 4th October 1964.

The species has nested in Yorkshire, but rarely. Chislett recorded breeding in 1932 and 1938, and possibly in other years. The site was on Skipwith Common, where, in the former year, seven young were reared and reported by both the keeper, a Mr J. Morris, and S.H. Smith, who wrote up the details in *The Naturalist*, 1934, p. 20. The same two gentlemen saw a duck with young on 2nd July 1938. H.F. Witherby asked Chislett to investigate the claims, and in 1938 he visited the locality and spoke to Morris, questioning him closely on the events. Morris was quite confident of the claim and 'could not be shaken'. The duck and brood kept among the vegetation on the far side of the water while Chislett was there.

There were no further reports of breeding until 1962, when a pair nested near Driffield. In 1966, a duck showed marked attachment to Pulfin Bog on 22nd and 28th May and was thought to have bred.

The old local name of Sea Pheasant is most fitting and doubtless applied to the bird's plumage, but it would appear from its popularity as a table bird that the name could equally apply to its culinary qualifications.

Garganey
Anas querquedula

The 'Summer Teal', a name used by Willughby in 1676, has become a more familiar bird to present-day watchers than it was to Nelson (1907), who said of it '... a bird of passage in spring and autumn, of rather rare occurrence ... has been known to breed in 1882'. In that year, J. Swailes of Beverley discovered a nest containing eight eggs from which the duck rose a few feet off. Nelson considered breeding to have taken place in several years in that general area of the East Riding as 'young had regularly been procured there in early autumn and adults in full plumage had been shot on the river close by for a period extending over ten years'. W.H. St Quintin recorded a nest at Scampston in May 1908, from which eight eggs were taken and four drakes and four ducks reared from them. Details were published in *The Naturalist*, 1909, p. 38.

The first record of breeding in the West Riding came in 1926 when, on 5th June, H.B. Booth found a duck with six ducklings aged about ten days on a moorland pool near Clapham. He published the incident in *The Naturalist* (1927, p. 17). G.H. Ainsworth watched a duck and two young on Burton Constable Lake in June 1947.

During the late 1940s, Garganeys were present on a few waters in the West Riding, notably Swillington Ings and Fairburn Ings, throughout the summer months and, although some breeding undoubtedly occurred, proof was frustratingly lacking except for an incident in 1947, when A.G. Parsons relieved a boy of 17 duck eggs at Fairburn Ings, six of which conformed to this species. Unfortunately, they did not hatch when placed in an incubator. Garganeys continued to spend the summer at these waters throughout the 1950s and 1960s, but proof of successful breeding was very difficult to obtain. Two pairs were, however, proved in 1952, in which year Chislett also found a nest near Easington containing nine eggs, a tenth being subsequently laid and successfully-hatched eggshells seen later.

At Fairburn Ings during the two decades, Garganeys arrived every spring; two on 2nd April 1960, increasing to six by 15th and nine birds present on 17th July, with the last of the year being seen on 2nd October, was typical of the events during that period. In 1965, the maximum number seen was 12 on 28th July, while ten were seen on 7th August in the following year. C. Winn saw two family parties on 28th July 1957.

In the south of the county, in the valleys of the Don and the Dearne, the species was behaving similarly at this time and, in 1955, up to 12 were in the latter valley after the breeding season. At the time of writing, Garganeys are still frequenting these areas, although in smaller numbers, and proof of breeding is still rare. Two pairs were successful at Low Ellers Carr in 1970, and R.J. Rhodes recorded a pair rearing five young near Doncaster in 1974.

Away from the general areas mentioned above, breeding has been infrequent and during the last 28 years has been proved at only three places. A pair reared five young near Settle in 1968 and was monitored by B. Shorrock. A duck and three young were seen at Hornsea Mere on 3rd July 1969. A duck with three young was seen by T.M. Clegg at Wheldrake Ings on 23rd August 1978.

That Garganeys breed more often than is proved is, I think, unquestionable, but it is still a fairly rare event. Chislett said that 'it is unfortunate that the species should visit most frequently an area that is so much over-run by egg hunting boys, in which this and other interesting species would probably breed regularly'. He referred of course to Fairburn Ings, but, in the absence of egg collecting and disturbance by youths under the watchful eyes of the RSPB wardens during the past few years, the Garganey has not fared any better.

This migrant species, which spends the winter months in Africa, south of the Sahara, returns to Yorkshire at the end of March and early April. Three drakes and a duck seen at Thornton Marishes on 14th March 1948 by R.M. Garnett were early, as also were two at Spurn Point on 15th March 1967, a pair at Tophill Low Reservoir on 14th March 1977 and one at Almholme on 5th March 1978. Some passage birds linger on into May, and occasionally later, before departing for breeding grounds farther north. In the autumn, most have departed by mid September but a few stay into early October. One was on a small pond at Flamborough from 23rd September to 14th October 1979. G.R. Bennett saw one at Hornsea Mere on 4th October 1969, and W.F. Curtis saw three there on 1st October 1970. In 1975, a duck stayed at the mere from 20th October to 5th November. The largest party ever recorded in the county was seen by S.C. and W. Norman on 25th August 1971, when 23 were on Coatham Marsh.

During times of passage, odd birds or pairs may turn up, sometimes for very brief periods, on any water in any part of Yorkshire, whether it be a large reservoir or a spring 'flash' in a flooded field. There has been little change in status this century and it can be summarised as a passage migrant and a very scarce and local breeder.

Blue-winged Teal
Anas discors

This North American duck entered the Yorkshire list of birds in 1967, and there have been records in six other years since then.

The first was seen by C.F. Turner at Wheldrake Ings on the Lower Derwent on 26th April 1967. He reported the occurrence to members of the York Ornithological Club and many people were able to see this exciting species during the next few days. It was last seen on 3rd May. The bird was very wary, and took wing readily at the least disturbance when R. Evison and I watched it on the evening of 28th April.

In 1971, a drake was watched and described in detail by J. Lunn at Wintersett Reservoir on 8th May, and what was probably the same bird was at Fairburn Ings on 15th May. Very many birdwatchers were able to add this species to their lists during its stay until 13th June. Among the first to see it were C. Winn, Dr J.D. Pickup and P.T. Treloar.

In the following year, on 1st April, a drake appeared again at Fairburn Ings. It was last seen on 2nd July, and even more surprising was the appearance of what was presumed to be the same bird on 16th February 1973. It stayed throughout the summer and was last recorded during August.

On 10th August 1974, at Hornsea Mere, R.G. Hawley saw a duck which he later watched with H.O. Bunce and D.I.M. Wallace and which was identified as a drake Blue-winged Teal in eclipse plumage. It fed close to the observation hide on the north bank and was sketched and photographed during its 16-day stay. Later in the same year, a female was seen at Fairburn Ings by C. Winn, and a drake was seen there on 12th September by M. Wells.

In 1980, one was at Blacktoft Sands from 27th to 29th September, and R.G.

Hawley saw a female at Hornsea Mere on 16th November. A drake frequented Blacktoft Sands from 23rd September to 19th October 1982.

There are now about 120 records of this Nearctic species in the British Isles. The chance of some being escaped birds from private waterfowl collections is fairly high, but some are undoubtedly vagrants from over the Atlantic, as evidenced by one which was shot in Suffolk on 9th October 1971 which had been ringed in New Brunswick, Canada, on 7th June that year.

Having crossed the Atlantic, for whatever reason, it is likely that the spring and autumn migrations are still performed and this no doubt accounts for birds turning up at the same waters in the springs of successive years. When I was in Majorca with R. Harrison in 1969, we watched a pair of Blue-winged Teals on the Albufera Marsh on 3rd May. They stayed for at least three days and could well have been returning north to Britain, having wintered in Africa.

Shoveler
Anas clypeata

As a Yorkshire bird, the Shoveler would appear to be far more common now than in Nelson's time, especially during the autumn, even allowing for the more efficient coverage today. No large numbers were quoted by Nelson and he said that it was best known as a more or less rare visitor on the spring and autumn migrations and also in winter . . .'.

Today it is common on most suitable waters in the spring and autumn, and at some in the winter, when it may occur in large numbers. Favourite waters are Fairburn Ings, Hornsea Mere and the floodwaters along the Lower Derwent Valley, especially since the 1970s at the latter. Swillington Ings was a favourite water from the 1940s, and there were maximum counts of 50 birds there in November 1941 and 60 on 5th December 1943. In 1957, K. Dawson counted 100 there on 22nd August and again on 26th October and 9th November. Nearby Fairburn Ings has attracted large numbers during the last 30 years. On 5th August 1957 W.C. Wakefield counted 180, and over 100 birds were present in most autumns into the 1960s, when the annual numbers started to increase. A total of 190 Shovelers on 26th September 1964 was eclipsed in the following year, when 308 were seen on 16th October. There were counts of 350 on 1st October 1967 and 420 on 28th August 1972. Hornsea Mere regularly held 100-150 Shovelers during the 1950s and 1960s and produced the county's largest ever assembly of 460 birds in November 1969.

The lake at Ripley Castle was regularly watched by A.F.G. Walker during the late 1940s, and flocks of 35 on 6th November 1948 and 20 on 22nd October 1949 were good numbers for the area at that time. Malham Tarn had 56 birds on 4th September 1972, most of which stayed to the year end.

In spring, the sight of a pair of Shovelers on any small pool and a build-up of passing birds at larger waters anywhere in the county is normal. Large flocks during the autumn, when immigrants join the ranks at the favourite waters, are now a familiar sight.

In Hewitson's *Eggs of British Birds* (1856, vol. ii, p. 400), Hornsea Mere is given as a breeding resort, and such it is today. The Shoveler breeds regularly and in good numbers, principally in the southeastern half of the county. Several pairs nested along the River Derwent in 1966, three pairs at Beverley Sewage-farm in 1969, and five pairs at Tophill Low Reservoir in 1980. The carrlands around

Doncaster are favoured haunts, while breeding has also occurred regularly at Fairburn Ings in the last few decades, and did so at Swillington Ings in that area's hey-day during the 1940s and 1950s. A few pairs breed on the moorland tarns and on 26th June 1965, while ringing young Black-headed Gulls at Locker Tarn in Wensleydale, I picked up and ringed a solitary young Shoveler which was later shot on the Somme in France on 21st March 1966.

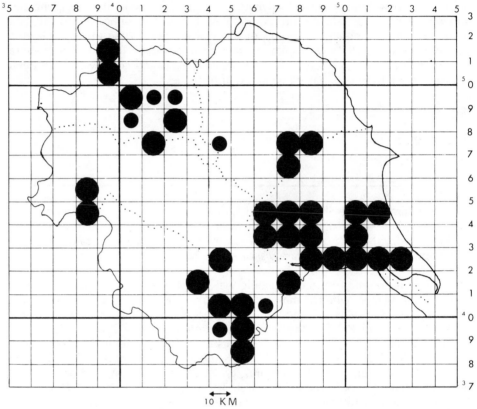

Shoveler. Most numerous in the lowland carrlands of the southeast and along the Humber Estuary and the Lower Derwent Valley; some isolated breeding stations exist on tarns in the high ground of the northern Pennines.

Red-crested Pochard
Netta rufina

Nelson recorded a male in good plumage, shot off a small pond on Coatham Marsh on 20th January 1900. He saw the corpse just after it was procured and bought it from the shooter. The mounted specimen is now in the Dorman Museum, Middlesbrough. No more were recorded in the county up to the publication of Chislett's *Yorkshire Birds* in 1952, but, since 1954, the species has occurred in almost every year with increasing frequency. Females have preponderated and, of the 60 or so records which are now to hand, only about 20 have involved males.

A female seen on 17th March 1954 at Swillington Ings by K. Dawson was placed in square brackets by Chislett in the county Annual Report for that year, with the presumed excuse of its having escaped from captivity as he goes on to say that 'the species has been introduced to ornamental waters in Central Yorkshire recently'.

In 1957, however, several occurred and Chislett ended his paragraph on the species in the Annual Report with 'this species is kept on some ornamental waters but it is unlikely the above occurrences are all escapes; it may well be extending its range westwards'. The records to which he referred in that year included 'several' ducks and 'several' drakes which J.E.S. Walker saw at Swillington Ings on 27th June. It is a pity that the actual numbers were not determined. 'Several' is naive and most unsatisfactory for a species which at that time was most unusual. A.H.B. Lee saw a duck at the same site on 29th June, and one was there on 17th July. A duck was also seen at Fairburn Ings on 21st July, and again from 11th to 14th August, by P.J. Stead and W.C. Wakefield among others. D.R. Wilson saw three ducks on Redmires Dam, near Sheffield, on 10th November in the same year. Whether these birds were escapes from captivity or not, they heralded the Red-crested Pochard's almost annual appearance in Yorkshire.

Hornsea Mere had two birds on 26th September 1959 and three ducks and a drake from 27th September to 18th October, two remaining into December. In that year, there was a duck at Finningley on 3rd May.

With the exception of 1964, 1969, 1973 and 1981, the species has occurred in every year since then up to 1984. Red-crested Pochards are usually seen from August through to February, but there have been records in every month except March and, as stated above, females are the most usual.

Occurrences have been more frequent since 1974, in which year there were records from no fewer than eight waters involving up to six drakes and six ducks. Hornsea Mere has held birds for long periods and a pair was present, though not always seen together, from August 1974 into January 1975 and again from July to November 1976, as well as on several dates during 1977 to 1979. The same individuals were no doubt involved. Other places to have attracted the species have included, in chronological order, Barnsley, Nostell Dam, Walton Hall Lake, Eccup Reservoir, Aughton Ings, Easington Lagoons, Low Ellers Carr, Thrybergh Reservoir, Gouthwaite Reservoir, Newmillerdam, Malham Tarn, Staveley Lagoon, Harewood Lake, Tophill Low Reservoir, Seamer Road Mere at Scarborough, Throxenby Mere, Potteric Carr and Bolton-on-Swale Gravel-pits. This random scatter suggests much local movement of the same birds and some, if not most, must have originated from captivity. The species is certainly plentiful in collections and breeds readily, the eggs often being hatched under broody hens or in incubators and some resulting young left unpinioned.

Some genuine immigrants may have come over to Britain from the Continent, and Hornsea Mere would be a most suitable place for such birds to make their first stop. That a few have arrived in this way is undeniable. That the species is now to be seen regularly, mainly singly or in pairs, at almost any time of the year and at any water, is an established fact, whatever their origin. If most are from captive stock or direct escapes, feral breeding will eventually take place.

Pochard
Aythya ferina

There has been a marked change in the Pochard's status during the last 30 years, and it is, without doubt, now far more numerous during the winter months than formerly. Nelson said of it: 'Resident; extremely local: breeds at several places. Also winter visitant, not very abundant.' Chislett, in 1952, agreed with that assessment, but added that it was perhaps an understatement and that 'extremely local' did not apply outside the breeding season,

In *Yorkshire Birds*, Chislett dwelt mainly on the breeding situation and was able to cite only a handful of sizeable non-breeding flocks. Swillington Ings seems to have been the most favoured water during the 1940s, with up to 100 birds during November 1941, 150 on 5th December 1943, 250 on 29th February 1948 and 97 on 11th December 1949. Fairburn Ings had 50 Pochards on 4th April 1948, and Coniston Cold Lake was worthy of mention with, in 1944, 29 birds on 6th March, 62 on 5th September and 38 on 20th December.

An exceptional increase in reported numbers in 1950 was perhaps due in part to more efficient coverage, but assemblies of 220 birds at Wintersett Reservoir on 4th March and 700 on 19th March were unprecedented at the time and such numbers could hardly have gone unnoticed before. In the same year, P.F. Holmes counted 100 at Malham Tarn in early January, 72 were at Blackmoorfoot Reservoir on 7th January, Swillington Ings held 160 on 5th February, and 75 were at Lindley Reservoir on 26th December.

During the following decade, Pochards occurred on their favourite waters at Hornsea Mere and the Fairburn/Swillington complex in numbers of up to 100 to 300 birds, with a large count of 850 at Hornsea Mere on 19th October 1957. In 1960, Hornsea attracted assemblies of up to 500 during February to March and up to 700 in late November and early December. Fairburn had up to 200 during these periods, and 138 were counted by A. Archer at Worsborough Reservoir on 13th March.

Even more Pochards were recorded in 1961, with maximum counts by G.R. Bennett at Hornsea Mere of 950 on 4th November, the flock increasing to 1,390 by 11th November. Worsborough Reservoir continued to attract large numbers, and 160 were seen by A. Archer and C. Bower on 2nd February and 183 on 2nd December. Southfield Reservoir, too, was pulling in birds, with 270 on 23rd November. At Welton Water in the Upper Humber, parties of 150 on 21st November and 170 on 3rd December were stated by B.S. Pashby to be very large for the area, and 200 were there on 25th January 1962. Hornsea Mere had large numbers at this time, when 713 were counted on 21st January 1962 and 870 in November.

Large flocks of Pochards during the non-breeding season were by now commonplace, and Hornsea Mere emerged as the stronghold for the species and provided the county's largest ever total of 2,000 birds on 21st November 1965, after another high count of 1,830 on the same November day in the previous year. Between 500 and 1,000 birds have been on the mere in most winters to the present time.

At Bretton Park Lake in November 1962, a count of 126 birds was stated by R.L. Brook to be unprecedented. The floodwaters along the Lower Derwent Valley were emerging as a popular haunt for the Pochard during the 1960s and 180 were there on 2nd April 1963, after which similar numbers appeared annually with an increase during the 1970s. The year 1970 was a typical one, when 270 birds were counted on 18th January and 1,100 on 1st February, reducing to 350 by 8th March, 200 by 15th March and with none seen at all on 22nd when H.O. Bunce checked the whole area. Numbers at the year end peaked at 800 on 22nd December, after a gradual build-up from October. The area is still popular, and in 1980 D.I.M. Wallace counted 1,300 between Aughton and Bubwith on 10th February, 3,115 along a larger stretch on 17th and 2,240 between Ellerton and Bubwith on 20th.

The reservoir at Tophill Low attracted 300 Pochards on 13th December 1970 and has figured annually since.

At the time of writing, Pochards can be seen on any water which is suitably deep and open enough for this most typical of diving ducks, in any part of Yorkshire including the estuaries of the Tees and Humber. Flocks start assembling during the late summer, increase during the autumn as immigrants arrive for the winter, and disperse in the spring when numbers decrease, often very rapidly, as birds leave for their breeding grounds elsewhere in Britain and eastwards into Europe. Small parties may be seen passing along the coast at times of migration. A female ringed in Finland on 2nd May 1965 was shot near Leeds on 6th December 1966.

Breeding during Chislett's time was sporadic and very local. Odd pairs nested at widely separated localities, such as Malham Tarn in 1906 (*The Naturalist*, 1907, p. 157), Throxenby Mere, near Scarborough, in 1936 and on Leyburn Moor also in 1936. Skipwith Common was reported in *Yorkshire Birds* to have 'usually held a few breeding pairs for many years', and breeding occurred at Rise Park Lake in

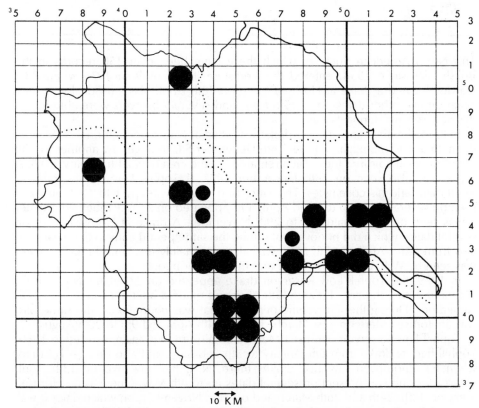

Pochard. A sporadic breeder on large and well-vegetated sheets of water, where it is nowhere common.

1950. Hornsea Mere has long been known as an established breeding haunt and remains so today. Fairburn and Swillington Ings, and latterly Mickletown Flash, are now established breeding areas and Tophill Low Reservoir has had a few breeding pairs in recent years.

In 1975, there were eight broods totalling 49 ducklings at Fairburn Ings, and a total of 14 pairs bred at Mickletown Flash, Newmillerdam, Potteric Carr and Denaby Ings, the latter having nine of these pairs. In 1977, breeding was reported from Hornsea Mere (two broods), Fairburn Ings (14 broods), Mickletown Flash (three broods) and in the Lower Derwent Valley (no details). There was proved breeding for 28 pairs in 1978, most of these being in the western half of the county. Brian Shorrock reported a pair breeding at Hellifield, near Settle, when a duck had seven young in July 1978, this being only the second breeding record for the area, the first having been in 1906 at Malham Tarn. In 1979, breeding occurred at Tophill Low Reservoir, Hornsea Mere and on the Lower Derwent, and 28 pairs produced 107 young in the central part of the county, nine of these broods, totalling 44 young, being at Fairburn Ings. In 1980, 32 pairs were proved breeding, 22 of which hatched 87 ducklings, and again most of these were in the south-central part.

Nelson's practice of listing the local names for various species included the following for the Pochard: Dunbird, Red Head and Poker as being commonly used, and, along the River Hull, Pokker, Dunpocker and Bighead.

Ring-necked Duck
Aythya collaris

This North American duck, of which there have been over 150 records in the British Isles since 1958, entered the Yorkshire list of birds in 1976 when R.G. Hawley located a drake at Hornsea Mere on 28th April. This individual was seen again on five other dates up to 15th May, and several observers were able to see this new species during its stay.

In the following year, another drake was seen at Newmillerdam on 31st May by P. Smith and G.J. Speight, and on 18th December S.C. Madge saw another (or the same) drake at Fairburn Ings which remained in the area until 24th January 1978. A drake was also seen on 18th December 1977 at Tophill Low Reservoir by K. Rotherham and his colleagues. This latter bird was still present into 1978 and was seen on several dates up to 22nd April; it re-appeared on 21st October, whereafter it was seen on many dates up to 29th November. A drake at Hornsea Mere on several dates (which did not overlap) during the same period early in that year, and also from 22nd April to 15th May, was almost certainly the same bird. The latter was seen by W.F. Curtis, S.M. Lister and many other people.

In 1979, the Tophill Low Reservoir drake appeared on 27th January, again on 18th and 25th February, 4th and 15th April and made a brief appearance on 17th November. During the intervening periods, what was undoubtedly the same bird was at Hornsea Mere on 31st March, 19th to 24th April and 9th to 20th August.

Tophill Low Reservoir, Hornsea Mere and Fairburn Ings again featured in 1980. Tophill had its drake from 6th January to 5th February, and also on 21st February when F.J. Thompson saw two drakes there. N.A. Bell saw two on 13th April, whereafter one was present on several dates up to 4th May. One was on Hornsea Mere on 18th, 24th and 26th March and on 16th November, on which dates it was presumed to have commuted from Tophill Low Reservoir. G.R. Welch and others saw one at Fairburn Ings from 14th April to 2nd May in the same year.

What were almost certainly the same drakes were again present at Tophill Low Reservoir in 1981, 1982 and 1983. One was there from 2nd January to 4th May 1981, with two drakes present from 6th to 11th January; a single drake re-appeared on 8th November, stayed until 3rd April 1982, and returned on 7th November. A single drake at Hornsea Mere from 24th to 26th March and again on 11th November 1981 was presumed to be one of these same two birds, one of which returned to Tophill Low on 7th November 1982 and stayed to at least the end of the year. N.A. Bell, P. Dove, K. Rotherham, B. Fendley and A. Lowe have supplied notes and details of all the above sightings, and the birds have been watched by very many other people. In 1983 a drake returned to Hornsea Mere, where it stayed from 26th February to 18th June.

In 1981, a drake was also seen at Wheldrake Ings by T. Barker, B.G. Pepper and D.R. Waudby from 14th to 20th April and again on 25th, and another appeared on 7th May 1983. In addition to the Tophill Low Reservoir records in 1982, mentioned above, there were single drakes at Pebley Pond, near Harthill, seen by D. Hursthouse on 9th February; and near Brandesburton, seen by W.F. Curtis on 10th February. An adult drake was seen at Potteric Carr by R.J. Scott on 14th April 1984.

Although some Ring-necked Ducks are kept in captivity, it is not an easy bird to breed, and it is unlikely that many, if any at all, are left unpinioned. Records are now considered to refer to genuine wanderers from over the Atlantic, justification for which came in 1977 when a drake which had been caught and ringed at Slimbridge, Gloucestershire, on 1st March 1977 was shot in southeast Greenland in the following May. That some can wander to the British Isles and then return across the Atlantic is most interesting. It had usually been supposed that, once here, these long-distance vagrants would stay on this side, as most undoubtedly do. Most of the Yorkshire records, during the last seven years, will refer to the same individuals, which may live for many years, and it is likely that no more than two or three different drakes have ever visited the county. The absence of females in Yorkshire is intriguing, as they occur at several places elsewhere in the country. They are more difficult to pick out among flocks of other diving ducks, but will surely occur and should be looked for.

Ferruginous Duck
Aythya nyroca

Yorkshire's first example of this south European duck was caught in Coatham Decoy on 17th January 1850 and recorded by T.S. Rudd in *The Zoologist* (1850, p. 2773). The second was shot at Dalton, near Huddersfield, in December 1858 (Hobkirk's *Huddersfield*, first ed., 1859, p. 145). Mr Thomas Boynton of Bridlington had a pair in his collection which were, as he informed Nelson, originally in the collection of W.W. Boulton at Beverley and probably of local origin.

On 23rd December 1876, Nelson saw a Ferruginous Duck for sale in a fish shop at Redcar and was told that it had been killed near the Teesmouth. Two were seen, and one of them shot, on 3rd October 1878 by the Reverend H. Smith on Coatham Marsh (*The Zoologist*, 1879, p. 211; and *The Field*, 15th February 1879).

A Major W.B. Arnold of Ackworth, in correspondence to Nelson on 20th April 1903, said that 'A pair of adults in excellent plumage were secured lately near here. The irides of the female were slaty brown.' In a later letter he said that two pairs were noticed, one of which remained all summer and the following winter (*The Zoologist*, 1904, p. 33).

Chislett listed three more occurrences. On 8th May 1918, a male was killed against telegraph wires in Upper Nidderdale and reported by Riley Fortune in *The Naturalist* (1918, p. 231). On 1st January 1947, G.R. Edwards saw one in company with five Pochards on Ringstone Edge Reservoir. On 18th March 1951, Dr Ian Brown saw a male at Wintersett Reservoir and notified P.E. Davis, who saw it on 19th and noted the white iris and deep chestnut colour of the head, breast, back and flanks with darker wings and white undertail-coverts, characters which separate this scarce visitor from the female Tufted Duck, a species with which the Ferruginous Duck often consorts. The Wintersett record was published in detail in *The Naturalist*, 1951, p. 138.

Since 1951, the species has been recorded in Yorkshire in 13 of the 30 years to 1981. Some of these sightings have been considered to refer to escapes from waterfowl collections.

Three birds were seen in 1957: the first, at Harewood Park Lake on 10th June, was thought by G.R. Naylor and M. Densley to have been an escape; R.G. Hawley described one on a pond at Owlerton, Sheffield; and C. Winn watched one at Fairburn Ings on 19th and 22nd October which was also seen by B. Lavery on 20th and identified as a drake.

In 1960, A.H.B. Lee saw one on Harewood Lake on 7th February which stayed to 23rd April. It visited Eccup Reservoir on 21st February and 27th March, and a second individual was seen at Eccup on 1st and 2nd May. G.R. Naylor identified one at Hornsea Mere on 5th January. R.F. Dickens recorded a female at Spurn on 3rd November 1962. From mid September in the same year, Mrs Malone of Scampston Hall (the daughter of W.H. St Quintin) noted two unfamiliar ducks on her park lake. She invited Sir Charles Richmond Brown to view them, but only one was present when he visited the lake. He described the bird well, and saw it again on 7th October with E.W. Taylor, who wrote up the occurrence in *The Naturalist*, 1963, p. 29. One was on Bretton Park Lake on 20th December 1964, and C. Winn and M.L. Denton saw one at Fairburn Ings from 28th to 30th October 1967.

In 1970, a female was seen on Hornsea Mere by W.F. Curtis on 16th October and a female was seen on Nafferton Mere by H.O. Bunce on 1st November. Two occurred in 1971, the first being a female at Bretton Park Lake from 7th to 27th November which was seen by J.E. Dale and R.L. Brook, with the second at Eccup Reservoir on 24th January. In 1973, records of a single bird at Langsett Reservoir on 4th September, Treeton Dyke on 20th and 21st October and Broomhill Flash on 28th October are likely to refer to the same individual.

Since 1973, this duck has occurred in every year up to 1982 with the exception of 1979. A drake stayed at Hornsea Mere from 1st May to 5th August 1974 and was seen by many people, including R.G. Hawley and S.M. Lister. A female was on John O'Gaunt's Reservoir, near Harrogate, from 1st to 11th January 1975, and again on 16th November and subsequently; Dr G.T. Foggitt, K. Moir and D.M. Pullan submitted notes. S.P. Singleton watched two birds at Eccup Reservoir on 3rd September in the same year. The bird at John O'Gaunt's Reservoir stayed over into 1976, and was seen up to 24th January and again in November and December, when I watched it with Dr G.T. Foggitt.

There was a remarkable series of records at Fairburn Ings in 1976, starting with a drake from 14th February to 2nd March, another from 31st May to 3rd June, and a third from 27th July to 31st August, with a duck from 16th November to 18th December. The three drakes were considered to be different individuals by S.C. Madge, who noted differences in plumage and bill markings. A drake was at Mickletown Flash on 17th April, also seen by S.C. Madge. R.G. Hawley recorded a drake at Hornsea Mere on 8th and 9th May and a duck on 9th June, and a drake was at Bransholme on 10th October.

A bird at Gouthwaite Reservoir on 18th January 1976, which was thought to be a Ferruginous Duck by some observers, was considered by D.J. Britton to be a hybrid between a Pochard and a Ferruginous Duck. The product of this cross-pairing is a recognised hybrid known as Paget's Pochard. The plumage details were published in the Yorkshire Naturalists' Union Ornithological Report for 1976, p. 65.

In 1977, a duck was at Knotford Nook Gravel-pit on 5th, 6th and 20th November and was watched and described by F.A. Wardman, D.M. Pullan and K. Moir; two ducks were on Castle Howard Lake on 13th November. In 1978, P.J. Izzard, D.J. Britton and others saw a drake at Tophill Low Reservoir from 26th February to 5th March; one was at Hornsea Mere on 12th March; three were at Potteric Carr on 10th September; and P. Smith saw one at Wintersett Reservoir on 2nd and 3rd December. P. Dunn and K. Rotherham watched a drake at Tophill Low Reservoir on 14th and 15th September 1980.

A drake was seen by C. Winn at Fairburn Ings from 14th to 16th June 1981, and an immature drake was seen by D. Waudby at Dringhouses Pond, near York, on 29th November 1981. In 1982, a drake was at Mickletown Flash from 12th to 25th May and again from 6th June to 9th August, during which period it occasionally visited Allerton Bywater. One was at Fairburn Ings on 11th July, and a duck was there on 30th July and 9th August. Another drake was at Potteric Carr on 29th and 30th September, yet another at Pugneys Gravel-pit on 20th November, with one at Pebley Pond, on the Yorkshire/Derbyshire border, on 19th December. In 1983, single birds were at Mickletown Ings on 24th and 26th May; Allerton Bywater from 4th to 17th July; Tophill Low Reservoir from 23rd October to 12th November; and at Pugneys Gravel-pit on 26th December.

It is extremely difficult to know from where such birds originate. Some will certainly have come from waterfowl collections where birds are left to fly freely. Several of the Yorkshire records will doubtless refer to the same individuals, which could live for ten or more years. That a few will have had a natural southern origin is quite possible, but unfortunately the escape element clouds the truth.

Tufted Duck
Aythya fuligula

The first quoted reference to this species as a Yorkshire bird was in Fothergill's *Wensleydale List*, where it is enumerated among the birds of that district (Nelson). Nelson's own summary of its status was 'Winter visitant; not uncommon on the coast in some severe seasons. Occasionally occurs inland, and nests at one or two localities.'

There has been a marked change during the 75 years since 1907, when Nelson published his avifauna, and the Tufted Duck is now a common breeding species over much of the county wherever suitable habitat presents itself. It has certainly benefited from the creation of gravel-pits and subsidence flashes, from both a wintering and a breeding standpoint. By 1911, Riley Fortune had referred to its increase as a breeding species, and in 1952 Chislett listed 13 major waters where breeding was taking place and said that it also nested at other reservoirs and at smaller sheets of water, which he did not name.

Historical breeding mentioned by Nelson included a pair on Malham Tarn, at an elevation of 1,300 feet (396 m), in 1849 (*The Zoologist*, 1850, p. 2879) and again in 1895, with three pairs in 1903. He also listed Nidderdale, the Washburn Valley, Castle Howard Lake and Hornsea Mere, a nest being reported at the latter in 1856. An injured drake remained at Worsborough Reservoir, near Barnsley, in 1901, and a female stayed with it, nested and hatched seven young (*The Zoologist*, 1904, p. 33).

Breeding records during the three years 1978 to 1980 give a good indication of its present status:

1978 VC 61: Five pairs bred near York and the species also nested at Hornsea Mere, Tophill Low Reservoir and Faxfleet.
VC 62: One pair bred at Hackness Lake and single pairs at Dalby and Seamer Road Mere; also proved at Scaling Dam.
VC 63: 90 pairs bred at 20 sites.
VC 64: 74 pairs bred at 18 sites and produced 325 young; 25 of these pairs were at Fairburn Ings and accounted for 127 of the young.
VC 65: One pair bred at Bolton-on-Swale Gravel-pits and hatched seven young.

1979 VC 61: Single pairs bred on the Lower Derwent at Aughton and Bubwith; probably bred on Hornsea Mere.
VC 62: One pair produced six young on Seamer Road Mere, and six young were hatched on the River Derwent at Brompton; bred at Scaling Dam.
VC 63: Nested at 15 sites, including Wentworth Park Lake where seven pairs produced 54 young.
VC 64: 86 pairs produced 500 young at 20 sites.
VC 65: No breeding reported.

1980 VC 61: Bred at four sites.
VC 62: Bred at two sites, including Scaling Dam.
VC 63: 47 pairs bred at 18 sites, and 222 young were hatched by 22 of these pairs.
VC 64: 48 pairs bred, 26 of which were at Fairburn Ings where 122 young were hatched.
VC 65: One pair bred.

The species can thus be considered a common breeder on many sheets of water, being most numerous in the west and south. It is more local in the east, owing mainly to the relative scarcity of suitable waters.

Winter assemblies at reservoirs and flashes began to increase during the 1960s, but there had been some large flocks in earlier years. On 17th January 1946, on the River Nidd near Ripley, the Reverend K. Ilderton estimated 600 birds, which had presumably resorted to the free water having been driven off a number of frozen reservoirs in the area. On 23rd March 1949, 300 were counted at Fairburn Ings, a water which was to attract many Tufted Ducks during subsequent years. R.F. Dickens saw 250 there on 11th March 1953, and in 1955 A.H.B. Lee counted 155 on 9th January and there were 195 present on 27th November; 319 were counted by C. Winn on 25th January 1959 and the water held good numbers during the next two decades, with peak counts of 360 on 6th March 1966 and 550 during January and February 1979.

Hornsea Mere has held the county's largest numbers during the past 30 years. There were 100 birds on 26th December 1955, 250 on 29th December 1956, 400 on 15th December 1957 and 460 on 29th November 1959. The figures give a good idea of the increase in annual maxima during the period. On 29th November 1960 the flock numbered 690 birds, and a further increase in maximum numbers occurred during the early 1970s. During late November 1970, 700 were there, with 860 in December and 880 in October 1971. The largest assembly ever recorded in Yorkshire was at Hornsea Mere on 24th September 1972; it consisted of 1,035 birds, many of which would have been newly arrived immigrants and which were later to disperse.

The floods along the Lower Derwent Valley, which were well watched during the 1960s by H.O. Bunce, A.F.G. Walker and Miss M.R. Sanderson, showed figures of 175 on 27th November and 150 on 27th December 1960. This area continues to attract large numbers of Tufted Ducks.

The relatively new reservoir at Tophill Low soon began to play host to this attractive diving duck: 500 were there on 27th January and 3rd December 1978, and P.J. Izzard counted 830 on 6th February 1979 and 700 on 13th January 1980. The high-altitude Malham Tarn has attracted upwards of 200 of these ducks on occasions, and smaller numbers regularly; P.F. Holmes counted 113 there on 27th October 1949 and 165 on 14th August 1975.

Almost any water, if deep enough to satisfy this duck's needs, will accommodate flocks during the non-breeding season. Favoured waters during the past 30 years have included Gouthwaite Reservoir, Eccup Reservoir, Wintersett Reservoir, Swillington Ings, Mickletown Ings, Newmillerdam, Bretton Park Lake and some waters in the Sheffield area. At any of these, up to 200-400 Tufted Ducks may be seen, numbers varying annually and with the season.

Chislett mentioned a bird ringed in St James Park, London, on 20th December 1945 which was recovered near Castleford on 29th May 1946, suggesting that it had moved south to London for the winter, probably from Fairburn. He also cited a bird ringed in Finland on 13th June 1933 and recovered in Yorkshire on 25th January 1935. A juvenile ringed in Czechoslovakia on 10th August 1961 was shot at Hirst Courtney in January 1963, and a duckling ringed in Holland in July 1967 was later found dead at Hornsea on 11th April 1970, giving an idea of the origin of some of our winter visitors. A juvenile ringed at Hollesley, Suffolk, on 22nd July 1979 was shot at Blaxton on 20th October 1979.

Scaup
Aythya marila

In Willughby's *Ornithology* (1678), the Scaup is mentioned thus: 'It is called Scaup Duck from its habit of feeding upon Scaup, ie, broken shellfish; varies infinitely in colour, especially in the Head and Neck, so that among a pack of forty or fifty you shall not find two exactly alike. A thing not unusual in this kind. We owe this description of it to Mr. Johnson.'

Nelson said that it was one of the latest of the winter ducks to arrive and did not appear until the end of October, 'at the time when we may expect Scoters, Longtails and other Norroway ducks'. He also said that its numbers varied greatly in different years, depending on the mildness or severity of the season. In the Teesmouth area, before the steamships, and when the area was sparsely populated, the Scaup was one of the commonest sea-ducks according to Sir Cuthbert Sharp in his *List of Birds of Hartlepool*. In the winter of 1788/89, they were in such quantities that above a thousand were caught in a week and sold for one shilling per dozen.

In 1906, an old fisherman aged 91 told Nelson that when he was a young man, about the 'thirties' or 'forties', the fowlers of those days did not as a rule trouble with Scaup. He, however, used to shoot them and sell them for 2$\frac{1}{2}$d each to a carrier who took them to Stockton Market. One stormy day at the Teesmouth, Nelson's informant crept close to a pack of fully 500 Scaup, but his old flintlock 'snapped'.

In the winter of 1864/65, when there were many wildfowl in the Humber Estuary, this species also occurred in immense flocks. In a letter to Nelson dated 9th January 1880, a Mr Francis Hoare stated that he had known them after strong northeast gales to go as far upriver as Paull Bight, where he had killed great numbers. In the winter of 1890/91 and in the early months of 1895, Scaup were unusually abundant in the Tees Bay and Nelson 'shot some fine specimens from the deck of Coatham Pier'.

Scaup were, according to W.J. Clarke, numerous in the harbours of Scarborough and Whitby during the period January to March 1940, and in early 1947, during the most prolonged cold weather of the century, A.J. Wallis reported large numbers off Scarborough, many of which died. A raft of 250 was in the mouth of the Humber off Spurn during December 1946 and January 1947, and this area has been favoured up to the present time. R.F. Dickens saw 100 there on 26th October 1953 and 500 were counted at the end of February 1954. Up to 70 were off Bridlington in December of the latter year. The Humber mouth attracted 120 on 2nd March 1956 and 200 on 18th and 19th February 1973. Scaup have been seen here in most recent years but numbers have varied annually, some years producing practically none at all, as in 1974 when the highest number seen was eight on 15th April. This was an exception, and from 100 to 200 have occurred in ten of the last 30 years with 450 birds on 18th January 1970 and 600 on 10th February, the highest number since Nelson's time.

Whitby Harbour and Bridlington Bay attract Scaup at times. In 1963, M. Densley counted 350 at the latter on 26th January and G.R. Bennett had 250 on 17th February. The Tees Estuary has had very few in recent years, and certainly no numbers approaching those quoted by Nelson.

The regular sea-watching at Flamborough Head in recent years has produced some excellent results. In 1979, 70 Scaup flew north on 1st January and 42 did so the next day, when 50 were also seen flying north off Spurn; on 3rd 194 passed, and another 40 on 6th. V.A. Lister saw 200 off Barmston on 7th and 80 were in Cornelian Bay on 14th. During this period, 200 were in the Humber mouth at Spurn, and this flock increased to 365 by 4th February and 700 by 18th March. The year 1979 was a good one for Scaup.

In 1906, Nelson summarised the status as 'Winter visitant, irregular in numbers, very abundant in some severe seasons, occasionally occurs in inland waters.' This remains very true today, except that far more now occur on the more numerous inland waters. The bulk of the comments on the species in the Annual Reports of the Yorkshire Naturalists' Union during the last 30 years have related to the inland occurrences and these are far too numerous to list in detail. Such records usually involve only one, two or three birds and larger parties are scarce. Birds may occur in any month, but mainly during the autumn and winter. Five at Gouthwaite Reservoir on 27th June 1965 were unusual.

To give some idea of the frequency of inland occurrences, I can do no better than present details from the Annual Report of the Yorkshire Naturalists' Union for 1976, when Scaup were seen at 35 inland waters in the western half of the county. Of these, Fairburn Ings had the most interesting series of records, with three on 1st February increasing to six by 8th and ten by 14th, declining to five by 23rd February. Southfield Reservoir had 11 birds on 18th January, 23rd February and 22nd March, but not on the intervening dates; that they were not seen at any other waters in the area when not at Southfield is curious. Records came from 26 waters in both 1977 and 1979, with maximum counts of six at Eccup Reservoir on 12th November 1979 and five at Worsborough Reservoir on 13th.

Apart from a very few pairs which nest in Scotland, the Scaup breeds no nearer to Yorkshire than Iceland and from Norway eastwards across northern Europe. Large numbers spend the winter in Holland, and severe weather in that region is often responsible for driving birds over to our east coast. An adult female ringed in Finland on 7th June 1972 was found dead at Barmby Marsh, Goole, during the winter of 1975/76.

In 1978, a female Scaup, which was probably not absolutely pure-bred, was watched at Fairburn Ings during April to June, in company with a drake Tufted Duck. It remained alone into July and possibly tried to breed, but the nesting area was flooded in mid May. In the following year, the same bird was again paired with a Tufted Duck and was later seen with a brood of eight ducklings (*British Birds*, 1980, p. 11, and 1981, p. 22). Both Scaup and Tufted Ducks are regularly kept in private collections and, under these forced conditions, matings between different species are far more common than in the wild; it is possible that the Fairburn female was the result of such a captive pairing, having been left unpinioned.

Eider
Somateria mollissima

In Nelson's day this large sea-duck was rare. He said of it in *The Birds of Yorkshire*: 'This handsome and conspicuous duck is a casual visitant in winter, generally in immature plumage, though, now that its numbers have so greatly increased at the Farne Isles, there seems every probability that its occurrence may be looked for with greater frequency on the Yorkshire coast.' How right he was to be.

When Chislett wrote *Yorkshire Birds* in 1952, he could only say of it '. . . wanders down to Yorkshire occasionally, probably from its Farne Island haunts. Although living near to Teesmouth, T.H. Nelson only recorded rather more than a dozen occurrences in the county prior to 1906, since when there have been fewer.'

The records listed by Chislett included two drakes and ten ducks seen on Gorple Reservoir by E.W. Watson on 1st November 1935. He commented that 'this was an extraordinary occurrence, but Mr. Watson saw them at close quarters and was quite certain of the unmistakable drakes'. Eiders have now been shown to occur quite regularly on inland waters.

Coastal records up to 1952 were few and came from Redcar, Scarborough, Bridlington and Spurn. Only one or two birds were seen at any one time, and of three seen on the Durham side of the Tees Estuary in late November 1950 two were shot and what was considered to be the surviving female was seen by P.J. Stead off Redcar on 26th November.

No sooner had Chislett's *Yorkshire Birds* hit the bookshelves than the Eider made its mark as a visitor to the Yorkshire coast. In 1954, a party of 16 was at Teesmouth on 18th February and odd birds were seen at Filey Brigg, Whitby and Flamborough, including four at the latter on 14th November which were seen by H.O. Bunce. It is most interesting to note that in the Ornithological Report of the Yorkshire Naturalists' Union for 1955, only three years after he had declared that there had been very few records during the period since Nelson published *The Birds of Yorkshire*, Chislett started the paragraph on the Eider by saying 'too many records of both sexes to enumerate, in January to April and September to

December near Teesmouth, Scarborough, Bridlington and Spurn. Four drakes and two ducks at South Gare from 20th November made up the largest party.'

The increase continued and was dramatic. In 1957, A.J. Wallis saw 30 in Filey Bay during a northerly gale on 10th November, the largest number ever recorded in the area at the time. Up to 16 were at Bridlington in November and December and up to 15 were at Spurn in November in the same year. A spectacular influx occurred in 1958 and the species was seen regularly at Flamborough in every month of the year, with peak counts of 71 on 9th January, 74 on 1st March and 61 on 9th April, numbers falling off gradually thereafter to leave only a few at the year end. No adult drakes were recorded, but H.O. Bunce and A.J. Williams said that the drakes remaining in September were probably second-winter birds. There were 12 at Spurn on 27th April, 19 on 27th September, and 45 on 6th November when 'two parties of motley drakes swam close inshore at 7 a.m.'; later in the day, a mixed flock of 33 birds flew down the Humber.

In 1960, the largest party was 33 off Hornsea on 17th October, and the first inland record during this new period was of one seen by A.F.G. Walker and Miss M.R. Sanderson on the Lower Derwent Valley floods on 4th December. This bird was seen again on 26th December by L. Smith, and another was seen on Scaling Dam by D.G. Bell on 27th November.

During the two decades from 1961, Eiders have been a regular feature of the Yorkshire coastline and flocks of up to 30 birds are now quite normal, some years producing larger numbers. The favoured localities were to be Spurn and Flamborough, the latter particularly so during the 1970s. After a record of 20 in November 1962, a flock of 40 was seen by R. Lightfoot in January 1972 which increased to 62 birds by 11th February; numbers dwindled to 52 by 22nd March and 30 by early May, with three remaining up to 10th June. Maximum counts in subsequent years have been 33 on 20th November 1976, 34 in December 1978, and 52 on 6th January 1979.

The mouth of the River Humber at Spurn Point attracts small parties annually, and during the past 20 years flocks of up to 30-40 have been regular visitors during the winter months. In 1978 there were more birds than usual, with 55 on 28th October being the most seen together, and 76 were there on 18th December 1983. On 25th December 1973, 48 were at South Gare and five at Redcar.

R.G. Hawley, W.F. Curtis and D.E. Murray counted 96 Eiders flying north off Hornsea on 9th November 1975. On the previous day, 39 had flown north at Flamborough, and 45 were also seen over the Humber on 9th. No fewer than 146 flew north at Spurn on 20th November 1983.

Filey Bay is occasionally favoured by this species. There were 30 there on 28th March 1964 and 47 on 2nd December 1980; 36 of the latter remained at the year end.

Anywhere along the Yorkshire coastline, from the Tees to the Humber, the Eider is now a regular visitor during the winter months, assembling mainly at the favourite places mentioned above but appearing in smaller numbers elsewhere. Females and immatures preponderate. Some perish in severe weather and I have found several dead ones along the sands of Bridlington Bay.

Inland occurrences have increased in coincidence with the coastal trend. Gouthwaite Reservoir in Upper Nidderdale has pulled down more than its fair share of Eiders, which could have been crossing the country from one coast to the other in either direction. An immature drake was seen on 10th November 1962 by Miss M.R. Sanderson and Miss A. Summersgill, and A.F.G. Walker saw another on 12th January 1964, on which day one was seen by G.R. Naylor on Eccup Reservoir. Single birds were at Southfield Reservoir on 28th November 1967 and at Wentworth on 15th December 1968.

On 21st November 1971, a remarkable flock of 20 Eiders arrived at Wintersett

Reservoir, coinciding with a small influx on the coast. By next morning, 15 had departed, the remaining five staying until 4th December, after which date a lone bird lingered on until 9th April 1972 when a flotilla of 30 yachts forced it to take wing and leave. P. Smith and P.B. Wordsworth were among the many observers to see this largest ever inland flock. Three of the five birds which left on 4th December moved to nearby Newmillerdam, where they remained until 26th December. Gouthwaite Reservoir was again favoured by two drakes on 7th May 1977 and two more on 14th March 1980. A drake was at Treeton Dyke Reservoir on 23rd and 24th December 1979, and in 1980 singles were at Broomhead Reservoir on 8th November and at Pugneys Gravel-pit on 9th November. Nine flew northwest over Fairburn Ings on 8th January 1981. A female was at Hay-a-Park Gravel-pit from 16th December 1982 until 2nd January 1983, when it was seen flying with Mallards over nearby Knaresborough Ringing Station by P.T. Treloar.

Eight birds were upriver at Blacktoft Sands on 7th December 1978 and eight flew down the river at Paull on 9th April 1981. In 1959, a juvenile male landed in a housing estate at Barugh Green, near Barnsley, on 19th November and died.

The increased frequency of winter records along the Yorkshire coast, with a few birds lingering into the late spring and summer, may eventually lead to a breeding attempt. It is possible that an odd pair may come ashore to do so at one of the rocky parts of the shoreline.

As has been assumed, the majority of Eiders along the Yorkshire coastline originate in the Farne Islands, although the recovery of an oiled bird on the beach at Withernsea on 23rd March 1969 that had been ringed as a duckling in the Dutch Frisian Islands on 13th July 1965 shows that some visit us from western Europe. This individual had been recaught on Texel Island on 15th August 1967 before being found in Yorkshire, and was only the third recovery in the British Isles of an Eider ringed abroad.

On 9th February 1983, A.M. Allport was sea-watching at Flamborough Head when a drake Eider flew in and landed on the sea below the cliffs. It was only about 50 yards (46 m) out and he noticed that it had an all lemon-yellow bill. He watched it through a telescope for the next ten minutes and was able to note that the whole bill was a bright, clear yellow with a paler, almost white nail and a very obvious black nostril. Such are the features of the race *Somateria mollissima borealis*, which breeds in the Arctic North Atlantic from Franz Josef Land and Spitsbergen to Iceland, Greenland, and the Baffin Island region of Canada.

King Eider
Somateria spectabilis

An example of this northern eider captured at Bridlington Quay in August 1846 remains the only Yorkshire record. The details were published in *The Zoologist*, 1851, p. 3036, by Joseph Duff. About 170 King Eiders have now been recorded in the British Isles, mostly in Scotland and mainly during the last two decades.

Steller's Eider
Polysticta stelleri

The Steller's Eider, which breeds in eastern Siberia and Alaska and spends the winter mainly in the Bering Sea, has occurred in the British Isles on only 13 occasions. The one Yorkshire claim concerns a male which was shot at Filey on 15th August 1845 and submitted to Yarrell for inspection. The specimen, which, according to Clarke and Roebuck (1881), was in the collection of Mr Thomas Boynton of Ulrome Grange, went eventually to the collection of Lord Scarsdale of Kedleston (*The Naturalist*, 1845, p. 1249).

It is interesting to note that the only Yorkshire record of the King Eider was in the following year, also in August.

Harlequin Duck
Histrionicus histrionicus

There have been three instances of this specialised duck's occurrence in Yorkshire, two of which are quite unacceptable. The first concerned a female, alleged to have been shot on the River Don a little above Doncaster by a Mr Cartmell. There is no date available and the record was published by Thomas Allis in 1844. The specimen was acquired by Hugh Reid, and he sold it to N.E. Stickland, in whose collection it was residing in 1881. J.H. Gurney considered the record of doubtful authenticity and, from what we now know of the species' occurrences away from its nearest breeding grounds in Iceland, the incident seems most unlikely.

A second example, alleged to have been captured at Hornby Decoy about 1860 and published in *The Handbook of Vertebrate Fauna of Yorkshire* (Clarke and Roebuck 1881), proved, on investigation by W. Eagle Clarke, to have been an imported specimen. The bird was at one time in the collection of George Savage, a keeper at Hornby Castle, Bedale.

The third record was more credible and was accepted by the editors of *The Handbook of British Birds*. The bird was a young male, which at the time of Nelson was in the collection of Mr J. Whitaker of Rainworth Lodge, Nottinghamshire. It was bought by him from Alfred Roberts of Scarborough, who procured it about 1862 from some fishermen at Filey who said that they had found it washed up on the beach (*The Zoologist*, 1878, p. 135).

In the absence of the more sophisticated present-day knowledge concerning migrations and habits of unusual birds, the old collectors and their suppliers often fabricated details of such in order to better their rivals, and several old records must be thus clouded.

Long-tailed Duck
Clangula hyemalis

This sea-duck has been known as a Yorkshire species since at least 1678, when it was mentioned in Willughby's *Ornithology* by Ralph Johnson of Greta Bridge, the friend and correspondent of John Ray. He had sent a description of a bird called the 'Swallow-tailed Sheldrake' which answers accurately to that of the Long-tailed drake.

Nelson knew it as a 'Winter visitant, not uncommon in immature plumage off the coast; rare in the adult stage, occasionally occurs as a straggler to inland waters.' Its status has changed but little since then, even allowing for the massive increase in observer activity, especially during the last 30 years.

'The adult male is rare, the mature female still more so' wrote Nelson in 1907. W.J. Clarke of Scarborough had one of the latter sent to preserve in November 1897, it being only the second example he had known. Nelson, however, had observed and secured some very good specimens of the adult male, and in February 1892 he watched, through the lifeboat telescope, two perfectly adult drakes disporting on the water about a mile offshore. Sea-watching is not all that new, it would seem!

Nelson also cited about 15 inland records during his period up to 1906, including one shot by John Cordeaux on a flooded meadow at Kilnsea in October 1882 which had been feeding on small red worms.

Chislett listed only ten coastal records and five inland ones during the period of his review up to 1951, including five seen in Bridlington Bay on 6th January 1945 by G.H. Ainsworth and three seen at the same place on 17th January 1951 by F. Wilcock. The other records involved single birds or 'pairs'. The five inland occurrences were a female at Ringstone Edge Reservoir on several days in January 1939 and a female at Swillington Ings from 3rd to 24th December in the same year, the latter seen by A. Gilpin and H. Walker; a male was seen on 22nd October 1950 at Eccup Reservoir by P. Davis and F.E. Kennington; and in 1950, J.C.S. Ellis saw a female on a Pennine reservoir on 24th November and B. Speake reported a pair on an ice-free corner of Swillington Ings on 24th December. Since 1951, the species has occurred mainly singly on some inland lake, reservoir or flash in every year except four up to 1984.

Coastal records have been more numerous than in Chislett's period, probably owing entirely to increased birdwatching activity rather than to an increase in Long-tailed Ducks. The species has occurred annually and mainly singly or in low double figures, but there have been a few larger parties. Ten were off Hornsea on 20th November 1955, and in subsequent years this area, well watched by G.R. Bennett and latterly by W.F. Curtis, has proved to be a favoured haunt. Nine were there on 10th November 1957 (after 13 had been seen at nearby Atwick on 13th October), seven on 10th November 1960, 18 on 26th January 1967, and 14 on 1st February 1971.

South Gare Breakwater at Teesmouth has provided sea-watchers with fair numbers of Long-tails. D.G. Bell and W. Norman saw parties of 17 coming in from the east on 17th November and 1st December 1963, with 14 present on 30th November. The Tees Estuary held 15 birds on 4th January and during late February 1964, and in 1966 a total of 39 flew north between 25th and 29th October, including one flock of 16 on the latter date. Six were seen there by D.G. Bell on 14th January 1973. Seven were off Redcar during January to April 1958, and S.C. Norman saw 12 flying north there on 3rd November 1970.

In 1973, a most remarkable and unprecedented influx of Long-tailed Ducks occurred off the Yorkshire coast. At the start of the year, Bridlington Bay had up to seven during January and two on 1st April. Filey Bay attracted one in January, three on 2nd March and eight on 10th, six remaining to the month end. Six were at South Gare on 14th January. One was on Hornsea Mere during January and February, with two from 25th February to 24th March and from 14th to 25th April. Tophill Low Reservoir had one on 28th January, 3rd March and 22nd May. It was, however, at the year end that the big arrival took place. The first was off Spurn Point on 21st August, followed by offshore movement involving mainly single birds on five dates in October with five on 24th as the maximum seen on one day. Filey Bay had three birds on 27th October and one or two were seen there on three later dates. Cornelian Bay, south of Scarborough, a popular place for sea-ducks, attracted six on 27th October; eight on 4th November; 11 from 9th to 20th November; 13 from 22nd to 27th November; and 14 on 28th November. It was in Bridlington Bay, however, that the most spectacular numbers congregated. R. Lightfoot saw the first flock of 15 on 14th December, which had increased to 35 by 16th and to 39 by 24th, with 36 birds present on Christmas Day. These birds stayed over into 1974 and Lightfoot, together with D.I.M. Wallace, counted 35 on 30th March and 13th April and 25 on 15th April. These numbers were quite exceptional, and have not been approached since.

The Long-tailed Duck can be seen during the winter months along any part of the Yorkshire coastline, and on any inland sheet of water, where birds may stay for a few hours or a few weeks. Single birds are usual inland with two occasionally, and such is more often the case on the coast, with small parties of under ten birds being seen in some years.

In the East Riding this duck used to be known as the Sea Pheasant, a name shared with the Pintail, and, according to Nelson, it was known as the Go-West at Redcar.

Common Scoter
Melanitta nigra

'Its case stuft was sent us first by Mr. Jessop out of Yorkshire.' Thus, the Common Scoter entered the county list of birds as written in Willughby's *Ornithology* (1678).

Allis, in his report of 1844, mentioned a most unusual circumstance of a flock appearing at Bretton Park in July 1834. We now know such an incident to be quite normal as birds drop in to rest before continuing their cross-country movements. In 1879, W. Eagle Clarke recorded a most extraordinary migration of scoters at Skipton-in-Craven. On 24th April, shortly after dusk, birds were heard passing overhead, and they continued most of the night, many being bewildered and flying against chimney pots and houses. At the railway station, they were immolated against the telephone wires and several were picked up on the following morning, one porter securing as many as 17. It was calculated that, in all, 150 had been taken, the majority of which were males. The migration continued on 25th and again on 26th, when the fowl were heard passing over for two hours between eight and ten o'clock. See *The Zoologist*, 1880, p. 355, for fuller details of the incident. What happened to the corpses is not known, and as the scoter was not considered to be very good for eating, being decidedly rank and fishy in taste unless properly cooked, it is unlikely that many found their way into the pot.

Nelson often related tales of strange happenings which relied on hearsay and exaggeration as much as on true fact. A bit of each must have been included in the following account from *The Birds of Yorkshire* (1907, p. 479).

'As a sporting bird, when in large packs, it affords excellent practise, comparable even to grouse driving, with the additional difficulty of a rocking boat to take into consideration. I have at times enjoyed capital shooting amongst the Black Ducks over the Redcar Scars by putting out decoy birds to attract the wild ones within range. As is well known, the Scoter can carry off a heavy charge of shot, and, even when knocked down and apparently helpless, a wounded bird has an annoying trick of diving if a spark of life remains, and so often baffles the shooter, for it is practically useless to pursue one under these conditions, while if hard pressed it will even cling to the rocks or seaweed and commit suicide by drowning. On several occasions, after a days shooting over the rocks, dead birds have been found at low tide with wings firmly clasped round a stone, or holding on by the bill to a piece of seaweed.'

It is hard to imagine that someone of Nelson's calibre could have believed such stories, or have interpreted the facts in this way. Dead ones at low tide there undoubtedly would have been, but intentionally holding on to stones and seaweed as described is too much!

Nelson knew the 'Black Duck' well, as he did most sea-ducks, and said that immense flocks may be seen in the autumn and winter months and that it could be found at most stations between the Tees and the Humber, Bridlington Bay being a favourite locality. Apart from the term 'immense', this assessment applies today. Scoters are most numerous from late July to October, when parties may be seen passing along the coastline either on migration or while undertaking feeding movements of a more local nature.

Chislett disposed of the Common Scoter's coastal involvement in seven lines. He stated that maximum numbers occurred in 1950, with 300 at Spurn on 31st July, 200 in Filey Bay on 27th October and 600 at Teesmouth on 26th November.

Flocks of scoters seen passing along the coast or resting on the sea usually number from just a few to 200 birds, but larger flocks sometimes occur. R.F. Dickens saw 500 in one raft at Spurn on 26th July 1952, and 750 were assembled in five rafts off Hornsea on 24th March 1957. On 19th August 1957 500 were in Bridlington Bay, and 450 were at Redcar on 16th November in the same year. On 9th November 1957, J. Cudworth counted flocks totalling 1,400 flying south at Spurn. In 1958, 500 in the Humber mouth on 12th July increased to 750 by 26th. Bridlington Bay, where there were 720 on 29th January 1983, and Spurn have produced the largest numbers over the years, the former attracting mainly feeding parties and the latter mainly passing birds.

Regular watching at Blacktoft Sands during the 1970s has shown that ducks and waders fly westwards up the Humber and continue inland. In 1974, flocks of Common Scoters were seen doing this: on 5th August, 180 flew west at 16.00 hours, 180 at 20.00 hours, 40 at 20.15 hours and 20 at 20.30 hours; with 42 more on 8th August and 44 on 26th August. Such birds will no doubt be crossing to the west coast and may stop off to rest on some of the Pennine reservoirs. Similar movements in 1980 involved 43 birds on 25th July, 37 on 27th, 50 on 13th August and 150 on 21st September.

Appearances at the high Pennine reservoirs are frequent, especially during late summer. Gouthwaite Reservoir in Upper Nidderdale is a favourite stopping-off place, and over the years some large flocks have occurred there. A.F.G. Walker counted 30 birds, including 20 drakes, on 2nd August 1954, in which year 160 flew up the Calder Valley in two lines in the evening of 10th August. In 1955, Gouthwaite Reservoir had 83 birds, of which 78 were drakes, on 21st August and 75, of which only two were females, on 24th July 1970. Further cross-country movement was noted on 31st July 1957, when J. Cudworth counted 130 flying southwest over Ossett and V.S. Crapnell and Irving Morley saw 200 flying over Whiteholme Reservoir, 35 of which dropped in to rest as the others flew on. An exceptional flock of 250 was at Swinsty Reservoir on 28th June 1958, and later in the year 60 were on Eccup Reservoir on 9th August and 31 were at Blackmoorfoot Reservoir on 18th October, on which date 250 flew north over the Tees Bay. Large numbers were at Spurn during the same October period, when 148 flew north on 17th and 459 on 18th.

In 1962, an overland movement was witnessed at 11 Pennine waters during early July which included 26 at Eccup Reservoir on 8th, with 21 at Gouthwaite Reservoir on the same day increasing to 57 by 11th. Movement continued during the month, and 36 flew east at Fairburn Ings on 19th and 45 flew west over Kirkheaton on 29th, with 34 at Gouthwaite Reservoir on 15th August and 40, all females or immatures, at Fairburn Ings on 10th November. Scoters often fly very high and appear only as long thin dark lines in the sky, especially in clear weather when some may pass too high to be seen. C. Winn picked up such a line over Fairburn Ings on 18th July 1966 and counted 74 birds. A similar string of 50 birds was seen flying over Burley Woodhead by J.K. Fenton on 6th August 1970, and C.E. Andrassy saw 80 flying east over Altofts on 29th July 1975.

The year 1977 was a good one for inland scoters. F.A. Wardman saw 27 drakes on Chelker Reservoir, near Skipton, on 13th April and Miss Joan Owen counted 26 drakes on Scargill Reservoir in Nidderdale on 26th June. On 27th July Swillington Ings had a flock of 49, including only one female, and on 30th July Blackmoorfoot Reservoir had a splendid flock of 75 drakes. In the same year, a coastal movement on 10th July included 71 birds at Scarborough, 150 at Burniston, 137 at Filey, 170 at Flamborough and 300 at Spurn. A good day for seabird movement on 17th September included many scoters, with 303 flying north at Burniston, 342 at Filey, 145 at Flamborough, 494 at Hornsea and 306 at Spurn. Smaller numbers were seen at Ravenscar.

In consequence of the foregoing, the Common Scoter can be seen to be a common duck along the whole of the Yorkshire coast, being most numerous during the late summer and autumn. It is not unusual to see the species on inland waters, especially those along the Pennines, often in large numbers, as birds crossing the county drop in to rest. Odd individuals or small parties may occur almost anywhere inland during the main periods of movement.

Surf Scoter
Melanitta perspicillata

The first Yorkshire record of this North American duck occurred at Spurn Point on 30th August 1961. At 17.45 hours on that day, G.R. Naylor and M. Densley were sea-watching behind the Warren Cottage when a group of three scoters was seen about 250 yards (229 m) offshore. The birds were casually examined through binoculars and it was noticed that one of them was slightly larger than the two accompanying birds and also showed some white about the head. Examination through telescopes showed this to be an adult drake Surf Scoter, and the two observers watched it for ten minutes before going to inform others who were staying at the bird observatory. R.F. Porter, B.A.E. Marr and P.J. Mountford were also able to see the bird, and they followed it down the peninsula as it drifted southwards with the tide. It gradually came very close inshore and gave excellent views.

A drake flew north at Filey Brigg on 20th January 1981 which P.R. Chambers and P.J. Dunn described and sketched. The *British Birds* Rarities Committee felt unable to accept the record, but the details submitted were considered perfectly acceptable to the Yorkshire Naturalists' Union Records Committee.

On 24th January 1982, S.C. Madge saw a lone scoter off Filey Brigg which he identified as an immature of this species.

An immature male was seen at Flamborough on 20th October 1984 by A.M. Allport, J.C. Lamplough and P.A. Lassey.

There have now been over 235 records of this Nearctic duck in British waters, about 165 of these having occurred during the last 25 years.

Velvet Scoter
Melanitta fusca

Nelson knew the Velvet Scoter principally as a sea-duck, and said of it in *The Birds of Yorkshire*: 'Essentially an oceanic species, this fine duck is almost entirely restricted to the seaboard, where it arrives in small flocks during the first October gales; the earliest date of its appearance of which I am aware is 21st September 1891, when one was captured after a strong on-shore wind; on 11th August 1877, four flew past me while at sea, but these were in all probability individuals which had remained throughout the summer as the Common Scoter often does.'

That assessment was basically correct, except for the fact that August birds need not, and indeed are most unlikely to, have summered.

Any of the large flocks of Common Scoters along the coastline may hold a few Velvets, with larger numbers on occasions. In early 1956, more than usual occurred and birds were seen from the Tees to the Humber. In February, 12 were off Redcar on 18th and 19 off Huntcliffe on 28th, while numbers at Scarborough during the early part of the month increased until 100 were seen by A.J. Wallis on 3rd March. A flock of 19 drakes was off Bridlington on 31st March and smaller numbers were in the general vicinity around that time. Some penetrated to inland waters and were seen at Fairburn Ings and Ogden Reservoir, where a female stayed until 25th February when it was trapped under the ice and was later found dead. The specimen went to the Bradford Museum. Nine birds were still off Redcar on 1st June, and one was seen there on 20th July.

In 1962, 21 flew south at Filey Brigg on 10th November, 14 were at Spurn on the same day, and 21 flew north off Flamborough on 18th November. On 10th August 1968, 31 were seen flying north off Flamborough, and regular watching there during the last ten years has produced relatively good numbers in most years, the highest daily counts being 20 on 29th October 1976 and again on 9th December 1978, and 15 on 23rd September 1979. Cornelian Bay, south of Scarborough, is a popular feeding place for sea-ducks, and in the early 1970s assemblies of from 16 to 27 birds were regularly seen there.

In 1977, there were good numbers at Spurn Point, building up from 18 on 6th January to 20 by 29th and 32 on 30th; up to 29 were present in March. During April, it was noticed that the scoters which often flew south along the coast were turning into the Humber, where they spent the day feeding before returning north again to spend the night. During the period 3rd to 8th April, between 37 and 50 Velvet Scoters were seen in the river mouth.

At inland reservoirs, lakes and other suitable waters, the species has occurred in 24 of the 34 years since 1950, in every month except June, and most numerously during October to February. These reports have involved mainly single birds, which are usually immature, with two on occasions. Larger numbers are scarce and, apart from nine birds at Redmires Dam on 8th October 1941 and eight at Scaling Dam on 9th December 1960, the largest parties have been four birds at Fly Flatts Reservoir on 17th November 1956, four at Wintersett Reservoir on 22nd November 1970 and four at Langsett Reservoir on 7th January 1979. On 7th December 1963, with Eric Gorton of the Bolton Museum, I watched a young drake at Copgrove Lake, near Knaresborough; on the following day it was found dead in the reeds, and is now preserved in the Bolton Museum.

Over 20 different waters, in all parts of the county, have induced Velvet Scoters to land and rest, sometimes only briefly before continuing their journeys to destinations which we can only conjecture.

Nelson considered this species to be very unusual inland, but listed occurrences at Doncaster Carrs, Clapham, Walton Park, Barnsley and Hiendley Reservoir, which probably indicate that it was as frequent then as it is now but undetected on lonely waters to which access was difficult in the absence of modern transport. His summary, quoted in 1952 by Chislett, who considered it still to pertain, 'Winter visitant in small numbers. Has occurred inland', is, in the light of our present knowledge, no longer true. The species may occur in small numbers along our coastline in any month, most commonly from October to March; and on any inland water, mainly singly, during most months, the frequency often being linked to the periods when it is most numerous at coastal sites.

Bufflehead
Bucephala albeola

There is one Yorkshire record of the 'Butterball', by which name this Nearctic duck is known to North American wildfowlers. It was an adult male in fine plumage, shot on the Bessingby Beck, near Bridlington, in the winter of 1864/65 by Richard Morris and preserved by a Mr Machen. The specimen went originally to the collection of J. Whitaker of Rainworth Lodge, and the occurrence was reported in *The Zoologist*, 1865, p. 9659, by John Cordeaux.

As with several species of rare waterfowl, the possibility of captive origin must be very high. For example, in October 1974, a shipment of 36 Buffleheads arrived in Britain from Canada. They had been wild-caught and wing-clipped and all died on the journey or shortly afterwards. Had they lived and gone to private waterfowl collections, the majority would probably have been left to moult and renew their wing feathers in the autumn, when they would have been free-flying and a potential problem for birdwatchers.

The Yorkshire claim was the second of only five British records, the others having occurred in 1830, 1920, 1932 and 1961.

Goldeneye
Bucephala clangula

The claim for this species having nested in Yorkshire at Swinsty Reservoir in 1891 and mentioned only briefly by Nelson was clarified by Chislett. He said that the report, concerning a drake which was stated to have stayed with a winged female, the pair subsequently having been seen with young of which one was caught, was discredited by H.B. Booth, who declared the duckling submitted in support of the claim to be a young Mallard (*The Naturalist*, 1930, p. 357). Nelson said that the old drake was afterwards secured and the specimen placed in the collection of the Leeds Naturalists' Club. *The Birds of Yorkshire* includes a photograph of the island in Swinsty Reservoir where the breeding was supposed to have taken place.

For odd birds to linger into late spring or stay throughout the summer is no longer a rare event. It is perhaps understandable for those early naturalists to associate such an event with breeding and to misinterpret the events.

Hornsea Mere is Yorkshire's main water for Goldeneyes, but Chislett referred to it very briefly in connection with a copulating pair on 17th February 1946 and much active display on 16th March, with a bird still present on 1st May. The first Annual Bird Report of the Yorkshire Naturalists' Union in 1940 mentioned 50 birds on the mere on 10th March. In 1950, this total was again given as the highest count — on 15th January. The first real indication of the popularity of this large water, if it was not a real trend of increasing numbers, came in 1960, when the maximum counts were 180 on 28th February and 142 on 13th November. G.R. Bennett was watching the mere regularly then, and higher numbers were to follow. In 1961, the spring peak was 302 during March. A high count of 320 birds on 6th April 1963 was eclipsed in the following year by 444 on 27th March, and in 1967 by 480 on 12th February. Peak numbers at the mere during the 1970s varied between 150 and 350 in the spring and 50 to 230 in the autumn and winter.

The reservoir at Tophill Low became popular with Goldeneyes during the early 1970s, and in 1972 there were 130 there on 5th February and 200 on 24th December. Numbers there in recent years have varied from 50 to a maximum of 172 on 7th March 1975.

The most popular water inland is perhaps Gouthwaite Reservoir, and Chislett gave it much attention in his *Yorkshire Birds*. He had 'never known more than about 15 birds there', but A.F.G. Walker counted 26 on 5th March 1950, 32 on 29th November 1953 and 39 on 29th March 1956. Regular counts during the next few years showed that up to 30 Goldeneyes could be expected in most winters. In 1965, the count was 31 birds on 20th November, and this was not exceeded until November 1973 when 43 were present.

In 1952, the Annual Report of the YNU stated that the Goldeneye had been reported from 25 waters within the county and gave maximum counts of 31 at Whiteholme Reservoir on 9th March with 24 there on 16th November, 23 at Fairburn Ings, also on 16th November, and 49 at Withens Reservoir on 23rd November. Chislett considered these figures abnormal for any Yorkshire water and 'probably connected with the early severity'.

In 1956, reports were sent in from 40 waters and the species was to be expected at any suitably deep lake or reservoir in any part of the county, from the upland areas of the north and west and, in the south, eastwards to Holderness. The floodwaters along the valley of the Lower Derwent were regularly monitored during the early 1960s, and 120 were at Bubwith on 11th December 1960. In the following year, there were 110 on 15th January and 120 on 12th February. The highest count in 1980 was 40 on 9th March. Seventy-six birds at Fairburn Ings on 6th March 1977 was a high number for that water.

The reaches of the Upper Humber attract this species, and in 1970 Welton Water showed maximum figures of 103 on 31st January, 125 on 4th February and 143 on 15th March.

Coastal occurrences are mostly during the autumn, when birds are coming in from their main breeding grounds in Scandinavia and eastwards across northern Europe. Small parties may then be seen either feeding in the sheltered bays or flying to and fro over the sea. In some years larger numbers occur, as in 1966 when, on the three days 25th, 26th and 27th October, 212, 48 and 76 birds respectively flew north at South Gare, Teesmouth. On 22nd October 1970 93 flew north there, and 101 were counted by S.C. Norman, again flying north, on 20th October 1972, the date on which several inland waters had their first main influx.

In 1975, 48 passed to the north off Hornsea on 16th February, 32 off Scarborough on 9th November and 23 off Burniston on 7th December. A marked coastal influx occurred in November 1977, evidenced by 60 off Scarborough during 10th to 15th, 12 in Filey Bay on 13th and 35 at Burniston on 15th.

At Spurn Point, Goldeneyes are regularly noted passing, usually to the south during the autumn and mainly during October. Forty-four on 28th October 1976 with 55 the next day, and 32 on 26th October 1978 were peak counts. Smaller numbers are present on many other dates around this period in every year.

In recent years, several birds have lingered late in the spring before finally departing, and some have stayed throughout the summer, often alone. By February, drake Goldeneyes may be seen displaying vigorously to attendant ducks, and the pairs are usually formed before the birds leave for their northern nesting quarters. The main return of immigrants in the autumn is often preceded at some waters by the early appearance in August of one or two immatures which may have spent the summer elsewhere in the British Isles. The 7th September 1981 was an early date for 11 birds to be at Nosterfield Gravel-pit.

On 30th November 1973, at Fairburn Ings, a duck Goldeneye was picked off the water by a Great Black-backed Gull and partly eaten.

The Goldeneye is, without doubt, now much more numerous in Yorkshire than formerly. Even allowing for the increased birdwatching activity and the much better coverage of isolated waters at the present time, Chislett's statement in 1952 that 'Flocks of more than a few birds rarely occur except on the coast in early autumn, and at Hornsea Mere' must have reflected the situation at that time.

Hooded Merganser
Mergus cucullatus

The claims for the inclusion of this North American sawbill on the Yorkshire list are quite inadequate, and the British Ornithologists' Union did not include them in the accepted records for the British Isles in *The Status of Birds in Britain and Ireland* (1971). None of the five accepted birds was recorded in England, there being one in Wales and the other four in Ireland, the latter being the most likely place for this transatlantic vagrant to appear.

It was first mentioned in connection with Yorkshire by Gould in his *Birds of Great Britain*, where he said 'Mr. W. Christy Horsfall, of Horsforth Low Hall informs me that he has a pair in his collection which were killed in the neighbourhood of Leeds.' W. Eagle Clarke was unable to trace these specimens, which he included in *The Handbook of the Vertebrate Fauna of Yorkshire*. Nelson pursued the matter and discovered that the British Museum of Natural History possesses a mounted example of this species which bears the following particulars: 'Colder (Calder) River, Yorkshire, 1843. Mr. Parke, presented by Mr. J. Baker'. It is possible, wrote Nelson, that this may be one of the specimens referred to, as the Calder flows into the Aire not far distant from Leeds.

Nelson's *The Birds of Yorkshire* includes a photograph of the old fowler Snowden Slights in his punt on the Derwent, near the place where he claimed to have shot a Hooded Merganser (see plate 47). The specimen, a drake, was inspected by Nelson in the collection of Captain Dunnington–Jefferson of Thicket Priory. Neither the owner of the stuffed bird nor its shooter kept a record of the date, and the only information that Slights was able to provide was that he shot it in the 'North Ings' when the River Derwent was in flood and much of the surrounding countryside was covered with water.

As stated, this record was also rejected and the species has thus never been satisfactorily recorded in Yorkshire. That the birds in question were Hooded Mergansers there is no doubt, but their origin is far from proven and the likelihood that they were labelled with false localities to enhance their value and to ensure their sale to the local landowners, who took a great pride in their collections, is great.

Smew
Mergus albellus

'The White Nun', by which name the handsome drake Smew was known to early wildfowlers, and the more soberly clad female occur in small numbers every winter in Yorkshire. The species' appearances at inland waters far outnumber those along the coast, and during the ten years 1971-80 there have been only eight coastal records compared with 68 inland.

Most records concern lone 'redheads', a term given to the females and young males, which look almost alike during the winter months. Adult drakes are relatively scarce. Two birds together are not unusual, and there have been records of up to four at some waters over the years. Larger numbers have been six, including one adult drake, at Eccup Reservoir on 24th February 1952; five there on 23rd February 1945, and six at Swillington Ings on 6th February in the same year; five, including one adult drake, at Harewood Park Lake on 5th and 12th February 1961; and an exceptional party of 11 redheads at Hornsea Mere on 10th March 1963. A flock of eight redheads seen at South Gare in 1966 is not dated. J.E. Dale watched five redheads fly into Blackmoorfoor Reservoir in the evening of 8th November 1974, all of which had left by dawn next day.

Some Smews arrive in Yorkshire during October, the earliest of which I have note in recent years being one at Gouthwaite Reservoir on 20th October 1968.

Chislett listed 28th October 1931 (one at Chelker Reservoir), on which date in 1978 one was at Hornsea Mere. A record of one at Hornsea Mere on 24th August 1943 by C.H. Wells is exceptional; Chislett, who published this record in *Yorkshire Birds*, does not say which sex it was.

After the scattering of birds during October, the main influx usually follows during November. In some years, the main increase in records does not take place until December or even January, probably as a result of birds being frozen off their preferred wintering areas in western Europe.

Most birds leave for their north European breeding grounds by March and few linger after that time. Later dates are 19th April 1958 and 12th April 1963 at Hornsea Mere, and 20th April 1979 and 21st April 1981 at Fairburn Ings, with the latest ever county record at Gouthwaite Reservoir where A.F.G. Walker saw a drake on 2nd May 1954.

The Smew is not a common visitor to Yorkshire, but during the main period of November to February mainly single birds but sometimes two or more may occur on any water, including rivers and the estuaries of the Tees and Humber. The beautiful adult drake is a fine but rare sight.

Red-breasted Merganser

Mergus serrator

Up to the time when Chislett published *Yorkshire Birds* in 1952, the Red-breasted Merganser had been known as an uncommon winter visitor with occasional occurrences at inland waters. Since the 1960s, presumably as the result of increased watching at both coastal and inland localities, the species has been shown to be far more numerous than was formerly supposed.

The largest parties mentioned by Chislett were 14 in Whitby Harbour on 18th February 1940 and ten in flight off Cloughton on 26th December 1948. Only five inland waters were mentioned as having had mergansers.

Anywhere along the coastline, mostly during October and throughout the winter, small numbers may be seen either flying offshore or feeding close in among the rocks, usually with other seafowls. Ones, twos and threes are usually encountered, but occasionally larger parties are noted and these may occur in any month. The main influx is during October, and it is at that time that mergansers are most likely to be seen.

On 18th October 1958, P.J. Stead saw 23 birds flying across the Tees Bay, and 12 flew north at Redcar on the same day. On 2nd October 1965 ten were seen at Spurn, with 14 there on 24th. A marked passage northward occurred at South Gare during October 1966, when totals of six, 19 and 24 were counted on 6th, 25th and 27th respectively; 22 passed up the coast there on 5th November 1957. In 1970, 45 flew north at South Gare on 21st October and 27 did so on the same date in 1972, when ten were also seen flying north at Filey Brigg. D.E. Murray counted 32 flying north off Filey on 7th October 1973, and 52 passed Flamborough on 12th November 1983. Smaller numbers occurred at other coastal watchpoints during these periods.

Inland occurrences are widespread and may occur in any month, the peak times often coinciding with the coastal influx. Ten were at Gouthwaite Reservoir on 20th October 1968, and seven were there on 11th September 1971. At most other places numbers are few, and an odd bird or a pair may stay for just a few days or less before moving on.

In 1957, K.G. Spencer watched a lone drake at Stocks Reservoir in the north-west of the county. Later in the year, on 28th July, Keith Fenton saw a duck with seven young, which Chislett said 'implied the possibility of breeding'. It most surely did! The birds were present during the following summer without evidence of successful breeding, but in 1959 nine eggs were found, from which five young eventually flew. In 1960, three clutches were located consisting of six, seven and seven eggs, but many of these were addled; the observers saw no more than eight chicks and believed that none was reared.

Three pairs bred again in 1961 and the species has been present during the summer in every year since then. Evidence of successful breeding is often difficult to obtain in the absence of hard searching for nests, a practice not pursued these days, but in most years some young are seen. More pairs are seen in early summer than are subsequently seen with young, and it could be that these are non-breeding birds, or those that have been unsuccessful. In 1967, four or five such pairs were present, and in 1969 seven drakes and four ducks were seen on 26th May but only one duck apparently produced young, two chicks being seen on 29th August. During the last decade, one or two pairs have been proved to breed with varying success under the watchful eye of John Fenton, who has supplied information during this period.

In 1975, G.D. Moore reported that a pair had nested on the River Tees near Piercebridge, and that a pair had done so since 1973.

The species can be considered established as a breeding bird at Stocks Reservoir and a pair or two may spread to other places if success continues there.

Goosander
Mergus merganser

Like the last species, the Goosander is a much more numerous bird than it was in Nelson's, or even in Chislett's days. This change is due to a definite increase in the number of birds visiting the county, rather than being the result of increased observer activity.

Chislett mentioned Eccup Reservoir as the place where Goosanders occurred with the greatest regularity, but added that, prior to 1920, it had been little in evidence there. This reservoir is certainly one of the most important wintering places, along with Stocks Reservoir and Hornsea Mere, and during the 1960s these three waters each regularly attracted between 60 and 80 birds. The two reservoirs at Leighton and Roundhill became popular waters during the mid 1960s and continue to attract good numbers.

On 2nd January 1970, W.F. Curtis was watching at Hornsea Mere when he counted 218 Goosanders, 179 of which were seen to fly in from the southeast. This was the largest number ever recorded in Yorkshire and remains so today. On the previous day 41 birds had been present, and the large numbers on 2nd soon dispersed, leaving only 51 on 5th.

During the 1970s, Eccup Reservoir continued to hold up to 90 or so Goosanders each winter, with a large increase in 1979 when there were counts of 176 on 25th January, 139 on 24th February and 141 on 8th March. This large influx was no doubt due to the severe weather which affected western Europe at the time and forced many aquatic species over to Britain. In the following year, the high numbers were repeated and 159 were seen on 20th January and 122 on 17th February.

During the last few years, the numbers visiting Hornsea Mere have decreased dramatically and no more than 27 have been seen there. Annual peaks of only 18 in 1973, ten in 1974, 27 in 1975, 20 in 1976, 15 in 1977 and 14 in 1980 illustrate this trend. Stocks Reservoir has fared similarly.

Apart from Hornsea Mere, the waters most frequently visited by Goosanders lie in the western part of the county. In addition to the most popular waters mentioned above, birds regularly frequent Malham Tarn, Chelker Reservoir, Ilton Reservoir, Gouthwaite Reservoir, the River Wharfe about Pool and the River Ure near Ripon. On 23rd February 1979, 118 birds were on the Wharfe between Pool and Arthington when Eccup Reservoir was frozen over. Goosanders are to be seen regularly along the river courses when severe weather forces them off the lakes and reservoirs. Some gravel-pits are now becoming popular, and the one at Hay-a-Park near Knaresborough held up to 36 birds at both ends of 1978 and 90 in December 1983.

Numbers visiting Yorkshire vary annually and, as stated above, their movements are very much affected by the severity of the weather, both at national and local level. Any large sheet of water, particularly those along the Pennines, is likely to

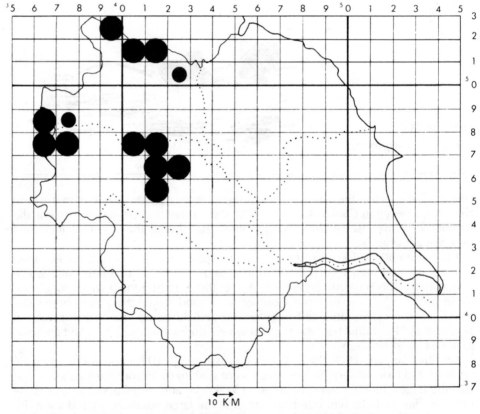

Goosander. A southerly extension of the breeding range brought the Goosander to Yorkshire in 1969. Further spread is likely along the hill streams and at moorland reservoirs.

attract this handsome bird, especially from November onwards when the main influx of immigrants from their breeding grounds in northern Britain and Scandinavia occurs. A flock of Goosanders flying over snow-covered ground with the light reflecting on the salmon-pink bellies of the drakes is a superb sight.

Coastal occurrences involve surprisingly few birds, and low single figures are usual. Ten birds off Flamborough Head on 25th September 1976 and nine on 18th November 1980 are the largest numbers seen together on the coast.

In 1952, Chislett wrote in *Yorkshire Birds*: 'the species appears to be slowly extending its breeding range southward. Breeding in Scotland was rare before 1871. In very recent years a few pairs have bred in Northumberland where I am informed they are increasing. It would give me little surprise if the species attempted to breed in Yorkshire in the fairly near future.' It was to be 17 years before proof of this prophetic comment was forthcoming when, in 1969, two pairs nested along the River Tees between Middleton-in-Teesdale and Barnard Castle and another pair bred at Dent, near Sedbergh. In the following year, four broods were seen on the River Tees above Barnard Castle, with five broods there in 1971 and a pair again near Sedbergh. A pair on the River Ure, near Leyburn, seen by G.E. Alderson in 1972, was the first such ocurrence in Wensleydale, where they were to become firmly established during the next few years; I am indebted to Alderson and to J. Hancox for monitoring their progress, which included three broods near Wensley in 1973 and three broods of six, seven and three in 1975. By 1975, seven pairs were also breeding in the Sedbergh area and G.D. Moore reported five pairs along the River Tees between High Force and Piercebridge. On 26th July, four well-grown 'flappers' were on Leighton Reservoir, where earlier in the summer an agitated duck had been seen by P.J. Carlton.

In 1977, a pair with seven young was on the River Tees near Wycliffe, and a duck with nine young was seen at Bolton Bridge on 3rd June. On 28th June, a duck on the River Dove in Farndale was joined by a drake and breeding was considered likely. In 1978, reports of breeding came from the River Ure, near Ripon, where a brood of nine was seen by C. Slater and S. Worwood; the River Ribble, near Settle, where there were two broods of eight in June; Bolton Bridge, where a duck accompanied no fewer than 16 ducklings in June; and also along the River Tees. Records also came from the high ground in Wensleydale, where birds were seen along some streams during the summer.

Nine broods reported in 1980 did not include the River Tees or the Sedbergh area, but did include the first breeding record for Gouthwaite Reservoir, as well as the regular areas on the rivers Ribble, Ure and Wharfe. In 1982, R. Sutton and I watched a duck with 11 young on the River Wharfe at Burnsall.

Few breeding species have become established so rapidly with such success, and there is little doubt that the Goosander is here to stay as a nesting species, with indication of increasing numbers and further spread. At least 14 pairs bred in 1983.

Nelson cited an incident concerning a bird shot on the River Tees, near Stockton, in March 1853, the gizzard of which contained part of a gold ear-ring, no doubt swallowed by the fish on which the bird had fed.

Ruddy Duck
Oxyura jamaicensis

Two specimens of this small North American 'stifftail' were seen at Fairburn Ings from 16th to 30th April 1968, and one was at the same locality between 19th and

30th October in the same year which I saw with C. Winn and M.L. Denton. In the following year, a duck was seen by C. Winn at Fairburn and another was on Harewood Park Lake on 26th October. Since 1974, Ruddy Ducks have occurred in Yorkshire in every year to the present time, with increasing frequency.

An established feral population exists, mainly in the West Midlands and originating from The Wildfowl Trust at Slimbridge, from where about 70 young birds dispersed during the late 1950s and early 1960s. The first record of successful breeding in a wild state came from Somerset in 1960, and the species was admitted to the British List in 1971.

In 1974, a duck seen at Gouthwaite Reservoir by P.J. Carlton and others from 21st to 29th September, a young drake seen at Masham Gravel-pits by A.F.G. Walker on 4th October, and a duck seen by R.G. Hawley at Hornsea Mere in November and December heralded the present-day annual trend of occurrence. Two ducks were on Hornsea Mere during February and March 1975, one of which remained into April. P.B. Wordsworth reported two ducks at Worsborough Reservoir, near Barnsley, on 23rd September 1976, and in the following year there were records from three waters: J.E. Dale and G.M. Yeates saw a drake at Blackmoorfoot Reservoir on 15th May; P. Smith and G.J. Speight saw two ducks, or young drakes, at Wintersett Reservoir on 10th September; and one was again at Worsborough Reservoir on 10th November and from 30th November to 7th December.

1978 produced even more birds, starting with a duck at Blackmoorfoot Reservoir on 18th August. This was followed by a pair at Bretton Park on 13th September, and single birds at Mickletown Ings from 18th to 25th November; at Harewood Park Lake from 25th October to 5th November; and at Staveley Lagoon from 22nd June to 13th July which greeted my colleagues R. Evison and G.T. Foggitt on their return from North America, where they had been watching the species in its native haunts.

A drake was on the river at Dewsbury Sewage-farm on 4th February 1979, and single birds were at Newington Flash from 11th to 19th February, Wintersett Reservoir on 8th March, Wath Ings on 27th and 28th April, and at Merehall Reservoir on 14th and 15th September. Two were at Southfield Reservoir on 6th October, with one staying up to 23rd December. One was on Seamer Road Mere, Scarborough, from 13th to 24th November, and single birds were at Knotford Nook Gravel-pits from 9th to 11th March, on 22nd October and from 17th to 20th November, and at Paul's Pond, Leeds, on 1st November.

From the above records, it will be seen that the distribution was becoming widespread within the county, with the long stays of several individuals suggestive of eventual breeding. This was to happen in 1980, when, after four drakes and a duck arrived at Harewood Park Lake in late March, three drakes eventually departed, leaving a pair which nested and reared two young, the first breeding recorded in Yorkshire. During that year, Ruddy Ducks occurred at 12 other localities, including Bolton-on-Swale Gravel-pits, Fairburn Ings, Tophill Low Reservoir, Treeton Dyke Reservoir, Sandbeck Park, Ingbirchworth Reservoir, Wintersett Reservoir, Mickletown Ings and two waters near Leeds, with five drakes flying south at Spurn on 31st October.

In 1981, single pairs were present at Harewood Park Lake from mid May to mid November, at Wheldrake Ings from 5th to 12th April, and at Potteric and Low Ellers Carrs from 18th to 31st May, but no proof of breeding was obtained. Mickletown Ings attracted two males from 9th August, then up to seven birds from 28th September to 26th November. Single birds were seen on various dates during the year at seven other waters.

Four pairs nested in 1982, two of these being at Allerton Bywater, where three broods were hatched, one at Mickletown Ings and one at Harewood Park Lake.

In 1983, five young were reared at Harewood Park Lake, three pairs bred at Mickletown Ings and single pairs at Swillington, Wintersett and on the Lower Derwent.

That breeding will occur at other localities during the next few years there is little doubt, and this small attractive duck is a welcome addition to the Yorkshire list of breeding birds.

Honey Buzzard
Pernis apivorus

A bird mentioned in Denny's *Leeds Catalogue* (1828), said to have been obtained at Harewood and later passed into the collection of a Dr Leach, is the first recorded occurrence of the species in Yorkshire.

Nelson knew it as a 'Bird of passage, of rare occurrence in spring and autumn; most frequently observed at the latter period and near the coast.' He had 'nearly one hundred published and communicated instances of its occurrence', not 200 as erroneously quoted by Chislett. Some intriguing stories were quoted in *The Birds of Yorkshire*, including one of a bird which was flapping against a window in Bridlington at midnight and making such a noise that the person got up and captured it (*The Zoologist*, 1850, p. 2649). Mr J. Backhouse presented to the York Museum a specimen which had been taken at 1 a.m. on 14th September 1883 against the Spurn Light. A bird caught alive at sea, 4 miles (6.4 km) off Whitby, in about 1875, while in pursuit of a pigeon which took refuge on board a fishing coble, is, as stated by Nelson, a most unusual occurrence. The bird hovered around the coble and was eventually knocked into the water and captured. This 'fine living specimen of the Honey Buzzard' was in the possession of a Mr J. Kitching of Whitby, but Nelson does not say definitely that he saw it, although his statement implies such. It is likely that the bird was exhausted, and attempting to land on the boat as a last resort.

In August 1902, the gamekeeper at Aske, near Richmond, killed an immature individual while it was in the act of carrying off a Woodpigeon. This was told to Nelson by the Marquis of Zetland in whose collection the bird was, but he had been at 'some pains to ascertain the correctness of the incident and the identity of the specimen', which suggests that he had some doubts. Could this bird have been a Goshawk, a much more likely bird to tackle a Woodpigeon?

Migrant Honey Buzzards pass through Yorkshire mainly during May and June and in August and September. Since 1912, the 49 Honey Buzzards recorded up to 1982 moving through the county have occurred in April (one, 30th); May (six); June (13); July (two); August (four); September (19); and October (two, 1st and 10th).

That some birds do not survive the North Sea crossing is evidenced by the discovery of dead Honey Buzzards along the shore. One was found on the sands at Marske in June 1911 (*The Naturalist*, 1912, p. 20); another was found dead on Filey beach on 7th March 1929, an extremely early date (*The Naturalist*, 1929, p. 174); a dark-phase juvenile was found dead on Filey beach on 17th September 1969; and one was similarly found on Filey Brigg on 4th June 1983. The 1969 specimen was very wet and bedraggled, but the skin cleaned up well and is now in my collection. I am grateful to A.J. Wallis for presenting the corpse to me, which proved on dissection to be a young female; it was very fat and had presumably weakened during its long flight and dropped into the sea. The 1983 bird was found dead on the rocks at the Brigg by C. Callaghan of Leeds, who took it to the sea-watching hut to show those present. It was very wet but otherwise in good condition, and was examined and identified by P.J. Dunn, H.J. Whitehead and others. Photographs show it to be a very pale and well-barred individual and the body was retained by Callaghan.

In addition to coastal occurrences in both spring and autumn, birds are frequently seen inland, most often in the vicinity of large sheets of water, where birdwatchers are most in evidence. In recent years, birds have been recorded singly flying over Leeds; Fairburn Ings; Wintersett; Tophill Low Reservoir; Knaresborough Ringing Station; Lindley Reservoir; Potteric Carr; Redmires Reservoir; Treeton, where two flew southeast on 26th August 1976; near Sheffield; Gouthwaite Reservoir; Deffer Wood; and Blacktoft Sands. Two flew over Hornsea Mere on 1st June 1974. On 29th April 1978, at Spurn, three birds identified simply as buzzards as they flew up the Humber were thought to have been Honey Buzzards, although the views were not good enough for certainty.

Nelson said that 'It has no doubt bred in the county, for Dr. Farrer informed Thomas Allis that a pair fixed their quarters in Wharnecliffe Wood in 1833, one of them being shot; and W.W. Boulton of Beverley was of the opinion that two young birds, which formerly constituted part of his fine collection, were bred amid the wooded margins of the Hornsea Mere.' In the catalogue of a sale at Steven's Rooms on 22nd April 1895, two eggs of the Honey Buzzard, taken at Hackness, were offered for sale. Nelson concluded his remarks on the breeding of the species by saying that 'it seems not improbable that some of the individuals seen in spring and early summer may have intended to nest in the county if allowed to remain unmolested'. How true that was.

In early August 1950, a Mr A.E. Felgate found a large nest about 30 feet (9 m) up in a larch tree in Roppa Wood in Riccaldale. The nest was surrounded by down and had green branches woven into it. The adult bird had yellow eyes and, when Felgate visited the site with Morris Ward some days later, the young were out of the nest and the adults 'glared down at them'. On 12th and 13th August, Felgate and Ward saw four birds in the air together and both observers said that they were definitely not common Buzzards, being longer in the tail, shorter in the wing and paler underneath. That description fits Goshawk better than the supposed Honey Buzzard. When the nest was first located, a dead young Cuckoo lay underneath and a wasps' nest had been dug out in the plantation about 100 yards away. When R. Chislett, R.M. Garnett, P.J. Stead and the two finders went to the nest on 19th August, there was no sign of the birds, but the party considered that the nest belonged to either common Buzzard, Honey Buzzard or Goshawk. Many aspects point to the latter and only the excavated wasps' nest would seem to indicate the presence of Honey Buzzards. It is very unfortunate that the attempt to confirm the species came too late, and in my opinion the incident is far from proven as a Honey Buzzard breeding record.

On 27th May 1976, a pair of Honey Buzzards was seen in an area which for the sake of security must remain undisclosed. There are still those who would take the eggs of such a rare breeding bird, and I am not even at liberty to give the names of those caring ornithologists who have watched and guarded the area over the years. Suffice to say that the pair of birds chose an area of mixed woodland and remained during the summer. The nest site was located by many hours of watching, from a distance, the flight-lines of the male bird during July and August. On 18th August, the male was seen entering and leaving the nest area regularly, and while circling about a mile from the site was joined by the female carrying a large spherical object, probably honeycomb, in her claws, which were held at full stretch. She left the male and entered the nest area in a long steady glide. The male's feeding flights continued up to 5th September, and the female was last seen on 8th September. No search was made for the nest and no young birds were seen.

In the following year, a male, first seen on 21st May, was presumed from its plumage and behaviour to be the 1976 bird. Display was witnessed on 26th May and was frequently performed, often at a great height and over a wide area, until 7th July. The male continued to soar over the woodland and enter and leave the nest site of the previous year until it was last seen on 27th August. A new, all-dark bird was seen on 3rd September. Whether or not this was a juvenile is not known.

In 1978, what was again presumed to be the male of 1976 appeared on 27th May and displayed for long periods from 3rd to 10th June. On 17th June, the male was visiting the nest area and a new individual was soaring overhead. On 29th July, the male visited the nest area and a new female left and soared away. The male displayed again on several dates between 3rd and 19th August, both at a height and low over the nest site, suggesting breeding failure; it was last seen flying westwards, still displaying, on 24th August.

In 1979 and 1980, there were only four sightings in total and the general area had been much disturbed by tree felling.

In 1981, however, a bird was seen at a new locality nearby and a pair was seen together on 29th and 30th July, with both birds displaying on the latter date. The male was seen during August and in early September on a probable nest flight-line, and breeding was considered possible. Both these birds were different from the original ones in 1976-78. This same locality was watched in 1982, but with no encouraging results. After a possible sighting on 26th May, nothing was seen until a pair was present on 21st and 22nd August. A watch during 1983 revealed no Honey Buzzards at all.

That these birds may breed again, or attempt to do so, and others settle in to nest in other parts of Yorkshire is more than likely. In order that a few pairs of this exciting raptor may become established in the county, they will need to be completely undisturbed. Their very specialised lifestyle inflicts no harm whatsoever on man's interests, and the species should go unmolested.

Evidence of the Scandinavian origin of some Yorkshire migrants comes from the finding of a dead bird on Martin Common, Bawtry, on 26th October 1976 that had been ringed in the nest at Göteborg, Sweden, on 12th August 1976.

It should be mentioned that a bird in Nelson's collection, which was presented to the Dorman Museum, Middlesbrough, by his widow in 1916, and labelled Buzzard in case number 168, is in fact a dark juvenile Honey Buzzard which P.J. Stead and I inspected in August 1984. The bird was shot at Sewerby in September 1907.

A buzzard found alive at Dunsdale, south of Guisborough, in early September 1966 was later released after being photographed by N.W. Harwood. The record was published by P.J. Stead in *The Birds of Tees-side* (1969) as a common Buzzard as it had been reported at the time. Stead and I subsequently saw the colour transparency taken by Harwood and the bird is clearly a Honey Buzzard.

Black Kite
Milvus migrans

The occurrences of this species in Yorkshire are few. Two large dark birds of prey which were seen in the Washburn Valley on 30th October 1959 and reported in the Yorkshire Naturalists' Union Ornithological Report for that year as this species leave some room for doubt, and I do not feel that the record is acceptable.

On 12th May 1975, C. Bielby saw a Black Kite flying along the edge of the Hambleton Hills near Kepwick and was able to take a photograph of the bird as it sailed overhead. The print is clearly recognisable as this species, and the date is also perfect for this south European species to wander north on its spring migration.

In 1979, Miss Joan Fairhurst and H.O. Bunce watched a Black Kite flying down the Derwent Valley at Bubwith on 19th May which they described in detail. Later in the year, on 8th July, Bunce was fortunate enough to see a second bird as it passed over his garden at Skidby, being mobbed by Carrion Crows. The *British Birds* Rarities Committee felt unable to accept this second bird, mainly on the grounds that the views were brief, but Bunce knows his birds of prey and there is no more careful and critical observer than he.

Records in 1981 of a bird at Southfield Reservoir seen by C. Wall and others on 3rd May, and another, or the same, on Thorne Moors seen by M. Limbert on 9th May were similarly considered unacceptable by the *British Birds* Rarities Committee, although the Yorkshire recorders were satisfied as to their correctness. Intimate knowledge of an observer's ability and attitude are at times more important than the written description when considering the record of a rare bird.

The Black Kite is spreading slowly northwards as a breeding species in Europe, and wandering birds are now occurring more regularly in Britain. That more will occur in Yorkshire is inevitable.

Red Kite
Milvus milvus

In *The Birds of Yorkshire*, Nelson had much to say about the Red Kite, including the first reference to it as a Yorkshire bird, when it was mentioned by George Stovin in the *Gentleman's Magazine* (1747, p. 23) as a native of the country about Hatfield Chase. Allis (1844) mentioned one being caught in a trap at Edlington Wood, near Doncaster, and a pair of young taken from the nest by H. Reid of Doncaster. Nelson considered there to be no doubt that it formerly nested in Yorkshire, but said that the old information on this point was difficult to obtain. The Edlington specimen was, in Nelson's time, in the Chester Museum.

In a manuscript list supplied to Nelson in 1880, a Mr J. Tennant wrote that one was shot from the nest at Murton, near Hawnby, by Charles Harrison, who obtained both birds. A pair was obtained in Redhouse Wood about 1850 and a pair passed over Wilstrop in 1874. Charles Waterton of Walton Hall said that 'of all the large wild birds which formerly were so common in this part of Yorkshire, the Heron alone can now be seen. The Kite, the Buzzard and the Raven have been exterminated long ago by our merciless gamekeepers. Kites were frequent here in the days of my father, but I, myself, have never seen it near the place.' (*Louden's Magazine Nat. Hist.*, 1835). The Red Kite was obviously scarce during the nineteenth century, Nelson listing only 15 occurrences and his assessment of its status being 'casual visitant, of very rare occurrence ...'.

It is surprising that between 1901, when a female was obtained at Flamborough on 15th October, and 1952, when Chislett published *Yorkshire Birds*, no Red Kites were recorded in Yorkshire at all, and Chislett said that it had ceased to be even a 'casual visitant, of very rare occurrence'. A further six years passed before the species was to be encountered in Yorkshire again, when, on 4th March 1958, G. Aynsley, a young observer, saw what he described as a Red Kite over Barnsley. Alan Archer questioned the boy about the claim and felt satisfied that it was correct. Chislett published the details in the Ornithological Report of the Yorkshire Naturalists' Union for that year, along with two other reports. The second was on 6th March, when D. Ward watched one at Arthington. He described the bird as being 2 feet (60 cm) in length with a long forked tail, and reddish-brown in colour with deeper red on back and rump. The wings were pale underneath, and the bird was flying close to the ground as it was being mobbed by Rooks. The third was on 18th April at Ogden Reservoir, near Halifax, where C. Williamson saw one in the company of Rooks and gulls. Other Red Kites were seen farther south in England in March and April that year.

A bird which was watched at Spurn Point on 10th November 1967 as it flew out to sea heralded the species' almost annual occurrence. On 23rd March 1968, David Alred was driving along the Dob Park road in the Washburn Valley when his wife pointed out a large bird in the sky. They stopped and were surprised to see that it was a Red Kite; they took full details. It was seen independently on the same day by three other people, including F.J. Steele of London. I went to the site next morning with R. Evison and, in pouring rain, saw the bird well. It stayed in the area until at least 27th March. On 11th March 1972, P.J. Carlton, D.W. Swindells and A.F.G. Walker watched one at Gouthwaite Reservoir as it drifted to the southeast. Later in the day, at 15.45 hours, a Red Kite, presumably the same one, was seen over Collingham, some 20 miles (32 km) southeast of Gouthwaite. On 12th, H.O. Bunce and Miss Joan Fairhurst saw one over Thixendale on the Wolds.

A Red Kite was in Farndale during June 1973, and later in the year one took up residence in the area of Bishop Wilton, east of York. It was first noted on 15th October by workers on the estate, and on 8th November Peter Hutchinson saw it from Garrowby Hill. The estate owner was very interested in the bird's welfare and gave instructions for its protection. That it stayed, unharmed, until 19th January 1974 must be, in no little way, due to that most encouraging attitude. On 3rd February 1974, what was presumably the same bird was seen at Leavening, a few miles farther north.

A bird which was seen circling over Kilnsea on 6th April 1975 later flew south down the Spurn Peninsula. This was the first of four records in that year, the others being at Gorple Reservoir on 28th July and in early August; at Walkley, near Sheffield, on 1st August; and at Dinnington, South Yorkshire, on 18th.

The late Colonel John Newman supplied me with details of a Red Kite which was found dead at Scagglethorpe, near Malton, on 13th April 1976 and which is now preserved as a study skin in the York Museum. One was seen by C. Straker over Crosshills, Keighley, on 10th July 1977 and another was seen by A. O'Neill near Harrogate on 21st January 1978. On 8th January 1979, one was observed at Spurn Point, and on 19th April one flew south over Easington Lagoons and later down the Humber at Spurn. It is interesting to note that what was presumably the same bird was seen flying southwest over Saltfleetby, Lincolnshire, later the same day. There were two records in 1980, both from the coast. One which flew southeast over Easington and Kilnsea on 29th March was seen by N.A. Bell and others, and on 15th April W.C. Clarke saw one coming in over the sea at Osgodby, Scarborough.

In 1981, one was seen near Birkenshaw on 22nd March, one flew east over Crosland Hill, Huddersfield, on 23rd April, and one came in over the sea at Flamborough on 17th May. In 1982, one flew south at Millington on 21st February and what was no doubt the same bird was seen over Everthorpe an hour-and-a-half later. One was at Harewood Park on 30th September; one flew south, then north, at Spurn on 17th October; and one was seen over the M62 motorway near Ferrybridge on 16th November.

The Red Kite is now more regular than during Nelson's days and can be expected almost annually, mainly during the winter and spring. Some of the birds seen along the coast in spring may eventually cross the sea into Europe, but others will undoubtedly come from the Welsh breeding population.

Nelson warned that records of kites should be treated with caution, as, in the mountainous districts of the county, the Buzzard is usually known by the name of 'Kite' or 'Glead'. He considered that the 'Glead', mentioned in the Reverend Edward Peake's *Avifauna of Ribblesdale* (*The Naturalist*, 1896, p. 42) as 'occurring in the memory of the old dalesfolk especially near Wharfe and Greygreth', is referable to the Buzzard. There is, I am sure, no longer a problem in that direction.

A mounted specimen in the Yorkshire Museum, which, according to the details on the label at the back of the case, was shot near Guisborough between 1859 and 1864, does not appear to have been recorded by Nelson.

Swallow-tailed Kite
Elanoides forficatus

Three occurrences of this American species were included by Nelson in *The Birds of Yorkshire*. Howard Saunders refused to accept the first of these, which had hitherto been generally accepted, but Professor Alfred Newton in his edition of Yarrell's *British Birds* considered it a good record. The incident was recorded by a Mr Fothergill of Carr End, near Askrigg in Wensleydale, whose original notes were produced by his son, Mr William Fothergill of Darlington, and the event was entered in the Minute Book of the Linnean Society dated 4th November 1823. The notes state that on 6th September 1805, during a tremendous thunderstorm, a bird, which was described perfectly, alighted on a tree and was knocked down by a stick thrown at it. It was not killed and was kept in confinement until 27th September, when it escaped after being shown to some friends of Fothergill. It rose high in the air and was mobbed by Rooks, before alighting on the same tree in which it was first seen. When approached, it flew off towards the south and was not seen again. Mr Charles Fothergill of York, a nephew of the old Fothergill, wrote to him saying that 'Unaccountable then as the facts may be, it rests on the evidence of perfectly competent witnesses, and there is accordingly no room for doubt in this case.' The editors of *The Handbook of British Birds* rejected the record and said 'the claims for the admission of this species are in our opinion insufficient'. It is impossible to say otherwise, although, on 4th December 1948, W.B. Alexander, in his presidential address to the Yorkshire Naturalists' Union at Scarborough, expressed the view that 'the Swallow-tailed Kite has as good a claim to a place on the British List as any other species which has been captured or killed on a single occasion in the British Isles'. Chislett agreed with that view entirely.

The second record referred to by Nelson concerned a bird in the collection of A. Clapham of Scarborough, who stated that he purchased it from Mr Graham of York, a taxidermist to whom it had been sold by Jonathan Taylor, a schoolmaster from Harome, near Helmsley. Before purchasing the specimen, Clapham made enquiries about its origin and wrote to Taylor, who replied 'In referring to my old books of memoranda is the following:– 25th May 1859, Little George [the name of the keeper at Duncombe Park] brought me today a Swallow-tailed Kite shot by himself in the Quarry Bank, near Helmsley, on the estate of the Earl of Feversham.' Clapham had several other letters from Taylor bearing out his claims, and in one he said that he greatly regretted selling it to Graham for a few shillings, not knowing its value at the time. About the same time as this bird's claimed appearance, the sighting of a Swallow-tailed Kite at Glaisdale was notified to Thomas Stephenson of Whitby, who took an interest in the birds of the northeastern part of Yorkshire, by a Mr Lister who, with his brother, saw the bird: it was black and white and its tail much more forked than that of the Red Kite.

The third example was in the collection of Alfred Beaumont of Huddersfield and supposed to have been obtained in Bolton Woods some 'forty or fifty years ago' (prior to 1907). It was formerly in the collection of a Brighouse or Halifax gentleman, on whose death the collection was auctioned and the bird bought by Beaumont for £11. Beaumont was apparently satisfied that the bird was a genuine Yorkshire specimen, but after paying that much for it I suppose he had to be. Nelson could not agree, because of the vague nature of the evidence. The extra value of a specimen taken locally was a great incentive for taxidermists and others to label falsely rare birds which had been imported, and the likelihood of this deception pertaining in this case is perhaps more than a probability.

Whether or not this beautiful bird of prey has ever crossed the Atlantic of its own accord will never be known for certain. The large sailing ships were operating at this time and several species of birds were brought over to Liverpool, a not unusual habit of sailors. This kite was doubtless more common in the southern United States then than it is now and vagrancy would not, however, have been impossible, even if most unlikely. The species is not included in the British and Irish list of birds on the grounds that its appearance here is so unlikely, and because of the unethical practices of some taxidermists and naturalists of the period, as mentioned above.

White-tailed Eagle
Haliaeetus albicilla

Nelson's opening remarks for this species echo the fate of many large birds of prey in those days, and even at the present time in spite of supposed protection:

'The White-tailed or Sea Eagle is but a very occasional visitor, occurring chiefly in the autumn and winter, on its passage southward from northern latitudes. Although most frequent on the coast, yet it is by no means confined to it, and visits our large inland woods and waters, where its size soon attracts the attention of the gamekeeper, to whose gun or snare it usually falls a victim.'

Nelson listed some 21 records up to 1898, including a few about which there were some interesting details. One bird, in the collection of the Duke of Devonshire at Chatsworth, was killed by a keeper in the Forest Moors near Bolton Abbey about the year 1871. It was unable to rise at the time, being gorged while feeding on the carcase of a sheep, and the keeper tried to capture it alive, but the bird fought so hard that he was compelled to kill it with his stick. John Cordeaux recorded the occurrence of two, one of which, an immature female measuring 8 feet (2.4 m) in extent of wings, was killed on 28th October 1889 by Mr G.E. Clubley, with a charge of number eight shot in the head, while skimming over the bents at Spurn (*The Naturalist*, 1890, p. 10). A fine male, trapped at Long Pain, Bedale Wood, near Scarborough, on 17th January 1865 and reported by Nelson under this species, was in fact an American Bald Eagle (see under that species).

Since *The Birds of Yorkshire* was published in 1907, there have been nine instances of this fine eagle's appearance in the county, seven of which were published by Chislett in *Yorkshire Birds*. The first of these, shot near Bickley on 1st May 1911, was said to have been in the district for three years (*The Naturalist*, 1911, p. 237). One was killed at Guisborough on 17th November 1915, and one was stated to have been seen by P. Horsfall and his brother on the Cleveland Hills between Kildale and Great Ayton on 1st December 1915 (*British Birds*, 9, p. 212). Chislett watched an immature bird above the hills on the Yorkshire side of the Derbyshire Derwent on 1st January 1921 and subsequently. At first thought to be a Golden Eagle, it was later identified by T.A. Coward and A.W. Boyd as this species, which was confirmed when it was shot some weeks later, an offence for which the offending keeper was fined. Another example frequented this same area on both the Derbyshire and Yorkshire sides from 20th February to 13th March 1939 and was seen by several observers. A male was picked up dead at Cloughton on 12th March 1942, after having been shot; it was in almost full adult plumage and W.J. Clarke noted that it had been trapped at some time, as evidenced by the absence of three toes from its left foot. The seventh bird was present for about a month from 20th January 1948 in northeast Yorkshire, where it was seen by R.M. Garnett, M.F.M. Meiklejohn, A.J. Wallis and others. On 8th February the eagle's nightly roost was located in an oak wood on the steep side of Dovedale Griff, below the Bridestones, and each day the bird flew down the valley and out onto the Vale of Pickering to hunt, returning to its roosting place each evening. It was last seen on 17th February and was believed to have left the area alive. See *The Naturalist*, 1948, p. 114, for full details.

Thirty-four years were to elapse before another White-tailed Eagle was seen in Yorkshire, when, on 28th February and 1st March 1982, an immature was observed on Thorne Moors by W.H. Priestley, G. Sellors and A.D. Warren. What was no doubt the same bird was seen later on 1st March at Spurn Point by A.G. and M.E. Blunt and others.

The year 1983 produced another record when, on 15th November, at Bridlington, one of the corporation gardeners working on the flowerbeds along the seafront just south of the harbour noticed a large dead bird on the tideline. He went to investigate the corpse and found that it was an eagle. He informed G. Brown, who in turn told Ivan Procter, the RSPB warden at Hornsea Mere, and together they inspected the specimen on the following day. Apart from having been pecked on the breast and at the back of the head, most likely by gulls, it was in very good condition and was sent to a Manchester taxidermist by Brown on behalf of the Bridlington Corporation, for eventual display in Sewerby Hall. The bird was an immature and it is indeed fortunate that the specimen was rescued before it had been too badly mutilated by gulls and dogs.

American Bald Eagle
Haliaeetus leucocephalus

The inclusion of the American Bald Eagle in this work is to lay to rest a possibly erroneous claim for its admission as a Yorkshire bird. That a specimen of this species does exist is not in doubt, as it is still at the Woodend Natural History Museum in Scarborough where I have seen it, stored uncased behind the scenes, but the link between this specimen and the White-tailed Eagle trapped at Long Pain, Bedale Wood, Scarborough, on 17th January 1865, as mentioned by Nelson, cannot be proved with any degree of certainty.

Nelson reported that a White-tailed Eagle was so trapped, that it was sent by Lady Downe to D. Graham of York for preservation, and that it was exhibited at a meeting of the Yorkshire Naturalists' Club (query Union), where Graham commented that the bird had been seen in the neighbourhood for several winters. If this information was correct, then where was the bird during the summer months? Presumably, on the assumption that it was a White-tailed Eagle, those who saw the bird would have expected it to have returned northwards each spring.

A stuffed eagle, apparently labelled as White-tailed Eagle, was presented to the Rotunda Museum in Scarborough by Mr E.P. Brett of Sawdon in 1937. At that time the museum was owned by the Scarborough Archaeological and Philosophical Society, and the chairman was E.A. Wallis. The specimen was seen by W.J. Clarke, a member of the society but not curator of the museum as mentioned by Chislett. Clarke doubted the correctness of the label and suggested to Wallis that the bird was in fact a Bald Eagle. A detailed description was sent to H.F. Witherby, who, from the notes supplied, declined to accept that it was other than a White-tailed Eagle. Clarke remained convinced of his identification but let the matter rest.

Later in 1937, the society gave the Rotunda Museum, and all the collections held in it, to the Scarborough Council. As part of the council's improvements to the museum service in the town, a building in The Crescent, known as Woodend, was converted to a Natural History Museum, which opened to the public in 1951. While going through the collections in preparation for the opening, the curator, P.A. Clancey, came across a Bald Eagle and claimed it to be the bird trapped at Long Pain, Bedale Wood, near Scarborough. By that time, the bird had been taken from its original case and remounted, whether by Clancey or prior to his arrival in Scarborough is not known. Clancey announced that the bird trapped in 1865 as a White-tailed Eagle was in reality an American Bald Eagle of the race *washingtonensis* and published the claim in *British Birds*, 1950, p. 339.

The facts were picked up by Ralph Chislett, who was by then preparing his book *Yorkshire Birds*, and on 6th December 1950 he wrote to A.J. Wallis seeking his opinion and requesting factual information about Clancey's claim. Wallis discussed the matter with his father, E.A. Wallis, who said that he could clearly recall that, when the bird was first given to the museum, the now missing case had painted on the back 'Bedale, January 1867' and also gave the name of the York taxidermist, D. Graham. He suggested that the discrepancy in dates was due to a mistake in either the information given to, or made by, Nelson. Chislett subsequently decided that the evidence for accepting the Bald Eagle as an addition to the Yorkshire list was not proven, and, although he wrote to Lord Downe asking if any information about the bird had been entered in the Estate Game Book at the time, it would appear that he got no reply, for he makes no mention of it.

No explanation can be found for the transference of the specimen from Lady Downe to Mr E.P. Brett, even though Wykeham, the ancestral home of Lord Downe, and Sawdon, where Brett lived, are neighbouring villages. There is also the discrepancy in the spelling of the name of the wood where the bird was trapped. If it was trapped near Scarborough, as it must be supposed is correct as the bird came into the hands of Lady Downe, it was in Bee Dale Wood; and, if E.A. Wallis remembered correctly that the case presented by Brett was labelled 'Bedale, January 1867', it could well have originally contained a completely different bird killed at Bedale, near Northallerton. We shall now never know, and the origin of the Bald Eagle in the Woodend Museum at Scarborough must remain in doubt.

Marsh Harrier
Circus aeruginosus

Miller's *History of Doncaster*, published in 1804, stated that the 'Moor Buzzard', by which name the Marsh Harrier was locally known, was very common on the morasses and moors. The breeding population in this area of South Yorkshire up to the beginning of the nineteenth century was gradually forced out by the advancing agriculture and the usual slaughter by gamekeepers. The last recorded instance of its successful breeding in the county in that century was in 1836, near Lindholme, when a nest containing three young was found.

For 100 years from the middle of the nineteenth century, the Marsh Harrier was a very scarce bird in Yorkshire and many years passed without one being seen at all. Some idea of its rarity will be gained from the fact that in only two of the 100 years up to 1945 was more than one bird recorded. The years concerned were 1872 and 1945, the latter being the start of an annual increase in sightings which was perhaps due, in part at least, to an increase in birdwatchers, although there is little doubt that the species was visiting the county more regularly as a passage bird from that time. From 1956, one or two birds occurred almost annually at Hornsea Mere, often over the large reedbeds at the Wassand end, and although an odd harrier occasionally summered there, with new birds appearing during August in several years, no breeding was ever proved or even suspected. During the early 1950s, occasional birds were being seen at the well-watched inland waters such as Fairburn Ings, Swillington Ings and Wintersett Reservoir, and there were records from the Upper Humber and more regularly at Spurn Point, where migrants passed along the peninsula.

In the spring of 1962, more birds than usual occurred in the county, and there followed in 1963 the first known successful breeding attempt since 1836. The site was at Blacktoft Sands and F. Gilleard of Fockerby, who had watched this area for many years, had always considered the possibility of breeding by this species. His patience was rewarded when, in late April 1963, he saw nest building by a pair which was eventually to fledge three young. Gilleard and two friends kept a watch on the area during the summer and were in no small way responsible for the birds' success, an effort which earned the payment of a reward by the Royal Society for the Protection of Birds.

In 1964, the male arrived in early April, soon to be followed by the female. In order not to disturb the birds, very few visits were made to the area; a brief one in May showed that all was well, and a food pass was witnessed. A check in July revealed that two pairs were actually breeding, the other about a mile away in a strip of reeds alongside the River Trent. Work on the river embankment by the

Trent River Authority posed a threat to the second pair, but owing to the efforts of M.K. Knothard, the work was suspended, and two young were successfully reared and flew in early August. The original pair meanwhile produced three young. It is most disturbing to note that someone posing as a Nature Conservancy Officer managed to take an egg from the clutch of three at the River Trent site.

Workings on the embankment near the River Trent continued into 1965, and the pair was deterred from taking up residence. A pair did, however, settle in on the north side of the estuary at Broomfleet Island and reared three young in a bed of sea aster growing along the old tidewrack. The pair at the original site also reared three young and the Broomfleet birds brought their young over the river to Blacktoft, where, in August, Gilleard saw three adults and four young in the air at once. A male bird, presumed to be one of the breeding adults, was shot on the Lincolnshire side of the river in the autumn. Only one pair returned to the area in 1966 when they took up residence at the original Blacktoft site, suggesting that, as had been supposed, the bird shot in 1965 was the male from the Broomfleet Island pair.

The presence of a gamekeeper at Blacktoft Sands from the winter of 1966 and increased activity from birdwatchers, who had, by then, learned of the harriers, probably contributed to the birds' failure to breed successfully after returning in the spring and building a nest. A watch from across the river by Miss Joan Fairhurst revealed that something was amiss and the site was eventually deserted. The male stayed in the area during the remainder of the summer, but there was no evidence of a second attempt. Although harriers arrived in the area each spring, some staying into the summer, no more breeding took place until 1977, when a pair hatched two young. With the presence of a warden for the RSPB at Blacktoft since 1973, the harriers are at least safe from disturbance while in that area. In spite of this, the birds which have summered since 1977 failed to produce young until 1982, when two were reared, although nest building had taken place during the interim. A pair summered in 1983, but did not breed. It has been estimated that the Blacktoft harriers hunt over an area of 7,000 acres (2,830 ha), of which only 472 acres (181 ha), consisting of reedbeds, are within the reserve boundaries. They are thus very vulnerable to outside pressures while hunting over the surrounding farmland and foreshore. Birds of prey will continue to be shot by gamekeepers and rough shooters, in spite of the protection afforded them by law, and such a sensitive species as the Marsh Harrier is, sad to say, fighting an uphill battle. For full details of breeding during the period 1962 to 1966, see *The Naturalist*, 1977, pp. 125-32.

Apart from the breeding birds and their progeny, the Marsh Harrier is now far more numerous as a bird of passage through the county than it has been for perhaps 150 years. Numbers have increased markedly since 1970, and no fewer than 20 different individuals were recorded at Blacktoft Sands between 7th April and 3rd October 1975. In 1976, 32 individuals were recorded there, and birds also occurred at 15 other localities ranging from Spurn in the southeast to Settle in the west. Most were seen during May, including three which passed through the Lower Derwent Valley. Nine individuals flew south at Spurn in 1980, and upwards of 50 birds were reported in the county during that year.

A nestling ringed in Norfolk on 9th July 1983 was found dead at Catterick on 2nd February 1984.

Nelson's assessment of this harrier's status as 'Casual visitant, of very rare occurrence' certainly needs amendment. During the spring and autumn, mainly the former, a lone Marsh Harrier may be encountered almost anywhere in Yorkshire. More pass in some years than others, and there are favoured places where some may linger before passing on, notably the Upper Humber, Hornsea Mere and the Spurn Peninsula.

Hen Harrier
Circus cyaneus

It is clear from the information given in Nelson's *The Birds of Yorkshire* that the Hen Harrier was once a fairly common breeding bird on the extensive moorlands over much of Yorkshire, especially in the north and west. The available information for the period in question is almost non-existent and Nelson was unable to shed much light on the extent or numbers of the breeding population. What he did have to say illustrated very well the pressure to which this species, together with all other birds of prey, was subjected and which ultimately contributed to its demise as a regular nesting species. John Hancock took four eggs from a nest on Wemmergill Moors in 1823, and in January 1834 J.H. Anderson of Kilham wrote that 'The Hen Harrier breeds among our furze brakes, and a few years ago I shot the cock bird on a nest, and found six eggs under him. I have also had young ones more than once.' P. Hawkridge of Scarborough, writing in 1838, said that 'Specimens are repeatedly shot on the moors near Scarborough. They also breed there.' Other instances of birds being shot and eggs taken from the moors of the North Riding during the early nineteenth century leave little room to doubt that the hand of man was directly responsible for the dramatic reduction which took place at that time. The last known instance of breeding in the county during the nineteenth century was in 1888, when a pair nested in Dentdale and the four eggs were taken.

The species was very scarce thereafter, and Nelson listed only four records up to 1906. During the next 30 years about 20 Hen Harriers were noted, mostly in the northeast and the East Riding. Doubtless some of those in the north would have been visiting the traditional breeding areas and likely met the same fate as their predecessors. From 1936 more records were forthcoming, with ten birds recorded in 1947, seven in 1948, five in 1949, and six in 1950. This increase continued annually, and by 1957 14 birds were seen, mainly during November and December. Similar numbers were seen each year during the 1960s, and at the end of that decade odd individuals were lingering on some moorlands during the summer. In 1970 there were 36 sightings scattered over much of the county, and in 1978 single Hen Harriers were reported from no fewer than 25 localities in vice-county 64 (the northern half of the West Riding). Also in 1978, the wintering populations at some sites give an indication of the relatively high numbers visiting Yorkshire: up to five birds were on Broomhead Moor, up to three on the moors about Halifax and Hatfield, and up to five on Thorne Moors. Similar numbers have occurred each year up to the present time, and Blacktoft Sands has attracted up to five harriers in recent winters.

At the end of the 1960s, it was clear that the species was about to re-establish itself as a breeding bird, and proof came in 1971 when a pair was successful on a moor in the mid west of the county. Since that time, breeding has been recorded annually at two or three localities, with varying success. If left alone, Hen Harriers would become a more regular sight during the summer over the extensive moorlands of the north and west, but some keepers are against them for no valid reason, and it is not being overly pessimistic to say that, apart from odd pairs which manage to survive unnoticed, there will never be more than the few which breed at the present time. For obvious reasons, I am not able to be more precise about the localities which are at present favoured as nesting sites. Egg collecting is not a past pursuit, and there are those who would add to the harriers' problems in this way.

In 1906, Nelson could only say of it 'Bird of passage, of rare occurrence.' It is thus most pleasing to record that nowadays, at any time of the year, though mainly between September and May, a Hen Harrier may be seen quartering the ground or skulking along on migration or going to roost in almost any part of Yorkshire, from the coast to the high moorlands. During the winter months, several Hen Harriers may assemble in one spot to spend the night, and gatherings of up to seven or eight birds have been recorded at a few places in recent years. Long heather, reeds or rough ground among forestry plantations are the most popular places for such roosts, which may attract birds from a wide area, often providing the only real clue as to how many are present in the locality.

A young bird ringed in the nest on Orkney on 1st July 1960 was found dead at High Grantley, near Ripon, on 31st January 1961, and a female ringed in Strathclyde on 8th July 1981 was found dead at Duggleby on 23rd January 1982. Some illegally shot birds will be wearing rings that are not reported, but one shot in the Ripon area on 15th December 1979 came to our notice and proved to have been ringed as a chick on Terschelling in the Netherlands on 24th July 1979.

Pallid Harrier
Circus macrourus

Nelson did not record this species in *The Birds of Yorkshire*, but under Montagu's Harrier he listed a female bird, obtained at Flamborough in the late autumn of 1896, which was in the possession of M. Bailey of Flamborough. This had no notch on the outer web of the fifth primary, and the notches on the outer and inner webs of its first and second primaries were situated 1 inch (2.5 cm) below the primary coverts, all characters which are diagnostic of the Pallid Harrier. The fact that these details were noted and published by Nelson without the identity of the specimen being questioned is curious. The Pallid Harrier had been known as a distinct species since 1771, although none had been recorded in Britain at the time of this bird and presumably the wing formula was not then known as an identification character. In his addenda to *Yorkshire Birds*, Chislett mentions the occurrence and concludes thus: 'As such are the features of the Pallid Harrier's wing formula, G.H. Ainsworth has rightly pointed out that this supposed Montagu's Harrier may have been a specimen of the eastern breeding Pallid Harrier .... '

If the wing formula as claimed by Nelson was accurate, then in my opinion this could have been only a Pallid Harrier and I see no reason why it should not be accepted as the first for the British Isles. There can be no question of fabrication in order to claim a rare bird, an aspect of early ornithology often implied in the conflicting stories which supported the claims for rarities in those days, as the specimen was never apparently claimed as anything other than a Montagu's Harrier and thus the given locality would be reliable; it is unlikely that a collector would claim Flamborough as a false locality for Montagu's Harrier, a species which was by no means a rarity. The occurrence was published in *The Naturalist* (1897, p. 237) by

John Cordeaux. For details of the wing formula, see *Vår Fågelvärld*, 1971 (no. 2), pp. 106-22.

Apart from the foregoing, only three Pallid Harriers have been recorded in the British Isles. A male on Fair Isle in April and May 1931, a male in Dorset in April 1938, and an immature in Yorkshire in 1952.

The details of the latter make interesting reading. On 2nd October 1952, at Hutton Cranswick, near Driffield, two harriers were present while partridge shooting was in progress. As the gamebirds were reluctant to rise while the harriers quartered the ground, one of the latter was shot; we are not told whether or not the partridges appreciated the action and behaved more accommodatingly afterwards! The corpse was sent to a gunsmith in Beverley, who kept it for a Mr F. Wood of Sproatley to identify, and by whom it was taken to the Mortimer Museum in Hull. It was eventually sent to Messrs Edward Gerrard of London for preservation, and taken by them to the British Museum (Natural History) where it was identified by J.D. Macdonald as an immature Pallid Harrier. Few corpses can be so well travelled. The specimen is now in the Hull Museum.

I would think that the species occurs in the British Isles more frequently than is recorded, and that the female or immature harriers identified simply as 'ringtails' could well include an occasional Pallid Harrier.

Montagu's Harrier
Circus pygargus

When Thomas Allis gave his report to the British Association at York in 1844, he commented that the Montagu's Harrier had been procured by Arthur Strickland in all stages from the nest, though it was by now seldom met with. Most of the other early references concerned birds that had been shot or trapped and Nelson stated that 'the species appears formerly to have been more widely distributed in this county than either of its congeners, the Marsh and the Hen Harriers, and it also was the last of the genus to depart from its former haunts'.

By 1907, when Nelson published his *The Birds of Yorkshire*, he could say only that it may occasionally breed on some of the less frequented moors. A pair did so in 1906 in the extreme south of the county, the female being trapped at the nest, which contained two eggs.

There is ample evidence that this harrier, along with most other birds of prey, suffered much persecution at the hand of man during the nineteenth and early twentieth centuries, and the handful of breeding attempts known to Nelson were all so thwarted. A pair with their two young and some addled eggs was 'obtained' at Crosscliffe, Hackness, near Scarborough, some years prior to 1906: 'The plumage of both the old birds was peculiar, being of a dull slaty mixed colour. The two sexes were very similar in plumage and size; the female being so diminutive that were it not for the fact that she was procured at the same time as her mate and the young, she might have been mistaken for a male bird.' A male was shot on the moors near Whitby in July 1854 and three eggs taken from the nest. One of the eggs and the head of the male bird were in Nelson's possession in 1906. A pair and their young were obtained on Barden Moor in Wharfedale on 12th July 1860, the nest being on the site now occupied by the reservoir of the Bradford Corporation. See *The Naturalist*, 1905, pp. 60-87, for details. A pair and their young were captured near Bridlington in 1871. A bird stated to be this species was flushed from cover at Stockton-on-Forest, near York, and a nest containing one egg was found.

The egg was compared with others of the genus and pronounced to be that of a Montagu's Harrier. Details were published in *The Zoologist*, 1880, pp. 362, 445 and 512.

Not until 1919 was another nest discovered when, near Ribblehead on 4th June, a keeper trapped a male at the nest and took the three eggs.

Because of the need for secrecy in the interests of the species, Chislett was able to mention only a few records of breeding in his *Yorkshire Birds*, but he said that 'the occasional Montagu's Harrier began to be seen with some little regularity in summer from about 1935 in one or two moorland districts'. Young were reared in one North Riding area in that year, and a nest with five young was found in another district in 1937. In 1938, four young were reared in the northwest. After reporting these occurrences, Chislett went on to say: 'Thence onward to the present time [1952] one or two pairs of Montagu's Harriers have attempted to breed in the county annually with some little measure of success.'

It is in fact very probable that one or more pairs bred successfully from the early 1920s in a central part of the North York Moors, and from the mid 1930s in another part of the same area. The period of peak success was during the 1940s, when as many as five pairs may have bred. The apparent population crash in the mid 1950s reflected a national trend, but may have been exaggerated by the loss of the main local observers.

Breeding during the 1920s was in the Wheeldale area, where a nest with young was found by a gamekeeper in long heather and an adult trapped in July 1925. Birds assumed by the keepers to be this species were seen regularly and were thought to be nesting up to 1943, when a fire started by enemy action cleared heather from a vast area of the moorland. In 1942, H.O. Bunce confirmed the species and saw a female with one juvenile. After the heather recovered, birds were seen again and probably nested from 1946 to 1950, in 1961 and in 1970, with confirmed breeding recorded only in 1969 when both adults and two juveniles were seen in August.

In 1944, a pair of birds which were almost certainly the Wheeldale adults from 1943 probably nested in a new locality, where breeding was finally proved in 1945 when four young were ringed in a nest among young conifers. A pair again bred successfully here in 1952, this time in heather, and reared four young. An attempt to breed in 1953 unfortunately failed. It is possible that a second pair was present in 1952 and 1953, while in some of the intervening years birds were present but no breeding was proved. This second breeding locality was in fact in Dalby Forest, where in 1937 foresters located a nest near the fire tower from which four young were reared. Successful breeding followed in 1938 (four young); 1941 (four young); 1942 (three young); 1946 (three young) and 1947 (four young). Birds were also present in 1939, when they failed on two occasions, in 1940, 1943, 1944 (known to have failed), 1945 and from 1948 to 1950. The breeding area was formerly heather moor planted with Scots pine and larch in 1930, and the actual nest sites were reported as being in 'sparse forestry' and 'young firs'; in later years, when the trees were getting higher, the birds nested in wide firebreak rides. H.O. Bunce, to whom I am indebted for much of the above information, considers that the final desertion of this area was caused by disturbance during road building and by the maturing forest becoming too high for the birds' needs. Young were ringed in the nest at this site in 1942, 1946 and 1947. In the latter year, Chislett ringed two young birds, both of which were recovered dead in the same year, one at Kilnsea on 18th October and the other in Portugal, also in October.

The breeding record published by Chislett for 1935 in the North Riding was in fact on Waupley Moor, north of the River Esk, where the species again attempted but failed in 1942. A pair reared two young on Gerrick Moor in 1943, and three young were reared within 2 miles (3.2 km) of Ampleforth in 1945. Montagu's

Harriers were reported in suitable breeding areas, but with no definite proof of success, at Saltersgate in 1940, Spaunton Moor in 1950, Danby Beacon and Bilsdale in 1953, Bransdale in 1956, and Fylingdales in 1961. In 1969, at a site in the northwest, a pair was seen during June and July, and also in August, when they were accompanied by two young.

Some reports of lone harriers from the 1960s may have included an occasional Hen Harrier, a species which by then was frequenting the moors during the summer in a few areas.

In 1968, J. and A. Denison located a pair of Montagu's Harriers near Foggathorpe and breeding was proved in a 10-acre (4-ha) hayfield, where three young were reared. In 1970, a pair nested in long grass along the sea-defence banks between Easington and Kilnsea, but the eggs failed to hatch. Both birds of this pair were considered to be sub-adult. G.E. Dobbs and A.W. Wallis, along with other observers from the Spurn Bird Observatory, kept watch on this vulnerable site.

During the period 1970 to 1976, occasional pairs of or single Montagu's Harriers were seen during the summer months in the county without any indication of breeding, but in May 1983 a pair was discovered in an upland area of the west. After various discussions had taken place between the Yorkshire Naturalists' Union and the RSPB, the latter placed a full-time warden on site until early August and his efforts were ably supported, wherever possible, by a handful of volunteers from the Yorkshire Naturalists' Union Bird Protection Committee. The owner, and his keeper, were extremely co-operative, despite having reservations about the birds' presence and their potential effect on grouse stocks. It is most encouraging to report, however, that three young were successfully reared and eventually left the site during the middle of August.

It is clear from the random pattern of breeding records that a pair of these harriers may arrive and settle down to breed in any suitable district anywhere in Yorkshire, whether it be on the high moorlands or in lowland agriculture. If such breeding is suspected, the event should be afforded the strictest secrecy and advice sought on possible protection. The Bird Protection Committee of the Yorkshire Naturalists' Union and the Royal Society for the Protection of Birds have the resources to organise the protection which this rare bird so much deserves.

As a migrant through Yorkshire, the Montagu's Harrier is known to have occurred in every year since 1940, when the Yorkshire Naturalists' Union started to collect and publish records. In some years, only an occasional individual has been recorded, and in very few years have more than just two, three, or four been seen annually. This most migratory of the three regular harriers usually passes through the county during the months of May, August and September, later birds being unusual. Seven sightings, mainly along the coast, in both 1979 and 1980 was an exceptional number. Of the 14 birds involved, nine were seen in May, one in June, three in July (two of which were at inland localities), and one in September. Occasional Montagu's Harriers, seen skulking over the moorlands in May or June may still be on their way to destinations unknown to us, and those seen along the coast during the autumn may have crossed the North Sea on their way south to the wintering quarters in Africa.

Goshawk
Accipiter gentilis

A specimen of this large hawk was shot at Cusworth in 1825, an occurrence mentioned by Allis in his report of 1844.

Nelson published records of about 20 Goshawks in Yorkshire between 1825 and 1897, most of which were inevitably shot or trapped. Some of the attempts to procure birds of prey were persistent and ruthless, as shown by the account of one at Flamborough which Matthew Bailey communicated to Nelson. It concerned 'a fine old female' that frequented the area for some weeks, baffling all attempts to shoot it until 23rd January 1899, when it was seen by the gamekeeper to kill a full-grown rabbit which it carried 20 yards (18 m), when he shot at it but missed; he concealed himself in an adjoining wood, and the bird soon returned to its prey, and was finally shot. Some of the other records published by Nelson occurred in widely scattered localities, including Oswaldkirk, Ripon, Ousefleet Grange, Wykeham, Dentdale, Levisham and Eskrick, near York, but the majority were taken near the coast, suggesting that they may have been immigrants. One, a juvenile shot at Filey in January 1906, is in the Dorman Museum, Middlesbrough.

Up to 1952, when *Yorkshire Birds* was published, Chislett could add only two more records: a bird seen hunting near Runswick Bay by W.S. Medlicott on 9th January 1939; and one at Ilton on 1st November 1949, seen by P. Young, a gamekeeper/naturalist with a very favourable attitude to birds of prey.

Nothing more was seen of the Goshawk until the mid 1960s, since when a few pairs have nested, or attempted to do so, in several parts of Yorkshire. On 22nd May 1965, D. and J.W. Atter, T. Hobson and A. Critchlow located a large nest about 45 feet (14 m) high in the fork of a beech tree amid a conifer plantation in the south of the county. The nest held four eggs, but was not successful owing to possible disturbance by gamekeepers. Although there is no direct evidence that the species nested in South Yorkshire before 1965, it is possible, judging from unconfirmed reports of large nests and large hawks, that they did so from at least 1955. During the period 1965 to 1974, only one pair, and at the most probably two pairs, nested in this area. On each occasion, the attempts were thwarted by gamekeepers and egg collectors.

In 1972, D. Herringshaw started a study of the species and I am grateful to him for supplying the information for South Yorkshire. His findings suggest that, although the Yorkshire birds were faring very badly owing to human pressure, a few pairs in neighbouring Derbyshire were being more successful and the resulting young were colonising the southern and western parts of Yorkshire during the mid 1970s. From about 1975, there was a steady increase in the number of breeding pairs, but at the time of writing there are probably still fewer than ten pairs and their success is very low. It is known that only 24 or 26 young have been reared to the flying stage during the 19 years from 1965 to 1983.

Elsewhere in Yorkshire, a few pairs have been recorded during the summer months, but with very little evidence of successful breeding, although this may have occurred in several districts.

It is now clear that this large hawk, a favourite with falconers, whose escaped birds certainly contributed over the years to the present breeding population, has re-established itself in some suitable parts of the county. If unmolested, it will continue to breed and become a more familiar sight.

The choice of prey is varied but usually large, and includes mountain hares, rabbits, Woodpigeons, Feral Pigeons, crows, Rooks, Jackdaws and some gulls. A Little Auk found at one nest site in 1983 was most unusual, but there were more than average along the coast in that year and this one is likely to have been found dead by the Goshawk after having been blown inland.

The ringing of young Goshawks in the nest in one part of Yorkshire since 1980 may eventually provide recoveries which will throw some light on the movements and longevity of this welcome addition to the list of breeding birds. The Goshawk breeds fairly commonly over much of Europe, and its absence as a breeding species from the British Isles since the nineteenth century and until very recently was almost certainly due to human persecution. Similar pressures in Europe have not eliminated the species so totally, and one must assume that the North Sea has acted as a barrier, preventing young birds from crossing to the British Isles and maintaining the breeding population. Now that small numbers are established, it is likely that some migrants will stay over here and augment the numbers.

Since the mid 1960s, the Goshawk has been recorded annually in Yorkshire and, in addition to the breeding pairs outlined above, an increase in sightings of single birds in other parts of the county since that time has coincided with the establishment of breeding birds. During the early years of recolonisation, sightings away from the known breeding area were few and sporadic, but these gradually increased until, by 1976, the Annual Report of the Yorkshire Naturalists' Union stated that there were records from 16 different localities during the year, a remarkable change in status in ten years. Most records were of lone birds on single dates, but some lingered for several days or even weeks. Two were shot at one locality in the northeast in the winter of 1973/74, and a pair was seen in this same place for several months from July 1974.

A bird found injured near Easington on 3rd October 1970 was claimed by a Lincolnshire falconer, and some sightings in subsequent years may well have been escapes.

I regret that I am unable to be more precise about localities or of the exact breeding situation, but there are, unfortunately, many who would use such information for illegal purposes to the detriment of the species. Suffice to say in conclusion that a Goshawk may now be seen almost anywhere in Yorkshire, and such may be either a wandering juvenile from some other part of Britain or a migrant from over the sea. The fact that this situation now prevails is most encouraging, and due in no small way to those who have sought to protect the small breeding population.

Sparrowhawk
Accipiter nisus

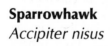

At the turn of the century, this hawk was a generally distributed resident, breeding in almost every part of the county where there were suitable woodlands. Nelson remarked that it was becoming much scarcer than formerly owing to the grudge cherished by the gamekeeper. It was common practice for the nest to be left alone until the young hatched, when the keeper would lie in wait and shoot both parents, leaving the young to die in the nest. The collection of A. Clapham of Scarborough contained 'many interesting varieties of the Sparrowhawk, thirty of which were obtained in Yorkshire'.

Chislett, in his *Yorkshire Birds*, considered that, although its numbers may have decreased on the large game estates, several factors were working in its favour and large suburban areas where no gamekeepers operated were refuges for breeding Sparrowhawks. The conifer plantations on large areas of the Yorkshire moors were also being favoured as nesting places. Chislett concluded by saying that: 'From the levels of Hatfield Chase where I have known a nest quite low down in birch, to the last hanging wood on the verge of the high moors in the north-west, the Sparrow-hawk is always a possibility.'

The species continued to be well distributed, if thinly, throughout most parts of Yorkshire until the mid 1950s, when the use of organochlorine insecticides for dressing seed grain had an indirect effect on the breeding capability of the Sparrowhawk and several other diurnal birds of prey. The toxic residues in the tissues of grain-eating passerines, which were in turn caught and eaten by Sparrowhawks, caused serious side effects including infertility and a thinning of the eggshell, which resulted in many eggs being broken in the nest. A marked decline in the breeding population, particularly in the south and east of England, became evident and was illustrated by the analyses of the British Trust for Ornithology Nest Record Cards. The decline was very marked in Yorkshire, and in 1961 one recorder for the Yorkshire Naturalists' Union said that it 'Continues to disappear at an alarming rate.' The Annual Bird Report of the YNU for 1961 listed every record received, and, apart from those at Spurn and Filey which were likely immigrant birds, Sparrowhawks were reported at only 17 places.

In the annual report of the Knaresborough Ringing Station for 1979, Peter Treloar analysed the Sparrowhawk records for the years 1955 to 1979. This showed that birds were seen on only four days in 1955 and 1958, with none in between and none during the years 1959 to 1965, only one in 1966 and 1969, and on only two days in 1970. After occurring on six days in 1971, records increased annually and in 1977 there were 32 records, with 42 in 1979. Regular watching at such sites can often produce invaluable results, and a similar constant effort in the Settle area, conducted over the years by Brian Shorrock, showed the same increase during the early 1970s when he had 52 sightings in 1972, 83 in 1975, and no fewer than 122 in 1978, compared with only eight ten years earlier. Reports from many parts of the county around this time were most encouraging and several observers were noticing a general increase, especially in the western half. Reported sightings became far too numerous to list in detail, and in 1977 Sparrowhawks were seen more regularly than the Kestrel in some parts of the West Riding. Sparrowhawks' nests are not easy to find unless really searched for in known breeding woods, but evidence of success was often forthcoming in the form of dis-playing birds and subsequent family parties. Brian Shorrock estimated that at least 20 pairs bred in the Settle area in 1978. The species was widespread and increasing around Sheffield in 1979 and spreading into former breeding localities in the east of the area. It is now possible to see this hawk almost anywhere in Yorkshire, even over our town centres, at any time of year, and it is commoner now than at any time during the last 30 years. As a breeding bird it is scarcest in the southeast of the county, especially in Holderness, and about the Pennine moorlands of the extreme southwest.

Many Sparrowhawks visit or pass through Yorkshire during the autumn, and coastal watchpoints such as Filey, Flamborough and Spurn Point record varying numbers each year. Return passage each spring is also evident. Numbers passing daily rarely exceed three or four, but may occur on several dates during both the spring and autumn passage periods. Where such migrants originate is not known for certain, but some come from Scandinavia or western Europe, perhaps to spend the winter in Britain or to pass through on their way to more southerly parts.

A female ringed at Spurn on 8th September 1955 was found dead in Essex in the following October, and a young female ringed at Spurn on 28th September 1966 and found dead in Norway on 15th May 1967 was only the third British-ringed Sparrowhawk to be recovered there at that time. A bird ringed as a chick near Carlisle on 14th July 1969 was retrapped at Burley-in-Wharfedale on 12th November 1969 and eventually found dead at Norwood, near Otley, on 3rd February 1973. A nestling ringed at Opland in Norway on 7th July 1979 was found dead at Scalby, near Scarborough, on 28th October 1979. There are other records of Sparrowhawks ringed in southwest Scotland, Cumbria and Northumberland and recovered in Yorkshire during the autumn and winter months.

Buzzard
Buteo buteo

According to Nelson, the Buzzard once bred at Bishop's Wood, Selby, where up to three pairs occurred annually. This information was provided by a William Harland, the keeper, who used to procure the young when he was a boy. At the same time it was abundant in the fells of Upper Wharfedale, where the eggs and young were by no means rare. Breeding was recorded on the summit of Great Whernside, and two young birds were obtained from a nest in the vicinity of Kilnsey, lower down the valley. Other references to Buzzards breeding at Hebden Bridge and Tadcaster are less satisfactory. There is a record of five young being reared on Red Crag, Richmond, about 1852. A note in *The Naturalist* (1892, p. 319) by J.E. Tinkler states that, up to 1870, it bred on Buzzard Scar in Swinnergill. Both this species and the Raven used to breed in Swaledale and fierce competition for the possession of the best nest sites took place. During the mid nineteenth century, it was reputed to be really 'common' in Wensleydale, and it formerly nested in Cleveland on the high ridge between Waupley and Danby and also in Douthwaite Dale, near Kirkby-moorside. Statements that 'It is still occasionally obtained in these districts, noticeably in the Grinkle and Mulgrave Woods, where specimens were trapped in 1886, 1887, and 1895; as also at Ingleby-in-Cleveland, the latest record at that place being in 1887, when an adult female was captured' give some clue as to why it was soon to disappear from the area.

Nelson also said that 'There is authentic evidence of a pair or two nesting in the unfrequented mountainous districts of north-west Yorkshire in 1878 when the eggs were taken and the old birds shot at, in the belief that they were Golden Eagles . . . .' He was not able to name the exact locality, as the birds 'continue to maintain a precarious existence in their fastness, where they are able to pass undetected and undisturbed, and, so recently as the year 1906, succeeded in bringing off young ones'. Continued attempts to breed in this remote part of the county were regularly thwarted, and even up to the 1950s birds were being shot and eggs taken.

During the mid 1950s, myxomatosis severely affected the rabbit populations in the hill country over much of western Yorkshire, and wandering Buzzards were thus deprived of their main food supply. Four pairs nested in the northwest in 1955, just before the disease took a hold in that part of the county and elsewhere, and any possibility of an increase in breeding pairs was probably thwarted. Up to four pairs, however, continued to nest annually thereafter until 1961, when no fewer than nine pairs were located and seven nests actually found by the Sedbergh School Society, whose members ringed 17 youngsters. Seven to eight pairs nested each year up to 1970, and there was a welcome increase to 15 pairs in 1976, when 22 young were reared.

Several pairs still grace the county with their presence during the summer months, with varying success. Hopefully, those who purport to 'keep' game will accept the fact that they have no enemy in the Buzzard, and if left in peace a few pairs may extend the range into other suitable areas of the Pennines. A marked preference for rocky outcrops and cliffs, often with a lone tree clinging to the face and thus providing a nest site, is perhaps one factor which prevents spread into more lowland country, where hanging woodlands, a popular habitat in Lakeland and in southwestern England, would appear to be suitable.

During the spring and autumn, a solitary Buzzard may be seen almost anywhere in the lowland half of Yorkshire, east of the Pennines, or along the coast. Most of these wandering or immigrant birds are seen during the months of April/May and September/October, but occasional individuals can be seen in any month. Occurrences are usually of single birds, but at times more are seen together. In 1976, at Staveley, near Knaresborough, R. Evison and P.T. Treloar regularly observed a party of five Buzzards between 25th August and 18th September. Included among them was a very pale bird which showed a marked dark tail band, a feature of the Rough-legged Buzzard. It was intriguing to speculate that this was a family party which had not travelled far to hunt over the low ground before dispersing. It is possible that some of the birds which spend the winter months in the eastern half of the county are from the Continent, but it is equally likely that they have originated in the extreme northwest of England or in Scotland.

Ringing has proved that not all Buzzards seen along the east coast have come over the North Sea. One young bird that had been ringed in the nest in Westmorland in June 1936 was at Marske in October. Two birds ringed in the Pennines in June 1944 and 1945 were recovered near Whitby and near Barnard Castle respectively, six and nine months later, and a chick ringed in the New Forest in Hampshire in 1962 was found dead at Hornsea on 17th September 1962. Some areas along the Pennine foothills are regularly visited during the winter and small parties, exceptionally of up to six birds, may frequent a particular area for varying periods.

Lowland Buzzards during the summer months are a rare sight. Single birds at Lissett on 18th June 1970, at Askern on 15th June 1974, and over York on 18th June 1977 were well east of their range at that time of year. Others nearer the hills at such places as Grantley, Halifax and Redmires could be non-breeding birds spending their time on the nearby moorland areas. The origin of a few Buzzards which have been seen passing along the coast in July is difficult to speculate on. One flew north near Hull on 23rd July 1972 and one flew south at Bempton on 17th July 1973. A bird coasting southwards at Spurn on 19th May 1974 was equally mysterious. Some June buzzards are not specifically identified and the possibility of migrating Honey Buzzards should always be borne in mind at that time. In 1971, there were three such sightings: one at Sprotborough Flash on 1st June, one near York on 20th and one at Kirkbymoorside on 21st.

Nelson's assessment of the Buzzard's status as 'Resident; but confined to one or perhaps two pairs; also an irregular spring and autumn migrant' needs amending only in that there has been a slight improvement in the breeding situation, and that more intensive watching has proved the 'irregular' migrants to be somewhat more numerous than formerly.

An interesting historical tale was told by Nelson, who was informed by a W. Walton of Middleton-in-Teesdale that his grandfather kept a pet 'Buzzard Hawk' which he 'pitted' against gamecocks. Cockfighting was a popular sport at that time and the Buzzard was invariably victorious. Not surprising!

Rough-legged Buzzard
Buteo lagopus

'Winter visitant, occurring occasionally in varying numbers, and chiefly near the coast. Rarely observed on the spring migration', is how Nelson summed up the status of this attractive buzzard. The same can be said of it today, the only obvious difference being that nothing equalling the 'large flights' mentioned by Nelson has occurred in recent years. The most impressive such influx was in 1903, when no fewer than 70 or more individuals were recorded, many of which were trapped. Birds arrived along the east coast from Holy Island to Spurn, the first being on 10th October when two were at Flamborough. One of these was captured and shown to Nelson. On the same date two more were at Bempton, where they remained for several days. Also on 10th, two were seen at Kilnsea and several others were noted daily for a week or more afterwards, their presence being a common topic of conversation among the local people. Between 13th October and 7th November, no fewer than 20 were on Seamer Moor, near Scarborough, ten of which were trapped. Four were on the moors near Loftus-in-Cleveland, one of which was trapped and later went to Nelson's collection. It is now in the Dorman Museum at Middlesbrough (case number 159). Up to seven were in Bransdale, one of which was caught, and one or two birds occurred at eight other places, including one washed up on the beach at Whitby on 12th. During November, several occurred in Wharfedale and it was calculated that nine birds were seen and four others captured. Examination of the ones that were obtained during this invasion, and of those from a smaller influx in 1876/77, showed that all except one were immature birds in pale streaked plumage, the exception being uniformly dark brown, a phase occurring commonly in North America. The only record in spring which Nelson knew of concerned an adult washed up on the shore at Redcar on 25th May 1877.

The rabbit warrens, which were carefully managed in the nineteenth century, appear to have been a favourite hunting place for this species. In 1839, H. Doubleday, a friend of T. Allis, sent him a live bird which was one of more than 50 caught at a warren. The locality is not given. Also mentioned by Allis in his report of 1844 was that this buzzard was frequently met with at Black Hill when that was a rabbit warren.

Chislett was apparently reluctant to accept records of this bird unless they had been shot or trapped, actions which he most certainly did not condone, but said that 'it is frequently impossible to determine with certainty the species of a bird seen in the air'. He listed eight records of birds which had been available for examination and their identity confirmed, four of which occurred during the month of November. He also acknowledged that, of the many other records of buzzards which were 'certainly', 'almost certainly' or 'thought to be' of this species, most no doubt were, and that some of them, and others, would be shot by gamekeepers without being ornithologically recorded. How right he was! With modern optical aids and expertise, the Rough-legged Buzzard is not a difficult bird to identify, especially in flight, and in more recent years the species has been recorded annually. Most are seen during October and November when they arrive from Scandinavia, and often along the coast before they disperse to their favourite wintering grounds, or pass through the county to haunts farther south.

In the autumn of 1973, large numbers came into Britain and the influx was reflected in Yorkshire. The first report came from Haxby on 28th September, and this was followed by ten other birds which were seen at Lindley Reservoir on 12th October, Whitby and Scarborough on 18th, Spurn on 21st and 28th, Knaresborough Ringing Station on 28th, two on the Broomhead/Langsett moors from 28th October to 27th April 1974, Thorne Moors on 28th November, Baysdale Moor on 21st November, and on the North York Moors on 9th December. Up to seven frequented Bransdale during the first three months of 1974, and single birds were seen at five other places during the same period.

A smaller influx occurred in 1974, when single birds were reported from ten localities during October and November. On 31st October, two flew west over Blacktoft Sands, and there were up to three there regularly up to mid March 1975. Four were on Thorne Moors on 15th December 1974, and up to two in Bransdale where R.H. Appleby saw up to seven during late March 1975, the last being seen on 13th April. Some birds lingered on into the spring of 1975 and were seen at ten places, including three flying north together over Hornsea Mere on 30th April, with the last over Buckton Hall, near Flamborough, on 10th May.

Bransdale has been a favourite wintering locality since Nelson's time and a few Rough-legged Buzzards are to be seen there annually. Some birds have been satisfactorily recorded during August and September, but, as will be seen from the foregoing, October and November are the main months of occurrence. Almost any part of the county may provide the sight of a Rough-leg, from the coastal strip as they arrive, to the high ground of the western part and the lowland carrs in the south, where they choose to spend the winter.

Golden Eagle
Aquila chrysaetos

The first Golden Eagle to be recorded in Yorkshire was shot on 29th November 1804, at Stockeld Park, near Wetherby, by Mr Cummins, gamekeeper to the Countess of Aberdeen, in the grounds near the house. It was still alive on being retrieved. A bird which was accused of committing 'numerous depredations for a week before its capture' was trapped in January 1838 at Beningborough. The wingspan was given as 7 feet 10 inches (2.4 m). An immature bird was taken at Hunmanby on 24th July 1844, on the estate of Admiral Mitford, who presented it to the Scarborough Museum. A specimen at one time in the collection of Captain Turton of Upsall Castle, near Thirsk, was obtained about Christmas 1851 on Court Moor, Kildale, near Stokesley, by his father's keeper.

In the winter of 1850/51, one was shot at, and wounded in one wing, at Helwath, Harwood Dale, near Scarborough. It was captured alive and lived in captivity until 1864. The bird was eventually preserved by Graham of York, one of the very best taxidermists around at that time, and went to the collection of Mr Hill of Thornton-le-Dale, the son of its original owner. A young female was captured in December 1861, at Skerne, near Driffield, while eating a hare. It was set up by

Alfred Roberts of Scarborough and went to the Norwich Museum.

On 17th November 1902, a young male was killed at Kettlewell in Upper Wharfedale by a river watcher called Mallinson. His attention had been attracted to it by a noise in a tree which proved to be caused by the eagle knocking a steel rabbit trap, which was fastened to its left foot, against a branch as it prepared to take flight. It flew about 200 yards (180 m) before alighting on the ground, where Mallinson killed it with a stick. It was 3 feet 1 inch (94 cm) in length, had a wing-span of 8 feet 2½ inches (2.5 m) and weighed only 9½ lb (4.3 kg). The bird was preserved by Widdas of Bradford and was at the time in the possession of its captor.

It was to be 68 years before this majestic bird was seen in Yorkshire again. On 6th December 1970, P.J. Carlton and P. Hooper watched an immature Golden Eagle on the hills above Gouthwaite Reservoir in Nidderdale. It remained in the area, sometimes visiting Leighton Reservoir, until 7th March 1971 and was seen by several observers. On 12th December 1970, A.F.G. Walker saw it kill a rabbit, a common animal on the moorland fringes and an important prey item for such large wandering birds of prey. Its occurrence coincided with breeding in the Lake District, and was at a time when a few birds were wintering on relatively low ground in southwest Scotland.

On 19th September 1976, that stalwart birdwatcher R.J. Rhodes watched an eagle which he identified as a Golden, flying in a southeasterly direction over Almholme. On 3rd April 1977, P.J. Carlton, this time in the company of A. O'Neill, was fortunate to see another immature Golden Eagle at Gouthwaite Reservoir. It re-appeared on 8th May and stayed in the area until at least 16th, when it was seen by Miss June Atkinson and others. An immature seen by P.J. Carlton at Leighton Reservoir on 18th March 1978 may have been the same one.

An adult was watched by B. Unwin and P. Gill at Long Grain Beck, Lunedale, on 20th May 1979, and a juvenile was in Arkengarthdale on 3rd September 1980, in which year an immature re-appeared at Gouthwaite Reservoir on 18th November. It stayed in the area during the winter and was last seen on 26th January 1981, having been observed by many people, including M.G.H. Garnett and A.F.G. Walker. What was presumably the same individual was present on 28th December 1982 and on several dates subsequently until May 1983, when it was last seen by W. Wiltshire circling over the nearby moors.

On 11th April 1982, T. Marshall saw one flying towards Holme Moss and a few minutes later P.D. Bell, while watching from his car on the road overlooking the Wessenden Valley and Holme Moss, noticed a large bird flying from the direction of the latter. At first thought to be a Grey Heron, its true identity soon became obvious when the large bill with a yellow cere and the creamy-coloured crown and nape were seen as it turned and flew away towards West Nab.

It is perhaps the interest shown in these large and magnificent birds by the regular birdwatchers that prevents some of them being shot by those who would otherwise hope to get away with such an act of vandalism.

In *Yorkshire Birds*, Chislett referred to an article in *The Naturalist* of November 1923 by F.J. Stubbs which referred to the possibility that Golden Eagles might, at one time, have nested in Yorkshire. After referring to John Ray's account of an eyrie occupied in 1668 on the Derbyshire side of the Derwent at Woodlands, Stubbs discussed the reliability of a poem by one Samuel Bottomley of Saddleworth, published about 1790, which referred to the breeding of eagles on Ravenstones, above the Greenfield Valley, and to the taking of their young. The story was repeated by James Butterworth in his *History of Saddleworth* in 1828 and, although Nelson made no reference to the story, Stubbs considered that it was unlikely to have been an invention. We shall never know for certain, but the possibility remains.

Osprey
Pandion haliaetus

The Osprey was known in Yorkshire as far back as 1678, when Willughby, in his *Ornithology*, said that 'It preys often upon our rivers.' Nelson knew of at least 70 occurrences during the 'past century', the majority of which had been near the coast. We now know that there is no such coastal bias, and there probably never was, the inaccessibility of the reservoirs on the high ground and the rivers in the remoter parts of the county simply ensuring that the Ospreys passed through unnoticed and unharmed. The fact that no Osprey was seen in Yorkshire between 1906 and 1938 was doubtless due to the same factor, and to the scarcity of observers at that time.

Chislett listed in *Yorkshire Birds* the occurrence of 17 Ospreys between 1938 and 1951, since when the species has been seen annually. Better coverage of the lakes, reservoirs and rivers, where migrant Ospreys call in, sometimes for only a few minutes, or linger for several days, has ensured that few pass through unnoticed. Of the 138 birds which have been recorded during the ten years 1971 to 1980, 63 have occurred during April and May, 12 in June, nine in July, nine in August, 31 during September and October, and five in November/December, with an early bird at Hornsea Mere on 25th March 1979. The autumn of 1976 was a good one for passing Ospreys, which were encountered at 13 places. The spring of 1977, which probably reflected the numbers passing during the previous autumn, also produced good numbers, with records coming from 14 localities.

Together with the Grey Heron, the Osprey is not the favourite bird of some fishermen, and that some are shot there is no doubt. One was so disposed of near Driffield on 6th May 1951 and sent to the York Museum, and another was shot near York on 8th September 1956. No other recent incidents have come to my notice, but the bird-protection laws would ensure that any such illegal act was kept quiet.

Occasionally, an Osprey may frequent a suitable feeding water for several weeks, as did one in 1938 at Semerwater, where it was seen several times during the summer and autumn and during the winter of 1938/39. About 20th August 1959, an Osprey landed on board the pilot cutter off Spurn Point during a period of fog. It was very exhausted, but finally ate fish offered to it during the next few days. The bird wore a ring and was eventually released on 26th August, when it flew off towards Spurn Point. Later in the same day, it was stated to have been found dead by a keeper at an East Riding lake. He fed the body to his ferrets but kept the ring, which he produced. This bird had been ringed on 8th July 1958 on a small islet near Stockholm. The pilots did not release the bird until 11.25 hours and it is most unlikely that it died just a few hours later; it was probably shot.

Gouthwaite Reservoir is a favourite place for passing Ospreys and one has been seen there in most recent years. Fairburn Ings and Castle Howard Lake have also attracted birds regularly. At any large sheet of water, almost anywhere in Yorkshire and at any point along the coast, a migrant Osprey may be seen. April, May, September and October are the most likely months of occurrence.

Lesser Kestrel
Falco naumanni

This south European species entered the British list on the strength of a bird shot near Green Hammerton. About the middle of November 1867, John Harrison of Wilstrop Hall noticed a small falcon flying about his farm and, his curiosity being aroused by its diminutive size, he shot it. Thinking it to be only a freak Kestrel, he took it to Graham, the York taxidermist, who correctly identified it and persuaded Harrison to donate the mounted specimen to the York Museum. Nelson inspected the bird there, and I examined it on 6th September 1984 with P.T. Treloar. It is a second-year male with a few spots on the breast and near the scapulars and the central tail feathers are new. The claws appear to be somewhat short, but there are no other signs of its having been in captivity, although this is often impossible to detect. The finder was unable to furnish the exact date as he did not make a note of it at the time, but his story was not questioned and the record was accepted as the first for the British Isles.

The second Yorkshire example was reported by a Mr Robert Lee of Thirsk, who wrote in *The Field* (23rd April 1892) that a Lesser Kestrel had been brought to him for preservation. It was an adult male and showed no signs of confinement. The specimen was acquired by Mr B. Foggitt of Thirsk, who presented it to The Hancock Museum in Newcastle on 16th June 1943 where I inspected the mounted specimen on 23rd August 1984. It is indeed a beautiful male and in perfect condition. According to the label, written from the information on the original case, it was shot on 12th April 1892.

On 14th October 1909, C.B. Ticehurst shot a Lesser Kestrel at Spurn. This was recorded by Chislett as 'on the Holderness coast', but J.K. Stanford, in a letter to B.S. Pashby in 1964, said that his friend Ticehurst shot the bird on the 'ridge' at Spurn Point, which refers to the area of the Narrow Neck. The bird's gizzard was full of grasshoppers and beetles, but there is no information concerning the ultimate fate of the specimen.

On 4th June 1979, at Fairburn Ings, S.C. Madge and S.C. Ellis watched an adult male as it flew along the east side of the area and gave excellent views to both observers.

There are only about 20 accepted records of this species in the British Isles, and Yorkshire was to provide the latest when, on 14th June 1983, at Atwick on the Holderness coast, W.F. Curtis saw a male perched on an electricity pole. The unspotted back and general paleness of the bird attracted his attention, and further inspection revealed the other salient points of this rare falcon. The blue-grey crown and nape, buffish forehead, reddish-chestnut mantle, blue-grey wing-coverts, grey-blue uppertail with a broad black subterminal bar and pale buffish underparts were all seen well before the bird took off and circled up and then flew off to the north, when its silvery underwings were also noted.

Kestrel
Falco tinnunculus

The Kestrel is certainly the most familiar bird of prey in the Yorkshire countryside, being well known to almost anyone who travels within the county. Anywhere, from the sea-cliffs in the east, throughout the central vales and across the Wolds to the high ground of the Pennines, the 'Windhover' is a common sight. Even our city centres often hold a pair of breeding Kestrels, and hunting over suburbia is now commonplace. This species, more than any other, has learned to live with man and has in some ways benefited from the latter's activities. One cannot drive very far along any of the county's motorways without seeing at least one Kestrel hovering over the grassy embankments, where its prey of voles, shrews and beetles must be easy to find.

The choice of nest site is very varied, ranging from holes in trees or on crags to old buildings, barns, haystacks, old nests of crow or Magpie, nesting boxes, and even on the ground in upland, treeless areas. This ability to breed successfully in such differing sites is undoubtedly one of the reasons for its continued success.

For several years, a pair has reared young on, or in the vicinity of, Leeds Town Hall, and in 1978 single pairs nested on the Corn Exchange building in the centre of Leeds and also in New York Street. A trusting pair chose to breed on Wakefield Prison in 1982. An electricity pylon at Knostrop was chosen as a nest site in 1974; the lack of suitable bases on which to lay eggs, or on which crows can build nests which could eventually be used by Kestrels, prevents these structures from being exploited more frequently. Some idea of the numbers of breeding pairs in certain areas can be gained from the 1978 figures: 15 pairs in the Leeds area; 14 in the Doncaster area; 13 in the York area; six definite and 12 probable in the Huddersfield area; and seven in Lower Nidderdale. In 1949, four pairs nested within half-a-mile (0.8 km) of the centre of Batley, where it was unusual to walk along the main street without seeing one.

That some Kestrels are shot there is no doubt, but this falcon does absolutely no harm to the interests of the shooting fraternity. In Nelson's days it was 'subject to the rule of wholesale extermination which is applied to all the hawks', and a gamekeeper, when questioned on this point, admitted the harmless character of the bird, but added 'it frightens the young pheasants by its hovering'.

Perhaps the most serious problem that the Kestrel has to face these days is the taking of its young by youths. The film 'Kes', which had as its main theme the relationship between a boy and a pet Kestrel, sparked off a drastic increase in the taking of young Kestrels for pets during the 1960s and 1970s. Many were handed in to the RSPCA, having been found abandoned and unable to catch prey for themselves: in 1978, no fewer than 16 such birds were received by the society in Barnsley, and in most years the local officer handles several from the Harrogate/Knaresborough area. Efforts to 'hack' these birds back to the wild are rarely successful and death often comes quickly owing to their inability to fend for themselves.

During the month of August, when the young birds are becoming independent and start their wanderings, Kestrels become more evident. This obvious autumn increase will include birds which have been bred locally, but also migrants from other parts of Britain. Autumn numbers are greater in some years than in others, no doubt owing to variations in breeding success. In 1971, for instance, six were hovering in the air together at Almholme on 19th August, seven did likewise at Settle and 12 at Gouthwaite Reservoir on 30th August. Concentrations in the spring are not so apparent. Seven at Leighton Reservoir and eight at Gouthwaite Reservoir on 8th April 1972 may have been the local breeders which had newly arrived on their territory.

Coastal passage is at times quite spectacular, especially at Spurn Point where the birds bottle up before crossing the Humber. Watchers at other coastal watchpoints witness similar movements, and regular counting during the past ten years or so has produced some interesting figures. In 1969, more Kestrels than usual arrived along the coast and Spurn had more than ever before. Birds were passing during August, September and October, with 98 individuals counted on 22nd September. Many were found dead or dying through exhaustion and, of the few that came into my possession, one bird, a young female, was exceptionally pale, unlike any from the British breeding populations and almost certainly from some part of northern Europe. In most autumns during the 1970s, movement along the coast involved large numbers. At Spurn, in 1975, the most seen on any one day was 35 on 26th September, with 32 on 3rd October and 23 on 6th October. The year 1976 produced similar figures and Flamborough Head had up to 20 on most days, with 25 on 25th September as the maximum; on 28th October, D.I.M. Wallace watched four Kestrels catching exhausted passerine migrants there. In 1978, at Spurn, 104 birds moved south on eight September dates and 107 did so on 12 dates in October. Some birds may linger in one area for a few days, probably in order to feed and gain strength after crossing the North Sea, but most eventually drift south. Nelson said: 'I have, almost yearly, noticed individuals flying in from the east or north-east, and have occasionally seen them crossing when at sea off the Cleveland coast.'

There are several recoveries of foreign-ringed Kestrels in Yorkshire, including one each from Germany, Sweden, Denmark, the Netherlands, Belgium and France; all had been ringed as chicks in the nest. Some of the recovery dates suggest that birds hatched abroad may subsequently spend the summer in Britain, and this is indicated by two Yorkshire recoveries: a nestling ringed in Sweden on 23rd June 1959 was found dead near Rotherham on 18th June 1960 and another, ringed in Denmark on 5th June 1981, was found dead at South Cave on 19th July 1982. A young Kestrel ringed in Friesland on 16th June 1978 was caught off Spurn Point on 1st August 1978, showing that immigration can occur quite early. Yorkshire-ringed Kestrels have also been recovered abroad: one ringed at Sedbergh on 22nd June 1952 was in the Pas-de-Calais, France, on 10th June 1953, suggesting either an interchange of breeding stock or that immatures spend their first summer south of their breeding places. Most of the others have been recovered between October and February while spending the winter to the south, mainly in France.

Red-footed Falcon
Falco vespertinus

This small dainty falcon, which breeds regularly no nearer than the Balkans, was first recorded in Yorkshire in April 1830 when one was shot near Doncaster. Thomas Allis (1844) gave details of five birds, one of which, a female, was 'shot a few years back near Easingwold, and sent to H. Chapman of York, with a message that "if it was a Cuckoo" he was to stuff it, and return it to the person who shot it, but, if it was not a Cuckoo, when stuffed he might keep it for his pains'. The other records are clouded by the usual vagueness of the period, but Nelson published two of these as acceptable, one being killed near Sheffield, which was in the Museum there, and the other, a fine female, being shot by a keeper in Stainer Wood, Selby, in May 1844.

In November 1864, a mature female was shot from a ship entering the Humber as it hovered above the vessel. The specimen went to W.W. Boulton of Beverley 'in the flesh' and was recorded in *The Zoologist*, 1865, p. 9415. An adult male was killed at Bempton Cliffs on 6th July 1865 and was purchased by J. Whitaker of Rainworth Lodge for his collection.

In his *Birds of the Humber District*, John Cordeaux gives details of another adult male, which T. Boynton of Ulrome Grange told him had been captured at Bempton on 18th July 1869, which was at the time in the possession of T. Machin of Bridlington.

One was captured at Egton Bridge, near Whitby, in 1876 or 1877, and two birds, supposedly a pair of adults, bought at the sale of a Mr Hall's collection in 1878 at Scorborough and said to be of local origin, went to the Hull Museum. Mr A Clapham of Scarborough stated that an adult in his collection was trapped by Lord Londesborough's keeper near Hackness and that the keeper had another specimen that was taken near Scarborough.

A 'fine female' was obtained in Wadworth Wood, near Doncaster, during the last week of April 1884. It was preserved by A. Paterson of Doncaster, who communicated the information to Nelson.

On learning that a pair of birds had been reported at Ackworth in 1895, Nelson asked a Major Arundel of that place to investigate and received the following information:

'17th March 1903. For a fortnight or more during the spring of 1895 two (probably a pair) Red-footed Falcons were seen several times at Brockadale and Stapleton, and one of them eventually fell to the gun of the gamekeeper, Savage, who shortly afterwards left the district and is now dead. I did not see the birds myself, but they were reported to me by Mr. G.P. Rhodes, a competent observer, who saw them on the wing, and examined the specimen that was shot, in the flesh.'

One can do no more than report such an incident as it was told at the time. Whether the birds concerned were in fact this species is open to the element of doubt which so often surrounds records of rare birds from that period.

Between then and 1952, when Chislett published *Yorkshire Birds*, no other Red-footed Falcons were reported in the county, and it was in 1954 that the species next received a mention. In the Yorkshire Naturalists' Union Ornithological Report for that year, Chislett referred to one that was reported to have been shot at Skelton Park, near Saltburn, in the spring months, but he added that corroboration, or otherwise, had not been obtained.

In the report for 1956, Chislett included in square brackets a report of one seen as it sat on a roadside stone on Wheddale Moor in October. The observers did not know what the bird was at the time and later identified it from a painting in *The Field*. Some doubt must attach to such a report.

On 21st June 1961, P.J. Mountford, the Spurn Bird Observatory warden, was watching at the Point dunes when he had good views of a Red-footed Falcon that passed low over him. R.J. Rhodes was fortunate enough to see one at Burnt Ings Plantation, near Doncaster, on 5th July 1964, and a first-year bird frequented the Spurn Peninsula from 12th to 18th September 1968.

A male at Fairburn Ings on 27th and 28th July 1972 was watched by several people, including the 'man on the spot', C. Winn. The year 1973 was a good one for Red-foots in Britain and Yorkshire had its fair share. The first was at Spurn Point on 23rd May, when a first-year female was seen that stayed until 26th; a first-year male appeared there on 2nd June and a second-year male on 9th June. An adult male was seen at Hornsea on 14th June, and an immature flew over Knaresborough Ringing Station on 27th August which I watched with P.T. Treloar and D.T. McAndrew.

G.J. Speight, P. Smith and J.S. Armitage watched one at Wintersett Reservoir between 28th August and 1st September 1976. P.A. Lassey, Miss Irene Smith and D.I.M. Wallace reported a second-year male at Flamborough on 1st May 1978.

Three were reported in 1979. On 21st May an adult male was seen at Hornsea by R.G. Hawley, a very careful and extremely competent observer, but it was not accepted by the *British Birds* Rarities Committee who considered that the views were too brief for certainty. Hawley could not mistake anything for such a distinctive bird and would certainly not have claimed it if he was in any doubt whatsoever; I have no doubt at all that an adult male Red-footed Falcon was at Hornsea on that date. The second report also concerned an adult male, perhaps the same one, this time at Flamborough on 27th May and which was seen by P.A. Lassey and Miss Irene Smith. The third bird was an adult female which W.F. Curtis saw as it flew south at Mappleton on 22nd August.

On 21st June 1980, an immature male flew south at Spurn and later returned north to the Warren area. It was seen by R.P. Council and Miss B. Jackson, but the *British Birds* Rarities Committee did not feel able to accept the record.

P. Warham reported a female at Allerton Bywater on 19th and 20th May 1981, in which year a second-year male which flew south at Spurn Point on 1st June was seen by B.R. Spence, R.P. Council and R. Scott. A male was seen at Fairburn Ings on 7th June by P.D. Kirk and C. Winn.

On 15th May 1982, at Mickletown Ings, B. Townend saw a male Red-foot as it flew past him at close range. He noted the all-dark-grey plumage with rufous undertail-coverts and the red legs. On the same day, a first-summer male appeared at Potteric Carr, where it stayed until 1st June and was seen by L.J. Degnam, R.J. Scott, N.P. Whitehouse and many others. Later that year, on 13th September, an adult male was seen at Fairburn Ings by P.D. Kirk and C. Winn.

From 2nd September to 2nd October 1983, a female was near Ingbirchworth, where it was seen by several observers including B. Armitage, J.E. Dale and D. Sykes. A male was seen near Sledmere by Miss E. Longhorn on 8th June 1983.

There are certainly more records of this bird in Yorkshire now than formerly, and whether this is due solely to more intensive watching or to a definite increase in the number of birds that now visit us is uncertain. That much pleasure is to be gained from the sight of this migratory, insect-eating falcon there is no doubt.

Merlin
Falco columbarius

The breeding area of the Merlin in Yorkshire given by Nelson in his *The Birds of Yorkshire* included the whole of the Pennine moorlands from near Sheffield in the south, northwards to the Tees, and on the North York Moors in the northeast. In 1952, Chislett reiterated this but added that its distribution was rather more sparse. For several years after that time it fared badly and was a scarce breeding bird over all its range during the 1960s and early 1970s, owing in part to the effects of harmful pesticides. Four infertile eggs from an abandoned nest in Wharfedale, sent by

E.S. Skinner in 1965 to the Nature Conservancy Council for analysis, contained very high organochlorine residues, particularly of dieldrin and heptachlor epoxide. The eventual ban imposed on these persistent chemicals allowed this and other birds of prey to breed more successfully, and a slight increase in the breeding population followed.

A survey undertaken in 1983 by the Yorkshire Naturalists' Union Protection of Birds Committee, working in conjunction with the Yorkshire Dales Protection Group and the Royal Society for the Protection of Birds, showed that, of 72 territories checked over the whole of the Yorkshire breeding area, 47 were occupied with 34 pairs eventually breeding; 31 of these were successful and 81 young were reared.

The *Atlas of Breeding Birds in Britain and Ireland*, organised by the British Trust for Ornithology and published in 1976, gave a total of 600-800 pairs in the whole of Britain during the period 1968 to 1972, in which case Yorkshire would appear to have held a fair percentage of the British breeding population in 1983, especially as the weather during June in that year was the wettest on record and quite disastrous for some species. In 1921, W. Rowan, writing in *British Birds*, located only four regularly used sites in 20 square miles (52 km^2) of Yorkshire moorland, although there was an apparent abundance of suitable alternatives. Each pair had a range of approximately 3,000 acres (1,214 ha). Of the 72 territories checked in 1983, it is possible that some were alternative sites within the range of just one pair and these may be used in different years. Whatever the true situation, it appears that the

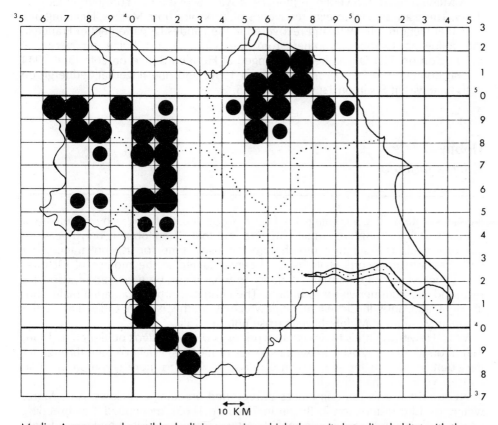

Merlin. A scarce and possibly declining species which shares its breeding habitat with the Red Grouse, in consequence of which it is persecuted on some moorlands. Much suitable habitat is without Merlins.

species is now known to be faring a little better than previously supposed and studies in 1984 have revealed even more pairs than were located in 1983.

Between 1881 and 1890, on the moors about Bowes and Scargill in the northwest, 16 nests with eggs or young were destroyed and 44 old birds were killed, the majority in pole traps. Some details of the persecution to which the birds were once subjected were published in *The Naturalist*, 1892, p. 320.

As is the case with most other birds of prey, the actual breeding localities must be kept secret, a sad reflection on man's attitude to this small passerine-hunting falcon. The Merlin's main prey item on the Yorkshire moorlands is the Meadow Pipit, and investigations by W. Rowan in 1922 showed that 90 percent of their diet was made up of this species. During the winter months a variety of other small birds is taken, with occasionally larger quarry. On 17th March 1943, a female was trapped at a half-eaten Golden Plover in the East Riding.

Outside the breeding season, the Merlin may be encountered almost anywhere in Yorkshire, but mainly on the low ground during the winter months when very few are to be seen on the high moors. Merlins passing along the coast during August to November may include birds from northern Europe and perhaps an occasional one from Iceland, where a larger race originates and moves south to spend the winter mainly in Ireland and western Britain. Coastal movement is evident in every year, especially at the well-watched places such as Flamborough and Spurn, where single birds are seen on many days, mainly during September and October, flying south or lingering to hunt on their journey.

A Merlin ringed in Sweden in June 1934 was recovered in Yorkshire in January 1935. There are several foreign recoveries of Yorkshire-born Merlins, including one ringed at Dent in July 1938 and recovered in the Landes Département of France in the following October, another from the same brood being recovered at Warrington on 31st December. One ringed at Hebden Bridge on 26th June 1944 was at Rochefort in France on 30th March 1950, and one ringed at Sedbergh on 18th June was in Spain on 1st October 1965.

Hobby
Falco subbuteo

Nelson's statement concerning this falcon suggested that it was by no means a regular visitor to Yorkshire at that time. He said that 'The Hobby is only occasionally observed. The summer months are the usual time for its appearance, but instances are on record of its having been obtained in the months of October (31st), December and February, contrary to what might be expected of a species regarded as a summer visitor to Britain.' The February bird was an adult male, shot in 1894 at Danby-in-Cleveland, and which is in the Nelson Collection at the Dorman Museum at Middlesbrough (case number 153).

W.C. Hewitson, in his two-volume work *Eggs of British Birds* published in 1856, said about the Hobby 'This beautiful species of hawk is, I believe, rare throughout the country, and, as far as my own observation goes, is more common in some parts of Yorkshire than elsewhere.'

Nelson listed only three instances of recorded breeding as follows. A.G. More, writing on bird distribution in Britain in *The Ibis* (1865), mentioned it as breeding occasionally in Yorkshire, but in reply to later enquiries said that he knew of only one record, in Rossington Wood, near Doncaster, and that his informant was Hugh Reid. The keeper at Bishop's Wood, near Selby, recorded an instance of breeding there about 1809 and said that the eggs were taken from a crow's nest and were at the time in the possession of a Mr A.R. Kell of Barnsley. A nest was recorded in Everingham Park, near Market Weighton, in 1875.

Chislett could add only two other instances of successful breeding when he published *Yorkshire Birds* in 1952. The first was near Terrington on 9th July 1925, when V.G.F. Zimmerman examined a nest with four young and published the record in *The Naturalist* (1926, p. 11). The second concerned a nest found in South Yorkshire by M. Darlow and a gamekeeper on 12th June 1948, when it held three eggs; two young hatched on 15th June and left the nest on 9th July. In conclusion, Chislett said 'Information received that a pair of Hobbys has bred in South Yorkshire very recently may be correct, but must be treated with reserve.'

Since that time, there has been slight evidence that Hobbies have nested in Yorkshire, and a pair or two may do so at the present time. The number of sightings over much of the county suggests that it is becoming established as a breeding species in the north of England.

Nelson listed about 20 records up to 1906, most of which were inevitably shot, and Chislett listed a further nine, the details of which are as follows. In June 1907, one was killed near Harrogate and reported by Riley Fortune in *The Naturalist* (1908, p. 25), while Nelson's annotations to his personal copy of *The Birds of Yorkshire* recorded two shot at Seamer, Scarborough, in August 1907 which were shown to him by the keeper who shot them. W.S. Medlicott saw a Hobby as it passed 10 yards from him near Goathland on 16th May 1920 (see *British Birds*, 15, p. 63 for details), and the same observer saw two more over Goathland on 2nd August 1941. P. Baldwin saw one at Methley on 7th June 1942. An adult male was found in a vermin trap at Hornsea on 24th July 1948 and inspected by C.F. Proctor and G.H. Ainsworth. A.F.G. Walker saw one at Ripley on 7th May 1949, and E.W. Taylor saw a bird at Easingwold on 8th November 1950 which he considered to be a Hobby, despite the late date.

Single Hobbies seen at Ossett on 10th August 1954 by J. Cudworth and at Knaresborough Ringing Station on 1st October 1955 by myself and J.A.S. Borrett heralded the annual appearance of the species in Yorkshire from 1957 to the present time. The number of sightings increased from just one or two birds during the period 1957 to 1964, to seven in 1965 and 1968, 22 in 1974, 24 in 1976, 36 in 1977, 42 in 1979 and 43 in 1980. Half of all the birds seen occurred during May and June, 30th April 1977 at Wheldrake Ings being the earliest of which I have note. The remainder have been seen during the period July to October, the latest date being 29th October 1979.

Coastal movement, mainly to the south, has been recorded in most recent years at the well-watched coastal localities, particularly Spurn Point where, in 1970, single birds passed on seven dates between 30th May and 24th September. In 1979, nine birds were seen singly at five watchpoints between 13th May and 25th June, and 12 were seen singly at five places between 13th August and 29th October.

On 20th September 1974, a Hobby at Fairburn Ings was catching Swallows at their roost in the reedbeds. In the same year, one was attending a roost of Swallows and Sand Martins at Hay-a-Park Gravel-pit, Knaresborough, from 22nd to 24th August, when R. Evison and I saw it catch five swallows, including three in half-an-hour on one evening. On 9th August 1977, at Gouthwaite Reservoir, P.J. Carlton and A. O'Neill saw one catch a Sand Martin.

At any time from May to October, a Hobby may now be seen in Yorkshire, mainly singly and often very briefly while dashing through, or a bird may frequent a particular area for a few days, especially in the autumn when young birds are about.

Eleonora's Falcon
Falco eleonorae

In late October or early November 1981, the young son of Mr P.R. Greensides of Elm Tree Farm, Patrington, told his father that there was a dead hawk in the garden. Mr Greensides did not pay much attention as dead crows were often found, and he thought nothing more of it. Two days later, he went into the garden to pick Brussels sprouts and lying between the rows was a dead falcon. It was in good condition, and he took it indoors and remembered showing it to some friends on 'bonfire night' before putting it into the freezer. On learning that a man called Baker from Hedon did a bit of taxidermy, he took the corpse to him for preservation. Baker identified it as an Eleonora's Falcon and set it up as a mount.

Some time in 1982, on a visit to Spurn Point, Greensides told B.R. Spence, the Yorkshire Wildlife Trust's warden, about the incident and arranged to let him see the specimen. This he did in early 1983, and, much to everyone's amazement, the bird was in fact an Eleonora's Falcon.

It is a second-year example in good plumage, with new feathers moulting through on the mantle and wing-coverts. The pale tips of the old feathers are abraded off, a quite natural process, and are otherwise in normal condition, showing no signs whatsoever of the bird ever having been in captivity.

This south European species, which nests on the islands and adjacent coasts of the Mediterranean and winters in Madagascar and East Africa, has been recorded in the British Isles on only one other occasion, when one was seen at Formby, Merseyside, on 8th and 9th August 1977.

Mr Greensides very kindly allowed the Yorkshire specimen to remain for a while at Spurn, where it was seen by several people including myself, and I am indebted to him for making the details known. This very important occurrence could, so easily, have gone unrecorded. A photograph of the mounted specimen appears on plate 64.

Gyrfalcon
Falco rusticolus

The Gyrfalcon was formerly split into three species and Nelson published ten references to its occurrence in Yorkshire, four of which were referable to the Greenland Falcon (*candicans*) and six to the Iceland Falcon (*islandus*). He said: 'and it is satisfying to know that the specific names of some of them, which would otherwise have been open to grave doubt, have been determined by the highest authorities'. All the former 'species', which were in reality merely geographical races, have now been grouped under the one circumpolar species.

Of the four records referable to the very white and striking Greenland Falcon, three were shot and one captured. The first was shot at Sutton-on-Derwent on 13th March 1837 and passed into the possession of Thomas Allis. It was injured in each wing, but not in the body, and 'Like most birds of the family when in captivity, it sulked and entirely refused all food for the first four days; it was still alive on 26th April and seemed likely to do well.' John Hancock saw the specimen and confirmed the identification.

The second bird went to the Scarborough Museum, where Nelson saw it, after it had been shot on 25th November 1854 on the moors near Robin Hood's Bay. The record was published in *The Zoologist*, 1855, p. 4558, by A. Roberts of Scarborough, by whom it was preserved.

The third is no more than a probability and concerns a bird recorded by John Cordeaux in his *Birds of the Humber District*, in which he stated that 'several years since, a bird was shot by a man engaged in shooting Rock Pigeons from Speeton Rocks. The bird looked quite white but at close range showed black speckles on its plumage. It fell to the bottom of the cliff and attempts to retrieve it failed.'

The fourth occurred on the moors in North Yorkshire in the autumn of 1892, when a 'fine female' was captured and went to a Mr Foulds of Bradford, going eventually to Joseph Morley of Scarborough, where Nelson examined it.

Those records referable to the Iceland Falcon number six as follows. The first was shot on the moors between Guisborough and Normanby in March 1837 and was described as a young bird (*The Zoologist*, 1845, p. 1052). The specimen went with the Hancock collection to the Newcastle Museum, where it was seen by P.J. Stead in 1963. Another was captured on Marston Moor in December of the year 1826 or 1836, and went to the collection of Admiral Oxley of Ripon.

The third occurred in November 1860, when a 'fine young female' was obtained at Upper Poppleton and reported in *The Zoologist*, 1861, p. 7312, by D. Graham of York, the taxidermist who purchased the bird for five shillings. The specimen went to the collection of Mr A. Clapham of Scarborough, who also acquired the fourth example. This was a bird killed on Filey Brigg on 4th October 1864 'while in company with another of its kind which escaped'. At first thought to be a young Peregrine, it was sent to H.E. Dresser for his opinion. He replied: 'the bird is not a Jer Falcon but an Iceland Falcon, not in mature plumage and most probably, if not certainly, a male. It is a capital specimen.'

In 1865, a taxidermist from Whitby found a bird nailed on a wall with other 'vermin' at Newton House, near Whitby. It was an Iceland Falcon and had been placed there by the gamekeeper, who had shot it.

The last one mentioned by Nelson concerned a bird which occurred in the spring of 1846 but had hitherto gone unrecorded. It was one of two that appeared on Wemmergill Moors in North Yorkshire. It was bought in the flesh by Joseph Duff of Bishop Auckland, and later passed to his son. The collection was sold in 1901 and Nelson bought the specimen, which I have seen in the Dorman Museum at Middlesbrough (case number 170).

Chislett knew of no other records up to 1952, and there have been only a handful since then up to the present time. In January 1954, a fisherman at Coatham Sands saw a large pale hawk, described as banded all over with brown markings, that came in over the sea, pounced on some Starlings and took one. Chislett placed the record in square brackets and said that it might have been of the Iceland or Greenland race of this species. Whatever the bird was, it can be regarded only as a probable. A young bird brought into Hull on 11th August 1964 had landed on the ship in the Bear Island region; it was released by the RSPCA at Bempton on the following day.

A grey-phase bird was seen at Flamborough on 22nd January 1983 by P.A. Lassey. On 15th September 1983, J. Cudworth saw a large falcon fly over the Warren at Spurn; on 17th, it flew south at the Narrow Neck. Later on 17th, G.E. Dobbs was birdwatching in the area of Easington Lagoons when suddenly all the gulls and Lapwings 'exploded' into the air. He noticed a bird of prey circling low over the pools which he identified as a large falcon. The evening light made positive identification difficult and the bird was left unspecified. On 25th September, K. Rotherham and B. Fendley saw a very large falcon sitting in a dead tree on the western side of Easington village. They watched it for five minutes before it took off and began hunting over some bushes. It eventually returned to the dead tree and started to preen, enabling them to make detailed field notes of its plumage before it finally flew off and out of sight. It was seen in addition by R.H. Appleby and R.N. Hopper, who also had good views. It was a buzzard-sized falcon, grey-brown above and pale, with streaks, below, and with very heavily feathered 'trousers'. All the observers agreed that it was a Gyrfalcon. The bird remained in the area until mid October, being seen again on 18th December by C. Massingham.

Peregrine
Falco peregrinus

Nelson's summary of the Peregrine in 1907 was 'Resident, restricted now to a few pairs nesting on the north-western fells, an occasional pair on the sea-cliffs, and possibly another pair in Cleveland. Observed fairly regularly on migration at the coast.' He said that 'A pair or two bred almost annually until 1879 in the stupendous cliffs of our coast at Flamborough and Speeton, where its favourite prey, the Rock Pigeon, is numerous.' On 3rd June 1876, W. Eagle Clarke was on the clifftops near Bempton when he saw three downy young in the possession of the egg-collecting 'climmers'. They had been taken on 30th May and, as they were proving difficult to feed, were offered for sale to Clarke, who declined the offer in the hope that they might be returned to the nest. This was not to be and they eventually found their way to Barnsley. In 1879, one of the breeding pair was killed and the nest deserted. Various attempts to re-establish met with little success until a pair settled in near Danes Dyke in 1906. Nelson asked the climbers to locate the eyrie, which they did on 6th June, when it contained three young which fledged about 21st June. In 1910 the nest was at Bempton, but the eggs were taken and the birds were shot. One young bird was reared in 1911 and two in 1912. In 1914, two eggs were taken by J. Hodgson and acquired by the Hull Museum. Two young were reared in 1918. In 1920, only one adult was seen, and there were no records after that until 1938, when a pair attempted to nest for what is thought to be the last time at this site. Two young hatched and were photographed on the nesting ledge by J. Petty, but they subsequently died.

A pair frequented the Bempton Cliffs during the summer of 1954, and may have bred. On 5th August, the male harried a Herring Gull, causing it to drop its food which the Peregrine caught before it hit the water. The last coastal breeding was recorded in 1956, when a nest at Bempton held half-grown young on 27th May.

In the winter of 1900, a pair took up residence on a cliff a few miles from Scarborough. They nested in the following year, when they reared two young. The male was killed in the autumn of 1901, but the female found a new mate and bred in the two following years. A pair reared three young on the cliffs northwest of Whitby in 1935, and nested again in 1936. They were seen in the area in April 1939, and this, or another, pair attempted to nest south of the town in the same year. The coastal sites are no longer occupied, although they would seem to be the safest, both from egg collectors and gamekeepers, their main coastal prey of pigeons and gulls not conflicting with the moorland sporting interests.

The Peregrine has nested traditionally at a few sites in the northwest for many years, and Chislett recorded an annual occurrence with fair success up to 1939. In that year, protection was removed from the Peregrine in the interests of the carrier pigeons of the Royal Air Force. Some birds survived and two young were reared at one eyrie in 1948. Two successive clutches were robbed at another site and a third site was thwarted by gamekeepers. Only one young was known to be reared in 1949. In 1950, a pair was shot at one site and the young from the second clutch of another pair taken. A late brood was successful in 1951. One young was reared in the Craven area in 1947.

This species, along with some other birds of prey, fared very badly during the 1960s, being seriously affected by persistent and harmful chemicals in pesticides used for seed-corn dressing. The eventual ban on these products allowed the birds to breed more successfully and a slight improvement in the breeding population followed. During the last few years, at least nine pairs are known to have occupied nesting sites and some of these have reared young. During the three years 1981-83, at least 29 young Peregrines have fledged from Yorkshire eyries. This most encouraging trend is due in part to the watchful eye kept on the nest sites by the Bird Protection Committee of the Yorkshire Naturalists' Union, the Royal Society for the Protection of Birds and the Yorkshire Dales Protection Group. For obvious reasons of security, I am unable to be more precise about the breeding localities chosen by this fully protected species, as their young are highly prized for falconry and are often taken in spite of the protection afforded. Two young were taken from a nest in 1982 and a nest was robbed of eggs in 1984.

Outside the breeding season, a Peregrine may now be encountered almost any-where in the county, mainly during the autumn when young birds are dispersing and wandering. Occurrences along the coast undoubtedly include immigrant birds, as evidenced by ringing recoveries and sight records. On 19th October 1959, one seen flying in over the sea at Spurn alighted on the beach in an exhausted state; single birds were watched flying in at Filey Brigg on 13th September 1975 and 23rd December 1979; and W.F. Curtis saw an immature coming in over the sea at Mappleton on 23rd November 1975.

A young bird ringed in the northwest of the county on 9th June 1938 was shot at its nest on the Mull of Kintyre on 20th April 1942; and another, ringed in the same place on 5th July 1949, was at Tayport in Fife on 11th August 1950. An immigrant Peregrine was recovered inland at Eskrick, near York, on 11th November 1947; it had been ringed as a young bird in Sweden on 10th June 1946.

The prey of this falcon is varied and its catching methods often spectacular. One took a Greenshank at Cherry Cobb Sands on 19th September 1952, one chased a Curlew Sandpiper at Spurn on 19th September 1959, and an immature chased House Martins at Flamborough on 1st September 1974. At Stocks Reservoir on 11th November 1974, one was seen chasing gulls, and on 14th December one was seen to chase ducks and a Grey Heron.

Now that the species is breeding more successfully, it is likely that sightings away from the nesting areas will become more regular during the autumn and winter months and it is to be hoped that they will be left unmolested by those on whose land they choose to hunt.

Red Grouse
Lagopus lagopus

As stated by Chislett in his *Yorkshire Birds*, the Red Grouse is a common resident on all the high moors from the Derbyshire boundary in the south to the borders of Durham and Westmorland in the north and northwest, and less commonly on the Hambleton and Cleveland Hills.

Heather moor is the favourite ground, and wherever this occurs so does the Red Grouse. In normal circumstances few birds wander away from the heather, the new shoots of which form their main diet, and although some frequent areas of crowberry, on which they also feed, heather is never far away and they will live at relatively low altitudes if heather is dominant.

In former times, when heather grew more commonly in some lowland districts, the Red Grouse could be found there. Nelson quoted a Mr F. Boyes, who said that he could recall when heather was abundant in the Market Weighton, Cliffe and Holme-on-Spalding-Moor districts in the East Riding before cultivation removed it and that he remembered the last grouse being shot there. He thought that they had been introduced but had not thrived.

According to Nelson, larger numbers of Red Grouse were forced to undertake movements away from the moors in severe weather in his time than we have records for in recent years. He wrote:

'In severe winters when there is a great depth of snow, birds are driven down to the cultivated valleys literally by the thousand, the moors being utterly deserted by them. In 1886 and 1895 they left the moors "in immense packs" to feed on corn and turnip leaves in the fields and on the buds of the blackthorn, haws and hedgerow buds. In weather like this they may be seen perched in hundreds on the hedgerows and on the lower branches of trees. Large numbers have been observed on the sea beach in the Cleveland district, and on one occasion during a lengthened snowstorm a pack of several hundred birds passed over; these, however, were only present when the tide was down, and as the water flowed they returned to the moors.'

Such incidents are difficult to imagine in view of our present-day experience with the species, although it must be assumed that there was some truth in the statements. In December 1878, Nelson passed within 5 yards of a hen grouse feeding on a hawthorn bush behind the Redcar sandhills, and in the severe winter of 1879/80 they were seen at Oswaldkirk, near York, and at Bridlington. Nelson, again in *The Birds of Yorkshire*, wrote:

'In the storm of 1886, when heavy snow on 24th January was succeeded by a partial thaw, accompanied by rain, and then followed by frost, large packs of birds came down into the lowlands, and were noticed in Swaledale, Wensleydale, Arthington, Weeton, Leeds and other places remote from their usual haunts, as many as five hundred being seen in one day; numbers were killed by flying against the telegraph wires, others were shot by pot-hunters or died of starvation and many doubtless never returned to the moors.'

Similar weather prevailed in 1895 and many birds appeared in the vicinity of Harrogate and Lower Nidderdale. A record of 'scores' of birds feeding on oat stubbles adjoining the moors in Wensleydale in the mild winter of 1903/04 by standing on the stooks and stripping the ears of corn is most interesting, as grouse seldom leave the heather in mild weather.

Recent instances of grouse being affected by severe weather occurred in the winter of early 1947 when the depth of snow forced birds down onto the low ground, where they fed on berries and hawthorn buds. They appeared along the banks of the River Wharfe near Ilkley and in gardens, one bird being found in the cellar of a house. Similar behaviour was recorded in Rosedale and some other areas. One was seen at the High Royd Sewage-farm near Halifax on 16th and 18th March, and another was caught in a Halifax street. High winds kept patches of heather clear of snow on Lord Bolton's estates in Wensleydale, where grouse fed until a late snowfall at the end of March robbed them of this food source and many succumbed.

It was inevitable that the severe winter on 1962/63 would produce some interesting observations, and during January and February 1963 there were several records of birds feeding on hawthorns below the moors; one bird roosted in mature roadside hawthorns near Catterick Camp. During mid February several records of packs of up to 400 grouse were reported, and an estimated 5,000 were on the Airedale side of Rombalds Moor on 15th and 16th February. Bingley Moor attracted 1,000 on 17th February and some birds were found dead under wires there.

An interesting account in *The Field* of 23rd March 1940, p. 461, tells of the gamekeeper of Bertram Parkinson of Creskeld Hall, Arthington, being surprised to see a pack of about 40 Red Grouse feeding on a potato pie in the centre of Creskeld Wood on 18th February. The thaw, after a severe period, had been in evidence for a fortnight and the grouse were not seen again after this date, presumably having returned to the moors some 8 miles (12.8 km) distant.

Shooting grouse on the wing would seem to have been first practised about 1687, as mentioned in Hunter's *Hallamshire, S. Yorkshire* (vol. ii, p. 183), and Yarrell, in his *British Birds* (1843, vol. ii, p. 318), mentioned that Lord Strathmore's keeper was matched to shoot 40 brace on the Teesdale Moor on 12th August and 'performed the feat with great ease, bagging 43 brace by two o-clock'. About 1805, grouse were 'driven' on the low moor at Rayner Stones, an area subsequently cultivated during Nelson's time. There were regular drives in 1841, but no butts had been built. Three brace per gun for one drive was considered a good bag, and a total bag of 50 brace in 1843 was considered 'a great day'.

At High Force in Teesdale in 1886, eight guns killed 2,616 brace between 13th and 17th August. The year 1872 was a record one on the Yorkshire grouse moors and some very large bags were made on 6th September. At Broomhead, 1,313 were killed by 11 guns in one day, and a further 1,040 brace were said to have been shot by seven guns in the same season. On Wemmergill Moors in the same year, a staggering 3,931 brace were shot by six guns and a total of 17,074 was killed during the season, 5,668 of which were claimed by Sir Frederick Millbank. The average bag on this moor over 12 seasons was 4,133 brace, the largest single day's shoot accounting for 1,035 brace from six guns of which Sir Frederick shot 96 brace in one drive lasting 23 minutes. A granite monument erected on Wemmergill Moors commemorates this feat.

Nelson gave details of several other spectacular shoots, including 1,070 birds shot in 20 drives on Blubberhouses Moor on 30th August 1888 by Lord Walsingham's party. In the year 1901, a game dealer in Richmond sent away, during one week in August, no fewer than 17,352 Red Grouse, the price ranging as low as two shillings per brace.

The importance attached to the grouse moors in the nineteenth century is evidenced by a legal charge in the minute book of the township of Harmby in the North Riding under the heading of 'Ling': '... And if any person shall burn any Ling, Heath, Furze etc. between 22nd February and the 24th June he shall be sent to the House of Correction for any time not exceeding a month, there to be whipt and kept to hard labour.'

In 1952, Chislett, in his *Yorkshire Birds*, gave no details of recent bags, but I doubt if the numbers quoted by Nelson have occurred during the twentieth century. In the 1966 season, 600 were shot on Rombalds Moor, where 600 brace were shot in 1974; 900 brace were shot on the Bingley, Hawkesworth and Burley Moors in 1970, despite extensive fire damage during the breeding season, and 920 brace were shot on these same moors in 1971. Shooting results for the Midhope Moors in the south of the county showed bags of 1,000 brace in 1974, 600 brace in 1975 and 400 brace in 1976.

The Red Grouse reaches the southern limit of its distribution in the Peak District. A study undertaken by D.W. Yalden during the years 1969-72 showed a total of 10,000 pairs, the Yorkshire part of the area holding at least 1,300 of these in 1971.

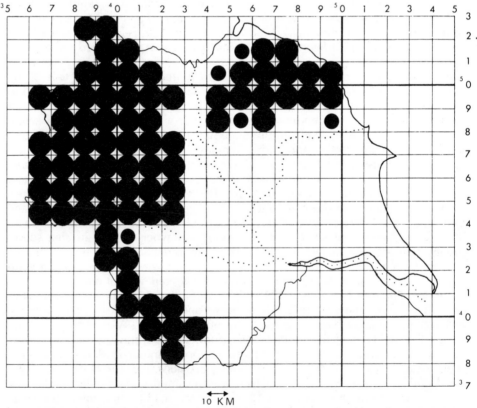

10 KM

Red Grouse. The most characteristic of all Yorkshire heather-moorland breeding species; it is common on the rigorously managed estates, some Yorkshire moors providing the best grouse shoots in Britain.

For details of this interesting study see *The Naturalist*, 1972, pp. 89-102, and 1979, pp. 5-8.

After enemy bombs had set fire to large areas of the moors near Helmsley on 31st August 1940, small parties of grouse were seen at night near the Malton road. Three birds seen by R.H. Appleby at Burniston Tip near Scarborough on 21st January 1978 were quite exceptional and were presumably driven down by snow on the high ground. A most intriguing record concerns two Red Grouse that rose from some trailing brambles and flew past Ralph Chislett on the Spurn Peninsula on 19th September 1938. The typical elongated droppings of the species were found at the spot from where the birds had risen. He was informed that two grouse had been about the peninsula all through that spring and summer and that they had probably come from the North Riding moors in the previous winter. A farmer near Goldsborough reported two grouse on his land in the autumn of 1972, and on 7th November 1974, in thick fog, a Red Grouse landed beside a tractor driven by Miss A. Summersgill in the same locality.

Very few Red Grouse are reared in captivity, and there is little chance of these out-of-context birds having that origin. To the inexperienced, the sight of a Grey Partridge in the dark brown *montana* plumage could give rise to thoughts of Red Grouse, but that plumage variety of the partridge is rare. Aberrant plumage in the Red Grouse is not unusual; Nelson cited two white birds, one of which was an albino with pink eyes and legs, and he mentioned a brood of cream-coloured young on Grimwith Moor, three of which were procured. The most recent records concern a pure white bird at Hebden Bridge on 30th October 1976, and a hen bird with a white breast shot in Colsterdale on 8th September 1966.

The afforestation over much of the North York Moors has seriously affected the grouse population there. As early as 1941 the Annual Report of the Yorkshire Naturalists' Union stated that they had been almost driven away 'but four were seen on Harwood Dale Moor on 3rd November', and a few others have been noted occasionally.

Peter Young, an experienced gamekeeper/naturalist, reported the nest of a Red Grouse on Sourmire Moor containing four Mallard's eggs and some of the owner's on 8th April 1980. Inspection on 18th May showed that three of the Mallard's eggs and all the grouse eggs had hatched. It would have been interesting to have learned the fate of the young ducklings.

This most indigenous of British birds is so very typical of the Yorkshire moorlands and some of the best grouse moors in Britain are situated within our boundaries. It was apparently much more numerous in the nineteenth century than today. The continued interests of the shooting fraternity, some of whom pay very large amounts of money for a day's shooting, and the landlords who provide such, will ensure it a continuing place albeit at the expense of other, perhaps more exciting species, the presence of which is often wrongly assumed to be detrimental to grouse.

Black Grouse
Tetrao tetrix

'Resident, local, occurring chiefly on the western borders of the county. Has been introduced in several districts.' That is how Nelson summarised the status of this attractive species. Proof that it was indigenous and possibly abundant in prehistoric times was evidenced by the discovery of its bones in the Teesdale caves by James

Backhouse. Marmaduke Tunstall of Wycliffe-on-Tees wrote in 1784 that it was scarce all over the north of England, the principal reasons seeming to be the great improvement in the art of shooting flying birds; enclosure of moors and commons; and burning of ling, which was difficult to prevent, 'being commonly done by stealth in the night'.

Lengthy investigations by K.G. Spencer into a comment in the *Journal of Nicholas Assheton of Downham, Lancashire* which states that, on 23rd December 1617, he killed three Heath Cocks at 'Rowe Moore' indicated that the locality was in Yorkshire. He was unable to locate the name on any modern map, but a district lying about 2 miles (3.2 km) north-northwest of Slaidburn was, however, formerly well known as 'Rawmoor' and Spencer concluded 'with fair certainty' that the two places were the same. For details see *Bolland Forest and the Hodder Valley* (1955) by M. Greenwood and C. Bolton, and *The Naturalist*, 1965, p. 50.

The Reverend George Graves, in his *British Ornithology* (1813), wrote that poachers took considerable numbers of Black Grouse by imitating the call of the female and as many as 50 males could be lured by this means in the course of two days. Thomas Allis in his report of 1844 said that, according to J. Heppenstall, they were pretty common in some woods near Sheffield.

At the time of Nelson, this species still bred in a few localities near Sheffield and was introduced into the Holmfirth and Penistone districts, where a few pairs bred annually. Several attempts to introduce the species were made around this time. Young hatched and reared under domestic hens were released in the Hebden Valley, but did not fare well and soon died out. The same happened at Whitewell-in-Bowland, the last, a female, being shot on Holden Clough in 1885. Similarly, attempts to introduce it at Arncliffe in Wharfedale and near Huddersfield both failed. An introduction at Meltham met with some success, and a few still bred there in the early 1900s, with some being shot annually.

In the game book of Sir Thomas Frankland for the year 1798, referring to the Blubberhouse Estate in Washburndale, is written the following: 'Pullan, keeper, says that when a boy he shot nine Blackgrouse one morning on these moors, and that his mother made them into a pie for the haymakers.' After that time the species apparently decreased, as some were subsequently released by J. Yorke of Pateley Bridge, but these did not survive.

Around this time a few birds were seen, and some were shot, in the general area of the western dales and, in the Sedbergh area, a few nested annually. In Upper Teesdale, three or four plantations were specially devoted to the Black Grouse and it apparently did quite well. It would appear to have been successful also in the Lartington area after its introduction there. Mr E.B. Emerson shot several on Bowes Moor in the 1870s, and a small population survived on the North York Moors during the mid nineteenth century.

An attempt was made to introduce birds onto Thorne Waste, whereafter a few were seen at long intervals and a nest found in 1880. A male was shot in October 1896 near the Vermuyden River. Chislett recorded Black Grouse 'once or twice on Hatfield Moor and west of Sheffield'. In his *Yorkshire Birds* he listed Swaledale, Wensleydale, Wharfedale, Nidderdale, Ribblesdale, the Forest of Bowland, Hubberholme, Lunedale, Dentdale, Mashamshire, Richmond and the Washburn Valley as places where the species had been shot or reported in the years up to 1952. One shot on Danby Moor in October 1941 was the only occurrence that Chislett knew of from the northeast, but W.J. Clarke reported one seen near Scarborough on 9th April 1930.

A.H.V. Smith, in his *Birds of the Sheffield Area* (1974), referred to breeding in the Strines area in 1948 and again in the late 1960s, although the latter is considered suspect. Leks were known to D. Herringshaw during the 1940s and 1950s, but there are very few in the area today. A single male in 1975 and a female seen on 7th March 1976 are the only recent indications that a small population may still linger there.

The Forest of Bowland around Stocks Reservoir was a good area for Black Grouse in the 1950s and remains so today. In 1950, 13 birds were seen by J.K. Fenton and young were reported in the same year. An old established lek at Tan Hill in the northwest held 17 males in 1962, 19 on 4th May 1969, 11 on 6th May 1973, with fewer up to the present time. On 21st February 1971, 37 males were on Wemmergill Moor near Selsett Reservoir, where 16 were counted on 22nd February 1981.

The increase in conifer plantations on many moorland areas during more recent years has undoubtedly benefited the Black Grouse, and the most noticeable increase has been in Upper Wharfedale in the Greenfields area of the Langstrothdale Chase. During the early 1970s, reports were coming in from the foresters of large numbers, including one count of 150 lekking males in March 1974 and 51 birds in one small area on 15th November that year. These numbers were quite exceptional, and B. Shorrock and S. Ralph visited the area in the following year and found the species to be indeed numerous. On 18th February 1975, 48 males and 23 females were seen from the road and the whole area of young conifers may have held many more. A check on 24th October produced 20 males and ten females. The foresters' count may have been exaggerated, but their ability to cover the whole area away from the road could well have enabled them to locate those numbers. During the 1970s, this was certainly the best area in Yorkshire for

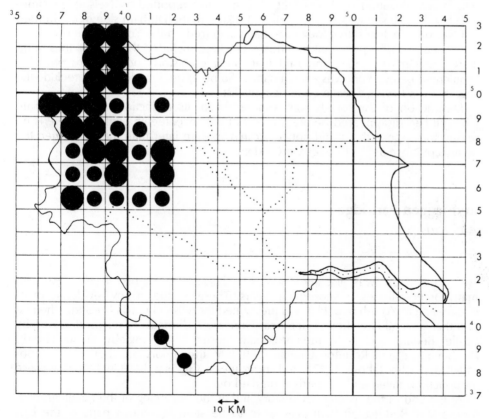

Black Grouse. This species has benefited from the forestry plantations on the uplands of the northwestern Pennines. Some areas have relatively large breeding populations, particularly in Langstrothdale.

seeing Black Grouse but, as the conifers grew and became less suitable, so the numbers fell as birds doubtless moved into other areas. It is still possible, however, to see upwards of 20 birds during the spring in this area.

The area from Bowes Moor in the northwest, southwards through the heads of Swaledale, Wensleydale and Wharfedale to Settle and the Forest of Bowland is the stronghold of the Black Grouse in Yorkshire. Birds are now being reported more frequently from lower down the valleys into the Pennine foothills, and will no doubt continue to increase as they find their favourite habitat in young plantations of conifer. On the North York Moors and along the moorland districts of the south-west, the species is very thinly distributed and hard to find.

Capercaillie
Tetrao urogallus

Nelson included the Capercaillie in his *The Birds of Yorkshire* on the strength of evidence in the form of bones found among the remains in Victoria Cave, Settle, and summarised its status as 'Formerly resident in the forests of north-west Yorkshire; now extinct.' Bones were also found in one of the caves of Upper Teesdale at an elevation of 1,600 feet (488 m), and reported to Nelson by James Backhouse. The site was in fact 2 miles (3.2 km) on the Durham side of the border, but Nelson concluded that they must have occurred on the Yorkshire side, too.

Chislett, with his penchant for square brackets, included the species thus in his *Yorkshire Birds* in 1952, and said that 'Such prehistoric bones were probably sepulchred before York was even a name.' So be it; but that does not preclude the species from having a place on the county list.

Destruction of the forests was responsible for its extinction in England, from where it had disappeared before the end of the seventeenth century. There is no reason to suppose that it did not occur in Yorkshire later than the time when the owners of those ancient bones were extant.

Red-legged Partridge
Alectoris rufa

The 'Frenchman' was first introduced into England in Suffolk about 1770, with many other releases in subsequent years. There is little, if any, evidence of its occurrence in Yorkshire until it was mentioned by Allis in his 1844 report, when he said that 'several have been killed near Doncaster'. Birds were released at Hornby Castle, Bedale, and at Swinton, Masham (about 1846); Ingleby Manor (1860); Pinchinthorpe and Rounton Grange (1890); Warter Priory and between Scarborough and Filey (about 1892); and in northeast Cleveland (1906). Most of these introductions failed and the birds soon died out.

At the end of the nineteenth century and at the beginning of the twentieth century, a few Red-legged Partridges were to be seen in various parts of the East Riding. Several were turned down at Mulgrave by the Maharajah Dhuleep Singh some years prior to 1897. It would be interesting to know from where these birds came; if from his native homeland, they could well have been Chukars (*Alectoris chukar*), a species which is commonly kept in captivity today and sometimes crossed with the Red-leg to produce the 'Ogridge', a sporting hybrid which is reputed to 'spring' instead of running as does the Red-leg.

E.W. Wade, writing in *The Naturalist* (1911, p. 43), said that the species had spread all over the Wolds and was extending into Holderness, and Riley Fortune recorded a continued increase south of Harrogate to beyond Church Fenton. A bag of 29 brace, shot in one day at Ganton Hall in 1914, was said by W.H. St Quintin to be unprecedented.

By the 1950s when Chislett wrote *Yorkshire Birds*, the Red-legged Partridge occurred 'fairly commonly from Spurn northward to Scarborough, inland across Holderness into the southern parts of the West Riding and across the Wolds and the Vale of York to the Boroughbridge–Leeds–Sheffield line. North and west of that area the bird occurs less frequently and with growing scarcity until the Pennines are approached where it becomes rare.' With a few minor amendments, that assessment still applies.

By the late 1950s, some were penetrating up the lower valleys of the Pennine foothills, and a pair had young on Masham Moor in 1956. In 1964, at Catterick, P.J. Stead saw one on 31st May and two on 28th June, and one was shot at Rogan's Seat, near Tan Hill, in that year (*The Shooting Times*). Also in 1964, there were two near Kettlewell on 19th April, one killed near Redcar on 22nd April and one at Boulby Cliffs on 27th June. Two birds shot at Colsterdale in 1965 were the first that P. Young had seen there. A pair with ten chicks was at Ilton on 1st July 1970, and

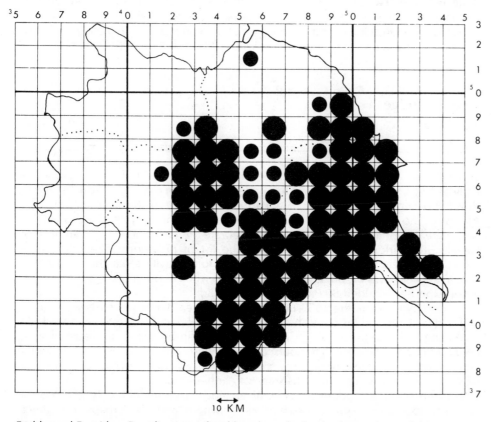

Red-legged Partridge. Breeding is confined largely to the lowland agriculture of the southeast, but it has spread into some foothill valleys in recent years. Stocks are augmented annually by birds released for shooting.

the first breeding record for Wharfedale occurred in 1971 when a nest containing 14 eggs of this species, plus two of the Grey Partridge, was found on 21st June. Two birds at Ellestring in Wensleydale, seen by G.E. Alderson, were the first he had recorded so far up the dale, and one was near Hawes in late May 1979. In 1976, two were on Skelding Moor on 4th April, two were on Grewelthorpe Moor on 16th April, and 25 were shot at nearby Ellington in October. A bird seen by M.G.H. Garnett at Angram Reservoir in Upper Nidderdale on 29th June 1976 was quite unexpected. Two seen by D.J. Britton in Farndale on 25th December 1977 were also well above their normal range. In 1978, single pairs were on Ilton Moor (800 feet/244 m elevation) on 11th March, Dallow Moor (850 feet/259 m elevation) on 13th May, and Low Bishopside (950 feet/290 m elevation) on 15th April.

Coveys of up to 20 or 30 birds are not unusual in the species' main range in the southeastern half of the county. In 1977, 71 pairs located in the Doncaster area included 50 pairs on Hatfield Moor, where five coveys totalled 51 birds on 30th October, and several coveys of up to 30 birds were seen in the area south of York in that autumn. Arable land adjacent to Skipwith Common attracted a covey of 47 on 9th November 1978, and 54 were together on Hatfield Moor on 31st December 1977 with 60 on 19th October 1980.

It is known that many hybrid 'Ogridges' are reared by the shooting concerns and are put down annually in late summer, and that Chukars are kept in captivity by aviculturists. All birds should be carefully examined and the black streaking below the throat band looked for. The absence of such streaking will indicate hybrid or pure Chukar blood. Two birds walking along the road in front of my car in the early morning of 26th March 1983 at Kirkbymoorside were in all respects pure Chukar.

A marathon Red-leg ringed at Spurn on 29th September 1956 travelled 40 miles (64 km) to Thwing, west of Bridlington, where it was shot on 30th December 1958.

Grey Partridge
Perdix perdix

This popular gamebird was mentioned in literature connected with Yorkshire as early as 1313, when, according to the price of victuals in the City of York, issued by Royal Proclamation, the value of a Partridge was 2d. In the accounts of Selby Abbey for the years 1413-14 is an item 'paid for catching Partridges at Crowle, 2s.' At the great feast at Cawood in 1466 to celebrate the enthronisation of Archbishop Nevell, 500 Partridges were included in the list of provisions. The price of 40 Partridges bought for the marriage feast of Sir John Neville's daughter at Chevet, near Wakefield, was 6s. 8d, and two years later, when Sir John was High Sheriff, his list of expenses included 80 Partridges at £1.6s.8d.

At Hornby Castle in the 1859/60 season, no fewer than 5,359 birds were killed, and Earl de Grey and his party shot 303 birds near Ripon on 23rd September 1884.

Writing of its status in 1952, Chislett said '... can be seen and heard in open country from the Teesmouth to Spurn coastline westward to the lower slopes of the Pennine moors. As the moors are approached birds become fewer and on the high fells, the species is unknown.' This summary applies today.

The pressures of modern agricultural methods have undoubtedly affected the Grey Partridge population in Yorkshire, as elsewhere, and it is perhaps commonest in the low-lying uncultivated land in the south of the county, where some large coveys have occurred in recent years. High Melton had 100 birds on 12th October and Wath Ings had 100 on 4th December in 1976. Ten coveys totalling 100 birds were on Swinefleet Common on 20th October 1974, and 150 were counted there on 13th February 1978. The area around Blacktoft Sands often attracts good numbers, and 60 were there on 31st October 1975 with 80 on 11th February 1978.

Coveys of between 20 and 40 birds can be found regularly in the agricultural land east of the Pennines, and larger parties occur not infrequently. Adverse weather during the spring and early summer can severely affect the breeding success, and in some years numbers may be well down as a result. Towards the end of the severe winter of 1962/63, 101 birds were assembled at Harrogate Sewage-farm on 2nd February, doubtless attracted by the soft open areas of sludge, and 58 were at Adwick-le-Street on 9th February. On the Wentworth Estate in 1975, 84 brace were shot on one October day.

The species is well known for its pugnacity in defence of the nest or young. The Yorkshire Naturalists' Union Annual Report for 1951 records an incident at Scruton in the North Riding when a hen bird was picked off her brood of 17 chicks and, before she was replaced, the cock flew into the man's face, forcing him to retreat with bleeding cuts.

Birds with aberrant plumage are sometimes recorded, and Nelson mentions one taken in a net in about September 1797 which had delicate milky-white plumage and which was thereafter kept in confinement. Four pure white birds were killed from a brood at Scarborough in October 1869 (*The Zoologist*, 1869, p. 1954), and five more similarly plumaged birds were included in a covey of 11 and recorded in *The Field* for 28th November 1885. The dark-chestnut-plumaged '*montana*' variety may occasionally occur.

The number of Grey Partridges reared in captivity and released by shooters is not large, and this indigenous gamebird survives well in a fairly hostile environment. Chislett ended his chapter on the species by saying: 'It is not a species that calls for much comment and its status in Yorkshire has scarcely varied since 1906.' The records available to me at the present time provide no evidence to suggest otherwise.

Quail
Coturnix coturnix

A hundred dozen 'Quayles' were included in the provisions for the great banquet at Cawood in 1466, given in honour of Archbishop Nevell. Obviously the Quail was much more common then than it is now, and even by 1844 T. Allis, when he gave his report to the British Association at York, spoke of its casual appearances in various parts of the county: it was apparently becoming scarce by that time. Nelson said that it was formerly an abundant species, but could say of its status in 1906 only that 'it still nests irregularly and in limited numbers in several localities'. The latest breeding record of which he had note was in 1896 in Glaisedale in Cleveland. Chislett was able to cite breeding in 14 of the years from 1906 to 1952. Many of the nests were destroyed by harvesting activities, and there is no doubt that this hazard has been one of the prime causes of the bird's scarcity at the present time.

In *The Naturalist*, 1918, p. 37, W.H. St Quintin stated that more than one pair nested in the East Riding in 1917. W.J. Clarke recorded nesting in the North Riding in 1920 and near Hunmanby in 1921, which he reported in *The Naturalist* (1921, p. 37, and 1922, p. 38). A brood was reared at Lothersdale in the West Riding in 1924 and reported in *The Naturalist*, 1925, p. 24. A clutch of 11 eggs at Sedbergh in

1927 was passed over by a reaper without being damaged (*The Naturalist*, 1927, p. 357). A nest with 11 eggs was found on Selby Common on 26th July 1929 (*The Naturalist*, 1929, p. 377). A Quail laid 14 eggs in a nest in the garden of Eskrick Hall in 1941. In 1943, there were three reports. The first was at Sherburn, where a deserted nest containing 12 eggs was found. The second concerned a bird flushed from 11 eggs by a reaper on 9th August near Scarborough, with four adults and a brood of chicks seen in the same field on 14th August. The third was a record of six Quails flushed from a barley field at Reighton on 4th September and an injured bird caught there on 25th September. Two nests, both containing eggs smashed during the harvest, were found in 1945 at Aldborough and above Ashbury Head. A nest was found near Hunmanby on 21st July 1945 and two eggs taken to W.J. Clarke for confirmation. In 1947, a nest was destroyed during haymaking at Grassington, some 1,300 feet (396 m) above sea-level, and another nest was destroyed at Holme near the Cheshire border. Seven were flushed at Warter Priory on 24th September 1947, and Lord Middleton said that Quails bred on five of his farms around Birdsall in that year. A nest with eight eggs was mown over in the Vale of Pickering in July 1947. In 1949, two pairs were reported breeding in an East Riding dale where the species had been heard calling during the early summer, and birds bred on two farms on the Birdsall Estate. Seven were flushed at Balne, near Goole, on 16th September 1950. A nest with eight eggs was found in a clover field near Kirk Hammerton during the harvest on 25th July 1952 and they were taken because 'there seemed no prospect of the birds returning'.

Since 1952, the Quail has been recorded in Yorkshire in every year except 1962. A nest was cut over at Fadmoor on 4th July 1953, and a pair with their brood was reported in a Wolds area in September 1955 (Lord Middleton in *The Field*). A pair reared a brood near Hutton-le-Hole in 1957, and a hen bird with seven newly hatched chicks was on a road near Sutton-on-Derwent on 29th June 1958. Single pairs at Muston in 1960 and 1961 were thought by J. Temple to have nested successfully, but proof was lacking. A pair with six young was seen near Fountains Abbey on 30th June 1961.

Apart from the foregoing proven cases, Quails had been heard calling in summer at several other localities in all the Ridings, and most frequently about the areas of Wolds chalk and where the limestone outcrops.

Reports of Quails came from over 20 localities in 1964 after the first bird was seen at Spurn on 25th May. These mostly concerned one or two calling birds, but seven were in the Dearne Valley near Mexborough on 29th June.

Although varying numbers of Quails have occurred in every year but one since the breeding record in 1961, no other proof of nesting has been forthcoming, although it surely must have taken place. Calling has been recorded from all parts of the county, from Holderness in the southeast up to some parts of the Pennines and the Cleveland Hills. Several have been heard calling from barley, and the species could well nest successfully in cereal crops now that its traditional hayfields are cut too early in the year to allow the birds time for successful breeding.

There were more records than usual in 1981, especially in the eastern parts of the county, and reports came from nine places between May and July including six at Flamborough on 11th July. An increase during August and September probably indicated that breeding had taken place in some areas. Up to five called near Holme-on-Spalding-Moor during August and several were seen during harvesting in the Bielby area. One was killed by a harvester at Hagg Bridge in August, and three were flushed during harvesting near Newton on 25th August with two there on 14th and 16th September. Birds also occurred at Bempton, Blacktoft Sands, Wheldrake, Pocklington Airfield, Ravenfield and Burnby.

The year 1982 was also above average, and records came from no fewer than 28 localities between 12th May and early August. Three were at Bubwith on 22nd

May; three at Flamborough on 1st June; up to four in the Bolton and Wath Ings area from 28th May to 27th June; up to three at Hagg Bridge near Elvington during June, where there were five on 4th September; three at Spurn on 6th June; and one or two at the other places.

Exceptional numbers occurred in 1983, with records from 20 localities including up to seven birds calling along the River Ouse near Cawood during the summer. Breeding was proved for two pairs in the York area, at Wheldrake (seven young) and at Holtby (four young).

The Japanese Quail *Coturnix japonica*, now considered to be a separate species, is a very common bird in captivity and is intensively reared for the table. There are some instances of its being released, but it appears not to thrive, having been too inbred. The call is very distinct, being a loud, harsh rattle, quite unlike that of the ordinary Quail.

Pheasant
Phasianus colchicus

The Pheasant was established as a Yorkshire bird as early as 1466, as evidenced by the provision of 200 for the banquet at Cawood given in honour of the enthronisation of Archbishop Nevell. It inevitably featured in all the great feasts of that time, and in 1528 the price of 12 'ffesants' was £1.

In 1844, Thomas Allis wrote that Pheasants were 'As common as shooters and poachers allow them to be.'

At one time thought to be entirely dependent on man for its food and requiring re-introductions, the Pheasant became completely feral and, although many thousands are reared and released annually, a sizeable population exists of its own volition. The species may be seen almost anywhere in Yorkshire, especially during the autumn when released young birds are wandering.

In the breeding season, the Pheasant will nest in any well-sheltered site among vegetation and in a variety of other situations that provide cover and seclusion, and may even choose to nest off the ground in old nests or on tree stumps. In 1965, I flushed a hen from a nest with eggs among the thin grass on an exposed moorland slope above Carperby in Wensleydale.

The Annual Reports of the Yorkshire Naturalists' Union have contained some interesting references to this bird. In 1951, J.P. Utley reported that there were five nests of this species and one of the Grey Partridge along a 200-yard (180-m) stretch of the central grassed reservation between the carriageways of the Great North Road (now known as the A1) near Sinderby. E.W. Taylor saw a hen leading newly hatched chicks near Yearsley on the very late date of 2nd October 1955. On 3rd November 1956, J.P. Utley examined the crop of a Pheasant which contained 36 beechnuts. At Eccup Reservoir on 27th April 1958, a bird flew low over the water before dropping in, some 30 yards (27 m) from the bank, to which it swam with its head jerking like a swimming Moorhen and its tail held under the water.

The race originally introduced into Britain was the nominate *P.c. colchicus*, which lacks a white neck-ring and originates in the area between the Black and Caspian Seas. Some birds showing the plumage characters of this western race still occur, but few are pure and the majority of the Pheasants are now interbred with the race *P.c. torquatus* from southeastern China, which has a broad white neck-ring. Mixtures of several races now occur in the artificially reared stocks, and melanistic and leucistic examples are not rare. Pure white birds are also met with.

The continuing interests of landowners and rough shooters will ensure that this colourful introduced species remains a regular feature of the Yorkshire countryside.

Golden Pheasant
Chrysolophus pictus

This small and colourful pheasant is now admitted to the British list on the strength of a few small feral populations, the most successful of which are in the Brecklands of Norfolk and Suffolk and in southwest Scotland.

A few birds have been seen in recent years in Yorkshire, all without doubt being escapes from captivity, and it is most doubtful if any have survived long in the wild, most being taken back into captivity.

Commonly kept in aviaries, both in public parks and in private collections, and very easy to breed, it is inevitable that some will escape or be left by their owners to run free and it is not impossible that a pair could settle down to breed in a wild state.

In the event of such an occurrence in the future, the monitoring of these early escapes will prove useful.

Water Rail
Rallus aquaticus

That the Water Rail was once very common in the undrained carrlands of the southeastern part of the county there can be no doubt. Even today, more birds are actually present, both in the breeding season and in the winter months, than are ever seen.

Nelson said that 'the nest has rarely been found in Yorkshire, but young birds are occasionally captured ...'. According to Hatfield's *Historical Notes of Doncaster* (1866), it bred in that district in former times before the drainage and reclamation of the carrs. Only a few other widely scattered localities where breeding had been recorded were reported by Nelson, and Chislett, in 1952 when he published *Yorkshire Birds*, said 'I have yet to see a nest in Yorkshire where proved breeding is rare.'

Since 1952, definite proof of breeding has been obtained in only 11 years. A pair nested at Skipwith in 1953; an adult with six chicks was seen at Harewood Park in July 1960; one with a chick was at Almholme in 1967; a nest with six eggs was found on Thorne Moor on 12th May 1968, and six pairs were thought to have bred there; two pairs bred at Low Ellers Carr in 1970; one bird with a chick was on Thorne Moor in 1972; two pairs nested at Blacktoft Sands in 1974, one pair in 1976 and three pairs in 1977; also in 1977, single pairs were proved to nest at Wheldrake Ings, on the Pocklington Canal, and at Fairburn Ings where three chicks were seen; two pairs bred at Hornsea Mere and one at Potteric Carr in 1979; and two pairs bred at Blacktoft Sands in 1980. In the intervening years, breeding almost certainly occurred at some of these places and doubtless at several others. The majority of breeding records have come from Thorne Moors and Blacktoft Sands, but intensive watching at other likely places would reveal the necessary proof.

In the autumn, many Water Rails visit us from the Continent and elsewhere in the British Isles. A bird ringed at Spurn Bird Observatory on 11th January 1959 was recovered in Germany in May of the same year, and a young bird ringed in Sweden on 14th September 1965 was found dead at Beverley on 12th January 1970, illustrating the two-way traffic. Each October, birds may be encountered along the coastline anywhere from Spurn to the Teesmouth. What are undoubted immigrants are often seen in strange places: one was flushed from a shelter on Hornsea Promenade by H.O. Bunce on 13th October 1957, one was caught in a Beverley street on 29th November 1957, and one was found in the City of York on 20th October 1966. A bird landed on board a ship off Portugal on 10th October 1953 and was brought into Hull, where it was fed by the RSPCA before being released. A journey in the opposite direction would have been more beneficial!

During the migration period, several Water Rails have been found dead or injured beneath wires or as a result of flying into other obstacles. A young bird in my collection, for instance, killed itself against the radar globes on Fylingdales Moor on 24th November 1965.

A Water Rail may be flushed unexpectedly from almost any waterside vegetation during the autumn and winter, and some large numbers may be found at the favoured places. During the last ten years, with regular watching by the wardens at bird reserves, a better indication of the numbers present has been gained. Fairburn Ings has had between 15 and 30 birds during the autumn and winter months in some years, and Blacktoft Sands has attracted between 20 and 40 birds. In 1959, Chislett said in the Yorkshire Naturalists' Union Annual Bird Report that 'to have Water Rails reported from 20 areas inland was most unusual'. With more bird-watchers on the scene in recent years, that situation is seen to be normal and the species is widespread during the non-breeding season. Those wishing to see this skulking rail, however, should not expect to do so without patient watching in the right habitat.

A resident breeding bird of patchy but widespread distribution and in small numbers, and a bird of passage and winter visitor, is how our present knowledge of this elusive species allows its status to be summarised.

Spotted Crake
Porzana porzana

Nelson summarised this crake as a 'Resident; very local and limited as to numbers. A spring and autumn migrant; in some years not uncommon during the latter period.' The report given by Thomas Allis to the British Association in 1844 mentioned it, on the authority of Hugh Reid, as frequenting the 'Carrs' of Doncaster, and stated that it was found breeding in most years near York. F. Boyes considered that it bred annually in Holderness, where he found a nest with eggs on the banks of the River Hull on 21st May 1882. A pair bred at Hemsworth Dam near Ackworth in 1899 and it was said to have occurred on the Harrogate Irrigation Farm during the breeding season.

Since those early days, breeding reports have been very few. A pair bred at Hornsea Mere in 1912 on the authority of G. Bolam, and Chislett ended his chapter on the species by saying 'I have reliable information of breeding by this species in Yorkshire very recently but can do no more than state the fact, for obvious reasons.' The locality was in the south of the county.

During Chislett's period of review (1907-1952), there were only 12 records of the Spotted Crake apart from the known breeding birds, the majority being seen in May, September and October. Since 1952, it has occurred in all but 11 years up to 1981. Most records have concerned lone birds, some of which were found dead, as was one picked up on the road at Branton, near Doncaster, on 2nd December 1961. On 29th October 1966, a Knaresborough postman, who took a keen interest in birds, saw a 'rail' type bird walk across the road and hide behind some stones in a garden. He dismounted his cycle and caught it. The bird was a Spotted Crake, which died shortly afterwards. He phoned to ask me to collect the corpse, but unfortunately, while he was out, his wife burned the body, believing the green legs to be the result of radio-activity picked up on its migration!

Evidence supporting immigration comes from records along the coast: single birds were at South Gare on 19th October 1966 and on 7th November 1967; at Coatham Marsh on 25th November 1968; at Spurn from 14th to 27th September with another on 12th October 1969; again at Spurn on 26th August 1970, one being caught and ringed and last seen on 1st September; at Hornsea Mere on 19th November 1970; at Spurn on 29th October 1972; at Seamer Road Mere, Scarborough, on 25th October 1975; at Flamborough on 21st March 1976; at Spurn on 2nd May 1976; at Hornsea Mere from 11th to 24th August 1976; at Flamborough on 8th April 1978; at South Gare from 2nd to 5th May 1978; and again at Flamborough on 4th April 1981.

Inland records have come from Welton Water on 17th December 1959; Almholme on 13th April 1968; Stanley Sewage-farm on 13th and 14th September 1969; Clapham (found dead) in October 1970; near Settle on 20th March 1973; Tophill Low Reservoir from 18th August to 9th September 1975; Sutton-in-Craven on 10th October 1976; Scout Dyke Reservoir on 14th August 1977; Swillington Ings on 28th August 1977; near Wilton from 8th to 10th September 1977; Blacktoft Sands from 8th to 10th August 1981 (immature) and an adult from 23rd August to 12th September 1981; Tophill Low Reservoir on five dates between 29th August and 10th September, and again on 19th October 1981; Sprotborough Flash from 9th September until November 1981; and at Blaxton Gravel-pit, where one was found dead in late October 1981.

There were three records in 1982: at Sprotborough Flash on 30th October, at Flamborough on 14th November, and by the River Don at Barnby Dun on 18th November. In 1983, two were seen by several observers on 2nd September at South Gare, where one bird stayed until 10th, and single birds were at Fairburn Ings on 7th August, at Naburn Sewage-farm from 12th to 20th September and at Tophill Low Reservoir from 2nd to 4th October. One was at Blacktoft Sands on 13th September 1984 and subsequently.

Spotted Crakes have been seen more regularly at Fairburn Ings than at any other locality. Single birds were present on 16th May 1959; from 3rd to 19th September and from 14th to 25th October 1969; from 27th August to 18th October 1970; from 30th August to 31st October 1971; on 20th August 1972; and on 27th and 28th October and from 3rd to 11th November 1973. In 1975, there was an interesting series of records during the autumn: an adult was seen on 11th August, and by 17th at least five birds were present, with from two to five being seen subsequently almost daily up to 21st September. One was present on 8th February 1976. A Spotted Crake was seen regularly between 21st May and 16th June 1977 at a site south of York.

It is possible that one or two pairs are breeding in the county but, as with the last species, proof will be difficult to obtain.

Little Crake
Porzana parva

W. Fothergill of Carr End, near Askrigg, wrote 'The *Rallus pusillus* of Gmelin, was shot on 6th May 1807 by Mr. John Humphrey of Wensley, on the banks of the Yore, near that place. It was alone, and suffered itself to be approached very near without betraying any sense of danger. It ran with great rapidity, carrying its tail erect.'

Thomas Allis, in his report of 1844, said 'H. Reid tells me that a specimen of this rare bird was taken alive at Cantley; it ran into a tuft of grass and was captured by a boy, and came into his possession [Reid's] about eighteen years ago.'

In 1836, one was captured near Scarborough, and recorded by Professor W.C. Williamson. One was caught alive on a canal boat on 6th May 1862 at Aldwarke Bridge, near York, and went to the collection of Mr Johnson of Masham, being later acquired by J.C. Garth of Knaresborough in whose collection Nelson saw it. At the dispersal of Garth's effects in December 1904, the specimen was bought by Riley Fortune of Harrogate.

The last of Nelson's recorded occurrences was on 17th October 1892, when one was taken alive at Green Hammerton. The specimen was sent to Lord Lilford, who identified it.

On 28th December 1946, at Spurn, G.H. Ainsworth and J.H. Barrett had views at ranges down to 5 yards (4.6 m) of a small crake with chestnut-brown wing-coverts streaked with black; its flanks, throat, chest and sides of neck were uniform slate-grey, its legs apparently grey, and the short bill green except near the base. The bird skulked among the tangles of rusty barbed wire in the area at Chalk Bank known as the 'wire dump'.

There have been no records since the above, which Chislett published in *Yorkshire Birds*.

The species is very rare in the British Isles, and only about one individual has occurred in each of the last 15 years. There are about 96 records in all.

Baillon's Crake
Porzana pusilla

Nelson recorded three Baillon's Crakes up to 1892 and Chislett added one more for 1912.

The first was killed by George Challard on 29th May 1874 at Hors Dam, Kirkheaton, and was mentioned by J.E. Palmer in *The Zoologist*, 1874, p. 4159. The specimen went to the collection of S.L. Mosley of Huddersfield.

One was reported at Holmpton, Holderness, in 1880. It went to the collection of H.H. Slater.

The third was killed by hitting telegraph wires between Pocklington and Wilberfoss at Whitsuntide 1892. It was an adult male and the specimen went to the York Museum, where I have inspected it (*The Naturalist*, 1892, p. 308).

The record published by Chislett was of a bird shot by J.M. Charlton at East

Harsley, near Northallerton, on 2nd October 1912 (*British Birds*, 6, p. 258).

Since the foregoing there have been two further records. On the evening of 10th May 1965, N.W. Harwood flushed a small crake from the side of a small stream known as Model Beck about 3 miles (4.8 km) north of Guisborough. He returned later with A. Barnard, and together they had excellent views and were able to identify it as an adult Baillon's Crake. The bird was present until 12th May and was also seen by D.G. Bell, E.C. Gatenby and P.J. Stead (*The Naturalist*, 1966, p. 80).

The other was at Fairburn Ings from 6th to 13th June 1970, and was watched by P.J. Carlton, B. Eaton, C. Winn and others. This was only the fourth British record since 1948 of this central European species.

Corncrake
Crex crex

Nelson considered that the Corncrake, although less abundant than formerly, was not the 'rara avis' that Allis's records inferred. Allis had said that the bird was seldom heard and that incessant persecution by the birdstuffers and others had nearly exterminated it. Some indication of its former abundance can be found in Nelson's *The Birds of Yorkshire*. A note in *The Zoologist*, 1845, p. 820, said that six or seven might at that time have been killed on their arrival at Spurn. W. Talbot, author of *The Birds of Wakefield* (1876), remarked that he had seen 41 sent to one man in a season.

Nelson summarised it as a 'Summer visitant, generally distributed, common except in manufacturing districts.' Chislett knew the bird well during the early 1900s, and remarked in his *Yorkshire Birds* (1952) that there was 'no thought of the possibility of the practical disappearance of a species which then bred everywhere'. In 1905, when he set up house one mile from the centre of Rotherham, six Corncrakes called that summer from the fields adjoining his garden and the bird was common in the direction of Wickersley and Maltby. E.W. Wade reported that the species was becoming much scarcer in the East Riding by 1907, and that it had almost disappeared from the Wolds by 1909 (*The Naturalist*, 1907 and 1909).

Between 1920 and 1924, the Corncrake had almost gone from south and central Yorkshire, except for an occasional breeding record or calling bird. It fared better in the Dales country, where the hay harvest was later, but numbers were reducing there by the end of the 1930s. A.J. Wallis recalls seeing a nest with eggs and newly hatched young at Ackworth in 1933. Since 1940, the Corncrake has been an extremely rare bird in Yorkshire and, although the species has occurred in every year since then, proved breeding records have been very few. The 1950s were the last years of the Corncrake's stand in the county. Single pairs bred near Austwick and Lawkland in 1952, and five pairs were located within 2 miles (3.2 km) of Sedbergh in 1953. In 1954, three pairs hatched young near Reeth, some of which were killed by the reaper; Corncrakes also bred near Sedbergh and nested near Bingley, where three young were seen on 14th July, and also near Halifax, where five or six young managed to escape the reaper on 13th July. A pair bred near Whitby in 1958.

Apart from the Sedbergh area, where one or two pairs nested up to the mid 1960s, only one pair, near Pateley Bridge, is known to have been successful in recent years. Two pairs were located near Sedbergh in 1965, eight young from one brood being killed by a reaper.

During the years from 1960 to the present time, between two and eight

Corncrakes have been recorded annually. Most of these have been calling birds during May, many, if not all, doubtless in vain for most moved on. From the few that stayed for a week or more, no evidence of breeding was forthcoming.

Some immigrants are recorded along the coast in most years, and there have been 19 such records between 1961 and 1982: one at South Gare, two at Flamborough and the remainder at Spurn. Apart from five birds during April, May and June, the rest have been seen during August and September, with one on 9th October. The latest bird of which I have note concerns one caught by Miss A. Summersgill in a kale field at Bewerley in Nidderdale on 10th November 1961.

There can be little doubt that modern farm machinery and the earlier harvesting of hay have accelerated the Corncrake's decline. A few pairs may still nest undetected in the hill country of the northwest, but success in the lowland pastures is now virtually impossible. Two birds calling from corn near Helmsley for a period during the spring of 1983 attracted birdwatchers from all over the county — a sad reflection of the situation for a bird which was relatively common at the beginning of the century. In 1959, Chislett said that fewer Corncrakes were noted during the year than Water Rails, 'which would have been impossible in my younger days'.

Moorhen
Gallinula chloropus

There is no evidence to suggest that the Moorhen is any less numerous now than it was in Nelson's time and before. It can certainly cope well with the increase in built-up areas if open water is available, and may even have benefited from the creation of artificial waters such as gravel-pits during recent times. Public parks, small farm ponds, rivers, lakes, reservoirs, sewage-farms and moorland tarns all provide the needs of this ubiquitous bird. Nowhere in Yorkshire, if suitable water, no matter how small, exists, is the Moorhen completely absent.

Its choice of nest site is as varied as the type of water on which it chooses to build it. Traditionally it nests among waterside vegetation or among overhanging branches, but it may nest on floating planks and oil drums or high up in bushes and trees. Chislett knew of a nest 20 feet (6 m) up in a yew tree at Roche Abbey. A nest in 1956 was built 18 feet (5.5 m) from the ground on top of an old pigeon's nest, and F.A. Wardman found a nest 30 feet (9 m) up in a riverside alder near Swinsty Reservoir in 1978. Nelson records a case of a bird incubating an egg in a hole of a tree 8 feet (2.4 m) above the ground.

During the winter months, many birds may be seen congregated at suitable localities. At the larger waters, numbers may reach treble figures, the highest of which have been 150 at Fairburn Ings on 1st February 1948, 150 at Hornsea Mere on 6th March in the same year, and 150 at Swillington Ings on 20th December 1952. A.H.B. Lee saw 100 on the big lagoon at Knostrop Sewage-farm on 27th December 1954. A. Chapman counted 73 birds on the Humber Wildfowl Refuge on 27th July and 141 on 10th September 1972. Thrybergh Reservoir had 140 birds on 10th February 1980, and earlier in the year 80 were at Gouthwaite Reservoir on 12th January. Gatherings of 20 or 30 birds are commonplace at several large waters or sewage-farms during the non-breeding season.

In very severe weather, the Moorhen may wander away from water in order to find food and at such times may often be found perching high up in hedges or trees of hawthorn, where it feeds on the berries. Sewage-farms are a favourite habitat at such times, when the damp sludge is easily picked over.

The severe winter of 1962/63 severely affected the Moorhen, and several areas had reduced numbers during the 1963 breeding season; a reduction of up to 50 percent was reported from some areas around Doncaster. The species was quick to recover, and observers were reporting an almost complete return to normal after the 1964 breeding season.

A Moorhen ringed at High Royd, Halifax, on 7th April 1950 eloped to Gretna Green, Scotland, where it was found only 14 days later on 21st. Another from the High Royd trap, ringed on 6th October 1957, was recovered at Nidd, near Knaresborough, on 23rd May 1958. One ringed at Ossett on 26th March 1961 was found dead at Newton Burgoland, Leicester, on 26th July 1961.

Nelson examined a specimen that had killed itself against the Flamborough lighthouse. He also stated that birds are occasionally picked up in the streets of sea-coast towns in the autumn, suggesting immigration.

Birds are often seen along the Spurn Peninsula in circumstances indicating recent arrival. Some appear during March and April, probably on their homeward journey, whether that be to other parts of Britain or across the North Sea. An adult ringed there on 13th April 1979 was recovered in Denmark on 23rd March 1981. Evidence of incoming birds is provided by the recovery at Driffield in January 1951 of a bird ringed in Denmark in May 1950, and of one at Rise on 26th February 1963 which had been ringed on Texel in the Netherlands on 30th November 1962.

In 1978, six birds were on the canal at Spurn during most of October, with nine there on 21st and 11 on 30th. Up to seven remained throughout November, and up to nine were present in December. A similar situation exists in most years, and more ringing would doubtless provide the recoveries to shed further light on their origins and destinations.

Moorhens with abnormal plumage have been recorded on a few occasions. Nelson reported a buff-coloured specimen in the collection at Thickett Priory which had been taken on the River Derwent. A white bird was near Blaxton during the early months of 1959 and again in December 1960. One at Knotford Nook Gravel-pit from 24th February to 28th May 1970 was described by F.A. Wardman as having a pale brown back and ash-grey underparts. D.E. Murray saw a pale leucistic bird at Tophill Low Reservoir on 23rd May 1975.

Coot
Fulica atra

Nelson summarised the Coot's status as 'Resident throughout most parts of the county, excluding the manufacturing districts, and on the high moorlands though even on some of the latter it is not altogether absent.' That is more or less true today, but the numbers involved would seem to be far greater than during the nineteenth century. Nelson did not mention actual numbers, but statements such as 'large numbers on Hiendley [Wintersett] Reservoir in February 1872', 'resident but not common on the "Carrs" of Doncaster', 'fairly common on the lakes at Harewood and Allerton Mauleverer', 'rather scarce on Fewston but on Malham Tarn it is abundant' all suggest that it did not occur in the often huge flocks with which we are familiar today.

Chislett published figures showing that certain waters were obviously favoured, among which were Hornsea Mere and Fairburn Ings. At the former, numbers in December 1946 and 1947 were estimated to be about 800. At one time it was the practice to shoot Coots at Hornsea, and on 16th February 1924 392 were so killed.

Fairburn Ings attracted 500 birds during the winters of 1950 and 1951. P.F. Holmes, the warden at the Malham Tarn Field Study Centre during the late 1940s and 1950s, watched the autumn build-up each year, starting in August and peaking at around 150-200 birds by November.

Records in recent years show that these three localities are still favourite places for Coots to assemble. In 1956, G.R. Bennett's figures for Hornsea Mere showed a peak count of 500 during the early months, with 500 again in October, increasing to 800 by 9th December and 1,050 by 27th December. In the following year, commenting in the Yorkshire Naturalists' Union Annual Report, Chislett described a count of 1,700 on 30th December as 'phenomenal'. That high figure is now recorded almost annually, and in 1972 there were 2,370 during January, 1,500 during February and March, with a population of between 500 and 850 during the summer, increasing to 1,150 by 23rd September, 1,040 during November, with a sharp increase to 3,880 on 26th November, 4,050 on 17th December and 5,200 on 24th December. Since then, numbers have not exceeded 2,000, and the annual maxima have varied from 500 in October 1978 to 2,000 in January 1980 and 1,350 in February 1981.

At Fairburn Ings there have been counts of 1,000 in July 1974 and 950 in October 1975, with that latter figure during the period August to October 1976, 1,051 on 27th July 1980 and 1,000 on 1st August 1981. At Malham Tarn, numbers were increasing by the mid 1970s. There were 950 present on 3rd January 1976, and 500 or more have occurred in most years to the present time.

Wintersett Reservoir has attracted Coots since Nelson's time and is still one of the main waters in Yorkshire, with maximum counts of 550 birds on 25th December 1974 and 809 on 20th December 1975. Mickletown Ings now holds large numbers, and since the mid 1970s the highest counts have been 450 in November 1974, 612 in January 1980 and 738 in November 1981. The floodwaters along the River Derwent held 300 Coots in March 1978 and 950 on 14th February 1981 as maximum counts. The highest counts at Tophill Low Reservoir in recent years have been 600 on 1st October 1972 and 685 on 13th October 1980. The new gravel-pits at Bolton-on-Swale started to attract this species during the late 1970s; 595 were there on 30th December 1979, and 1,098 feeding on tipped grain and potatoes on 16th December 1980.

Most of the other deep waters in the county have good numbers of Coots during the same periods. The reservoirs along the Pennine foothills and the gravel-pits on the plains are equally attractive if the conditions of deep open water prevail. After a gradual build-up during the late summer, flocks of between 200 and 500 are a regular sight at any of these waters. Gravel-pits may take several years to mature and to establish a growth of weed suitable for Coots. When such development has taken place, the species is quick to take advantage.

The origin of the Coots that arrive suddenly each year during July and August is not fully understood, but it is known that some come to Britain from the Continent. Ringing recoveries prove such a crossing of the North Sea and large-scale ringing would provide much useful information. The bird is shot for food on the Continent and recoveries should be forthcoming thereby.

In severe weather, ice may force Coots onto small areas of open water, where they assemble in large and often spectacular packs. They are sometimes forced to vacate their favourite haunts altogether, when they disperse to other reservoirs or lakes, or onto the rivers where they are normally seen only at such times. Some move to the coastline, and during a spell of very hard weather in 1979 no fewer than 100 were counted in Scarborough North Bay on 5th January and 22 were on the sea in Jackson's Bay the next day, when single birds were also at Filey and Barmston and eight were feeding in Bridlington Harbour. The long and severe winter of 1962/63 also forced birds to the coast and along the Humber, where small numbers were seen on some small areas of open water, and the River Ure at Ripon was visited by 100 birds in late February that year.

The numbers of breeding birds following the 1962/63 winter were much reduced in some areas. It was estimated that the population at Almholme was down by 25 percent and that at Lindholme Lake by 18 percent. Flock sizes in the following autumn were also slightly lower than usual.

Hornsea Mere and Fairburn Ings hold the largest breeding populations and a careful check by C. Winn at the latter locality in 1957 showed some interesting results. On 16th May he counted 28 broods totalling 146 young birds; three days later, 87 nests held 488 eggs or small chicks, and on 12th June 39 broods added up to 273 young birds. In 1976, the RSPB warden counted only 45 breeding pairs. At Hornsea Mere, in 1977, R.G. Hawley, the warden, said that breeding numbers were well down on the established 200 pairs of the early 1970s. Elsewhere in the county, Coots breed at most waters, and in 1979 a pair attempted to nest at Blacktoft Sands for the first time. Often, a solitary pair will build its large and conspicuous nest on a lone branch in the water or may conceal it in the vegetation along the water's edge. Wherever they choose to build, the presence of a pair of these very noisy and aggressive birds is always obvious.

The Coot is now one of the commonest waterbirds in Yorkshire, both during the breeding season and in the autumn and winter months when their numbers are swollen by immigrant birds from other parts of Britain and the Continent.

A Coot ringed at Duddington Loch, Midlothian, on 13th November 1960 was found dead at Burley-in-Wharfedale on 11th January 1962. An adult ringed at Fairburn Ings on 29th December 1961 was recaught at Elstree, Hertfordshire, on 13th January 1963.

A white Coot was seen on a small pond at Staddlethorpe in November 1959, and an all-white bird frequented a small pond at Kilnwick Percy during the years 1975 to 1977.

Crane
Grus grus

Now an extremely rare visitor on its migrations to and from northern Europe, the Crane was undoubtedly far more common in Yorkshire up to the end of the fifteenth century, when it finally ceased to breed in East Anglia. At the great feast given at Cawood in 1466, Cranes were included in the bill of fare; and at the marriage feast of the daughter of Sir John Neville, the High Sheriff of Yorkshire, on 14th January 1526, in the nineteenth year of Henry VIII's reign, £1.10s. was paid for nine Cranes — a fair price in those far-off days, suggesting that they were hard to come by.

One was recorded in Fothergill's *Orn. Brit.* (1799, p. 7) as having been shot near York in 1797. One was also noted by J. Cordeaux in *The Naturalist*, 1893, p. 203, where he states that he saw a Crane in the house of a Flamborough fisherman that had been obtained by a local farmer from a field near his house in the last week of

February 1892. It had been preserved by Jones of Bridlington and was a young bird of the previous year.

Whether a record of two Cranes, seen with the naked eye and also through a glass, at Bolton-by-Bowland on 25th August 1884 would stand up to the scrutiny of the modern records committees is doubtful, but Nelson published the details in *The Birds of Yorkshire* and said that the observer was 'perfectly familiar with the appearance of the bird, having often seen it in Germany and other places on the Continent' (*The Zoologist*, 1884, p. 470). An adult bird in the York Museum is labelled 'Adult, Strickland collection, probably local', but no other details were available to Nelson.

The sub-fossil of a 'nearly perfect left tibiotarsus' was found during excavations at Walton Abbey in the East Riding, and identified by E.T. Newton as belonging to a Crane. It was reported in *The Naturalist*, 1923, p. 284.

Chislett knew of no other records up to 1952, but several were soon to follow. One was found dead near Auburn, Bridlington, on 5th April 1954 by R. Little (*British Birds*, 1955). In 1957, at North Deighton, near Wetherby, six unusual birds, tall enough to look over a fence 3 feet 6 inches (1.1 m) high, frequented fields of barley stubble undersown with rye-grass and clover from 17th November to 7th December. The landowner, G.E. Sturdy, wrote to the *Yorkshire Post* on 2nd December and Chislett asked A.F.G. Walker of Harrogate to visit the farm and speak to Sturdy, who described the birds perfectly. On one occasion, he had passed them at 70 yards' (64 m) range while driving his tractor and could see the red patch on the head and their black and white necks. They always stood and flew together 'never more than a yard apart.' A Crane frequented the Lissett area from 16th to 27th April 1960, and was seen by C.H. and S. Voase, B.S. Pashby and H.O. Bunce.

John Temple of Muston, near Filey, saw one near his farm on 23rd April 1966 which stayed until 14th May, when it was last seen during the morning by R.H. Appleby and H.E. Scott; at 14.18 hours on 14th, what was undoubtedly the same bird flew south at Spurn. Later in the same year, Temple was fortunate enough to see four more Cranes as they flew south over Muston on 15th October. They later passed over Flamborough, where they were seen by A.F.G. Walker and friends. A crane at Gargrave, near Skipton, on 14th October in the same year was not specifically identified, but in a year when Cranes were passing through the county it would almost certainly have been of this species. One frequented the area of Spurn Point from 21st to 26th May 1967. In 1970, C. Winn saw one flying low over Fairburn Ings on 6th August and S.L. James saw what was very likely the same individual as it flew over Thorne Moor on 8th.

One was present on some flooded fields in the vicinity of Owston Wood near Almholme from 14th to 16th April 1976, on which latter date it was seen to leave to the north at 07.15 hours. In the same year, on 30th May, P.J. Carlton watched one as it flew over Leighton Reservoir and finally landed on the moor. Later in the year, on 29th October, three birds, including a juvenile, flew north off Spurn and alighted briefly in Kilnsea before continuing their journey northwards. In 1977, C. Winn saw one at Fairburn on 17th March; several observers including T.D. Charlton, Dr J.H. Lawton and G. Smith watched a bird at Wheldrake Ings from 24th April to 9th May; two birds were seen by J.E. Adlard and S. Taylor flying south off Hornsea on 1st October; and M.J.A. Thompson saw one at Haxby from 8th to 17th October. One was seen at Thorn Park, Mowthorpe, near Scarborough, by M. Francis and F.A. Whitford on 5th May 1978.

In 1979, there were five acceptable records of the Crane, in a year in which 34 were seen in the British Isles. One at Burniston from 20th to 28th April was seen by P.J. Dunn, T. Hobson and others; one was seen by R.G. Hawley at Hornsea Mere on 27th May; one in the Newington area on the Nottinghamshire/Yorkshire border from 20th June to 1st July was seen by many people, including D.J. Britton and C.H. Wear; one was seen by M. Coverdale and K. Rotherham in the Lissett area from 15th to 23rd August; and one was seen by M. Hobson, M. Lynes and W.H. Priestley on Thorne Moor from 26th October to 11th November. On 10th June, a bird seen by P. Dove at Gate Helmsley was accepted by the *British Birds* Rarities Committee only as a species of crane, but in a year when there were many Cranes passing through the country I could see no reason to doubt Dove's identification.

Three birds flew down Nidderdale over Scar House Reservoir on 6th April 1980 and were watched by P.J. Carlton and A. O'Neill.

On 10th November 1982, A.J. Last watched three Cranes flying over Kilnsea before they turned and flew westward over the Humber. At the same time, J. Cudworth was watching three more flying south off Spurn about a mile (1.6 km) out to sea. This party consisted of two adults and a juvenile. One was seen flying north over Ellerton Ings on 12th April 1983.

Four birds occurred in the spring of 1984; one at Flamborough on 11th April; two flying north at Blacktoft Sands on 26th April; and one at Wheldrake Ings on 19th May which was seen by D. Waudby. In the autumn, one was seen on 7th September at Crabley Creek and later in the Spurn area, where it remained throughout the following day; the bird subsequently spent a few weeks in the Sunk Island/Welwick area. One occurred at Barmston on 24th November 1984, where it was seen by S.T. Holloway.

Only in the years when adverse weather in Europe blows the migrating Cranes off course to westward do we see them in Yorkshire and elsewhere in the British Isles. That they have occurred in 12 out of the last 31 years is remarkable when compared with the paucity of records during the previous 100 years.

Demoiselle Crane
Anthropoides virgo

Whether all the British records of this species have referred to birds that have escaped from private collections will never be known for certain. Chislett made the point, in 1952, that 'a bird that is frequently kept in captivity need not necessarily be an escape when it occurs in a free flying state at a migrational focal point but the question should certainly be borne in mind'. I agree entirely and have long considered the species to be deserving of more serious consideration than has attended its occurrences in recent years.

Several have occurred in Yorkshire in a healthy and free-flying state and I can do no more than list them for future researchers to treat as they think fit.

On 12th September 1948, H.O. Bunce and E.M. Rutter watched a Demoiselle Crane as it flew with some Rooks over the 'Long Bank' at Kilnsea, near Spurn Point. It was fully described by the observers and Chislett published the record in his *Yorkshire Birds*, but placed it in square brackets, necessitated by the possibility of its having had a captive origin.

In 1967, one frequented the area around Atwick and Leven in Holderness between 19th May and 20th June. In the same year, three birds were at Bank Newton, near Gargrave, where they remained from 10th July into early August.

Mrs Joan Webb watched, and described in detail, a Demoiselle Crane in the area of Hundale Wyke and Staintondale, north of Scarborough, on 10th and 11th May 1977. Another was seen by the same observer and by F.A. Whitford at Burniston, near Scarborough, on 3rd December 1978.

Little Bustard

Otis tetrax

Two birds at Flamborough in the winter of 1814/15, one of which was shot, constituted the first occurrence of this species in Yorkshire. These were mentioned by Thomas Allis in his report of 1844, together with four more, none of which was dated: one shot in Bolton Wood, near Bradford, 'about five years ago'; one shot near Beverley; one killed at Boythorpe on the Sledmere Wolds; and one from the Wolds in Arthur Strickland's collection.

Nelson cited the following records. A female was procured by the Reverend W. Blow at Goodmanham, near Market Weighton, on 19th January 1854; it went to the York Museum. Another female was killed at Leven, near Beverley, on 31st January 1862, by the keeper of Canon Wray. Two occurred at Allerston Marshes in October 1886. One was taken at Scarborough a few years prior to 1881. One was killed at North Burton in 1868. A female in splendid condition was obtained in a turnip field at Burton Pidsea in Holderness during the last week of December 1895.

On 5th December 1902, near Spurn, G.E. Clubley of Kilnsea shot one at dusk which was not recovered until next morning, when it had been partly eaten by a cat. Nelson examined the preserved remains in Easington in the following October.

A Little Bustard in the possession of Captain E.W.S. Foljambe of Osberton, Nottinghamshire, was one of two shot near Wadworth, south of Doncaster, on 9th December 1922. It was brought to the notice of H.F. Witherby by Alfred Hazelwood, and was identified as belonging to the western race *Otis tetrax tetrax*, the first British specimen to be ascribed to this form (*British Birds*, 31, p. 334; and *The Naturalist*, 1938, p. 138).

Since the publication of Chislett's *Yorkshire Birds* in 1952, there have been two examples of this species in the county, both in 1956. The first occurred on 10th November, when it was shot when flying to a small pond near Aldborough in Holderness, and the second was shot from barley stubble undersown with trefoil near Preston, 6 miles (9.6 km) from the Aldborough pond, on 20th November. A Hazelwood of the Bolton Museum, to whom both birds were sent, diagnosed the former as a first-winter male of the rufous western race and the second as an adult female of the grey (and more usual) form *Otis tetrax orientalis*. Colonel R. Meinertzhagen confirmed the racial diagnosis, and I have inspected both specimens, which are in the Bolton Museum.

That two Little Bustards, each ostensibly belonging to a separate population, should occur within 6 miles of each other and in the same month in most intriguing.

Houbara Bustard

Chlamydotis undulata

There are only five records of this southeast Palearctic bustard in the British Isles. Four occurred between 1847 and 1898 and all were in October. The fifth was seen in Suffolk during November and December 1962.

Included in the nineteenth century records are two from Yorkshire, both of which are detailed in Nelson's *Birds of Yorkshire*. The first was seen on 5th October 1892 by some boys, in a field at Windy Hill Farm near Marske-by-the-Sea. It was quite fearless and allowed stones to be thrown at it. Later the same day, as it rose from the ground, it was shot at by a man named Richardson and badly wounded on one side. Nelson saw it in the flesh before it was sent to the Hancock Museum in Newcastle, where it was preserved as a mount and is on display at the present time. A coloured painting of the mounted bird appears in Nelson's *The Birds of Yorkshire* (vol. II, opposite page 560).

The second bird occurred on 17th October 1896, and was not to survive long after first being seen on Clubley's Field behind the Warren Cottage on Spurn Peninsula. It was fired at on the first day by a Colonel White, who evidently missed it. On the following day, it was observed through binoculars by W. Eagle Clarke and H.F. Witherby at about 150 yards' (137 m) range and, after being fired at several times, was eventually killed by G.E. Clubley. It was a young male and weighed 3lb 11oz (1.7 kg). The stomach was filled with vegetable matter, chiefly ragwort heads, and also some beetle fragments. W. Eagle Clarke and J. Cordeaux dined off the body and found the flesh dark and tender, tasting of wild goose with a savour of grouse. The skin went to Colonel White of Hedon (*The Zoologist*, 1896, p. 438; and *The Naturalist*, 1896, p. 323).

It is interesting to note that, like these two birds, the one in Suffolk in 1962 was also remarkably approachable.

Great Bustard
Otis tarda

Nelson devoted over eight pages to this magnificent bird and summarised its status as 'Accidental visitant from Continental Europe, of extremely rare occurrence; formerly resident in great numbers on the Wolds of eastern Yorkshire, when in their virgin state as undulating barren sheep-walks.'

The date of its final extinction as a breeding species is uncertain, but a bird seen at Foxholes, near Scarborough, about the year 1835 was considered to be the last of the resident population. It had been very poorly documented during the eighteenth century and Nelson could publish only two references to its occurrence during that time. He considered, perhaps rightly, that this lack of records might have been explained by 'the very abundance of the species'; even today, observers rarely report on the common birds. That it was formerly very common can be in no doubt. Marmaduke Tunstall, writing in 1784, said that 'some still remain on our Yorkshire Wolds. An acquaintance of mine pursued for three days last summer, without effect, a brood of seven; and one of twelve, at least, he had heard of.' The only other eighteenth century reference was in the *Sporting Magazine* dated October 1792, where it is stated that '... a Bustard was killed at Rudstone-on-the-Wolds, by a gamekeeper belonging to Sir Griffith Boynton. The width of the wings was seven feet over.' In 1720, Sir William St Quintin of Wansford paid his grandfather two shillings each for bustards.

The last stronghold was apparently on the northern part of the Wolds, about Flixton, Hunmanby and Reighton. It was in this area that, early in the seventeenth century, a Miss Charlotte Rickaby of Bridlington, when a girl, counted 15 bustards in a field while riding with her father from Bridlington Quay to Flamborough.

The grandfather of Sir William Strickland could remember a flock of about 25 birds on the Wolds between Reighton and Bridlington, and that the last of them was 'eaten' at Boynton. A farmer living at Reighton in 1830 said that, when he was a boy, flocks of eight to ten together were found all over the district. Quoting from a letter from W.H. St Quintin dated 4th March 1902, Nelson said that a gamekeeper called Agars once killed 11 Great Bustards at one shot on the Wolds, at a place called Borrow, near Sledmere, in March 1808. When this occurrence took place, the Wolds had not been ploughed up, but consisted of unenclosed rolling downs, on which the Great Bustard bred, and some were shot every year. The equipment of a Wolds keeper at that time consisted of a stalking horse, a coat made of horse hide with the hair outside, and a blunderbuss.

Five Great Bustards on Flixton Wold in 1811 continued to be seen there for at least two years, before two were killed. The remaining three stayed in the same area for a further year, when two disappeared, leaving a solitary bird. This was eventually wounded by Sir William Strickland's keeper and found some days later, in a turnip field near Hunmanby, by a huntsman of Scarborough Harriers; it was cooked at a supper given by the hunt (*The Zoologist*, 1870, p. 2063).

Very few were recorded during the early nineteenth century, up to the last at Foxholes in about 1835. Information regarding this bird was supplied by a Mr Foord of Foxholes, who also said that his father once saw 11 birds together in that district and that he had heard his uncle speak of running bustards with greyhounds.

In the early 1830s, a Mrs Metcalfe of Bridlington Quay told Mr Boynton that she and her husband, then the Vicar of Reighton, were invited to dine at Boynton Hall with Sir William Strickland, the principal dish being a Great Bustard which Sir William, in his note of invitation, described as 'probably the last of his race'. He was to be wrong by only two birds: a female trapped at Boynton in about 1833 and the one at Foxholes mentioned above.

The birds in the southern part of the Wolds frequented the vicinity of North and South Dalton, and the only Yorkshire egg known to exist was collected by James Dowker of North Dalton in 1810. It was presented to the Scarborough Museum in March 1840. In 1816 or 1817, Dowker killed two birds with one shot near North Dalton, one of which was presented to George IV, then Prince Regent; the other was eaten by Dowker.

Since the date of its final extinction as a resident breeding species, there have been only four records. A female, shot on Rufforth Moor, near York, on 22nd February 1861, went to the York Museum, and another female was picked up dead, but still warm, in the sea near Bridlington Quay on 11th November 1864. Nelson examined this latter specimen in the collection of Thomas Boynton at Bridlington (*The Zoologist*, 1861, p. 7507, and 1865, p. 9442). On 1st March 1926, at Islebeck Grange Farm, near Thirsk, a female was picked up dead after having been in the area 'since Christmas' (*The Naturalist*, June 1926).

The tail feather of a Great Bustard was picked up above high-water mark on Spurn beach in late March 1950. It was sent by Miss E. Crackles to A. Hazelwood of the Bolton Museum, who confirmed the identification. Chislett said that its source could not be surmised: 'all possibilities seem equally unlikely'. A Great Bustard resting unseen along the Spurn Peninsula is not all that unlikely.

The claimed sighting of a Great Bustard on Goathland Moors on 18th August 1973 is no longer considered a genuine record.

Oystercatcher
Haematopus ostralegus

The Oystercatcher was mentioned in connection with Yorkshire in 1512, when the Household Book of Earl Percy recorded a list of birds to be provided for the kitchens, including 'See Pyes for my Lorde at Princypall Feestes and non other tyme'.

When Nelson wrote *The Birds of Yorkshire* in 1907, he said of the Oystercatcher that breeding in the county was unknown until 1888, when three pairs nested at Spurn. Breeding thereafter did not occur regularly and the species had only limited success up to 1906. An assumption that it may have also nested at the Teesmouth could not be substantiated, as even the 'oldest inhabitant' could not recollect it having done so. He considered it to be strictly a winter visitor, very local, but common in some places, particularly the Tees Estuary.

The Yorkshire coastline for the most part is not suitable for breeding Oystercatchers and a survey in 1971, organised by M.E. Greenhalgh (*The Naturalist*, 1972, pp. 49-51), showed that only nine pairs were nesting along the 100 miles (160 km) of coast. In subsequent years, some pairs have nested at Spurn and along the Humber, the latter often being on arable land. A pair bred at Sunk Island in 1961; six pairs nested between Easington and East Hull in 1966 and at least eight pairs bred between Spurn and Hull in 1971, in which year a pair bred on the south side of the Tees Estuary.

Breeding at inland sites has been known since 1936, when a pair nested on the Upper Aire. Two pairs nested on the Ribble banks in 1938 and two more pairs by the Aire. A spread to other areas in that district soon followed. In 1943, Chislett suspected breeding on a shingle bed of the Swale, which was subsequently proved by A. Baldridge in 1949. Breeding was proved by the River Wharfe in 1944, and on the River Ure at Aysgarth in 1946. Young were seen by the River Ure near Ripon in 1950, and the species bred near Jervaulx in the same year. By 1951, Airedale had eight nesting pairs, a brood was reared in Swaledale, and Chislett said that it was now well established in other western dales. A bird was present on the River Rye, near Helmsley, throughout March 1951. Breeding occurred in Wharfedale in 1953, when a pair bred in the Sedbergh area. By 1957, the Annual Report of the Yorkshire Naturalists' Union was able to record breeding in the valleys of the Ribble, Aire, Ure, Wharfe, Swale, Hodder, and the Rye where the species first bred successfully in 1955. At this latter locality, two pairs bred in 1961, both of which were just upstream from the old disused Harome station, and an odd pair still nests there today.

The survey by Greenhalgh in 1971 showed that 82 pairs bred in the Yorkshire Dales as follows: Airedale, 18; Nidderdale, one; Wensleydale, 19; Swaledale, 31; Wharfedale, 12; and Rydale, one. A tendency to spread eastwards out of the dales was noted at this time, after a pair had nested by the River Ouse at Poppleton and another pair at Wetherby in 1971. In 1973, two pairs reared young at Masham, one pair at Otley and two pairs by the River Wharfe near Pool, while several pairs lingered at gravel-pits without proof of breeding. The first breeding record for Lower Nidderdale occurred in 1974, when a pair nested at Staveley Lagoon, and in the same year four pairs bred by the River Ure near Ripon. In 1975, ten pairs nested within the Leeds–Ilkley–Ripon triangle, mainly at gravel-pits. In 1977, a pair hatched young in a kale field near Melbourne on the Lower Derwent, and birds were seen on arable land in the same area during the summer. In 1979, H.O.

Bunce reported three to four pairs nesting in this area between Bubwith and Wheldrake and one pair at Melbourne near the Pocklington Canal. In 1981, at least six pairs bred along the Lower Derwent.

A pair bred at Malham Tarn, 1,200 feet (366 m) above sea-level, in 1978, but the nest was preyed on. Other localities away from the northwest where breeding occurred in 1978 included Fairburn Ings (one pair), Hay-a-Park Gravel-pits (one pair), Masham Gravel-pit (one pair), Nosterfield Gravel-pit (three pairs), and Pool-in-Wharfedale (one pair on river shingle).

Numbers frequenting the coast at the estuaries of the Tees and Humber have undoubtedly increased during the last 25 years. In 1954, 'the largest number recorded anywhere was 200 on the mud in the Teesmouth on 3rd January' (YNU Annual Report). Redcar regularly had 150 to 180 in the autumn during the late 1950s. The Tees Estuary attracted 600 on 2nd January 1960, but no more than that number, and usually fewer, have been counted there in recent years.

The Humber Estuary at Spurn had the relatively low maximum count of 100 birds in late August 1962, but counts of 860 in February 1970, 500 in April 1970, 1,000 on 24th November 1971 and 800 on 28th December 1971 heralded a much larger presence there than formerly. In 1974, there were 1,490 on 20th January, 1,500 on 10th February, 1,540 on 3rd March, then fewer to May, building up again in autumn with 450 by 10th September, 1,065 on 24th October and 1,100 on 29th December. Smaller numbers occurred in each year thereafter, but in recent years numbers visiting the area have increased. In 1979, 3,400 in November and 3,120

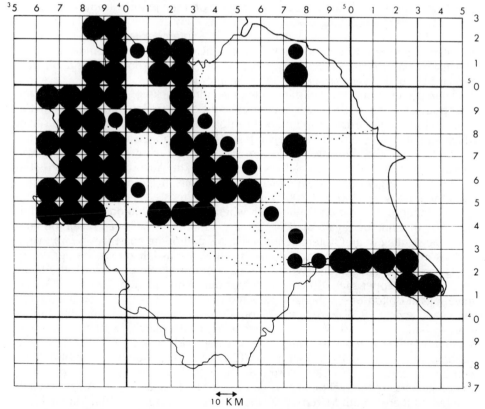

10 KM

Oystercatcher. Traditionally a breeding bird of the high ground in the northwest, a small population along the Humber extended its range during the present century and lowland gravel-pits are now regularly used for breeding.

in December were the highest counts for 30 years. In 1980, there were 4,000 on 14th February and 3,000 on 2nd November, and a count along the whole estuary from Spurn to Goole showed totals of 5,120 on 27th January and 3,350 on 24th February.

In addition to the birds feeding on the Humber mud, a marked southerly passage of Oystercatchers has been noted annually off Spurn and elsewhere along the coast during the last 25 years. The majority move during the period July to September and some spectacular counts have been made. In 1967, the annual report of the Spurn Bird Observatory read 'Movement south occurred on 19th July and became regular in small numbers on 21st July. Peak days occurred in early and late August with 517 flying south on 6th and 259 on 26th. Regular passage ended on 10th September but 392 flew south on 18th November.' Such is the situation every autumn, with fluctuating numbers. In 1975, there was southerly passage on eight days in July (163 birds in total), on 29 days in August (3,067 birds in total, with 500 on 12th as the daily maximum), and on eight further days to 13th September (168 birds).

In 1981, watchers along the coastline monitored the passage during August, with some interesting results. On 7th, over 200 passed south at Scarborough in one hour, 157 were counted passing at Filey and 203 at Flamborough. On 8th, a marked passage included 1,148 at Filey, 493 at Flamborough, and 530 coming in over the sea at Spurn. On 15th, there were counts of 140 off Filey, 245 off Flamborough and 659 off Spurn.

Nelson was aware of an immigration each autumn and he noted that, after the breeding season, small flocks began to appear 'on their journey from more northerly or Continental breeding places, occurring as early as 13th of July'. He went on to say: 'Many more arrive in August, whilst in September large migrating flocks, sometimes numbering three or four hundred individuals, are noted on passage ....' The flights often occurred as late as November, as they do now, and on 16th November 1898 several struck the Spurn lighthouse.

Other places along the coastline attract feeding flocks of Oystercatchers, the most popular being Scarborough South Bay and Cornelian Bay. A factory at Cayton making chips for the frozen-food market disposes of its potato waste into the sewer which empties into the sea in Cornelian Bay. This vegetable waste has changed the marine fauna of the shore, which in turn has attracted many birds. In 1973, Ivan Procter counted 220 Oystercatchers there on 27th August and 244 on 30th October, the largest counts ever made at that time in the Scarborough district. From then, between 200 and 300 were present in most years during January and from October to the year end until 1979, when there were 700 on 5th October followed by that number again on 15th January 1981. A.J. Wallis can recall the time when the sighting of an Oystercatcher along this part of the coast was a rare event.

Birds may be seen on passage at any inland water, mainly during the periods of spring and autumn migration. Twenty were at Gouthwaite Reservoir on 15th August 1962, and B. Pepper saw 20 flying northeast over York on 18th August 1973. The gravel-pits at Bolton-on-Swale have attracted passing Oystercatchers during the last few years, and in 1976 there were 21 on 22nd February and 29 on 29th. In that year, 43 birds were at Morley's Pool, near Settle, on 1st March. In 1978, 17 were at Bolton on 19th March, a date when several waters had passing birds including 37 at Masham Gravel-pit. In 1979 Bolton had 42 on 25th March and 32 on 14th April, with 23 on 23rd March 1980, illustrating the popularity of this site for migrating Oystercatchers. The gravel-pit at Masham is also used regularly, and A.F.G. Walker counted 30 there on 5th March 1977; there were 37 present on 19th March 1978, 57 on 11th March 1979 and 46 on 8th March 1980. In 1978, 11 flew over Eccup Reservoir on 8th August and 34 were at Ringstone Edge Reservoir on 28th. On 22nd March 1980, 53 were at Kilnsey in Upper Wharfedale.

In the Settle area, where several species regularly cross the Pennines through the Aire Gap, Oystercatchers are included. There have been counts of, for example, 25 on 2nd March 1978, increasing to 42 by 21st, and 42 on 15th March 1979.

Westerly passage is noted along the Humber, and regular watching at Blacktoft Sands in recent years has shown this to be an annual event. In 1978, there were counts of 19 on 5th August, 32 on 10th, 20 on 18th and 30 on 23rd. In 1979, 1,186 birds flew west on 18 days between 23rd July and 9th September, the maximum in one day being 352 on 3rd August.

A leucistic example frequented the Redcar area in 1971 from January to March and again in April and September. A similar bird seen at South Gare by D.G. Bell and W. Norman on 28th December was doubtless the same individual.

Black-winged Stilt
Himantopus himantopus

Two Black-winged Stilts, an adult and an immature, were shot at Aike Carr, near Beverley, by Lord Hotham's keeper in about 1851. The specimens were in the possession of James Hall of Scorborough and, at the sale of his collection, were purchased by a John Stephenson of Beverley, who was informed in a letter dated 25th July 1881 that they had been shot 'about thirty years ago'. Mr Stephenson knew a woman who lived at Aike, and who remembered the birds being killed and shown to her on account of their long legs.

The third specimen was procured at Kilnsea, near Spurn, 'many years ago' (Nelson 1907) by John Clubley, 'who described the bird to F. Boyes so accurately as to leave no doubt as to its identity'. He did not know the exact date, but it was in late spring.

There are two recent records, the first of which was seen at Woodhouse Mill, Sheffield, on 1st August 1963 by R.G. Hawley. The second concerned two birds which were present at Blacktoft Sands on 12th May 1983 and were seen to mate on one occasion.

Avocet
Recurvirostra avosetta

The last known instance of the Avocet nesting in Britain before 1947 was at the mouth of the River Trent about the year 1837. Hugh Reid of Doncaster, writing to A.G. More on 1st June 1861, said that eggs had been taken on a sand island at the mouth of the Trent about 24 years previously. A spring tide almost covered the island and the eggs were floating in the water. The man who took them also shot one of the adult birds. Nelson wrote: 'The county boundary being at this place drawn in the centre of the River Trent, Yorkshire will share with Lincolnshire the honour of possessing the last British breeding station of the Avocet.'

Thomas Allis referred to the Avocet thus: H. Chapman had two, killed on Skipwith Common, near Selby, about twenty years since, one of which is now in the Museum of The Yorkshire Philosophical Society.' Several birds were obtained at Spurn Point before 1844 'according to Allis's friend and correspondent Arthur Strickland'.

In 1827-28, one occurred at the Teesmouth. J.H. Gurney reported that it had appeared there 'two or three times', and these latter records may have included one in the spring of 1849 which was in the collection of J. Duff of Bishop Auckland; another, killed by a Stockton gunner, in the Tees, about 1870, may also have been so included.

An adult taken at Scarborough about 1864 went to the Museum in that town. An adult male, formerly in the collection of James Hall of Scorborough and believed to be a local specimen, went to the Hull Museum.

Two birds frequented the vicinity of Flamborough lighthouse for several days in April 1893. One was 'procured' by Mr Coates of the Lighthouse Farm and preserved by M. Bailey; the other was killed on 16th April at Marton Lodge, near Bridlington. Nelson examined both these birds and reported the facts in *The Naturalist*, 1893, p. 171.

Chislett added three more records when he published *Yorkshire Birds* in 1952. 'An authenticated Avocet' was supposed to have been shot on the Ouse 'not very long ago' prior to 1930. The second was watched by J.P. Utley at Teesmouth on 9th September 1947, the year in which the species first returned to England to breed in Suffolk. The third record concerned two birds seen by L. Greenwood at Redmires Dam, Hebden Bridge, during September 1950 and reported by G.R. Edwards.

Since 1950, the Avocet has occurred in Yorkshire in 21 of the 34 years to 1984, and in every year except four since 1963. Two were seen on the North Sands at Scarborough on 30th September 1955 by F. Hastings, who described them perfectly to R.S. Pollard, and another had been seen near Paull in mid August by A. Credland and other wildfowlers. One was seen at Cherry Cobb Sands on 25th September 1956 by M.K. Taylor. Two were at Spurn in the 'canal zone' area on 6th April 1958, three were present on 7th and one on 8th and 9th; they were watched by E.S. Skinner, G.R. Naylor and others.

An Avocet was at Wath Ings on 6th June 1963 and later on the same day at Almholme, where it remained until 7th. A. Credland reported one at Burstwick, near Hedon, on 8th April 1964. In 1965, H.O. Bunce watched one at Cherry Cobb Sands on 14th May and K.S. Cliff saw two flying south at Filey Brigg on 22nd May. Two birds stayed at the South Gare lagoon from 11th to 18th April 1966. One was at Flamborough on 23rd April 1968. Two Avocets flew west at Spurn on 1st June 1969, one flew south there on 3rd August, five flew south over the Humber on 21st September, and one flew north on 30th October, later to be seen on the Humber shore.

Two flew south at Spurn on 31st May 1970, and in 1972 three came in high from the north at the 'narrows' on 10th June and left to the east. Another was seen flying south on 28th September 1973.

The species occurred at five localities in 1974. One at Brough Haven on 9th and 10th March was seen by D.B. Cutts and D.I.M. Wallace; one was seen by A. Grieve at Blacktoft Sands on 12th March; D.J. Standring, J. Hewitt and P.B. Wordsworth saw two at Broomhill Flash on 28th April; eight flew west at Spurn on 4th May, and seven, probably the same party, flew into Fairburn Ings on the same date and were seen at Birkin later in the day.

In 1976, B.S. Pashby and his wife saw one at Cherry Cobb Sands on 27th

February and K. Rotherham saw two birds there on 23rd May; two were at Tophill Low Reservoir on 18th and 19th May, and one flew south at Spurn on 12th June. One was at Stone Creek on 13th February 1977, two were at Cherry Cobb Sands on 15th May, and one at the Beacon Pond, Kilnsea, on 28th May later flew down the peninsula at Spurn.

In 1979, there was an unprecedented series of records. On 3rd April A.M. Allport saw one at Hornsea Mere, and later in the day what was probably the same bird flew into Spurn from the northeast. W.I. Boustead and W. Norman saw one at Wilton, near Guisborough, on 7th April. W.F. Curtis and R.G. Hawley watched one at Sandsfield Gravel-pit on 4th May, and S.M. Lister saw another on Easington Ponds on 11th. A bird flew south off Hornsea on 4th August which was reported by E.H. and C.H. Wear. P.J. Dunn saw one at Tophill Low Reservoir on 18th August. Two Avocets were on Whitton Sands on 2nd September, and two days later W.F. Curtis saw a party of 11 flying south off Hornsea. Two birds were present at Blacktoft Sands on 8th July, eventually flying off up the River Trent, and two were there on 2nd and again on 7th September.

In 1980, one circled over Hornsea Mere on 27th January and was watched by N.A. Bell as it flew north, to be seen later at Barmston by H.T. James and then at Flamborough by P.A. Doherty and V.A. Lister. One was on the lagoons at Blacktoft Sands on 6th April and two were there on 13th May. H.O. Bunce saw one at Cherry Cobb Sands on 15th May, and two flew from Kilnsea Ponds, southeast over the sea, on 28th June.

Three birds flew north over the Humber at Spurn on 17th May 1981 and two were at Welwick on the same day. One at Tophill Low Reservoir from 26th May to 1st June was seen by several observers, including T.M. Clegg and K. Rotherham. On 22nd June two Avocets were at Whitton Sands and later at Blacktoft Sands, where they remained throughout the next day.

In 1982, one was at Cherry Cobb Sands on 17th January; two were at Whitton Sands on 17th April; one was at Blacktfoft Sands on 14th May; two were at Spurn on 13th June; and one flew south over the Humber at Spurn on 23rd June.

There were eight records in 1983, as follows: one at Easington on 25th April; one at Mickletown Flash from 16th to 21st May; an immature at Ardsley Reservoir from 19th to 23rd August; one at Catwick Gravel-pit on 23rd August; one at Fairburn Ings on 25th August; and one at Spurn on 13th November.

On 16th November 1984, 12 Avocets flew up the Humber Estuary at Spurn and alighted on the mud, and two birds were at Kilnsea the next day.

Stone-curlew
Burhinus œdicnemus

The Stone-curlew was formerly common on the Yorkshire Wolds and on the rough unenclosed tracts of heath and warren until the middle of the nineteenth century. Tunstall referred to it breeding in North Yorkshire at the end of the eighteenth century. Allis and Strickland mentioned it as breeding near Doncaster and regularly on the Wolds before 1844. Nelson commented that these old writers were apparently not aware that it was an abundant species in the warrens of the East Riding. It used to nest in the neighbourhood of Scarborough and the facts were reported by a Professor Williamson in the *Proceedings of the Zoological Society* (1836, vol. 4, p. 77). A Mr N.F. Dobree of Beverley observed that, up to 1870, the Stone-curlew was well known to him as a nesting species, and he possessed a fine series of eggs taken on the wastelands between Market Weighton and Selby. W.W. Boulton possessed examples of the bird taken in 1864 and 1865 from Holme-on-Spalding-Moor, where several pairs nested.

There is no better way to outline the decline of this species than to quote directly from Nelson's *The Birds of Yorkshire*.

'Before the enclosure of the Yorkshire Wolds, the Stone Curlew was, no doubt, pretty well distributed, and nested in considerable numbers all over the then sheep-walks and rabbit warrens which formerly extended over an enormous area, and were the home at that time of the Great Bustard. As the Wolds became gradually enclosed these two species, lovers of the lonely sheep-walks, were restricted to the remnants of these once famous downs, and as these became more and more circumscribed they were banished altogether, and what were once the uncultivated uplands are now waving cornfields. There were, however, still some portions, here and there, which were used as rabbit warrens, and in these the Stone Curlew continued to breed up to about 1874, when it finally ceased to do so, and it is now almost extinct in its old haunts.'

The exact localities of the last few pairs were not given by Nelson for obvious reasons of security, and he reported merely that its breeding grounds were restricted to one or two localities in the East Riding and to one in the North, the latter being the northerly limit of the species' breeding range in Britain. This northern site was probably on the Hambleton Hills, where, according to Nelson, the species used to breed.

J.H. Gurney wrote to Nelson on 15th May 1902, saying 'You may be interested to know that on 10th May Mr. Hugh Buxton found a nest and two eggs of the Norfolk Plover. He first saw a fox, which put the bird up, and that led to the discovery of the eggs.' The site was in southeast Yorkshire.

In 1910, five pairs nested in one locality and the details were published in *The Naturalist*, 1911, p. 45. In 1916, 17 birds were seen in October on the Wolds (*The Naturalist*, 1917, p. 37), whereafter references to its occurrences, according to Chislett, 'became very guarded . . .'. Nesting by the dwindling pairs continued until, in 1936 and 1937, only one pair was known to nest. In 1938 and 1939, only odd birds were seen, and breeding has not been attempted since.

While the Wild Birds Protection Acts Committee of the Yorkshire Naturalists' Union was subscribing to maintain the Stone-curlew in its last Yorkshire haunt, eggs labelled from the very district were on sale in Scarborough. There is no doubt, as Chislett concluded, that gamekeepers and egg collectors were responsible for contributing to the Stone-curlew's final extinction as a Yorkshire breeding species.

Nelson published three photographs in *The Birds of Yorkshire*, one showing a bird on its nest among stony ground near Pickering, the second showing two eggs laid on short turfy ground, and the third showing eggs laid at the base of a spruce tree with spreading branches in a Wolds plantation. This last nest is referred to in the text; it was apparently in the middle of a fairly large plantation of trees from about 12 to 14 feet (3.7-4.3 m) in height and was, it seems, a traditional site before the trees were planted.

The breeding birds used to depart during September and October, and on 9th October 1874 a flock of about 40 was seen on rough grassland at Ganton, 'evi-

Plate 1. Thomas Hudson Nelson, author of *The Birds of Yorkshire* which was published in 1907. *Photo by courtesy of David MacKenzie Booth*

Plate 2. Ralph Chislett, one of Yorkshire's most celebrated ornithologists; founder of the Spurn Bird Observatory, and author of *Yorkshire Birds* which he published in 1952.
Photo: J. Armitage

Plate 3. The plateau of the lofty Ingleborough at an elevation of 2,373 feet (723 m) above sea-level in the west of the county. An occasional pair of Ravens manages to nest on this, the third highest of the Yorkshire peaks. *Photo: C.H. Wood Ltd.*

Plate 4. Pen-y-ghent, the fourth highest peak in Yorkshire at an elevation of 2,273 feet (693 m) above sea-level. An occasional migrant Dotterel has been recorded on the top and Ravens sometimes nest. Twites are thinly scattered in the area. *Photo: B. Shorrock*

Plate 5. Stocks Reservoir in the west of the county showing part of the extensive Gisburn Forest on the right: the breeding place for a pair or two of Red-breasted Mergansers. *Photo: B. Shorrock*

Plate 6. Great Wegber Scar, a characteristic limestone ridge of the upper dales in the northwest. *Photo: G.E. Alderson*

Plate 7. Upper Ryedale showing extensive plantations of young conifers, the favoured habitat of Black Grouse and Whinchats. Sparrowhawks and a few pairs of Woodpigeons nest in the more mature stands. *Photo: G.E. Alderson*

Plate 8. Summer Lodge Tarn in Upper Wensleydale, typical of many such moorland tarns, frequented by Black-headed Gulls and a few pairs of Teals and Shovelers. A pair of Red-necked Phalaropes stayed here for three weeks in June 1966. *Photo: G.E. Alderson*

Plate 9. Semerwater in the west of the county, the second largest natural lake in Yorkshire, after Hornsea Mere. A favourite haunt of Whooper Swans in the winter months. *Photo: C.H. Wood Ltd.*

Plate 10. Agill on the edge of Dallowgill Moor. A typical moorland ravine and a classic breeding area for Ring Ouzels and Whinchats, with a few pairs of Willow Warblers near the trees. *Photo: M.F. Brown*

Plate 11. The River Wharfe as it flows southeast through Langstrothdale. The crag with the overhanging tree is a traditional site for breeding Dippers. *Photo: M.F. Brown*

Plate 12. Langstrothdale Chase at the head of Wharfedale. Common Sandpipers, Grey Wagtails, Dippers, Redstarts and Wheatears nest along the river and in the surrounding area. Black Grouse and Short-eared Owls are perhaps commoner here than anywhere else in Yorkshire. A few pairs of Goosanders also breed. *Photo: M.F. Brown*

Plate 13. Kilnsey Crag: a view looking south showing dry-stone walling in the foreground, many miles of which straddle the fells of the Pennines and provide nesting sites for Wheatears and Pied Wagtails. *Photo: M.F. Brown*

Plate 14. Kilnsey Crag in Upper Wharfedale: a view looking north showing the famous overhang on this striking buttress. One of the few natural sites in the county for nesting House Martins and the breeding place of Jackdaws, Swifts, Stock Doves and a pair of Kestrels. *Photo: M.F. Brown*

Plate 15. Upper Wharfedale, showing the pastureland of the wide valley floor and the many scattered deciduous trees typical of most of the Yorkshire dales. Much of the upland area is planted with conifers. *Photo: C.H. Wood Ltd.*

Plate 16. Dallowgill Moor in Upper Nidderdale; breeding ground for Red Grouse, Golden Plovers and Meadow Pipits and one of the best grouse moors in Yorkshire. *Photo: M.F. Brown*

Plate 17. The northwest corner of Gouthwaite Reservoir showing large areas of mud exposed by falling water levels: an important feeding area for migrating waterfowl and waders. The ridge beyond is used by occasional Buzzards and smaller raptors for hunting, particularly in westerly winds. *Photo: M.F. Brown*

Plate 18. Gouthwaite Reservoir in Upper Nidderdale: a view looking southeast. Haunt of many waterfowl and waders and an important stopping-off point as they cross the Pennines. A favourite locality for birdwatchers from all over the county. *Photo: M.F. Brown*

Plate 19. The River Strid as it flows through Bolton Abbey Woods. Haunt of Wood Warblers, Pied Flycatchers, Redstarts and Nuthatches, with Grey Wagtails and Dippers along the river.
Photo: M.F. Brown

Plate 20. The edge of Cropton Forest showing the North York Moors in the distance. A recent survey has shown this to be the best area in Yorkshire for breeding Nightjars; a few pairs of Siskins are colonising stands of mature conifers. *Photo: M.F. Brown*

Plate 21. A view looking northeast towards Bransdale on the edge of the North York Moors above Helmsley, with Beadlam Rigg on the right. *Photo: M.F. Brown*

Plate 22. A view near the head of Bransdale, the winter home of a few Rough-legged Buzzards. Red Grouse, Golden Plovers, Curlews, and Lapwings breed here. *Photo: M.F. Brown*

Plate 23. A view looking south along the Hambleton Hills near Sutton Bank, showing the well-wooded scarps and the sharply contrasting agriculture in the valley bottom. Site of the 1969 record of Rock Thrush. *Photo: M.F. Brown*

Plate 24. The old bridge over the River Derwent near the Ferry Boat Inn near Wheldrake in 1977, subsequently washed away by floods and never replaced. *Photo: A. Gilpin*

Plate 25. The floods in full spate on the Lower Derwent, showing the ancient and fascinating cantilevered bascule bridge over the river north of Wheldrake, now replaced by a modern bailey-type structure which forms the access to the Yorkshire Wildlife Trust reserve at Wheldrake Ings. *Photo: H.O. Bunce*

Plate 26. D. Waudby and the author at Wheldrake Ings on the Lower Derwent, a Yorkshire Wildlife Trust reserve. Controlled flooding of the water meadows attracts many waterfowl and waders. The site of the first county Blue-winged Teal in April 1967. A few pairs of Greylag Geese and Shelducks breed here, as well as Shovelers, Teals, Mallards, Redshanks, Snipe, and an occasional pair of Pintails. *Photo: M.F. Brown*

Plate 27. The Plain of York showing the patchwork of intensive agriculture with very few large stands of timber. Some pairs of Lapwings and Curlews breed, but the area is very thinly populated with bird species; Yellowhammers and Corn Buntings are relatively numerous. *Photo: C.H. Wood Ltd.*

Plate 28. Skipwith Common, near York, a Yorkshire Wildlife Trust Reserve. A few pairs of Woodcocks, Nightjars and Long-eared Owls nest here and there are small colonies of Black-headed Gulls around the peat pools. Tree Pipits and several species of warblers also breed. *Photo: John R. Mather*

Plate 29. Typical scrubland on Thorne Moors, clothing abandoned peat workings; birch, heather, purple moor-grass and bracken are extensive. Whitethroats, Willow Warblers and Whinchats breed here, with Wrens, Willow Tits and Redpolls more obvious in the winter. *Photo: A.G. Phillips*

Plate 30. A drain on Thorne Moors in the south of the county, flanked by birches and sallows and lined with reeds, rushes and cotton-grass. The drain is devoid of fish, but holds much invertebrate life. Mallards, Teals and Moorhens occur and Snipe frequent the margins. Raptors hunt the area, including Hen Harriers, Merlins and Hobbies at the appropriate season. *Photo: A.G. Phillips*

dently assembling for migration'. Birds were occasionally seen away from the breeding haunts while on passage. Nelson records a bird near Saltburn in 1845 and single occurrences at the estuaries of the Humber and Tees. A pair in the collection of the Reverend G.D. Armitage was 'inadvertently killed' in the summer of 1865 on Crossland Moor, near Huddersfield; one was taken on Coniston Moor in Craven in August 1866; one was recorded at Bilton, near Harrogate, about 1865; and one was seen on Malham Ings at the end of April 1895. Nelson also recorded some six instances of the species' presence during the winter months and thought these records to refer to late-hatched individuals unable to migrate at the usual time.

In recent years, the Stone-curlew has been a very scarce visitor to Yorkshire. Chislett recorded two birds seen in a Wolds area in May 1950 where one had been seen in 1949, but they were not seen subsequently. In the evening of 13th August 1950, K.G. Spencer and J.R. Govett saw a bird in flight over Leeds which they considered to be this species. In the same year, a Stone-curlew frequented the 'wire dump' area on the Spurn Peninsula from 14th to 25th August and provided several observers with their first view of this rare visitor. In 1951, A.B. Walker reported a wounded bird found on the beach at Sandsend which died during the same night. One occurred north of Kilnsea on 22nd August 1957. A bird was reported to Chislett by D. Clarke, who had seen it on Ilkley Moor on 21st July 1958. A.F.G. Walker and A.J. Williams saw one at Flamborough on 1st October 1960. R.G. Hawley watched one on a Sheffield refuse tip at Woodhouse Mill on 2nd September 1961. One was at Spurn on 27th June 1964, and another was at Cooper Bridge Sewage-farm on 2nd September in the same year. One was seen at the Spurn Chalk Bank on 2nd September 1965. One was at Durkar Sand-quarries on 5th September 1972. R.H. Appleby, F.J. Thompson and others watched one in the Vale of Pickering on 26th and 27th April 1975. One near Kilnsea on 8th May 1977 later flew down the Spurn Peninsula, where it was seen by I. Forsyth, K. Rotherham, H.J. Whitehead and others. One was seen by B.S. Pashby and his wife between Welwick and Haverfield Ponds on 11th May 1980. Two birds occurred in 1982: one at Wheldrake Ings on 9th August and another, or the same, at Elvington Airfield the next day.

Having occurred in only 12 of the years from 1951 to 1983, the Stone-curlew must now be termed an extremely scarce visitor to Yorkshire. It is certainly one of the greatest losses that the county list of breeding birds has suffered.

Cream-coloured Courser
Cursorius cursor

This rare vagrant from North Africa and Asia has occurred in Yorkshire on three occasions.

The first was in April 1816, when one was shot in a field near Wetherby by a Mr Rhodes. It was seen alone, frequenting a dry piece of fallow ground over which it ran 'with great swiftness', making frequent short flights, and was approached without difficulty. The specimen was badly damaged by the shot, but as the bill was different from any plover's, for which he first mistook it, he kept the corpse for several days before sending it to J. Walker of Killingbeck Lodge, near Leeds. Because of its stale and damaged condition, Walker was unable to preserve the specimen, but he made detailed drawings of it and these were inspected by H. Denny, who included the record in his *Catalogue of Leeds Birds*.

Thomas Allis gave a detailed account of this bird's occurrence in his report of

1844, in which he also mentioned two others on the authority of Arthur Strickland. One of these was killed in 1825 by the keeper of the Earl of Harewood, and the other in 1823 by the keeper of the Hon. Chas. Stourton of Holme-on-Spalding-Moor.

This interesting species, of which Nelson said 'It is difficult to understand the causes which impel this beautiful bird to wander from the deserts of Africa and Asia to these inhospitable shores', has not been so impelled to visit Yorkshire again in recent times.

Collared Pratincole
Glareola pratincola

This bird, which breeds from Iberia and northwest Africa, eastwards through southern France to southwest Asia, and also in Egypt and down the eastern side of the African continent, has been recorded in the British Isles about 70 times. Eight of these records have come from Yorkshire, the first being shot in May 1844 in the dangerous company of Dotterels on Staxton Wold, 5 miles (8 km) from Scarborough. The specimen went to a Peter Hawksworth (*The Zoologist*, 1848, p. 2023).

The second was taken at Bridlington in 1850 and was erroneously recorded by Joseph Duff of Bishop Auckland as having been received by him on 9th February 1850 from Bedlington, Northumberland. He later corrected the locality in a letter to Joseph Hancock, and subsequently discussed the matter with Nelson and confirmed the facts. The specimen eventually went to J.H. Gurney.

The third example was killed between Ruswarp and Whitby by William Wilson on 19th October 1871. It was a male and the stomach contained ants and a few feathers. The specimen went to the Whitby Museum.

Since that time, the Collared Pratincole has visited Yorkshire on five occasions. The first of these, at Spurn on 2nd April 1975, although undoubtedly a pratincole, was not specifically identified and the record was accepted as either this species or the Black-winged Pratincole. The latter is very rare and it is almost certain that the Spurn bird was a Collared Pratincole.

The second occurred on 28th June 1976 inland at Fairburn Ings, where it was watched at rest and in flight by S.C. Madge and C. Winn.

On 11th June 1977, a Collared Pratincole flew east over Blacktoft Sands and was seen by A. Grieve, P. Greaves and D. Page as it continued down the estuary. What was undoubtedly the same bird appeared the next day at Spurn, where it stayed until 19th June and was seen by J. Cudworth, C.D.R. Heard, I. Forsyth and others.

The fourth record concerns a bird seen by J. Cornelius, R.G. Hawley and S.M. Lister at Hornsea Mere on 15th May 1980.

The fifth occurrence was at Easington, where J. Cudworth, S.M. Lister and J.M. Turton watched one at 30th May 1982.

Black-winged Pratincole
Glareola nordmanni

On 17th August 1909, an example of this very rare eastern pratincole was shot by W.S. Charlton from a flock of Lapwings at Reedholme, near Danby Wiske. It was reported in *The Naturalist*, 1909, p. 372, by Riley Fortune, who examined the specimen and said that 'it differs distinctly from *G. pratincola* in the secondaries not being tipped with white and in having the under wing coverts and axillaries jet black'. The mounted specimen is now housed in the Dorman Museum in Middlesbrough, where I examined it with P.J. Stead in September 1984.

There are only 19 British records of this species, which breeds from Romania and southeast Russia eastwards across southwest Asia.

Little Ringed Plover
Charadrius dubius

This species nested for the first time in England in 1938, near Tring, prior to which it had been recorded only as a vagrant on some 15 occasions. The first record for Yorkshire was in 1947, when the Reverend J.E. Beckerlegge saw two birds at Swillington Ings on 7th May. On 25th, A.G. Parsons saw the two birds engaging in display, false brooding and scraping. Three birds were seen on 16th July, after which the original pair behaved as if they had young and breeding was considered to have been very probable. In the following year, a bird was seen by D. Leaver on 8th May. When R. Chislett visited the area with W.B. Alexander on 8th June, a nest containing four eggs was found before the breeding pair was seen. The eggs were fairly conspicuous against the dull shale on which they were laid. On 12th June the two observers watched a bird back to the nest, which unfortunately was empty, but five weeks later K. Dawson and F.R. Allison found two chicks about three days old. This was the first confirmed breeding record for the north of England and the details were published in *British Birds* (1948, pp. 384-5). In the same year, one occurred at an East Riding gravel-pit on 9th May, but was not seen subsequently.

In 1949, a nest at Swillington held three eggs on 22nd May and two chicks and an egg on 6th June, but the young were not seen again. Chicks were, however, seen on 2nd and 3rd August, but whether these were from a second pair or from a replacement clutch was not certain. Four adults had been present in the area.

On 18th June 1949, M.F.M. Meiklejohn found a pair of Little Ringed Plovers at Fairburn Ings, a few miles from the Swillington site, which behaved as if with young, but none was found. Another bird was seen by the same observer in a third area nearby. It is quite possible that birds had been at Fairburn Ings prior to this as nobody was watching the area regularly at that time. In 1950, three pairs nested at the Swillington site and young fledged for the first time, and it is possible that a fourth pair bred there also.

In 1950, a Little Ringed Plover was seen at Gouthwaite Reservoir by A.F.G. Walker on 24th June and one was seen by a pool at the head of Gordale by P.F. Holmes on 12th June. A search of the East Riding gravel-pits by F.E. Kennington in

1950 proved negative. Six pairs were known to breed in 1951 and some young were successfully reared. A few birds were starting to turn up at other localities by this time and single birds were at Dewsbury Sewage-farm on 10th September and at Malham Tarn on 2nd June. In 1953, seven pairs bred at Swillington and Fairburn Ings. In 1954, J.S. Trimingham found a nest with one egg by a gravel-pit in South Yorkshire, and three pairs hatched young at Fairburn Ings with two other pairs present at Swillington. In 1955, one breeding bird was wearing an aluminium ring and a blue colour ring, having been marked as a young bird in 1953. By 1959, Chislett reported that the species bred in several areas, where eight pairs certainly reared young and two more pairs probably did so.

In 1962, 15 pairs attempted to nest at seven localities; and in 1963 the number of breeding pairs had reached 20 at 12 sites, where 15 nests were found, 13 of which hatched young birds. The habitat distribution was as follows: seven pairs at five sandpits or gravel-pits; 11 pairs on five slag heaps; a pair each at two reservoirs; and a further pair possibly nesting at a sewage-farm.

Breeding occurred in each of the five vice-counties in 1964 as follows: VC61, one pair bred at a gravel-pit and birds were present at another gravel-pit and one other site; VC62, one pair bred at a gravel-pit; VC63, four pairs bred at two gravel-pits, three pairs bred at subsidence flashes and one pair bred at another site; VC64, one pair bred at a gravel-pit, six pairs by subsidence flashes and a pair nested on river shingle for the first time on record (*The Naturalist*, 1965, p. 32); VC65, six pairs bred at five gravel-pits and one pair on river shingle. A total of 29 breeding pairs, 22 of which were successful, was a most encouraging situation for the species to have reached in only 18 years.

By this time, almost any suitable habitat was likely to attract a breeding pair of Little Ringed Plovers, and 28 pairs were located in 1967 and 33 pairs in 1968. In 1970, at Gouthwaite Reservoir, where the water level was very low and the resulting large expanse of drying mud most suitable for breeding, three pairs nested and reared six young. Two pairs were seen to display at King George Dock, Hull, on 2nd May 1970 and another on Melton foreshore, where a pair nested in 1969.

The Yorkshire Naturalists' Union Ornithological Section organised an enquiry into the number of breeding pairs in 1972 and the following results were obtained:

VC61: ten pairs proved to breed, nine at gravel-pits and one on a disused runway. Two sites were used for the first time.
VC62: one pair bred successfully at a gravel-pit.
VC63: 16 pairs bred at ten sites, which comprised five gravel-pits, four spoil heaps and one sewage-farm. Young were seen at six of these sites.
VC64: ten pairs proved to breed at five sites and at least five others may have done so. The proven sites were two gravel-pits, two spoil heaps and one sewage-farm.
VC65: 11 pairs proved to breed at seven sites, four of which were gravel-pits and three river shingle. At least 24 young were reared. Two sites were new in 1972.

To summarise the foregoing: 48 pairs bred at 33 sites, comprising 21 gravel-pits (30 pairs), seven spoil heaps (11 pairs), three river shingle sites (four pairs) and two sewage-farms (three pairs).

As is often the case, reporting became less complete as the novelty of seeing this formerly rare species wore off. In the 1970s records for some years were known to be incomplete, but 35 pairs were reported in 1975, 45 pairs in 1976 and 39 pairs in 1977. In the last year, places where breeding was reported included Tophill Low Reservoir; Wold Newton; Seamer Gravel-pit; near York; Mickletown Ings; at eight sites in the Doncaster area; Gouthwaite Reservoir; Staveley Lagoon; Masham

Gravel-pit; Fairburn Ings; and Bolton-on-Swale Gravel-pit.

In 1978, the species bred at Tophill Low Reservoir (one pair); Wheldrake Ings (two pairs); Naburn Sewage-farm (one pair); Seamer Road Gravel-pit (one pair); at nine sites in VC63 (17 pairs); at nine sites in VC64 (18 pairs); Bolton-on-Swale Gravel-pit (one pair); and on river shingle at Leyburn (one pair probable). Swillington Ings and Fairburn Ings were still being used as breeding places, although the nature of the ground was constantly changing. The latest count of breeding birds in the county was in 1981, when 41 pairs were notified, but it is possible that several more than that number are now nesting.

By the early 1960s, Little Ringed Plovers were occurring on passage at places other than the regular breeding areas. In 1961, single birds were at Gouthwaite Reservoir on 13th July, at Barmston on 7th June and at Hornsea Mere on 7th August. In 1962, one was at Spurn on 8th May and two to three juveniles were seen at Beverley Sewage-farm from 23rd to 25th September. Birds were recorded on passage in 1963 at Worsborough Reservoir, Beverley, Knaresborough Sewage-farm, Otley Sewage-farm and at Spurn; 12 birds were also present at one locality in the south of the county, where two pairs bred, on 21st May. In 1964, a similar situation prevailed, including four juveniles at Scaling Dam on 18th July. By 1969, passage birds were a regular sight at many waters, and there were maximum counts of 33 at Fairburn Ings and 26 at Gale in July and August that year. J.D. Pickup saw 22 at Fairburn Ings on 9th August 1972 and 11 were at Wath Ings on 1st September. The autumn passage in recent years has included counts of 18 at Wath Ings from 23rd to 26th July 1974 and also eight at Knaresborough Ringing Station on 6th July, with 14 there on 10th and 15 on 11th. Wath Ings had 20 birds on 5th May and again on 27th July 1976 and 21 on 17th July 1978. Fairburn Ings had 24 on 16th July 1977; 15 were at Newington Flash on 17th July 1978; and 20 were at Nosterfield Gravel-pit on 23rd July 1978. Such parties are typical of the situation at the present time.

The first birds to arrive in the county each year usually come during the last week of March and early April, the earliest records being of two birds at Beighton on 20th February 1982 which were seen by D.J. Glaves, and one at Arthington on 10th March 1979. In the autumn, most have left the breeding grounds by the end of September or early October, but some linger on. The latest dates on record are 29th October 1973 at Wintersett Reservoir; 20th October 1974 at Hay-a-Park Gravel-pit, Knaresborough; 16th October 1975 at Tinsley Sewage-farm; 22nd October 1977 at Wath Ings; and 17th October 1981 at Pugneys Gravel-pit, near Wakefield.

A chick ringed at Farnham Gravel-pit, near Knaresborough, on 4th June 1981 was found dead at Seine-Maritime, France, on 25th July 1981.

Nelson did not accept the species to the Yorkshire list, but mentioned one bird recorded by J.C. Garth of Knaresborough as being taken at Whixley on 30th July 1850 (*The Zoologist*, 1850, p. 2953). When Nelson saw the specimen in Garth's collection, he believed it to be 'merely a small example of the common species *hiaticula*', an opinion shared by J. Backhouse and Riley Fortune. In 1851, three were said to have been killed on the Calder and were reported in Talbot's *Birds of Wakefield*, p. 25, and W.W. Boulton recorded the occurrence of one at Spurn on 5th October 1861 in *The Field* of 15th October that year. Nelson considered that these birds may also have been referable to the larger species. In the absence of the specimens we shall never know for certain, but there is no reason why the Little Ringed Plover should not have occurred then.

Ringed Plover
Charadrius hiaticula

The first mention of this species in Yorkshire was in the Allen Manuscript in connection with the Tunstall Museum (1791), where it is stated: 'Sea-Lark - frequent our shores in summer but are not numerous .... ' Allis said in 1844 'A few of these birds may generally be met with on the sands in autumn or winter, generally in pairs or small numbers and never in large flocks .... '

Nelson summed up its status in 1907 as 'Resident, very local; is common, and nests in the Tees and Humber districts. Also spring and autumn migrant. Of occasional occurrence inland.' That assessment remains true today, with the addition of inland breeding by an annually increasing number of pairs during the past two decades.

The number of breeding birds along the coast is now much smaller than formerly. Riley Fortune recorded no fewer than 70 nests along the Spurn Peninsula in 1914, and C.F. Procter counted 36 nests there in 1936. In spite of the restricted access to the peninsula during the war years, Chislett said that it was doubtful if more than 20 pairs nested there in 1949. In 1952, 25 pairs bred there and five pairs did so at Teesmouth. By 1955, the Annual Report of the Yorkshire Naturalists' Union could only say 'A few pairs bred at Teesmouth and at Spurn.' Fifteen young birds were ringed at Spurn in 1957, ten pairs nested there in 1965, eight in 1971 and ten in 1972 and 1973. In 1978, 12 pairs were located between Spurn and Hull, but only two nests were actually found. Disturbance by the public in ever-growing numbers along the Spurn beaches and industrial activity at Teesmouth have reduced the number of Ringed Plovers at their seaside habitat and only very few pairs have been successful in recent years. Much of the coastline between the two estuaries is unsuitable for this beach-loving wader, and it is a sad fact that the breeding population is now only a shadow of what it was 50 years ago.

Some consolation comes from the trend to nest at inland localities. In 1937 a pair nested at Malham Tarn, where two young were found on 17th July. Riley Fortune said that young had been reared in Upper Nidderdale, and a nest with four eggs was found by the River Ribble near Settle in 1938 and the details published in *British Birds* (1938, p. 126). Two young were reared by the River Ure near Ripon in 1952. A pair nested at Grimwith Reservoir in 1959 and in several subsequent years, with two pairs in 1974 and three pairs in 1975. Broods of two, three and three were reared in the latter year. M.V. Bell reported four pairs there in 1976, but extensive workings started at the site in 1977 and this no doubt disturbed the birds in that year and subsequently, although a pair bred in 1981. Work on the enlargement of this reservoir is now nearing completion (February 1984) and, having established itself at the locality, the Ringed Plover will doubtless continue breeding there.

A pair bred at Scaling Dam in 1967 and 1968 and near Settle in 1969, 1970 and 1976. A pair nested near Catterick in 1970, the first breeding record for vice-county 65, and breeding has occurred there in most years up to 1979, with two pairs in 1971. A new site in 1975 was Pallett Hall Gravel-pit, where one pair nested. Single pairs bred at Stocks Reservoir in 1975 and 1976, five pairs in 1978 and four pairs in 1980. Nosterfield Gravel-pit had one breeding pair in 1976, one again in 1977, three pairs in 1978, two in 1979 and four in 1980. The nearby Masham Gravel-pit had three pairs in 1977, two in 1978 and one in 1979. Gouthwaite Reservoir had its first breeding record in 1977, when three pairs nested, followed by one pair in 1979 and three in 1980.

From 1977, the species started to spread to other inland waters, and since that year has bred at Staveley Lagoon, Mickletown Flash, Eccup Reservoir, Fairburn Ings, Bolton-on-Swale Gravel-pit, Tudworth Sand-quarry, Preston-under-Scar, Tynham Hall Gravel-pit, Blaxton Gravel-pit and Pugneys Gravel-pit. It is thus now well established as an inland breeding species, and there is every indication that the trend will continue.

Along the Holderness coast, birds began to nest some miles inland on the ploughed fields during the early 1970s. One pair did so, 2 miles (3.2 km) from the coast near Lissett, in 1973 and a few pairs have bred southwards from Barmston in recent years. A pair nested in a railway siding near Hull in 1975, and six pairs bred at Welton Water in 1975. In 1970, eggs were found on the Humber shore west of Hull and three pairs nested in King George V Dock, the first proved breeding for the upper reaches of the estuary.

Flocks of Ringed Plovers gather along the Humber Estuary, and to a lesser extent at Teesmouth, during the peak migration periods in May and August/September. Gatherings of around 100 birds have been regular during the last 30 years, and a count of 550 at Teesmouth on 24th August 1950 was considered by Chislett to be 'unusually large'. Spurn had 500 birds on 1st September 1952 and 400 on 2nd September 1955, but in recent years flocks on the Humber there have not exceeded 300. Regular watching at Cherry Cobb Sands from the mid 1950s by H.O. Bunce and G.R. Bennett showed this to be a popular haunt of the species. Maximum counts during the period were 500 on 21st May 1955; 'hundreds' in May 1956; 700 on 14th May 1957; 500 on 2nd May and 700 on 16th May 1958; 600 on 10th May 1960, decreasing to 250 by next day and to 100 by 25th; 450 on 15th May 1965; and an exceptional count by G.R. Bennett of 1,300 on 21st May 1962. These figures illustrate the value of this site for migrating Ringed Plovers. There have been no reports of such large flocks in more recent years, although the area is still frequented by good numbers.

The open sandy beach south of Bridlington is a popular place for the species, and up to 50 birds can regularly be seen there.

Southerly passage offshore is recorded annually, mainly during August and September, and some birds are seen coming in directly over the sea. A few may pass south on many days during the period, the most in one day being usually about 20 or 30 birds.

The Arctic race of the Ringed Plover *Charadrius hiaticula tundrae*, which is smaller and darker on the upperparts than the typical form, occurs each year on spring migration during May and early June. A small flock frequented the Humber mud at Spurn from 12th May to 3rd June 1981, the majority of which were of this race, as were a roosting flock of 109 birds at Easington on 25th May, with several others passing at Blacktoft Sands during the same period. A bird in my collection which hit wires at Spurn on 22nd September 1968 is a typical example of this race (see plate 68).

Migrating Ringed Plovers are seen each year, both in spring and in autumn, at inland waters. They may occur in any month but mainly during May and August/September. Numbers vary from single birds to flocks of 20 or more, and in some years larger numbers occur, often coinciding with arrivals on the coast. Some maximum counts have been 18 at Fairburn Ings on 17th May 1962; 38 at White-holme Reservoir on 19th August 1964; 27 at Tophill Low Reservoir from 23rd May to 8th June 1966; 44 at Fairburn Ings on 25th May 1969; 30 at Gouthwaite Reservoir on 20th August 1969; and 42 at Fairburn Ings from 25th to 28th May 1970.

In June 1971, a marked passage was witnessed at many inland waters during the early part of the month, and some birds were considered to belong to the Arctic race. Gouthwaite Reservoir had the most, with 38 on 7th June, 13 remaining on 12th and seven on 14th; 12 were at Fairburn Ings on 12th and one to eight birds at several other places at this time.

In 1974, 25 were at Blackmoorfoot Reservoir on 17th August, on which date ten were at Masham Gravel-pit. The North Ings at Mexborough attracted several passing birds in 1979 with 16 on 12th May and 41 on 19th May, 35 of which were still present on 22nd. In the same year, 28 were at Newington Flash on 8th and 31st May.

Ringing recoveries show some interesting movements. A juvenile ringed at Spurn on 24th July 1954 was at Rhyl, Flintshire, on 4th February 1955; one ringed at Spurn on 30th August 1957 was shot at Chatelaillon, France, on 25th September 1957; one ringed at Spurn on 14th September 1962 was shot at Blyth, Northumberland, on 16th May 1964; an adult ringed at Inishkea Island, Mayo, on 16th December 1963 was retrapped at Spurn on 10th May 1965; one ringed at Barnby Dun, Doncaster, on 6th August 1966 was retrapped at Snettisham, Norfolk, on 24th July 1967; one ringed at Angle Bay, Pembroke, on 16th November 1974 was retrapped at Spurn on 29th August 1976 and caught again at Angle Bay on 11th December; and, finally, a chick ringed at Masham Gravel-pit on 30th May 1977 was trapped at Beaumaris, Anglesey, on 29th December 1978.

Killdeer
Charadrius vociferus

On 29th November 1975, S.L. James was watching birds at the Shoulder O'Mutton Well area on Thorne Moor when he noticed a medium-sized wader running about on a muddy area. He identified it as a Killdeer, and later in the day several other observers including M. Limbert were able to see the bird. It was still present the next day and detailed notes of its plumage and behaviour were taken.

When first seen it was relatively confiding, as is usual with its kind, and when flushed it did not fly very far. It fed mainly among small rushes on the more open soft peaty mud. It frequently employed the technique of foot-trembling to disturb prey in the mud and, on 30th, a very cold and frosty day, the bird continued this activity despite a covering of ice.

This was the first occurrence of this North American plover in Yorkshire and the twentieth record for the British Isles. Full details were published in *The Naturalist*, 1976, pp. 135-6.

Kentish Plover
Charadrius alexandrinus

Nelson listed seven Yorkshire occurrences between 1857 and 1891 of this plover, which at that time used to breed on the south coast of England. It last did so at Rye Harbour, Sussex, in 1956 and, although it is a common breeder on the coasts of the adjacent Continent and in the Channel Islands, it has never recolonised England.

The first Yorkshire record, at Flamborough in 1857, was, inevitably, 'obtained' and the specimen went to Matthew Bailey, the taxidermist. There were two birds in 1869, both obtained on the sands at Ulrome, one on 25th May and the other on 28th. The details of these two were published in *The Zoologist*, 1869, pp. 1843-4. Another was procured by Mr Boynton, also at Ulrome, in 1875. One was taken near Flamborough in 1881 and was in the possession of a Mr Foster of Bridlington, where Nelson inspected it. The last of Nelson's records concerned two birds killed at Cayton Bay, near Scarborough, on 12th September 1891, the details of which were communicated to Nelson by W.J. Clarke.

Up to 1952, when Chislett published *Yorkshire Birds*, only two more had been recorded in the county, both in 1947. The first was seen at Swillington Ings by K. Dawson as it fed with a Ringed Plover on 11th May, and the other was watched by R. Chislett and H.G. Brownlow at Hornsea Mere on 15th September.

Since that time there have been no fewer than 25 records of Kentish Plovers in Yorkshire between 1957 and 1983. One fed in the Spurn 'wire dump' area on 31st October 1957 and was seen by E.C. Sterne and J.C. Leedal. A female was seen by S.C. Norman at South Gare, Teesmouth, on 9th September 1963 and another female was at Spurn on 18th April 1964. One was at Spurn on 10th April 1966 and another occurred there from 16th to 18th April 1968. C. Winn saw one at Fairburn Ings on 16th May 1970, in which year another was at Spurn on 30th May. Fairburn had a second bird on 8th May 1971 which was seen by P.T. Treloar and C. Winn, and yet another in 1972 when Winn and others saw one on 6th May. One was at South Gare, Teesmouth, on 18th June in that year and was seen by S.C. and W. Norman. In 1973, J.D. Pickup and I.H. Dillingham watched one at Fairburn Ings on 19th and 20th May and D.G. Bell saw one at Scaling Dam from 21st to 24th May. In 1976, two birds were at Stanley Sewage-farm, near Wakefield, on 6th May, D.I.M. Wallace saw one on Whitton Sands on 2nd September, and a fourth was on the Humber mud at Spurn on 27th August where it was watched by H.J. Whitehead. A bird at Filey Brigg on 29th and 30th May 1978 was seen by A. Botterill, W.A. Clarke and H.J. Whitehead as it fed on the mussel beds. At Hay-a-Park Gravel-pit, Knaresborough, on 3rd May 1980, R. Evison located three Kentish Plovers, two males and a female, the most seen together in the county; I saw them the next day with P.T. Treloar and other members of Knaresborough Ringing Station. Two occurred in 1981: a female seen by T.E. Dixon at North Duffield Carrs on 22nd May and a male seen on the Humber mud at Spurn on 24th May. A male was on the Humber shore at Spurn on 16th May 1982, and single birds were at Barnby Dun on 4th May 1983 and at Blacktoft Sands on 12th May 1983.

The fact that more have been recorded in Yorkshire since the species became extinct as a British breeding bird in 1956 than during Nelson's time is curious, and probably explained quite simply by more efficient coverage resulting from increased observer activity.

Greater Sand Plover
Charadrius leschenaultii

On the morning of 29th July 1981, E. Crawford, J. Rose and Mrs J. Thompson located a wader on the Humber mudflats opposite the Crown and Anchor Inn at Kilnsea. They suspected that it was a Greater Sand Plover and, after watching it for a while, went to the Spurn Bird Observatory and informed the warden, B.R. Spence, who immediately went to look and found it feeding some 50 yards (46 m) from the road.

It was eventually seen during the day by several observers who arrived unsuspectingly en route for the Spurn Bird Observatory and were able to add this bonus species to their lists. When the tide rose in the late afternoon, the bird flew off in the direction of Spurn Point and was relocated by B.R. Spence and R.P. Council half way down the peninsula towards Chalk Bank; here it was to spend much time during the course of the next few days, when, with other waders, it roosted there at high tide. It was seen regularly opposite the Crown and Anchor as it fed on the mudflats during its nine-day stay. The last sighting was by R. Evison, G.T. Foggitt and P.T. Treloar at Chalk Bank on 6th August.

What was presumably the same bird was seen on the Lincolnshire coast at North Coates next day, after which it was not seen again (*British Birds*, 1983, pp. 574-5).

This was a new county record and only the fifth in the British Isles for this species, which did not appear in these islands until December 1978. It breeds on the dry steppes of southern Russia and eastwards to Mongolia, and winters south into Asia and in Africa down the east coast to the Cape.

Dotterel
Charadrius morinellus

In Nelson's time and before, the Dotterel was a passage bird in both spring and autumn, especially along the coast, where parties of birds often lingered for two or three weeks. Birds also occurred on the high ground at these times and many were shot or trapped. 'They are stupid birds easily enticed into a net' wrote one early naturalist in 1791. The breast feathers were formerly prized by fly fishers, and the practice of shooting Dotterels was regular in spring. Some old gunners claimed to have shot 50 couples in a season, and no fewer than 42 couples were secured in one day on the Wolds of Ganton, Sherburn and Knapton. Writing in the *Field Naturalist* in January 1834, J.H. Anderson stated that 'The Dotterel visit our large open fields every spring and autumn, and dire is the slaughter committed amongst them.'

The numbers were much reduced by 1844 according to Strickland, who wrote, stating such, to Thomas Allis. About the middle of the nineteenth century, numerous flocks were still found on the Hambleton Hills, and J.H. Phillips had put up 'hundreds' on the moors between Dialstone Inn and South Woods (*The Naturalist*, 1890, p. 15). It was also sought on the Wensleydale moors every year for anglers' feathers (*The Naturalist*, 1886, p. 186).

The Dotterel Inn, near Reighton, was built by one of the Strickland family and designed for the accommodation of gamekeepers, who came from all parts of the neighbourhood for the purpose of shooting Dotterels in the spring. The original inn sign, depicting a Dotterel, was painted by Mrs Strickland. I wonder if it was any better than the one now adorning the front of the building (see plate 37).

When Nelson wrote of the bird in 1907, he considered it to be a fairly regular visitor to its old haunts in limited numbers, while on passage in spring and autumn. The earliest date of which he had note was 18th February 1901, when two were seen at Kilnsea. The usual time of arrival was at the end of April or early May and the bird was then encountered in trips of between two and 50 individuals. The largest flock that Nelson had seen consisted of 30 birds at Teesmouth in May 1903, but on 6th May 1897 a flock of 50 was seen near the Dotterel Inn. There was, apparently, a field near Easington where they had occurred 'from time immemorial'.

Return passage was during August and September, and the latest date on record at the time of Nelson was 29th November 1900, when one was seen on Coatham Marsh during a strong southeast gale. Nelson shot one of two Dotterels which passed over the butts while he was grouse shooting in August 1893.

References to breeding at High Stake in Wensleydale up to about 1866, and at the head of Swaledale and Arkengarthdale up to about 1866, appeared in *The Naturalist*, 1886, p. 186, and 1892, p. 324, and it was reported as nesting in Ribblesdale and on Marsden and Slaithwaite Moors. Nelson investigated several of the claims, but was not able to obtain the proof necessary to establish the fact beyond doubt. It has long been accepted that breeding used to occur on Mickle Fell in the extreme northwest of the county, and in a letter to John Hancock from J.E. Anderson, writing from Holy Island in April 1875, it is stated that they build 'on another fell top a few miles south of Crossfell'. Anderson had forgotten the local name for the fell but it may well have been Mickle.

Riley Fortune saw a pair of birds on a hilltop in the northwest and young birds were seen in the summer of 1895, 1902 and 1904. A pair on one of the high fells during the summer of 1902 disappeared in the middle of June and two empty cartridge cases were found at the site.

In his personal copy of *The Birds of Yorkshire* published in 1907, Nelson wrote the more up-to-date details in the margins and included: 'A small trip at Teesmouth from 20th April to 5th May 1907; a large flock at Easington, several of which were shot in May 1907; 100 on the Wolds near Bempton from 11th to 18th May 1907 and 30-40 on Bempton cliff-top on 2nd June 1907.'

Chislett listed 12 occurrences during the period 1909 to 1951, all but one record referring to only one or two birds. The exception was on 12th May 1947, when P. Young saw a party of six birds on Ilton Moor. The other localities mentioned were near Boroughbridge in 1909; Lindley, near Huddersfield, in 1914; Fly Flatts Reservoir in 1916; Kilham in 1921; Bolton Abbey in 1928; Whiteholme Reservoir in 1933 and 1934; near Kilnsea in 1936; near Skelder on the Whitby to Guisborough road in 1942; and Middlesmoor in 1947.

Since 1951, the Dotterel has occurred in all but six years and has become more frequent since 1970. Following a few records of single birds up to that time, three were seen by L. Smith on a ploughed field near Strensall, York, on 11th May 1970. In 1971, a party of six was seen by H.O. Bunce and Miss J. Fairhurst on arable land at Lissett on 9th May; one was seen in a beet field at Cawood on 25th May; two were on Blubberhouse Moor on 22nd May; and one was at Spurn between 15th and 23rd August. In 1972, there were ten on Danby Moor in Cleveland during early May, and five different individuals were seen at Spurn on several dates from August to the late date of 18th November. In 1973, two were seen by F.J. Roberts on a fell near Settle on 6th May, four were on Buckton clifftop on 7th May where another was seen on 7th September by S.C. Madge, and 12 were seen by D.J. Britton on Danby Moor on 22nd May. A female, seen by W.F. Curtis at Mappleton on 5th May 1974, heralded a good spring migration, with eight on Rombalds Moor on 8th May, three on Danby Moor on 16th May and a pair on Houndkirk Moor on 25th and 26th May; in the autumn, one occurred at Bempton on 31st August.

A good series of records in 1975 began with one on Baildon Moor Golf Course on 4th May; three seen by N.W. Harwood on Danby Moor on 15th May; one near High Bradfield from 17th to 20th May; and two at Bempton from 31st May to 2nd June, one of which stayed until 3rd. A report in the local newspaper stating that Dotterels had been 'breeding' in the clifftop fields should of course have said 'feeding'. Two occurred in the autumn, one at Wilsthorpe on 6th September and a single bird at Spurn from 21st to 24th August.

In 1976, one was near the summit of a hill in the west on 25th April, and R. Houlston saw three on Howl Moor, near Whitby, in late April. Ten were on Ocean View Farm at Flamborough Head on 8th May, all of which were in full plumage, and some were displaying. Nine were at Lissett on 11th May; seven were on Roils Head Playing Fields, near Halifax, from 10th to 14th May with two still there on 15th; two were at Spurn on 22nd August and two more on 18th September, one of which stayed to 21st.

No spring birds were seen in 1977, but a few occurred in autumn. One was on Ingleborough on 23rd August; one at Spurn on 9th September; a juvenile at Fairburn Ings on 10th September; one on Great Shunner Fell on 15th September; and a juvenile at Chelker Reservoir with Golden Plovers on 28th September.

There were only two spring records in 1978: a party of 12 on a hill in the west on 20th May and three at Nawton Mulgrave in the northeast on 20th and 21st May, one being killed by a car on the latter date. In the autumn, a juvenile was found dead by the roadside in Commondale on 1st July, one was at Bempton on 12th August and one was at Filey from 16th to 18th August.

In 1979, there was one on Whitley Common, near Ingbirchworth, on 26th April; six at nearby Spicer House Lane on 20th and 21st May, with two on 22nd; and one record in autumn at Kilnsea, where one was seen on 12th September.

The year 1980 must have been somewhat reminiscent of former times. One was at Hopewell House Farm, Knaresborough, on 27th April, and a flock of seven was on Whitley Common on 9th May, increasing to ten birds on 11th, some remaining until 19th when four were still present. One was on Thorne Moor on 10th May, with two next day. The largest flock recorded since 1907 occurred at Ravenscar on 10th May, when M. Francis saw a flock of 24 birds. R.H. Appleby visited the area the next day and saw 18 birds, six of which stayed until 15th. Two were at Flamborough from 22nd to 28th May. The only autumn record was of one at Spurn on 25th September.

Two birds were at Blacktoft Sands of 19th and 20th April 1981, with five on 4th and 6th, seven on 5th May and 11 on 8th. D. Hursthouse saw eight at Harthill on 5th May, 12 on 6th and 16 on 7th, with two birds from 8th to 12th. Three were at Ravenscar on 6th May and four on Burley Moor on 7th. One flew south at Spurn on 8th May and one flew north on 24th. Single birds were at Flamborough on 17th and at Filey on 31st May. One occurred at a locality on the North York Moors on 15th June.

There were 49 birds recorded at 11 widely scattered localities in 1982, including

16 at Ravenscar on 14th May, and all but three occurring during late April and May. In 1983 there were 29 birds at six localities, all but one in May and including nine at Church Fenton on 6th, ten at Flamborough on 14th and seven at Atwick on 20th.

At the end of April 1984, a few Dotterels frequented the pea fields adjoining Swinefleet, near Goole, and on 5th May I visited the area with D.R.J. Watkins, R. Evison and his wife and was able to watch 25 birds as they fed in the field. The pea shoots were about 3 inches (7.6 cm) tall and when the birds sat down, which they often did for long periods, they were sometimes completely invisible from the road. When feeding, they picked off pieces of pea shoots as well as taking food from the ground. The flock increased to 39 birds by 12th May, and during their stay the birds were seen by many observers who were treated to some excellent views during a long spell of fine warm weather. A remarkable movement was detected on 10th May 1984, when M. Natrass counted 51 birds on Shunner Howe on the North York Moors and a second observer saw others in the same area and considered that no fewer than 100 were present there on that day.

It would appear from the foregoing that the Dotterel is once again becoming a regular visitor on migration to some parts of the county, and it is quite possible that a pair or two may settle down to nest on one of the remote fells, where hopefully they will go unmolested.

Lesser Golden Plover
Pluvialis dominica

On 1st September 1975, S.C. Madge, while acting as warden on the RSPB reserve at Bempton Cliffs, located a plover in a clifftop field near Wandale Farm and identified it as this species. He watched it for 30 minutes and made full notes and drawings, from which the bird was accepted as the first for Yorkshire. The species breeds in Arctic North America and across the Siberian tundra to Alaska. There are two distinct races, based on colour tones, those breeding in North America (*dominica*) being much richer in colour than their greyer counterparts from Siberia (*fulva*). The Bempton bird was considered to belong to the latter race (*The Naturalist*, 1976, p. 107).

A second example occurred on 30th October 1977 at Faxfleet, where it was watched among a flock of Golden Plovers by D.I.M. Wallace. Five others occurred in Britain in 1977.

Between 14th and 19th October 1981, a bird considered to belong to the North American form frequented an area of large open coastal fields between Redcar and Marske. It was seen by D.J. Britton and subsequently by several other observers.

On 5th September 1982, D.I.M. Wallace watched a bird at Flamborough which he considered to belong to the Asiatic race *fulva*. This record has not yet been submitted to the *British Birds* Rarities Committee.

A bird in almost complete breeding dress was seen at Wath Ings by J.M. Turton on 18th July 1984. Another bird in almost full plumage was seen near Misson by J. Coleman on 8th and 9th September 1984. An adult at Easington from 15th to 18th September 1984 was seen by A. Cawthrow, J. Hewitt and J.M. Turton.

Golden Plover
Pluvialis apricaria

This species was known and valued as a table bird as long ago as 1393, when Richard II issued a Royal Proclamation fixing the price of a Golden Plover at 1d. Other ancient household books and records of banquets in Yorkshire listed the bird among the provisions to be supplied.

Nelson knew it as a resident on the fells and moorlands of the Pennines, the Cleveland Hills and the North York Moors. They were at that time also to be seen in large numbers on the carrs and low grounds of East Yorkshire, especially in wet weather when the carrs were flooded. Vast flocks would then 'form together into enormous congregations, and acres of ground were covered with them'. On 12th December 1878, during a winter of Arctic severity, the sands and muds at the Teesmouth were absolutely covered with plovers at low tide and, according to Nelson, 'as the water flowed the noise made by the masses of birds, forced by the rising waters to the circumvented space of dry sand, was marvellous, and finally the host rose like an immense cloud ...'.

Anywhere along the coastal strip where suitable arable or pastureland exists, especially in Holderness, large flocks of up to 2,000 birds can be found from September until March or April. Inland areas also attract large numbers and some localities have been favoured haunts for many years. Hangthwaite, in the Doncaster area; the Lower Derwent Valley; Southfield Reservoir; Pool-in-Wharfedale; and Menwith Hill, near Harrogate, are some of the most regularly used areas and have attracted flocks in excess of 2,000 birds in several years. Many other areas may hold flocks of up to 1,000 Golden Plovers and sometimes more. Lapwings are usually attracted to the same areas and the two species are usually associated.

The Humber Wildfowl Refuge in the Upper Humber is a good place for Golden Plovers and flocks of 2,000 to 4,000 are a regular sight there. In 1979, the largest numbers recorded in modern times occurred there when A. Chapman and B.S. Pashby counted 6,000 on 28th January and 8,000 on 8th December. In 1981, 5,300 were there on 21st November, having increased from 4,240 on 13th September.

In 1961, up to 15 birds wintered on Baugh Fell, near Sedbergh, for the first time on record.

Many of these birds come to Yorkshire each autumn from northern Europe, immigration and passage being witnessed along the coastline during late July, August and September. Flocks still assembled on their feeding grounds during April and early May are usually in active moult to summer dress and may exhibit the striking black and white characters of the northern race *Pluvialis apricaria altifrons*, which breeds from Scandinavia eastwards across northern Europe. These birds are evident every spring, and some of the larger flocks in recent times have been 200 at Wigglesworth on 17th April 1966; 500 at Ingbirchworth on 20th April 1974; 1,500 at Thorner Lane, near Leeds, during April 1976; 1,000 at Settle from mid March to 23rd April 1978; 400 near Ripon and 400 at Whitley Common during late April 1981.

During the years of World War II, the large expanse of grassland which forms the Harrogate 'Stray' was put under the plough for growing cereals, and Golden Plovers were quick to use the area during the autumn and winter months. A.F.G.

Walker watched regularly there during the late 1940s and made counts of 600 on 31st January 1948 and again on 18th November 1948, and 600 on 24th December 1949. The Stray was returned to grass in 1950 and the numbers of Golden Plovers soon dwindled.

The species breeds in varying densities all along the Pennine range from the southwest county boundary, northwards to Upper Teesdale and along the ridges which project eastwards to enclose the dales. The North York Moors are less favoured and fewer pairs breed.

Unless affected by deep snow, some breeding birds may be back on their upland breeding territories by mid February. Song flight was witnessed at Gouthwaite Reservoir by A.F.G. Walker as early as 9th February 1957, and ten birds had returned to the moors round about by 6th February 1960. Three birds were also on their breeding grounds on Ilton Moor on 4th February that year and 15 were near Middlesmoor in Upper Nidderdale on 9th.

A study of the breeding populations on the moorlands of Upper Wharfedale was undertaken by M.V. Bell during the summers of 1970 to 1975. He calculated that a population of 160 pairs was attainable in this area during a good year, but may be reduced to half that number in a bad one. Densities of from three to five territories per square kilometre were estimated on most of the moorlands surveyed. Full details were published in *The Naturalist*, 1979, pp. 95-100. A survey of five moors lying to the southwest of Huddersfield (Saddleworth, Howden, Wessenden, Wessenden Head and Standage) by D.W. Yalden in 1972 gave a total of 35 breeding pairs. In 1974, P. Bray and J.E. Dale counted 26 pairs holding territory on two of

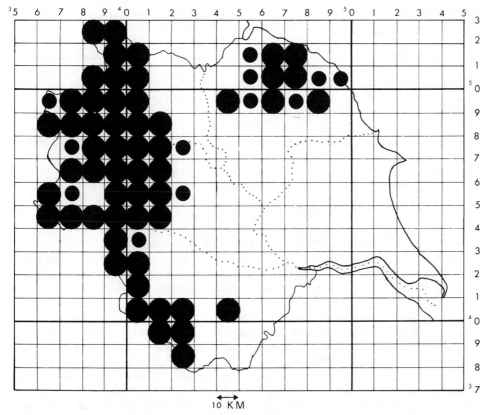

10 KM

Golden Plover. Essentially a bird of the high barren heather moorland of the Pennines and North York Moors, and one of the most characteristic birds of such habitat.

these moors (Wessenden and Wessenden Head) in mid June.

Some Yorkshire-hatched Golden Plovers spend the winter far to the south of their natal moorlands. A bird ringed at Danby in Eskdale on 13th June 1975 was shot at Camelford in Cornwall on 4th December 1976, and one ringed in Commondale on 17th May 1980 was shot near Rabat in Morocco on 20th December 1981. A bird shot at Stanley, near Wakefield, on 12th January 1960 had been ringed as a chick at Allenheads in Northumberland on 18th June 1957 and was no doubt on its way south for the winter when it fell to the gun.

It would appear from Nelson's assessment of its status that fewer pairs are now breeding on the Cleveland Moors than did in his time.

The present-day assessment of its status in Yorkshire differs little from that written by Nelson in 1907 as 'Resident, breeding on the moorlands in the western part of the county and more sparingly in the north-east, with large numbers of immigrants arriving in early autumn and dispersing over much of the lowlands where they may remain until spring.'

Grey Plover
Pluvialis squatarola

A passage migrant in considerable numbers, with a few resident in winter, is how Chislett summarised the status of this shore-loving bird. Nelson knew it similarly, and its status remains the same today. The estuaries of the Tees and Humber are its main haunts, and Nelson said that in some years at the former there may be as many as 100 individuals in summer dress in late July and August, the young following in September.

Numbers are never very large, but at times of peak passage some assemblies may reach treble figures. A count of 250 birds at Spurn on 6th April 1947 was considered to be 'unusually large'. There were counts of 200 there on 9th October 1948 and 250 on 10th September 1949, with 150 at Teesmouth on 1st October 1949.

Since the publication of Chislett's *Yorkshire Birds* in 1952, more efficient coverage of the estuaries has shown that large numbers do not occur every year, and the largest assemblies on the Humber mud at Spurn during the last 30 years have not exceeded 100 birds, except for an isolated passage peak of 400 on 12th September 1956, and have usually been around the 75 mark. At Teesmouth, the majority collect on the north side at Seal Sands and fewer gather on the Yorkshire side. D.G. Bell and P.J. Stead counted 340 on Coatham Sands on 28th September 1957, which was the largest number they had recorded in the Tees Estuary at that time.

The largest counts elsewhere have not exceeded 100 birds except at Cherry Cobb Sands, a favourite haunt for the species. Maximum counts of 300 on 11th May 1956, 200 on 22nd May 1959, 218 on 21st May 1962 and 200 on 20th May 1978 are reflective of spring passage through the area, as were 118 flying east at Stone Creek on 15th May 1979 when a further 90 birds were resting in the fields there. S.C. Norman saw 98 flying north off Redcar during a gale on 3rd November 1970.

The Birds of Estuaries Enquiry organised by the British Trust for Ornithology since 1971, which in part co-ordinated counts along the north shore of the Humber from Spurn Point to Goole, has not produced any spectacular numbers. The figures for 1972 are typical of most years and showed monthly maxima of 12 on 23rd January; 22 on 20th February; six on 5th March ; six on 9th April; 29 on 7th May; 20 on 7th September; 255 on 25th October; and 85 on 26th November. There is some annual variation, and on 28th February 1971 102 were counted. In 1973 the maximum count was 320 on 23rd September, and in 1979 100 on 7th January. S.M. Lister counted 830 from Cherry Cobb Sands to Sunk Island on 15th May 1983.

In most months, some Grey Plovers are present, birds in spring and summer often being in full breeding dress. Away from the two estuaries the species is scarce, but a few can be found feeding on some beaches, the sands at Filey and Bridlington often attracting small numbers.

The species has occurred regularly at inland waters during the last 30 years, and there have been records in every month at waters too numerous to mention in detail. The main months of occurrence are May and during August to October, the majority being seen during September. During the ten years up to 1981, birds have been recorded annually at an average of 13 inland sites. There were inland records from 21 different places in 1976, the most ever recorded in the county. Any reservoir, flash, sewage-farm, river bank or even arable land may attract an occasional bird. Records are mainly of single individuals and larger numbers inland are rare, but up to four or five have been seen together on occasions. On 14th September 1975, 11 Grey Plovers flew south over Wintersett Reservoir. Wath Ings regularly attracts the species, and there are several records of up to four birds there, with an unprecedented party of 14 on 19th September 1976. Nine birds were at Fairburn Ings on 18th September 1976, another nine on 17th October, and seven were at Wheldrake Ings on the first date.

Thomas Allis, in his report to the British Association at York in 1844, said that J. and W. Tuke had informed him that they saw a pair on Hambleton in June which no doubt had eggs or young, as they would not leave the place, although watched for several hours. This interpretation of the events is typical of the attitudes of the time and the two birds would certainly have been migrants. In addition to the passing birds seen at inland waters in late spring and autumn, there will be others that make short stops by moorland pools and go unrecorded. A bird in almost full breeding plumage was picked up dead on the moors at Blubberhouses on 27th September 1966 which the finder, C. Horner, brought to me for preservation.

Lapwing
Vanellus vanellus

There is no more familiar bird in the Yorkshire countryside than the Lapwing. 'It can claim ancestry of great antiquity' wrote Nelson, who said that 'Selby was of the opinion that the Egrittes to the number of 1,000, served at the celebrated banquet to Archbishop Nevell in 1466, were referable to this species.' It was also mentioned in the 'Northumberland Household Book' in 1512 under the name of 'Wype', where the price was fixed at 1d each. It also figured in *Wildfowl at Hull* in 1560, where the price was stated at three-halfpence each.

In his report of 1844, T. Allis mentioned the arrival of enormous numbers on the coast each year during October and November and sometimes into December and even January. Great numbers occurred in November 1881, and in 1887 there was a constant migration from mid October to mid November. He said that on some days the passage lasted from dawn until about 3 p.m., the birds 'crossing incessantly in immense hordes'. In October 1899, it was estimated that they were coming in over the coast at the rate of 10,000 in a quarter of an hour.

There is absolutely no doubt that the Lapwing has decreased dramatically as a breeding species during the last 50 years. If the figures quoted by Allis above are correct, it would also seem that the reduction is reflected in the much lower numbers that now come to Britain each winter, although there have been indications of an increase in the size of wintering flocks in recent years.

Nelson knew the Lapwing as a 'generally and widely diffuse breeding species, being found in all suitable localities from the marshes and coast lands up to the highest elevation on the fells and moorlands of Cleveland and the north-west of the county', but he was aware of reducing numbers, which he concluded was due to drainage, more intensive cultivation and the taking of eggs for sale. Today, it is still a widespread nesting species but in severely reduced numbers, especially in the agricultural lowlands from where it has been almost banished by modern farming methods involving the increasing use of machinery. Pastureland, especially in the damper areas, is where the Lapwing hangs on as a regular breeding species, and only on the wetter moorland areas and the adjoining pastureland can it now be considered common.

The first eggs are laid in March and many of these are lost under the roller or harrow in arable areas. Even second layings are not safe and are often similarly destroyed, and large tracts of suitable habitat are now devoid of breeding Lapwings.

D. Hird monitored the breeding population on Sutton Moor, near Keighley, during the years 1972-75, with the following results:

1972:   33 nests, only eight of which produced young, with 19 eggs hatched from 130 laid.
1973:   92 pairs nested with a 39 percent success rate.
1974:   53 pairs nested with a 45 percent success rate.
1975:   78 pairs nested with a 28 percent success rate.

Flocks of Lapwings may be seen in Yorkshire during the non-breeding season, scattered all over the lowland and foothill areas of the eastern and southern parts of the county. At any time from late June, when post-breeding flocks gather and move from the high ground, until the numbers are augmented by immigrants in late autumn, gatherings of up to 1,000 birds are commonplace. Larger numbers often occur, and in recent years there has been a definite increase in the size of flocks in several parts of the county.

In 1961, A.F.G. Walker counted 4,000 birds along the Lower Derwent on 12th February and 5,000 there on 20th. The area around Settle is a popular place for Lapwing flocks and in 1970 there were 2,500 there on 24th January and 3,000 on 19th August. Another favoured area is the flat grassland around Pool-in-Wharfedale, where concentrations of Lapwings and Golden Plovers, with the attendant Black-headed Gulls, are present every year. In 1971, 3,000 were there on 20th December.

Cold weather at the end of January 1972 forced many birds to move, and on

30th there were counts of 1,040 flying south-southwest in 90 minutes over Melton Wood; 750 moving southwest over Thorne Moor; 1,300 flying southwest in two hours over Wintersett Reservoir; and 1,620 flying southwest in three hours over Swillington Ings. A cold snap in December that year affected birds similarly and there were small flocks moving on 24th at many places, including 700 flying west at Knotford Nook Gravel-pit and 200 flying west at Knaresborough Ringing Station.

In January 1976, a cold-weather movement involved many birds, and on 25th January 2,830 flew southwest over Knaresborough Ringing Station up to midday; 2,572 flew west over Wintersett Reservoir; 2,300 flew over Wath Ings; and small flocks were seen passing overhead in many other areas during the day.

After a period of cold weather in February 1978, the subsequent thaw induced birds to move and large numbers were involved. On 24th February, 'many' were reported moving over Scarborough in the morning and 1,534 passed in one hour in the afternoon; 1,500 flew south over Blacktoft Sands; 2,200 flew over York in two hours; and the movement continued during the next two days. On 24th and 25th, exceptional numbers moved southwest over the Doncaster area and the same movement was witnessed at Spurn, with 1,244 on 24th, 850 on 26th and 1,111 on 27th.

Feeding flocks may be numerous and widely scattered. Typical of events during recent years was the situation in 1974 when 1,000 to 1,500 birds were seen at several places, including Ulleskelf Mires in January; Denton, Scalby and Wintersett in February; Almholme, Blacktoft Sands, Southfield Reservoir, Chelker Reservoir, Wath Ings and Birkin in December; and smaller gatherings frequenting many other areas during the same periods.

Since 1976 there have been some very large feeding flocks, and in that year there were 4,000 at Birkin Pond on 17th January; 3,400 at Bewholme on 2nd February; and 4,000 on 18th September at Staveley Lagoon, where P.T. Treloar counted 6,307 flying west on 5th December.

Larger flocks than usual were counted in December 1979, when there were 4,500 at Bubwith on 7th; 3,000 at Pugneys Gravel-Pit, near Wakefield, on 8th; 3,500 at Wath Ings and 7,500 at Aughton Ings on 9th; and 5,000 at Southfield Reservoir during the early part of the month.

On the night of 8th/9th March 1980, an exceptionally large influx brought many birds into the Lower Derwent Valley and no fewer than 17,000 were counted between Wheldrake and Bubwith, the largest single concentration recorded in the county in modern times. About 8,000 were in the same area during November. There were many other large flocks in 1980, with between 1,000 and 4,000 recorded at 30 other localities during the winter months at both ends of the year.

The large numbers in the Lower Derwent Valley persisted into 1981, with flocks of 3,000-4,000 during January and February. Cold weather during December forced birds to leave the area and they were seen passing westwards over York on 8th and 9th; few remained along the Derwent and Humber after that time.

Movement along the coast in late autumn provides evidence of immigration. In 1953, birds were passing over Middlesbrough all morning on 31st October and a continuing stream of small flocks passed south-southwest over Teesmouth on the same day, when birds were also coming in at Spurn. Between 07.05 and 10.55 hours on 3rd November 1958, a movement at Spurn involved 1,967 birds, 1,300 of which passed in the first 50 minutes. Smaller numbers occur every year, and on 22nd October 1961 1,580 flew south at Atwick, while 3,591 passed at Spurn in three hours the next day.

Lapwing movements are affected very much by the weather and this very 'visual' species is easy to monitor. At any time during the winter months, a sudden cold period will induce birds to move to new feeding areas and a subsequent thaw will often bring them back. Flocks of failed or early breeders and juveniles are sometimes well on the move by July and often during late June, the numbers varying annually depending on the breeding successes.

Lapwing chicks have long been popular with bird-ringers, being easy to find, and there are many interesting recoveries of Yorkshire-ringed birds as well as records of foreign birds recovered in Yorkshire. Of the 20 or so more important recoveries published in the British Trust for Ornithology ringing reports over the years, the majority of Yorkshire-ringed young have been found in France, with others in Spain, Portugal and the Netherlands. Foreign-ringed Lapwings have come to Yorkshire in winter from Norway (six), Denmark (four), the Netherlands (three), Finland (one) and Sweden (one). A chick ringed in Harewood Park on 10th May 1966 was shot at Casablanca in Morocco on 17th Janaury 1967, but perhaps the most interesting of all concerns a chick ringed at Gargrave on 20th May 1956 which was shot at Tobolsk in the USSR on 8th May 1959. It is unlikely that the bird would have returned to its native Yorkshire to breed, and it would have been interesting to know whether it was in breeding condition when shot. Several have been reported from Eire, where many Lapwings go when forced out of Britain by severe weather. In such conditions, there may be a spate of foreign recoveries.

There are several records of birds with abnormal plumage. Nelson mentioned one with light brown and cream upperparts at Oswaldkirk in about 1884, a cinnamon-coloured bird at Redcar in December 1892, and a white bird near Fewston Reservoir in 1903. I saw a fawn example at Copgrove in 1950; an oatmeal-coloured bird with a normal black gorget was seen by R.M. Garnett at Marishes in the Vale of Pickering on 23rd March 1952; one at Malham Tarn, seen by M.V. Bell on 10th September 1974, had white wing feathers; and a pale cream bird was seen by F.A. Wardman at Chelker Reservoir on 18th November 1978.

Knot
Calidris canutus

The Knot is a common passage migrant and a winter visitor along the Yorkshire coast from Teesmouth to the estuary of the Humber, where it regularly penetrates as far west as Whitton Sands. Birds may be seen in all months, those still undergoing their northward journey to the Arctic breeding grounds in May, or even June, often being in full red breeding dress.

The first immigrants usually appear during July and August, when many of the adults are still showing signs of summer plumage, and these are followed by the main influx during September and October. They assemble anywhere along the coastline, but most numerously on the mud of the two estuaries. Here, they may rest for a while before continuing their journey southwards, or settle in to spend the winter in the general area. Numbers along the Humber shore fluctuate widely, often daily, as birds seek new feeding or roosting sites depending on the weather or tide. On 24th and 25th January 1959, for example, 8,000 birds were seen each day, leaving the mudflats at Spurn in the direction of Lincolnshire at high tide.

The most regularly watched area is the wide expanse of mud known as Kilnsea Clays at Spurn, where there have been counts of between 1,000 and 5,000 birds in most years since the 1950s. Larger gatherings have been 7,000 on 1st January 1956 and 8,000 on 8th November 1964. There were 5,000 birds between Welwick and Cherry Cobb Sands and another 5,000 from Cherry Cobb to Paull on 5th February 1967.

Numbers in the Tees Estuary are similarly large, and high counts have been

6,000 at South Gare on 11th January 1959; 6,000 on 9th January 1960; 6,000-10,000 in February 1961; and 7,000 in early March 1963. A flock of 1,000 was on Redcar Rocks on 28th November 1959.

The Birds of Estuaries Enquiry organised by the British Trust for Ornithology since 1970 has in part monitored the populations on the north shore of the Humber Estuary from Spurn Point to Goole, and has shown the importance of this area as a feeding ground for Knots. Birds were counted during a co-ordinated watch on one day in each month from September to April and the figures are shown below. I am most grateful to D.B. Cutts of South Cave who organised the enquiry in this area and who has provided the information. The great majority of these birds have been in the eastern part of the estuary between Cherry Cobb Sands and Spurn Point.

	Sep.	Oct.	Nov.	Dec.	Jan.	Feb.	Mar.	Apr.
1970					4,100	7,872	9,280	205
1970/71	175	812	373	6,850	5,290	1,960	4,550	570
1971/72	20	140	1,810	19,300	9,900	8,450	4,450	1,665
1972/73	190	1,500	5,575	NC	8,125	7,100	NC	4,070
1973/74	1,370	420	6,700	NC	11,200	22,650	14,900	60
1974/75	18	136	1,250	6,150	2,420	4,740	307	70
1975/76	NC	NC	NC	4,050	NC	10,500	NC	NC
1976/77	NC	NC	NC	6,416	32,000	29,500	NC	NC
1977/78	NC	NC	NC	5,140	7,070	18,000	NC	NC
1978/79	NC	NC	NC	11,430	23,300	10,000	NC	627
1979/80	NC	NC	NC	5,350	10,600	6,540	NC	NC
1980/81	NC	NC	NC	6,000	15,500	17,950	7,250	NC

NC = No count

Before the invention of the breech-loader, the mudflats of the estuaries were less frequented by gunners than they were at the turn of the century, after which time Nelson said that some large bags of Knots were secured by fishermen and professional fowlers. He knew of instances, told to him by the old sportsmen, of more Knots and godwits being shot than could be conveniently carried. Nelson himself gathered 32 Knots killed with a 'right and left' from a 12 bore shotgun. 'Knottes' were priced at 1d each in 1512, as recorded by the Percys in the 'Northumberland Household Book'.

John Cordeaux, in his *Birds of the Humber District* (1872), gave a graphic account of an experience with Knots on the Humber. The extract from his note-book was published in *The Zoologist*, 1866, p. 75, and is worth repeating here:

'November 4th. This evening, shortly before sunset, I witnessed a most extra-ordinary gathering of Knots on the Humber flats. When at some distance from the bank I was attracted by the noise made in their occasional short flights along the coast — the roar, or rather rush, made by their wings in flight reminding me, more than any thing else, of the noise made by a mighty host of Starlings when settling down for the night. On cautiously peering over the embankment, a beautiful and very striking scene met my gaze. The tide was coming in, and from three to four hundred yards of the flats were still uncovered; in the west the sun was going down in a blaze of glory, and the usual grey and dreary mud plains had borrowed the gorgeous colours of sunset — they were purple with reflected light, — while beyond, the great river in all its tranquility, and almost unbroken by a ripple, was barred and streaked with purple, gold, and crimson. Thousands and thousands of Knots were massed together on the foreshore, here crowded as closely as they could sit, then again straggling out into a more open line, and then again massed together by thousands. Some hundreds of yards length, and about thirty breadth, along the edge of the water, were fairly crowded with them. One part or other, of this great congregation was almost constantly on the wing, flying over the heads of those sitting, and then settling again. All the time they kept up what I may call a continual warbling; the blended notes of so many birds was so completely unlike the usual sharp cry of the Knot, that at first I could scarcely believe it came from that species; it more resembled the twitter-ing of a countless flock of Linnets. Shortly before sunset the flock rose, taking a course directly across the Humber: they did not all rise together, but, commenc-ing at one extremity, gradually took flight. When all on the wing, their appearance was that of an immense dark undulating line of smoke from the funnel of a steamboat.'

Thomas Allis referred to Knots being recorded inland at Hebden Bridge, near Leeds, and at Killingbeck in 1839 where a pair was shot. Nelson mentioned also Halifax, Cold Hiendley Reservoir (Wintersett) and East Cottingwith. Many more birds must have passed unseen at inland waters in those early days, for we now know it to be a regular migrant across the county in small and varying numbers each year.

Chislett mentioned occurrences at a few inland waters up to 1951, since when it has occurred in every year. In some years there may be records of single birds or small parties at many waters, especially at those about the southern part of the Yorkshire Pennines. In other years, fewer birds visit fewer waters. Some fairly large flocks have been seen; Chislett mentioned a party of 20 birds at Redmires Reser-voir on 6th August 1939 and said that Knots had been known to visit Whiteholme Reservoir since 1935. During the last 30 years, they have been seen at very many inland localities, usually during May and September, but there are records in all months.

The more interesting records are as follows: 27 at Blackstone Edge Reservoir on 4th September 1957; 25 at Whiteholme Reservoir on 22nd September 1959 and 24 there on 1st September 1960; 40 at Eccup Reservoir on 25th July 1961; 28 at Fairburn Ings on 1st September 1969 and 23 there on 15th May 1970; ten at Blackmoorfoot Reservoir on 2nd September 1973, in which year there were also nine at Eccup Reservoir on 4th September and 35 flying west over Wintersett Reservoir on 13th September; 12 flew west at Eccup Reservoir on 15th August 1974.

The year 1975 was a good one for inland Knots. Ten were at Wheldrake Ings on 7th March and nine flew west at Wath Ings on 10th March. At Fairburn Ings, 12 flew west on 8th September, seven flew east on 12th September and six flew west on 7th December. A flock of 17 birds dropped into Wath Ings and stayed for only two minutes on 20th October, and smaller numbers, mainly single birds, were seen at several other waters.

Strong gales on 11th and 12th September 1976 brought some Knots inland, with five at Blackmoorfoot Reservoir and two at Gouthwaite Reservoir on 11th, four at Staveley Lagoon on the same day and six at Wintersett Reservoir on 12th.

The autumn of 1978 produced more Knots than usual at inland waters, the largest parties being 11 at Blackmoorfoot Reservoir and five at Fairburn Ings on 17th August, 15 flying west at Wintersett Reservoir on 28th August, and 12 flying west at Worsborough Reservoir on 29th September.

Not all Knots stop off at the Pennine reservoirs and a few have been recorded on the open moorland. One bird in full summer plumage was seen on Pen-y-Ghent by the road leading to Halton Gill on 24th July 1960. During a grouse drive on Burley Moor on 28th August 1967, an adult and a juvenile were shot both of which came into my possession. Eight were seen on Bingley Moor on 10th October 1968.

A bird ringed at Revtangen in Norway on 3rd September 1949 was shot in the mouth of the Tees on 7th February 1954.

Sanderling
Calidris alba

This spring and autumn migrant and winter visitor arrives in Yorkshire in fairly large numbers each year. The sandy parts of the estuaries of the Tees and Humber and the expanse of sand fringing the wide sweep of Bridlington Bay are its favourite haunts. Numbers peak as migrants pass through during the spring and autumn, and most birds have left for their northern breeding grounds by May or early June, the first to return in autumn usually appearing as early as July. A passage from *The Birds of Yorkshire* (1907) sets the scene:

> 'These first arrivals are wholly composed of old birds in summer plumage, and at the end of the month they are found in flocks from about ten to a hundred strong; birds of the year are seldom noted before the first week of the succeeding month, and by the middle of August large flights of guileless youngsters, together with mature birds fast losing the mottled throats, swarm on the beach by the tide-line'.

Nelson went on to say that 'in September the immature birds outnumber the old, and at times large bags may be made by those gunners who are desirous of shooting such "small deer".'

Nelson knew the Teesmouth well and considered it to be the county stronghold for the species; it remains so today. Coatham Sands, Bran Sands and Redcar Sands are the most popular areas and large numbers often gather there to roost at high tide. During the last 20 years, assemblies of from 200 to 400 have been seen regularly, with larger numbers occasionally. On 16th April 1972, S.C. Norman counted 424 on Coatham Sands; P.J. Stead reported a flock of 460 on Bran Sands on 14th April 1974; the largest county flock was seen in 1977, when birds peaked at 800 during February and 600 were assembled there in August; 722 birds, most of them on Coatham Sands, were present on 21st May 1978; and 573 were on Bran Sands on 10th February 1980.

At Spurn, the numbers have been fewer. The most seen there were 430 on 31st October 1978, but counts of between 100 and 300 have been made in most recent years.

The sandy beach between Bridlington and Barmston is the easiest place to see Sanderlings on the Yorkshire coast, and good numbers are always present during the winter and at times of migration. During the last 20 years, maximum counts have been 260 in January and February 1963; 230 on 3rd March 1975; 337 on 23rd February and 450 on 7th March 1976; 354 on 25th February and 250 on 7th March 1977, seven of which were seen to be wearing metal rings; and 417 on 3rd February 1979.

The beaches at Filey, Scarborough South Bay and Jackson's Bay attract smaller numbers, and 20 to 50 birds are often seen there. A flock of 60 was in Jackson's Bay during January to March 1980.

Birds flying south offshore are noted at Spurn every autumn, their numbers varying annually. Passage may continue from July to September, with some stragglers still moving through in October and November. Numbers passing each day vary greatly and may range from just a few birds to 100 or more. Maximum counts have been 194 on 22nd July 1974, in which month a total of 828 birds flew south during the last ten days; 249 on 22nd August 1978; and 270 on 17th August 1979.

More birds occur at inland waters than Nelson knew of, presumably owing to lack of coverage in his day, and we now know the Sanderling to be a regular cross-country migrant, mainly during May and in August and September. Intensive watching at inland waters during the last 20 years has shown them to occur in all months, mainly singly but occasionally in small parties of up to five birds, and any reservoir, flash, gravel-pit or sewage-farm may act as a feeding and resting place.

In some recent years, the species has been recorded at up to 20 different waters, mainly in the western half of the county along the Pennines and mostly at those adjacent to the Aire Gap. The largest parties have been 13 at Almholme on 13th May 1967, with ten at Fairburn Ings next day; 15 in the Upper Humber at Trent Falls on 7th October 1972; 12 flying north at Wintersett Reservoir on 20th May 1973; nine at Blackmoorfoot Reservoir during late July 1974; nine at Eccup Reservoir on 9th May and six at Staveley Lagoon on 29th September 1978; a relatively large inland movement in 1980, with 20 at Wath Ings on 30th May, nine at Fly Flatts Reservoir on 27th May, 13 at Blacktoft Sands on 2nd June, nine of which flew west, seven flying west at Swillington Ings on 29th November; and seven at Nosterfield Gravel-pit on 6th August 1981.

The Sanderling is thus a winter visitor to the coast and a passage migrant in both spring and autumn, some birds moving through during the summer months; small numbers also migrate overland and occur at many inland waters, mainly during May and September.

Semipalmated Sandpiper
Calidris pusilla

A juvenile, watched at Faxfleet by D.I.M. Wallace on 6th October 1978, was a new species for the Yorkshire list and only the sixth for Britain. There have now been 45 British records of this small North American wader.

Little Stint
Calidris minuta

Nelson's assessment of the status of the Little Stint in Yorkshire as a 'Bird of passage on the coast on the spring and autumn migrations, chiefly at the latter period. Very rare inland' needs but a little amendment today. There are certainly more inland records now than in Nelson's time, but his summary remains otherwise very true. He was aware of the erratic appearances of the species and said that these were 'due to the fact that the Yorkshire coast lies to the westward of its chief line of flight, and it is only under extraordinary circumstances that large numbers are met with'. He went on to say 'On first arrival the Little Stint does not, as a rule, associate with other shore birds, and occurs in small parties of half-a-dozen up to forty and fifty, or even more, but later in the season it is seen consorting with the Dunlin and Curlew Sandpiper, the latter of which is generally associated with it on migration.'

Chislett mentioned only a few years when the Little Stint was more numerous than usual. In 1946, S.K. Wainwright saw six at Dewsbury Sewage-farm on 5th September, 16 were with Dunlins at Swillington Ings on 3rd October, and G.R. Edwards and W.B. Alexander saw 11 at Spurn on 11th October. The following year was also considered worthy of mention: R.F. Dickens saw 11 at Spurn on 24th May, with nine remaining on 26th, and single birds were present on a few other dates; the only inland record was a lone bird at Swillington Ings on 27th September. Chislett's typical caution was illustrated in the Yorkshire Naturalists' Union Report for 1955 when he referred to the Spurn Bird Observatory logbook thus: 'The figure "one" inserted in the roll call at Spurn on 20th September is insufficient as a record in the absence of a note in the log.' How times have changed!

An obvious increase in records since the 1950s is doubtless due to the change in status of birdwatchers rather than that of Little Stints. In the YNU Report for 1960 it was stated that the year was a most remarkable one for the species. A brief summary followed thus: numbers began to increase during the first half of September, with 30 at Teesmouth on 11th and single birds at seven other places along the coast and up the River Humber, where there were 13 at Cherry Cobb Sands on 11th. A second influx brought 200 to Teesmouth on 17th September, when there were also 48 at Scaling Dam; ten at Flamborough on 18th; 150 on Brough Salting on 21st; and 17 at Primrose Valley, Scarborough, on 24th. Inland records were numerous, too, with maximum counts of nine at Wintersett Reservoir on 17th, 36 the next day and 30 on 20th. Smaller numbers occurred at several other localities, both along the coast and inland. Such years are quite exceptional.

In 1970 and 1979, there were records from 23 and 28 localities respectively, both on the coast and inland, the majority being in the southeastern part. A marked passage through the county occurred during July to October 1981, when one to three birds were recorded at 13 inland sites, with up to six at Fairburn Ings during mid September. Spurn had up to 13 on 19th September and 11 on 21st and 22nd, and a quite exceptional build-up of numbers occurred at Blacktoft Sands from 12th September, on which day there were 14 present, increasing to 42 next day, 65 on 14th, 85 on 15th and 86 on 19th. These were easily the largest numbers recorded in the county since 1960.

The majority pass during the autumn and birds may be seen from July to November, the peak numbers usually occurring during September. Many fewer are seen during the spring passage period, when most occur in the latter half of May and into early June with an occasional bird in April.

A single bird spent the winter of 1979/80 at Blacktoft Sands and was last seen on 9th April. What was very likely the same individual was at some nearby localities in January and February.

Temminck's Stint
Calidris temminckii

Nelson was able to record only six occurrences of this stint, but added that it was quite probable that the species was overlooked among flocks of Little Stints.

On 1st June 1939, G.R. Edwards and W. Greaves watched seven Temminck's Stints at Ringstone Edge Reservoir, and the birds were still present the next day. Edwards had found the first recorded nests of this species in the British Isles while he was visiting Scotland in the years 1934 to 1936. One was seen at Elland Sewage-farm on 24th September, also in 1939.

K. Dawson and B. Speake watched one at Swillington Ings on 19th October 1947, and one was seen there again by Speake on 23rd August 1949, in which year H.O. Bunce saw one at Cherry Cobb Sands on 29th August and 1st September.

Yorkshire can lay claim to the only English breeding record of the Temminck's Stint. On 1st July 1951, A.H.B. Lee and S. Jackson watched a stint fluttering aimlessly over the slag heaps at Swillington Ings about 150 yards (135 m) from the nearest water. The bird eventually flew off and a search revealed a cup-shaped hollow lined with a few dried grasses and containing four eggs. When the observers retired a few yards, the bird returned and gave the 'broken wing' distraction display before eventually going to the nest to sit on the eggs. Chislett, R.M. Garnett and others saw the bird on 3rd July and watched it return to the nest. Regrettably, on 12th July, the bird was found mauled and dead nearby, probably having been killed by a rat or weasel. A lone bird, presumably its mate, was seen in the area on 14th July. The eggs were taken to the York Museum, and proved to be fertile and highly incubated with well-developed embryos. An excellent photograph of the sitting bird taken by G.A. Newby appears in Chislett's *Yorkshire Birds* and another appears on plate 70. This breeding record was quite extraordinary as the species normally breeds only on the tundra from Norway to northeast Siberia, being very local in southern Scandinavia. One bird was seen in the same area on 24th August 1952.

Temminck's Stints have been recorded in Yorkshire in every year except three since 1952. Up to 1972, one to three records in a year were usual, but since 1973 there has been a definite increase in the number of sightings reported, with eight records in 1976, eight in 1977 including four birds at Mickletown Ings on 24th May, seven in 1980, seven in 1981 including three birds at Wath Ings from 23rd to 25th May, nine in 1982 and four in 1983.

May and August/September are the main months of occurrence and records have come from most areas of the county, including the coast and some of the many reservoirs and gravel-pits of the Pennines.

White-rumped Sandpiper
Calidris fuscicollis

On 19th October 1957, driving from Spurn to the Crown and Anchor Inn at Kilnsea for breakfast, in the company of R.F. Dickens, B.S. Potter and S.J. Weston, I noticed a dead bird lying on the road which on inspection proved to be an example of this North American species. It had a wound on the breast consistent with its having collided with the telegraph wires overhead, but was otherwise in good condition. It was taken back to the observatory, where it was photographed and details of its plumage and measurements taken (see plate 71). It was a juvenile and the corpse was sent to A. Hazelwood of the Bolton Museum, where the specimen is now housed. This was the first recorded instance of the species' occurrence in Yorkshire and full details were published in *The Naturalist*, 1958, p. 81.

As is often the case, once the first record has been established, others follow. One was caught and ringed at the Easington Lagoon area by B.R. Spence and M.A. Hollingworth on 9th September 1969, and seen again on 10th. H.O. Bunce, D.E. Murray and D.I.M. Wallace watched one on the Humber mud at Welton Water between 13th and 15th July 1975. An adult in almost full winter plumage was seen on 27th September 1978 at Wath Ings, where it remained until 12th October. It was caught and ringed on 1st October and was seen by many people, including N. Addey, J. Hewitt and J.M. Turton. The fifth record for the county occurred at Tophill Low Reservoir, where one was seen from 27th July to 1st August 1981 by several observers, including P. Dove, P. Izzard, I. Forsyth and K. Rotherham.

In 1983, one was at Blacktoft Sands from 10th to 14th July which was seen by A. Grieve and others, and another was seen at Melbourne, near Wheldrake, on 26th September by T.J. Barker and T.E. Dixon.

Baird's Sandpiper
Calidris bairdii

The first record of this Nearctic wader in Yorkshire occurred at Fairburn Ings on 6th September 1967, when M. Densley, T.G. Gunton and C. Winn saw and described a bird in detail. It was still present the next day and several other people were able to see this rare visitor, which has now visited the British Isles on some 115 occasions.

On 15th August 1981, a second example was seen at Blacktoft Sands, where it remained until 31st August. It was seen by literally hundreds of birdwatchers from all over the county and beyond, including A. Grieve, D. Page, D. Hursthouse and myself.

The Baird's Sandpiper breeds across North America and into northeast Siberia.

Pectoral Sandpiper
Calidris melanotos

Nelson published six records of this American species as follows. One was shot near Redcar on 30th August 1853, and another was shot in a field near Coatham on 17th October 1853 (*The Naturalist*, 1853, p. 275). One was recorded at Filey by the Reverend F.O. Morris, the details of which were published in *British Birds*, 1854, p. 316. One was shot on the coast near Kilnsea on 2nd October 1888 and sent to J. Cordeaux for identification; the specimen was figured by Lord Lilford in his *British Birds*, vol. 5, pl. 31 (*The Naturalist*, 1888, p. 354, and the *Zoologist*, 1891, p. 366). One was shot at Bridlington on 15th August 1891, and another was 'obtained' at Easington near Spurn on 28th September 1897; this latter bird, a male in full plumage, was examined by J. Cordeaux, H. Saunders and W. Eagle Clarke.

Chislett was able to add only two more records up to 1951, the first of which concerned two birds seen at Leeming Reservoir near Bradford by A.W.A. Swaine in the early spring of 1948. No further details are available and the record is, in my opinion, far from proven. The other referred to a bird at Cherry Cobb Sands on 4th September 1951 and for a few days thereafter. It was found by J.M. Laws and seen subsequently by G.H. Ainsworth, H.O. Bunce and J. Lord.

Since that time, the Pectoral Sandpiper has occurred in Yorkshire on at least 24 occasions as follows. G.R. Edwards watched one at Spurn on 10th October 1952. One was in the Easington Lagoons area on 15th September 1957, where it was seen by J. Cudworth, A.H.B. Lee, C. Winn and others. One was seen at Fairburn Ings from 17th September to 12th October 1959 by several people, including M. Densley, G.R. Naylor and C. Winn. One was at Settle Sewage-farm from 22nd to 28th September 1967 which J.G. Ireland and F.J. Roberts described in detail. Three birds were seen at Cherry Cobb Sands on 27th September 1970 by A.W. Wallis and R.G. Wallis. One was seen at Birkin on the unusual date of 17th July 1972 by R.F. Dickens and S. Gwillam (*The Naturalist*, 1973, pp. 69-70). One was seen at Hornsea Mere from 28th September to 7th October 1972 by many observers, including D.T. Ireland and J. and A. Denison. One was seen, again at Birkin, on 25th and 26th May 1973 by R.F. Dickens, S. Gwillam, Dr J.D. Pickup and others (*The Naturalist*, 1973, p. 90). One was at Hornsea Mere from 11th to 21st September 1975, where it fed along the water's edge in the field at the northeast corner and was watched by many people including D.E. Murray, who supplied detailed notes; on the last day of its stay, its behaviour changed and the bird became restless, finally departing high to the south with some Ringed Plovers (see plate 72). One was seen by P. Reid at Rosscarrs, Selby, on 6th August 1976, and another was seen by G.D. Moore at Bolton-on-Swale Gravel-pit on 25th August 1976. There were five records in 1977: one was seen at Tophill Low Reservoir on 23rd and 24th July by S.L. James; one was at Potteric Carr on 28th July; one was seen at Coatham Marsh, near Redcar, from 3rd to 18th September by several observers, including S.C. and W. Norman and G.W. Follows; one was at Fairburn Ings on 18th September, seen by S.C. Madge and J. Martin; and finally one was seen at Tophill Low Reservoir from 12th to 29th October by J.H. Lawton and P.J. Izzard. Single birds were at Blacktoft Sands from 29th July to 1st August 1981 and at Tophill Low Reservoir on 13th and 14th September 1981. One was at Nosterfield Gravel-pit on 22nd July 1983 and another at Spurn on 3rd October 1983. In 1984, singles were at Alltofts on 1st September; at Kilnsea on 8th

September; at Tophill Low Reservoir from 14th to 26th September; at Jackson's Bay, Scarborough, from 25th to at least 27th September; and again at Nosterfield from 1st to 27th December.

As is evident from the above records, this North American wader now appears almost annually, and a lone bird may be seen by the side of any water. The most likely time for such an occurrence is in May or during the autumn migration period from July to September.

Sharp-tailed Sandpiper
Calidris acuminata

The first Yorkshire record of this species, which breeds in northeastern Siberia and winters in Australasia, occurred at Blacktoft Sands on 17th September 1982, when it was seen by A. Grieve, C. Jarvis, C. Nimick and others.

The news of its presence travelled quickly, and at dawn on 18th large numbers of observers were queued at the hides hoping to see this rare bird. They were hampered by early morning fog, which eventually lifted to reveal that the sandpiper was not there. It was subsequently learned that what was presumably the same individual had moved down the estuary into Lincolnshire and had been seen at Killingholme, where it remained until 20th September.

This was only the sixteenth record for the British Isles and the first since 1978.

Another appeared on 9th September 1983, at Flamborough, where it was seen by P.A. Lassey and A. Speck.

Curlew Sandpiper
Calidris ferruginea

Nelson mentioned five years at the end of the nineteenth century that were numerically good for this species. 'An extensive migration' occurred in 1873; it was abundant at both the Tees and the Humber in 1881 and in 1887; 'upwards of a hundred were obtained at the Tees' in 1890 and many were killed at Spurn, several of which had red breasts, in 1892.

Chislett considered it 'generally scarce', with no years providing such migrations as were recorded by Nelson. During the last 30 years, a similar situation has prevailed and only the years 1959, 1969, 1972, 1975 and 1978 can be termed above average.

Chislett started his paragraph on the species in the Yorkshire Naturalists' Union Report for 1959 with the words 'A most extraordinary number was recorded compared with the few of most years', going on to list occurrences of one to two birds at Spurn on several dates from 1st August to the end of October, ten birds on 2nd September being the largest flock. Records came from 14 inland waters on several dates between 25th July and 2nd November. The largest numbers seen were nine at Fairburn Ings from 1st to 9th September, six at Wintersett Reservoir on 1st September and 13 on the Humber near Welton Water on 1st September.

The autumn of 1969 produced 'an exceptional number', mainly at Teesmouth, with 66 birds on the Yorkshire side on 28th August, and at Spurn, where there were

82 on 30th August and 78 on 6th September. Further up the Humber, there were 26 at Brough on 6th September, and up to 11 at four other places along the river from late August to late October. From one to nine birds occurred at six inland waters, from the first at Fairburn Ings on 24th July to the last at Withens Reservoir on 8th November.

There were many records in 1972, almost all being in August and September. The Easington Lagoons area attracted many birds, with peak counts of 14 on 31st August, 35 on 2nd September and 37 on 9th September. Sunk Island also had good numbers, with seven on 9th September and 43 on 10th. Tophill Low Reservoir had 15 birds on 19th August, 19 on 5th September and six on 11th September. Smaller numbers occurred at four other coastal and estuarine localities during the same periods. Inland records were also numerous and came from seven waters, the highest numbers being seven at Wath Ings on 29th August, six at Stocks Reservoir on 1st September, three at Knostrop Sewage-farm on 2nd September and six at Masham Gravel-pit on 9th September.

Records in 1975 were slightly above average, the maximum counts being 15 flying south at Filey on 31st August; 27 at Patrington Haven on 3rd September; 20 at Faxfleet on 4th September; ten flying west at Blackmoorfoot Reservoir on 25th August and nine more on 8th September; up to six at Redmires Reservoir between 30th August and 14th September, with eight on 13th September; 13 at Fairburn Ings on 8th September and eight from 30th August to 14th September; and ten at Morley's Pool, near Settle, on 11th September.

The largest migration in recent years occurred in the autumn of 1978, with a marked influx in mid August and another in mid September. Birds were passing from late July to late September along the coast and the Humber shore and at 17 inland waters. The largest numbers were 17 near Paull on 14th September and 65 in the Faxfleet/Whitton Sands area on 16th and 17th September. Blacktoft Sands had birds from 6th August with a few lingering on into early December, the most seen together being 25 on 6th September. Seven were at Nosterfield Gravel-pit on 6th September; seven at Blackmoorfoot Reservoir on 7th September; ten at Newington Flash from 7th to 9th September and 12 at Ingbirchworth Reservoir on 30th September.

The present status of the Curlew Sandpiper in Yorkshire can be summarised as a passage migrant in both spring and autumn, mainly during the latter period, the estuaries of the Tees and Humber being the most favoured coastal localities but small numbers occurring at inland waters. Annual numbers fluctuate greatly.

Purple Sandpiper
Calidris maritima

The first reference to this most littoral of waders in Yorkshire is in Leyland's *Halifax Catalogue* (1828), where one is recorded as shot on Ovenden Moor in December 1827. According to T. Allis, another was shot on Sowerby Moor in the winter of 1832.

The numbers of Purple Sandpipers along the Yorkshire coast during the last 25 years have certainly been larger than in Chislett's time and before. Nelson mentioned a flock of 40 to 50 birds on West Scar, Redcar, on 13th November 1893, from which he 'secured six with one barrel'. The largest flock mentioned by Chislett was 75 birds in Whitby Harbour during the winter of 1930/31 (*The Naturalist*, 1932, p. 26), but he said that flocks were usually considerably smaller.

The favourite places for Purple Sandpipers have changed little over the years, and at the present time the species may be found anywhere from the South Gare Breakwater and the rocks about Redcar, along the boulder-strewn bases of the cliffs southwards to Filey Bay, Flamborough and Bridlington Harbour. South of Bridlington, the sandy beaches of Holderness are quite unsuitable for this rock-loving bird and records from that area are relatively scarce.

Since the 1970s, some large flocks have been reported from the favoured localities at Whitby, Scarborough, Cornelian Bay, Filey Brigg, Flamborough and Bridlington Harbour. Filey Bay is undoubtedly the most popular haunt and up to 300 birds can be seen there regularly during the winter months. A large flock of 400 was present on 16th December 1978 and the county's largest gathering of 500 birds was seen there on 1st March 1983. Peak counts in other recent years have been as follows. In 1975 there were up to 175 present during January and February, and a build-up from 130 on 30th October to 260 on 19th November and 320 on 6th December; a similar situation prevailed in 1978, with 235 birds on 4th January, 262 on 11th March and 140 flying north off the brigg on 15th April, the autumn having 100 in November, increasing to 250 by 3rd December and to the peak of 400 mentioned above. In 1980, the figures were 276 on 5th January, 210 on 24th February, 320 in March, 280 on 7th April and 250 as late as 3rd May, the latter flock being quite exceptional. It is probable that the highest counts at Filey are due to a movement from Cornelian Bay, about 4 miles (6.4 km) to the north, at times of high tides.

The southern end of the Scarborough South Bay and Cornelian Bay farther south have become very attractive for wading birds during the last few years as a result of discharged waste from a potato chip factory running across the beach and enriching the marine life. Purple Sandpipers have discovered the improved food source, and in recent years average counts of up to 300 birds have been made there (see A.J. Prater, 1981, *Estuarine Birds of Britain and Ireland*, p. 358). Jackson's Bay, north of Scarborough, Cayton Bay to the south of the town, and the rocks below the Marine Drive all play host to good numbers from time to time and make the Scarborough area a good one for the species.

During 1965, while C.J. Feare was attached to the Leeds University Wellcome Marine Laboratory at Robin Hood's Bay, he studied the feeding behaviour of a small flock of Purple Sandpipers and made other observations on a second flock at Filey Brigg. The principal food items were small winkles and young dogwhelks, small mussels and crabs being important reserve foods. Full details of the study were published in *British Birds*, 1966, pp. 165-79.

Most have departed for their breeding quarters in northern Europe by the end of April, but a few linger, or pass through, into early May. A late bird was at Spurn on 28th May 1928 (*The Naturalist*, 1928, p. 315). The first birds of autumn usually appear during early August, but occasionally a few are seen in July and exceptionally in late June, as on 22nd June 1977 when one was on Filey Brigg and on 30th June 1980 when six were seen there.

Inland records are scarce. Apart from the two birds shot on the moors near Halifax (see first paragraph), Nelson mentioned one seen on Cam Fell in Ribblesdale in November 1891. Chislett could add only one more: a bird seen on Malham Moor in November/December 1906, the details of which were published in *The Naturalist*, 1907, p. 29.

Since 1952, when Chislett published his *Yorkshire Birds*, there have been 14 inland records as follows. One at Elland Gravel-pit on 20th November 1954; one found dead under wires at Castleford on 23rd September 1962; one at Settle Sewage-farm on 23rd November 1966; one at Faxfleet in the Upper Humber on 12th November 1967; one at Gouthwaite Reservoir on 18th November 1972; one at Marley Sewage-farm on 29th August 1974; one at Broomhill Flash on 8th September 1975; one at Blackmoorfoot Reservoir from 12th to 18th August 1976; one at Deer Hill Reservoir on 2nd September 1978; one at Wintersett Reservoir on 11th November 1979; one at Pugneys Gravel-pit on the very early date of 4th July 1980; one at Faxfleet on 10th August 1980; another at Faxfleet on 17th August 1981; and one at Hay-a-Park Gravel-pit on 31st October 1981 which was caught and ringed the next day.

Dunlin

Calidris alpina

The Dunlin occurs in Yorkshire as a breeding species, a passage migrant and a winter visitor. In Nelson's time, it nested in limited numbers and irregularly on the fells of the west and northeast and sparingly on the Tees marshes, but ceased to do so at the latter after 1907. Today it breeds only on the fells of the Pennines from the southwest northwards to Upper Teesdale, and anywhere on these high and barren moors a pair or two may be found. Birds feeding by the side of moorland tarns in May or June need not indicate breeding in the area; such individuals may still be on passage northwards.

There have been few detailed studies of the breeding population, but D.W. Yalden, D. Herringshaw and J.E. Dale have watched the moorlands of the southwest in recent years. In 1974, at least seven pairs bred on Wessenden Moor and five pairs on moorland west of Sheffield. M.V. Bell surveyed the fells of Upper Wharfedale in May and June 1974, when he located 24 nests and estimated a further 12 pairs to be breeding. The moors surveyed were Old Cote Moor, Moss Top, Cosh Inside, Fountains Fell, Darnbrook Fell, Gray Moss and Yockenthwaite Moor to Fleet Moss (see *The Naturalist*, 1979, pp. 95-100). Areas of wet cottongrass or those adjacent to small moorland tarns are the favoured places for nesting, and wherever these occur breeding Dunlins are likely to be encountered. Although probable breeding was reported for a pair on the North York Moors in the early 1970s, there is no proof of successful nesting there at the present time. Chislett said that breeding pairs were very rare in this area and he knew of no recent record.

The Dunlin is perhaps the most familiar of wading birds, occurring as it does in huge flocks along the shore, especially in the estuaries of the Tees and Humber. The Birds of Estuaries Enquiry organised by the British Trust for Ornithology since 1970 has shown some spectacular figures. Birds were counted along the north shore of the Humber from Spurn Point to Goole on one day each month during the winter periods. The table on page 283 shows the results.

Most of the birds counted were concentrated towards the mouth of the estuary between Paull and Spurn Point. For instance, of the 15,375 birds counted in December 1978, 12,000 were to the east of Paull, as were 18,000 of the total of 19,350 in December 1977.

Whitton Sands in the upper part of the Humber Estuary is a favourite place for both birds and birdwatchers, and good numbers of Dunlins can be found there. Large counts at this locality have been 1,800 on 14th March 1976, with 1,130 on

Plate 31. A view looking southwest over Kilnsea Clays to the Spurn lighthouse; favourite haunt of many waders, Brent Geese and other waterfowl. *Photo: A. Gilpin*

Plate 32. A view looking east over Whitby, down the River Esk, showing the two piers which shelter areas of mud in the estuary at low tide. The harbour is frequented by large numbers of gulls during the winter months. *Photo: C.H. Wood Ltd.*

Plate 33. A view looking north over Scarborough, showing the South and North Bays and the prominent Castle Hill which dominates the harbour. Scalby Mills can be seen at the top of the North Bay. The general area is very popular with gull-watchers during the winter months. *Photo: C.H. Wood Ltd.*

Plate 34. The famous Castle Hill Cliff at Scarborough, breeding site of 1,660 pairs of Kittiwakes in 1980. The colony is unique in being the only one in the British Isles with a main road running between it and the sea, which is just off the Marine Drive on the left of the picture. Herring Gulls and Fulmars also breed in good numbers. *Photo: M.F. Brown*

Plate 35. A view looking east along the eroded boulder-clay cliff of the Carr Naze to Filey Brigg. The sheltered bay and fringing beach attract many waterfowl and waders during the winter months. *Photo: R.H. Appleby*

Plate 36. Looking north from Filey Brigg during a 'northeaster'; a favourite sea-watching place for many birdwatchers. *Photo: A. Gilpin*

Plate 37. The Dotterel Inn at Reighton, built by the Strickland family for the use of gamekeepers and 'sportsmen', who gathered from all over the north to shoot migrating Dotterels in the spring during the end of the nineteenth century. *Photo: M.F. Brown*

Plate 38. The impressive chalk cliffs at Bempton, breeding place of Gannets and many thousands of Kittiwakes and Guillemots, with large numbers of Razorbills, Puffins, Herring Gulls and Fulmars. *Photo: A. Gilpin*

Plate 39. Flamborough Headland. This imposing promontory, which juts 6 miles (9.6 km) into the North Sea, is an important locality for migrant and vagrant passerines and many interesting seabirds have been recorded from the point. *Photo: C.H. Wood Ltd.*

Plate 40. A basketful of Guillemots' eggs, many thousands of which were taken until 1953 when the Protection of Birds Act came into force.

Plate 41. Some of the old climbers at Bempton at the turn of the century with their equipment and spoils.

Plate 42. Two views of the climbers in action on Bempton Cliffs at the turn of the century.

Plate 43. Joseph 'Joss' Major, who was killed by a falling stone while climbing for eggs near Staple Neuk on the Bempton Cliffs on 6th June 1910 (see page 371).

Plate 44. A selection of Guillemots' eggs collected on the Bempton Cliffs during the early part of the present century and showing the great variation in size and colour markings. The Yorkshire cliffs were famous for the excellence of some of the eggs, which were prized by collectors.

Plate 45. Sam Leng, one of the most famous of the Bempton climbers, who died on 5th March 1935. A booklet outlining his exploits and entitled *Reminiscences of a Bempton Cliff Climber* was published some little time before his death.

Plate 46. Edgar Ellis of Ossett, who was befriended by the climbers and went down the cliffs regularly towards the end of their activities during the post-war years.

Plate 47. Snowden Slights in his punt on the River Derwent near the place where the Hooded Merganser was said to have been shot. Slights was born at East Cottingwith in 1829 and lived there all his life. He was a basket-maker by trade and owned two shops in the village from which his wares, made from local osiers, were sold. His income was supplemented by wildfowling during the winter months, and he made a record profit of £90 in one season. He was acknowledged as an expert shot with all types of weapons, some of which can be seen on the following page, and some 'bags' with the large punt gun seen in the above photograph were quite spectacular. Between 1890 and 1907, the only period for which he kept records, he shot a total of 5,355 birds, the main species being Mallards (2,434), Lapwings (1,755), and Wigeons (455). The birds were usually sold at Pocklington and the following prices were paid: Whooper Swans 7s, Great Crested Grebes 3s 6d, Bitterns and Mallards 2s, Sparrowhawks and Snipe 6d, and larks 1d. It is interesting that Bitterns and Mallards were valued at the same price. He was buried in the churchyard at East Cottingwith, and with his passing the art of wildfowling, as he knew it, died also. None of his successors followed the pursuit and his armoury is now housed in the Yorkshire Museum at York. *Photo: S.H. Smith by courtesy of the Yorkshire Museum*

Plate 48. Snowden Slights, the most famous and last of the Yorkshire wildfowlers, with his armoury.
Photo: S.H. Smith by courtesy of the Yorkshire Museum

Plate 49. Craggs Clubley, one of the famous Clubley family who were responsible for several bird records in the Spurn area, here seen 'digging in' on Kilnsea Clays for a duck shoot in the early 1900s. He died in 1946 at the age of 86.

Plate 50. Miss Carrie Leonard, at whose cafe at Kilnsea visitors to the Spurn Bird Observatory during the 1950s were always fed, and who became well known to birdwatchers from all over the British Isles. She is here seen feeding 'Stergie', an oiled Puffin which she cared for in 1951.

Plate 51. A group of visitors to the Spurn Bird Observatory outside the Warren Cottage in April 1953. Left to right: D. Robinson, P.C. Quin, J.K. Fenton, Miss Audrey Leach, Miss Margaret Haydock and the author. Fenton was secretary of the observatory for many years and played a major part in its organisation. *Photo: E.S. Skinner*

Plate 52. Knaresborough Ringing Station on the banks of the River Nidd showing the Heligoland trap, and goats used for controlled grazing. Over 100,000 birds have been ringed here since 1953; a Great Reed Warbler, an Icterine Warbler, two Yellow-browed Warblers, a Bluethroat and two Wrynecks have been recorded and the site produced the first county record of Savi's Warbler. *Photo: M.F. Brown*

Plate 53. The observation tower at Knaresborough Ringing Station, affording an uninterrupted view of the area and from which several interesting species have been seen passing overhead, including Honey Buzzard, Osprey, Marsh Harrier, Red-footed Falcon, Night Heron, Common Scoter, Arctic Skua, Fulmar and Leach's Petrel. *Photo: M.F. Brown*

Plate 54. Members of the *British Birds* Rarities Committee at a meeting at the author's house at Knaresborough in March 1982. Left to right: M.J. Rogers, B. Little, P.J. Grant, J.R. Mather (standing), D.J. Holman, T.P. Inskipp, K.E. Vinicombe, D.J. Britton, Dr J.T.R. Sharrock and R.F. Porter. *Photo: M.F. Brown*

Plate 55. Five White-billed Divers found dead or dying on the Yorkshire coast between 1953 and 1973. Top to bottom: juvenile, Hornsea, December 1973; the remainder, all adults, from Robin Hood's Bay, February 1966; Filey, March 1963; Hedon, February 1953; and Scarborough, January 1953. *Photo: M.F. Brown*

Plate 56. Three Fulmars found dead on Yorkshire beaches: upper, the large white form typical of the Yorkshire breeders; centre, an intermediate 'blue' form; and lower, an example of the Baffin Island race *Fulmarus glacialis minor* from Withernsea on 7th January 1982, showing the small bill. The shorter wing length of the latter is not apparent in the photograph. *Photo: M.F. Brown*

Plate 57. Capped Petrel found dead at Barmston on 16th December 1984. Only the second British record of this rare species, which breeds in the West Indies. *Photo: J. Cudworth*

Plate 58. A male Little Bittern which frequented Millfield Flash, near Wakefield, during the last week of September 1976 and was caught and ringed on 30th. *Photo: J.S. Armitage*

Plate 59. Green-backed Heron at Stone Creek in November 1982. The first record for Yorkshire and only the second for the British Isles. *Photo: P.A. Doherty*

Plate 60. The first and only Cattle Egret to be recorded in Yorkshire, near Rievaulx Abbey from 5th to 7th April 1981, in a typical setting among cattle. *Photo: P.J. Dunn*

	Sep.	Oct.	Nov.	Dec.	Jan.	Feb.	Mar.	Apr.	May
1970					11,980	12,520	11,450	7,900	NC
1970/71	4,192	6,513	6,524	8,900	13,500	9,650	4,340	NC	NC
1971/72	2,330	13,110	15,050	12,800	26,365	16,275	13,555	22,560	7,180
1972/73	6,810	18,835	16,145	NC	17,880	16,715		17,325	14,920
1973/74	15,150	15,240	13,540	NC	10,700	18,250	17,250	11,400	11,325
1974/75	4,000	9,100	10,000	14,750	6,875	10,995	9,330	15,110	18,408
1975/76	NC	NC	NC	13,200	NC	17,630	NC	NC	NC
1976/77	NC	NC	NC	16,835	44,000	29,000	NC	NC	NC
1977/78	NC	NC	NC	19,350	22,745	19,900	NC	NC	NC
1978/79	NC	NC	NC	15,375	23,580	16,060	NC	7,820	NC
1979/80	NC	NC	NC	7,300	10,300	12,200	NC	NC	NC
1980/81	NC	NC	NC	5,735	9,100	12,500	8,930	NC	NC
1981/82					25,900	16,900	11,190		

NC = No count

4th May and 2,000 on 23rd September; and 5,000 on 9th November 1977. Cherry Cobb Sands is also favoured, and B.S. Pashby counted 10,000 there on 20th November 1977.

The mouth of the River Tees holds many Dunlins, not all of which are on the Yorkshire side of the estuary, and 57,000 were present on 13th February 1972. Cornelian Bay attracts this species and 1,000 were there on 26th January 1975, in which year Filey Bay had 1,000 on 26th February. Dunlins, along with other waders, resort to grassland along the coast, especially at high tide when they assemble to roost, or at times of flooding when they feed along the water's edge. There were 1,800 on floodwater at Cayton Carrs on 25th January 1975 and 1,000 on 28th January 1977. D.I.M. Wallace counted 590 on grassland at Flamborough on 3rd January 1977, and there were 220 on floodwater at Hollym Carrs on 16th January.

The majority of those visiting Yorkshire on migration in autumn are of the longer-billed northern race which breeds from Norway, eastwards across Europe into Siberia, and it is sometimes possible to see such birds in the company of the shorter-billed British race, formerly known as the Schinz Sandpiper.

Small flocks of Dunlins may be seen on any beach or coastal pool during the winter months and at times of migration in spring and autumn. They also occur on migration at inland localities, and any type of water from the largest reservoir to the smallest gravel-pit or sewage-farm may pull down migrating birds at such times. The moorland reservoirs of the southern Pennines and the waters along the Aire Valley are the most favoured stopping-off places, lying as they do on the direct route from the Humber to the Morecambe Bay area.

Mud along the edge of the River Don near Thorne attracted 143 Dunlins on 30th November 1973 and 154 on 23rd November 1975. Wath Ings had 66 birds on 10th March and 50 on 19th October 1974, and there were 75 at Fly Flatts Reservoir on 27th April, 32 at Redmires Reservoir on 23rd July and 60 at Potteric Carr on 12th September. In 1975, Potteric Carr had 57 on 23rd March, Redmires Reservoir had 70 during late October and floodwater near Settle had 46 birds on 9th October.

In 1976, more Dunlins than usual crossed the county and were seen at many inland waters, mainly during the spring and autumn migration periods. The Lower Derwent Floods attracted many birds, with a high count of 300 on 25th January. Potteric Carr had 35 on 18th January, 65 on 27th February, 60 on 18th March and 40 in November. During February, 150 were at Swillington Ings and 60 were at Fairburn Ings. On 30th January, 50 flew west at Southfield Reservoir, and 65 were seen at Mickletown Ings on 15th February. Gouthwaite Reservoir had 22 birds on 17th March and 27 on 11th September as peak counts in spring and autumn. Up to 50 Dunlins were near Settle during January to March. In May, there were 23 at Wath Ings on 5th, 100 at Wheldrake Ings on 8th and 24 at Fly Flatts Reservoir on 18th. The movement was similarly heavy in the autumn, and during a gale on 11th

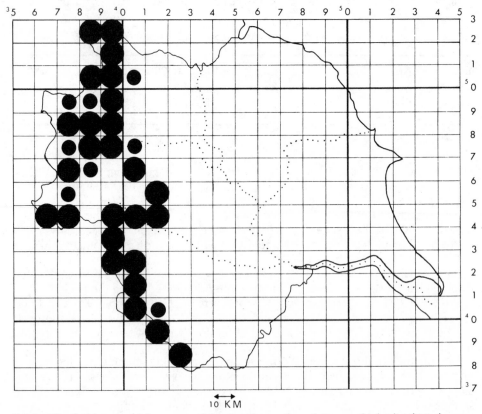

Dunlin. Confined to the higher parts of the Pennines, where it is very thinly distributed.

September 74 flew southwest over Staveley Lagoon and 76 did so next day; 50 were at Nosterfield Gravel-pit on 31st October, with 32 on 2nd November, and 101 flew west in four flocks over the Ewden/Langsett Reservoirs on 4th December.

That was an exceptional year, but cross-country passage occurs annually in smaller and varying numbers. The floodwaters along the Lower Derwent have become a regular wintering area since the early 1970s. H.O. Bunce counted 100-200 there during January and February 1971, 200 in January 1972 and 150 during February and March that year. Very large numbers were seen there in 1974, when 350 were counted on 29th January, 600 on 31st March, 100 on 4th May and 200 in December. In 1978, no fewer than 700 were present during March and 200 during April, all of which had moved out by the end of May. The highest count in 1980 was 420 on 23rd February.

There are several recoveries of ringed Dunlins in Yorkshire, including 37 birds marked in Finland, Norway, Sweden and Denmark, the Netherlands, Germany and Poland during the autumn, all but one of which have been recovered along the coastline during the winter months. A bird ringed at Spurn Bird Observatory on 7th October 1960 was recovered in France on 25th December 1960, having apparently continued south for the winter. Of the 6,683 Dunlins ringed at the Spurn Bird Observatory, 29 have been recovered abroad: in Fenno-Scandia (16), the Netherlands (two), Denmark (four), France (one), Germany (five) and Poland (one).

Known as the 'stint' in ancient times, Dunlins were 'formerly a great dish at our tables'. In 1512, 'Styntes' were sold at six for one penny, and in 1526 the marriage feast of Sir John Neville's daughter included 'five dozen stints at nine pence'. The price quoted in *Wildfowl at Hull* in 1560 was four pence a dozen.

Yorkshire can claim the first written description of the Dunlin, which was communicated by Ralph Johnson of Greta Bridge to Willughby, who published the detailed notes in his *Ornithology* (1678, p. 305).

Broad-billed Sandpiper
Limicola falcinellus

There are now almost 90 records in the British Isles of this species, which breeds from Scandinavia, eastwards across northern Europe to Siberia. The first Yorkshire example was shot from a flock of Dunlins at Hornsea Mere in late April 1863 by Thomas Ellotson; the specimen went to the collection of Sir Henry Boynton at Burton Agnes, where Nelson examined it.

The species was not encountered in the county again until 1984, when A. Grieve and others saw one at Blacktoft Sands on 18th May; another was present there from 28th May to 1st June and another, or the same, appeared on 13th June and stayed until 15th.

Stilt Sandpiper
Micropalama himantopus

The first record of this North American wader in the British Isles occurred in the area north of Kilnsea Beacon now known as the Easington Lagoons. After the coastal floods of 1953, a high bank was created some distance from the shore dunes between which an area of marshy ground developed. This soon became a favourite resting and feeding place for migrant wading birds and it was the practice of those staying at the Spurn Bird Observatory to visit this area and check the birds present.

On 31st August 1954, E.E. Jackson and P. Waterton made such a visit and noted a wader which was completely new to them. It could not be found that same evening, when R. Chislett, G.H. Ainsworth and R.F. Dickens visited the area, but Jackson and Waterton relocated it the next day, and on 2nd September, in the company of R.F. Dickens, watched it again and took detailed field notes. It stayed until 3rd September and was seen by 14 observers, all of whom made notes and sketches.

R.F. Dickens later examined over 50 skins of Stilt Sandpiper at the British Museum of Natural History and confirmed that the Yorkshire bird was in almost complete breeding dress, lacking only the rust colour on its cheeks. The heavy barring on the lower breast, belly and undertail-coverts which the bird exhibited is diagnostic of the species in summer plumage. Full details of the bird's stay were published in *British Birds*, 1955, pp. 18-20 and plate 32, which shows two sketches drawn by J. Cudworth.

Buff-breasted Sandpiper
Tryngites subruficollis

The first representative of this Nearctic wader in Yorkshire occurred at the Easington Lagoons area on the morning of 6th September 1954, when it was located by J.K. Fenton, Miss A.E. Leach and S. Martin. Other people staying at the Spurn Bird Observatory were informed and were able to watch the bird as it fed among waterlogged grass for the remainder of the day. It was still there the next morning and during the early afternoon, but could not be found later (*British Birds*, 1955, pp. 328-9).

In 1975, many Buff-breasted Sandpipers came to Britain, and Yorkshire claimed its fair share of records. One was seen at Wath Ings from 28th to 30th August and another, or the same bird, seen again on 20th and 21st September by R. Wells, J. Hewitt and J.M. Turton. One was seen by M.L. Denton, G.M. Yeates and J.E. Dale at Blackmoorfoot Reservoir on 28th and 29th August, on which latter date it moved to nearby Deer Hill Reservoir where it was seen by J.E. Dale. This same bird, or another, was at Deer Hill from 15th to 17th September, when it was watched by F.J. Roberts, M.L. Denton and others. One was seen at Redmires Reservoir from 10th to 26th September by D. Herringshaw, D. Gosney and others, and what was probably the same bird was seen there from 10th to 14th October.

One occurred in 1977 at Ringstone Edge Reservoir, where it was watched by J. Bray, N. Leece and J.E. Dale from 13th to 16th September.

In 1981, a juvenile bird was seen at Blacktoft Sands from 31st August to 8th September, and again from 27th September to 6th October, by several observers, including A. Grieve, G.P. Catley and G. Sharpe.

Ruff
Philomachus pugnax

The account of the great banquet at Cawood in 1466 included a statement that 'of the fowles called Rees there were supplied 200 dozen'. In 1512, 'Reys' were priced at 2d each and they were evidently a delicacy at the better tables of the period. In Pennant's *British Zoology* (1766, ii, p. 363) it is stated that 'These birds are found in the East Riding of Yorkshire where they are taken in nets and fattened for the table, with bread and milk, hempseed, and sometimes with boiled wheat; but if expedition is required, sugar is added, which will make them in a fortnight's time a lump of fat: they will then sell for 2/- or 2/6d a piece.'

The species once nested in Yorkshire, certainly on Riccal Common, near Selby, and on Hatfield Moors and Skipwith Common, but they ceased to do so after the middle of the nineteenth century. Collecting of both eggs and skins coupled with drainage and changed agricultural practices, was no doubt a contributory factor to its extermination as a breeding species. Breeding at the Teesmouth in 1901, 1902 and 1903, originally reported as being on the Yorkshire side, was corrected by Nelson in his *The Birds of Yorkshire*, having in fact occurred on the north side of the river.

We know the Ruff as a bird of passage both in spring and in autumn, mainly during the latter period, and increasing numbers are now spending the winter months in the county, especially in the Humber estuary, where it has been known to do so in very small numbers since Nelson's time, and also along the Lower Derwent Valley. Ruffs may be seen in any month of the year, but principally during April/May and during August to October, when the majority are on passage through the county.

In Nelson's time, it was known mainly as a coastal species, being most numerous in the estuaries of the Tees and Humber, but regular watching at some inland waters in recent years had shown it to be equally numerous at such places, and in fact more so at some. A party of 16 birds seen by J. Cudworth at Dewsbury Sewage-farm from 18th to 27th August 1948 was described by Chislett as being very exceptional and numbers at Teesmouth were said to be large in 1950, when 11 birds were seen there on 31st August and 12 on 7th September.

Numbers of Ruffs passing through the county have increased in recent years. Maximum numbers counted at any one place during the 1960s were usually about 20 to 30, with a large assembly of 100 at Cherry Cobb Sands on 9th September 1965 and a flock of 60 on Brough Salting on 11th September in the same year being unusual. Up to 76 birds were on Coatham Marsh during October 1969.

On 6th October 1974, 60 were on stubble at Stone Creek, with 65 there on 13th October 1974. In 1976, 108 were present on 27th September, during which period a marked influx was noted at several other places, including 28 at Hornsea Mere on 18th September, 50 at Wheldrake Ings on 28th September and 50 in fields at Easington on 2nd October. Later in the autumn of 1976, 30 were on stubble at Stone Creek on 7th November. Many were seen at inland waters during the same period, maximum counts being on 31st August when there were 17 at Fairburn Ings, 14 at Masham Gravel-pit and 12 at Wath Ings; Staveley Lagoon had 16 birds on 1st September. During mid April 1977, 30-45 birds were on flooded grassland in the Patrington–Winestead area. The Upper Humber area had 100 birds on 3rd September 1978.

In 1980, a spectacular passage occurred, with a marked influx during mid September, and birds were about in large numbers at several places. Blacktoft Sands had 15 on 29th July; 25 by 14th August, increasing thereafter to 62 by 6th September; 105 by 8th September; 205 by 12 September and 220 on 13th September, whereafter numbers declined slowly leaving 120 birds by 9th October and 30 still in the area on 19th November. Whitton Sands also attracted larger numbers than usual, with 20 on 12th August, 30 on 12th September, 110 on 14th September and 123 on 16th September. Wheldrake Ings on the Lower Derwent had 30 on 29th August, 70 on 30th August and 55 on 12th September. Tophill Low Reservoir had 21 on 9th September, 64 on 16th September and 38 on 22nd September.

There were 150 birds at Blacktoft Sands on 18th August 1981, 130 during September and 135 on 11th October.

Ruffs occur at several inland waters during these same migration periods, usually just a few birds, but occasionally up to 20 or more being seen. Maximum counts have been 18 at Stanley Sewage-farm on 25th August 1964; 36 at Stanley and 31 at Beverley Sewage-farm on 13th September 1965; 18 at Allerton Bywater on 2nd June 1971; 17 at Knostrop Sewage-farm on 1st September 1971; and 17 at Fairburn Ings on 26th August 1973. In September 1978, 28 were at Wheldrake Ings and 24 were at Newington Flash; and, on 29th-30th August 1979, 16 were at Nosterfield Gravel-pit, where there were 17 on 10th September 1980.

Numbers passing through the county vary annually and in some years very few occur. The areas adjacent to the Humber Estuary are the most favoured. A few have lingered into the summer at one locality in recent years, and in 1968 one did so on floodwater near Settle where it remained from 3rd May to mid July.

A Ruff ringed in Swedish Lapland on 2nd June 1948 was recovered at Redcar on 23rd August in the same year. A young bird ringed at Almholme, near Doncaster, on 29th August 1966 was shot in the Niger Inundation Zone of Mali on 4th March 1973, being the first Ruff to be recovered in that part of Africa.

A bird of passage in both spring and autumn, most numerously during the latter period, also occurring at many inland waters, with numbers seen varying annually, is the present status of the Ruff in Yorkshire. This differs from the summary given by Nelson, who considered it to be chiefly a coastal bird and only a rare straggler inland.

Jack Snipe
Lymnocryptes minimus

Claims for the Jack Snipe to have nested in Yorkshire in the neighbourhood of Huddersfield and occasionally near Doncaster and Halifax, as written by T. Allis in his report to the British Association at York in 1844, were, according to Nelson, referable to the Dunlin.

Nelson knew this as a winter visitor, being generally distributed in suitable places, arriving in October and departing in April. Apart from a few extensions of dates, there is nothing to add to that assessment, and it can be found anywhere in the county from the coastline to the upland tarns and bogs of the Pennines.

On 23rd October 1900, Nelson 'bagged' four out of six which rose from a small marshy tract in the Tees marshes, at the same place where 14 Common Snipe and three Jacks were killed at one shot in the autumn of 1890 as they sunned themselves on a small open grassy spot.

In recent years, the highest counts of Jack Snipe have been at Wath Ings: ten on 7th November 1971; eight on 27th October 1972 and 20 on 4th November 1972; 14 on 20th October 1974, 21 on 10th November and again on 24th November 1974; 23 on 9th March 1975 and nine on 13th April 1975. Other large counts have been 12 at Clifton Ings, near York, four of which were shot, on 20th November 1957; 23 flushed at Aughton Ings in the Lower Derwent Valley by G.R. Bennett on 16th November 1961, in which year there were more birds than usual in the county with up to four at several places and seven at Armthorpe Sewage-farm on 23rd December; eight at Hay-a-Park Gravel-pit on 19th November 1970; eight at Adwick-le-Street Sewage-farm on 6th February 1971; and eight at Hornsea Mere on 19th October 1971, with records of up to four or five birds from several other areas during October and November in that year.

Most birds have departed for their northern breeding grounds by mid April, but a few linger into May. The Annual Report of the Yorkshire Naturalists' Union for 1962 said that none was seen that year between 16th May and 31st August, the former date being late for a Jack Snipe to be still in the county. More than usual lingered late in 1978, with one at Hornsea Mere on 3rd May, one at Tophill Low Reservoir on 5th, one at Flamborough on 6th and one at Welwick on 8th.

The first to return in autumn usually appear from mid September, but there is an earlier bird in most years. The earliest on record is one at Potteric Carr on 13th August 1976 which was well seen by seven observers. Single birds at Adwick-le-Street Sewage-farm on 14th August 1965 and at Hornsea Mere on 15th August 1971 are the next. A thorough search of any suitably damp area near to water may produce more Jack Snipe than are thought likely to be present. They are reluctant to rise and flush only at the last minute, to drop in again a few yards off. On 24th December 1964, R.G. Hawley was walking through some boggy ground near Sheffield when he heard a flapping noise on the ground behind him. Inspection revealed a dying Jack Snipe fluttering in his footprint, having sat too long and been inadvertently trodden on. The bird, a female, was quite healthy and very fat.

A Jack Snipe ringed at Hornsea Mere on 14th January 1967 was shot at Keele in Stafford on 26th December 1969.

Snipe
Gallinago gallinago

The Snipe is a common bird over most of Yorkshire, from the coastlands to the high fells of the west and north. It breeds in any suitably damp habitat within this wide altitudinal range and the population is augmented by large numbers of immigrants each autumn.

The familiar 'drumming' sound of the displaying male can be heard from April onwards over the breeding grounds, which may be a lowland water meadow or a boggy peat moss high on the moorlands. A nest at Hotham Carrs in 1955 held six eggs, a very unusual number and probably the product of two females.

During September each year, birds visit Yorkshire from the Continent, and at that time the species becomes very evident, especially along the coast, when single birds or several together may be flushed. They soon move inland, and numbers often increase markedly at some reservoirs or gravel-pits at this time. Gouthwaite Reservoir has long been a favourite feeding place for Snipe, which gather on the muddy margins at the northern end, their numbers being affected by the water levels. Gatherings of up to 100 birds are commonplace in most years during the autumn, with 200 being counted on 1st September 1976.

The largest gatherings in recent years have been seen at Wath Ings, where good numbers are always present in autumn and winter, and the maximum counts have been 220 on 22nd November 1974; 200 to 300 during September and October 1976; 400 on 24th and 25th February and 300 during late September to mid November 1977; and 300 on 10th April, 200 in September, 250 on 6th October and 300 on 4th November 1979. Fairburn Ings is also good for the species and may hold upwards of 100 or more, with a high count of 300 on 7th October 1976. Swillington Ings attracted large numbers during the 1950s and 1960s, with a maximum of 300 on 18th August 1953. Low Ellers Carr had 200 on 20th February 1970; and Potteric Carr had 200 on 8th October 1961, 250 on 4th November 1961 and 300 on 2nd January 1975. Bolton-on-Swale Gravel-pits had 475 on 24th October 1976 and 162 on 11th November 1979. Hampsthwaite Sewage-farm in Nidderdale is most suitable and up to 100 birds are regularly seen there, with 200 in mid August 1970, 150 on 24th August 1976 and 185 on 12 October 1976. Many other places in the county are attractive to Snipe and may have up to 100 birds during the non-breeding season, some sites being of a temporary nature as the land-use changes.

Numbers in spring are fewer as birds disperse to their breeding grounds, and 182 at Flamborough Head on 6th March 1977 would no doubt be returning immigrants.

Some Yorkshire-bred Snipe move south and into Ireland for the winter, as evidenced by ringing recoveries. A juvenile ringed at Gouthwaite Reservoir on 3rd August 1959 was shot in County Cork, Ireland, on 2nd October 1959; another ringed at Ilkley on 31st July 1959 was shot in Westmeath, Ireland, on 1st January 1961; and one ringed near Pateley Bridge on 8th June 1977 was shot in France on 17th September 1977. Evidence of immigration from the Continent can be witnessed in most years, when birds fly directly in over the sea, and ringing recoveries also shed some light on the origins of our winter visitors. A bird ringed in southern Finland on 18th August 1970 was shot at Patrington on 3rd February 1972; one ringed in Czechoslovakia on 20th July 1971 was shot at Wansford on the Humber on 1st January 1979; and a bird ringed in West Germany on 14th August 1973 was retrapped at Knaresborough Ringing Station on 7th October 1973. In addition, two birds ringed in Yorkshire during the winter months have subsequently been recovered abroad. One ringed at Ilkley on 4th October 1959 was shot in Jutland, Denmark, on 10th October 1961, probably while on its way back to Britain for the winter; and one ringed at Marske, near Redcar, on 23rd December 1972 was shot in Norway on 19th September 1973.

A bird picked up dead in a Harrogate street in September 1979 and brought to me for inspection showed the characteristics of the Faeroe Snipe, a race which is more finely marked with narrower lines along the back and a generally paler plumage (see plate 74). Apart from the very dark-plumaged variety known as Sabine's Snipe, aberrant Snipe are rare. One at Adwick-le-Street Sewage-farm in late September 1972 had patches of white feathers in its plumage; it remained throughout the winter and was last seen on 17th March 1973.

Great Snipe
Gallinago media

More Great Snipe occurred in Nelson's time and before than are recorded now. Nelson knew this species as a 'Bird of passage, of uncommon occurrence' and said in his *The Birds of Yorkshire* 'The communicated and recorded occurrences number upwards of sixty, and are too voluminous for particularisation. It may, perhaps, suffice to say that eighteen have been shot in the North Riding, seventeen in the East Riding, and in the West Riding twenty-nine.'

Even allowing for some misidentifications, it would appear to have been met with more regularly at that time, probably owing to the fact that most were shot and their identity thus in no doubt. It seems that it appeared usually during September, but there were records of earlier ones: one shot on 11th August 1879 near Sheffield; on 23rd August 1901 at Cherry Cobb Sands; and in the last week of August 1877 and again in 1887 near Beverley. One shot on the River Hull near Beverley weighed just over 8 ounces (227 g), and its gizzard contained a few seeds and vegetable matter (*The Zoologist*, 1864, p. 8890). The average weight given by Nelson for the species was 7½-8 ounces (213-227 g), but one from near Pickering, reported in *The Field* for 5th October 1895, weighed 10½ (298 g) and a specimen in the York Museum, shot at Hayton in September 1878, was said to have weighed 14 ounces (397 g). One shot on Sowerby Moor on 27th September 1836 went to the museum of the Halifax Literary and Philosophical Society. W.H. St Quintin mentioned one being shot at Scampston on 18th September 1884 and recorded one near Helmsley on 28th September 1919.

Chislett could add only two more possible occurrences up to the publication of *Yorkshire Birds* in 1952. The first was seen on Ilton Moor by P. Young, who described the bird as large and with a flight quite different from that of the Snipe. It is impossible to accept such a record on these meagre details. The second was seen by Lord Bolton during a grouse shoot in September 1949 on the moors above Wensleydale. He saw it on two occasions and noted the large size and the silent dead-straight flight. The bird was flushed a third time, when Lord Bolton was able to get his glasses onto it and noticed a lot of white about the tail; it was again silent. This may well have been a Great Snipe, a species which, in spite of the supposed difficulties of identification, is very characteristic in appearance, being more like a small Woodcock than a large Snipe, although care should certainly be taken.

The Ornithological Reports of the Yorkshire Naturalists' Union for the years 1954 and 1955 published details of two birds which cannot be considered fully proven. The first was seen at 10 yards' (9 m) range in a gutter at Carnaby on 7th February 1954; the bird showed white outer tail feathers, had a slower and more laden flight than that of the common Snipe and did not zig-zag on take-off. The second record concerned a bird seen at Farnley Gravel-pits on 18th August 1955; the details were not really conclusive and Chislett placed the record in square brackets.

It was to be 20 years before another Great Snipe was claimed in Yorkshire, when, on 6th September 1975, D.I.M. Wallace saw a bird at Crabley Creek. Full details were submitted and the record was accepted by the County Records Committee and the Rarities Committee of *British Birds*. The same observer saw another individual at Weighton Lock on 28th August 1976 which was also well documented and accepted by the two committees.

There are now some 230 records of this rare snipe in the British Isles, 180 of which were before 1958 when the *British Birds* Rarities Committee was set up. The species breeds in northern Europe from Norway, across Russia into western Siberia, and spends the winter mainly in tropical Africa.

Long-billed Dowitcher
Limnodromus scolopaceus

Of the two closely allied American dowitchers, the Long-billed and the Short-billed, only the former has been proved to visit Yorkshire. It is often impossible to be certain of the exact species as the two are very similar and such records are published simply as dowitchers.

A Long-billed Dowitcher in full summer plumage at Hornsea Mere on 24th July 1974 was watched by R.G. Hawley and J.E.S. Walker. Detailed notes and sketches were made by Hawley and his drawings appeared in the Yorkshire Naturalists' Union Ornithological Report for that year.

On 23rd May 1976, R. Evison saw a bird in summer plumage at Staveley Lagoon which he identified as a Long-billed Dowitcher. On 30th August that year, a bird in transitional plumage was seen at John O'Gaunt's Reservoir, near Harrogate, by M.F. Brown and subsequently by many observers during its stay until 11th September (see plate 75). A bird in almost complete winter plumage appeared at Farnham Gravel-pit on 23rd October and stayed until 7th November. It was first seen by R. Evison and later by myself and A.F.G. Walker. It is possible that the same individual was involved in all three records.

A juvenile Long-billed was at Fairburn Ings from 7th to 16th October 1981 which S.C. Madge, C. Winn and many others were able to watch. One was seen at Muston, near Filey, on 2nd August 1983 by M. Francis and H.J. Whitehead.

In addition to the above four birds which were specifically identified, there have been six other records of undoubted dowitchers not seen well enough for positive identification.

The first was mentioned by Nelson in *The Birds of Yorkshire* and concerned a bird shot on Norland Moor in September 1864. The information was supplied by A. Crabtree of Halifax, who forwarded the specimen for inspection by Nelson and W. Eagle Clarke. It was an adult changing into winter dress and was formerly owned by James Cunningham, whose collection went to the Halifax Museum. The label read 'Brown Snipe. Shot on Norland Moor, September 1864. Shot and cased by James Cunningham.'

On 15th May 1965, on the mud at Patrington Haven, H.O. Bunce saw a dowitcher on which he took detailed notes. From the views obtained, he felt unable to be certain of the exact species.

On 26th and 27th August 1967, one occurred near Wigglesworth Hall, Settle, where it was watched by W.R. Hirst, J.G. Ireland and F.J. Roberts. Again the specific identity was not established, although the colour of the underparts, described as a dark rich brown, suggest that it was a Long-billed Dowitcher. For very full details of this bird see *The Naturalist*, 1968, pp. 47-8.

On the afternoon of 25th September 1974, C. Winn saw three dowitchers flying over Fairburn Ings. They circled for a brief period before leaving to the west. Inevitably, the views obtained were brief, and, although Winn was certain of his identification, the *British Birds* Rarities Committee felt unable to accept the record as proven.

A bird at Potteric Carr on 12th September 1978, seen by P. Greaves, L. Degnam and N. Whitehorn, was also not specifically identified. On 10th August 1980, at Staveley Lagoon, D.R.J. Watkins watched a dowitcher feeding in front of the hide, before it was disturbed by a passing Short-eared Owl. With the exception of the

Fairburn Ings birds, the remainder have been accepted as dowitchers.

On 9th September 1979, two birds flew south along the Humber shore at Spurn. They were first seen by D. Page and J.M. Turton as they passed Kilnsea, and later by J. Cudworth as they passed the Narrow Neck on the Spurn Peninsula. All three observers concluded independently that they were dowitchers, but the *British Birds* Rarities Committee declined to accept them, even as dowitchers. It is difficult to imagine these three very experienced observers being mistaken.

Woodcock
Scolopax rusticola

This strange, crepuscular species is more generally distributed in Yorkshire than is apparent from the number of times one comes across it during the breeding season. The 'roding' call of the male may be heard almost anywhere where damp woodland exists, and only in the extreme southeast corner of the county and on the dry Wolds areas of the East Riding is it at all scarce. A bird roding at Hornsea Mere in June 1975 was the first evidence of possible breeding there for many years.

The lowland birch woodland at places such as Skipwith Common and on the carrlands in the south around Hatfield are favourite breeding haunts, but wooded gills along the Pennines are equally popular. In 1976, 18 pairs were located around Barnsley and ten pairs in the Huddersfield area. There were eight pairs on Hatfield Moor in 1981. Eggs are usually laid in April but may be found in March; a nest containing a full clutch of four eggs was found near Roche Abbey on 27th March 1938.

Thinly distributed certainly, but widespread over much of the county as a breeding species, the ranks are swollen each autumn by immigrants from abroad which arrive in numbers varying with the year. Ringing recoveries have shown that the majority of our native Woodcocks are mainly sedentary, but two are known to have left the county for the winter: one ringed as a chick on 27th March 1913 was recovered in France on 16th November 1913, and another ringed as a chick at Ilkley on 24th May 1958 was shot at Finistère in France on 18th December 1958. Several birds ringed abroad, either on their breeding grounds or while on passage in autumn, have been recovered in Yorkshire. A bird ringed on Heligoland Island on 28th March 1944, probably on its way back to Europe for the summer, was recovered at Egton Bridge on 31st October 1944; one ringed at Spurn, as a newly arrived migrant, on 16th October 1960 was found dead in Sweden on 25th July 1961; an adult ringed in Finland on 19th May 1961 was shot at West Ardsley on 1st February 1962; an adult ringed in Denmark on 18th October 1960, presumably while on passage, was shot near Huddersfield on 3rd December 1960; a chick ringed in Sweden on 29th May 1966 was shot near Richmond on 27th December 1968; and a chick ringed in Finland on 2nd June 1974 was shot near Guisborough on 4th January 1975. There are two records from Ireland of birds ringed on the east coast of Yorkshire and one of a bird ringed in Ireland and recovered at Filey, indicating that some immigrants continue their journey across the Irish Sea. A bird ringed as a chick in Lancashire in June 1934 was at Bridlington on 5th December 1935, proving that not all east coast Woodcocks are of Continental origin. There is thus ample evidence that birds from Scandinavia and western Europe pass through Yorkshire, or stay for the winter, and there is also visual proof every autumn, usually during the period October to December, when birds may be flushed along the coast, often in unlikely situations — they have been seen in small gardens or even in the streets of coastal towns.

Nelson said that 'on dark and foggy nights, they strike the lanterns of our sea beacons, many being thus immolated at Spurn and Flamborough'. He also stated that, on arriving at Flamborough, 'they frequently drop at the foot of the cliffs, being sometimes found amongst the boulders on the shore or seeking shelter in the small ravines running up from the beach'. The coastal gunners were ever watchful for arrivals of Woodcock, when they would go out 'to take advantage of the opportunity to make a good bag'. The birds were said to be in good condition on arrival 'for of their estimable qualities [Nelson] had personal experience'.

Small numbers may be flushed anywhere along the coastline during the migration seasons, usually singly, but occasionally in larger numbers. The main influx in 1978/79 did not take place until 1st January 1979, when 46 appeared at Flamborough. R.G. Hawley counted 100 in the woods around Hornsea Mere during the period 3rd to 6th January, on which latter date 96 were at Flamborough. A total of 50 birds was shot at Winestead on 13th/14th January and 50 were still at Flamborough on 14th. The most spectacular arrival in recent years happened in 1981, when there were three distinct waves of immigration. On 24th October, 17 were at Flamborough and six at Spurn; 20 were at Flamborough and four at Spurn on 7th November, with 12 at the former locality on 15th November. A second arrival took place during the period 18th-19th December, when W.F. Curtis flushed up to 150 birds along the hedgerows south and west of Atwick and 46 were at Flamborough, 40 at Filey and 100 at Hornsea Mere on 19th. A third arrival occurred on 26th December, when 30 birds were at Filey and up to 80 at Atwick during the last few days of the year. On 12th December, during a spell of cold weather, 47 were shot at Buttercrambe.

The arrival of Woodcocks along our shore in the autumn often coincides with the arrival of Goldcrests, and the latter have acquired the name of 'Woodcock Pilot'. It is not impossible that a tired Goldcrest could 'hitch' or at least temporarily land on the back of a migrating Woodcock flying low and steadily over the sea, and such an incident witnessed in the early days doubtless gave rise to this supposed association.

A few Woodcocks with aberrant plumage have been recorded in Yorkshire. One shot in 1766 near York had all the large feathers perfectly white; one in the collection of W. Talbot of Wakefield was a uniform rufous or light brown shade; an all-white specimen was killed at Strensall Common in October 1975; an almost white bird with faint yellow markings was reported from Ormesby-in-Cleveland in the first week of November 1904; and one flushed near Helmsley on 16th November 1954 had wings of a light yellow colour.

Nelson's 1907 assessment of its status in Yorkshire needs no amendment today: 'Resident, in limited numbers. Best known as a winter immigrant, arriving in October and November, sometimes in large flights. Appears on the coast in March and April preparatory to returning to its northern haunts.'

Black-tailed Godwit
Limosa limosa

The Black-tailed Godwit was formerly a resident in Yorkshire and certainly nested on Hatfield Moor, where Hugh Reid of Doncaster once found young birds. Nelson said that it doubtless bred in the carrs of the East Riding, but cited no evidence. It ceased to breed shortly after the middle of the nineteenth century, its demise being no doubt accelerated by human pressure and intensive agriculture.

Over 100 years elapsed before the species nested in Yorkshire again, but in 1952 Chislett said that, following successful attempts to nest in Britain in places as far separated as Lincolnshire and Caithness, he thought it quite possible that the species might breed in Yorkshire again. This it possibly did in 1974 and 1975, when a pair was present at one site and two pairs attempted to breed at a second site in 1975. A pair was present at one locality from April 1976 and young were seen. In 1977, two pairs were rumoured to be present at one site, and another pair attempted to nest at a second site where two pairs were seen in 1978.

When he wrote *The Birds of Yorkshire* in 1907, Nelson considered this to be a rare bird and said that it had occurred more frequently at Spurn than elsewhere, mainly in August and September, singly or in small parties. He mentioned one being killed there as late as 9th December 1875 and listed six places where the species had been seen inland.

During the 1940s and 1950s, there were relatively few records and most of these came from Spurn and along the Humber Estuary, with six at Spurn on 26th August 1950 as the maximum count during the period. Inland records came from a few localities, usually of single birds but six were seen at Swillington Ings on 13th July 1947 by K. Dawson. An exceptional party of 46 birds was at Marishes in the Vale of Pickering on 26th April 1947, being seen by R.M. Garnett, and 27 were seen by J.P. Utley as they flew south over Osmotherly from the direction of Teesmouth on 14th September 1948.

There have been more records during the past 30 years, but appearances are very sporadic and in some years very few are seen. Occasionally a large party may appear in isolation at some inland water, but more usually single birds or small parties are scattered about the county during the spring and autumn migration periods as the birds drop in at the Pennine waters on their cross-country journeys.

On 18th June 1961, nine birds flew in from the west at Fairburn Ings and continued southeast, and on 7th August in the same year 35 birds left Teesmouth and flew past South Gare. B. Shorrock saw 65 birds in summer plumage at Settle on 26th April 1965. C. Winn and F.A. Wardman saw 57 arrive at Fairburn Ings from the east on 20th April 1974 (see also Bar-tailed Godwit); after two hours, 17 of these departed, leaving the remainder to rest and feed until 16.30 hours when another 35 left, the remaining five birds staying until 17.10 hours. Four were at Wath Ings on the same day. At Blacktoft Sands 31 flew west on 25th April 1977, and small numbers are seen doing so at that locality almost annually now. Nine were at Staveley Lagoon on 18th August 1980; 16 were at North Duffield Carrs on 16th April 1981, with 11 on 20th and six until early May; and small numbers spend the winter in the Humber Estuary, with 21 at Cherry Cobb Sands on 22nd October 1961.

There is now as much chance of seeing a Black-tailed Godwit on migration at an inland water as along the coast, except perhaps for the small wintering flock in the Humber Estuary. Few birds occur at Teesmouth, but one or two are now being seen in winter there.

The Black-tailed Godwit's status is now that of a bird of passage in small numbers during the spring and autumn, large parties sometimes being seen during the former period; it occurs at inland waters as well as along the coast, especially in the estuaries of the Tees and Humber where a few birds spend the winter. One or two pairs have nested in the county in recent years.

Hudsonian Godwit
Limosa haemastica

On 10th September 1981, A. Grieve entered one of the hides at Blacktoft Sands to check the waders present on the lagoons and noted a party of six sleeping godwits which included five Black-tailed and a smaller individual which at first was thought to be a Bar-tailed. They eventually took off and the smaller bird showed a wingbar similar to its companions and appeared to be a small Black-tailed. Further views, and reference to the literature, enabled its correct identity as a North American Hudsonian Godwit to be established.

It remained in the area until at least 3rd October and during its stay was seen by very many people, including K. Atkin, S.C. Madge and J.E. Dale. Very full and detailed notes were taken by the finder and the bird was accepted as the first for the British Isles.

On 26th April 1983, what was almost certainly the same bird re-appeared in full summer plumage at Blacktoft Sands, where it remained until 6th May.

The Hudsonian Godwit has a very limited breeding range in North America, but undertakes a long offshore migration each autumn to its wintering grounds in South America and it is likely that some have gone unrecorded in the past.

Bar-tailed Godwit
Limosa lapponica

The earliest reference to this species as a Yorkshire bird was made by Pennant, who referred to the 'Red Godwit' in 1766 in his *British Zoology*, in which he said that it had been shot near Hull.

As with several other species of shorebirds, the impression given by Nelson was one of much greater abundance than at the present time, but it is difficult to be certain of the comparative status, as the descriptive writings of the early days are perhaps prone to exaggeration and misinterpretation of the facts. More abundant in some years than others, 'immense' assemblies were met with in the Humber and Tees Estuaries and, 'being unsuspicious of danger and easily "called", their ranks are speedily decimated by the shore shooters', wrote Nelson in 1907. On 7th September 1895, one of the largest arrivals that Nelson had witnessed occurred at Redcar, when fully 400 birds alighted on the sands. They were soon driven off by boys throwing stones at them and fled towards Teesmouth, where they allowed a gunner to walk within easy shot, and did not take flight until he had fired three shots at them.

In more recent times, there have been other large gatherings which could be termed 'immense'. A. Baldridge reported a flock of 400 at Teesmouth on 15th August 1948 when the autumn passage was at its peak. The exact situation in the Tees Estuary during the last ten years or so has been clouded by the practice of giving figures for the whole estuary, including both the north and south shores, but Bran Sands is a favourite feeding and roosting place and, on 4th January 1970, P.J. Stead and E.C. Gatenby counted 142 birds there. On 18th January 1970, no fewer than 727 were counted at this locality, 715 of which were in one flock; this was the largest number ever seen on the Yorkshire side of the Tees Estuary and it remains so today. S.C. Norman counted 246 on 15th September 1970; 260 were present in January 1978; and the area holds a high proportion of the estuary total in most years.

The Humber Estuary, especially the mud at Kilnsea Clays and Cherry Cobb, attracts large numbers. The Birds of Estuaries Enquiry, organised by the British Trust for Ornithology since 1970, has shown some high totals. Counts during the winter months from December to February have regularly ranged from 100 to 300 birds, with larger counts of 1,000 on 16th January 1977; 750 in February 1977, 550 of which were at Cherry Cobb; 503 on 15th January 1978, 400 of which were at Cherry Cobb; 407 on 27th January 1981; and 908 on 24th February 1981, 750 of which were also at Cherry Cobb.

Birds start arriving at the estuaries in July and numbers build up during the ensuing weeks. Coastal passage is witnessed every autumn at Spurn, where 900 birds were counted passing south on 21st December 1976 and 56 came in over the sea on 5th July 1977. On 1st May 1972, 118 flew south off Hornsea, another 65 did so on 31st August and 54 more on 17th August; in 1977, 43 flew south on 4th August. Birds were seen flying south in 1978, when 70 passed Filey on 30th August and 80 passed Flamborough on 31st. On 22nd August 1981, 100 birds were seen flying in over the sea at Filey.

Thus, anywhere in the estuaries of the Tees and Humber, Bar-tailed Godwits may be seen, mainly from August through to April in varying numbers. Southerly passage along the coastline occurs every year.

The species appears at many inland waters, mainly during the spring and autumn migration periods although it has been seen from February to November in several years. Single birds are mostly involved, but small parties may be seen, with occasionally larger numbers when strong passage is in progress. The largest inland flocks have been 13 at Fairburn Ings on 28th August 1967, with 22 there on 11th November 1967, on which date eight were at Settle and 23 flew west at Blacktoft Sands; 19 flew east at Wath Ings on 10th September 1972. Many birds occurred on 20th April 1974, when 63 were at Fairburn Ings at 06.50 hours, followed by another 62 at 06.57 hours, then a single bird; a passing train caused 117 to leave shortly afterwards, the remaining nine staying until midday (see also Black-tailed Godwit). On the same day, ten were at Wath Ings, seven at Blackmoorfoot Reservoir, four at Swillington Ings and one to three at four other waters.

Birds are seen passing westwards over Blacktoft Sands in most years from late June until October, as migrants arrive and move across country to the west coast. Maximum daily counts have been 51 on 5th July 1977; 24 on 17th July and 22 on 24th July 1978; 213 flew west on 23 dates between 17th July and 4th September 1979; 43 on 27th July and 27 on 15th August 1980; 24 on 14th July, 39 on 29th August and 28 on 1st September 1981.

The recovery of two ringed birds gives an indication of the origin and destination of some Bar-tailed Godwits passing through Yorkshire in autumn. One ringed at Cherry Cobb Sands on 20th April 1964 was shot at Krasnoyarsk in the USSR on 8th June 1973, being only the third recovery from that region; and one caught and ringed at South Gare on 13th October 1982 was found dead near Largoub in the western Sahara on 18th October 1982, having travelled an average of 730 km (456 miles) a day. This area, lying south of the western Sahara, is known to be an important wintering area for the species.

The Bar-tailed Godwit is thus a passage migrant and a winter visitor to Yorkshire in varying numbers each year, often occurring at inland waters in small numbers with occasionally larger flocks at times of peak passage.

Whimbrel
Numenius phaeopus

Yorkshire can lay claim to the first British description of a Whimbrel, when Ralph Johnson of Brignall, near Greta Bridge, gave details in a communication to Francis Willughby, who published them in his *Ornithology* in 1678, p. 294, as follows:

'The Whimbrel *Arquata minor*. Mr Johnson, in his papers communicated to us, described this Bird by the name of a Whimbrel, thus: It is less by half than a Curlew, hath a crooked bill, but shorter by an inch or more; The Crown deep brown without speckles. The Back under the Wings white, which the Curlew hath not. Besides the colour of the whole body is more duskish or dull. It is found upon the sands in the Teesmouth.'

They were once shot for the table along with other species of shorebirds, and in 1528 the price of 32 Curlew Knaves (an old name) was £1.12s. By 1560, the price had dropped to 4d each.

Thomas Allis said that Strickland had never met with it in this county, which Nelson said was 'passing strange' as he (Strickland) resided at Bridlington, where the Whimbrel's rippling notes were a familiar sound to ornithologists.

Its regular appearance during the month of May has earned it the name of 'Maybird' and Nelson knew of its appearance in that month 'with unfailing regularity', saying that few ever occurred in late April. We now know it to pass through the county regularly from mid April every year, with a few earlier records (see below), but never so numerously as during the autumn passage, which starts in July and continues through to September with a few still moving during October. There are records of later ones: two were at Cherry Cobb Sands on 20th November 1961; two were seen by G.R. Bennett at Hornsea on 10th December 1961; and one was at Flamborough on 29th November 1978.

Small numbers may be heard calling overhead along the coast from the Tees to the Humber on many days during these periods and larger numbers may pass on some days in the autumn. Maximum counts in recent years, which are typical of the situation annually, have been as follows: at Spurn, 130 on 30th July 1965; 133 on 4th August 1966; 110 flying south there on 26th July 1970, with 56 on 8th August and 54 on 16th August; 44 coming in over the sea on 25th July 1974 and 95 flying south on 27th July, on which date 52 were seen at Filey. The following were all flying south: 61 at Spurn on 23rd July 1977; 59 at Bempton on 3rd August 1977; 57 in one flock at Grimston on 27th August 1978; 55 in one flock at Mappleton on 26th July 1979; and 88 in one flock at Grimston on 18th August 1979.

There have been a few very early spring records, a bird at Spurn on 2nd February 1947 being most unusual. Three were at Whitton Sands on 20th March 1949; one flew west at Blacktoft Sands on 26th March 1977; one was at Cherry Cobb Sands on 15th March 1981; and one flew over York on 29th March 1981.

Occurrences at inland waters are numerous and often reflect the peak coastal passage. In some years, birds may occur at many waters, often those along the Pennines, usually singly or in small parties of under ten birds; in other years there are fewer. Some large parties have been seen, the largest being as follows: 16 at Eccup Reservoir on 28th August 1962; 20 at Almholme on 26th April 1964, the largest inland spring flock recorded in the county; 23 at Auckley Common on 2nd

July 1964; 23 at Fairburn Ings on 21st August 1966; 12 flying west at Eccup Reservoir on 26th July 1977; 19 at Blackmoorfoot Reservoir on 22nd August 1977 and 19 again on 26th; 21 at Elsecar on 15th August 1979; and 15 over Markington on 4th September 1979. Birds are seen flying west over Blacktoft Sands in the Upper Humber during most autumns, and a few do so in spring.

Nelson recorded that a few Whimbrels stayed on the Humber foreshore during the summers of 1833 and 1896 and that odd birds occasionally did so at Teesmouth. These could have referred to birds on late spring passage in June and early autumn passage in July, and it would be very difficult to prove actual summering.

An aberrant leucistic Whimbrel was at Spurn on 1st May 1979. It was all white except for a buff wash on the mantle and wing-coverts. D.G. Hobson and others recorded a pale bird at Flamborough from 11th to 16th October 1980.

A bird seen at the high-tide roost at Whitton Sands on 17th September 1978 showed a uniform dark rump and lower back, characters usually associated with the Nearctic race *Numenius phaeopus hudsonicus*, which has been recognised once on Fair Isle. Another was seen flying south at close range at Flamborough Head on 12th September 1982, and P.A. Lassey and D.I.M. Wallace consider that these birds are just as likely to have originated in the east and were probably examples of the Siberian race *Numenius phaeopus variegatus*, which has not yet been recorded from the British Isles.

Curlew
Numenius arquata

There is no doubt that the Curlew is now more widespread as a breeding bird in Yorkshire than in Nelson's time. The moorlands of the West and North Ridings were the strongholds at the beginning of the century, with mention of breeding in meadows adjacent to the high ground west of Harrogate, and occasionally, according to Chislett in *Yorkshire Birds* (1952), a few pairs still called in the summer about the rough pastures of the Hatfield/Thorne area, and near to Skipwith, Allerthorpe and Strensall Commons. Chislett went on to say that nests in fields quite a distance from the moors were quite normal in too many districts to enumerate. They are now more widespread than ever, and birds can be found in the breeding season on any lowland pasture, or even among cereal crops, along the lower reaches of the Pennine rivers and out on the plains in the centre of the county. Only in the southeast corner, east of a line drawn from Filey, through Great Driffield to South Cave, is it absent as a breeding species. Within the remainder of Yorkshire, the familiar call can be heard anywhere from March onwards. In 1960, Chislett told me that he considered the trend of breeding in lowland areas probably not a new development, but simply a return to former status, the species having once been forced off the lowlands by drainage and intensive farming.

On the eastern edge of its Yorkshire breeding range in the East Riding, nesting was suspected near Millington on the chalk Wolds from 1957 and proof came in 1960, when two nests were found. Birds attempted to nest just below the chalk at Nunburnholme in 1956 and 1957, and successfully in 1958. Several pairs nested just off the chalk near North Grimston from 1955 and these records showed an interesting spread onto the Wolds uphill country, where nesting had never been recorded before. Breeding birds have colonised lowland sites south of Huddersfield since 1978, and more birds are now breeding in the York area, and in the Vale of Pickering.

K. Williamson, writing in *Field Studies*, 2: pp. 651-68, said that the calcareous mires and limestone lings of the West Yorkshire Pennines had a density of 14 to 18 pairs per square kilometre. In 1961, the Doncaster and District Ornithological Society conducted a survey of breeding Curlews within a 10-mile (16-km) radius of Doncaster. They concluded that about 32 pairs were present in 20 localities in the eastern half of the circle, where the land is low-lying and mainly arable and rough grazing interspersed with moor and marsh and subject to occasional flooding. The western part of the area, consisting of higher ground rising to 400 feet (122 m) above sea-level, did not appear suitable for breeding Curlews. See *The Naturalist*, 1962, pp. 130-2, for details summarised by R.J. Rhodes.

Some breeding Curlews return to the moors during February in most years, the majority arriving during March, when flocks of birds are common at waters along the length and breadth of the county. Such flocks may number upwards of 100 birds, but more usually below 50. Often they assemble at such places at dusk to feed before moving on. Bolton-on-Swale Gravel-pit had 206 present on 27th February 1977, with 200 on 10th February 1980, and 500 were at Ellerton-on-Swale on 10th February 1981. On 9th February 1978, 90 birds were probing in snow-covered fields at Leyburn.

Some birds spend the winter at inland waters, and have done so at Gouthwaite Reservoir since at least 1950. The flock has varied from 50 to 100 birds over the years, with high counts of 200 on 27th November 1960; 148 on 14th October, 255 on 5th November and 295 on 26th November 1961, but only ten were present on 31st December during a freeze-up; with 120 on 2nd November and 113 on 16th December 1970. Numbers in recent years have been fewer and usually below 50.

The Humber Estuary is the winter stronghold for Curlews and the Birds of Estuaries Enquiry, organised by the British Trust for Ornithology since 1970, has shown that the favourite places in this region are Stone Creek and Cherry Cobb Sands. At the latter locality, there were 5,000 on 28th August 1969; 2,000 on 10th August 1979; and 1,600 on 24th February 1980, when the total count for the estuary was 2,069. Stone Creek had 1,300 on 14th February 1981.

Numbers wintering on the Tees are much smaller, and 200 to 400 for the whole estuary has been usual in recent years.

Recoveries of ringed birds reveal that some Yorkshire-bred Curlews spend the winter in Ireland: 13 birds ringed as chicks in June have been recovered across the Irish Sea between 29th August and 4th April. Four others, also ringed as chicks, have been recovered in France (three) and Portugal (one). Three birds ringed in Sweden and two in Finland during the summer have been recovered in Yorkshire while on passage, or spending the winter here, in the months of April, May, September, October and November.

A leucistic bird was seen by M.G.H. Garnett in Upper Nidderdale on 13th May 1978 and another was seen at Bishop Monkton on 16th March 1980.

Along with other shorebirds, the Curlew, inevitably, featured among the items of food at the ancient banquets. 'Curlewes 100' were provided for the Nevell banquet at Cawood in 1466, and in the early sixteenth century the price of 20 Curlews was £1.6.8d.

To summarise, Curlews are one of the familiar sights in Yorkshire during the breeding season, anywhere from the lowland pastures to the high moorlands. They are common during the late summer and autumn when dispersing, and undergoing their migrations, and during the winter months, when they can be seen feeding along the coast and estuaries. Some birds also spend the winter at the larger inland waters.

The species is synonymous with the dark satanic moorlands of Yorkshire and 'The North' and no film set in that part of the country has ever been made without including the birds' familiar bubbling call, whether it be in summer or in the depths of winter!

Upland Sandpiper
Bartramia longicauda

On 6th August 1973, G.D. Moore watched a bird at Bolton-on-Swale Gravel-pit which he described in detail and identified as this species.

The Upland Sandpiper breeds in North America and winters in southern South America, and there are now some 38 records in the British Isles. This was the first and only recorded occurrence of the species in Yorkshire.

Spotted Redshank
Tringa erythropus

The Spotted Redshank was thought to be a rare bird of passage in Nelson's time and he recorded only 12 occurrences, including a flock of 12 at Sunk Island in November 1891, five of which were 'procured'. The other records referred mainly to birds at Teesmouth and the Humber, with one killed at Hornby, near Catterick, in August 1864 and one shot by Snowden Slights at East Cottingwith in August 1896.

Nelson inspected a specimen killed on the beach at Redcar in September 1896 by a fisherman, who was intending to dispose of it as a common Redshank. The last dated records he mentions were both in 1902: at Seamer, near Stokesley, on 27th August and at Teesmouth in September.

No more were reported until 1938, when Chislett saw two birds at Spurn on 22nd September. From that time, it was recorded much more frequently and the coverage of inland waters in more recent years has shown it to be a fairly regular passage migrant in small numbers over much of the county during both seasons, but mainly in autumn.

Birds occurring at the Pennine reservoirs and elsewhere inland during the autumn will no doubt be on their journey across the county to the west coast then southward, to winter in the Mediterranean and Africa.

During the 1950s, maximum counts at inland waters were of five at Fairburn Ings from 28th to 30th August 1953 and four at Swillington Ings on 4th September 1955. More were recorded during the 1960s and subsequently, and from one to five birds were regularly seen at inland waters. A good passage occurred from mid August to mid September in 1962, when there were up to six at Scaling Dam; eight at Bottomboat on 1st September; four at Wintersett Reservoir on 8th September; and six at Chelker Reservoir and at Patrington Haven during the period. A flock of 17, seen by A. Credland at the latter locality on 23rd September, was described by Chislett as 'remarkable'. It was the largest flock recorded in Yorkshire at that time.

In 1968, Wath Ings had six birds on 14th September, ten on 15th September and nine on 21st and 22nd September, with seven there from 27th September to 5th October 1969.

During the 1970s, up to five birds were seen both in spring and in autumn, mainly during the latter period, at inland waters too numerous to mention. Maxima were 13 at Worsborough Reservoir on 31st August 1974; and 19 flying northeast at Wath Ings on 2nd September 1974, with 23 there on 8th September 1974. Twelve were at Blacktoft Sands on 27th August 1981, and 15 flew west at Whitton Sands on 15th November 1981.

One was at Spurn on 31st December 1955 and a few birds have wintered in the Upper Humber Estuary since about 1960. Five were present on 11th January 1962, but usually only one to three birds are seen.

There have been records in every month of the year, some spring passage birds lingering until June and some autumn ones arriving during July. A few individuals have stayed for periods of up to two weeks at inland waters.

Redshank

Tringa totanus

Nelson said that the Redshank had prospered in Yorkshire during the few years prior to 1907 when he published *The Birds of Yorkshire*, having established itself in 'places where hitherto its querulous call note was almost unknown', and small breeding colonies could be found in suitably marshy areas from Thorne Waste to the fells of Upper Teesdale.

In 1952, Chislett said that it was generally, but sparsely distributed in spring about marshy areas throughout Yorkshire at almost all altitudes up to well over 1,000 feet (305 m). It would be wrong to repeat that general statement, as there are areas of the county where it is not a regular or numerous breeding bird, particularly in the eastern half and in some parts of the extreme south. Much of the Vale of Pickering is without Redshanks during the summer, mainly as a result of increased drainage and intensified agriculture, and so too are the eastern parts of the chalk Wolds. Along the Pennines and their foothills it is most numerous. In 1979, about 20 pairs nested in the Sheffield area, reflecting a recent increase. The Lower Derwent Valley is an established nesting area and 20 pairs bred there in 1980. Land drainage in many places has robbed the species of much suitable breeding habitat, notably wet tussock pasture which it favours, but new gravel-pits have often provided alternative sites around their margins.

As a passage migrant and winter visitor, the Redshank is well known along the coastline, where it is one of the most obvious shorebirds from the Tees to the Humber and in the estuaries of these two great rivers. During the non-breeding season flocks of up to 100 birds, and sometimes more, may be seen anywhere along the rockier parts of the coast, and small numbers feed regularly in the harbours of Bridlington, Scarborough and Whitby. The Humber Estuary, however, holds the largest numbers and the Birds of Estuaries Enquiry has shown some large concentrations. A count along the whole shoreline from Spurn to Goole on 9th April 1972 revealed a total of 3,300 birds. In 1977, the total count was 5,150, 5,000 of which were between Patrington Haven and Easington, and smaller numbers are present each year. Cherry Cobb Sands is a favourite locality and 1,000 were there in mid August 1958 and 1,850 in mid March 1977. A good percentage of the total estuary population is usually in this area. Patrington Haven is also very popular and there were counts of 900 on 29th July 1951, 1,100 on 1st September 1957 and 2,100 on 26th August 1961. The highest estuary count in 1979 was 2,440 on 7th January, 2,000 of which were at Patrington Haven. Cornelian Bay, south of Scarborough, now attracts Redshanks and there have been maximum counts of 432 on 24th February 1975, 300 on 1st September 1973, and an unprecedented count for the Scarborough area of 4,392 on 9th November 1973.

The Redshank figures prominently as a visitor to inland waters during the spring and autumn migration periods. On 20th April 1974 32 birds flew northeast over Wintersett Reservoir, and small numbers occur at many other waters during these passage periods. Parties of up to ten birds are usual. In recent years, some birds have tended to winter at inland waters, the most notable place being near Settle, where they have wintered since the 1960s: maximum counts have been 25 on 3rd December 1970; 57 on 24th January and 80 on 13th February 1974; 60 during January and February 1975 and 1976; and 50 on 2nd January 1980. In recent years smaller numbers, sometimes just one or two birds, have wintered at up to ten waters, including Gouthwaite Reservoir, Bolton-on-Swale Gravel-pit, the Washburn Valley reservoirs, Fairburn Ings and Almholme.

The Redshank breeds from the British Isles and eastwards from Scandinavia to western Siberia, and also in Iceland and in the Faeroe Islands. Birds from these latter regions are known to visit us every year and, when caught for ringing, their larger measurements indicate the areas of origin. Some Yorkshire-ringed Redshanks

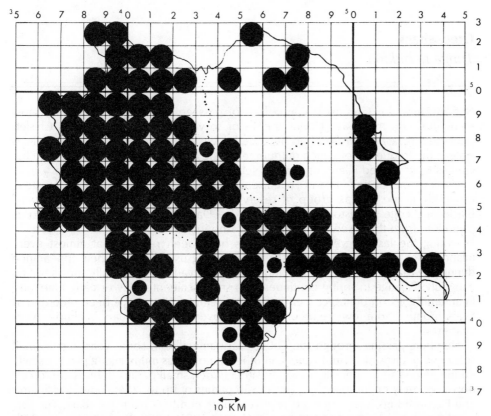

Redshank. Breeds most numerously on the higher ground of the northwestern part of the county, but also in low-lying pasture in the east and along the Humber Estuary. Scarce or absent on the chalk Wolds, over much of the North York Moors, and the intensively cultivated Vales of York, Pickering and Mowbray.

have been recovered abroad and in other parts of the British Isles. Five birds ringed as chicks during May and June have been recovered in France (four) and the Netherlands (one); one in France was recovered in July, only two months after being ringed, and the one recovered in the Netherlands was in its seventh year.

On 29th December 1973, L.S. Higgins and a friend were walking along the coast to the Easington Lagoons area near Spurn when they noticed two Carrion Crows flying low. One crow suddenly veered upwards and engaged a smaller bird which appeared to be a wader. The wader was apparently attacking the crow, which finally turned in mid-air and caught the smaller bird with its feet. It then landed with its prey and, when flushed by the observers, left behind a dead Redshank which had already been plucked along the back and had a head and breast wound (*The Naturalist*, 1974, p. 70).

During December 1975 and January 1976, H.M. Frost saw a Redshank regularly attending a flock of feeding Redwings on the playing fields of Thorngumbald County Primary School. It would frequently chase a Redwing to make it drop newly found food, presumably earthworms, which were then retrieved (*The Naturalist*, 1976, p. 148).

The Redshank, known also as the Pool Snipe in the seventeenth century, was mentioned in connection with Yorkshire in 1512, when it featured in the 'Northumberland Household Book' at Earl Percy's Yorkshire Castles, where it was listed among the birds to be bought for 'my Lordes owne mees' at 1½d each.

Greenshank
Tringa nebularia

Nelson knew the Greenshank as a bird of passage in spring and autumn, most numerously on the coast. During the 15 or so years prior to 1952 when Chislett published *Yorkshire Birds*, it had become known as a very regular visitor to inland waters, the frequency of which outnumbered the occurrences along the coast. That Greenshanks passed inland unseen in Nelson's time there can be no doubt.

Chislett mentioned inland occurrences almost annually at many waters, especially at the Halifax group of reservoirs — Whiteholme, Fly Flatts, Withens, Blackstone Edge, Ringstone Edge, Cold Edge Dam, Gorple and Ogden. Records came also from the reservoirs along the Washburn Valley.

During the last 30 years, Greenshanks have been recorded at almost every inland water in Yorkshire. The first birds in spring usually make their appearance during late March and early April, and the autumn vanguard normally shows during early July. Passage in spring continues on a small scale into May or early June, and in autumn goes on until October or early November. Birds have been recorded in every month, and a few are recorded from November to February in almost every year now.

Numbers passing through the county vary annually, in some years just a small scattering of birds at several waters, in others an obvious influx taking place, usually during August and especially in wet weather, when small parties of birds are forced down and may occur at many places, with parties of up to 20 at some. Swillington and Fairburn Ings have attracted relatively large numbers over the years. The former locality had 13 in one party on 27th August 1955, 14 on 31st, 14 again on 27th August 1961 and 19 on 12th September 1963. Fairburn Ings had 13 on 21st August 1965 and 15 on 12th August 1981, in which year there were good numbers passing through the county. Mickletown Flash had 15 on 20th August 1958, and other maxima have been ten at Settle on 17th August 1965; 15 at Almholme in mid August 1966; 20 at Newington Flash from 2nd to 9th September 1975; 24 at Blacktoft Sands on 15th August 1980; 14 at Pugneys Gravel-pit on 26th August 1980; and 20 at Wheldrake Ings on 30th August 1980.

The Humber Estuary has held gatherings of up to 20 birds fairly regularly over the years, the most ever recorded in one area being 40 at Cherry Cobb Sands on 2nd September 1969. Three flocks totalling 30 birds (22, four and four) flew north at Spurn on 21st August 1970. Numbers in the Tees Estuary have been fewer, with South Gare and Coatham Marsh being the favoured places.

Nelson said that there were exceptional instances of birds remaining during the winter, but Chislett knew of none during his period of review. During most recent years, a few birds have been seen in the winter months in the Humber Estuary and at a few inland waters.

A bird ringed at Redcar on 4th October 1981 was shot at Minho, Portugal, on 8th November 1981. The Greenshank breeds from Scotland eastwards across northern Europe and Asia to the Pacific, birds from the west of the range wintering as far south as South Africa and those from the east moving as far south as Australia. Most of the Yorkshire birds will originate in Scandinavia and beyond, but will doubtless include some Scottish breeders.

Lesser Yellowlegs
Tringa flavipes

On 27th May 1973, R.H. Appleby took his wife and son to Seamer Gravel-pits, near Scarborough, to show them a Little Egret which he had watched earlier the same day. To his surprise it had now been joined by a medium-sized, slim and lanky wader which he was able to identify as a Lesser Yellowlegs, the first record for the county. It was also seen later the same evening by B. Cockerill and F.J. Thompson and again by Appleby on 5th June, when it re-appeared, having been absent during the intervening period. Full details were published in the Yorkshire Naturalists' Union Ornithological Report for 1973, p. 6.

On 16th September 1978, P.A. Lassey, Miss Irene Smith and D.I.M. Wallace watched another at Flamborough Head; it was still present the next day.

The third county record occurred at Broomhill Flash, where P. Brady, J.M. Cattle, G.J. Speight and others saw one on 20th and 21st September 1982.

The Lesser Yellowlegs breeds across North America and spends the winter in the southern United States and into South America.

Green Sandpiper
Tringa ochropus

The Green Sandpiper visits Yorkshire in fair numbers while on passage, during the late summer and autumn, and a few birds remain in the county during the winter months. The return passage in spring is less obvious.

Green Sandpipers breed across northern Europe into eastern Siberia as far north as the Arctic Circle, and the majority spend the winter in the Mediterranean region and southwards to tropical Africa, India and southeast Asia.

The secluded edges of large waters and deep ditches or river banks are favourite feeding places for Green Sandpipers and birds are rarely seen far from cover. In most years there is a scattering of records over much of the county, mainly in the western half, where sheets of water in the form of moorland reservoirs, gravel-pits and flashes are numerous. Numbers vary with the season, and in some years more birds than usual are obvious as small parties are seen and single birds flushed from many places.

There have been some relatively large concentrations in recent years and some localities have emerged as favourite places. Swillington Ings, Wath Ings and Thorne Moor are three such, where the county's largest gatherings have been noted. When Swillington Ings was at its best during the 1950s and 1960s, Green Sandpipers were regularly seen there with a maximum count of 30 on 17th August 1952. Wath Ings had seven birds on 7th August 1966; 11 on 20th August 1972, with 14 on 25th September 1972; 15 on 26th August 1980; and 21 on 24th August 1981. Regular watching at Thorne Moor has revealed the presence of good numbers in most years, and since 1970 there have been counts of between ten and 25 birds. In 1971, for instance, there were eight on 27th June, 15 on 28th July, 19 on 1st August, 22 on 8th August and nine on 10th September. Other large numbers have been 20 along the River Hertford near Staxton on 22nd August 1954; seven at Flamborough on 29th June 1963; ten at Muston, near Filey, on 22nd August 1966; seven at Hampsthwaite on 17th August 1970, in which year eight were at Spurn on 3rd August and six at Stanley Sewage-farm on 13th September; 12 at Sandsfield Gravel-pit during early August 1975; 14 at Tophill Low Reservoir on 2nd August 1980; and 13 at Flamborough on 3rd August, 11 at Blacktoft Sands from 13th to 18th August and 19 at Knostrop Sewage-farm on 9th August 1981.

The few birds that spend the winter months in the county may be seen at several waters in most years, sometimes for only brief periods as they move about the area.

The main periods of passage are during April-May and August-September, but some birds arrive as early as late June and some linger into November before moving south. Some early spring birds may have wintered in Yorkshire, and it is often difficult to judge the exact status of birds at the limits of their main migration periods.

Chislett said that one or two recorded dates, presumably those during June, suggested the possibility of breeding, and such had been suspected, without proof being forthcoming. He published reference to an incident mentioned by Nelson in *The Birds of Yorkshire* where it is stated that a gamekeeper named Roberts, at Hunmanby, told Alfred Roberts of the Scarborough Museum that he had shot one when it was leaving an old nest in a tree. A. Roberts stuffed the bird for the shooter, but no details of its sexual condition are given, in the absence of which there is no justification for claiming even probable breeding. It is difficult to imagine such an event and the presence of a bird or two in Yorkshire during the summer need not suggest even a slight probability, so extended are the migration periods as outlined above.

The local name of Drain Swallow, mentioned by Nelson as being used in the Spurn area, is particularly apt.

Wood Sandpiper
Tringa glareola

More Wood Sandpipers have been recorded in Yorkshire during the last 30 years than before, almost certainly as a result of increased observer activity.

Nelson knew this species as a rare visitor on passage, mainly during the autumn, and he listed records of some 27 birds between about 1844 and 1904. Most were inevitably shot, one by a boy with a pistol; and two out of three birds on the River Hull on 4th August 1878 were shot by F. Boyes, the third being procured later by another person. Such was the fate of many birds in those days.

In the annotations to his personal copy of *The Birds of Yorkshire*, Nelson included a bird shot near Beverley on 14th August 1906, after which date none was officially recorded in Yorkshire until 1935 when G.R. Edwards saw one on 25th May at High Royd Sewage-farm (*The Naturalist*, 1936, p. 28).

Chislett was very guarded concerning the acceptances of the Wood Sandpiper, and in his *Yorkshire Birds* the opening paragraph on the species reads:

'Although I already knew the species well on its breeding ground in Swedish Lapland, I have twice seen birds that I suspected of belonging to this species in late summer at Swillington Ings, but failed in both cases to get to quarters close enough for identification completely to my satisfaction.'

From then on, the species was seen regularly during the autumn in most years, and less so in spring, by the increasing number of birdwatchers at inland waters all over the county, but especially those along the southern Pennine foothills and adjacent to the Aire Valley. Several birds were also being seen in the southeastern part of the county and at Spurn and along the Humber shore. April and May is the time of spring passage, when a few pass through, 16th April 1966 at Ripon Sewage-farm being the earliest of which I have note. Some autumn birds start arriving during July, the main passage taking place during August and September with a few birds lingering into early October. One at Settle Sewage-farm from 13th to 23rd October 1966 was unusual, and a very late bird was at South Gare on 31st October 1981. Single birds are usual but there have been records of up to three on several occasions and larger parties in some years: five birds at Swillington Ings on 26th August 1953; four at Scaling Dam on 4th August 1960; four at Burniston on 27th May 1961; a marked influx in 1963, when nine appeared at Flamborough on 29th June, six at Ripon Sewage-farm on 4th August, five at Flamborough on 8th August, 17 at Beverley Sewage-farm on 12th August with eight on 16th and six on 24th, and from one to three birds at 20 other inland waters between 22nd July and 6th September; six at Fairburn Ings on 10th August 1969; seven at Coatham Marsh on 8th July, and eight at Fairburn Ings on 21st August 1970; and five at Scaling Dam on 16th July 1973.

One at Spurn on 16th May 1970 performed song flight over Clubley's Field.

More than usual occurred in 1980, when there were records from 14 places in spring and from 36 places in autumn, the maximum together being six at Spurn on 30th July. Up to 24 birds were in the Teesmouth area during August.

The Wood Sandpiper breeds from Denmark and Scandinavia eastwards across the whole of northern Eurasia to Kamchatka and Amurland, and winters from the Mediterranean south to South Africa, India and Australia. A few pairs have nested in northern Scotland since 1959. In Yorkshire, it is a passage migrant at both seasons, mainly during the autumn and generally in small numbers, at any inland water and along the estuaries.

Terek Sandpiper
Xenus cinereus

On 4th August 1971, J. Lord saw a Terek Sandpiper by the side of Scaling Dam between Whitby and Guisborough. He watched it for some time and made detailed notes. This was a new bird for the county list and only the seventh in Britain.

There are now some 23 records for the British Isles of this small and unique wader, which breeds from Finland eastwards to Siberia and winters south to South Africa, India, southeast Asia and Australia.

Common Sandpiper
Actitis hypoleucos

Nelson summarised the status of the Common Sandpiper as 'a characteristic Yorkshire bird of our sub-alpine streams, local in its distribution, and occurs more frequently on the higher reaches of the valleys running towards the west and north-west than elsewhere, though it breeds not uncommonly on the lower portions of the North and West Riding Dales, including those of Cleveland, where I have found it very abundant on the moorland reservoirs; it also nests in the neighbourhood of Whitby and Scarborough.'

Chislett (1952) mentioned a recent tendency to breed in lowland areas by private lakes and subsidence flashes. Several pairs bred around a flooded area in the Dearne Valley, southeast of Barnsley, in 1941 and one or two pairs occurred annually at such places in south and central Yorkshire. It breeds mainly along the upland streams and by the side of moorland tarns and reservoirs if these have rocky shores, and also along the rivers running down the eastern Pennines, along which it may breed until they reach the flat plains and become too slow-running to suit its needs. It has pushed a little farther east during the last 30 years and now breeds at several gravel-pits in the Knaresborough area and elsewhere. Breeding was suspected at Blaxton Gravel-pit in 1962 and a pair bred successfully at Treeton in 1979. There are no breeding records for the southeastern part of the county below a line drawn from Scarborough, through York to Sheffield.

The first Common Sandpipers of the spring arrive during late March in some years, but April is the main month of occurrence when several scattered waters often record their first birds. The tendency in recent years for a few birds to over-winter has complicated the picture, and some very early spring records could refer to birds that have spent the winter either in Yorkshire or elsewhere in Britain. One at Elland Gravel-pit on 25th February 1976 is an example. A bird at Lindley Reservoir on 10th March 1977 was probably the one that had been there each winter since 1974. Two birds at Swinsty Reservoir on 19th March 1975 may have been genuine early arrivals. Birds have also wintered at Farnham/Hay-a-Park Gravel-pits in 1978 and 1979, and single birds have occurred at Atwick on 3rd December 1960; at Bentley Tilts on 29th January 1977 and Wintersett Reservoir on 11th December 1977; at Broomhill Flash on 2nd November 1978 and Low Moor on 12th February 1978.

Numbers seen on migration are seldom large, as the Common Sandpiper is not a flocking species, and it occurs mainly in ones and twos. Concentrations at some waters in autumn are usually made up of local breeders and their young, although some passage migrants may augment the numbers. Gouthwaite Reservoir has held the largest numbers by far during the last 25 years since A.F.G. Walker and others have watched it regularly. Every July, birds congregate along its shores and on the exposed mud, when such exists at the northern end, and the highest annual counts have been as follows: 70 on 19th July 1957; 52 on 5th July 1959 with 50 on 22nd; 50 on 9th July 1961; 55 at the end of July 1970; 78 on 10th July 1971; 56 on 16th July 1977; and 79 on 8th July 1978. Other large assemblies have been 34 at Fly Flatts Reservoir on 18th May 1961; 44 at Hornsea Mere on 24th August 1971; 29 at Wintersett Reservoir on 25th July 1978 and 20 on the foreshore at King George Dock, Hull, on 6th August 1978. Smaller groups occur at several other waters, but nowhere do the numbers approach those at Gouthwaite Reservoir.

A chick ringed at Gouthwaite Reservoir on 14th June 1965 was shot at Manche, France, on 14th July 1968. Three birds ringed at Abberton Reservoir, Essex, while on passage have been recovered in Yorkshire: one of these is most interesting in that it was at Wetherby only three days after being ringed at Abberton on 10th May 1965. The other two were recovered at Aysgarth and at East Tanfield, both in May;

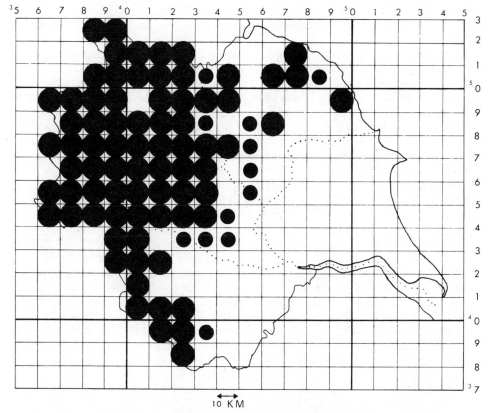

Common Sandpiper. Common along moorland streams and rivers and also by upland reservoirs, with a tendency in recent years to nest at gravel-pits in the foothill country.

whether they were Yorkshire breeders or still on their way to more northerly parts is not known, but either possibility is equally likely in that month.

An interesting note by G.E. Alderson and R. Chislett on flycatching by this species appeared in *The Naturalist*, 1955, p. 160. On 2nd July 1955, the two observers watched from their car as a Common Sandpiper stalked flies attracted to fresh sheep droppings in the road by a North Riding reservoir. The bird walked cautiously but intently to within inches of a fly, crouching with its head held low, and finally stretched its neck slowly before snatching the insect. Several flies were caught but some snatches were unsuccessful.

The Common Sandpiper is perhaps more numerous now as a breeding species than formerly, owing in the main to a recent tendency to breed at the many newly created waters along the Pennine foothills.

Spotted Sandpiper
Actitis macularia

Of the three records mentioned by Nelson, only one appears to be acceptable: a bird killed on the beach just north of Whitby Pier on 29th March 1849 by a sailor and sent the next day for preservation to D. Graham at York, where it was set up for Sir William Milner's collection. It was said by Milner to be 'a beautiful adult female', but E.T. Higgins of York, who saw it in the flesh, stated that the sex could not be determined. The bird was supposedly very tame and was with a flock of Dunlins.

The other two records were considered doubtful by Nelson. They came from Bridlington in about 1848 and Rowlsone in Holderness in October 1892.

In *The Naturalist*, 1911, pp. 100-101, W. Greaves reported a Spotted Sandpiper which had been shot near Hebden Bridge about 1899. H.F. Witherby apparently had doubts about the record, but later accepted it and it was included in *The Handbook* together with the Whitby bird of 1849 (*British Birds*, 4, p. 369). The latter record is not, however, cited in the British Ornithologists' Union publication *The Status of Birds in Britain and Ireland* (1971), although it seems to be the most detailed and satisfactory of the two.

On 7th May 1979, R. Evison saw a Spotted Sandpiper in breeding dress at Farnham Gravel-pit, near Knaresborough, and informed other local observers who were able to watch it at close range during the next four days as it fed along the grassy edge of the lagoon.

Another adult in breeding dress occurred at Blacktoft Sands on 27th August 1981, when it was watched by G.P. Catley, A. Grieve, K. Rotherham and others.

The county was to be treated to yet another adult, when one appeared at Wath Ings on 24th May 1982. During its two-day stay it was seen by several people, including N.W. Addey and J. Hewitt, and a photograph of the bird taken by J. Seeviour appeared in *British Birds* 1982, p. 394.

One was seen by G.J. Speight and others at Ingbirchworth Reservoir between 13th and 28th September 1983.

One stayed at Worsborough Reservoir from 29th July to 5th August 1984 and was seen by M. Kilburn, T. Kilburn and J.D.H. Brown.

The Spotted Sandpiper breeds across North America and there are now about 70 records in Great Britain and Ireland.

Turnstone
Arenaria interpres

The Turnstone can be found along the Yorkshire coastline at almost any time of year. During the spring, passage migrants in bright breeding plumage pass northwards, a few remaining throughout the summer. Autumn migrants appear from July to September, and many birds remain during the winter months. The earliest date known to Nelson for the autumn migration to start was 26th July, but it is often difficult to separate such birds from the few that have summered, perhaps along another part of the east coast.

The largest numbers have been recorded at Spurn, where R. Chislett and G.H. Ainsworth saw 500 on 8th September 1947, and the numbers recorded there in most recent years have usually reached a maximum of about 300 during the autumn but there were 530 there on 18th September 1974. A typical year, illustrating the pattern of occurrence at Spurn, was 1977 when, after small numbers during January and February, there were maximum counts of 150 in March; 233 in April; 180 in May; 41 in June; 160 in July; 258 in August; 436 in September; 160 in October; and smaller numbers to the year end. With minor fluctuations in numbers, that is the pattern in most years.

At Teesmouth, 150 at South Gare on 11th January 1959 was the highest number seen there 'for many years'. Bran Sands is a favourite roosting place at high tide, and there have been counts of 202 on 14th December 1980, 110 during October and November 1981, and 247 on 15th August 1982. South Gare had up to 200 birds during March 1981.

Cornelian Bay, south of Scarborough, attracts Turnstones, and since the early 1970s gatherings of around 200 have been commonplace. The harbour wall at Bridlington is also a popular place for Turnstones and they can often be seen resting in the shelter of the fishery buildings, where there were 50 on 15th March 1971 and 80 on 18th November 1971. Other good flocks have been 57 on Bridlington beach on 3rd February 1979; 108 along the Humber shore between Kilnsea and Easington on 8th September 1979; 71 along the beach between Bridlington and Fraisthorpe on 24th November 1979; and up to 100 frequent Jackson's Bay, Scarborough, in most winters. Filey Brigg is a favourite feeding place, and in 1980 there were counts of 70 in January, 110 on 8th March, 340 on 7th April and 120 on 17th December, with 153 there on 22nd November 1981.

Inland occurrences were seldom recorded in Nelson's time and he listed only the following: one was shot from a flock of pigeons at Boroughbridge in October 1849; one was at Cold Hiendley Reservoir in September 1868; one was shot from a flock of seven on Eldrick Moor in 1883; and one was at Harrogate in 1896.

By the time Chislett published *Yorkshire Birds* in 1952, he was able to say that, during the previous 15 years, inland occurrences were too numerous to list in detail. More regular watching at the Pennine reservoirs was responsible. Turnstones can now be expected at almost any inland water during the period April to

October, mainly during May-June and August-September. Usually single birds are seen, but small parties of up to five and sometimes more occur occasionally. There were 14 at Whiteholme Reservoir on 14th August 1935 (*The Naturalist*, 1936, p. 17) and ten on 19th August 1938 (*The Naturalist*, 1939, p. 12).

Flocks passing inland have all been flying westwards in recent years as follows: eight at Fairburn Ings on 14th August 1967 and 11 there on 14th August 1975, in which year 11 passed at Blacktoft Sands on 18th August, two flocks of five and ten on 19th and eight on 30th; 15 near Barnsley on 18th November 1976; 13 at Southfield Reservoir on 17th September 1979; five at Blackmoorfoot Reservoir on 16th August and six on 31st August 1980. Nine also flew west at Pugneys Gravel-pit on 7th May 1981, on which date one would have expected them to be flying east; the movement was perhaps local.

On 5th February 1976, during a period of hard frost, Mrs Joan Webb watched two Turnstones pecking at a Razorbill corpse on Scarborough north beach, and A.J. Wallis tells me that during frosty weather small numbers can frequently be seen on the fish pier pecking at fish remains dropped or thrown out by the fishermen preparing their catch for market.

An adult Turnstone ringed at Spurn on 25th July 1959 was found dead at Fleetwood in Lancashire on 3rd May 1962; a juvenile ringed at Spurn on 10th August 1960 was caught at Sheppey in Kent on 6th August 1966; and a chick, ringed at Vaasa in Finland on 29th June 1974, was recaught at Hull on 21st August 1974, indicating how quickly the young leave the breeding grounds.

Wilson's Phalarope
Phalaropus tricolor

On the afternoon of 20th June 1965, a female Wilson's Phalarope in full breeding dress was identified at Scaling Dam by T. Bradbury and W. Norman. It stayed until 21st, being present for most of that day. The bird spent most of the time on the muddy margins of the reservoir, occasionally wading into the water, and was seen by over 20 observers including D.G. Bell, E.C. Gatenby, D. Summers-Smith, A.J. Wallis and P.J. Stead. It was the first record for Yorkshire and full details were published in *The Naturalist*, 1966, p. 86.

In the following year, on 22nd June, a Wilson's Phalarope was found dead at Scaling Dam by D.G. Bell, who contacted me. I went to his home in Guisborough to inspect the corpse, which was in an advanced state of decomposition. Although the plumage was in a clean and dry condition when found, the body was full of fly larvae and it was not possible to preserve the skin. It was a female and very likely the one seen in 1965. It is not possible even to guess where the bird spent the intervening year. The skeleton is in my collection.

At midday on 7th September 1972, P. Jones of Castleford saw a pale grey wader in front of the new hide at Fairburn Ings. He correctly identified it as a Wilson's Phalarope, and the bird was seen independently by C. Winn later the same day and subsequently by several other observers, including R.F. Dickens and Dr J.D. Pickup. (*The Naturalist*, 1973, p. 28.)

At 13.30 hours on 27th September 1973, one was seen flying over the canal zone at Spurn. It alighted on a small pond near The Bluebell and stayed until 17.00 hours, when it was seen to fly off to the northwest. It was watched by A.O. Aitken, B.R. Spence and R.A. Williams.

T.M. Batten and C.J. Sollitt saw one at Barmston on 8th and 9th September

1979. R.P. Council, G. Neal and B.R. Spence saw another bird at Spurn on 16th September 1980; it later moved to the Beacon Lane ponds at Kilnsea. A female was at Blacktoft Sands on 23rd June 1983.

There are now over 170 records of this North American phalarope, which did not enter the British list until 1954 and which has occurred almost annually since 1961.

Red-necked Phalarope
Phalaropus lobatus

The first information on the Red-necked Phalarope in Britain concerned a bird supplied by Ralph Johnson of Greta Bridge and which Willughby described in 1676 as follows:

> 'Mr. Johnson's small cloven footed gull; — when I first saw the skin of it stuft at Mr. Johnson's at Brignall in Yorkshire, from the make of its feet I judged it to be of the Coot kind. But afterwards being informed by Mr. Johnson that it is much upon the wing, hath sharp wings, and cries like a small gull, differs also in the fashion of the bill, I changed my opinion, and thought that it might rather be referred to the Gulls, to which I have subjoined it.' (Willughby's *Ornithology*, 1876, p. 355).

Nelson was aware that the species occurred less frequently than the Grey Phalarope and said that it was a rare and casual visitor. He listed 19 occurrences in *The Birds of Yorkshire*, all but four of which had been obtained at or near the coast. The first inland records came from Wilberfoss, near York, where one was shot in May 1854 while it was swimming with some ducks on a pond; from near Hambleton in the spring of 1854; one in summer plumage which was obtained while swimming on a pond near Scampston about 1860; and one in the collection of J.C. Garth of Knaresborough was labelled 'Arkendale, 7th October 1871'. The last of Nelson's records was at Bridlington in 1898.

The next was seen at Hornsea Mere by P.F. Holmes on 29th September 1935 (*British Birds*, 29, 1936, p. 252). One was seen on 15th August 1937 at Whiteholme Reservoir by V.S. Crapnell, G.R. Edwards and others (*The Naturalist*, 1938, p. 31). A bird in full summer plumage was seen at Kilnsea on 16th July 1939 by H.O. Bunce and L. Smith (*The Naturalist*, 1939, p. 236) and one was seen by A. Baldridge at Teesmouth on 12th October 1947.

Since then, there have been records in 15 years up to 1982 and annually during the period 1974 to 1978. One was at Wath Ings on 24th September 1955; one was swimming on the River Aire at Brotherton on 3rd November 1957; one was at Scaling Dam on 14th September 1958; one in summer plumage at Harlington Flash on 7th June 1961; one at Flamborough on 19th May 1962; one at Eccup Reservoir on 12th June 1963; one at Whiteholme Reservoir on 16th August 1964; one at Malham Tarn on 3rd June 1965; one at Settle Sewage-farm on 21st May 1966, in which year a pair was seen intermittently at Summer Lodge Tarn from 30th May to 19th June; one in summer plumage near Atwick on 24th June 1967, and one at Redmires Reservoir on 5th September 1967; one at Wintersett Reservoir on 28th September 1974; one in summer plumage at Wath Ings on 13th and 14th June 1975, and another similarly garbed bird at Gouthwaite Reservoir on 18th June 1975; one at Worsborough Reservoir on 27th May 1976, another at Wintersett

Reservoir on 17th June 1976 and one in summer plumage at Fairburn Ings on 28th June 1976; one at Hornsea Mere on 25th September 1977; one flew north at Flamborough Head on 1st October 1978, one was at Spurn on 6th October 1978, and two first-year birds were seen at Flamborough Head by P.A. Lassey, Miss Irene Smith and D.I.M. Wallace on 6th December 1978, an exceptionally late date for this species; and finally a juvenile was at Coatham Marsh from 6th to 8th August 1979.

In 1982, one was at Blacktoft Sands on 20th June; a juvenile was at Tophill Low Reservoir from 28th to 31st August; and one was watched at the entrance to Scarborough Reservoir on the exceptionally late date of 7th November by R.N. Hopper and M. Feather.

Three birds occurred in 1983: one was at Blacktoft Sands from 24th to 29th July; one was at Gouthwaite Reservoir from 6th to 9th August; and one was at Flamborough on 29th October.

The breeding range of the Red-necked Phalarope is circumpolar in the tundra and boreal zones. It extends somewhat farther south than that of the Grey Phalarope, with which it winters off the coasts of South America, West Africa and southeast Asia.

Grey Phalarope
Phalaropus fulicarius

As with the last species, the first known description of the Grey Phalarope as a British bird came from an example obtained in Yorkshire. The bird in question was killed at Warley Clough, near Halifax, by Thomas Bolton and sent to George Edwards, who described it in the *Philosophical Transactions* and afterwards figured it in his *Gleanings of Natural History* (1743-76). It was procured for Edwards by his 'obliging friend, Mr. Thomas Bolton, florist, of Warley Clough in Yorkshire, near which place it was shot in January 1757'.

The first known British example of the Grey Phalarope, shot near Halifax. Described and figured by George Edwards in February 1757.

The Grey Phalarope occurred in 15 of the years during the period 1906 to 1952, in which latter year Chislett published *Yorkshire Birds*. Since then it has been recorded in 25 of the years up to 1982, and annually since 1969. During this period, occurrences have been between September and April, the majority being seen during November, December and January. Single birds are usual, but at some well-watched places several individual sightings of lone birds have been proved, on plumage differences, to be of different individuals and during the winter of 1975 ten different Grey Phalaropes were recorded in the Scarborough area between January and April.

S.C. Norman saw four birds land on the sea at South Gare on 25th January 1969; P.A. Lassey and Miss Irene Smith saw three flying north at Flamborough on 26th November 1978 and A. Grieve, S. Rooke and D.I.M. Wallace saw three more there on 28th November 1978. There have been some records outside the usual winter period and these have concerned birds in full summer plumage. W.F. Curtis and R.H. Appleby saw one at Hornsea Mere on 27th May 1974; R.H. Appleby saw one at Scalby Mills on 15th May 1975 and another on 7th August 1975; and P.A. Lassey and Miss Irene Smith saw one flying north at Flamborough on 4th June 1977.

Coastal records have come mainly from South Gare; the Scarborough area including Jackson's Bay, Cornelian Bay and Scalby Mills; Filey Brigg; Flamborough and Bridlington; with other occurrences at Spurn, Patrington Haven and Cherry Cobb Sands.

Birds have occurred singly at inland waters in 16 of the years since 1950 and mainly since 1970. All have been between August and December, except for one at Fairburn Ings on 16th July 1956 which was in full summer plumage and seen by A. Gilpin, A.H.B. Lee, E.C. Sterne and C. Winn. Sightings have come from the Lower Derwent Valley, Tophill Low Reservoir, Broomhill Flash, Midhope Reservoir, Gouthwaite Reservoir, Blackmoorfoot Reservoir, Ingbirchworth Reservoir, Horbury Sewage-farm, Withens Reservoir, Beighton, Swillington Ings, Ben Rhydding Sewage-farm, Bolton-on-Swale Gravel-pit and Staveley Lagoon.

Numbers appearing in the autumn vary annually. In some years there may be only one record; in others there may be several, as in 1972 when single birds were recorded on 13 dates and two birds on one date. In 1977, single birds were seen on 12 dates. Occasionally a bird will stay in one area for several days and may move up and down the coast, giving rise to several records from different places. Nelson said that it occurred most regularly during strong gales and 'as it is of a remarkably tame and confiding nature, it falls victim to the first gunner who notices it'.

A winter visitor in small but fluctuating numbers, with birds in full summer plumage being seen occasionally during the spring and early autumn, summarises the Yorkshire status of this ocean-going species. The majority spend the winter at sea off the coasts of West Africa, southern Arabia and South America, to where they migrate from their breeding grounds in northern Europe, Siberia and North America.

Pomarine Skua
Stercorarius pomarinus

'Bird of passage off the coast in autumn; chiefly in immature plumage, and uncertain as to numbers. Large flocks have occurred at irregular intervals.' That is how

Nelson summarised the Yorkshire status of the Pomarine Skua and he followed it with seven full pages of details concerning the occurrences up to 1906. Prior to 1879, it had been considered an uncertain and rather scarce autumn or winter visitor to the coast, adult examples being almost unknown or very rare, and the headland at Flamborough was said to be the best place to see them.

Nelson witnessed a great passage in early October 1879 and wrote in graphic detail in *The Birds of Yorkshire* thus:

'In the early part of October in the year mentioned, great numbers of skuas were noticed in the Tees Bay, and on the 8th, when off at sea, I procured an adult and two immature Pomatorhines, at the same time seeing some fifty others in small parties of four or five, all flying to the north-west. This in itself was so unusual an occurrence as to excite great interest amongst local naturalists. On the following day seven more Pomatorhines were obtained, and about a hundred others, in small flocks, were noted going in the same direction as those previously observed; while, during the succeeding four days, I observed one while punting in the Tees, others being seen and some killed by various gunners. Then came the memorable "Skua" gale on the 14th October, which created an amount of interest and speculation amongst ornithologists equalled only by the famous irruption of Pallas's Sand-Grouse in 1888. About 11 a.m. on the day named the wind suddenly flew round to the north, changing to north-east and blew with great violence, being accompanied by torrents of rain. I had gone to the Teesmouth at the outbreak of the storm, and soon after noon the first flight of Pomatorhine Skuas appeared, coming from eastward; more flights followed, their numbers increasing as the day wore on, and scarcely had one party gone by before another hove in sight; they flew in flocks of from seven to ten in number, skirting the shore, and on arriving at the Teesmouth many of them alighted on the sands, apparently exhausted by battling against the storm. They allowed a close approach as they sat on the beach, only taking flight when an intruder came within a few yards' distance; possibly they were ignorant of the effects of a gun, and had not had any experience of their arch-enemy, man. Thus they continued to pass for several hours, until by dark some thousands must have gone by; then the approach of night prevented further observations. On the sand-hills, on both sides of Redcar, many gunners were out, taking toll of the passing birds, but, as they afforded little sport, the shooters abstained from firing at them after obtaining a few specimens. The majority of the Skuas constituting these flocks were adults, their white breasts and long twisted tail feathers rendering them very conspicuous, and easily distinguishable from the immature dark-breasted birds; a considerable number of Buffon's and a few Richardson's Skuas accompanied them. In endeavouring to form an approximate idea of their numbers, after careful consideration and consultation with those of my acquaintance who were witnesses of the great flight, it was calculated that a total of between five and six thousand birds passed Redcar. On the day following they continued to fly by during the morning; on the 16th the wind slackened, and none were observable; but the gale freshened on the 17th, and I saw about fifty in small bands of seven or eight together, whilst on the 28th two adults were seen.'

The movement was also noted at Scarborough and 30 specimens were taken to Alfred Roberts, who said that many others were obtained and that these were the first birds he had had during his 30 years as a taxidermist. Heavy toll was also levied on the birds at Filey, Flamborough and Bridlington. Many were driven inland by the force of the gale and were reported from several parts of the county. According to Nelson, E.T. Booth was of the opinion that this movement was not unusual, except that the storm had driven the birds onshore as they passed south out to sea, where they normally migrated unseen from the shore. That theory was in part correct, but the majority pass westward around the top of the British Isles and move south off western Ireland to winter off West Africa; large numbers come into the North Sea only when forced south by severe gales before they have rounded the north of Scotland, as in 1879, a classic situation for heavy skua passage off Yorkshire.

In the following year on 28th October, another large passage occurred during a terrific northeaster; most of the skuas seen were adults and, during the height of the storm, several hundreds passed Redcar, flying close to the esplanade and struggling to make heavy headway against the wind, rain and sleet. Yet another flight occurred on 14th October 1881 during a northwest gale. On this occasion the birds came downwind and flew high over the town of Redcar and into the country. The year 1886 was also a skua year when large numbers were reported offshore on the fishing grounds, one fisherman saying that they had not seen so many since 1879. Several hundreds passed south at Flamborough in 1887, and larger numbers than usual were recorded in the autumns of 1889, 1892, 1901 and 1903.

It is inevitable that the accounts of such movements were flavoured with exaggeration and misinterpretation of the facts, but there is no doubt that they were very spectacular and nothing on a similar scale has occurred since. Alfred Roberts said that in October 1879 he saw several at Scarborough pursuing the smaller Buffon's Skuas (Long-tailed) and snipping off their elongated tail feathers so as to impede their flight in the scramble for food, and he also saw them attacking members of their own species in a similar way. Snipping off tail feathers I do not believe! M. Bailey of Flamborough recorded an instance of one which clung to a wounded Kittiwake 'until it fell victim to its own rapacity', and Nelson records that an adult dark-phase bird which he shot on 14th October 1879 disgorged a perfectly fresh Grey Plover. That is physically impossible.

Chislett dismissed the Pomarine Skua in one page of text, and made only passing reference to the spectacular movements of the late nineteenth century of which Nelson had said '... without which [details] a history of the birds of Yorkshire would be incomplete'.

A northeasterly gale on 30th September 1911 produced good numbers when about 200 skuas, including both Arctic and Pomarine, were seen passing over the South Gare at Teesmouth (*British Birds*, 1911, p. 170). After that time, up to the publication of *Yorkshire Birds* in 1952, the Pomarine Skua was a rare sight along the Yorkshire coast. Chislett listed very few birds, some of which he did not consider conclusively proven.

A large-scale movement of skuas at Teesmouth during a north-northeast gale on 15th October 1955 was described by P.J. Stead as unapproached in scale since Nelson's time at Redcar. Small parties totalling up to about 100 birds passed, of which 30 were definite adult Pomarines and 20 most probably juveniles. Good numbers also passed South Gare on 3rd and 4th October 1966, when 41 and 34 respectively were counted flying south. In the following year, 13 passed on 4th October and 14 on 29th, and 20 flew south in one flock there on 11th October 1972.

The best year in recent times for this interesting species was 1976; the only spring record was of 12 pale-phase adults flying east over the Spurn Peninsula on 29th May, but the autumn passage involved larger numbers than for many years. The first ones were seen off Long Nab, Burniston, and at Hornsea on 23rd July, after which date they were seen regularly off several coastal watchpoints until 18th November. On many days only one or two were identified, but at Flamborough 16 passed on 10th September, seven on 11th and 21 on 25th; 18 on 1st October and nine on 28th October; and seven on 20th November. On 9th September 19 flew south off Long Nab, and 15 flew south at Hornsea on 15th October. A total of 45 birds, mainly in parties of ten, flew south off Filey Brigg on 29th October, and ten flew north off Mappleton on 10th October.

The majority of Pomarine Skua records in 1980 came from Flamborough Head, where there were five on 3rd August, eleven on 10th August, ten on 24th August and 25 on 25th August. A good passage off Flamborough in 1982 had peak counts of 41 on 7th October, 42 on 14th October and 31 on 6th November.

Occurrences in spring are few, but some birds pass north during April and May and occasionally into June. In some years, the first birds of autumn are seen during late June, but more normally from mid July. Occasional birds are seen during the winter months, and this skua is the most likely one to be seen passing south in November and December.

Inland records are rare. Chislett knew of none during his period of review from 1907 to 1952, but a bird killed while attacking chickens near Steeton Reservoir on 17th September 1942 and which went to the Keighley Museum, originally identified as an Arctic Skua and published in *Yorkshire Birds* under that species, was in fact a Pomarine. It was at one time labelled as a Great Skua, and finally identified correctly by Chislett on 2nd October 1953 after doubts about its identity had been expressed by C.D. Robinson and the curator, J. Ogden. A large skua at Eccup Reservoir on 4th November 1959, described as larger than a Common Gull, was thought by G.R. Naylor to be a Pomarine, which would be most likely on that late date. A dark-phase adult flew over Broomfleet Island in the Upper Humber on 8th November 1970, and one frequented the area of Hessle, and Barrow on the Lincolnshire side of the river, during early January 1979. The only record in recent years concerns three birds flying west inland at Blacktoft Sands on 27th July 1981, the destination of which would be most intriguing.

The Pomarine Skua is thus a regular passage migrant in varying numbers along the Yorkshire coast in spring and autumn, most numerously during the latter. A few birds occur during the winter months. The strength of passage is almost entirely dependent on the weather, being most apparent during periods of strong winds from the northern quarter, when they often go northwards in autumn, flying into the gales in the lee of the shore.

Arctic Skua
Stercorarius parasiticus

Nelson knew the Richardson's Skua, as it was then known, as the commonest of the four skuas frequenting the Yorkshire coast, and he said that from the middle of August to the end of September and into October it was very abundant at sea. He knew of no spring records, but commented that 'it doubtless occurs on the spring passage northwards but has, so far, escaped observation at that period'.

During the spectacular skua movements of 1879, it was very numerous in August and September, when it occurred with the Pomarines. Nelson had previously seen two flocks, each of 20 birds, on 8th October 1877, and during October 1886 several parties passed Redcar during a southeasterly gale. In September 1887, a flock of 30 flew high overhead to the northwest making a continuous screaming call. Larger numbers than usual occurred in 1881, 1885, 1886, 1887 and 1891 at Teesmouth; and it was abundant off Flamborough in 1865 and 1879, and especially so in 1877 when flock after flock was seen passing south, some extending for a mile in length. It is difficult to imagine numbers of that inferred magnitude as nothing remotely approaching them has occurred since.

Observations along the coast were very spasmodic in the years prior to World War II and few records were forthcoming. With the end of the war and the establishment of a permanent observatory at Spurn Point, skuas were recorded annually but no large numbers were seen. The only double figures published by Chislett in *Yorkshire Birds* were 28 seen moving south in one hour by G.R. Edwards on 21st September 1947 and 'About a dozen' at Teesmouth and Spurn in 1949.

In the Yorkshire Naturalists' Union Ornithological Report for 1960, Chislett said that 'For seven to pass Spurn on 7th June was curious', but such a record would not be considered curious today. Intensive watching during the last 20 years has shown that birds may be seen in any month of the year, small numbers passing through during April and May and sometimes into June, and from July to October when the main passage takes place, with occasional birds in the period November to March.

Since the early 1960s, Arctic Skuas have been recorded in large numbers every autumn, mainly during August and September and fluctuating with the weather, most birds appearing during periods of strong winds from the northwest to the northeast. In 1976, a heavy southerly passage was noted at Spurn when the following counts were made: 150 on 27th August; 150 on 28th August; 320 on 29th August; 140 on 4th September; 562 on 9th September; and 260 on 10th September. During August 1980, a three-day movement on 21st, 22nd and 23rd involved the following numbers; 167, 170 and 188 at Filey; 235, 277 and 154 at Flamborough; and 487, 254 and 154 at Spurn. Later in the same month, on 30th, during a northwesterly gale, skuas began to move south at midday and were in evidence all along the coastline. The maximum counts were 623 at Filey, 523 in one-and-a-half hours at Flamborough, 344 in two hours at Hornsea, and 471 at Spurn.

Another good year followed and, in August 1981, the three major watchpoints at Filey, Flamborough and Spurn recorded large numbers as follows. On 15th August there were 148, 140 and 140, and on 16th August there were 112, 130 and 222 respectively. Spurn recorded the highest numbers on 20th August when 460 flew south, and during the next three days birds continued to pass along the coast with 121 at Flamborough on 22nd and 132 on 30th. Flamborough also had 185 birds on 20th September, and 123 passed Filey on 2nd October.

Maximum counts in 1982 were 215 at Flamborough on 31st August and 190 at Spurn on 6th September. In 1983, there were peak counts of 332 at Filey and 547 at Flamborough on 28th August, with 403 and 417 respectively at these two localities on 3rd September.

Anywhere along the coastline from the Teesmouth to Spurn, particularly at Filey, Flamborough and Spurn, during April and May and from July to October, Arctic Skuas may be seen passing on their journey to or from their northern breeding grounds, but the direction need not be the expected one for the season. During strong winds from the northern quarter in autumn, birds may be flying purposefully northwards into the wind, seeking some shelter in the lee of the shore, or perhaps southwards as they sweep along the wave tops, going with the wind in loose parties. Such movements may occur at any time during the peak migration periods if the weather is as described. In calm conditions, birds may pass high and farther out to sea and go unrecorded, or small numbers may be seen drifting steadily southwards, stopping to chase small gulls and terns as they go.

There have been well over 50 records at inland waters during the last 30 years and to list them all in detail is unnecessary. They have occurred in every month from April to November, the majority being during August and September, and their appearance often being linked with gales and passage along the coast. Ten birds have occurred during April to June, which suggests that a few cross the country from the west coast on their northward journey in spring.

Records are usually of single birds, but occasionally more are seen together. At Fairburn Ings, two were seen on 17th September 1976, five on 18th September and one on 20th September, and three flew west there on 19th July 1977. In 1978, four flew southeast at Swillington on 28th August, on which day two were seen at Wintersett Reservoir. A few birds penetrate up the Humber Estuary, where they may chase waders and gulls. In 1962, two birds chased wader flocks at Cherry Cobb Sands on 19th August and one was west of Hull on 9th September. One was at Cherry Cobb Sands on 31st July 1978; another was at Sunk Island on 26th August 1978; and one was near Hessle Haven on 7th January 1979. Arctic Skuas have been seen flying to the west over Blacktoft Sands in recent years: two did so on 4th August 1975; three on 12th September 1976; five on 18th August 1977; four on 10th August and three on 19th September 1979; and four on 26th September 1981. Fairburn Ings and the Aire Valley are directly in the path of these birds.

One flying south with three normal birds at Filey Brigg on 26th November 1978 was described by H.J. Whitehead as appearing almost all-white with off-white underparts and some grey on the upperwing.

A bird found dead at Skeffling on 17th August 1965 had been ringed as a chick on Fair Isle on 7th July 1959.

Long-tailed Skua
Stercorarius longicaudus

Prior to the great invasion of October 1879, the Long-tailed Skua, or Buffon's Skua by which name it was formerly known, had been recorded in Yorkshire only on some four or five occasions, at Redcar and Flamborough. During the large movements in 1879, no fewer than 15 adults were captured at Redcar and several others were seen (*The Zoologist*, 1880, pp. 18-19 and 365). Alfred Roberts of Scarborough received eight adult birds, and others were procured at Whitby, York and Thirsk. Nelson recorded one at Redcar on 20th June 1849, and a late bird on 6th November, the locality and year of the latter not being specified. He knew of no spring records, but published details of coastal Long-tailed Skuas in 16 years between 1849 and 1902, including the birds in 1879 listed above. There were also three inland records: an immature at Hopperton, York, on 6th November 1853; one found half-starved on Strensall Common, near York, on 18th October 1879; and another found dead at Slingsby, near Thirsk, on 19th October 1879 — the last two being associated with the big coastal movements.

Chislett could add records in only three years up to the publication of *Yorkshire Birds* in 1952, and two of these concerned birds recorded by Nelson after the publication of *The Birds of Yorkshire* in 1907: two immatures were shot and an adult seen off Flamborough in October 1908; an immature was picked up near Whitby in October 1911 and sent to Nelson for identification; and the third was picked up dead near Helmsley by Adam Gordon in September or October 1950, and E.W. Taylor exhibited the mounted specimen at a meeting of the Yorkshire Naturalists' Union on 21st October 1950.

Since 1952, it has occurred in 27 of the 30 years up to 1983. During the years of occurrence to 1974, from one to five birds were seen annually, but intensive watching along the coastline, especially at Spurn, Hornsea, Flamborough and Filey, has shown it to be a fairly regular bird of passage in autumn. Numbers seen each year from 1975 to 1983 have been as follows: 7, 48, 12, 37, 12, 17, 14, 31 and 27.

In 1975, single birds were seen at Bempton on 17th August, Flamborough on 30th August, Spurn on 31st August, Kettleness on 27th September and Filey on 28th September. A juvenile with a badly smashed wing was found at Spurn on 14th September (see plate 77), and the wings and tail of another juvenile were found there on 12th October. Both these specimens were sent to me for preservation.

There were more Long-tailed Skuas in 1976 than had been recorded since 1897. The first was on 7th August at Spurn, where there were two more on 27th August and two again on 28th; one at Hornsea on 21st August was followed by single birds at Scarborough and Bempton on 28th and at Hornsea on 29th. Four adult birds were off Filey on 31st August, and singles were off Hornsea on 12th and 25th September and at Filey Brigg on 9th October. One was found dying at Scarborough on 14th September (see plate 77). At Flamborough, P.A. Lassey, D.I.M. Wallace and others saw a total of 28 birds passing during the period August to October, including 14 birds in the Bridlington/Flamborough area on 25th September. J. Hewitt saw an adult flying east over Wath Ings on 29th May and J.M. Turton saw an immature there on 2nd September. An ailing bird found at Marske on 22nd September was given antibiotics by M. Blick and eventually flew off on 28th September.

Another good year followed in 1977, the first bird being seen flying north at Flamborough by D.I.M. Wallace on 24th July. One was at South Gare on 31st July; an adult was off Filey on 9th August; an immature at Flamborough on 13th August, an adult on 20th August, and an adult and an immature on 27th August; and an adult flying south at Hornsea and an immature flying north at Bridlington, both on 16th September.

In 1978, one was at Flamborough on 1st May, whereafter 26 birds were recorded during the autumn on 14 dates from 6th August to 1st October with one on 15th July. Single birds were recorded on 12 dates during the same period off South Gare, Coatham, Scarborough, Filey, Hornsea and Spurn.

There were 12 birds in 1979, more or less evenly spread between the first at Flamborough on 27th July and the last off Scarborough on 13th October.

One flew southeast over Kilnsea on 10th May 1980, and in the autumn there were records of 16 birds, mainly from Flamborough where there was one on 9th August; three on 24th; singles on 12th and 21st, 23rd, 25th, 30th and 31st August, on which latter date three juveniles were seen, and on 12th October. The other records came from Spurn on 21st August and 11th October and from Filey Brigg, also on the latter date.

In 1981, there were 15 records between 25th July and 26th September from Redcar, Flamborough, Filey, Spurn, and Easington where two flew south on 20th September.

A total of 31 birds was recorded in 1982. All except three were at Flamborough, which had nine on 7th October, four on 8th and four on 14th; 12 of these 17 birds were juveniles.

Of the 27 birds recorded in 1983, 20 were seen at Flamborough between 9th August and 27th September. One flew over Thrybergh Reservoir on 6th May 1984.

Both adults and immatures pass, the latter being in the majority. There is no definite peak period of passage; single birds or perhaps two or three in a day may be seen at almost any time between late July and October, but mainly during September.

On 12th October 1963, a bird presumed to be an Arctic Skua was found dead on Burley Moor and the wings removed. They were given to me some days later and proved to be those of a juvenile Long-tailed Skua. R. Atkins found a dead skua in a railway cutting between Mickletown and Sherburn-in-Elmet on 1st November 1967 and retained the wings, from which the species was identified as a juvenile Long-tailed Skua.

A bird found dead at Filey on 19th September 1973 and identified as an Arctic Skua was sent to Doncaster Museum for preservation. It was subsequently examined in 1976 and correctly identified as a Long-tailed Skua by C.A. Howes, to whom I am grateful for reporting the details.

Great Skua
Stercorarius skua

The 'Bonxie' was known as a scarce autumn visitor along the Yorkshire coast during Nelson's time at the turn of the century, and like the Arctic Skua had eluded detection during the northward passage in spring. Nelson said that it was a bird of the offshore zones, where it attended the gulls and terns on the herring shoals and was well known to the deep-sea fishermen. Its occurrences inshore were, in consequence, few in number and only some 20 records were listed in *The Birds of Yorkshire.* The monthly distribution of these was March (two); August (one); September (one); October (five); with one 'in summer' and four undated.

Three inland records were published: at Nun Monkton 'several years ago' (i.e. prior to 1907); Pateley Bridge in 1864; and at Tollerton Ings, near York, on 18th October 1879, the year of the great skua invasion.

During the period from 1907 to 1952, a few Great Skuas were seen in several, but by no means all, years and mainly at Spurn. Not many years after Chislett published *Yorkshire Birds* in 1952, the pursuit of sea-watching became popular and the regular manning of the Spurn Bird Observatory, where many seabirds may be seen from the peninsula, provided more sightings than previously recorded. By 1958, the Great Skua was becoming known as a regular passage bird during the autumn in varying numbers, its appearance close inshore often being dependent on strong winds from the northwest to northeast. Over 30 birds were seen in that year, including six on 15th October and 12 on 18th October at Spurn and five flying northwest at Redcar on 17th October. After that time, birds were seen regularly in small numbers every spring, as well as during the autumn when larger numbers passed. During the 1960s, the highest annual counts ranged from ten to 50 birds, but in 1963, at Spurn, 17 were seen on 27th September, 26 on 28th September and 70 on 13th October. In the 1970s, especially since 1976 when Flamborough Head became regularly watched by P.A. Lassey, Miss Irene Smith, D.I.M. Wallace and others, the numbers seen each autumn have been higher than before, and with more being seen in the spring and during the winter months. A heavy passage was witnessed off Spurn in September 1974 when 102 birds flew south on 24th and smaller numbers on other days.

At Flamborough in 1976, 18 birds passed north on 21st April with smaller numbers to the month end; and, during a period of gales in September, 30 passed on 10th, 90 on 11th and 52 on 12th, with a grand total of 286 Great Skuas passing between 24th July and 20th November. Daily counts of up to 60 or 70 birds have been regular off Flamborough in September during recent years, 94 on 21st September 1979 and 144 on 10th September 1983 being the highest numbers.

Birds may be seen offshore in any month, a few appearing during the period late November to February, which probably suggests that some spend the winter in the southern part of the North Sea. Spring passage begins in March, when birds can be seen flying northwards, and continues into early June. By July, the first autumn birds are moving south, and from then until early November the species passes in varying numbers with occasional periods when strong winds bring larger numbers closer inshore.

The Great Skua has occurred inland on some 13 occasions, three involving birds wearing rings: one found dead on Goathland Moors on 17th September 1938 had been ringed in the Shetland Islands on 14th July 1938; one found dead at Mexborough on 16th March 1960 had been ringed on Noss in the Shetland Islands on 22nd June 1958; and one caught at Wilsden, Bradford, on 18th January 1968 had been ringed on Foula on 22nd July 1967. In addition to the above inland recoveries is a bird ringed in Iceland on 31st July 1963 and recovered dead at Reighton Gap on 30th March 1964.

Other inland records are as follows: one was killed by hitting power cables at Thornton-le-Dale in December 1932; one was seen at Swillington Ings on 27th October 1946; one was at Almholme on 30th and 31st October 1966; single birds were at Fairburn Ings on 7th January and 26th October 1968 (see penultimate paragraph); one was found dead under wires at Stainton on 1st September 1971, the skin of which is in the Sheffield City Museum; one was at Swillington Ings on 22nd August 1977 which settled on the water for ten minutes; one was at Fly Flatts Reservoir on 5th September 1978; one was at Worsborough Reservoir on 1st September 1979; and one was at Wheldrake Ings on 26th April 1981.

Some birds have been seen well into the Humber Estuary at Skeffling, Barrow Haven and Whitton Sands, and a few have been recorded at, or flying west over, Blacktoft Sands: one on 8th September 1976 and three more during the gales on 12th September 1976; one on 14th September 1979; two on 26th September 1981; and two in May 1982. It is possible that these autumn birds will cross the country onto the west coast, then head southward to their wintering grounds in the eastern Atlantic south to the Tropic of Cancer.

The record at Fairburn Ings on 26th October 1968 concerned a bird which appeared over the water at midday and caused a sudden outcry among the gulls, which flew up in a crowd as the skua landed. It eventually flew off, and, keeping low over the water, pounced on a Coot, first with its feet and then attacking it with its bill. A terrific struggle ensued and both birds were often half submerged. Eventually the Coot went limp and was lifted into the air and dropped into the water, before being picked at by the skua for the next half-hour. Miss G. Grainger reported the incident in *The Naturalist*, 1969, p. 4.

On 17th August 1984, while watching from the Marine Drive at Scarborough, R.H. Appleby saw a Sooty Shearwater flying leisurely northwards when suddenly a Great Skua appeared behind it, presumably having been sitting on the sea, and gave chase. The shearwater weaved and dipped to avoid its pursuer and then suddenly ditched into the sea, followed closely by the skua. Both birds took off again and the performance was repeated several times during the next five minutes, before the Sooty ditched again, whereupon the skua went in with a great splash and finally killed it.

Great Black-headed Gull
Larus ichthyaetus

A bird seen at Lingerfield Tip, near Knaresborough, from 31st March until at least 14th April 1967, originally believed to be an immature example of this species, has since been re-appraised and is now considered to be an immature Great Black-backed Gull with aberrant head markings.

The bird was most striking in appearance, with dark areas on each side of the head and on the crown, and its behaviour was subtly different from that of the Great Black-backs present. Its head shape was much 'finer' than is normal in that species and it exhibited other small differences which were difficult to relate. During its stay, it was seen by very many people from all over the British Isles.

Examination of skins in the British Museum at Tring revealed that a pale grey mantle should have been moulting in on a bird of this age, and in addition the species is altogether much more lightly built. Having subsequently watched several Great Black-headed Gulls in northern India, I am quite satisfied that a mistake was made and the record must be deleted from the Yorkshire list.

Photographs were published in *British Birds*, 1968, plate 48, one of which is reproduced on plate 82 of this work.

Mediterranean Gull
Larus melanocephalus

An example of this species, said to be an adult in winter plumage, was shot on the Yorkshire coast in November 1895. Nelson was in possession of the full details of its occurrence, but the owner of the specimen did not wish them to be published. A photograph of the mounted bird appears in *The Birds of Yorkshire*, and it is clearly not an adult as claimed. The outer primaries are black with white spots near the tips and the bird is thus in its second-year.

The next Mediterranean Gull to be seen in the county was not until 63 years later. On 12th October 1958, D.M. Burn, K. Hardcastle, R.C. Parkinson, A.F.G. Walker, C. Winn and myself put to sea off Scarborough in a small coble skippered by 'Blondie' Wood, who made several such trips for me in the late 1950s. The sea was calm and fairly uninteresting except for a Sooty Shearwater which passed us when about 3 miles (4.8 km) offshore. When we were 5 miles (8 km) out, the engine was cut and we drifted while having some lunch. A small group of Herring, Common and Black-headed Gulls assembled near the boat and came to feed on bread thrown to them. The day was warm and the sea mirror-calm, and hundreds of spiders were drifting along just above the surface of the sea, each on a long strand of gossamer, being carried by only the slightest breeze. We noticed an unusual gull among the assembly, and for the next half-hour or so watched it at close range as it flew around and sat on the sea. It was a second-year individual, with the outer webs of the first primary black and some black bands near the tips of the third and fourth primaries. The bill was mainly black, yellowish towards the base and with a cream-coloured nail. There was a dark area behind the eye and the mantle was very pale grey. The bird stayed with the other gulls and followed the boat for some time as we returned to the harbour.

The Mediterranean Gull at one time nested only in the area of the Black Sea, Turkey and Greece, but a few pairs nested in Holland during the 1960s and occasional pairs have bred in Hampshire since 1965.

Since 1958, it has occurred in Yorkshire in almost every year up to 1970 and has done so annually since then. An adult with a full black hood flew south at Spurn during a heavy passage of Common Gulls on 2nd May 1959 and was seen by K. Hardcastle and C. Winn. T.M. Clegg watched an adult at the Scarborough sewage outlet on 30th January 1960, and G.R. Bennett saw a first-winter bird at Atwick on 16th October in the same year. An adult was at Spurn on 21st October 1962 and was watched by J.M. Butterworth, M. Densley and P.H.G. Wolstenholme; a second bird was there on 9th November 1963. An adult in summer plumage was seen by R.H. Appleby, D.I. Fotherby and A.J. Wallis at Scarborough on seven dates between 21st March and 14th May 1965, and a first-winter bird was seen there on 30th August by T.M. Clegg. Single adults were seen at Spurn on 21st July and 18th October 1967. In 1969 three occurred: at Filey Brigg on 1st March, when one was watched by R.H. Appleby, C.R. Clark and F.J. Thompson; an adult at Hornsea on 13th July, seen by M.G. Hodgson; and the third, seen by A.J. Wallis at Scarborough, on 1st October. An adult was seen at South Gare on 1st March 1970 by N. Jackson and H. Mitchell, and a first-year bird was seen at Hornsea Mere on 15th and 16th October 1970 by W.F. Curtis. In 1972, an adult flew south at Spurn on 13th August, a first-year bird was on the Humber there on 1st October, and W.F. Curtis watched a second-year individual on the sea off Hornsea on 26th August.

No fewer than eight birds occurred in 1973 as follows: single adults were seen at Spurn on 1st April, 30th September, 13th October and 10th November; a sub-adult was seen by P.M. Ellis at Bridlington on 19th May; an adult was seen by W.F. Curtis at Hornsea on 9th August; a second-winter bird was seen at Jackson's Bay, Scarborough, on 14th October by D.I. Fotherby; and a different second-winter individual was seen at Scalby Mils, Scarborough, on 3rd November by R.H. Appleby and B. Cockerill, full details of this bird being published in the Yorkshire Naturalists' Union Ornithological Report for 1973, pp. 6-8.

There were six records in 1974, some probably referring to the same individual. One was at Jackson's Bay on 24th March; another at Scalby Mills on 9th April, with two different immature birds from 11th to 21st April; an adult was at Tunstall on 31st March; and an adult flew south at Spurn on 24th July.

Since that time, the Mediterranean Gull has increased dramatically as a visitor to Yorkshire and records during the period 1975 to 1983 have been far too numerous to list in detail. The first real increase came in 1975, when it was estimated that at least 24 individual birds visited the county. Most were in the Scarborough district, Scalby Mills with its freshwater stream running out over the tidal rocks being the most popular haunt with up to six birds present on some dates during February and March. Others were seen at Filey Brigg, Flamborough, Spurn and Skeffling. The first inland records also came in 1975, when a first-year bird was seen by P. Bray at Blackmoorfoot Reservoir on 4th August and another first-year was seen at Fairburn Ings by P.D. Kirk and C. Winn on 10th and 14th September.

Similar numbers have occurred along the coast in each year since, with up to nine different individuals in the Scalby area in 1976. A first-winter bird appeared in Bridlington Harbour on 31st October 1978 and has occurred there in every year to the present time.

Coincident with the coastal increase was an increase in sightings at inland waters. Birds occurred at five places in 1976; one in 1977; four in 1978; four in 1979; three in 1980; seven in 1981; and at three in 1982. Fairburn Ings had Mediterranean Gulls in 1976, 1978, 1979 and 1980, all of which were seen during the summer months; a first-winter bird was there on 31st May 1976, another first-summer bird on 4th June 1978, a first-summer bird on 1st June 1979, and another of the same age on 10th June 1980.

Other places where Mediterranean Gulls have occurred are Elland Gravel-pit, Broomhill Flash, Blackmoorfoot Reservoir, Roundhay Park in Leeds, Tadcaster, Wheldrake Ings, Bradford, Stamford Bridge, Eskrick near York, Wath Ings, Eccup Reservoir, Wintersett Reservoir, Pugneys Gravel-pit, Greasborough Tip, Carlton Marsh, Langsett Reservoir and Scaling Dam.

The change in status of this gull from that of a very rare vagrant, which it was up to 1958, to the very regular visitor that it is today is quite remarkable, and reflects a westward breeding spread in Europe. It can now be confidently expected to occur along the Yorkshire coastline from Spurn to Teesmouth in every year, mainly during the non-breeding season, but with a few during the summer, and it is being seen with increasing regularity at inland waters. The species has come a long way during the last 25 years, since the forerunner appeared off Scarborough in October 1958 and was originally rejected by the *British Birds* Rarities Committee, who were not tuned in to the species at that time.

For full details of Mediterranean Gull records in Yorkshire up to and including 1977, see *The Naturalist*, 1979, pp. 135-43.

Laughing Gull
Larus atricilla

This North American species entered the Yorkshire list of birds with a flourish in 1978. On 24th September, an adult was seen by P.D. Kirk and C. Winn at Fairburn Ings where it re-appeared on seven occasions up to 7th October, but did not spend any time there as it was always seen in flight over the ings. An adult bird was seen at Flamborough Head on 19th September by A. Grieve, P.A. Lassey and Miss Irene Smith; a first-year individual was seen by D.I.M. Wallace in Bridlington North Bay on 24th September; and an adult was seen by S. Rooke at the Bridlington sewer outlet on 13th November. The two adult sightings may have referred to the same individual.

T.E. Dixon saw an adult bird in winter plumage at Faxfleet on the Upper Humber on 5th September 1983, details of which have not yet been submitted to the *British Birds* Rarities Committee.

On 16th April 1984, P. Coupland saw an immature example in East Park, Hull, while he was photographing the ducks and geese. It was swimming with Common and Black-headed Gulls and eventually sat on a log with three of the latter, when photographs were taken which clearly show a second-year Laughing Gull.

In the evening of 23rd July 1984, at Filey, H.J. Whitehead checked the gull flock feeding at the end of the brigg and located a Laughing Gull which he aged as a second-year bird moulting into winter plumage. It was also seen by W.A. Clarke, T.L. Hobson, F. Nendick and A. Whitehead.

Later in the year, on 9th November 1984, A. Wrightson found an unfamiliar gull on a small playing field surrounded by houses in a Hull suburb. He identified it as a Laughing Gull and many people were able to watch it, as it sat on the goalposts and fed with Black-headed Gulls, during its stay until at least the end of the year.

It is very likely that the same bird was involved in these last three sightings.

The Laughing Gull is a common breeding bird in North America and has been recorded in the British Isles on some 40 or more occasions.

Little Gull
Larus minutus

At the beginning of the twentieth century, the Little Gull was known as an autumn and winter visitor to Yorkshire, irregular, and varying in numbers. According to Nelson, it had occurred more frequently on the Yorkshire coast than in any other part of the British Isles and was therefore of more than passing interest to Yorkshire ornithologists. It was, at that time, expected during September and October, especially during stormy weather, and was most numerous at Bridlington and Flamborough. No fewer than 150 were 'obtained' at these two localities during Nelson's time. Mr T. Boynton of Bridlington procured 30 birds, most of which he shot himself between the years 1868 and 1872, and M. Bailey, the Flamborough taxidermist, had 40 birds through his hands up to 1881. Bailey told Nelson that he once observed a flock of about 12 Little Gulls, and Nelson considered that he (Bailey) had perhaps done more than anyone to make it known as a Yorkshire species.

J.H. Gurney had 13 sent to him in 1868; 30 were obtained in Bridlington Bay during a full easterly gale between 12th and 14th February 1870, 19 of which were adults; about 20 were taken at Scarborough between 1836 and 1902; and Redcar and Teesmouth claimed 15 specimens between 1849 and 1902. In his annotated copy of *The Birds of Yorkshire*, Nelson included a flock of 30 off Redcar in October 1905.

Chislett knew of no large numbers up to 1952 when he published his *Yorkshire Birds*, and he listed only one or two birds at any one place during the autumn and winter months. He said they were very rare at inland waters and had only four records to report: one at High Royd Sewage-farm on 23rd October 1947; two adults and two juveniles at Swillington Ings on 19th November 1949; one at Eccup Reservoir on 14th October 1950; and a juvenile at Dewsbury Sewage-farm from 7th to 12th September 1951.

The species was probably overlooked to some extent during the 45 years of Chislett's review as more were certainly seen thereafter, and since the late 1960s there has been a definite increase in the number of Little Gulls visiting Yorkshire. This cannot, however, be attributed solely to an increase in observer activity and there seems to be a real tendency for the species to visit Britain in larger numbers than formerly.

In 1970, 96 birds were at Spurn on 7th October and 52 flew south off Filey in four hours on 25th October. On 14th and 15th October 1972, P.A. Lassey saw 29 and 86 birds fly south off Kettleness. Hornsea Mere became a popular feeding place for the species at this time, and in 1974 there were maximum counts of 28 on 27th August; 23 on 31st August; 50 on 6th September; 49 on 18th September; and 22 on 1st October. Ten birds were at Swillington Ings on 15th April 1974, and Fairburn Ings recorded 22 individuals between 15th April and 19th May in the same year.

In 1976, 85 flew east, then north, at Flamborough on 25th September; 21 on 1st October; 73 flew east, then turned north there on 28th October, and smaller numbers passed into November. At Spurn, there were 40 on 27th October, 55 on 29th October, 19 on 30th October and 46 on 17th November. Inland at Fairburn Ings, there were 44 birds between 25th April and 10th May, mostly adults in summer plumage. One at Scalby Mills on 18th July 1976, seen by R.H. Appleby, was in full summer plumage with a definite pink flush on the underparts.

The maximum counts in 1978 were on 1st October, when 66 flew north at Spurn, 107 flew north at Hornsea and 89 flew north off Flamborough.

There were more birds in 1980, the build-up at Hornsea Mere starting on 17th July and reaching 14 birds by 29th, 170 on 22nd August, 85 on 23rd August, 30 on 18th September, with the last bird on 25th September. Little Gulls were also over the sea off Hornsea during the same period, with 105 on 10th August and 113 on 13th August. Birds were seen at Spurn from 16th April to 2nd November, with a maximum of 71 flying north on 25th October. There were records from 13 inland waters between 18th April and 21st September, one to three birds being usual, but a flock of 20 dropped into Treeton Reservoir for two minutes on 7th May.

In 1982, a very large movement of Little Gulls occurred off the watchpoints at Flamborough Head and Filey Brigg. Between 24th September and 7th October, 5,413 were counted passing, mainly to the south, off Flamborough, and 1,304 off Filey. The main passage took place after periods of low pressure with heavy rain, and usually coincided with winds from the south-southeast. It is likely that these birds were forced over to the west side of the North Sea by these winds and would otherwise have moved south off the Dutch coast. Very full details of the movements have been written up for *The Naturalist* by P.J. Dunn and P.A. Lassey.

A count of 174 birds at Hornsea Mere on 18th August 1983 was the highest number ever recorded at that locality.

The Little Gull is obviously more numerous now than formerly and occurs in Yorkshire in all months of the year, most numerously during April-May and from July to October. During these periods, it can be seen almost anywhere along the coastline, but particularly off Flamborough Head, Hornsea, and Spurn Point, where large parties often pass north or south depending on the season or the weather. At any suitable inland water, small numbers may feed for short periods before passing on, with an occasional larger party at times of peak migration. Hornsea Mere is a most popular feeding place and large numbers occur there annually in both spring and autumn.

The species breeds mainly in northern and eastern Europe, from the Netherlands, the Gulf of Bothnia and north Russia southeast to the Black Sea and eastwards to Siberia. During recent years, a few single adults have been seen in attendance at breeding colonies of Black-headed Gulls in Britain, and on 17th June 1958 an adult was seen among a colony of Black-headed Gulls at Fairburn Ings. The bird called and displayed over the colony and showed particular interest in one small area. Flooding on 28th June, however, washed out the whole colony, which was then deserted.

In 1966, H.O. Bunce watched an adult in full breeding plumage at a small colony of Black-headed Gulls in the Lower Derwent Valley, between 14th and 28th May. Single immature Little Gulls attended Black-headed Gull colonies on Thorne Moors on 8th June 1969, 6th and 7th June 1970 and 20th May 1972 (*British Birds*, 1979, p. 190).

In 1978, breeding was attempted at Fairburn Ings where, on 27th May, two adults and an immature were located at a colony of about 100 pairs of Black-headed Gulls. On 3rd June, one adult was seen to carry nest material to a site and building continued throughout the following day. The nest was virtually complete by 5th June and on the following evening a bird was sitting and shuffling on the nest, suggestive of turning eggs. The nest was closely watched during the next few weeks and everything went well until one of the adults was found injured on 25th June, by which time the eggs should have been ready for hatching. Inspection of the site on 27th June to ascertain the exact situation did not reveal any conclusive proof that the attempt had been successful, and it was difficult to locate the nest in the growing vegetation. One nest, however, which was regarded as that of the Little Gulls, was empty. This was only the second known breeding attempt in the British Isles, and very full details written by S.C. Madge were published in *The Naturalist*, 1979, pp. 143-6.

Sabine's Gull
Larus sabini

T.H. Nelson listed records of 48 Sabine's Gulls in Yorkshire between 1866 and 1905. Of the 36 for which an age is given, 15 were adult and 21 were immature. Nelson inspected 12 of the preserved specimens and a case containing an adult and two juvenile birds can be seen in the Nelson Collection at the Dorman Museum at Middlesbrough. It is possible that a few juvenile Little Gulls were erroneously identified as Sabine's Gulls at this time, and a case containing a juvenile Little Gull in the Nelson Collection is labelled 'Sabine's Gull — immature'. This is one of only two cases for which there are no details available, and it is possible that the museum was responsible for the incorrect labelling when the collection was prepared for exhibition.

The first record came from Bridlington on 5th September 1866. It was an adult female and the specimen went to the collection of Thomas Boynton, where Nelson saw it.

During the 45 years between the publication of *The Birds of Yorkshire* in 1907 and *Yorkshire Birds* in 1952, only 11 Sabine's Gulls were recorded, one of these inland at Wintersett Reservoir from 19th to 29th September 1950 which was watched and described by J. Cudworth, P. Davis and others (*The Naturalist*, 1951, p. 11). The locality for this bird was erroneously published by Chislett in *Yorkshire Birds* as Ossett Sewage-farm.

Since 1952, the species has been seen with increasing frequency each year, doubtless as a result, at least in part, of the more intensive and efficient sea-watching during the last 20 years. During the period 1953 to 1970, a total of 18 birds was recorded during August, September and October along the coast of Spurn, Filey, Whitby and South Gare. There were four records in 1971, five in 1972 and four in 1973, all ocurring between 26th July and 9th November.

D.I.M. Wallace saw an adult bird off Flamborough Head on the unusual date of 10th February 1974. At Spurn, during August 1974, the species occurred offshore with a flock of feeding Kittiwakes and single adults were seen on 14th, 22nd and 23rd of that month, with two Sabine's present on 24th and 25th and one on 26th. Adult birds were seen flying south there on 1st, 2nd and 3rd September; a young bird flew north on 29th September; and adults flew north on 22nd and 23rd

October. Three first-year birds were off Bempton on 18th September in the same year, two adults flew north off Scarborough on 3rd October and a first-year bird frequented the harbour sewage outlet on 12th October. The year 1974 also produced the second inland record for the county when an adult bird was seen by C. Winn at Fairburn Ings during the late afternoon of 14th October.

Only three birds were seen in 1975, all off Flamborough and all adults: one flew north on 17th May, one flew southwest on 9th August and one flew north on 3rd September. There were two spring records in 1976, one at Filey on 6th March and the other at Flamborough on 3rd April, while in the autumn Flamborough had 12 birds as follows; one on 28th August, single birds on 10th, 11th and 25th September and on 15th, 18th, 28th and 29th October, with two on 30th October and singles again on 9th and 11th December. Immature birds were off Filey on 9th and 11th September, and an adult was off Withernsea on 17th November.

In 1977, D.I.M. Wallace saw one flying north off Flamborough Head on 15th January; P.A. Lassey saw a first-year bird flying south there on 21st May; and a first-year bird was at Spurn on 19th June. At the year end, 14 birds occurred between 15th August and 31st December, mainly during late August and mid September, at Spurn (one), Hornsea (two), Flamborough (nine) and Scarborough (two).

More Sabine's Gulls were recorded in the county in 1978 than ever before. Most records came from Flamborough Head, where two adults flew south on 28th January; one adult flew north on 8th April; four birds, including three definite adults, flew north on 1st May; and a first-year bird flew north on 12th June. The autumn produced one at Flamborough on 28th July; six birds in August, including two adults in full summer plumage at Flamborough and another at Mappleton; nine birds in September, at Spurn (one), Flamborough (six) including four adults on 19th, Filey (one) and Burniston (one); six in October, at Hornsea (one), Flamborough (one), Filey (one), Scarborough (one) and Scalby Mills (two); no fewer than 11 in December, at Spurn (one) and Flamborough (ten) including three adults and three first-year birds on 31st, and finally one off Redcar on 30th December. The third inland record also came in 1978 when D.M. Pullan saw and sketched an adult bird in full plumage at Knotford Nook Gravel-pit on 5th September.

Regular watching by D.I.M. Wallace at Flamborough Head during the early part of 1979 revealed passing Sabine's Gulls on 11 dates from 1st January to 8th April. A total of 25 was seen, 12 of which flew north, seven south or southeast and six east. The birds passed within, or just beyond, the regular stream of gulls that rounds the headland and were always in the company of Kittiwakes. It was thought that some of the same individuals were involved on several of the dates. Full details of these records appeared in the Yorkshire Naturalists' Union Ornithological Report for 1981, pp. 57-8. One flew north at Filey on 23rd February; one flew north at Spurn on 11th June; and six others were seen between 8th August and 30th September, at Spurn (one), Hornsea (two), Mappleton (one), Flamborough (one) and Filey (one).

Of 12 coastal records in 1980, ten came from Flamborough with single birds on 19th March and 23rd May and the remainder between 22nd August and 10th November. One was up the River Humber at Whitton Sands on 9th August, one was at Spurn on 22nd August, and the fourth inland record came from Blackmoorfoot Reservoir, where P.D. Bell saw an adult on 29th August.

Flamborough Head produced eight of the ten records in 1981, single birds being seen on 4th January and 25th April and two each in August, September and October, and single birds were at Spurn and at Withernsea in September.

There were records of 17 birds in 1982, at Spurn, Flamborough, Burniston and Scarborough between 24th July and 12th November, with one at Flamborough on 10th April and one inland at Blackmoorfoot Reservoir on 1st October which was reported by M.L. Denton.

Far more is now known about the status of the Sabine's Gull on the Yorkshire coast than formerly, and there appears to be a small presence in the North Sea during the winter months as evidenced by the records in December and January in several recent years. September is undoubtedly the main month of occurrence.

Bonaparte's Gull
Larus philadelphia

This small gull, which breeds in the northern part of North America in Alaska and Canada, and spends the winter months on the Great Lakes and along the Atlantic and Pacific seaboards of the United States, has occurred in the British Isles on some 47 occasions, three of which have been in Yorkshire.

The first, at Swillington Ings on 11th February 1948, was seen by K. Dawson and F.R. Allison as it swam among Black-headed and Herring Gulls and was observed to bathe and preen before flying around eventually to land on the mud, where it was watched for half-an-hour. Chislett examined sketches and very detailed plumage notes, which he published in full in *Yorkshire Birds*, pp. 283-4.

The second was seen at Filey on 20th June 1969 by L.G. Dewdney, who was there on holiday with his wife and family. While birdwatching from the promenade, he saw a small gull approaching along the wall which he identified as an immature of this species and for which he submitted detailed notes and sketches.

The third occurred at Flamborough Head, where D.I.M. Wallace saw an immature bird on 13th September 1973.

Black-headed Gull
Larus ridibundus

There is no doubt that the Black-headed Gull is now more numerous during the breeding season in Yorkshire than it was at the turn of the century. Nelson said that it was very local in the nesting season and knew it mainly as a coastal bird during the spring and autumn.

A drastic national decline in breeding numbers occurred in the latter part of the nineteenth century, reducing the population to near extinction, but a recovery was under way by the end of the century although it was then a much scarcer breeding bird than it is today. Clarke and Roebuck, in their *Handbook of Yorkshire Vertebrata* published in 1881, listed only two places where the species bred; a large colony existed on Thorne Waste and a few pairs were revisiting Strensall Common in 1881. The inaccessibility of the high Pennine moorlands at that time would have made it difficult to know the exact status, and it is almost certain that scattered moorland colonies existed then.

By 1952, Chislett was able to say that it bred at more inland localities in Yorkshire than at any time, although he doubted whether the bird was any more numerous than before land drainage schemes robbed it of the lowland marshes where large colonies once existed. Some of these had been destroyed during the late nineteenth century, and by 1907 there were 'but a few small colonies and scattered, or isolated, nesting sites'.

The earliest known colony was near Thornton Bridge, Bedale, where Bishop Nicholson of Carlisle, on a journey from Carlisle to York in 1702, said that 'thousands of Blackcap Mews' were breeding on a nearby moss. Nelson reported a large colony on the island in Hornsea Mere during the late nineteenth century which was eventually deserted when the ground was planted with potatoes. Today, the island is covered with large trees and quite unsuitable for breeding gulls. A large colony existed on Strensall Common until about 1880, by which time it was almost deserted. About 30 pairs bred up to 1884, but the eggs were taken and no young were hatched. Drainage and military activity caused the eventual desertion of this old site. Riccal and Skipwith Commons were also mentioned as breeding places, and the species still nests there. In 1940 there were about 200 birds at the Skipwith colony, and 500 pairs in 1980 and 1981. The moors about Goole and Thorne also held breeding colonies which still exist today, and in 1975 no fewer than 1,500 pairs bred at the latter locality. Potteric Carr held 250 breeding pairs in 1978.

Nelson mentioned the existence until 1865 of a small colony of four pairs at Summer Lodge Tarn, where today several hundred pairs nest annually. At Locker Tarn, a colony was founded in 1888 when a single pair nested. By 1902 there were about 40 or 50 pairs at Locker Tarn and at the present time there are many more, a count of 1,000 pairs being made in 1965 and subsequently. The species has nested at Fairburn Ings since at least 1942, when about 30 pairs were present; numbers have never been large at this locality, and 83 and 92 pairs were counted in 1980 and 1981 respectively.

The creation of reservoirs, sewage-farms and gravel-pits in more recent years has provided the Black-headed Gull with ample opportunity to extend its breeding stations. Rotherham Sewage-farm had 100 pairs in 1948 and 700 birds were there on 7th May 1949. The gravel-pits at Masham and Nosterfield now have breeding colonies, with 250 and 83 pairs respectively in 1981. No fewer than 6,000 pairs were reported by J. Fenton at Stocks Reservoir in 1978. The floodwaters along the Lower Derwent Valley have regularly hosted small breeding colonies, and in 1980 there were 30 pairs at Wheldrake Ings and 150 pairs at North Duffield Ings.

The moorland tarns and mosses of the Pennines are well established breeding haunts, and in recent years, in addition to Summer Lodge Tarn and Locker Tarn mentioned above, good colonies exist at Whitaside Tarn (500 pairs in 1965); Bowes Moor (1,000 pairs in 1950 and 1,200 pairs in 1951); Haworth Moors (500 pairs in 1950); Black Moss (70 pairs in 1975, 150 in 1978 and 120 in 1980); Dallowgill Moor (500 pairs in 1975); Grassington Moor (115 pairs in 1975); and Arnagill Moor (500 pairs in 1980). The smaller moorland colonies may shift from time to time and new ones often spring up, perhaps for only a short period. Twelve pairs bred at Lower Gorple Reservoir for the first time in 1975, and four pairs nested at Crow Hill above Halifax in 1978. Many other gulleries, for which there are no up-to-date figures, exist all along the Pennine chain from the south of the county northwards to Bowes Moor, and there are many more at lowland places where the right conditions exist. Such may be of a temporary nature as sewage-farms or gravel-pits change, the latter often being restored to agriculture or 'tidied-up' for recreational use.

Many breeding colonies have suffered badly over the years, mainly from game-keepers and egg collectors, and it was a popular pastime at many moorland sites for local farmworkers to collect the eggs for food. Gamekeepers have destroyed nests in the supposed interests of their grouse, whose chicks are thought to be taken by the gulls. A small colony on Whernside in 1943 was robbed by soldiers with buckets which they filled with eggs. In spite of these pressures, the species is doing well and expanding, and is a very common bird in the breeding season over almost every part of the county except in the southeastern corner, east of a line drawn through the Wolds from Scarborough to Market Weighton.

H.B. Booth undertook a survey of the gulleries in 1920 (*The Naturalist*, 1921, pp. 159-66), and R. Chislett attempted a similar one in 1938 (*antea*, 1939, pp. 125-30).

During the non-breeding season, reservoirs along the edge of the Pennines attract large numbers of Black-headed Gulls which often spend the night there on the water. The most popular during the last 15 years have been Wintersett Reservoir (12,000 on 18th December 1976, 10,000 on 22nd January 1977, 15,000 on 2nd January 1978 and 6,000 in January 1981); Southfield Reservoir (6,250 on 16th December 1962, 8,000 on 16th August 1976 and 12,000 on 14th October 1977); Blackmoorfoot Reservoir (7,000 on 18th January 1975 and 6,000 in January 1981); Eccup Reservoir (21,000 on 12th October 1955, 10,000 on 4th November 1961, 14,000 in January 1977, 10,000 in November 1977, 15,000 in December 1979 and 13,000 on 1st February 1981); and Ardsley Reservoir, where there were 13,500 on 25th November 1972. Several other waters regularly hold smaller numbers, ranging from 1,000 to 5,000 birds. Waters at a lower altitude also hold large roosts, notably Fairburn Ings where high counts in recent years have been 20,000 on 4th April 1964, again on 4th March 1965 and on 9th November 1968; 9,000 on 23rd January 1972; 10,000 in February 1975 and again in January 1976; 8,000 on 26th December 1979; and 6,000 in January 1981. Blacktoft Sands and the Upper Humber area around Whitton Sands often attract very large concentrations. The former locality had 25,000 on 21st August 1975 and again on 15th September 1979. A large roost in the Whitton Sands area held 20,000 during September 1976 and again on 24th October 1977, and 50,000 on 16th September 1980.

The floodwaters along the Lower Derwent Valley have attracted spectacular numbers over the years. In March 1959, 10,000 came in to roost, and in 1980 there were counts of 50,000 on 17th February, 40,000 on 1st March reducing to 12,000 by 9th March, and 15,000 on 22nd November.

Along the coast, some roosting assemblies form offshore each evening during the non-breeding season. Scarborough North Bay is such a place and 12,000 were counted there on 12th April 1975 and 8,000 on 13th January 1981. The rocks at Scalby Mills are a very popular feeding and resting place and gatherings of 1,000 to 5,000 birds are regular during the winter months. S.M. Lister counted 14,000 gathering on the sea off Barmston in the evening of 12th March 1978.

Many of the Black-headed Gulls which are present in Yorkshire during the autumn and winter months come to us from Scandinavia, Denmark and sometimes farther east. Ringing recoveries of birds ringed as chicks, which are too numerous to list in detail, have shown that those subsequently found in Yorkshire during the winter months have come from Norway, Sweden, Denmark, Bavaria, Czechoslovakia and Poland. There are very many recoveries of birds ringed as chicks at Yorkshire gulleries, mostly from places elsewhere in Britain and Ireland, but some from abroad; these include two ringed on Heptonstall Moors in 1954 and 1962 which were recovered in France and Spain respectively, and one ringed at Swillington Ings in June 1952 which was recovered at Rabat in Morocco in March 1954, the most southerly recovery for the species.

The large roosts and coastal feeding assemblies start to disperse during March as birds return to their breeding grounds, either elsewhere in Britain or across the North Sea. In the early autumn, the first birds to appear in non-breeding areas are moulting adults, followed soon afterwards by juveniles which, having left their natal colonies, start to flock together for the winter.

The Black-headed Gull is perhaps most familiar to countrymen as the gull which follows the plough, although the Common Gull also does so regularly in some areas. It often consorts with Lapwing flocks for the purpose of robbing them of earthworms and other food items, which it forces them to drop by chasing and harrying. Tunstall referred to it as the Peewit Gull in 1784, doubtless because of this association.

The present status of this familiar gull is that of a common breeding bird over much of the county, its numbers being greatly augmented each autumn by birds from Continental Europe. Some Yorkshire-bred young disperse into Ireland, southwards throughout England, and there are ringing recoveries in France, Iberia and North Africa.

Ring-billed Gull
Larus delawarensis

This North American gull did not enter the British list of birds until 1973 and since that time it has been seen almost annually.

On 10th October 1978, P.A. Lassey watched a gull at Flamborough which he identified as this species. The *British Birds* Rarities Committee declined to accept the record, but the observer was convinced of his diagnosis and remains adamant.

On 19th December in the same year, a first-winter bird was seen at Coatham Marsh, near Redcar, by D.J. Britton and the record was accepted by the *British Birds* Rarities Committee.

The third Yorkshire record came from Blackmoorfoot Reservoir, where J.E. Dale watched an immature bird for 20 minutes on 23rd December 1979.

T.A. Ede watched one at Whitton Sands on 30th September 1981, and a second-year bird was seen by M.L. Denton at Blackmoorfoot Reservoir on 11th February 1982.

That more will be seen in the county I have no doubt. Gull-watching is now a favourite pastime for many birdwatchers, and this species is high on the list of expected discoveries.

Common Gull
Larus canus

Known by Nelson as a fairly abundant winter visitor with a few birds remaining about the estuaries of the Tees and Humber during the summer months, the status of the Common Gull has probably changed very little during the last 75 years, although better coverage of the many reservoirs and other inland waters and also along the coast has shown that many more birds frequent Yorkshire than were known to Nelson. In Chislett's *Yorkshire Birds*, only a handful of records involving large numbers were quoted, including 1,000 at Easington on 4th August 1947 and on 19th May 1950; 1,000 roosting on Malham Tarn on 5th November 1950; and 6,000-8,000 passing eastwards from floodwater near Kellythorne in the East Riding on 4th April 1947. Such spring movements are well known today, and many birds can be seen moving northwards or across the county during April on their way back to the breeding grounds in Scotland and Scandinavia.

During July each year, the first immigrant Common Gulls arrive along the coast, where some spend the winter months, others passing inland to cross the country. Anywhere along the coastline from the Tees to the Humber, from that time until October, birds can be seen moving southwards. Numbers are sometimes large and many thousands are involved; more pass in some years than in others. The

Humber Estuary holds spectacular numbers and the Birds of Estuaries Enquiry count on 27th January 1980 showed a total of 55,857 along the Humber shore from Spurn to Goole. In 1978, 15,000 were gathered in the upper estuary on 19th February and 50,000 gulls were present on 18th October, most of which were of this species. The Tees Estuary held 12,000 in February 1977; 15,000 were on Coatham Sands on 14th January 1978, and the Birds of Estuaries Enquiry count for that year revealed 34,000 there on 27th January, 7,000 of which remained up to mid February; 8,700 were in the estuary on 14th January 1979 and 6,000 on 4th January 1980. After a period of easterly gales in January 1979, which deposited a huge quantity of wrack along the beach southwards from Bridlington, I saw at least 10,000 gulls feeding there on 25th January, at least 4,000 of which were of this species.

Some roosts at inland waters may be large and involve birds from over a wide area. Eccup Reservoir undoubtedly holds the largest gatherings, and maximum counts over the years have been 5,900 on 24th August and 600 on 2nd October 1960; 3,500 on 21st August and 600 on 26th September 1974; 5,000 during September and 4,000 during December 1975; 4,000 during December 1977; 8,500 on 1st January and 6,500 on 7th December 1980; and 6,000 on 1st January and 6,750 on 13th December 1981. Many other inland reservoirs and gravel-pits attract birds to spend the night in safety on the open water and roosting assemblies of 1,000 to 2,000 birds are not rare, smaller numbers being quite commonplace. Large areas of open short grassland such as playing fields, and especially The Stray at Harrogate, are favourite feeding places where birds often attend Lapwings to rob them of their catches of earthworms. Arable land is also favoured and the species often follows the plough with Black-headed Gulls. On the Wolds, flocks are more often than not solely of Common Gulls.

Common Gulls start returning to their northern breeding grounds by March and the passage is usually in full swing by April, when loose flocks may be seen passing at inland localities or steady streams of birds moving up the coast. It has been noted at Spurn, and elsewhere along the coast, that birds passing northwards in spring are, as would be expected, all adults while a southerly movement of immatures has often occurred at the same time.

There have been several recoveries of ringed birds in Yorkshire, showing Scandinavia and Denmark to be the origin of some of our winter visitors.

The species was not known to nest in the county until 1955, when a pair built a nest on a rock at Malham Tarn. The birds incubated from 23rd June and the eggs hatched in late July, but no young were reared. In 1957, P. Young, a gamekeeper naturalist with a healthy attitude to natural history, located a nest on Ilton Moor. Two small chicks were lying dead by the nest and a Lesser Black-backed Gull was skulking around the area. The site was on high rocky ground about 1 mile (1.6 km) from the nearest water. A pair nested on the moors above Scaling Dam in 1966 and 1967 (see plate 79). In 1970, M.V. Bell found a nest with two eggs by a moor-land tarn in Upper Wharfedale on 6th June and a pair with one newly hatched chick at another site in August. A pair was thought to have been successful in 1971, and a pair had three eggs on 6th June 1975. In 1976, two pairs attempted to breed: one nest with a single egg was seen on 7th June, and a dead chick and two empty nests were located on 19th June while the anxious adults flew overhead. B. Shorrock reported that one pair nested near Settle in 1976, 1977 and 1978, and single pairs bred at Stainmore in 1980 and at Fountains Fell Tarn in 1981.

T.H. Nelson recorded an incident at Teesmouth when a cyclone hit the area on 2nd July 1914 and hail and falling lumps of clear ice killed several hundreds of gulls, most of which were of this species (see *British Birds*, 1914, pp. 67-9).

Lesser Black-backed Gull
Larus fuscus

The Lesser Black-backed Gull is a scarce breeding bird in Yorkshire. Nelson said that he had 'abundant proof' that they nested in one or two localities near Whitby among the colonies of Herring Gulls. When he visited the cliffs in 1878, two pairs were seen, and a few pairs occurred every year after that time up to 1907 when *The Birds of Yorkshire* was published. According to Chislett, one or two pairs continued to breed at this locality up to 1952 and some have done so since then. P.J. Stead found a pair at Boulby on 30th May 1954, and another pair had three eggs at Kettleness on 30th June 1954. In 1973, a pair frequented the cliffs at Bempton and probably bred but, although a close watch was kept by H.O. Bunce and S.C. Madge, the site was not easily visible from the clifftop and confirmation was not possible. A few pairs attempted to nest on the islands in Stocks Reservoir in 1940 and 1941, and in some subsequent years, but the eggs were taken by keepers.

A large gullery on the moors in Bowland at Roeburndale, which straddles the border between Yorkshire and Lancashire, has been known since at least 1947. Most of the 1,000 pairs counted in 1950 were on the Lancashire side of the border and, of the 1,500-2,000 pairs in 1951, very few were actually on the Yorkshire side. Many chicks were ringed at this site during the 1950s by P.E. Davis. R.F. Dickens, D.B. Isles and P.C. Quin, who also supplied much useful information on the numbers present at the colony. The eggs were collected by gamekeepers in 1953, and the gullery suffered much at the hand of man over the years. In spite of persecution, however, the colony increased from 2,000 pairs in 1966 to a staggering 17,000 pairs in 1972, most of which were in Lancashire (see *Birds in Lancashire* by K.G. Spencer, 1973, p. 38).

During the early 1950s when Davis and Isles were visiting the colony regularly, they took note of the food items brought in by the birds to feed their young. These included seafish, crabs, seashells, potato chips, bones, hens' eggs and a pot egg, a golf ball, orange peel, metal milk-bottle tops and the heads and feet of fowls, no doubt most collected at some rubbish tip.

A small colony of about 20 pairs was established near Tan Hill at the head of Arkengarthdale in 1960, but had moved into Westmorland in 1963. A few pairs were on the Yorkshire side of the border in several years thereafter, and 40 nests were counted in 1968 and 1969. On 30th May 1976, G.E. Alderson counted about 300 birds at the gullery, which was spread over half-a-mile (0.8 km) of flat moorland at Bog Moss.

M.V. Bell found a nest with three eggs at Grimwith Reservoir on 22nd June 1973 and another nest on Grassington Moor on 13th July 1974. A.F.G. Walker and C. Slator reported that a solitary pair settled in to breed at Nosterfield Gravel-pit in 1975 and was successful. What was presumably the same pair nested again in 1976 and reared one chick.

The species is perhaps best known as a bird of passage each spring and autumn, particularly during the former period. The majority breed along the western part of the British Isles, with other major colonies in Scotland and the Shetland Isles; relatively few large gulleries exist along the east coast, the largest and nearest being on the Farne Islands. In consequence, more birds pass through the western half of Yorkshire, mainly along and over the Pennines, than do along the coast on their way to the breeding grounds. During the peak passage period in April, some large flocks may be seen flying over or resting by reservoirs, flashes or riverside fields and on ploughed land in the west of the county.

Although many birds migrate southwards to the Mediterranean and the coasts of Africa, some spend the winter in the British Isles and Yorkshire acts as host to fairly large numbers in most winters. In company with other gulls, Lesser Black-backs assemble to roost at many inland waters during both migration seasons and in the winter months, the most notable sites being Eccup Reservoir, Fairburn Ings, Blackmoorfoot Reservoir, Redmires Reservoir, Ardsley Reservoir and Wintersett Reservoir, with smaller numbers occurring at several other waters. Gulls have roosted at Eccup Reservoir for many years, and in 1960 up to 4,000 Lesser Black-backs were counted during August and September. Between 2,000 and 2,500 were there in August and September 1961, but in more recent years the numbers have declined and have not exceeded 1,000 birds since the 1960s. Assemblies of up to 500 birds are regular there during the winter months.

Fairburn Ings attracted up to 2,000 Lesser Black-backs each autumn during the late 1960s, but in recent years there have been considerably fewer. Ardsley Reservoir had exceptional counts of 3,000 birds on 28th August 1972 and 4,000 on 20th September 1973, and numbers at Redmires Reservoir topped the 1,000 mark in October 1975. Gouthwaite Reservoir held around 2,000 during November 1965, and in the following year there were 1,500 on 29th September, 3,300 on 5th November and 2,500 on 19th November.

Newly formed gravel-pits at Masham and nearby Nosterfield are now popular

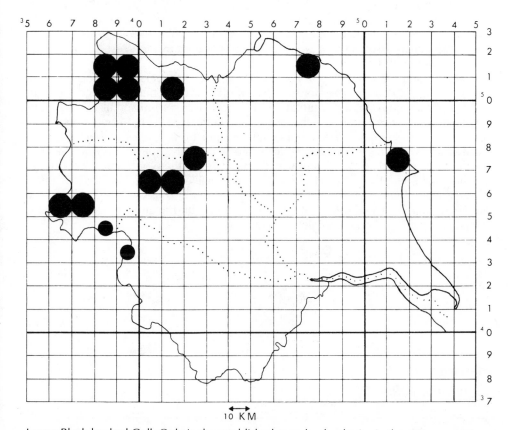

10 K M

Lesser Black-backed Gull. Only in the established moorland colonies in the extreme west and northwest do large numbers breed. Very few pairs breed at the other sites and not necessarily every year.

with the species and between 500 and 1,000 birds have been counted there during the autumn since the mid 1970s. The new gravel-pit at Pugneys, near Wakefield, held 470 birds on 28th September 1981, and Skellbrooke Tip had 700 on 13th October 1981. Such roosting or resting assemblies may occur at almost any water in the western part of the county and may become annual at some.

Birds gather in the Humber Estuary, where D.E. Murray described a flock of 135 resting at Patrington Haven on 14th August 1974 as 'an incredible number for the East Riding'. A flock of 200 birds was seen there on 10th August 1975. Birds in the upper part of the estuary in spring are likely moving westwards to the Pennines and beyond, returning by the same route in autumn. Large numbers at Blacktoft Sands in recent years included a count of 1,740 on 20th September 1979. A count along the estuary from Goole to Spurn on 16th January 1977 produced 100 birds between North Ferriby and the River Hull, where 52 were seen on 13th February and ten on 18th December.

The Scandinavian Lesser Black-backed Gull *Larus fuscus fuscus*, which breeds from Denmark northwards to the Kola Peninsula, visits Yorkshire on its migrations southwards in the autumn and to a lesser degree in spring. The darker back of this race can be picked out among flocks of grey-backed British birds at inland sites during the non-breeding season as well as along the coast, where it is regularly seen in small numbers in almost every month during most years. Recoveries in Yorkshire of birds ringed as chicks in Norway show the origin of some of these visitors.

Of the many chicks ringed at the Roeburndale colony during the 1950s, there have been many recoveries of birds moving south to their winter quarters, in the following countries: France (one), Spain (13), Portugal (16), Morocco (five), Algeria (one), the Canary Islands (two), and the coast of Mauretania in West Africa (three). The list is not complete.

Nelson stated in *The Birds of Yorkshire* that large numbers, in association with Herring Gulls, passed to the northwest at Redcar in October 1884 and again in 1887, and that many passed south at Spurn in September 1880 and also in 1884. In the latter year, he reported that the movement continued for ten hours on each of four days and birds passed at the rate of 280 per hour. Such numbers are now quite unknown along the coast. He also said 'inland, the species has occurred in the centre of the county as also in the remote dales of the North and West Ridings but not so frequently as the Herring Gull, and unlike that species, it is not often observed on ploughed land'. This statement is difficult to understand, as it is now the Lesser Black-backed Gull that is the commoner bird inland and certainly fond of loafing on ploughed land while on migration.

Herring Gull
Larus argentatus

Herring Gulls were noted among the multitudes of birds at Flamborough by Pennant on 3rd July 1769, and it is still the most familiar gull along the coast today.

The species is resident and breeds commonly along the cliffs from the Hunt Cliff at Saltburn, south to Flamborough. It was abundant on the cliffs at Gristhorpe, between Scarborough and Filey, at the turn of the century, and 180 eggs were collected there on 13th May 1899 and 76 in one day in May 1900. In 1903, upwards of 1,000 eggs were taken at Kettleness by Whitby fishermen. It was much persecuted on the chalk cliffs at Bempton and thereabouts because of its competitive effect on the auks, whose eggs were much sought after. The cliffs at Boulby, Kettleness and Ravenscar are still breeding strongholds and the cliffs at Cloughton Wyke, Scarborough Castle, Filey, Bempton and Flamborough hold many pairs now that persecution has stopped.

There were counts at Bempton of 1,000 pairs in 1975, 1,200 pairs in 1978, 810 pairs in 1979 and 1,000 pairs in 1981. In 1980, 234 pairs nested between the North and South Landings at Flamborough.

In 1942, some pairs nested on rooftops at Whitby, and in 1947 at Robin Hood's Bay, Cowbar and Staithes. Counts at Whitby gave totals of 37 such nests in 1949, 26 in 1950 and 42 in 1970. Two pairs bred at Scarborough in 1967, one on a house roof and the other on the Mormon Church, each pair rearing one chick. Eight pairs each reared one chick in 1969 and, by 1972, several pairs were nesting on house tops in North Marine Drive and Aberdeen Walk. Permission was sought for some birds to be shot, and this was granted by the local authority because of the excessive noise in the early mornings. Rooftop nests were recorded at Runswick Bay in 1969 and at Fylingthorpe and Filey in 1976. The total number of breeding pairs on town buildings in 1979 was 666, compared with 109 pairs ten years earlier.

The Yorkshire sea-cliffs and buildings in some coastal towns hold the largest concentrations of breeding Herring Gulls on the east coast of England, and a survey carried out in 1978 and 1979 showed a total of 5,634 pairs, compared with 3,749 pairs in 1969 and 1970. The full details of the 1978-79 survey were published in *The Naturalist*, 1980, pp. 107-14.

The large colony of Lesser Black-backed Gulls at Roeburndale included several pairs of Herring Gulls in 1955, and D.B. Isles counted 100 pairs there in 1958. Ten pairs were at the gullery near Tan Hill in 1969. Chislett reported that, during the Second World War, the North Pier at Bridlington was closed to the public and Herring Gulls nested on the flat surface of the pier and on the ledges of the parapet.

The Herring Gull is undoubtedly the most familiar gull along the coastline, especially about the resorts, where large numbers may occur during the non-breeding season, their ranks being swollen during the winter months by birds from farther north in Britain and Scandinavia. Birds are more evident in some years than in others, the severity of the weather often affecting the numbers frequenting the harbours. Filey usually attracts large gatherings and in 1978 there were 1,100 during January and March and 1,200 on 7th October. In the same year, in December, Spurn had 5,900 on 30th and 9,900 on 31st. A very large quantity of wrack, deposited by the tide on the beach south of Bridlington by gales in early 1979, attracted about 10,000 gulls on 25th January, 4,000 of which were of this species. Watchers at Flamborough counted 8,500 birds on 5th April 1981, and during December that year 1,500 were at Filey. Similarly large numbers may be seen in most years at these and other places along the coastline, large flocks regularly following the fishing cobles into the harbours.

The Birds of Estuaries Enquiry counts in 1977 gave totals of 3,900 birds between Spurn and Goole on 25th January and 3,400 on 13th February. The Tees Estuary holds more Herring Gulls than does the Humber and maximum counts in recent years, not all of which would be on the Yorkshire side, are 10,000 on 21st July 1971, 17,000 on 30th January 1977 and 18,250 on 22nd January 1978.

Large roosts at inland waters are a regular feature in every year. Eccup Reservoir attracts large numbers, and maximum counts have been 1,000 during January and February and from August to December 1950; 2,000 in December 1951; 4,000 on 12th January and 7,500 on 5th November 1955; and 2,000 on 9th April 1967. A large percentage of the total of 60,000 roosting gulls at Eccup Reservoir at the end of 1969 were Herring Gulls. For full details of this gull roost during the winter of 1953/54 see *The Naturalist*, 1956, pp. 1-7.

Stocks Reservoir also holds a large gull roost and 5,000 were counted there on 6th December 1951. Many other waters have held from 1,000 to 3,000 birds from time to time, principally Swillington Ings (3,000 in January 1952); Wintersett Reservoir; Almholme; Fairburn Ings; Ardsley Reservoir (3,000 during November-December 1972); Hay-a-Park Gravel-pit; Langsett Reservoir; Broomhead Reservoir; Pugneys Gravel-pit; and Blackmoorfoot Reservoir. During January 1977, up to 2,000 frequented Scaling Dam.

Rubbish tips have provided gulls with an abundant source of food over the years, and the Herring Gull is the most regular visitor to such places. Where tips are adjacent to water, as they often are when gravel-pits or flashes are being filled in, they provide perfect conditions, for the gulls like nothing more than to drink, bathe and preen after feeding on the tips.

There have been several records in Yorkshire between October and May of birds ringed as chicks on breeding grounds in Norway, Finland, Denmark, Murmansk and on Great Ainov Island (USSR). Three of the birds ringed near Murmansk were recovered as follows: one at Leeds on 16th February 1940, one at Ripon on 20th May 1954, and one at Robin Hood's Bay on 30th May 1974. Several birds showing the darker mantles of the nominate form *L.a argentatus*, which breeds from Denmark to Scandinavia and on the Kola Peninsula, have been seen annually during recent years since birdwatchers have become more aware of the different races that can visit us. They have occurred along the coast at several places and are now identified annually at Flamborough, where they are included in the large numbers of Herring Gulls which pass the headland. They have occurred from October to April, and the largest counts have been 57 birds passing on eight December days in 1978; 16 on 27th November and nine on 2nd December 1979; and 19 on 19th January and 12 on 15th November 1980.

Inland at Blackmoorfoot Reservoir, the gull roost included examples of this race in late July and in September 1980, and single examples have been seen at Knotford Nook Gravel-pit on 28th August 1979; Seamer Gravel-pit on 19th May 1980; and Blacktoft Sands and Pugneys Gravel-pit on 31st January 1981. The leg colour of this darker race varies from pink in the western part of its range to yellow in the east and several birds exhibiting the latter feature have been seen.

There are many records of abnormally plumaged Herring Gulls, some of which have caused confusion with Iceland or Glaucous Gulls. Nelson recorded a pure white bird shot at Filey on 26th September 1844. Chislett knew of no records of aberrant examples when he published *Yorkshire Birds* in 1952, but there have been several since then. An all-white bird at Hornsea Mere on 11th September 1955 was considered by G.R. Bennett to be an albino, which would have needed pink eyes to qualify as such. Most all-white birds have dark eyes, as did one which frequented the Bridlington area in 1981 and subsequently. Some leucistic examples have been recorded in recent years. Two such birds were at Scalby Mills in 1976, and there were similar birds at Filey, Barmston and Bridlington in 1979 and at Filey on 21st November 1981. A bird in Scarborough Harbour on 14th December 1977 was considered by S.C. Madge to be a hybrid Glaucous × Herring Gull, a pairing which is known to occur in Iceland.

Iceland Gull
Larus glaucoides

The status assessment of the Iceland Gull given by Nelson in 1907 as that of an occasional visitor to the coast in winter, when immature birds were met with at irregular intervals and adults were extremely rare, was echoed by Chislett in 1952 and applies equally well today. Nelson listed 17 records between 1846 and 1902, and Chislett published another 23 in *Yorkshire Birds* in 1952. The majority of these latter occurred at Scarborough between 1924 and 1949, most of the earlier ones having been recorded by W. Eagle Clarke. Chislett remarked that the spate of Iceland Gulls at Scarborough was due partly to the fact that the town had capable resident ornithologists.

During the period 1952 to 1974, between one and eight birds were recorded annually along the coast from South Gare to Spurn. Most were immature and only about ten of the 50 or so birds were full adults. From 1975, there was a marked increase in the number of birds seen each year and from nine to 16 have occurred annually up to the present time; again, very few have been fully adult. The coastal increase has also been reflected at inland waters where, in some years, there have been as many as along the coastline.

The favourite places are inevitably about the harbours at Bridlington, Filey, Scarborough and Whitby, where they consort with other large gulls to scavenge on the fishing-industry waste. Some individuals remain for long periods and provide many birdwatchers with excellent views. Present-day observers are able to identify this species more readily than was formerly the case, but the increase in records would appear to be a real one and not simply the result of more intensive watching.

The first inland record for the county was on 26th February 1938, when P. Stokes identified an adult example among the gull roost at Eccup Reservoir. Another, considered to be this species, was seen by K. Dawson and B. Speake at the same place on 4th January 1947. A third bird, in 'creamy' winter plumage, occurred there on 29th January 1949 which K. Brown claimed as an Iceland Gull. Since then, the concentrations of gulls at inland waters and rubbish tips have attracted Iceland Gulls annually since 1964. Eccup Reservoir, Blackmoorfoot Reservoir and Fairburn Ings have had most birds, but there have been records from at least 17 other localities, mainly at waters along the southern Pennines and their foothills. During the 1960s and early 1970s, records came from one to three waters each year. Since 1975, birds have been seen at up to eight waters, several individuals being involved at some, and have occurred from September to April, mainly during the period December to March. A late bird was seen at Blackmoorfoot Reservoir from 5th to 7th May 1973.

The Iceland Gull breeds only in Greenland and northeastern Canada, and moves southwards to spend the winter along the eastern seaboard of North America and eastwards to Iceland and the British Isles.

Glaucous Gull
Larus hyperboreus

This large and exciting gull, known by the Danes as the 'Burgomaster', occurs in Yorkshire in varying numbers every winter. Since the mid 1970s, the numbers have increased annually and there are now far more records than it is possible to enumerate.

It was known to Nelson as a winter visitor to the coast, most numerously during severe weather, and, like the Iceland Gull, mainly in immature plumage. Chislett was very cautious about acceptance of the 'white' gulls, the points of differentiation being poorly appreciated at that time. Problems still exist today, and Herring Gulls in aberrant plumage sometimes cause confusion.

W.J. Clarke recorded 'several' at Scarborough in 1945, and A.J. Wallis noted 'several' in January 1946, with up to four birds from 9th November 1946 and five on 28th. On 11th January 1942, T.N. Roberts saw 12 at Scarborough, only one of which was an adult. Four immatures were still there on 16th March, and at the year end eight immatures and one adult were on the pier on 16th November. During a period of intense cold in the early part of 1940, several were in the harbour at Scarborough and also at Whitby, where six were seen on 11th January and nine on 12th.

Since the publication of Chislett's *Yorkshire Birds* in 1952, the Glaucous Gull has been seen with increasing annual frequency. From five or so records each year during the 1950s and early 1960s, the annual number of sightings rose steadily until by 1971 there were 42 records along the coast and several others inland. In 1974, there were 55 coastal sightings, including one bird in June.

The first birds usually appear during September and may be present until April, with a few lingering into May. November to April is the main period of occurrence, the latter month often producing several records, possibly as birds pass through from farther south in England on their journey northwards to the breeding grounds.

From one to three individuals have occurred annually along the coast from the Teesmouth to Spurn, the majority of records coming from the main harbours and in the Filey Brigg area. Severe weather may produce more birds than usual and there have been records of up to five and more individuals in some years. In 1978, 12 individuals frequented Scarborough Harbour during January to April, with seven seen together on 22nd March, two of which were fully adult. An influx occurred on 12th January 1980, when there were five at Filey, one at Sewerby and nine at Flamborough, which had 12 on 13th January; several records of single birds came from other coastal areas during the same period. At the year end, five first-year birds were at Filey on 29th November. Birds were seen on 32 days at Flamborough in 1981, with maximum counts of four on 11th January, six on 15th March and five on 5th May, and there were five different individuals at Spurn up to the last bird of the spring on 20th May. A first-year bird at Filey on 26th July 1979 was very early.

The general increase in gulls at inland waters and rubbish tips during recent years has provided many more records of Glaucous Gulls than formerly. The major gull roosts at Eccup Reservoir, Blackmoorfoot Reservoir, Fairburn Ings and several other waters, including Wintersett Reservoir, Southfield Reservoir, Ardsley Reservoir and Wath Ings, attract the species almost annually. Records have occurred between October and April, with one in early May.

Many Glaucous Gulls occurred inland in 1980 and records came from 20 localities. At Greasborough Tip, there were seven individuals between 20th January and 3rd April; at Pugneys Gravel-pit there were six birds between 19th January and 30th April; and Fairburn Ings had single birds on 18 days between 9th January and 28th April, with two birds on three dates. Records at the other 17 places involved mainly single sightings, but the species occurred on several dates at some.

To summarise the present-day status: the Glaucous Gull is now a much more numerous bird, both along the coast and inland, than it was up to the 1950s, and the increase is almost certainly a real one along with that of the Iceland Gull. At any time from September to April, the harbours along the Yorkshire coastline may attract this large voracious species. Inland localities also have their share of birds, especially at gull roosts and rubbish tips. Numbers fluctuate annually and are often influenced by the severity of the weather. Scarborough is one of the most frequently visited places and anyone wishing to see this species could do little better than to visit the harbour in winter.

Great Black-backed Gull
Larus marinus

The Great Black-backed Gull is a passage migrant and winter visitor to Yorkshire in large numbers. Formerly known mainly along the coastline, an increasing tendency to occur inland along with other large gulls in more recent years has altered the status considerably. Nelson mentioned a few inland occurrences on sheets of water along the valleys of the Aire, Nidd, Ure, Swale and Tees and in the centre and south of the West Riding, and, although he did not give any real indication of the numbers, it was apparently an unusual event.

In *Yorkshire Birds*, Chislett said that he ceased to include inland records in the county bird reports 'some years ago' except where they involved large numbers. He listed 40 birds at a manure heap near Wakefield during the severe frost of early 1947, and other flocks of 40 at Swillington Ings on 18th January 1948 and 20 at Eccup Reservoir on 23rd November 1949. From ten to 20 birds visited the Eccup Reservoir gull roost during the 1940s and increasing numbers did so thereafter. During the early 1950s, other inland waters were attracting this species: 32 roosted at Ardsley Reservoir on 7th February 1953 and 22 were at Wintersett Reservoir on 19th December 1953. In 1955, Gouthwaite Reservoir had 14 birds on 10th December, and there were occurrences at several other waters scattered along the Pennines.

During the 1960s, Great Black-backs occurred at more inland waters and a remarkable increase took place during the decade. Eccup Reservoir had 110 birds at the gull roost on 20th January 1960 and around that number annually thereafter, until 500 birds were counted in April 1967. By 1960 Gouthwaite Reservoir was attracting up to 50 birds during the winter months, and 165 were there during hard weather on 25th December 1961; an increase followed, with 350 on 25th February 1962. Fairburn Ings had 100 birds in January 1965 and this site was to become one of the major inland roosts in the county during the 1970s: there were counts of 960 on 9th November 1968; 500 in December 1970; 1,800 on 12th December 1971; 1,400 on 23rd January 1972; 1,500 on 6th December 1975; 1,200 on 20th January 1977; and a staggering 2,000 birds in February 1979. The well-known gull roost at Blackmoorfoot Reservoir held 500 Great Black-backs on 24th December 1971, 400 on 14th January 1972 and 600 on 1st January 1974. Ardsley Reservoir had 50 birds in December 1962, and a continuing winter roost had built up to 500 by 2nd December 1972. One of the major waters for the species in recent years has been Wintersett Reservoir, where there have been maximum counts of 520 on 30th November 1975, 650 in January 1976, 1,100 on 1st January 1978, and 1,500 on 30th December 1978. Pugneys Gravel-pit had 400 birds on 17th February 1981, and 1,000 were counted as they flew west over Swillington Ings on 11th January 1981. Several other waters hold smaller numbers, which roost with other species of gulls, during the winter months.

Although the Great Black-backed Gull has become a very familiar gull to those who watch at inland localities, it is really a bird of the sea — as its name *marinus* implies. A movement off Redcar on 23rd October 1881 and for some days previously was described by Nelson in *The Birds of Yorkshire* as 'a great passage of mature birds ... as many as 100 going by to the north-west in one day'. Up to 1952, the maximum numbers along the coast were 500 on 10th September 1949 and 600 at Teesmouth on 24th August 1950. Chislett said that 'day after day, week after week, the birds come down the coast, practically continuously on many days ...'. How correct that observation was, for it is in fact possible to see birds passing in loose parties or singly, one after the other, at any time during the spring and autumn migration seasons. During the early months, the numbers passing are not large, but may reach treble figures on several days.

A marked increase occurs during March as the peak northward movement to the Scandinavian breeding grounds is under way, and there have been maximum daily counts during this period at Spurn of 400 on 15th March 1964, 600 on 17th March 1968 and 950 in March 1972. On 15th March 1981, 900 flew north at Flamborough.

A few birds are usually present during the summer, and the autumn passage gets under way by August, peaking during September, October and November. Many Great Black-backs pass during periods of rough weather, but a constant movement is evident throughout the autumn. At any time during this period, daily counts of up to 500 passing birds are not uncommon anywhere along the coast and there may be more on some days. The maximum daily autumn counts at Spurn have been 1,500 on 6th October 1955; 3,000 on 24th September 1958; 1,500 in October 1969; 1,500 in September 1970; 900 in September 1973; 850 in October 1974; 1,100 in December 1978; and 1,020 in October 1981. Counts at Flamborough Head in recent years have been 1,800 on 28th September 1978, 950 on 1st November 1980 and 850 on 7th October 1981. Most pass southwards and are mainly adult birds, but on some days the movement may be to the north in autumn, depending on the wind direction and strength, as they seek some shelter in the lee of the shore. In addition to the large numbers seen passing along the coast, there are favourite resting and feeding places along the shore. The rocks at Scalby Mills, near Scarborough, where the Scalby beck flows into the bay, provides a resting and bathing place for many gulls, including this species. They are always to be seen there during the non-breeding season and the numbers may reach several hundreds, 800 on 6th December 1975 being the highest count. A roost at Hornsea Mere attracts large numbers, with high counts of up to 600 during the winter of 1975; 600 in October 1976 and again on 13th January 1977; and 1,200 on 17th January 1979. On 3rd November 1975, 650 flew east at Hornsea to roost on the sea.

The Tees Estuary holds very many Great Black-backs and, although records in recent years have not separated the numbers on the Yorkshire side of the estuary, it is known that Coatham Marsh and Bran Sands attract good numbers; there were 600 at the former in July and September 1970, and 700 at the latter on 13th September 1970. The Birds of Estuaries Enquiry counts along the north shore of the Humber from Spurn to Goole have shown maximum totals of 1,400 on 16th January 1971 and 1,834 on 27th January 1980, mainly between Hessle and Hull.

Most of the birds of this species visiting Yorkshire during the winter months or those passing through during the autumn come from breeding grounds in Norway and the Kola Peninsula. There are at least ten ringing recoveries in the county of birds marked as chicks on their nesting grounds in Norway, and one from Great Ainov Island, Murmansk — a bird which was found dead at Wintersett Reservoir in March 1975. A bird ringed on Fair Isle in October 1972 was found at Tophill Low Reservoir on 10th March 1979.

There are many instances on record of Great Black-backs forcing tired migrant birds into the sea and swallowing them. Starlings, Blackbirds, Redwings and Fieldfares migrate over the North Sea in large numbers every autumn and are thus attacked. Herring and Common Gulls also harry them, the latter seldom following up the initial attack as the prey is far too large to swallow, although Herring Gulls, and of course the Great Black-backs, swallow them with ease. On 3rd November 1957, J. Cudworth watched a Great Black-back catch a Blackbird in mid-air; it eventually struggled free, only to be caught by a second bird and carried off. For details of these and other incidents at Spurn, see *The Naturalist*, 1955, pp. 155-9, and 1959, pp. 91-2.

This species is well known for its ability to kill large birds. It is able to swallow, whole, birds up to the size of Puffins, and there are several instances of such behaviour in Yorkshire. Nelson recorded one shot at Redcar which had swallowed a Redshank; and another from Bridlington that had swallowed a Little Auk which was so little damaged that the taxidermist was able to preserve the victim as well as its captor. On 15th January 1972, at Fairburn Ings, G. Thrussell saw one drop on to a Moorhen on the open water and carry it off for some yards before pecking and shaking it to death; the gull pecked at the corpse for half-an-hour before flying off (*The Naturalist*, 1972, p. 121). Also at Fairburn Ings, on 30th November 1973, G. Carr saw one pick up a female Goldeneye which it then killed and partly ate. On 9th August 1978, again at Fairburn Ings, the same observer saw one drop onto a fully grown juvenile Moorhen which it picked up and swallowed whole, head first, in three gulps; the feet protruded from the bill for some while.

A bird with an aberrant pale brown back was seen at Scarborough and at Scalby Mills during the winters of 1974 to 1978, and D.I.M. Wallace saw a pure white individual at Flamborough on 19th February 1978.

The large colony of Lesser Black-backed Gulls at Roeburndale on the Yorkshire/Lancashire border included some Great Black-backs from 1949 and probably earlier. Three pairs were present in 1951, and numbers increased to at least 20 pairs by 1958. Chicks were found in each of the years. For full details, see *The Naturalist*, 1959, pp. 98 and 128.

Ross's Gull
Rhodostethia rosea

Nelson devoted two pages to the occurrence of the first Ross's Gull for the British Isles, near Tadcaster in the winter of 1846/47, and detailed all the known correspondence concerning the record. Chislett (1952) summarised the affair in four lines.

This important record is interesting in that there are certain discrepancies, often the case in the publication of 'passed-on' details in various journals of the day — and subsequently. According to Nelson, Sir William Milner of Nun Appleton purchased the specimen from Mr Graham, the bird-preserver of York. It was said by

Graham to have been killed on 22nd December 1846 by Mr Thomas Robinson of Saxton, near Aberford. In a later communication from Mr Henry Miller of Nun Appleton, it was stated that 'Ross's Gull was killed by Horner, Lord Howden's keeper in February last (1847) in a ploughed field near the hamlet of Milford-cum-Kirby in the Parish of Kirby and Charlesworth.' The area mentioned is close to Tadcaster and gives no cause for concern. The difference in dates, however, is difficult to understand. According to Nelson, 'considerable scepticism has prevailed with regard to the reliability of Graham's assertion that the bird was obtained in Yorkshire, and it has been surmised that Sir William Milner was imposed upon by the professional bird stuffer'. The bird was in winter plumage, which stage was unknown at the time of the occurrence.

In subsequent correspondence in *The Field* (1885), Mr Foljambe, a relative of Sir William Milner's, stated that Graham had the bird in the flesh and confirmed that it had been killed by Horner, Lord Howden's keeper, in February 1847 in a ploughed field near Milton-cum-Kirby. Another correspondent, C.R. Garwood of Acomb, York, said that his brother, the Reverend W. Garwood of Staveley, remembered seeing the identical bird in the flesh at Graham's shop in Spurriergate, York (*The Field*, 5th December 1885).

Nelson summed up by saying 'as Foljambe and Garwood are both of the opinion that the bird was seen in the flesh, the evidence in favour of it being a Yorkshire specimen seems to be conclusive'. The editors of *The Handbook* admitted the record as the only one for the British Isles, and I see no reason to disagree. What is believed to be the mounted specimen is now housed at the City of Wakefield Museum, and its history has been thoroughly checked by M. Densley. It appears that no specimens in first-year plumage were ever imported into Britain and, although the bird in question was originally housed in the City of Leeds Museum and thought to have been destroyed when the museum was bombed during World War II, Densley is of the opinion that it may have been out on loan at the time and did in fact survive.

The second record for the county has never been in doubt. On 17th February 1962, while walking along the south beach at Bridlington, Brent Richards saw an unfamiliar gull and eventually obtained close views. He confidently reported it to H.O. Bunce as an adult Ross's Gull in winter plumage, and it was seen the next day by Bunce; on 19th by R.H. Appleby, Mr and Mrs J.A. Bailey and A.J. Wallis; and again on 22nd by G.R. Bennett. It frequented the general area of the south beach, the sewage outlet and the harbour, and was often missing for long periods, being under observation for a total of only 90 minutes during the four days on which it was seen. Most of this time it was on the wing, but it was observed to settle briefly on the sea on three occasions and three times on the beach. Full details of the record were published in *British Birds*, 1962, pp. 480-1.

On 27th January 1974, M. Densley and his wife were birdwatching in the harbour area at Bridlington. At 14.30 hours they were on the north pier and noticed a small solitary gull sitting on the sea about 30 yards (27 m) distant. It was a Ross's Gull in sub-adult plumage and they watched it for 15 minutes. It eventually drifted towards the harbour entrance and was disturbed by a fishing boat, which caused it to take wing and fly off across the bay to the south. Full details were published in *The Naturalist*, 1975, pp. 26-7.

Two years later, on 27th March 1976, an adult was seen by R.H. Appleby at 13.00 hours as it sat on a flat-calm sea on the leeward side of the cliffs at Jackson's Bay, near Scarborough. It was with Black-headed Gulls and Kittiwakes but did not associate with them too closely, preferring to sit on its own. It remained in the general area of Scalby Mills and the Scarborough North Bay until 28th April, although it was not seen between 30th March and 22nd April, and was observed by very many people who travelled from all over Britain to see this rare Arctic visitor. What was probably the same bird was found farther north at South Shields from 9th to 11th April. Full details appeared in the Yorkshire Naturalists' Union Ornithological Report for 1976, together with two excellent photographs taken by D. Bryan and J. Seeviour (plates 83 and 84).

Yorkshire was to have yet another Ross's Gull in 1980, when an adult bird appeared at Filey Brigg on the afternoon of 7th December. It was first seen by H.J. Whitehead, and subsequently by very many other observers, as it flew up and down the brigg and provided several people with their first ever views of this dainty and delightful gull which breeds only in the extreme northeastern part of Siberia.

In 1983, one was seen by Miss R. Bowmand, P.J. Dunn and many others at Filey, where it stayed from 17th to 20th February (see plate 85). A first-winter bird was seen at Flamborough on 12th February 1983 and another on 10th December, details of which have not yet been submitted to the *British Birds* Rarities Committee.

Kittiwake
Rissa tridactyla

The Kittiwake's association with Yorkshire dates as far back as 1770 when Pennant said 'It inhabits the romantic cliffs of Flamborough Head where it is called Petrell.'

During the first part of the nineteenth century, it was particularly abundant on the cliffs at Bempton, Speeton and Flamborough, and Charles Waterton, in 1834, found the nests so numerous as 'totally to defy any attempt to count them'. Shortly after this time, the demand for feathers for the millinery trade caused many thousands to be slaughtered. A single gunner could earn from £15 to £18 per week during the season for feathers. In one year, 4,000 birds passed through the hands of one shooter and were sent to the London plumassiers. Most birds were shot during the period when they were collecting grass roots along the clifftop for nest building. The old climber, Edward Hodgson of Buckton, remembered when Kittiwakes cleared a whole field of 'twitch', which had been worked out of the land, in two days.

In a letter to *The Times* dated 29th October 1874, the Reverend F.O. Morris wrote at length on the subject of the Sea Birds Protection Act and, after discussing a proposed extension of the closed season for seabirds, continued:

'... through a policeman appointed for several years past to take down the number of persons who, with or without a gun licence, have been found shooting sea birds about Flamborough and Speeton cliffs, they have ascertained that in the first two weeks only of August, eighty-nine persons were stopped by the said officer, no fewer than twenty of whom had not even the ordinary gun licence. Most of these persons were cheap excursionists, and at Flamborough alone the number of birds brought on shore in that short time was 336, and the lowest number computed to have been destroyed, including those left dead and wounded in the water, was upwards of 1,000. This estimate is considered to be much under the mark. One of these would-be sportsmen laid a wager that he would shoot eighty sea birds within an hour, and he had the discredit and disgrace of having succeeded in doing so. In fact, the very tameness of the birds, through the unwonted protection extended to them for the summer months, proved in the end an element of danger to them. "They trust in our humanity, and suffer in consequence." I went three or four years ago from Bridlington to Scarborough for the day in a steamboat, and one of these cheap excursionists employed himself for the whole of the way back in shooting at every unfortunate sea bird which the vessel came near in passing the "stupendous cliffs of Speeton," as Waterton well called them, and those of Flamborough, or wherever else the tameness of the birds kept them without fear in the track; and these, of course, as there could be no stopping to pick them up, could only be left on the sea, to die, maimed and mangled, utterly useless to the wretched shooter himself or any one else; a painful and pitiable sight. I am, Sir, your very obedient servant, F.O. Morris.'

This slaughter by the local people, and by the townsfolk who came purely for the sport, contributed to the near extermination of this formerly abundant species, the seriousness of which led to the Seabird Protection Act of 1869, which in turn put an end to the mindless persecution. The numbers began to increase soon after the killing stopped, and Chislett considered them to be back to their former numbers by the 1950s. Further increase followed, and today the thousands of birds breeding annually must surely reflect the scene of those early days when Charles Waterton visited the cliffs.

W.J. Clarke reported that a pair of Kittiwakes nested on the Scarborough Castle Cliff in 1940, whereafter a colony formed and has increased annually since then. In 1966, there were 650 pairs, which almost doubled to 1,250 pairs by 1967; 1,394 pairs in 1968; 1,712 pairs in 1974; 2,800 pairs in 1975; and 1,660 pairs in 1980. This colony is unique in that a busy major road runs beneath the cliffs and separates it from the sea (see plate 34).

New colonies were formed at Boulby and Staithes in 1950, when 80 nests were located, and 6,200 nests were counted between Saltburn and Staithes in 1977. A small colony on Huntcliffe, near Saltburn, had six or seven nests when first located in 1961; 49 nests in 1964; 586 in 1969; 2,355 in 1975; and 2,651 in 1976. Such is the speed of increase once the species has chosen a suitable breeding cliff. The cliffs just north of Long Nab, Burniston, hold a small colony which numbered 408 pairs in 1977 and 300 pairs in 1978, in which year M. Williams saw several birds lying dead on their nests on 26th June having been presumably shot. The colony has now extended around Hundale Point into Cloughton Wyke.

The most spectacular breeding area is of course along the chalk cliffs of the Flamborough Headland and the precipitous cliffs to the north at Bempton and Speeton. The colonies have increased in recent years and have also spread southwards towards Bridlington. In 1973, H.O. Bunce noticed a few old and used nests on the cliffs at 'Old Fall', about half-a-mile (0.8 km) around the headland, where in 1974 there were 40 nests. In 1975, a count between Speeton and Lang Ness revealed 53,160 nests. The Bempton Cliffs held 65,000 nests in 1977 and the RSPB warden, S. Rooke, estimated 100,000 nests on the whole headland in 1978. A complete check of the cliffs between Reighton and Bridlington, a distance of 12 miles (19.2 km), in 1979 gave a total of 83,000 nests, 64,180 of which were on the cliffs of the RSPB reserve. A total count of 80,000 nests between Filey and Flamborough in 1980 included 13,748 between the North and South Landings at the latter locality.

In 1978, several nests were built on the window ledges of a building above the Gypsy Race beck which flows out through the harbour at Bridlington. This colony flourishes today.

The 'climmers' took many Kittiwakes' eggs when they went down the cliffs for eggs of the Guillemot, and these were sold at four or five for a penny in the years before the great slaughter. If the first clutch was taken, the birds usually laid again and one climber had frequently taken eight eggs from one and the same nest, consisting of four clutches of three, two, two and one.

I visited the cliffs on 2nd June 1948 and watched the climbers at work. On the clifftop were wicker baskets full of eggs, some of Kittiwakes and Herring Gulls and others of Guillemots and Razorbills. There was some magic in the atmosphere of that hot summer day, accentuated by the clamour of the thousands of Kittiwakes and the croaking of auks, coupled with the characteristic smell drifting up the cliffs from the nests below. I did not realise then, as a teenager, that I was witnessing some of the last climbs to be made at this historic site, but I am pleased to have witnessed what to most people is now just a legend. Although the climbers asserted that their activities had no adverse effects on the populations of Kittiwakes, a steady increase during the last 20 years, both in numbers at the main colonies and in the establishment of new ones, suggests that there must have been a controlling factor, which in view of the huge numbers of birds involved would have been difficult to detect in the absence of a properly organised survey.

Movements along the coast are complex and difficult to interpret. They are often very erratic, few birds passing on some days and many hundreds or more on others. The direction is not constant with the season, and may be to the north and south on alternate days or even on the same day. Such movements are no doubt associated with food supply and may be dependent on the location of fish shoals. Large movements may occur in almost any month of the year. At Flamborough, on 7th May 1960, A.J. Williams counted 6,000 per hour passing between 06.00 and 08.00 hours. In 1971, 2,240 per hour were moving south at Filey on 6th March and 4,000 in one hour on 8th April. Watchers at Flamborough and Filey witnessed similar movements in 1975, when 4,000 per hour were moving north at Flamborough on 15th March and 4,000 per hour were moving south at Filey on 21st March. This is the time when birds return to the breeding cliffs after spending most of the winter out at sea, and these may have been local feeding movements. D.I.M. Wallace counted 4,850 flying north off Flamborough in one-and-a-quarter hours on 8th January 1977 and 6,000 flying north in one hour on 27th March 1977. In the spring of 1979, 9,000 flew north on 16th April, 13,000 on 27th April and 17,300 on 28th April; and, in 1981, a total of 61,000 birds flew north on four spring dates: 15th, 22nd and 29th March and 4th April. Birds flying north at Spurn on 17th and 18th June 1981 totalled 10,600. Movements in the autumn are similar in numbers and may also be in either direction, as in 1974 when 5,700 flew north at Spurn on 13th October, 2,250 flew south there on 28th October and 3,000 flew north on 29th October. On 20th October 1970, 10,000 passed Spurn, where they were streaming south all morning. Such variable movements are undoubtedly of a local nature and connected with food supply or weather.

Many birds congregate at the Teesmouth to feed, especially on sprats, and D.R. Seaward estimated 10,000 there on 14th August 1962 with around 6,000 up to early September. Large concentrations occur offshore at several places along the coast, mainly during the winter months, depending on the location of fish shoals.

Birds occur at inland waters far more commonly than Chislett was aware of up to 1950, and since that time their appearance at one or more waters has been an annual event. Numbers seen have increased over the years, probably owing in part to better coverage of the more remote reservoirs and to an awareness of gulls which was perhaps lacking 30 years ago. Birds have occurred in every month, but most numerously during April and May, when it is likely that some cross the country from the west coast to the breeding cliffs in Yorkshire and farther north; and again during August and September, when the juvenile birds are dispersing and the adults leaving for their North Atlantic wintering grounds and when a cross-country movement to the west may take place. Most records concern single birds or small parties, but large flocks have been seen, often coinciding with gales which force them inland. During the last few years, they have been seen at up to 20 different inland waters and it is possible that many more actively cross the county than are seen. At Angram Reservoir in Upper Nidderdale, on 11th November 1972, A.F.G. Walker and F. Symonds saw 14 Kittiwakes passing through, and on 29th January 1978 M.G.H. Garnett saw a tight pack of 75 adults circle Lumley Moor Reservoir, also in Upper Nidderdale, before they left to the southeast. On 10th January 1981, 89 birds came into Gouthwaite Reservoir, again in Upper Nidderdale. A party of 19 birds occurred at Wintersett Reservoir on 28th March 1979, another 27 on 30th March, and ten more on 1st April, when 11 were at Ingbirchworth Reservoir and five at Gouthwaite Reservoir; and there were ten at Fairburn Ings on 7th April.

In recent years Kittiwakes have been seen in the upper part of the Humber Estuary at Blacktoft Sands, often coinciding with strong northerly winds, and the records in 1979 illustrate the situation: 44 were present on 16th April; 29 on 7th May; 90 on 9th May; 22 on 15th May; 100 on 26th May; 42 on 20th May; and 32 on 30th May.

Recoveries of ringed birds give some clue as to the movements. A chick ringed on Lundy Island in 1953 was found dead at Scarborough in August 1954; and another, ringed at St Abbs Head in July 1957, was at Scarborough in August 1957. Several chicks ringed on the Farne Islands have been recovered in Yorkshire. A first-year bird ringed at Cuxhaven in Germany on 15th March 1958 was found dead at Bridlington on 9th April 1958, and a chick ringed in Denmark on 20th June 1956 was dead at Easington on 6th May 1960. I ringed several young Kittiwakes at the Scarborough Castle Hill colony during the early 1960s, and two were recovered: one in the Bay of Biscay, five months after being ringed, and the other in the Netherlands, two years after ringing.

In mid February 1892, Nelson noticed a vast assemblage of Kittiwakes about a mile (1.6 km) off Redcar in calm and hazy weather. He went out in a boat to investigate and found them sitting on the water and feeding on some small objects. He shot two or three specimens to establish the nature of the food and found the birds' bills to be full of small crustaceans with which the sea was literally alive. Some samples were sent to the Reverend Canon A.M. Norman, who identified them as *Euthemisto compressa*, a species which was new to the British Isles at that time (*The Naturalist*, 1892, pp. 175-6).

Nelson recorded a few examples of Kittiwakes with abnormal plumage, including a leucistic bird at Flamborough on 23rd October 1880 in which the plumage was entirely white except for fawnish wing tips. A similar bird was obtained near Flamborough on 15th November 1887.

Ivory Gull
Pagophila eburnea

Seven examples of this Arctic gull are mentioned by Nelson in *The Birds of Yorkshire*. The first, which was in Allis's report given to the British Association at York in 1844, concerned a specimen shot at Scarborough 'many years ago' by C. Watson of York. Allis said that 'Watson was no ornithologist, but from the account he gave me of the bird which was pure white all over, there can, I think, be no doubt about the species; I believe the bird was not preserved.' I find it very difficult to accept a record like this without question. A pure white gull need not necessarily be an Ivory Gull and, as most experienced field ornithologists today are aware, many abnormal individuals of several gull species have been recorded and originally claimed as one or other of the 'white' gulls. An example was published in the Yorkshire Naturalists' Union Ornithological Report for 1954 by Chislett, which he included under Ivory Gull in square brackets, thereby inferring doubts, concerning an all-white gull, smaller than Herring Gulls which were also present, flying along the river between Huddersfield and Leeds and seen from a train. It was most likely an albino or leucistic Herring or Common Gull and could never be considered as even a possible Ivory Gull.

The second of Nelson's records was an adult male obtained in Filey Bay in August 1875 by T.M. Edwards, who had the specimen preserved.

A bird in second-year plumage was seen on 2nd October 1879 at East Scar, Redcar, while feeding on a dead fish. It was fired at by a fisherman, who missed it, and the bird flew away but returned later to feed and was killed. It went to the collection of E.B. Emerson of Tollesby Hall.

An adult was obtained at Filey in the autumn of 1880 and reported by J. Backhouse in the *Friends' Natural History Journal*, 1881.

The next three occurrences mentioned in *The Birds of Yorkshire* are not supported by very much detail. One at Filey on 26th September 1884 was reported by J. Fountain; and one seen at Flamborough on 5th April 1904 went eventually to the collection of W. Hewitt (involuntarily one assumes). One recorded at Whitby by J. Kitching was reported to Nelson by T. Stevenson, who said that he had no reason to doubt the authenticity of Kitching's statement; be that as it may, what should be in question is whether the bird being claimed was in fact an Ivory Gull or merely thought to be.

Since the publication of *The Birds of Yorkshire* in 1907, there have been only three more records, one of which was published by Chislett in *Yorkshire Birds*. This was seen by A. S. Frank and F. Snowden on 2nd March 1925 in Whitby Harbour, where it remained for the next five days before being killed. It was fairly confiding and was captured alive by a fisherman on 7th March. The specimen, a male in its first winter, was acquired by the Whitby Literary and Philosophical Society, and a photograph appeared in *The Naturalist*, 1925, p. 149.

The second record came from Hornsea beach, where W.F. Curtis watched an immature Ivory Gull on 1st February 1971 as it sat on a groin.

The third bird also occurred at Hornsea, where, on 25th January 1976, S.L. James, D.Fleet and S. Morgan watched a first-winter individual as it flew along the sea-wall and later as it rested on a ploughed field with Common Gulls, which it constantly harried.

This exciting gull, which breeds only in the high Arctic, has now been recorded in the British Isles on some 100 occasions.

Gull-billed Tern
Gelochelidon nilotica

Prior to 1976, only one specimen of this large tern had been recorded in Yorkshire. It was a mature bird, shot at and wounded on a mill reservoir on the York road, near Leeds, during the last week of July 1843, and was taken alive to H. Denny. See *Annals and Magazine of Natural History*, 1843, p. 297.

There have since been ten other records. One was seen at Spurn on 11th July 1976 by J. Cudworth, C. Massingham and B.S. Pashby, and an immature was seen at Flamborough by D.I.M. Wallace on 25th September in the same year. A.M. Allport saw an adult flying north offshore at Hornsea on 19th July 1978.

The following records have not yet been submitted to the *British Birds* Rarities Committee but have been accepted by the YNU: D.I.M. Wallace saw one at Flamborough on 15th May 1979. A.M. Allport, P.A. Lassey and D.I.M. Wallace recorded single birds at Flamborough on 29th September 1981, 10th July 1982, 5th and 11th June 1983 and on 10th June and 20th August 1984.

This almost cosmopolitan species has its nearest breeding stations in Denmark and is known to have occurred in the British Isles on some 220 occasions.

Caspian Tern
Sterna caspia

One example of this impressive tern was cited by Nelson: a bird shot at Filey in early September 1874 which was sent to a Mr Baker at Cambridge for preservation. The mounted specimen was seen on Baker's premises by Professor Alfred Newton.

This remained the only record for the county until 1939, when a dead Caspian Tern was picked up on the beach at Whitby in August. It was wearing a ring and had been marked as a chick on Shoe Island in Lake Michigan, North America, on 14th July 1927 (see *The Auk*, October 1940). Caspian Terns recorded on the east coast of Yorkshire need not, therefore, have come from Europe, although that origin is most likely.

On 19th March 1940, one was picked up dead by a Mr Hitching of Kirby-in-Cleveland and sent to the York Museum, where it was identified as an immature of this species.

J.P. Utley had good views of one near Battery Point, Teesmouth, on 23rd August 1948. A bird in full breeding dress was seen just north of Kilnsea by G.R. Edwards on 26th July 1964. One was at South Gare, Teesmouth, on 26th September 1965 and was seen by S. Norman, T. Bradbury and others.

In 1972, A.J. Wheeldon watched one on Coatham Sands near Redcar on 7th

August; and later in the month, on 29th, P.A. Lassey saw one flying north at Kettleness, which is about 16 miles (25.6 km) farther down the coast. The same bird may have been involved.

One at Bolton-on-Swale Gravel-pit on 24th and 25th April 1973 was seen by W. and Mrs E. Hallet and G.D. Moore. Later in the year, S.C. Madge saw one at Bempton on 18th July. R.F. Porter watched one flying south at Spurn on 3rd August 1974. One was at Waterloo Lake, Roundhay Park, Leeds, on 3rd July 1976 and later at Eccup Reservoir, where it was seen by I.H. Dillingham, S.P. Singleton and E.C. Sterne. Single birds flew south at Spurn on 3rd and 14th August 1979, the former being seen by D. Garrett and the second by B. Banson and B.R. Spence. A. Grieve saw one at Blacktoft Sands on 24th June 1982, and P.A. Lassey watched one flying north on 22nd August 1982 at Flamborough, where another occurred on 25th June 1984.

This species, which breeds in the Baltic and in southeast Europe as well as in southern Asia, Africa, Australia and North America, has occurred in the British Isles on some 160 occasions, the majority being since 1958.

Lesser Crested Tern
Sterna bengalensis

An example of this rare tern occurred on the north side of the Tees Estuary near Seaton Carew on 17th June 1984. On 18th, it made its way across the river to South Gare, where it was seen on 18th and 19th by D.J. Britton. On 20th, it had moved farther along the coast to Redcar, where it was seen fishing offshore by B. Foster.

The species breeds along the southern shore of the Mediterranean Sea, into the Red Sea and down the coast of East Africa, and eastwards to India, Malaya and Australia.

Sandwich Tern
Sterna sandvicensis

The Sandwich Tern does not breed in Yorkshire but occurs commonly along the coast from April to October, some birds also passing overland and being seen at inland waters.

The first birds of the northward spring passage usually arrive during the second half of April, but there have been several records in March and early April, one at Filey on 3rd March 1980 being the earliest ever recorded in the county. Three at Hornsea Mere on 18th March 1972, one at Spurn on 29th March 1968 and one at Redcar on 30th March 1963 were also well ahead of the main arrival.

From mid April throughout May and into June, small numbers may be seen passing northwards along the coast to their breeding grounds in Northumberland and Scotland, or perhaps across the North Sea.

During the autumn, from July onwards, the Sandwich Tern is the most familiar tern along the coastline, as adults, often with their young ones which they feed while dispersing prior to migration, and also many independent young, pass offshore, or linger to feed, where their familiar grating call is one of the most characteristic sounds of the Yorkshire coast. During the early part of the autumn, movement is very often northwards and probably made up of birds dispersing from breeding grounds to the south of the county before the southerly migration starts in earnest during August and September, when some spectacular numbers can be seen. The first large movement recorded in the county was witnessed at Spurn on 3rd September 1953, when, after a gale from the west had abated, R.F. Dickens counted 1,000 birds passing south between 18.00 hours and 18.30 hours; a further 206 passed in five minutes between 18.55 and 19.00 hours, and it was estimated that 3,000 Sandwich Terns passed south during the day.

There have been regular counts at Spurn during the last 30 years, and the largest numbers passing in the autumn have been as follows: 3,425 on 9th August 1964; 1,000 on 29th August and 500 on 11th September 1966; 2,000 on 18th August, 2,300 on 30th August, and 1,300 to 3,400 daily from 1st to 10th September 1967; 1,050 on 4th August 1969; 900 to 1,400 on several dates between 26th July and 4th September 1971; 2,800 flying to the north on 26th July 1973, the direction probably indicating a local feeding or roosting movement; and 1,800 on 23rd August, 4,000 on 2nd September and 2,300 on 4th September 1974.

As with the other terns, Sandwich Terns often pass to the south or to the north during the late afternoon, and on 25th August 1984 G.T. Foggitt, D.R.J. Watkins and I watched a steady stream flying north off Long Nab, Burniston, into a strong northeasterly wind between 14.00 and 17.00 hours.

Similar numbers may be seen anywhere along the coast and observers at the regularly manned watchpoints at Flamborough, Filey, Burniston and Teesmouth have witnessed large numbers every year.

Several Sandwich Terns passing south at Spurn during late August and to the end of September 1964 were seen to be wearing yellow rings, which it was learned had been affixed to young birds on Coquet Island and on the Farne Islands in Northumberland. There are Yorkshire recoveries of birds ringed at colonies in Scotland, and one recovery of a chick ringed by a Yorkshireman at Salthouse in Norfolk on 15th June 1934 which was found at Skipsea on 12th August 1934. Two birds ringed in Denmark and one ringed in Holland have been recovered in Yorkshire during the autumn, two in their year of birth and one two years later.

Sandwich Terns often occur inland, presumably while crossing the country from the west coast in spring and the reverse in autumn. Nelson listed only three inland records up to 1907 and Chislett could add only three more up to 1952. There have been records in several years since 1950 and in every year since 1966. Occurrences have usually involved single birds, but two, three or four have been seen on several occasions and five on a few. Five were at Ilkley Sewage-farm on 27th June 1961 and five were at Gouthwaite Reservoir on 15th September 1969. They have occurred from April to October, the majority passing through during April and May and again during August and September. Their appearance inland is not necessarily connected with gales and they may be seen during calm settled weather, suggesting that the cross-country movement is a voluntary one.

Roseate Tern
Sterna dougallii

Nelson knew the Roseate Tern as a rare visitor to the coast on its way to and from its breeding grounds farther north, and Chislett said of it in 1952 that it was an exceedingly casual and occasional visitor to Yorkshire. Most of the records listed by Nelson were quite unsatisfactory; he knew of several instances of erroneous claims for the species and said in *The Birds of Yorkshire* that there was not an authentic instance of its capture on record within recent years. The only records listed by Chislett up to 1952 were a juvenile picked up at Teesmouth on 7th August 1949 which had been ringed on the Farne Islands on 21st July 1949, and two seen at Spurn by J.K. Fenton on 9th July 1950.

Since then, Roseate Terns have occurred along the coast in every year since 1954, with increasing frequency during the last few years, and some have occurred at inland waters. Since 1975, between six and 15 birds have been recorded annually, and there were 18 in 1967 and about 20 in 1968. Most have been seen passing up the coast during late May and June and returning during July to September, with a few records in April and October.

Occurrences at inland waters have come mainly from Fairburn Ings, where birds have been seen in ten years between 1958 and 1976. On 6th July 1958, C. Winn found a dead Roseate Tern in full pink breeding plumage on the slag heaps. Single birds have been seen during late April and early May in seven years and during July and August in five years, with two birds on three May dates and on 28th July 1967.

R.J. Rhodes and J.A. Platt saw one at Southfield Reservoir on 28th April 1962; H.O. Bunce saw one on the Lower Derwent Floods on 21st May 1966; D.J. Standring saw one at Wintersett Reservoir on 15th May 1971; P.M. Wright had three at Chelker Reservoir on 9th May 1972; J.S. Armitage saw one at Wintersett Reservoir on 24th May 1977, in which year J. Hewitt had one at Wath Ings on 29th May; and P.J. Carlton saw one at Knotford Nook Gravel-pit on 4th June 1979.

This 'greyhound amongst terns', as it was called in Nelson's time, has been observed in the county on more occasions during the last 30 years than had been recorded prior to that time, but one must presume that it was overlooked to some extent in those early days. It is not a common bird on passage even today, and very few are recorded in some years, though its occurrence is now annual.

The nearest breeding colonies are in Northumberland, on and around the Farne Islands, to and from which some of the Yorkshire birds will be en route.

Common Tern
Sterna hirundo

The Common Tern is best known as a regular bird of passage along the coast in both spring and autumn, and in recent years occurrences at inland waters have been more numerous. The first birds of spring usually appear during early April and the main passage takes place during the latter half of that month and throughout May, many birds being identified only as 'Commic' (Common or Arctic) Terns. Many more birds pass in autumn than during the spring, and on some days in August and September several hundreds may be counted flying south. On some autumn days, birds are seen flying to the north and such movement may be fairly local and connected with feeding or roosting. Many birds may linger for several days along a particular stretch of coast if the feeding is good, before continuing their journey southwards. During this time of year large numbers of birds often fly south, and sometimes north, in the evenings, the reason for which is not fully understood although it is likely connected with roosting behaviour.

Some large movements in recent years have been as follows: 1,000 flying south at Spurn in the evening of 10th September 1978; 1,132 flying south at Filey in one hour at midday on 21st August and 605 in four hours on 23rd August 1976; 850 flying north at Hornsea on 28th August 1976; 1,940 flying south at Spurn in the evening of 9th September 1976; and in 1980 700 flying south at Spurn on 29th August, 1,300 on 5th September and 1,800 on 12th September, on which date 1,729 flew south at Flamborough. These figures refer to birds specifically identified as Common Terns, but many more pass unspecified, being either Common or Arctic Terns, and the following figures are of such terns not specifically identified. In 1967, 5,000 passed south at Spurn on 18th August and 3,000-3,500 did so daily during the first week of September, with 1,000-1,750 during the first week of October. In 1969, 5,000 terns were at Spurn on 5th September. Large numbers are present every year as adults pass with their young, which they often feed while on migration, and the sight of birds carrying fish to begging young need not indicate breeding in the vicinity.

Most birds have passed through by early October, but a few linger to the month end and into early November. In 1969, several unspecified terns were seen in November, with birds at Filey Brigg, South Gare, and Spurn where there were three on 16th and two on 23rd. H.O. Bunce and A.J. Williams saw one at Flamborough on 6th December 1959.

On 28th October 1967, R.H. Appleby discovered 57 dead terns floating in the sea in a close bunch among the rocks on the incoming tide at the end of Filey Brigg. A wounded bird was also seen and 11 others were flying around. After examining the bodies, he concluded that they had been shot on the rocks that morning and were being picked up by the rising tide. It was later learned that a youth with a shotgun had been seen walking off the brigg earlier in the morning. The wounded bird and 38 of the corpses were sent to me later in the day, and all proved to have been shot. Of the 58 corpses examined by Appleby and myself, 55 were Common Terns and three were Arctic Terns. All were juveniles. These birds, together with 66 others seen at Spurn on the same day, are the largest number ever recorded in Yorkshire in late October. For full details of the incident and the analysis of plumage and measurements, see *The Naturalist*, 1970, pp. 63-6.

Regular watching at the Pennine reservoirs and gravel-pits along the foothills and elsewhere during the last 30 years has shown the Common Tern to be a regular passage bird at such places in every year. Chislett said that it was 'not very infrequent' inland and cited a few instances of large numbers. A 'considerable cross-country passage' in May 1947 involved many Arctic Terns, but some were identified as Commons. As with terns passing out at sea, many seen at inland waters are identified only as Common or Arctic, but I have included the maximum counts under this species, since the majority, but certainly not in every case, are likely to be Common Terns. Birds cross the county and visit inland waters, sometimes very briefly, at any time during April to October, mainly during May and June and again during August and September.

Numbers vary from single birds to parties of 20 or more, and may include both species at the same time. The largest counts are usually during the autumn, and have included 20 at Blacktoft Sands on 21st August 1970; 22 at Wintersett Reservoir on the late date of 28th October 1972; 57 flying west-southwest in small parties at Wintersett Reservoir on 28th July 1973, and 44 flying east-northeast there on 21st August 1973; and, at Blackmoorfoot Reservoir, 30 on 14th August 1974 and 34 on 26th August 1974. Spring occurrences are more erratic but occasionally involve good numbers, as in 1978 when many waters had passing birds, the maximum counts being 90 flying east at Wharncliffe Chase on 2nd May; 37 at Main on 2nd May; 40 at Potteric Carr on 5th and 6th May; 40 at Thrybergh Reservoir on 6th and 7th May; and 26 at Wath Ings on 6th May.

B. Shorrock saw 20 birds flying west at Settle on 12th September 1970 and 18 flying east in a tight pack on 5th May 1974. In 1971, 25 were at Swillington Ings on

9th May and 40 were at Wintersett Reservoir on 6th May. Parties of terns are regularly seen flying west up the Humber in the autumn, and such are recorded annually at Blacktoft Sands.

Breeding in Yorkshire has been irregular and the only records in recent years have been at inland sites. Nelson mentioned that it probably bred at Teesmouth in the seventeenth century, but there are no confirmed records until a pair produced two clutches on the Yorkshire side of the estuary in 1950. A Baldridge reported that one nest held three eggs on 15th June and the other had two eggs on 29th, both of which were later robbed. K. Baldridge found a nest in 1952, and P.J. Stead considered that the species probably bred there in 1955 but proof was lacking. In 1961, a pair nested successfully in South Yorkshire and another did so in the North Riding, the latter nest containing one egg on 23rd June when it was found by D.G. Bell. A pair in South Yorkshire in 1962 was unsuccessful. In 1980, two pairs reared five young at Bolton-on-Swale Gravel-pits, and a pair was present in 1981. A pair reared three young at Fairburn Ings in 1982, and in the following year two young were reared and a second pair was present. It is quite possible that inland breeding will increase now that the trend has commenced.

There are several ringing recoveries in Yorkshire of birds ringed elsewhere in the British Isles and abroad, the most interesting being a Common Tern found dead near Huddersfield on 6th October 1982, having been ringed as a chick in Poland on 19th July 1982. A chick ringed in Norway on 9th July 1979 was recaught at South Gare on 26th August 1979. Several chicks ringed at Walney Island in Lancashire, at Ravenglass in Cumberland and at Blakeney Point in Norfolk have been recovered in Yorkshire in the year of their birth, indicating a random dispersal prior to the southward migration.

Thus, anywhere along the coastline from the estuary of the Tees to Spurn Point and along the Humber, the Common Tern is a numerous bird of passage during both migration seasons. More occur at inland waters than were detected 20 years ago, and a few pairs are now breeding at inland sites.

Arctic Tern
Sterna paradisaea

Many of the birds passing in both spring and autumn along the coast and at inland waters include this species in varying numbers, but, as with the last species, many go by unspecified.

A bird at Filey on 24th March 1978 was very early, but this species does pass through slightly ahead of the Common Tern. In the autumn, most have departed by the end of October but there are a few records for early November and a late bird was at Filey Brigg on 19th November 1967.

Occurrences at inland waters match those of the Common Tern and there have been several specific records in recent years. In 1976, several passed through Fairburn Ings, with 40 birds on 21st April, 45 on 25th April and 20 on 15th May. A marked movement through the county occurred in 1978, when several waters recorded Arctic Terns during April and May, the majority being seen at Fairburn Ings, where there were counts of 22 on 20th April, 25 on 3rd May, 123 on 6th May, 67 on 8th May, 40 on 10th May and 15 on 15th May. All flew northwest. Also on 6th May were 50 at Knotford Nook Gravel-pit and 30 at Nosterfield Gravel-pit. In 1980, 46 flew northeast at Wintersett Reservoir on 5th April and 40 were at Fairburn Ings on 7th May. The spring passage in 1981 was heavier than usual and birds were seen at many waters, the maximum numbers being on 25th April when there were 35 at Blacktoft Sands, 29 at Fairburn Ings, 13 at Pugneys Gravel-pit, 12 at Swillington Ings, 11 at Wintersett Reservoir, and eight at Thrybergh Reservoir. Passage continued into May, and there were 53 at Wheldrake Ings and 18 at Fairburn Ings on 3rd.

An exceptional inland passage occurred on 2nd May 1983, when birds were recorded at several waters, the maxima being as follows: 27 at Blacktoft Sands, 23 at Whitton Sands, 36 at Wintersett Reservoir, 70 at Thrybergh Reservoir, 378 at Pugneys Gravel-pit, and 369 at Fairburn Ings. Most flew west or north.

The Arctic Tern has bred in Yorkshire on only one occasion. On 25th June 1939, J. Lord and G.H. Ainsworth saw a tern feeding young at Spurn and erected a screen from which to watch and determine the species. A pair of either this species or the Common Tern remained at Spurn throughout the summer of 1910, but did not breed.

An Arctic Tern, ringed as a chick in Estonia on 22nd June 1955, was found dead at Oswaldkirk on 11th August 1960; and another, ringed at the same place on 25th June 1960, was found dead at Spurn on 9th August 1960. Two birds ringed in Germany and one in Sweden have been recovered in Yorkshire in August, and an adult bird caught at Spurn on 1st August 1965 was recaught at a nesting colony in the Elbe Estuary, Germany, on 25th May 1966.

The status of the Arctic Tern in Yorkshire is that of a bird of passage during both migration seasons, with varying numbers occurring at inland waters during these same periods.

Little Tern
Sterna albifrons

When Nelson published *The Birds of Yorkshire* in 1907, he said of the Little Tern 'Summer visitant; breeds at Spurn; very rare inland.' Writing in his *Yorkshire Birds*, Chislett said that it had bred along the coast south of Kilnsea from 'times ornithologically immemorial'. The account of a visit to Spurn during the last week of May 1861 stated that the nesting site was on the seaward side about half-a-mile (0.8 km) from the point and that from 40 to 50 pairs were noted. The colony extended its limits thereafter, and Nelson said that it 'now includes nearly the whole strip of shingle from [the 1861 site] to opposite the Warren'. The nests were mercilessly plundered by egg collectors and excursionists, but in 1895 the County Council made an effort to protect them under the powers of the Wild Birds Protection Act of 1895. Spurn was declared a protected area and a watcher was appointed. The venture was apparently successful, for in 1900 about 200 young were hatched.

In 1912, 80 nests were situated north of Kilnsea and two to the south; eight were on the Humber side and four at Spurn Point. The breeding north of Kilnsea decreased after this time and evidently ceased except for returns in occasional years. In 1935, a few pairs bred on pastureland a little way inland, and in 1936 C.F. Proctor recorded 94 nests containing 259 eggs for the whole area. These numbers were maintained up to 1939, but decreased during the war years. The new hard road along the peninsula, built during the war, enabled easier access to the remoter parts of Spurn Point, and the Little Terns suffered much disturbance in the post-war years. During the late 1940s watch was maintained on the breeding pairs by The Yorkshire Naturalists' Union Protection Committee, and in 1950 some 60 pairs nested. Only about half of these reared young, but this was an improvement on the previous few years.

In 1952, the birds suffered much human interference and 18 eggs were found piled in a heap on the beach one day. The species fared badly thereafter, and in 1953 55 pairs produced 101 eggs but only one young bird was seen. A few pairs attempted to nest north of Kilnsea in 1954, but no young were produced. In both 1956 and 1957 about 20 young were hatched, but the colony then declined. During the late 1960s, from three to six pairs nested with some little success at Spurn, and foxes took the chicks of six pairs in 1967. In 1970, three pairs bred at the Point, but their nests were destroyed when a helicopter made an unauthorised landing on the beach; three nests on the Humber shore in 1977 were washed away by the tide.

In 1977 a small colony was formed again at the Easington Lagoons, north of Kilnsea, where there were three birds incubating on 4th June. Two young were seen by S.M. Lister on 9th July, when four birds were each incubating two eggs and 15 other adults were present. The colony persisted, and on 27th May 1978 26 birds were present including four apparently sitting on eggs, but no young were subsequently seen. No breeding was attempted at either Spurn Point or Easington in 1979, nor subsequently at the former locality, although one pair probably did so at Easington in 1980 and a few pairs have been present with varying success since then; five pairs reared 14 young in 1983.

Nelson's annotations to his personal copy of *The Birds of Yorkshire* gave details of breeding at Teesmouth. In 1908 and 1909, S. Duncan found three nests, and in 1911 about nine pairs hatched young. In 1912 about 20 pairs bred, and by 1931 some 30 pairs were breeding. Numbers dwindled after this time, but a few pairs persist to the present day. In more recent years, 11 pairs attempted to nest in 1950 at two sites, but few were successful; five pairs nested in 1951, one pair in 1957 and eight pairs in 1961. Two pairs produced two young at Redcar in 1963, and in 1967 four pairs were successful at South Gare, where from one to six pairs have nested annually since with little success.

Little Terns move along the Yorkshire coast from mid April and pass through on their journey to nesting areas farther north. The earliest arrival dates are 13th April 1979 at Filey; and 15th April 1980 and 16th April 1981 at Spurn. Numbers are never large, and some of the highest counts in recent years have been in the vicinity of Easington during May and June; up to 20 birds are regularly seen there and there were 37 present on 5th July 1980. On 7th May 1960, 58 flew north at Spurn; 30 were counted there on 19th July 1972, and 52 rested on the Chalk Bank at high tide on 22nd July 1975. The maximum counts in 1981 were 38 on 17th May and 42 on 18th June.

At any time from mid April to September, a few Little Terns may be seen along the coastline away from the two major estuaries, especially during the autumn when migrants are heading south. Most birds have departed by September, but a few have been recorded later: two were at Spurn on 9th October 1957, one on 19th October 1962 and one on 13th October 1964.

Up to the publication of *Yorkshire Birds* in 1952, Chislett could record only four inland records, although Nelson knew of several instances of its occurrence in the nineteenth century. After single records in 1953 and 1954, the species has occurred inland in every year since 1961. Better coverage of the many waters since that time has no doubt played a part in this new development, but in more recent years there has been a definite increase in the number recorded. May and June are undoubtedly the best months in which to see an inland Little Tern, and there have been over 60 records from about 20 waters since 1961. During the autumn, there have been fewer records from scattered localities between mid July and October. One to three birds have usually been involved, but there were nine at Blackmoorfoot Reservoir on 20th September 1976. Some birds linger for a few days before moving on, but usually the visits are brief. Two birds at Apperley Bridge on 3rd October 1965 and one at Wintersett Reservoir the next day were late.

A bird ringed as a chick at Spurn on 10th July 1914 was recovered in Portugal on 29th September 1914, and one ringed in Fifeshire on 10th July 1949 was recovered at Teesmouth on 20th August 1949.

Whiskered Tern
Chlidonias hybridus

A Whiskered Tern was shot on the River Swale in 1842 by one of the keepers at Hornby Castle, the residence of the Duke of Leeds (*The Naturalist*, 1885, p. 393).

On 18th May 1963, G.R. Edwards, T.D. Bisiker and R.F. Dickens visited the Easington Lagoons and saw a Whiskered Tern, which they were able to watch at close range as it fed over the marshy areas, dropping to the surface to catch insects. It was seen again on 19th and stayed for most of the day (*The Naturalist*, 1964, p. 32).

An adult was watched on Coatham Sands by W. Norman on 30th August 1964. It gave excellent views and enabled him to take detailed notes.

On 13th September 1975, H. Shorrock and others saw an adult at Fairburn Ings. I. Corbett, P.W. Izzard and B.G. Pepper saw an adult bird in full summer plumage at Tophill Low Reservoir on 26th and 27th May 1976. A similarly garbed adult frequented the canal area along the Easington to Kilnsea road from 24th April to at least 30th 1977. It was watched by many people, including D.J. Britton, G.P, Catley and S.M. Lister. M.G. Richardson and D. Waudby saw a first-summer bird at Castle Howard Lake on 4th June 1982, and D.I.M. Wallace saw an adult bird at Flamborough Head on 23rd July 1982.

There have been about 80 records of this Mediterranean tern in the British Isles, 60 of which have occurred since 1958.

Black Tern
Chlidonias niger

In *The Birds of Yorkshire*, Nelson said that, according to Arthur Strickland, the Black Tern used to breed in the East Riding of Yorkshire near Driffield. Chislett commented that there was little doubt that it also bred in parts of South Yorkshire before Vermuyden carried out his great drainage schemes.

It was purely a bird of passage by the middle of the nineteenth century and such it remains today. Its appearance in spring is dependent on the winds, and a period of good easterlies will bring Black Terns to several of the many inland waters. It has occurred in every year since records were first published by the Yorkshire

Naturalists' Union in 1940. May is the main month of occurrence, when, if the right winds prevail, birds may be seen hawking over inland waters ranging from sewage-farms to reservoirs and over large rivers. Numbers vary annually; in some years very few appear, in others a marked passage may be witnessed. In 1954, such a day was 9th May, when 34 were at Fairburn Ings, 26 at Chelker Reservoir, 21 at Malham Tarn, ten at Wintersett Reservoir, and smaller numbers at six other waters. In 1957, Hornsea Mere attracted 46 birds on 11th May, 15 of which were still present on 13th. Fairburn Ings had 38 birds on 23rd May 1959, 51 on 13th May 1962 and 42 on 12th May 1965. It was also a good year in 1966, when 67 were at Fairburn Ings on 25th May and 41 on 31st; 26 at Almholme on 29th May; and 25 at Stocks Reservoir on 30th May. An easterly wind brought 34 into Fairburn Ings on 6th June 1970. Along the coast, birds are usually more numerous during the autumn, but 62 passed at Spurn on 2nd May 1965, on which date 18 were at Fairburn Ings. In 1980, the peak spring passage occurred between 11th and 13th May, when single figures were seen at 18 localities and from 12 to 19 birds were at Fairburn Ings and Hornsea Mere. On 3rd May 1981, 50 birds flew west over Blacktoft Sands and small numbers were seen at many inland waters.

In autumn, most birds pass along the coast, and inland waters rarely have large numbers at this time. Anywhere along the coastline, especially at the favourite watchpoints at Filey, Flamborough and Spurn, daily counts of Black Terns in August and September number up to 20 birds on some days, with more occasionally. In 1958, 48 flew south at Spurn on 14th August and 35 did so on 28th August. The latter date was to provide the year's maximum count in 1960, when 57 passed at Spurn. The largest count in recent years occurred in 1965, when 165 birds flew south at Spurn on 26th September. A count of 126 flying south there on 17th August 1979 included only 29 adults, and on the same day 76 were in the Humber Estuary west of Hull. Several others were recorded during the next few days at other coastal places. A good autumn passage occurred in 1981, and 81 flew south at Spurn, including one party of 37 on 11th September. Only small numbers were seen at Flamborough during the period.

Autumn birds have been recorded between late July and mid October, but in 1954 single birds were seen by G.R. Bennett at Hornsea Mere on 7th and 21st November.

In the Yorkshire Naturalists' Union Ornithological Report for 1955, R. Chislett reported that he had been told by J. Armitage that a Mr L.C. Ballard had seen three heavily blotched eggs of the Black Tern in a nest built on a rotting mass of reed-mace in a marsh in central Yorkshire on 28th May 1950. The birds remained in the area up to the end of June. Ballard informed the British Trust for Ornithology, who gave him Chislett's address, but he never communicated. Chislett considered the claim probably correct, but the opportunity for proof had gone. The Black Tern breeds in France, northwards to southern Sweden and eastwards across Europe, and winters in tropical Africa. Its annual occurrence in the British Isles suggests that the migration route is taken voluntarily, but larger numbers are certainly forced westwards if easterly winds occur at the time of their northward journey in May.

On 16th May 1974, R.F. Dickens was watching 16 Black Terns at Fairburn Ings when, quite suddenly, eight of the birds joined together in a compact group and flew low over the water before doing a 'belly-flop' and then rising again, shaking their wings and body feathers in flight. The procedure was repeated several times, though not by all the birds simultaneously. For full details see *The Naturalist*, 1975, p. 27.

White-winged Black Tern
Chlidonias leucopterus

Nelson published three records of this south European tern: one was shot near Scalby Mills, Scarborough, in 1860 which went to the collection of E. Tindall and later to the Scarborough Philosophical Society's Museum; a mature bird was seen at Flamborough for some days in the spring of 1867, but was not procured; another was seen at Scarborough on 26th September 1896 and subsequently shot (*The Zoologist*, 1896, p. 387).

When Chislett published *Yorkshire Birds* in 1952, he could add no further reliable records, but since then the species has occurred on some 22 occasions.

It was to be 65 years after the 1896 bird before the next was seen in the county, and the record concerned two birds which Miss O.M. Pennock, W.F. Fearnley and A. Riley watched at Chelker Reservoir on 13th May 1961. This is the only occasion that more than one bird has occurred at the same time. In the autumn of the same year, G.R. Bennett saw a juvenile at Hornsea Mere on 19th August.

An adult in full breeding dress was seen near Kilnsea by G.R. Edwards on 24th July 1964. Later on the same day it was observed flying south at Spurn by R.W.N. Knapton.

An immature bird was at Elsecar Reservoir, near Barnsley, on 18th September 1966. It was seen by several people, including H. Crookes, J.I. Martin and D.J. Standring.

One in full summer plumage was at Hornsea Mere on 12th May 1969 and reported by W.F. Curtis. A juvenile occurred at the mere from 1st to 13th September 1974, when it was seen and photographed by the warden, R.G. Hawley, and by D.I.M. Wallace.

An adult at Wombwell Ings and Broomhill Flash on 19th June 1975 was watched from 10.30 hours to 20.30 hours by J. Hewitt, R. Wells and J. Seeviour, who photographed it (see plate 86). On 28th August 1975, J.D. Pickup, C.G. Varty and J. Whitaker watched a juvenile at Fairburn Ings, where it stayed for three hours (*The Naturalist*, 1976, p. 76). K. Dawson saw an adult flying south at Filey Brigg on 3rd August in the same year.

A juvenile was seen by C. Winn at Fairburn Ings from 17th to 21st September 1976, and P.A. Lassey and Miss Irene Smith watched a similar bird flying north at Flamborough Head on 25th September 1976.

In 1977, a bird in full summer plumage was seen by A.S. Butler, P.A. Doherty and V.A. Lister at Tophill Low Reservoir on 7th June. A juvenile was seen by A. Grieve at Blacktoft Sands on 25th and 26th August. Another juvenile was seen at Hornsea Mere on 23rd August by A.M. Allport, I.G. Howard and W.F. Curtis, and an adult was seen there on 30th August by D.G. Hobson and D.P. Sharpe.

In 1978, N.A. Bell, G.E. Dobbs and R.G. Hawley watched a White-winged Black Tern in full summer plumage at Hornsea Mere on 13th May; and a juvenile bird was seen at Tophill Low Reservoir from 7th to 10th August by P. Bishop, B.S.

Plate 61. Duck Pintail on its nest. A very scarce breeding species in Yorkshire, with confirmed records at Skipwith Common during the 1930s, at two other localities in the 1960s and at Wheldrake Ings in recent years. *Photo: J. Armitage*

Plate 62. A male Marsh Harrier over Blacktoft Sands reserve, where the species nested during the 1960s and 1970s, the only locality where such has taken place in Yorkshire since the beginning of the nineteenth century. *Photo: K. Atkin*

Plate 63. Merlin at its nest in a typical moorland situation among heather. A declining species in some areas, but still relatively successful in parts of Yorkshire. *Photo: A. Gilpin*

Plate 64. Eleonora's Falcon found dead by a farmer at Easington in early November 1982 and fortunately set up by a local amateur taxidermist. Only the second British record of this Mediterranean falcon. *Photo: B.S. Pashby*

Plate 65. Peregrine on its nest during a rain shower. In addition to having its eggs and young taken by collectors and falconers, this rare and noble bird is illegally shot in some parts of Yorkshire. *Photo: G.V. Adkin*

Plate 66. Red Grouse on its nest. Some of the best grouse moors in Britain are on the Yorkshire Pennines. *Photo: A. Gilpin*

Plate 67. Blackcock on a 'lekking' ground at West Stonesdale in Upper Swaledale. Forestry plantations are never far away from such sites and have aided the spread of this species in the northwest in recent years. *Photo: G.E. Alderson*

Plate 68. Three Ringed Plovers found dead in Yorkshire: an adult and an immature of the nominate race (left) and a juvenile of the small and darker Arctic race *Charadrius hiaticula tundrae* (right) from Spurn Point on 22nd September 1968. *Photo: M.F. Brown*

Plate 69. A migrant Dotterel at Filey Brigg in August 1978. *Photo: P.J. Dunn*

Plate 70. Temminck's Stint on its nest at Swillington Ings in 1951, the first breeding record for England. The bird was subsequently found dead nearby, having been mauled probably by a rat or weasel. *Photo: G.A. Newby*

Plate 71. White-rumped Sandpiper found dead under wires at Spurn on 18th October 1957. The first county record. *Photo: S.J. Weston*

Plate 72. Pectoral Sandpiper which frequented Hornsea Mere from 11th to 21st September 1975. This North American wader now occurs annually in Yorkshire. *Photo: D.R.J. Watkins*

Plate 73. Part of a flock of 400 Purple Sandpipers with a few Turnstones and Sanderlings in 1982 at Filey Brigg, one of the most favoured haunts of the former species. *Photo: P.J. Dunn*

Plate 74. Three Yorkshire Snipe, the centre bird showing much narrower stripes on the back and an overall paler appearance, characters typical of the Faeroe Islands race *Gallinago gallinago faroensis*, found dead at Harrogate in September 1969. *Photo: M.F. Brown*

Plate 75. Long-billed Dowitcher at Beaverdyke Reservoir, near Harrogate, where it stayed from 30th August to 11th September 1976. *Photo: J. Seeviour*

Plate 76. First-winter Grey Phalarope at Filey in the winter of 1982/83. This locality, along with Scalby Mills, Jackson's Bay and the Scarborough Harbour area, are the best places to see this species during the winter months. *Photo: P.J. Dunn*

Plate 77. Two juvenile Long-tailed Skuas found dead on the Yorkshire coast. Juveniles in dark plumage (upper), this one from Scarborough on 14th September 1976, are not uncommon but apparently moult into normal pale birds as dark-morph adults are practically unknown; the paler plumage of the lower bird, from Spurn on 14th September 1975, is more typical. *Photo: M.F. Brown*

Plate 78. Juvenile Little Gull at Hornsea Mere in August 1983. The mere is one of the best places to see this species in autumn. *Photo: I. Glaves*

Plate 79. One of the few Common Gulls to have bred in Yorkshire, on its nest on the moors above Scaling Dam in 1966. *Photo: N.W. Harwood*

Plate 80. Herring Gulls nesting on the roof of the Rowntree building in the centre of Scarborough, a recent trend in several coastal towns, notably Whitby and Robin Hood's Bay. *Photo: A.J. Wallis*

Plate 81. First-winter Iceland Gull (upper) and an adult Glaucous Gull in Scarborough Harbour, January 1983. This is one of the most popular haunts for these northern gulls in winter and certainly the best place to see them. *Photo: J.A. Pollentine*

Plate 82. Immature Great Black-backed Gull with aberrant head markings which frequented Lingerfield Tip, near Knaresborough, from 31st March until at least 14th April 1967. Originally thought to be an immature Great Black-headed Gull, the record is now deleted. See page 323. *Photo: N. Carling*

Plate 83. A group of gulls at Scalby Mills, Scarborough, in March 1976. Left to right: two Kittiwakes, a Mediterranean Gull and a Ross's Gull. *Photo: J. Seeviour*

Plate 84. Ross's Gull which frequented Scalby Mills, near Scarborough, from 22nd to 28th April 1976. *Photo: J. Seeviour*

Plate 85. Ross's Gull which occurred at Filey Brigg from 17th to 20th February 1983. *Photo: P.J. Dunn*

Plate 86. Adult White-winged Black Tern at Broomhill Flash on 19th June 1975. *Photo: J. Seeviour*

Plate 87. Yellow-billed Cuckoo caught at Spurn Bird Observatory on 27th October 1978. The second Yorkshire record. *Photo: G. Neal*

Plate 88. Yellow-billed Cuckoo found at Armthorpe, near Doncaster, on 14th November 1981. The bird died shortly afterwards and is now preserved in the Doncaster Museum. *Photo: Doncaster Museum and Arts Service*

Plate 89. Barn Owl, a declining species and perhaps most numerous in the open country of the East Riding, especially in Holderness. *Photo: W. Higham*

Plate 90. Long-eared Owl incubating on the old nest of a Carrion Crow in a hawthorn thicket. This most nocturnal of owls has a patchy distribution in Yorkshire, but is probably under-recorded. *Photo: G.V. Adkin*

Plate 91. Short-eared Owl brooding its young. Although many are illegally shot, the species remains a fairly common breeding bird in some parts of the county, especially in the northwestern dales and fells. *Photo: G.K. Yeates*

Plate 92. Tengmalm's Owl which stayed at Spurn Point from at least 6th March 1983 until being last seen on 27th. *Photo: P. Harrison*

Plate 93. The 1983 Spurn Tengmalm's Owl having been caught and ringed on 7th March. *Photo: P. Harrison*

Plate 94. Nightjar on its nest in Cropton Forest on the North York Moors, a favoured locality for this species. *Photo: R. Leslie*

Plate 95. Swift with abnormal plumage caught at Knaresborough Ringing Station on 22nd June 1975. Although superficially resembling a White-rumped Swift *Apus affinis* from above, the white lower belly and undertail-coverts with a few white spots across the breast are exhibited by no normal species of swift. *Photo: D.R.J. Watkins*

Plate 96. The first Yorkshire record of Olive-backed Pipit, at Spurn Bird Observatory in 1981. The bird was caught and ringed and stayed from 24th October to 1st November. *Photo: K. Atkin*

Plate 97. Olive-backed Pipit caught and ringed at Flamborough Head on 27th September 1984. The fourth Yorkshire record. *Photo: P.A. Lassey*

Plate 98. Grey Wagtail, a bird of the fast-flowing streams and rivers of the Pennines and North York Moors. *Photo: A. Gilpin*

Plate 99. Dipper, one of the characteristic birds of the upland streams in the west and north of the county. *Photo: A. Gilpin*

Plate 100. Thrush Nightingale seen alive in Locke Park, Redcar, on 16th May 1967 and found dead there next day. The first Yorkshire record. *Photo: N.W. Harwood*

Bryan, P. Izzard and others.

An adult bird was seen at Filey Brigg on 1st June 1979 by T. Hobson and A.M. Paterson, and another in summer plumage was seen there on 2nd August by N.M. Bibby, P.R. Chambers and D. Waudby.

In 1980, a bird in full summer plumage was at Tophill Low Reservoir from 29th to 31st May. It was seen by several observers, including T.M. Clegg, M. Coverdale and A. Gibson.

A juvenile bird was seen at Hornsea Mere on 8th August 1981 by I. Forsyth and K. Rotherham, and another was seen at Flamborough Head on 9th August by P.A. Lassey, D.G. Hobson and others.

A.Grieve watched a juvenile at Blacktoft Sands on 20th September 1982.

Two birds occurred in 1983: an adult at Easington on 29th May, seen by G. Featherstone, R.J. Scott and P. Shepherd, and another adult at Tophill Low Reservoir on 22nd June which was seen by P. W. Izzard.

All the Yorkshire records up to 1975 were detailed by R. Wells in *The Naturalist*, 1976, pp. 59-60. There are now about 500 records in the British Isles and the species has occurred almost annually in recent years, mainly during the spring.

Guillemot
Uria aalge

To read Nelson's 13 pages written under this species in *The Birds of Yorkshire* (1907) is a revelation. For the benefit of those who do not possess a copy of this fine work, I have reproduced the first nine pages in full below. Nelson also included no fewer than 22 photographs depicting the Guillemot; its eggs; the breeding cliffs at Bempton and Speeton; and the 'climmers' in action.

'The most remarkable and interesting feature of the stupendous range of cliffs extending from the Headland of Flamborough westward to Speeton, a distance of five or six miles, and varying in height from 250 feet to 350 feet, is the great ''loomery'' or breeding station of the Guillemot, a species that is found there in the nesting season in such vast quantities as to be practically innumerable.

It may be termed a resident of Yorkshire, spending most of the year on the open sea off the coast, and returning for short visits to the cliffs about Christmas or early in January, and, in some seasons, not till February; in 1901 it did not put in an appearance until the 11th of the latter month. These visits become more frequent, and of longer duration, as spring advances, generally taking place at high water and in calm weather, when, at times, the birds congregate as thickly on some of the ledges as in summer, but are quiet and undemonstrative. On 12th March 1900 there were thousands at Buckton Cliffs, where they were clustering like bees on the breeding ledges, and were in full summer plumage. Towards the end of April they take up their quarters for the season, the first eggs being laid in May; the earliest that the cliff-climbers have known were seen on the 6th. Some years ago they were common by the second week, though the usual period is about the third week in the month.

By the middle or end of August most of the Guillemots have left the cliffs and dispersed over the sea along the coast, where they are found in more or less abundance during the remainder of the year. Although this species is more a wanderer than a migrant, there can be no doubt that a partial migration takes place, many of our Yorkshire birds probably going further south, whilst their places are taken by others from northern stations. On 22nd August 1881, great numbers of young Guillemots were noticed off the Humber; and, when at sea off Redcar in the autumn, I have frequently seen flocks passing for days continuously, to the south-east, in small parties of from three or four to twenty. In winter storms many are cast ashore, and occasionally they are driven inland, being reported from localities far removed from salt water. In the "Correspondence of Dr. Richardson of North Bierley", is an interesting remark, contained in a letter to Dr. Sherard, and dated "7th January 1724-25," as follows:– "About the middle of last March was brought me *Lommia hoieri*, called at Flamborough Head (about two miles from Bridlington), Whillocks, where they breed in great quantities. This bird was found alive (on a moor) four miles from hence, and fifty miles from the sea: it was brought hither alive, very brisk, and in good feather."

The practice of climbing, or "climming" as the local term goes, for sea-fowl' eggs, as carried out on the Yorkshire cliffs, has often been described, though not always with strict accuracy; some particulars of this interesting and daring pursuit, which I have many times taken part in, may be acceptable, and, with the aid of illustrations, I hope to make it perfectly clear. The right of gathering the eggs belongs to the farmers tenanting the adjacent lands, and this privilege is conceded to the men who work for them when egging is out of season. "Climming" is a very ancient institution, having been in vogue for upwards of two hundred years, while one family at Buckton can boast of four generations who have followed this profession, viz.:– William Hodgson; his son Grindale, who died at the age of eighty about the year 1864; Edward, son of the last named, who climbed for upwards of thirty years; and, lastly, John, son of Edward, who has been a "climmer" since about the year 1885. Seventy to eighty years ago, that is, about 1825 to 1830, there were four gangs, led respectively by Aaron Leppington of Buckton; old George Londesborough, or "Lowney," of Bempton; Grindale Hodgson, and — Fox. Old Ned Hodgson can recollect when, some fifty years ago, only two gangs of climbers went out at the Bempton, Buckton, and Speeton cliffs, who divided the ground between them; one of these was captained by George Londesborough, and the other by Grindale Hodgson. The gangs consisted of two men only, one to climb and the other to manage the ropes; as a boy, Ned Hodgson used to be taken to help his father in coiling up the ropes and to assist in hauling up, while sometimes the men's wives were requisitioned to give a helping hand. A few years later three in a gang went out, but dangerous places were not "clumb." The cliffs at or near to Flamborough were worked by the fishermen, and, at the period referred to, the birds bred abundantly from the Headland westward, while in little bays, now entirely deserted, there was then a large avian population, as is exemplified by a spot near Thornwick called "Chatter Trove," from the noise the birds are said to have made. Many other portions of these cliffs have appellations derived from some incident connected with the bird-life, and handed down from father to son, e.g., "Bird's Shoot," "Hateley (Hartley) Shoot," "White-wings," where for some years, up to 1897, a white-winged Guillemot used to fly out; "White Breadloaf," so called from a man asking Ned Hodgson's help, who replied, "Whatever's on that spot you shall have"; the eggs were given to the man, who purchased with the proceeds of their sale the first loaf of white bread he had eaten for months; "Broken Head"; "Fox's Broken Arm," where accidents occurred; "Jubilee Corner," first climbed in the late Queen's Jubilee year; while the name of "Seven Score Place" perpetuates the memory of the largest number of eggs taken at one climb by George Londesborough.

Then ensued the time when the poor birds were ruthlessly shot down in the breeding season by tourists and gunners, who often did not trouble to pick up the dead or wounded, while the young were left to perish on the ledges; at this time, Hodgson declares, climbing did not pay, and was almost discontinued for some years. It was chiefly owing to the indignation aroused by this wanton destruction that the "Sea-birds Preservation Act" was passed, and, as the birds afterwards increased under protection, the egg gathering was resumed. On the Bempton, Buckton, and Speeton cliffs there are now four gangs of "climmers," each having an apportioned part, beyond which they must not trespass; four men constitute the gang, viz., the "climmer," and three top men. The ground from Danes' Dyke for about a mile and a half westward to Bartlett Nab (excepting one field at Bempton Lane-end), is climbed by Henry Marr's party (until 1902 the leadership of this gang was shared by the late George Wilkinson). The second portion is worked by William Wilkinson and his mates, who climb as far as Buckton Lordship, about half a mile, and they also have the Bempton Lane-end field; then William Chandler has Mainprize cliff, and a small part beyond; whilst the Hodgsons climb the Buckton end to Raincliff, comprising a stretch of about three-quarters of a mile in length.

Within the past two or three years a few Guillemots have taken up their quarters on the Gristhorpe Cliff, near Scarborough, but are not sufficiently numerous to repay the labour of climbing. At Flamborough, where the birds had become scarce, the fishermen climbed irregularly and intermittently until the year 1903, when a gang led by E. Major commenced to climb more methodically.

The ropes used are of strong stout hemp, 300 feet in length, and are renewed about every second year. In wet weather little climbing can be done as the ropes become slippery, or "greasy" as it is called, and difficult to work.

We will in imagination accompany a party of "climmers" on a fine morning, and having arrived "at cliff," find all in readiness for the descent. The "climmer" dons what are locally called the "breeches," an arrangement consisting of two broad loops of flat rope with belt attached, which is securely buckled around his waist, and to the front of the belt is fastened the "body" or "waist" rope. His hat is thickly padded to protect his head from falling stones, and on the arm which uses the guide-rope he wears a leather sheave, termed a "hand-leather"; his boots have toe-plates with edges turned down like a horse's shoe to enable him to walk on the slippery ledges; over each shoulder is slung a stout canvas bag; and a long stick, with a hook fixed at one end, for the purpose of raking eggs out of crevices and crannies, completes his outfit. A hand, or guide rope is made fast to an iron stake driven firmly into the ground, and the slack is thrown over the cliff. One of the men, the "lowerer," then sits on the edge of the cliff, with his feet planted in two holes purposely made to prevent his slipping; he wears a leather belt, or saddle, round which the waist rope is passed and held with both hands resting on his thighs; both men gather bunches of grass in order to protect their hands from being blistered or scored by the ropes when running freely, and to enable them to secure a better grip when hauling. The "climmer" now takes the guide-rope in his right hand, and in the other an iron stake having a running pulley at the top; walking backward he fixes the stake on the extreme edge (or, when the cliff is much broken, two pulleys are used), and lays the waist rope over the wheel; this prevents it chafing on the sharp rock edges; the lowerer then slacks away, and the adventurous "climmer" swiftly descends on the face of the cliff, by a succession of backward jumps, keeping his feet to the rock and inclining his body outward. He sometimes in this manner descends a hundred feet without stopping. On arriving at a ledge where eggs are visible he rapidly transfers them to the bags he carries, then kicks himself free from the ledge, throwing his weight on the rope, and so is lowered to other places, where he repeats the operation, clearing off all the eggs he can find. The expedients a practised "climmer" resorts to in negotiating dangerous places and corners are very ingenious; sometimes he creeps along a ledge for some distance, and, to save the trouble of returning by the same way, swings off again into mid-air; in order to get round a projecting corner he throws the slack of the waist-rope round and then launches himself off, so swinging to the spot he desires to reach. In some parts of the cliff iron pegs are driven into the rock, round which the "climmer" winds the hand-rope to assist him in his work, and at Jubilee corner, where the crag overhangs considerably three wire ropes are permanently fastened, by means of which the inner shelves, otherwise inaccessible, are reached. I have seen William Wilkinson, at a depth of more than two hundred feet, stop and fasten the rope to a holdfast in the cliff side, and from there lower himself to the recesses of a cave almost within stone's throw of the beach; indeed, the gymnastic performances of an expert egg-gatherer are as clever as those of many a first-class trapeze artist. A regular code of signals is arranged, by which the man below can telegraph his wishes to the top-man, thus: - a single tug at the waist-rope signifies that the "climmer" is ready to ascend; the laconic command "Up" is uttered, and all three of the top party, seated in a row behind each other, their feet firmly planted in holes, haul up their comrade from below. Two tugs mean "more hand or guide rope wanted"; three tugs, "less hand rope"; and these orders are executed accordingly; but by long experience the men have become so much accustomed to each other's ways that the lowerer seems to know intuitively what his mate wants, and instinctively holds or lowers, while the unsophisticated bystander naturally is lost in wonderment at the facility with which he seems to anticipate the other's wishes. When the "climmer" gives the signal to haul up he keeps kicking himself clear of the rock until he reaches a part where he can ease the labours of his companions by walking on the face of the cliff, reminding one of a fly on a window pane, and on reaching the top he picks up the iron stake at the edge, and so to the grassy flat where his spoils are emptied into large market baskets. The other men meanwhile coil up the ropes and prepare for a move to the next spot. The day's work commences at seven o'clock, and, on an average, about thirty descents are made; at the end of the day the eggs are all pooled and shared out, each man taking six or eight, the "climmer" as his perquisite being entitled to first pick each time. The Flamborough gang usually lower a young man instead of a "grown-up." The work is so arranged that the whole ground shall be cleared bi-weekly, each portion being climbed every third day, thus ensuring a constant supply of fresh eggs; in wet weather it so happens, however, that it is impossible to work, in this case the eggs become partly incubated and are spoilt for edible purposes; they are therefore gathered and blown for specimens, and the birds are thereby induced to lay again. When any portion of the cliffs is "clumb out," and becomes "poor," it is fallowed for two years or until it recovers, and is then again visited. In fine weather the Guillemots often drop their eggs in the sea, and it is no uncommon occurrence for specimens to be found in crab-pots and trawling nets. Egg-climbing in the "sixties" and "seventies" commenced on 12th May, but is now a week or ten days later; it ends the first week in July, or in a backward season it may be extended for a few days; I have known it prolonged until the 13th, but in the year 1904 a movement was started to induce the men to cease operations on 1st July. The average daily take of each gang is from 300 to 400, the grand total approximating 130,000. As many as 1,400 eggs have been collected by one party in a single day; old Londesborough on one occasion took 1,700 after stormy weather had prevented him getting down the cliffs for several days, and a few years ago George Wilkinson and Henry Marr gathered 600 from two spots between six and eight o'clock. The first laying is, as a rule, the most productive, after which there is a slack time; then ensues the midsummer "shut" or "flush," and after another slack interval, there is a third "flush"; the numbers then gradually decrease again towards the end of June. It may be here observed that there are many dangerous parts which are never climbed, and in these places the birds hatch out their first eggs without interference, and so a constant supply of young blood is ensured. The climbers say the Guillemot does not lay until the second year, their reasons for this assertion being based on the observations made with reference to fallowed spots which, if rested for one year, do not improve, but in two years the young birds have matured, and add their eggs to the general stock.

Accidents during the pursuit of egg-climbing rarely occur: one or two instances are known of the men having been damaged by pieces of falling rock, and this happened to Fox, whose arm was broken; also to old Londesborough and William Wilkinson, each of whom had an arm severely torn. A few years ago I was present when two of the men narrowly escaped shocking deaths; I had requested the "climmer" to procure me some Kittiwake's eggs, and he commenced his descent at a place where there were no foot holes for the lowerer, who, to my horror, began to slide towards the edge, being dragged by the weight of the man below; the other two top men were some distance away; I was on a point of the cliff a hundred yards off, and it seemed as though nothing could avert a frightful catastrophe, when, fortunately, Mr. John Morley, a Scarborough naturalist, who chanced to be near, rushed to the rescue and clasped the man by the shoulders, holding him until assistance arrived. The "climmer" has since told me he knew perfectly well what had happened "top o' cliff," and he had just reached a ledge where he could stand when the sickening sensation of falling stopped. Visitors are sometimes allowed to make the descent of the cliffs, and, if space had permitted, many amusing stories might be related in connection with their experiences. I have been told by a Quondam climber that, when he was assisting his father, who used to climb at Flamborough, in the "seventies," soon after the Franco-German war, they received a visit from three foreign gentlemen staying at the Thornwick Hotel, the youngest of whom requested to be allowed to take some eggs; he was accordingly lowered, and succeeded in bringing up five specimens, with which he appeared to be highly delighted. The strangers visited the climbers each day for a week, helping them in their work, and it was not until they had departed that it was discovered the young visitor who had gone "ower cliff" was the Prince Imperial of France.

If the first egg is taken a second is produced, and, frequently but not invariably, a third, the intervals between the first and second layings being, on an average, fourteen days if the egg is fresh, but, in the event of it being slightly incubated, the time is extended to eighteen or twenty days, and, if much incubated, to twenty-four days. In the case of a female becoming "clocky" over both the first and second egg it is probable that she does not lay a third that season. I have been informed by an old Flamborough climber that he once found in a sitting bird an egg ready for extrusion and three others in a well developed state.

Notwithstanding the enormous quantities of eggs taken annually the climbers declare that there is no diminution in the number of birds, and my observations certainly lead me to believe this to be the case. In 1834, when Charles Waterton visited Flamborough, the common eggs were sold at sixpence per score; the price is now twelve to sixteen for a shilling, and these are eaten by the villagers, or are sent to one of the large Yorkshire towns for use in the manufacture of patent leather, while the well marked specimens are set aside for collectors. Flamborough, or strictly speaking, Bempton, eggs are celebrated amongst oologists for their remarkable beauty and variety, though some twenty-five years ago, when collectors were few, common eggs were sold at three a penny, and twopence was considered a good price for a special example. The competition for good specimens is now very keen, prices having accordingly advanced until as much as 5/-, 7/6, and even half a sovereign is now paid for "real fancy eggs," as the men call them.'

This is the fullest account of the climbing for eggs on the Bempton and Flamborough cliffs, but it includes the indication that the number of eggs taken in a year approximated to 130,000, a figure which has been queried by Athol J. Wallis, who writes as follows:

The practice of climbing for the eggs of the Guillemot on the cliffs of Buckton, Bempton and Flamborough has been referred to by several eminent ornithologists, notably by Seebohm (1885), Cordeaux (1885), Wade (1902), Nelson (1907), Cott (1953/54) and Chislett (1952). Only the latter two refer to this practice as causing a decline in the number of birds breeding on the cliffs and lay the blame for this decline on the climbers' activities. There is also a booklet written by the climber Sam Leng, which is undated but was, from dates which he quotes, written in 1931. Leng does not refer to the number of eggs taken but he does mention another point which is at issue and which will be referred to later.

All these authoritative ornithologists except Seebohm quote what appears to have been accepted, without query, the magical figure of 130,000 eggs being taken in a season. Some doubt as to the authenticity of this figure is given later by Williams and Kermode (1968), who quote it followed by an exclamation mark, and by Cramp *et al.* (1974), who say of the figure 'said to have been taken'.

John Cordeaux, writing in *The Naturalist*, and reporting on the 1884 season, was the first person to mention 130,000 eggs as the annual take when he said: 'There are four sets of climbers working the cliffs between Bempton and Flamborough. In the season of 1884 one party admit having taken, in seven weeks and three days, 30,000 eggs of various sorts. The fishermen also, in their leisure hours, take a considerable number of eggs by climbing from below. It would, therefore, probably be no exaggeration to say that altogether 130,000 eggs are taken in the season, chiefly those of the Guillemot. It is difficult to understand how any species can withstand such a wholesale drain in their nurseries without showing a perceptible yearly and increasing diminution, more especially when we take into consideration the large number of birds slaughtered by "sportsmen" after the close time, when there are yet quantities of unfledged young on the cliffs dependent upon them. Yet the number of seabirds, I was told this season by those best able to judge, is considered greater than ever.'

It would appear that Cordeaux based his total of 130,000 eggs being taken on the equation: one gang of climmers admit to taking 30,000 eggs, therefore four gangs together took 120,000, with the fishermen accounting for, say, 10,000, a total of 130,000. This was followed by E.W. Wade, who presented a paper on 'The Birds of Bempton Cliffs' to the Hull Scientific and Field Naturalists' Club on 19th February 1902. He included the following paragraph: 'The season, varying as the egg supply is early or late, commences about the third week in May and finishes about the end of June or the first week in July (latest date 10th July). During that time each gang will collect on an average about 300 to 400 eggs daily, or, allowing something for wet days, when climbing is impossible owing to the greasy state of the ropes, 130,000 eggs in all per season. In spite of this the birds increase yearly'.

Nevertheless these figures do not agree with other statements made by the climbers to other ornithologists. Wade refers to an average of 300 to 400 eggs taken daily, while Henry Seebohm, who visited the cliffs in 1885 and talked to George Londesborough, known locally as Old Lowney, was told that 200 to 300 eggs was a good day's take. Seebohm's report on his conversations with George Londesborough reads, in part, as follows: 'He divides his ground into three days' work, so that he takes it all twice a week, when weather permits; in very wet and windy weather he does not "clim". Operations commence about the 14th of May. For the first nine days he has a good run of eggs, as the birds that breed on the ledges he visits have most of them laid; for the next nine days eggs are scarce. At the end of that time a second egg has been laid by the birds whose eggs he took during the first nine days, and he has a second run of successful collecting. He considers from two to three hundred eggs a day a good take. He has a second nine days' "slack", and after that comes his midsummer "fling" or "shut", as he comically expresses it. This is a very precarious one, and in some seasons is not worth getting, whilst in others it is nearly equal to the first two takes'.

This gives the most accurate picture of the climbers' activities, and takes account of the breeding biology of the Guillemot, a species which will, in normal conditions, lay only one egg a year, but will lay a second if the first is lost, with a proportion of the population laying a third egg should the second also be lost. It is known that if a Guillemot loses its first egg it will be between 14 and 22 days before a replacement egg is laid, with an average time of 17 days (Birkhead and Hudson 1977). Birkhead also found that overall 52% of lost eggs were replaced and that eggs which were lost were more likely to be replaced if the loss occurred early in the season.

From all this information we can deduce that the pattern of collecting described by George Londesborough was correct, and that the largest number of eggs would be collected during May when the first eggs were freshly laid, when there would be about nine days of successful collecting, followed by nine days when eggs would be scarce. This was then followed by a flush of second eggs, and as it would take about nine days to clear the ledges it was about 18 days before a return to the ledges first collected was made, a timing which fits with the bird's breeding biology. The climbers admitted to Chislett that they would take eggs that they knew had been partially incubated to induce the birds to lay a second egg, but from Birkhead's findings the resulting replacement crop would be less numerous than when the eggs were collected fresh.

It must be queried whether Cordeaux mis-heard what the climbers told him. Was the total of eggs claimed by one gang really the take taken by all the gangs? For one gang to collect 30,000 eggs in a season of seven weeks and three days, which was longer than was usual as the season was normally from about the last week of May to the first week of July or some 42 days, meant an average take of over 570 eggs a day. This is much higher than a good day's take quoted in either Seebohm's or Wade's accounts of the climbers' activities. Such a total of 570 eggs a day must have been exceptional.

If George Londesborough's account of their success is accepted as describing the more usual pattern of collecting, then the pattern would be somewhere along the following lines:

Nine days with an average take of, say, 300 eggs per day	2,700
Nine days slack period with, say, 100 eggs per day	900
Nine days with second laying with, say, 300 eggs per day	2,700
Nine days second slack period with, say, 100 eggs per day	900
Six days of 'midsummer fling' with, say, 200 eggs per day	1,200
A total for the season of	8,400

With four gangs equally successful, this gives an annual take of 33,600 eggs, and if an allowance is added for those taken by fishermen climbing up the cliffs a grand total of approximately 35,000 to 36,000 would appear more realistic than the mystical figure of 130,000.

It was in the 1930s and 1940s that the Wild Birds and Eggs Protection Committee of the YNU was expressing concern about the reduction in the numbers of Guillemots breeding on the Bempton Cliffs, and the climbers were blamed for this decrease. At a meeting between the YNU Committee and the climbers on 6th May 1938 (see below), and referred to by Chislett in 1952 in his book *Yorkshire Birds*, the climbers accepted that there was a reduction in the Guillemot numbers but they blamed the increase in the Kittiwake and oil as the true causes. The YNU Committee could not accept that the increase in Kittiwakes was the cause of any decline in the Guillemot population on the grounds that the Kittiwake numbers had been decimated in the 1860s and were building back to the same population that was probably breeding on the cliffs prior to the activities of the shooters. In any case, it has been shown by Birkhead (1977) that, where a dispute over occupancy of a nesting ledge arises between Kittiwake and Guillemot, the Guillemot is usually the successful species.

On the other hand, there is evidence through statements made by the climbers themselves that they were finding oiled birds in increasing numbers. Sam Leng, writing in 1931, says: 'Unfortunately, last year (1930) one of the Gannets came to an untimely end owing to the pollution of the water by oil from passing ships. A friend of mine found it, and he and I tried to free it from the oil, but this proved unsuccessful, and it met the fate of hundreds of others. Owing to this pollution of the sea, I have seen hundreds of dead and dying birds of all descriptions. The death caused in this way is a terrible one, as once caught in the oil there is no escape, and the birds slowly perish. This fact is responsible for the great decrease of late years in the numbers of birds which visit these cliffs, as owing to the parent birds being trapped in this manner the young birds are left to perish on the ledges.' Many references can be found in recent literature to the effects of oil on a population of breeding seabirds, and recent research into the control of expanding populations, e.g. the Herring Gull nesting on town roofs, has shown that effective control can be exercised only by the removal from the population of adult birds, just the effect arising from persistent oiling incidents at sea.

The Guillemot is a very long-lived species, and this, too, can be illustrated from the evidence of the climbers. This species is well known for the diversity of colour and markings on its eggs, and where a particular bird laid an egg of a particular colour or with a characteristic pattern the climbers reported finding an identical egg on the same ledge for a number of consecutive years. Sam Leng, in his booklet, refers to such a bird when he says: 'A Guillemot laid a pure white egg which was gathered by a friend of mine for eleven years, and I myself gathered it for 13 years.' Old Lowney mentioned this aspect in his talk in 1885 with Seebohm, who wrote afterwards: 'He also thinks that each bird frequents the same ledge year after year, and lays the same coloured egg every year, although the variety of colour in the eggs of different birds is so wonderfully great. He told me that he used to get a very rare and highly-prized variety, of an almost uniform rich reddish-brown colour, on a certain ledge twice every year, which continued for fifteen years in succession, after which the poor bird died, or was shot or became a "shunted dowager".'

For such a long-lived bird, exploitation of its eggs could not be the sole cause for the massive decline claimed if 130,000 eggs taken each year was correct, bearing in mind that a proportion of the cliffs could not be reached by the climbers and that weather conditions often made climbing at the most lucrative part of the season impossible. That there was a decline in the Guillemot population is highly probable, but the evidence would indicate that it was not as great as was assumed by the use of the quoted egg-take of 130,000 per year. Had this total of eggs been correct, the decline would have been in the region of 86 percent between the turn of the century and the first full census of Guillemot numbers carried out in 1964 by Williams and Kermode (1968). The claim made by Chislett that 'many few eggs are taken today' is possibly true for another reason.

Where man actively exploited wild populations as a necessary part of his survival techniques such exploitation was carried out to a scale and in a manner which would ensure the supply for future years. Undoubtedly, in the early years of climbing at Bempton, the proceeds were a means by which the farm labourers employed by the farmers owning the clifftop fields could supplement their annual income. In later years the practice was carried on to uphold a tradition rather than as an essential activity, and the climbing stopped, voluntarily, in 1953, one year before the law would have made the practice illegal.

References

Birkhead, T.R. 1977. The effect of habitat and density on breeding success in the Common Guillemot *Uria aalge. J. Anim. Ecol.* 46: 751-764.

Birkhead, T.R., and Hudson, P.J. 1977. Population parameters for the Common Guillemot *Uria aalge. Ornis Scand.* 8: 145-154.

Chislett, R. 1952. *Yorkshire Birds.*

Cordeaux, J. 1885. Ornithological notes from the East Coast in the spring of 1885. *The Naturalist* 10: 267-269.

Cott, H.B. 1953/54. The exploitation of wild birds for their eggs. *Ibis* 95 & 96.

Cramp, S., Bourne, W.R.P., and Saunders, D. 1974. *The Seabirds of Britain and Ireland.*

Leng, S. Undated (?1931). *Experiences and Reminiscences of a Cliff-Climber.*

Nelson, T.H. 1907. *The Birds of Yorkshire.* Vol. 2.

Seebohm, H. 1885. *A History of British Birds.*

Wade, E.W. 1902. The birds of Bempton Cliffs, in *Transactions of the Hull Scientific and Field Naturalists' Club.*

Williams, A.J., and Kermode, D. 1968. A census of the seabird colony at Flamborough, June 1964. *Seabird Bulletin,* No. 6.

On 6th June 1910, a most untoward accident cast a gloom over the whole climbing fraternity when Joseph 'Joss' Major of Flamborough was killed by a falling stone (see plate 43). The accident happened when he and his brothers were climbing at Staple Neuk during a strong gale. He was lowered at 09.30 hours and, after suspecting that something had happened, his companions sent another man down who found Major hanging head downwards with blood gushing from a wound in his head. He was eventually lifted to the top at about 18.00 hours and taken to the hospital in Bridlington, where he lay unconscious until his death two days later. The Major family never climbed again, and only three gangs worked the cliffs from Flamborough Head to Speeton thereafter. For very full details of this incident, see *The Naturalist*, 1911, pp. 102-3.

In 1938, an approach was made to the climbers by members of the Yorkshire Naturalists' Union Wild Birds and Eggs Protection Committee to meet and discuss the effect that egg collecting was having on the auk and gull populations. C.F. Proctor arranged for a dinner to be given at Bempton on 6th May 1938 which was to be hosted by himself, R. Chislett and S.H. Smith. Ten climbers attended, led by Messrs J. Petty and J.R. Artley. It was proposed by the committee that a date should be agreed in early June after which no eggs should be taken. All agreed that a serious decline in Guillemot numbers had occurred, but the climbers blamed oil pollution. The climbers could not agree to the June date because of seasonal variations and thought it better to work on different stretches of cliff in alternate years, which some of them said they did already. Some climbers admitted taking eggs they knew to be partly incubated so as to ensure a fresh supply in better weather. Birds producing a third egg were estimated at 40 percent of those robbed a second time. A claim by the climbers that an increase in Kittiwakes was responsible for the decline in Guillemots was disallowed by the protectionists, the increase being no more than a restoration of the Kittiwake's former status when Guillemots were numerous also. During the shooting slaughter in the mid nineteenth century, the gulls had become so reduced that climbing was halted because it was not profitable. The climbers were apparently impressed by the discussion 'and the meeting ended in a good if smoky atmosphere'.

Egg collecting on the cliffs was the prerogative of local farm employees and had the sanction of 'ancient custom'. It continued during the 1940s and early 1950s, in spite of dwindling numbers, before finally coming to an end in 1953, one year before the passing of the Bird Protection Act. The Yorkshire Naturalists' Union Ornithological Report for 1955 said that 'it is believed the birds did better than in any recent year', and in 1956 it was said that the Protection Act was already benefiting the species.

In 1964, 12,950 birds were counted on the cliffs between Flamborough Fog Station and Speeton Red Cliff Hole between 7th and 13th June. In 1974, 13,801 birds were counted on the same stretch of cliff. In 1977, S. Rooke, the warden for The Royal Society for the Protection of Birds, estimated a decrease of 25 percent on the Bempton Cliff section: from 12,200 in 1976 to 9,224 in 1977. The numbers were well up again in 1978, when 13,250 were counted, but only about one-third of that total were breeding and the success was apparently very low. Small breeding colonies are now established on the cliffs just north of Filey Brigg and north of Long Nab, Burniston.

The breeding birds settle down on the cliffs from mid March, but there are large temporary visitations during the winter months from November, particularly after rough weather. Some birds frequented the Flamborough Cliffs on 25th October 1971, an early date for such a visit. A massive visitation was witnessed by H.O. Bunce on 27th December 1975, when far more birds arrived at the cliffs than are present in the summer; most were in summer plumage. In 1978, S. Rooke also said that these visitations after rough weather were often in excess of the breeding total.

During the breeding season, Guillemots and other auks can be seen passing up and down the coast as they seek food, and there is a general mêlée of birds on the sea beneath the cliffs. On 15th April 1976, 5,500 flying south off Filey in three hours would doubtless be associated with the breeding colonies, as would counts of 1,000 per hour on many dates in late May and June 1981 and no fewer than 24,700 in one hour in the evening of 9th June 1981. The adult birds desert the cliffs with their young during August and spend the winter months at sea.

Large movements are often seen during the winter months depending on the weather, gales often causing many birds to shift their pelagic location. Offshore movements at Flamborough in 1978 involved 6,500 birds on 28th November; 5,250 on 10th December; 8,150 on 17th December; and 5,600 in three-quarters-of-an-hour on 18th December. All flew north. In 1980, off Flamborough Head, 10,300 flew north on 7th January, 6,000 did so on 1st March and 8,000 on 7th November.

The auks suffer badly from oil pollution and some are affected every winter. There have been several incidents of severe oiling, when several hundreds have been found on the beaches.

Nelson published several records of birds with abnormal plumage; these included pure white ones, an all-black melanistic example, some cream-coloured leucistic ones, two with white wings, and others with pied plumage. When S.C. Madge was warden at the Bempton Cliffs in 1973, he saw a pure white Guillemot; it was also present in 1974 and 1975. A piebald bird was also there in 1975.

The only recovery of a foreign-ringed Guillemot in Yorkshire concerned a bird ringed as a chick on the Island of Heligoland on 1st July 1961 which was found oiled at Flamborough on 20th October 1963. Many Guillemots were included among several hundred auks washed up dead on the Yorkshire beaches in February 1983. Gales lasting for several days had made it impossible for them to feed at sea and starvation resulted. P.A. Lassey, B.R. Spence, H.M. Frost and myself collected over 500 dead Guillemots, many of which were measured to determine the races. See also under Razorbill. For very full details of this wreck, see *Bird Study*, 1984, pp. 79-103.

Many of the birds visiting Yorkshire waters during the winter months belong to the much darker-backed northern race which breeds from Berwick northwards to the Shetland Islands and beyond. I have collected oiled and dead birds over the years, many of which belonged to this race, and an account of the occurrences on the Yorkshire coast was published in *The Naturalist*, 1966, pp. 81-4.

Whether the Guillemot is now any more numerous during the breeding season than when the climbers were operating is not easy to determine. A.J. Wallis has discussed this problem on pages 368-71, and it would seem that some early figures were greatly exaggerated. That it is now a very common and welcome breeding bird on the Yorkshire chalk cliffs there is no doubt.

Brünnich's Guillemot
Uria lomvia

The occurrences of Brünnich's Guillemot cited by Nelson in *The Birds of Yorkshire* have since been shown to be examples of *Uria aalge* in winter plumage. Several supposed Brünnich's were picked up on the beaches during the winter of 1894/95 and two of these, which are in the Yorkshire Museum at York, are undoubtedly common Guillemots.

A paper was published in *The North-western Naturalist* in 1946 by R. Wagstaffe, K. Williamson and R.H. Broughton, who, after examining all the British records, found only one specimen to be authentic. They revealed beyond doubt that Thorburn's painting of Brünnich's Guillemot in Lord Lilford's book was executed from a winter-plumaged Guillemot found in the winter of 1894/95, and this subsequently led to others being erroneously identified as Brünnich's.

The species has occurred in the British Isles on only 19 occasions and none has come from Yorkshire.

It should be noted that the second page of the chapter on Brünnich's Guillemot (page 725) in Nelson's *Birds of Yorkshire* is erroneously headed Black Guillemot.

Razorbill
Alca torda

The Razorbill is a common breeding bird on the cliffs of the Flamborough Headland and thereabouts, and, like the Guillemot, its eggs featured in the spoils of the climbers. The eggs from this area were much prized by collectors because of the variation in their markings. An all-black egg was taken by Henry Marr of Bempton, and several coloured a deep chocolate were taken. The Jackdaw often raids the Razorbill's eggs, much to the annoyance of the old climbers, one of whom, John Hodgson, once showed the half-eaten remains of a deep chocolate-brown egg to Nelson. He said that it was the best specimen he had ever seen and that he vowed vengeance against 'those rascally Jacks'.

Nelson considered that the Razorbill was outnumbered by the Guillemot on the breeding cliffs by 100 to one. A small breeding colony is now established on the cliffs north of Filey Brigg, and a few are breeding to the north of Long Nab at Burniston. They usually arrive on the cliffs during March, but in 1884 M. Bailey noted some thousands on the cliffs on 21st February, a date which he said was the earliest he had ever seen them. Nelson also records a few on the cliffs at Buckton on 11th February 1901. The adults leave with their young during August, where-after the cliffs are deserted. At this time, rafts of adults and their young can be seen on the sea a little way offshore, as at Scalby Mills on 30th July 1975 when several such rafts were assembled on a flat-calm sea, many young birds being fed by the adults.

In 1964, A.J. Williams and D. Kermode counted 2,492 Razorbills on the cliffs between Flamborough Fog Station and Speeton Red Cliff Hole between 7th and 13th June. Birds on the sea, of which there were many, were not counted. S.C. Madge covered the same stretch in 1974 and counted 3,767 birds on the visible parts of the cliff. A count in 1975 from Crowe's Shoot to Lang Ness in late June produced 3,395 birds. The Bempton stretch had a total of 2,921 birds in 1977 and 3,000 in 1978. In 1980, 316 pairs nested between the North and South Landings at Flamborough.

When Guillemots are passing offshore during bad weather or during feeding movements in the breeding season, Razorbills are included in smaller numbers. The largest count was off Filey Brigg on 15th April 1976, when S.C. Madge saw 1,750 passing south in three hours. At any time during the winter months a few lone and ailing Razorbills and Guillemots may be seen about the harbours, where they seek shelter.

The species is much affected by oil, and dead birds are a common sight along the beaches in some winters. During February 1983, a prolonged period of gales prevented auks from fishing successfully at sea and many thousands, mainly Razorbills, perished along the east coast of Britain. The Yorkshire beaches were monitored by several people and the number of dead Razorbills was well in excess of 1,000. The first birds came in during the night of 8th/9th February, and at mid-day on 9th I collected 31 Razorbills from a mile-long (1.6 km) stretch of beach south of Filey. All were clean, with no oiling, but very thin and obviously starved. Also found on that first day of the wreck at Filey were 18 Guillemots, four Puffins and three Little Auks.

P.A. Lassey later checked the beaches from Flamborough to Hornsea and measured 743 dead Razorbills; and I measured a further 136 from the beaches at

Filey and Withernsea, the latter sample being kindly supplied by H.M. Frost. Birds were being washed in over a period of several days, and many more than were found must have perished. It is almost certain that the majority were from the breeding colonies in the Hebrides and the Northern Isles, and some had been ringed as chicks there in previous years (*Bird Study*, 1984, pp. 89-94).

The Northern Razorbill, which breeds on the coasts and islands of northern Europe, has undoubtedly occurred in Yorkshire waters. A dead bird found at Spurn in February 1974 had a wing length of 222 mm, which falls well within the range of the larger northern form. The skull, complete with its ramphotheca, and one wing are in my collection. Some of the birds from the February 1983 wreck were at the upper limit of the British race as regards wing length, but were considered to be of that form.

Nelson recorded three birds with abnormal plumage. In 1976 S.C. Madge saw a pale leucistic example, with the black parts replaced by creamy-fawn, on the cliffs during the summer; M. Francis saw a similar one at Long Nab, Burniston, on 7th August in the same year.

On 11th November 1976, M. Francis watched a grey seal eating a Razorbill off Scalby Mills.

Although less numerous than the Guillemot, this fascinating auk is still a common breeding bird on the high cliffs from Flamborough northwards to Speeton, and a few small colonies are now established near Filey and Scarborough.

Black Guillemot
Cepphus grylle

There is evidence that the Black Guillemot formerly nested at Flamborough Head. Nelson quoted the account by Pennant, who visited the headland on 3rd July 1769 and said of the multitudes of birds there that he 'observed among them a few Black Guillemots very shy and wild'. A. Strickland killed a specimen in full plumage from a small flock at the height of the breeding season, near the rocks off Flamborough 'about 30 years ago' (prior to 1844).

Professor Alfred Newton showed Nelson 'the unmistakable egg of this species', which had come from the collection of Charles Waterton and was labelled '1834, Flamborough'. Nelson was unable to obtain any proof of breeding during the latter part of the nineteenth century and, as far as can be ascertained, it has nested only once in recent times. W.J. Clarke, writing in *The Naturalist*, 1939, p. 15, quoted V.G.F. Zimmerman as follows: 'Early in July (1938) I saw a Black Guillemot on Bempton Cliffs on several occasions; and on July 24th I watched a pair of Black Guillemots feeding two young ones. I had the pleasure of watching them for two hours.' Chislett knew Zimmerman, and agreed with Clarke in accepting the record 'without hesitation'. Clarke subsequently saw a pair in summer plumage near Filey on 24th September 1938.

In his *Yorkshire Birds*, Chislett listed four other records. A bird in winter plumage was seen several times in flight near Todmorden on 2nd February 1948: it had a white head and mottled black plumage, and was seen to fly fast downwind and appeared to come down in a distant field; then almost immediately it came back upwind with fast level flight to within 15 yards of the observer, S. Cockroft, when white patches on the short pointed wings became obvious; after landing on a bank, it took off again with some difficulty and flew out of sight. The second was found dead at Filey by P.A. Clancey on 18th February 1950; the third was shot at

Flamborough on 29th December 1950; and the last was seen at Runswick Bay on 25th April 1951.

Since then, it has occurred in 19 of the 34 years to 1984 and annually since 1975 (except 1983). Records usually involve single birds, but there have been two together on occasions and four at South Gare on 16th November 1969. Records have been in all months except June, only 12 during January to May and the majority between July and December, mostly during October (13 records) and November (15 records).

One stayed on Peasholm Park Lake, Scarborough, for about ten days from 17th December 1959. Two adults in full summer plumage were at Flamborough on 2nd July 1978, on which date an adult flew south at Filey; and single birds in summer plumage were at Flamborough on 13th May and 12th August 1979. One flew into Filey Bay on 11th July 1981, and one was off Flamborough on 22nd October 1981; one was at Flamborough on 4th April 1982 and 12th April 1983, and single birds were at Filey on 19th September 1982, 2nd July 1983 and 1st January 1984.

A chick ringed on Fair Isle on 28th July 1969 was found dead at Filey on 5th February 1978. This was the second longest known movement of the species.

Little Auk
Alle alle

Nelson's assessment of the status of this visitor from the Arctic islands — 'Winter visitant, not uncommon in some years, though irregular in its appearance; occasionally driven inland during stormy weather' — applies equally well today.

Some large visitations occurred in Nelson's time and he mentioned several years when more than usual were seen. What he described as the most remarkable invasion 'recorded during the memory of living man' occurred during the latter part of 1894 and in early January 1895. This was a period of strong onshore gales, and during the first fortnight of January 'immense companies of Little Auks passed along the coast, many being shot, while more were driven in by stress of weather and cast up on the sands in a dead, or exhausted and dying condition'. The gales continued until the middle of February and the birds 'perished wholesale, and some hundreds were taken to the bird-stuffers'. At Beverley 84 were brought in on one day, and many thousands were observed close inshore between Scarborough and Spurn. Nine were found inland.

In 1900, a week-long gale in late February brought many birds inshore. Fifty were found at Redcar; 18 on the Holderness coast in one day; and upwards of 150 were taken to the taxidermists at Scarborough.

In November 1948, after a period of easterly winds, Little Auks arrived offshore in large numbers. On 7th, small parties of up to 30 birds were flying north all morning off Filey Brigg, while others were on the sea. On the same day, two alighted on Swillington Ing for a few minutes; another was flushed during a shoot at Blaxton and collided with a wire; and one was caught alive at Southowram. On 8th, one was found in a garden at Baildon and another was found at Haworth. One was picked up on Otley Chevin on 9th, another was found in a field near Penistone on 10th and, finally, one was found on a moor near Halifax.

On 22nd October 1955, after a strong northerly gale on 21st, 98 flew north across the Tees Bay. In 1957, 85 flew north at Spurn and 163 at Teesmouth on 9th November, and 95 and 181 respectively did so on 10th.

A good many were seen in 1959, when 57 were off Spurn and 52 flew north at Hornsea on 31st October, and 45 were seen at the latter locality on 1st November. Over 100 were picked up dead through oil pollution along the Yorkshire beaches during January to March 1970. About 100 birds passed north off Spurn during early November 1971.

The largest influx in recent years occurred in 1974. Northerly gales persisted from 21st to 29th October, and on the latter date 318 flew north at Spurn during an all-day sea-watch, the majority passing during the hour before noon. Farther up the coast at Hornsea, 179 were counted in two-and-a-half hours, the same birds undoubtedly being involved. Next day, 118 flew north at Spurn and 66 were seen off Scarborough in two-and-a-half hours, one party being so close under the wall of the Marine Drive that R.H. Appleby could hear them calling as they passed; 28 also flew north at South Gare.

A lone bird on the sea at Spurn on 2nd November 1975 was the forerunner of another spectacular movement, when 180 flew north on 7th November; 120 on 8th; nine on 9th; and 26 on 18th.

A few birds remain in Yorkshire waters until May in some years, but most have left for their northern breeding grounds by April. Records during the summer months, when Little Auks should be well to the north of the county, have involved one at Spurn on 27th July 1957; one flying north at Scarborough on 26th May 1975; one flying south with Razorbills at Filey on 21st May 1977; one in summer plumage at Flamborough on 6th June 1977, and another at Spurn on 10th July 1977; one at Filey on 11th June 1980; and one flying south at Spurn on 17th June 1981.

Little Auks occur every year in varying numbers, large visitations being dependent on strong winds from the northern quarter during late October and early November. When such movements are taking place, birds may be seen along the coast from the Tees to the Humber and invariably some are 'wrecked' at inland localities, where occurrences over the years have been too numerous to list in detail.

In February 1983, a wreck of auks along the coastline included at least 250 dead Little Auks and many more were seen alive close inshore: 64 at Withernsea, 76 in the Barmston area, 356 at Flamborough and 81 at Filey on 2nd; 140 at Atwick, 31 at Bridlington, 218 at Flamborough and 55 at Filey on 7th; 171 at Atwick, 755 in Bridlington Bay, 884 at Flamborough and 161 at Filey on 8th; and 166 in Bridlington Bay, 274 at Flamborough and 225 at Filey on 9th. Unprecedented numbers occurred in the autumn, with 6,244 off Flamborough on 29th October and up to 300 on three other dates up to 16th November. On 29th October, 36 were well into the Humber Estuary at the Humber Wildfowl Refuge, and 12 birds were found inland between 8th and 11th.

It is intriguing to note that an early allusion, perhaps the earliest, to this species was made in a statement by the Reverend W. Dalton of Copgrove, near Knaresborough, to the effect that the Little Auk had been found near his house (Montagu's *Ornithological Dictionary*, 1813, p. 5, in Newman's 1866 reprint).

Puffin
Fratercula arctica

The Puffin arrives on the breeding cliffs of the Yorkshire coast in April, somewhat later than the Guillemot and the Razorbill. It breeds in good numbers on the cliffs at Flamborough head, Bempton and Speeton, and small numbers are now nesting at Newbiggin Cliff, Filey, where H.O. Bunce saw 25 pairs on 22nd May 1976.

A count by S.C. Madge along the visible cliff faces from Speeton Red Cliff Hole to the Flamborough Fog Station, a distance of about 7 miles (11.2 km), in June 1974 gave a total of 2,564 Puffins. In 1975, 1,791 birds were counted on the cliffs at Bempton between Crowe's Shoot and Lang Ness in late June. The number of birds counted on the Bempton Cliffs in 1977 by S. Rooke was 4,876, a remarkable increase on the previous year. In 1978, approximately 2,000 pairs bred there, but the numbers present in the area varied greatly; on 12th June, between 6,000 and 7,000 were present in the late evening, where there had been virtually none the night before.

Concentrated sea-watching from Flamborough Head in recent years has shown that large numbers of Puffins, hitherto unrecorded, pass in every year. Most pass northwards, and P.A. Lassey and his colleagues have counted 190 in one hour on 6th April 1974; 1,035 in one hour on 8th August 1975; an astonishing 21,250 during a seven-and-a-half-hour watch on 30th July 1976, with 14,575 during a similar watch on 31st and 2,472 on 13th August; 2,000 on 30th July and 4,500 on 13th August 1977; 2,000 on 1st July, 7,000 on 8th July and 3,500 on 22nd July 1978; 2,450 on 14th April, 4,800 on 16th June, 3,500 on 22nd July, 4,200 on 27th July and 3,700 on 6th August 1979; 2,300 on 12th April, 1,530 in 35 minutes on 16th April and 1,200 on 12th July 1980; and 10,500 on 1st August 1982. These remarkable counts have never been witnessed before and are due entirely to the dedicated vigilance of the sea-watchers at this unique location. It would be most interesting to know the origin of these large numbers.

Chislett recorded a bird found running in a street at Acklam on 1st November 1945, and there have been only six inland records since. One was found in Barnsley in October 1954; one found alive at Terringham on 25th October 1955; one seen in flight at Fairburn Ings on 9th September 1956; one found dead at Beningborough on 12th November 1958; a juvenile found dead in Roundhay Park, Leeds, on 13th November 1959; and a juvenile found dead on a road near Harrogate on 8th November 1969.

Nelson recorded a few birds with abnormal plumage. These included a cinnamon-coloured individual at Marske; a pure white bird at Flamborough and another at Bempton in 1902; and one from Scarborough in 1896 which was all white except for a few black feathers on the back.

Three birds ringed on the Farne Islands have been recovered on Yorkshire beaches.

Pallas's Sandgrouse
Syrrhaptes paradoxus

This extremely rare vagrant from Asia found its way into western Europe with some regularity during the second half of the nineteenth century. The first great invasion occurred in 1863, when at least 80 birds were seen in Yorkshire and 28 more were procured. In 1876, several flocks were seen on the Continent, and during late August Nelson saw three on the sands at Teesmouth. They were very wild and did not permit approach nearer than 100 yards. A local shooter told Nelson that he had followed the three birds for a whole day but in vain. Full details of this invasion were published in *The Zoologist*, 1863, pp. 8688-9 and 8722-4, and 1865, p. 9563.

In May 1888, there occurred another great influx, on a grander scale than that of 1863. The first to arrive was a party of six birds at Teesmouth in the middle of May, while Nelson was 'unfortunately away from home'. They did not survive and several were found dead in the neighbouring saltmarshes, the remains of one being taken to Nelson on 12th June. On 22nd May, a waterlogged female was picked up on the sands, and another was washed up by the tide around the same time. On 7th June, five were shot near Marske from a flock of 30 or 40 in mistake for Golden Plovers; Nelson purchased these shortly afterwards. Two of these birds can be seen in the Nelson Collection at the Dorman Museum in Middlesbrough (case number 154). Small parties of birds were seen at intervals during the summer months, including a flock of 20 at Ormesby on 10th June; 50 or 60 at Flamborough on 24th May; 25 at Scarborough on 16th May; 50 at Mappleton on 7th June; 40 at Hollym on 19th November; 70 at Spurn on 31st May; at least 50 pairs near Beverley in July; 30 near Market Weighton in June; 42 near Burton Agnes during July, which, in spite of an instruction for their protection by W.H. St Quintin, were reduced to 22 by early August; 15 near Goldsborough on 30th May; and 21 near Masham in June. Many other smaller parties were scattered all over the eastern part of the county.

A pair in the Yorkshire Museum, shot in 1888 and presented by J. Backhouse, are of the dark variety, which is suffused with smoky-grey.

In spite of the almost impossible task of estimating the actual numbers present in the county, Nelson calculated the following:

	Observed	Killed
North Riding	230-250	25
East Riding	500	90
West Riding	95	10

On 24th May 1890, six were seen coming from the east by two boatmen while half-a-mile off the Spurn Light. The birds passed within 30 yards and were seen to alight on the sandhills (*The Naturalist*, 1890, p. 202).

In May 1891, a flock of six was seen and two birds shot on the cliffs at Roulston (*The Naturalist*, 1895, p. 327), and a small flight occurred at Easington on 13th May 1899 (*The Naturalist*, 1899, p. 175). A flock of 18 was seen in the second week of July 1904 at Millington, near Pocklington, by a keeper who had seen many during the 1888 invasion and who had handled several. He recognised them by their flight, long pointed wings and tail feathers, and also by their call note. A neighbouring keeper saw a small flock about the same time. I doubt if these last two records would be acceptable today, and it is likely that an error was made in this case.

During the great invasion year of 1888, two pairs produced eggs in Yorkshire. Both were near Beverley: the first nest, containing two eggs, was reported on 15th June on Newbald Lodge Farm by Joseph Long, a rabbiter; and the other at High Gordham on 5th July, when two eggs were found on bare ground by Johnson Swales. The specimens went to the collection of a Mr T. Audas, and a coloured plate depicting the eggs appeared in the *Transactions of the Hull Scientific and Field Naturalists' Club*, vol. III, plate 4 (1906).

In 1953, I was given a case containing a pair of beautifully stuffed Pallas's Sandgrouse by the landlord of the Bluebell Inn at Kilnsea. They had been shot at Spurn in 1888 by Clubley and I disposed of them some years later, an action which I have deeply regretted ever since.

Rock Dove
Columba livia

The true Rock Dove, ancestor of all the varieties of domestic pigeon, quite obviously nested along the Yorkshire coast in times past.

A regular infusion of feral blood over the years, from lost homing pigeons and 'town-hall' birds joining the cliff colonies, has produced a mixture of several colour variations, among which, nevertheless, are many showing the characters of the true blue Rock Dove.

Many hundreds frequent the caves and crevices along the cliffs at Flamborough, and those to the north, wherever suitable places occur. The warden at Bempton Cliffs estimated that 80 percent of the cliff population in 1975 consisted of pure blue types.

During August, when the many auks and Kittiwakes have left the ledges, Rock Doves take over and breed on the otherwise quiet and deserted cliffs. In 1979, it was estimated that at least 2,000 birds were present from August onwards. The fields adjoining the clifftops and those some miles inland provide food for the huge flocks which assemble in the winter months. In 1980, 4,500 were counted along the Flamborough and Bempton cliffs on 21st November. On 28th February 1981, over 800 birds flew south over Bridlington Harbour in under two hours, no doubt on their way to feed in the fields along Bridlington Bay, and S.M. Lister counted 2,500 at Buckton on 17th October 1981. On 24th October 1982, 5,000 birds were counted between Flamborough and Speeton, a distance of 7 miles (11.2 km).

In Continental Europe the Rock Dove breeds on inland cliffs, but claimed records of their doing so in Yorkshire have always been referable to the Stock Dove.

Stock Dove
Columba oenas

When T. Allis presented his report to the British Association in York in 1844, he commented that he had seen only one specimen of the Stock Dove, a bird which had been on sale in a market with Woodpigeons and was then in the Museum of the Yorkshire Philosophical Society. He also referred to two or three other birds in York Market in 1843 and recorded that they were not infrequent near Sheffield.

The increase that followed seems to be a genuine one and not the result of better recording, and Nelson referred to it as one of the most interesting events in connection with Yorkshire ornithology.

It apparently existed in some numbers on the Yorkshire Wolds 'long previously', i.e. prior to 1864, when it was numerous on the old Warren grounds. The reclamation and cultivation of the old rabbit-warren areas drove it from its preferred haunts and for a while it nested on the edges of these areas, under furze bushes and among roots in old pits. It used to nest commonly in the rabbit burrows on the managed warrens and the warreners took the squabs for food. Nelson thought that the greater part of Yorkshire had been colonised by these evicted Wolds birds, the existence of which was apparently not known to Allis and Strickland.

A letter in *The Field* of 12th May 1877 drew attention to the sudden increase in the Stock Dove near York. It colonised the foot of the southern Wolds and around Malton and Flamborough about 1865; the first bird seen by Canon Atkinson at Danby in Cleveland was in 1846, and it did not appear in the Esk Valley until the 1850s. The spread to the west was not until about 1875; in the Masham area it was first observed about 1842, and several people spoke of its extreme rarity there until the last quarter of the nineteenth century.

By the turn of the century, the Stock Dove was widely spread over the whole of Yorkshire, except in the manufacturing districts and on the moorlands, which areas were, according to Nelson, unsuitable for its existence. They are now quite suitable and the Stock Dove is a common bird of the barren uplands, nesting in old barns and quarries as well as among the old factory buildings of the southern Pennines.

In spite of a marked decline in the population during the 1960s, due to harmful pesticides, there have been several records of large concentrations of Stock Doves during the non-breeding season since that time and parties of up to 30 or 40 birds are fairly regular in some areas. Some larger flocks have been as follows: 150 at Lindley Reservoir in January and February 1960; 700 at Hornsea Mere in December 1962; 100 at Settle on 4th April 1970; 100 at Blubberhouses on 23rd January 1972; 200 at Staveley Lagoon on 27th October 1974; 340 at Denton, near Ilkley, on 27th December 1975; 200 near Huddersfield on 2nd January 1977; 200 at Warmsworth on 27th December 1977; 300 at Cadeby in January 1978; 160 at Harewood on 12th November 1978; 235 at Bolton-on-Dearne on 19th November 1978; 350 at Denaby Ings on 18th February 1979; 300 at Potteric Carr on 9th February 1980; 300 at Scabba Wood on 2nd November 1980; 202 at Wath Ings on 6th December 1980; and 200 at Wath Ings on 3rd January 1981, with 250 there on 27th October 1981.

On 17th February 1959, at Spurn, 44 birds flew south, and during the mornings of 29th February and 1st and 2nd March 1960 flocks totalling 43, 60 and 28 respectively flew south; 34 flew south on 2nd January 1962. Five flocks totalling 261 birds were counted flying south there by C. Winn on 25th January 1958. G.R. Bennett counted 98 birds flying south over the sea at Atwick on 28th December 1959 and four more on 29th. Such flocks are probably associated with feeding movements.

The Stock Dove is a familiar bird along the roadsides, especially in the early mornings, where it seeks grit and drinks from puddles. The species nests early and eggs are usual during March, but, like the Woodpigeon, the season continues throughout the summer and eggs may be found in any month to October. Those who have visited nests to ring the young birds will know that eggs or young can disappear mysteriously. Newly hatched chicks which would be old enough to ring some seven days later may have been replaced by fresh eggs at the next visit. Nesting boxes are occupied very readily, indicating a lack of natural nesting sites. The habit of these birds of associating in threes during the spring and summer is most intriguing and may account for the obvious disturbance and apparent turmoil at some nest sites. Why they keep together in trios is not understood, and it would be interesting to know the sexual composition of such parties.

An adult bird caught at Knaresborough Ringing Station on 8th July 1973 was shot in the Cleveland Hills on 9th December 1973.

I am very fond of the Stock Dove and the fact that this very attractive 'black-eyed' pigeon is now a common sight in Yorkshire is most agreeable.

Woodpigeon
Columba palumbus

Marmaduke Tunstall, who lived at Wycliffe-on-Tees, wrote of the Woodpigeon in 1784: 'Have many here, and what is singular, more in the winter than in summer, even in the severest weather. Are very mischievous in gardens, destroying all sorts of grains, cabbages, etc. ... They usually begin cooing in March, though I have heard them in January, in mild warm weather.' Two hundred years have not really changed the status of this ubiquitous species, and Tunstall's assessment suffices today.

In spite of much persecution from farmers and rough shooters, the Woodpigeon survives and its numbers are maintained. Its wide choice of habitat and nest site doubtless contribute to this success and it may nest wherever there are trees or bushes, from sea-level to the high moorlands where it now builds its nest in young conifers. Suburban gardens offer it a secure home, and I have seen nests on branches overhanging busy main roads. In 1975, a pair built a nest on a ledge in a gable end in Scarborough. The breeding season is a protracted one and eggs may be found from March to October, the peak season being quite late in the summer after the harvest, when grain and clover are available.

Many birds come to the British Isles every year from the Continent and Nelson recorded an enormous influx in October and November 1884, when birds arrived on the northeast coast from 20th October to the end of November. Several other years were mentioned when large immigrations took place. Birds from farther north in Britain, as well as immigrants, swell the ranks from October onwards. From

October to December, and sometimes into January, large numbers of Wood-pigeons can be seen moving along the coast, having come across the sea or having coasted down from farther north. Numbers vary annually, presumably depending on the success of the breeding season or the severity of the weather in their home-lands.

Flocks of up to 1,000 to 2,000 are not an unusual sight and there have been many much larger flocks over the years. In December 1961, large numbers came in at Spurn, when 500 flew south at 08.00 hours and 2,000 flew north at 12.30 hours on 5th. On 10th, a total of 10,000 birds was counted, some of which flew north and others south. At 13.55 hours, a vast straggling flock of 6,000 birds went south until lost to sight, with smaller parties flying north at a lower level. On 18th November 1969, 4,500 passed at Spurn in half-an-hour; 3,000 passed in one flock on 28th, with 7,000 moving through during the day on 29th. The birds pass inland very soon after arriving and form large roosts at which their numbers can be counted. Such a roost, of long establishment, at Hornsea Mere held 23,000 birds on 3rd December 1960 and 25,000 the next day; 15,000 were present on 25th November 1961, their numbers increasing thereafter to 20,000. In more recent years, the largest counts at this roost have been 6,000 in November and December 1977 and 5,000 on 12th December 1979. There are many other inland roosts at which there have been counts of up to 5,000 birds in many years. During December 1980, there were 5,000 at Allerton Park, 3,500 at Elsecar and 3,600 fly-ing over Swillington Ings to a roost, with many other flocks of up to 2,000 at other localities. On 10th February 1981 5,000 were seen on Hatfield Moor, and 4,000 were on Loscar Common, Harthill, on 10th November 1981. The main flocks away from roosts usually occur during severe weather, when many birds are forced together to feed in suitably available places. Cabbages or sprouts are favourite foods and stubble, undersown with clover, is also to their liking. Acorns and beech mast are taken with ease, and in 1942 Woodpigeons were noted feeding on pig-nuts brought to the surface of newly ploughed old pasture: one shot bird had 40 in its crop. In very severe weather, when snow covers the ground, Woodpigeons suf-fer badly and many may die through starvation. To list all the flocks in excess of 2,000 would take up an inordinate amount of space, and it will suffice to say that such gatherings of between 100 and 2,000 birds occur in every winter and in any part of Yorkshire where agriculture dominates.

In the spring, return passage of the autumn immigrants is noted along the coast. Every year at Spurn, Flamborough and elsewhere, birds suddenly appear in April and continue to pass northward during May and into early June. In 1977, at Spurn, 240 flew north on 19th March, 480 on 26th March, 800 on 2nd April and 440 on 14th April; and at Flamborough, 800 passed on 16th April. Similar numbers moved through in 1978, with 380 at Spurn on 24th March, 488 on 25th March and 216 on 26th March; and at Flamborough numbers peaked at 200 on 29th April, 450 on 5th May, 300 on 7th May, 140 on 14th May and 50 on 15th May.

A most interesting story was related to me recently by a pigeon-racing friend which is quite remarkable for this very shy and normally 'wild' bird. In the summer of 1981, a young and recently fledged Woodpigeon appeared in the garden of Mr Alan Davey, a Knaresborough pigeon fancier. It was in a weak condition and one of its wings was drooping slightly. He put it in a goat shed and fed it for a few weeks, after which it became fit and was released. It chose to stay and associated with the racing pigeons, flying with them when they were exercised and landing with the flock on the loft roof. Each night it entered the goat shed to roost. During the daytime it was often absent, but returned each evening to feed with the other pigeons and sometimes entered the loft, but always roosted in the goat shed. It was a male, and in the spring of 1982 became very aggressive towards the homers, attacking them when they were attempting to mate. It often visited a neighbour's pigeon loft some 50 yards (46 m) away and caused similar disturbance. Because of this, it was taken 3 miles (4.8 km) away and released, only to fly back to its 'home' loft, in spite of the slightly drooping wing. During the next few weeks it was taken with the racing pigeons on their training flights in the hope that it would return to the wild. Three times it was taken to Wetherby, 7 miles (11.2 km) away, and released, only to fly home again on the same day each time. It was then taken 18 miles (28.8 km) to Micklefield on three occasions, and again returned each time on the day after its release. In June 1982, in desperation, it was taken 60 miles (96 km) to Worksop with a batch of racers and this time it did not return. The story was not over, for on 8th May 1983, some 11 months later, Davey saw a Woodpigeon on the top of his loft. He could hardly believe that it was the same bird, but it came down to feed with the others and that night entered the goat shed to roost. It was quite thin and weak, but recovered quickly after being fed with glucose. He brought it to my house on 12th May and placed it in a large aviary, where it survived for several months before dying during the winter.

Ringed Woodpigeons from Yorkshire nests have travelled to Shropshire, Nottinghamshire and Lincolnshire, and birds from Northumberland (three) and Hampshire (one) have been recovered during the winter in Yorkshire. Several others have travelled shorter distances within the county.

Nelson referred to a pure white bird seen at Ingleby in the summer of 1901, a pale reddish-coloured bird in the collection of F. Boyes, and an albino shot at Scarborough on 4th August 1905. A bird coloured uniformly buff was at Buckton in the summers of 1974 and 1975; a pale leucistic bird was in Forge Valley, Scarborough, in January 1975; and a bird near Scalby on 26th April 1975 had pale creamy back and wings. One at Dringhouses, near York, on 26th February 1977 had the mantle, wings, rump and tail coloured pinkish-buff, with a darker crown and a discernible white collar. An identical bird, probably the same one, was at Castle Howard on 18th June 1977.

This species is so much part of our countryside that one must hope that, in spite of man's battle against it, the sight and sound of what is a very handsome bird will always remain as common as it is today.

Collared Dove
Streptopelia decaocto

The remarkable westward extension of the breeding range of this species across Europe since about 1930 first reached the British Isles in 1955, when a pair appeared and nested in Norfolk.

The first notice of its presence in Yorkshire was on 18th April 1959, when S.J. Wells saw two doves in his garden at Chapel Allerton, Leeds. He described them and their song perfectly and Chislett included the record in the Yorkshire Naturalists' Union Ornithological Report for that year, but placed it in square brackets — his method of inferring some doubt. A neighbour said that the doves had been present for ten days previously.

It was subsequently learned that the species was seen in the southeast of the county in 1958 and that a pair reared two broods in 1959. Another bird was seen on 7th October 1959 at another site in the southeast. A pair reared one young in the northeast in 1960 and two other birds were also present.

The spread followed quickly and records came from 16 localities in 1961, with proof of breeding at five of these. Although the sites were mainly along the coast, birds had reached Sheffield and Leeds and H.O. Bunce saw the first real flock, consisting of 20 birds, at Rudston on 26th November. In 1962, breeding reports came from ten localities in vice-county 61, including two new sites, and a considerable increase in the population took place in the Hull area. In the northern part of the county in vice-county 62, Collared Doves were present in Middlesbrough, Whitby, Kirkleatham, Malton and Thirsk. In the south, in vice-county 63, a continuing spread was noted in Sheffield, the species bred in Doncaster and possibly at Sprotborough, and there were birds in several Leeds areas.

The spread accelerated and infilling of colonised areas continued during the next few years. By 1967 birds were spreading into areas around Barnsley, Batley and Brighouse, and a pair bred at Beverley for the first known time. In 1969, breeding occurred at Huddersfield and the species also reached Carperby in Upper Wensleydale, where one was seen on 27th June. Some relatively large flocks were now being recorded: in 1967 there were 42 at Acklam on 3rd February, 80 at Byram Park on 21st March and 52 near Hornsea during April. Over 100 were on farm buildings at Lissett during the early part of 1968, and there was a roost of 400 at East Park, Hull, on 21st January 1969 with 90 in Hymer's College grounds in Hull during January. Up to 75 frequented a corn mill at Copgrove in 1969.

The species was by now breeding in almost every part of the county except in the high moorland areas along the Pennines, especially in the northwest, and vice-county 65 had only three records in 1971. The bird soon penetrated the Pennine dales, and in March 1972 it was seen at Gouthwaite Reservoir in Upper Nidderdale and in September over the watershed at Leighton Reservoir. A spread westwards was also taking place in the south of the county, and in 1973 20 pairs bred near Midhopestones and Underbank Reservoirs. A few were seen near Settle in 1975 and one was at Grassington in Upper Wharfedale about the same time. By 1976, the moorland fringes and the upland villages of the southern Pennines were being colonised.

Since the early 1970s, some large feeding and roosting assemblies give an indication of just how numerous the Collared Dove has become. Large flocks are most frequent in the lowland agricultural areas in Holderness and in the southern part of the county, east of the Pennines. In 1974, 200 were on Broomfleet Island on 22nd October and on 27th October 200 were at the Copgrove Mill site near Knaresborough, where around that number can be seen today. The Selby area has attracted large numbers, with 200 in the early months in most years since 1975; Swinefleet Common had 200 at a farm roost in 1978 and 1979; 250 to 350 were counted at Healaugh during January and February 1981; 200 were at Sprotborough Flash during December 1977 and during the early part of 1978, and annually since then; 200 roosted in an orchard at Thorne during January 1976; and 250 were at Rotherham on 28th September 1975. Many other areas have smaller flocks, often up to 100-150 birds.

In 1979, over 200 birds were destroyed by a 'pest'-control officer at a farm near Selby on two January days. Justification in the form of proof of resultant benefits would be interesting. It is a staggering thought that a species which was unknown in the county before 1958 would have to be shot in an attempt to control its numbers only 20 years later.

Collared Doves are still relatively scarce on the higher ground of the northwest and on some parts of the North York Moors, but the species is now breeding commonly at Richmond and is increasing around Masham and in other parts of Wensleydale and around Helmsley.

Examples of a fawn variety, which resembles the domesticated Barbary Dove in colour, have occurred at Buckton during 1975, at Fairburn Ings in 1976 and early 1977, and near Ripon in 1983. For details of this colour form, see *British Birds*, 1973, pp. 373-6.

A bird ringed as an adult at Bradwell-on-sea in Essex on 25th June 1966 and shot at Scarborough on 28th October 1966 may have been a recent colonist.

From the late 1970s, southerly movement has been noted along the Spurn Peninsula during April, May and June and also in the late autumn. On most days of movement, up to 20 birds may fly south, but in 1976 65 passed on 24th October. Whether these birds are wanderers from southern Holderness or from farther afield is not known.

This dove is now a very familiar sight to almost everyone, especially in suburbia, where it is very much at home. It frequently nests in ornamental conifers and other trees close to houses, and sings from television aerials and telegraph wires. It is a regular visitor to chicken runs, where it has learned to share the corn. In 1971 and 1972, a pair built its nest and reared two young on top of a telegraph pole at Townville, Castleford (*The Naturalist*, 1972, p. 121). It is in fact most numerous around human habitation, and I doubt if there is now a village or isolated farm-house anywhere in the county that has not yet played host to the species.

A. Gilpin published some interesting observations on breeding near Leeds University in 1961 in *The Naturalist*, 1962, pp. 43-4; and D.B. Cutts and B.S. Pashby published their observations on feeding flights in Hull in *The Naturalist*, 1966, pp. 53-4.

A.J. Wallis has reported to me an incident which illustrates the dependence of this bird on man. For some years an avenue in Scalby, near Scarborough, had a resident population which peaked at the end of the breeding season at between 50 and 60 birds. They were fed by a pigeon fancier, who put out corn for them daily. In 1983, this gentleman died, and within a week not a single Collared Dove could be found in the vicinity and only two have been seen since.

Turtle Dove
Streptopelia turtur

Known as a Yorkshire bird since about 1824, when one was shot near Rotherham, the Turtle Dove has increased as a breeding bird and its familiar purring coo can be heard during the summer months in any well-vegetated part of the county except along the higher parts of the Pennine chain, from where it is virtually absent. It is perhaps most numerous in the southern part around Hatfield Chase and Thorne Moors and about the flat country in the Vale of Pickering, the Plain of York and southeastwards into Holderness.

Nelson said that it was supposed to be a southern bird but had spread north-wards in recent years (prior to 1907). Thomas Allis knew of only half-a-dozen examples in the county when he wrote his report on Yorkshire birds in 1844. During the early part of the twentieth century, its breeding range in Yorkshire was given by Nelson as lying east of a line drawn through Ripon, Harrogate, Leeds and Wakefield to Sheffield. It is virtually the same today, except that there has been an incursion into the lower dales and an extension to the north, where it now nests as far as the county boundary with Durham beyond the North York Moors. Scarborough was the most northerly limit given by Nelson.

The increase in forestry plantations along the hills of the eastern Pennines and on the North York Moors has undoubtedly favoured the Turtle Dove. Many pairs now breed in such habitat, which has taken them to higher altitudes than formerly.

The first spring migrants arrive from mid April, but the main influx is not usually until well into May. The earliest records concern single birds at Wilton, near

Middlesbrough, on 26th March 1972, Bempton on 3rd April 1968 and at Elsecar Reservoir on 5th April 1980.

When he wrote *Yorkshire Birds* (1952), Chislett said that migration was seldom observed and added that the species was seen occasionally at Spurn, where two were recorded on 17th May 1948. It is a very different story today and birds can be seen passing south along the peninsula in both spring and autumn, mainly during the former period. Varying numbers occur every year during late May and early June. In 1979, for example, 46 flew south on 19th May and 76 were down on the peninsula on 26th, on which day another 176 flew south and 97 more were in Beacon Lane, Kilnsea; 193 flew south on 27th May, 174 did so on 28th May and 214 on 29th, with smaller numbers passing to 14th June. In addition to these passing birds, others are often grounded along the peninsula and 112 were counted on 26th May 1977. Similar movements are noted every year at Flamborough, but the numbers are never so large in the absence of the funnelling effect of the Spurn Peninsula, which concentrates birds from a broad front.

Birds have also been shown to be regular migrants in recent years westwards along the Humber during the spring, and at Blacktoft Sands in 1981 a total of 543 was counted between 8th May and 23rd June, including 55 birds on 24th May and 50 on 3rd June. In the autumn, 80 were present on 19th August, at which time an easterly movement was noted.

Large concentrations inland occur mainly during the autumn. For example, 40 were at Nosterfield on 9th July 1967; 70 were counted on telegraph wires at Kirk Sandall Common by M. Limbert on 11th August 1970; and 60 were gathered on wires over a pea field near Fairburn Ings on 13th July 1976. Other large counts include 70 at Potteric Carr on 24th May 1978; 91 at Southfield Reservoir on 19th August 1979 and 50 on Thorne Moors on the same date; and 50 at Denaby Ings on 8th September 1979.

Away from the southern part of the county, large flocks are scarce and only small parties are seen, mainly during the autumn when they often frequent the stubbles before these are ploughed in. Most birds have left for their winter quarters in northern tropical Africa by mid September, but some linger on and a few have been recorded in October. Late birds have been at Wath Ings on 31st October 1974; Wintersett on 20th October 1976; Selby on 3rd November 1977; Filey on 29th October 1978; Chapeltown on 28th October 1979; Thorpe Marishes on 18th October 1980; Wath Ings on 14th October 1981; with very late birds at Copgrove, near Knaresborough, on 30th November 1969 and at Wheldrake on 13th November 1982. Nelson also cited a November bird which occurred at Beverley on 18th in 1865. One at South Milford with Collared Doves on 26th December 1964 stayed until 7th March 1965 (*The Naturalist*, 1966, p. 56). Some Turtle Doves are kept in captivity and one escaped from an aviary in Bradford in October 1979. The possibility that these very out-of-season individuals are escapes cannot therefore be excluded.

Two Yorkshire-ringed birds have been recovered, in Germany and Portugal in August and September respectively.

Rufous Turtle Dove
Streptopelia orientalis

The first British example of this species came from Scarborough on 23rd October 1889. It was forwarded to H. Seebohm, who identified it as *orientalis* in first plumage and probably a wild bird. The specimen was presented to the Yorkshire Museum by J. Backhouse, who had acquired it from a Mr Head of Scarborough.

Yorkshire was to have a second record of this eastern species, which has occurred in the British Isles on only eight occasions up to 1982, when one was seen in the Warren area at Spurn Point from 11.00 hours to 15.00 hours on 8th November 1975. It was watched by several people, including J. Cudworth and B.R. Spence who made detailed notes and considered it to belong to the western race *S.o. meena*, which breeds from western Siberia, south through central Asia to northwest India.

A bird at Flamborough on 26th June 1983 was considered by A.M. Allport and D.G. Hobson to belong to the race *S.o. orientalis*, which breeds east of the range of *meena*. Full details have yet to be submitted to the *British Birds* Rarities Committee.

Ring-necked Parakeet
Psittacula krameri

This familiar cagebird is now breeding in a feral state in some parts of southern England and has been admitted to the British list.

Records of birds seen in Yorkshire have been published in the Annual Reports of the Yorkshire Naturalists' Union since 1976. All will undoubtedly have originated in captivity, but are published here to aid future researchers in the event of colonisation in the county.

Two birds flew south at Spurn on 8th March 1975, one was on the peninsula on 16th April and one flew south on 14th June. One flew high over Knaresborough Ringing Station on 16th September 1975, and what was probably the same bird was seen flying over Copgrove, some 5 miles (8 km) farther north, ten minutes later. One fed on apples in a Knaresborough garden on several days in December 1975.

One was at Spurn on 7th July 1976; two were in the vicinity of Hornsea Mere from 1st to 22nd January 1977, one of which was later found dead; one flew over Harrogate on 27th January 1977; and one flew south at Spurn on 25th June 1977. One was at Bolton-on-Swale on 22nd March 1978. One flew south at Spurn on 21st August 1979, another was seen there on 25th September 1979, and single birds were present on 24th September 1980 and 19th November 1980; one was at Scawthorpe, near Doncaster, on 18th May 1981 and one was at Wilsic on 9th August 1981.

That several others have occurred without being reported is inevitable.

Great Spotted Cuckoo
Clamator glandarius

On 16th October 1982, N.A. Bell and G. Neal were walking along the Humber bank from Easington Lane end to Sammy's Point when they noticed a bird flying towards them from the direction of the Crown and Anchor which they recognised as a Great Spotted Cuckoo. A strong easterly wind was blowing at the time and the day deteriorated towards evening, when there was heavy rain, but the bird was still present next morning. Just before midday, it disappeared from the Easington area and was seen flying through the Warren area at Spurn, then flying south at the Narrow Neck and finally at the Chalk Bank, before returning to the original area between Easington and Welwick. It is strange that the bird should make such a journey and return to where it was first seen; this possibly suggests that it had been in the area for a while and had become accustomed to the Humber bank hedges and fences, where it was to remain until 6th November.

It was a juvenile, and during its stay many people gathered to see this exciting bird which was new to the Yorkshire list and which has occurred in the British Isles on only 25 previous occasions.

Cuckoo
Cuculus canorus

The Cuckoo was spoken of by Ralph Johnson of Brignall, near Greta Bridge, in a communication to John Rey published by Willughby in his *Ornithology* (1683, p. 22). Nelson's assessment of the species' status in the county was 'Summer visitant, generally distributed, common. Arrives about the third week in April, departing in August. ...' This applies equally well today. It may be found in May or June from sea-level to the North York Moors, and along the Pennine moorlands. It is perhaps easiest to see in this latter barren habitat; here it sits on walls and buildings and is often seen flying over the open moorland where its favourite fosterer, the Meadow Pipit, is common.

In several years, a few Cuckoos arrive early, but some claims can be attributed to human impersonators and in more recent years to the Collared Dove, whose distant notes can be deceptive. Although the majority do not arrive until the third week of April, there are a few records during the first week of that month in most years. In 1945, a remarkable series of exceptionally early birds was reported: on 15th February, one was seen at Scalby by W. Harland and one at Ayton by Dr S. Robertson; on 15th March, an exhausted bird was found in Scarborough which flew off after being rested; and another was present in Stainton on 27th March. The only other March bird on record was in 1946, when one was seen at Methley on 31st.

Most birds have departed before the end of August, but a few, usually juveniles, have lingered on until mid September in several years. After the middle of September birds are scarce and occur mainly along the coast, having probably crossed the North Sea on their journey south to the winter quarters in tropical Africa. Single birds were at Spurn on 17th September 1950, 22nd September 1968, 23rd September 1969, 19th September 1971 and on 5th October 1973. One was at Flamborough Head on 21st September 1980; one was at Atwick on 10th October 1959 and another on 2nd October 1960.

Inland, one was at Knostrop on 30th September 1978, and a bird on Royd Moor on the exceptionally late date of 27th October 1977 was described in detail by an experienced observer.

Migrating birds are seen regularly along the coast, especially along the Spurn Peninsula, between late July and the end of August. Numbers seen daily are usually small and have not exceeded nine birds on any one day.

The hosts of this parasitic species are many and varied. On the moorlands, the Meadow Pipit is undoubtedly the most popular, and there are also records of eggs being found in the nests of Twite and Ring Ouzel. The Chaffinch and the Greenfinch have also been recorded as hosts near Sheffield and near Rotherham. Many other species are known to act as foster parents and several have done so in Yorkshire, but to list them all is unnecessary.

Aberration in plumage has been recorded on several occasions. Nelson mentioned three birds with much white in the wings and tail as well as about the head, and also a bird of a dark cream colour. Single pure white birds were on Embsay Moors in four consecutive years from 1929, in which year one was shot in July.

There are several foreign recoveries of Yorkshire-ringed Cuckoos. Six birds ringed on migration at Spurn have been recovered in Denmark, Tunisia, Holland, Germany and Italy (two), and one ringed at Grimston, near Withernsea, on 29th June 1975 was recovered in France on 19th April 1976. A nestling ringed on Goathland Moor on 29th June 1910 was recovered at Southend-on-Sea on 2nd August 1910; and a bird ringed as a nestling at Bilton, Harrogate, on 23rd June 1979 was retrapped in Groningen in the Netherlands on 7th August 1979, illustrating well just how quickly the young birds pull out after leaving the nest.

Cuckoos are more evident in some years than in others and reports vary from 'fewer than usual' to 'more than usual'. Whatever the reason, the species is certainly widespread and common over the whole of Yorkshire between late April and August.

Black-billed Cuckoo
Coccyzus erythrophthalmus

On the evening of 23rd September 1975, G.W. Follows and W. Norman were mist-netting Blackbirds as they came in to roost in Locke Park, Redcar. The park was closed for the night, and the nets were set along a public footpath between holly trees in which the birds were going to roost. While the netters were standing some 30 yards away looking along the line of nets, a bird which they recognised as a small cuckoo flew over their heads and along the line before landing in a bush beside the path. It soon flew into a net and on examination proved to be a Black-billed Cuckoo, the first example ever recorded in Yorkshire. As it was getting dark, the bird was kept overnight and released next morning, after which it was not seen again.

It was only the seventh record for the British Isles of this rare cuckoo, which breeds in North America, east of the Rockies, and spends the winter in South America south to Peru.

Yellow-billed Cuckoo
Coccyzus americanus

The first Yorkshire record of this bird occurred at Cloughton, near Scarborough, from 14th to 17th November 1953. It frequented the garden of Mr E.H. Ramskir and was also seen by R.S. Pollard, E.A. Wallis, R.M. Garnett, R. Chislett and others. The bird fed on the pupae of the large white butterfly, the larvae of which had earlier been abundant, having crawled up the house wall to pupate. On one occasion the bird flew up to the window frame to take pupae while Chislett watched from inside. It was successfully photographed by W.R. Grist and a picture was published in *British Birds* (1954, plate 36, and see also p. 173). It appeared to be in less than perfect condition and was reasonably 'tame'. The tail feathers in particular were somewhat bedraggled and it is likely that it did not survive. (*The Naturalist*, 1954, p. 78)

In 1978, B.R. Spence caught a juvenile Yellow-billed Cuckoo in the Warren trap at Spurn on 27th October. At the time, I was at the Crown and Anchor Inn having lunch, and at 13.30 hours I returned to the observatory to be told that it was being ringed in the laboratory. It was a new bird for me and for many of the other people who saw it in the hand, including P. Higson, G. Hainsworth, S.E. Connel, and G. Neal who took an excellent photograph of it (see plate 87).News of its presence travelled quickly, and a friend of mine who was on the Isles of Scilly at the time knew of the bird before I did. After being released, it flew into a small bush and disappeared into the middle where it was virtually impossible to see, especially as it remained motionless for a very long time, a habit typical of the species.

On 14th November 1981, a Yellow-billed Cuckoo was found in Shaw Wood near Armthorpe and taken to the local RSPCA, where it died the next day. The specimen was taken to the Doncaster Museum on 17th and was identified by M. Limbert as a first-year individual of this species. For very full details of the occurrence see *The Lapwing*, 1983, pp. 8-11 (see also plate 88).

Barn Owl
Tyto alba

Nelson said of the Barn Owl 'Resident, generally distributed, fairly common; most numerous in the south of the county.' It is still generally distributed over much of Yorkshire, albeit in sadly reduced numbers, and is completely absent as a breeding species only on the high moorlands of the Pennines and the North York Moors. The removal of old timber, for whatever reason, in our overly tidy countryside has robbed the Barn Owl of many of its nesting sites. It does, however, use barns and any old building with suitable nesting cavities and will utilise boxes provided in such places.

The breeding season is a protracted one. Nelson recorded a late brood at Walton Hall in November 1828, and a half-grown young one was in a nest in an old ruin on the island in the lake there on 1st December 1823. Young were found in a nest at Knaresborough in October 1947; young were being fed at Gouthwaite Reservoir on 13th October 1964; young were in the nest at Rotherham on 30th November 1965; a pair had young near Pontefract in December 1970 (*The Naturalist*, 1971, p. 71); and a pair had young in a barn at Leathley, near Otley, on 8th March 1973.

The open agricultural areas of Holderness hold a good population of Barn Owls, and in the relative absence of large trees the majority nest in barns or similar sites. During the 1940s, G.H. Ainsworth and J. Lord found more Barn Owls than Tawny Owls in the East Riding, doubtless owing to the scarcity of old timber, so necessary for the latter species, and Chislett said in his *Yorkshire Birds* that this status comparison applied nowhere else in the county. J.E. Dale, writing in the Yorkshire Naturalists' Union Ornithological Report for 1981, said that it was probably most numerous around the villages of Holderness and along the coast in the Hornsea area.

The species seemed to suffer a decline during the 1960s, but has since recovered and today a pair may be found wherever suitable nest sites exist. Records of proved breeding are scarce: for instance, in 1970, there were sightings of single birds reported from 20 localities in vice-county 64 (the West Riding north), but breeding was proved at only three sites; and, in 1971, there were records from 35 localities and breeding proved at only four. A similar situation exists annually in all parts of the county. The bird is thus generally, but thinly, distributed over the whole county, most numerously in the southeast, and lone pairs may take up residence wherever a suitable nest site can be found. These sites may range from old tree stumps to barns and holes in any old masonry. In the early 1950s, a pair bred in an old dovecote built into the top of a barn at Lower Dunsforth; the cote was in use and the owl shared its home with upwards of 100 pigeons.

The Barn Owl is a fairly common road casualty, especially in the open country where it crosses low over the roads while hunting along the hedgerows.

The dark-breasted form of the Barn Owl *Tyto alba guttata* which breeds in central Europe has occasionally been recorded in Yorkshire. Nelson did not mention its occurrence, but Chislett gave details of a bird at Goathland on 14th October 1944 which W.S. Medlicott watched for five minutes flying close to him as it hunted and sat on the ground less than 10 yards (9 m) away; the breast was decidedly apricot in colour and the upperparts were greyer than usual. On 6th October 1959, a bird of this form landed on board the Humber pilot cutter and, being unable to fly, was taken ashore at Spurn, where it was inspected by G.H. Ainsworth. One at Flamborough on 21st November 1976 was considered by P.A. Lassey to be a typical dark-breasted bird. G.E. Dobbs saw one at Skeffling on 7th November 1976 and D.I.M. Wallace saw an exhausted migrant at Flamborough on 23rd October 1976 which was buff-breasted but not typically dark. One at Flamborough on 23rd October 1982 was probably of this race. The degree of buff on the breast varies considerably, and it is possible that more come to Britain each year than are detected.

There are no ringing recoveries in Yorkshire of Barn Owls ringed abroad, but there are several which show movement within the British Isles. A young bird ringed near Sheffield in July 1954 was found dead in Epping Forest in March 1955; one ringed at Clitheroe in Lancashire in June 1954 was at Dent in September 1954; one ringed in Durham in July 1962 was near Driffield in February 1963; one ringed at Leigh in Lancashire in July 1964 was at Leeming Bar in August 1965; one ringed at Godalming in Surrey in July 1975 was found dead at Seamer in March 1979. Others have moved shorter distances within the county.

An analysis of pellets collected from barns at East Ayton, near Scarborough, gave a good indication of the prey species. These included all the usual small rodents and insectivores. Full details were published in *The Naturalist*, 1972, pp. 11-13.

Scops Owl
Otus scops

There are only about 80 records of this small owl in the British Isles, most of which occurred during the nineteenth century with only about 15 since 1950.

All the Yorkshire occurrences, of which there are about seven, occurred before the turn of the century. The first instances of its occurrence in the British Isles included one believed to have been shot in Yorkshire, and another shot in the spring of 1805 near Wetherby which went to the collection of Charles Fothergill of

York. Nelson published the remarks of Thomas Allis in full and they are worth repeating here for those who do not possess a copy of his *The Birds of Yorkshire*:

'F.O. Morris mentions this bird as having been met with at Womersley; two pairs have been shot at Ripley, near Harrogate some years ago; the birds shot at Ripley were a pair of old and a pair of young birds; when shot they were nailed to a house, and, after being there for a fortnight, and spoiled, were seen by Mr. Stubbs, animal preserver, of Ripon. The gamekeeper of Matthew Wilson Esq., of Eshton Hall, in describing his exploits to a gentleman, said that some years ago he shot such a thing as he never saw before or since; it was a regular formed Hullet not bigger than his fist, with horns above its eyes; this, it is almost certain, could be nothing else but the Scops. Another specimen was shot near Driffield about 1839, and Arthur Strickland says "a beautiful specimen of this little bird appeared in July 1832, in the grounds at Boynton, and, from its loud and distinct note, attracted general attention; this note was like the sound of a single note on a musical instrument, repeated at about half-a-minutes' interval, and was so loud that it could be distinctly heard in the house when all the doors and windows were shut, and the curtains drawn, and when the bird was in some tall trees some distance from the house; after some time it was shot by firing at the sound, as it was too dark to see the bird — it is now in my collection." Another instance has been mentioned to me, and, from the description, I have no doubt about the species; it was in the grounds of Mr. Beaumont of Bossal, near Sand Hutton, and I think it was stated to have been heard for more than one spring. Three other specimens are mentioned in Yarrell's *British Birds* as having been obtained in Yorkshire.'

One was captured on the Egton Estate, near Whitby, in 1865 and an undated pair, formerly in the Hull Museum until destroyed by bombs during the Second World War, were stated to have been obtained at Marton, near Bridlington.

The true origin of some of these old records must be in some doubt and the 'pair' aspect is always a worrying one.

That ship assistance for this small owl is a possible cause of its occurrence here was confirmed in 1968 when I received a live Scops Owl which was brought into Hull on board a ship on which it had alighted, and broken its wing, while the ship was off the coast of Spain. The bird died shortly after I had received it, but had it arrived in Hull uninjured it could well have been released by the crew and lived to be recorded ashore.

There have been no genuine Yorkshire occurrences during the last 100 years.

Eagle Owl
Bubo bubo

Nelson mentioned 12 occurrences of the Eagle Owl in Yorkshire, one of which, shot in March 1845, was known to have been an escape from captivity at Hornby Castle. The earliest record is mentioned by Pennant in 1768 in *British Zoology*, i. p. 157, where he stated that it had once been shot in the county.

Thomas Allis mentioned two birds. In 1844, he wrote that one had been shot at Horton, near Bradford, about 1824 and quoted Denny's *Catalogue of Yorkshire Birds* as the authority; and that another, taken alive in a wood near Harrogate in the summer of 1832, went to the Yorkshire Museum.

On a 'very dark November day', C.C. Hanson of Greetland, near Halifax, snapped an old flint gun at an Eagle Owl, but it 'misfired as usual' and the owl stared at him for a moment 'with eyes like a leopard' and then flew off.

One was obtained at Loftus-in-Cleveland on 5th November 1875, and another was captured by two farm servants on Rombald's Moor in July 1876. The plumage of the latter was waterlogged and the bird was unable to fly; it was kept in captivity for some time afterwards, which was very likely its origin in the first place.

A 'very large' Eagle Owl flew past A. Roberts in a Scarborough back street at one o'clock in the afternoon of 30th September 1879. One seen at Easington in the winter of 1879/80 stayed all night in a tree in a cottage garden. A male was killed by J. Firth at Fixby, near Huddersfield, on 1st January 1885 and the specimen went to the Shepherd's Rest Inn at Cowcliffe.

Cordeaux (1899) recorded that 'an immense owl, presumably of this species, said to be the largest ever observed at Spurn, was reported in October 1888'. It was seen in the sand dunes and at the Warren, both in flight and on the ground.

Chislett knew of only one other record. On 17th December 1943, J.P. Utley watched a huge owl sweep low along a glade and then fly up into a pine tree in Yarker Bank Wood, Wensleydale. The wingspan appeared to be double that of a Tawny Owl and tufts were seen on the dark head. The upperparts were dark with reddish mottlings. The bird flew off to another wood after only a glimpse had been obtained.

One or two of the above records may have been of genuine vagrants, but there is as much, if not more, likelihood that they were escapes from captivity. The British Ornithologists' Union Records Committee, in their eighth report (March 1974) (*The Ibis*, 1974, p. 579), considered the 1943 record together with others during the last 50 years and decided that none was acceptable on the grounds of their being either inadequately documented sight records or suspected of captive origin. The Yorkshire bird falls into the first category and the species has therefore not been reliably recorded in Yorkshire since 1885.

Snowy Owl
Nyctea scandiaca

There are six instances of the Snowy Owl's occurrence in the county published in *The Birds of Yorkshire*. Some of these are not very satisfactory.

The first was mentioned in the report of Thomas Allis in 1844 and concerned a male shot on Barlow Moor, near Selby, on 13th February 1837 which was in the possession of A. Clapham of Potter Newton. At the time of the occurrence, Barlow Moor, which was rented by Clapham's father for sporting purposes, was covered in furze and abounded in rabbits. The bird was first seen by a neighbouring miller on 12th and mistaken for a goose. On seeing it the next day, he shot at it but only wounded one wing. On being approached, the bird threw itself on its back and fiercely resisted attempts to capture it. It was eventually caught and killed, and exhibited at a meeting of the Zoological Society in the same year.

During the winter or early spring months between the years 1849 and 1853, the same Mr Clapham saw a large white bird flying towards Scarborough Castle. From its size and soft, steady, broad-winged flight he concluded that it was of this species. A Snowy Owl was fired at but missed on the rocks at Filey a day or two afterwards; it was assumed to be the same bird.

J. Cordeaux wrote in *The Zoologist*, 1868, p. 1026, that a large owl, chequered all over black and white and as large as a Great Black-backed Gull, was seen in a turnip field at Flamborough on 14th October 1867.

One is said to have occurred near Scarborough in December 1879 which was shot at but not killed. E. Thompson, who reported the record in *Land and Water* for 27th December 1879, said that it frequented the New Park and was frequently seen.

One was obtained on the Lancashire border in 1880 and reported by a Mr Stuart of Skipton.

Strangely, Nelson considered the last of his published records as 'less satisfactory'. It was claimed by Messrs J. Cordeaux and H.B. Hewitson, who saw a fully adult example in a field near Easington on 27th September 1891 which Cordeaux reported in *The Field* of 3rd October of that year and in *The Zoologist*, 1895, p. 59. These two naturalists are not likely to have misidentified such a bird, although the date is unusual for a genuine immigrant.

Chislett published just one other instance of the Snowy Owl's occurrence in his *Yorkshire Birds*. On 24th January 1945, a very large white owl with grey-brown spots on the back was seen on the ground of a valley in the Yorkshire fells near Sedbergh by C.R.B. King, a member of the Sedbergh School Ornithological Society. As he watched, the bird rose with slow wingbeats.

There has been one recent record. On 15th June 1975, P.J. Carlton watched a bird on Lofthouse Moor in Upper Nidderdale. It was perched on the heather and was also seen in flight several times at ranges down to 200 yards (180 m). It was described as about 2 feet (60 cm) high, white all over, with dark spotting and large yellow eyes.

The Snowy Owl is an irregular winter visitor from the tundras of northern Europe and occurs in very small numbers. It is a common bird in captivity, both in zoos and in private collections, and the escape risk is fairly high, thus clouding most records.

Little Owl
Athene noctua

When T.H. Nelson published *The Birds of Yorkshire* in 1907, the Little Owl was an 'Accidental visitor from Continental Europe, of extremely rare occurrence.' In 1952, when Chislett published his *Yorkshire Birds*, he said that 'today, it is a common breeder over the whole of the county, excepting on the high moors'. Today, it is to be found among most of the moorland areas wherever there are suitable nesting sites in old buildings or walls. In recent years, counts in the recording areas of the various birdwatchers' clubs have given a good indication of its status. It was recorded at 18 localities in the Huddersfield area and at 50 localities in the Settle area in 1976 (none was recorded at the latter locality in 1938 when the British Trust for Ornithology organised a Little Owl survey); at 18 localities in Nidderdale and at 26 in the Leeds area in 1978; and at 18 localities in the York area in 1981. It is decidedly less numerous in the Vale of Pickering than it was before the use of organochlorines in the 1960s.

The Little Owl was introduced into the British Isles in the nineteenth century and Yorkshire had no reliable record of its occurrence until 1842, when Charles Waterton liberated five pairs in Walton Park. He had bought the birds in Rome. The introduction was not, however, successful and the owls did not establish themselves.

Nelson listed only four records, which he considered referable to migrant birds from the Continent: one was obtained at Flamborough in 1860; one was captured on a fishing boat off Scarborough in November 1884 (but see under Tengmalm's Owl); one was trapped at Seamer, near Scarborough, in May 1885; and the last was procured at Eskrick, near York, on 24th December 1896.

W.H. St Quintin released some Little Owls at Scampston Hall about 1890 and again in 1905, but in 1908 he had 'given up any hope of naturalising the birds here'. The eventual colonisation of Yorkshire came as the result of a spread from the south, where, after the release of several birds by Lord Lilford during the 1880s, breeding followed and the species spread in Nottinghamshire (1896), Lincolnshire (1902) and Derbyshire (1906). There were other introductions around this time in Kent in 1874-80, 1896 and 1900.

After one was shot at Leconfield in early October 1911, several reports followed, mainly from the East Riding and in the south of the county. A pair nested at Ledston in 1921, and the species was described as being 'well established' in the Derwent Valley and around Pocklington in 1922. One was shot in Teesdale in 1923 and another at Plompton, near Harrogate, on 9th January 1924. A pair bred between Harewood and Pool in 1925 and near Skipton in 1926. By 1927, game-keepers' gibbets began to include Little Owls when such were found in Houghton Woods and Eskrick. In 1940, a bird was seen at Cayton Bay, near Scarborough, and in 1941 a gamekeeper took one from a rabbit hole near Clapham, where it was well established by 1944. By the end of the decade, Little Owls had penetrated to all parts of the county, and breeding was taking place in Upper Ribblesdale, Wensleydale, The Vale of Mowbray, Lower Teesdale and north of Helmsley. One stood at the entrance of a hole on Bempton Cliffs on 24th June 1950 and occasional pairs are to be found at other coastal localities.

In 1948, in the garden of F.C. Niven at Ferriby, a pair of Stock Doves took over a hole in which Little Owls had nested in previous years. The hole was very shallow and the sitting dove was visible from outside. On 7th July, a Little Owl flew to the hole and the Stock Dove 'cracked' its wing down onto the intruder, which fell to the ground and hopped under some bushes, where the pigeon, in pursuit, could not locate it. On examination, it was found that one of the owl's legs was fractured. Exactly the same thing happened in 1949, when the two Stock Doves followed up the attack and killed the owl.

Ringing has shown that Little Owls do not move very far, and of the several recoveries the majority have travelled only up to 10 miles (16 km). A bird ringed at Little Crosby in Lancashire on 14th December 1958 and found dead at East Witton, near Leyburn, on 26th April 1960 was an exception.

One was seen in Park Square, Leeds, on 14th and 15th April 1975.

Some unusual food items have been recorded in Little Owls' nests: a nestling Jackdaw ringed near Harrogate on 7th June 1958 was found in a Little Owl's nest only 70 yards (64 m) away a week later; on 20th April 1958 I found a headless lampern in a nesting box at Knaresborough; and, in July 1984, a dead blue Budgerigar was found in a nest hole at Knaresborough. On 9th June 1977, at Led-sham, a Little Owl was seen to kill a grass snake. These small owls do absolutely no harm to game, and those who purport to 'keep' it should leave them alone. Now generally distributed over much of Yorkshire from the coastal areas of Holderness and northwards, to the high moorland areas of the west and north, it is most interesting that it has become so well established in spite of early and continuing persecution. It suffers too in very severe weather, as in 1947 and 1962 when the populations were drastically reduced, but it is able to recover to its former status in a very short time.

The only local name of which I am aware, used in parts of the Wolds, is Root Owl.

Tawny Owl
Strix aluco

This familiar owl has been widespread and common in Yorkshire since Nelson's time and before, and its status has probably changed but little during the present century. Nelson considered that the earliest reference to it as a Yorkshire bird was made by Graves in his *History of Cleveland* (1808), where he listed it under the name of 'Brown or Wood Owl'.

It favours well-wooded country, but may be found among young forestry plantations provided that suitable nest sites are available in the area, and in relatively open country so long as a few old trees exist. In the absence of holes in old trees, eggs are often laid in old nests of Magpie or crow or even among tree roots and in holes in cliff faces or buildings. Nesting boxes are readily occupied and their provision is to be encouraged. In 1950, a pair drove Magpies from a nest in Wharfedale and then stripped off the dome and reared three young on the resulting platform. A pair nested on the cliff face of Cronkley Fell in 1964.

Nesting begins early in the year and eggs are usually produced in March. Earlier breeding may be due to very mild weather or to the habits of a particular pair of birds. On 2nd February 1964, a bird was flushed from a hole containing two eggs in a pollarded willow tree at Clifton, York; the hole was inspected by Clifford J. Smith on 5th February (*The Naturalist*, 1964, p. 52). On 10th February 1970, an old and dangerous tree was felled in Valley Road, Scarborough, in the interests of public safety, and two young Tawny Owls were killed when the tree hit the ground. The two chicks were buried by the workmen and retrieved one week later at the request of A.J. Wallis, who sent them to me for preservation; they are now in my collection. They were well fed and one bird had the tarsus of a Starling in its crop; other Starling remains were in the nest hole. (*The Naturalist*, 1970, p. 56.) On 6th March 1971, a half-grown youngster was found on the ground in the same place and was killed by a dog; this specimen is also in my collection. In 1975, another young bird, about three weeks old, was found on the footpath on 14th March, indicating the continued presence of this early nesting pair.

A pale leucistic bird was found sitting on a nest at Millthrop, near Sedbergh, in 1960; it had a few brown feathers on the facial disc, a slight rufous tinge on the crown and wing-coverts, and faint buff bars on the primaries and secondaries, but otherwise its plumage was all white. It nested again in 1961 and 1965, in which latter year two young were reared.

The Tawny Owl is now a common bird in suburbia and in city parks, a niche that has become most suitable for its needs with the development of old timber and the complete absence of persecution from gamekeepers. The sight of one flying along a well-lit street is not a rare event.

The prey is varied, both in size and in range of species taken. Leverets, rabbits, rats, Magpies, Jackdaws, and many other small bird species have all been found in Yorkshire nests. Pellets collected at Cardigan Fields in Leeds contained crabs' legs, indicating that the bird had been scavenging on the nearby destructor. Very severe weather affects most owls, and in 1947, after one of the worst winters in recent times, 'scores' of dead Tawny Owls were picked up in the Helmsley area and others were found dead in Middlesbrough (one), Hull (four), Sheffield (several), Gorple Reservoir (three), Gouthwaite Reservoir (two); Lord Bolton picked up six in his grounds, where they were often seen vainly trying to find food during the day-time. Doubtless many others perished too.

Several recoveries of ringed birds have shown only local movement, but a bird ringed at Slaley in Northumberland on 19th May 1982 was found dead in Swinton Park, near Masham, on 8th December 1982.

Several vernacular names are applied to the owl family and to the Tawny Owl in particular, the most commonly used being Brown Owl. Jenny Howlett, Hoolet and Hullot are among those used in various parts of the county.

It is most pleasing to record that this most typical of owls is thriving in every part of Yorkshire, from the coastal areas to the upper fells of the Pennines.

Long-eared Owl
Asio otus

The Long-eared Owl was known as a Yorkshire bird as long ago as 1678, when Willughby, in his *Ornithology*, stated that Francis Jessop had 'sent it to us out of Yorkshire'.

Nelson considered it to be common where found and qualified this by saying that it was resident, local and confined to wooded districts. The same applies today except that it is now less common than formerly, a situation which, according to Chislett, started in the 1930s, when a noticeable decline in numbers was noted by several people. The decrease continued during the next decade, accelerated by the felling of timber during the war years.

Today, it is a very local breeding species, being most numerous among the southwestern Pennine conifer plantations, and on the flat carrlands southeast of York to around Doncaster. Counts of breeding pairs in recent years have revealed between ten and 20 pairs in this region, others undoubtedly being overlooked. A few pairs breed in Holderness, on the Cleveland Hills and on the North York Moors, where conifers at the latter locality have provided the necessary habitat. In the lowland areas, it prefers hawthorn thickets, where it lays its eggs on the old nests of Magpie or Woodpigeon, or on the ground under dense vegetation. On 3rd May 1964, R.J. Rhodes and some friends found a bird sitting on three eggs in a hole some 12 feet (3.7 m) up in an old birch stump. The major publications made no reference to this type of site up to that time (*The Naturalist*, 1965, p. 32). A pair bred successfully at Wold Newton in 1975, and a pair attempted to breed at Fridaythorpe in 1977 but one of the birds was shot off the nest by a local farmer, an ignorant and groundless act.

In the autumn, small numbers of Long-eared Owls arrive along the east coast from northern Europe. They are often evident during October and November, when single birds may be seen flying in over the sea and when newly arrived immi-grants can be seen in small bushes or trees. On 28th October 1950, at Spurn Point, R.F. Dickens and A.W. Gladwin counted 12 Long-eared Owls, 11 of which were sitting in one bush (*The Naturalist*, 1951, p. 5). Smaller numbers occur in every autumn, and in 1975 a large influx occurred on the northeast coast of England, being witnessed in Yorkshire when birds were more in evidence than usual. After one at Spurn on 11th October, there were records during most of the month: one was watched as it came in over the sea on 12th October, two more on 19th and another on 20th, all at Spurn; two birds were seen over a stubble field at Filey on 18th, and single birds were recorded during the next few days at Flamborough, Withernsea, Kilnsea and Skeffling. On 19th, no fewer than 14 were seen by D.A. Rushforth in the headlights of his car as he drove from Spurn to Filey, and a dead bird was found on the road which he sent to me for preservation. On 25th October, R.H. Appleby and C.R. Clark watched one flying in over the sea at Scarborough, being harried by gulls. During the following spring, the return passage of these autumn immigrants was witnessed: Spurn had a total of 12 between 26th March and 31st May, and several were seen at Flamborough during the same period, with five in Dane's Dyke on 14th February and four there on 21st March.

During the winter months, when the local birds are joined by immigrants, some large roosting assemblies may be found. These are often traditional and are used every year. In recent years, some of the larger ones, most of which are concentrated in the southeastern part of the county, have held between ten and 20 birds, with a count of 30 near Patrington in December 1975. Such roosts are often in conifers or hawthorns, but up to seven roosted in sallow bushes near Wetherby in 1979. A roost at Haw Park, Wakefield, has been used since at least the 1950s and held up to 13 birds in 1969 and 1976. J.S. Armitage made a study of this roost during the winters of 1963/64 and 1964/65, paying particular attention to the prey items. See *The Naturalist*, 1968, pp. 37-46, for very full details of this study.

Ringing recoveries have given evidence of the origin of some of the winter visi-

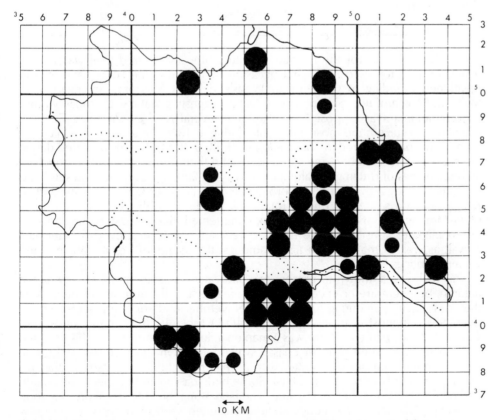

Long-eared Owl. Perhaps more widespread than supposed, this owl is one of the most difficult to detect. Conifer plantations and hawthorn thickets are equally popular for nesting.

tors. A bird ringed in Sweden in May 1950 was recovered at Boroughbridge in March 1951; one ringed at Falsterbo in Sweden while on migration on 19th October 1952 was found dead at Selby on 16th March 1956; and one ringed as a chick in the Netherlands on 20th May 1964 was retrapped at Spurn on 7th October 1964. Three birds ringed as adults in Yorkshire have been recovered abroad: one ringed at Newmillerdam on 9th November 1963 was found dead in Sweden on 25th March 1967; two birds ringed at Spurn on 20th October 1975 were found dead in Denmark in January 1978 and in West Germany in May 1979 respectively; and a late migrant ringed at Spurn on 6th June 1979 was found dead in Sweden on 15th August 1982. A bird ringed on the Isle of May on 5th November 1963, and no doubt an immigrant, was at Blaxton, near Doncaster, on 9th March 1968. The recovery at Whitby on 20th August 1928 of a bird that had been ringed on the Island of Heligoland on 27th December 1927 is interesting in that the recovery date is very early for an immigrant, which one would assume the bird to be.

This species is the most nocturnal of all the owls and breeding birds are seldom seen hunting during daylight hours. It is therefore difficult to locate in the absence of a systematic study and, although the known breeding distribution within the county is probably correct, the density within that area may well be under-estimated.

Short-eared Owl
Asio flammeus

Up to the early part of the twentieth century, the Short-eared Owl was known mainly as a winter visitor, though it occasionally nested in the county and Nelson mentioned breeding at Carperby in Wensleydale, at Masham, Arkengarthdale, Malham, Bentham, near Skipton and at Otley, suggesting that it was probably more widespread than was supposed. He also listed several years in which large immigrations had occurred, the most spectacular being in 1876, an account of which, by John Cordeaux, appeared in *The Zoologist*, 1887, p. 9. Many birds occurred during the night of 23rd October, and Cordeaux found them the next morning crouching among patches of rough grass along the coast and farther inland on drain sides and in pastures. They arrived off Flamborough Head in flocks of ten to 20 birds; and, at Redcar, Nelson saw them on the rocks at low tide on 17th October, with many others among the sandbanks. Cordeaux commented that 'It is astonishing any are left to migrate, considering the number, year after year, destroyed on their first arrival, as well as many which figure amongst the "sundries" of the autumn and winter shootings.'

This owl is well known to present-day birdwatchers as an immigrant during the autumn, but there are no recent instances of large arrivals. Birds are evident along the coast each year during October and November and some are seen flying in over the sea in most years, as at Filey on 14th October 1978 when four birds were watched as they came in; there was a marked influx along the coast at this time and other birds were seen at most coastal watchpoints. On 9th October 1959, one landed on the Humber pilot cutter with a small bird clutched in its foot; the owl was caught and later released in Hull. Some birds pass inland to spend the winter, and others stay along the coastal strip. The land along the Humber shore is a good wintering place and some concentrations are often seen there. A. Credland saw seven birds at Patrington Haven on 7th January 1962; five were over Welwick Saltings during January 1968; nine were at Trent Falls on 17th November 1973; and up to ten birds were at Blacktoft Sands during February and March 1975. Rough ground at the practice bombing range at Cowden attracts the species during the winter months and six were there in January 1981. Single birds may be seen almost anywhere along the coastline or estuary wherever there are rough grassland or marshy areas, over which the birds hunt during the daytime.

To what extent immigrant Short-eared Owls feature at inland localities is not known, but it is certain that such birds will be included in the many sightings in all parts of the county during the winter. Seven were counted by G. Smith on 16th December 1973 along the Lower Derwent Valley between Wheldrake and Bubwith, a typical area for the species. During April and May, when immigrant birds are returning, their appearance along the coastline is evident every year, but never so obviously as in the autumn, their departure being of a more leisurely nature. On 28th April 1966, at Spurn, one flew out to sea until lost to view, and seven were at Flamborough on 12th May 1979.

The high ground of the Pennines and the North York Moors is favoured for breeding, although a few pairs nest annually in lowland areas, mainly along the Humber Estuary. The moors in the extreme southwest of the county, and from Bowland northwards to the county boundary, hold the largest number of breeding pairs. Breeding was proved for 20 pairs in these areas in 1971 and it is likely that several more also bred. Plantations of young conifers provide excellent breeding grounds and have doubtless contributed to this owl's increase as a breeding species during the present century. The moorland plantations in Langstrothdale are a good example and hold a relatively large breeding population, up to 20 pairs

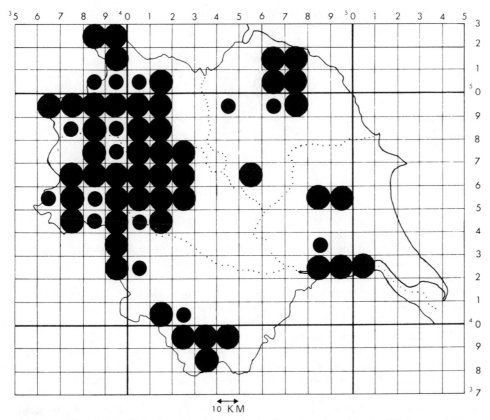

10 K M

Short-eared Owl. Breeds both on the high moorlands and on low-lying marshy ground in the East Riding. It is attracted to plantations of young conifer in the former habitat.

being reported there during the summer of 1976. From one to three pairs have nested on the RSPB reserve at Blacktoft Sands in recent years, and display during the breeding season has been noted at other sites along the Humber.

During the years 1972 and 1973, D. Herringshaw and D. Gosney studied the population on the moors west of Sheffield and located eight breeding pairs in an area 7 miles (11.2 km) square in the extreme south of the county. The average altitude was 1,000 feet (305 m) above sea-level, with deep ling, bilberry and bracken. For full details of the study, see *The Naturalist*, 1974, pp. 35-6. Attempted breeding on Strensall Common in 1982 was thwarted by a fire.

Young birds ringed in Yorkshire nests have been recovered in Kent, Galway and France, showing that some of our breeding population moves south after the nesting season. A chick ringed in Finland on 27th June 1981 was caught alive near Hornsea on 24th October 1981.

This species is known as the Woodcock Owl along the coast, as its appearance in autumn often coincides with that of the Woodcock, and in the fell country of the northwest it is known as the Moor Owl.

Nelson's assessment of its status in 1907 as 'Winter visitant; fairly common in some seasons. Arrives usually in October and November. Occasionally nests in the county' differs from that of today only in the apparent scarcity of breeding birds, which was probably due simply to the inaccessibility of the remoter areas at that time. The breeding population is subject to much annual variation, owing chiefly to the abundance or scarcity of the short-tailed vole, its chief prey.

Tengmalm's Owl
Aegolius funereus

Yorkshire had more than its fair share of Tengmalm's Owls during the second half of the nineteenth century, and of the 20 British records up to the publication of Nelson's *The Birds of Yorkshire* in 1907 no fewer than 12 were credited with occurrence in the county.

The first was from Sleights Moor about 1840. It went to the Whitby Museum, but, 'having been imperfectly cured, it decayed'.

About 1847, one was shot in Hunmanby Woods by the keeper of Admiral Mitford. It went unrecognised until 1849, when David Graham, the York taxidermist, saw it and had the record published in *The Zoologist* (1849, p. 2649).

A female was killed at Lowthorpe in the year 1860 and went to the collection of Sir Henry Boynton at Bridlington.

On 1st October 1963, after a severe gale from the northeast, 'a splendid specimen in exquisite plumage' was captured at Flamborough during the daytime by a man who ran it down in a field,' the bird being dazzled by the light and almost helpless'. It was preserved by M. Bailey of Flamborough, and the specimen went to the collection of J. Stephenson of Beverley and finally to T. Boynton at Bridlington.

W. Lister of Glaisdale had a Tengmalm's Owl which he obtained at Egton, near Whitby, on 19th November 1872. It went eventually to the Whitby Museum.

One was trapped by T. Metcalfe, a keeper in Handale Woods, Loftus-in-Cleveland, in January 1872 (*The Naturalist*, 1899, p. 139).

A third Whitby bird occurred on 30th December 1880, when a Tengmalm's Owl was taken at Normanby, above Hawsker, by a rabbit shooter as it flew from a patch of broom and furze. The specimen was sent to W. Eagle Clarke for identification (*The Zoologist*, 1882, p. 177).

One was killed at Holmpton, in Holderness, on 18th November 1884 and purchased by P. Loten of Easington. Details were published in *The Naturalist*, 1884, p. 12, and in *The Zoologist*, 1891, p. 364.

Three other records dated only as 'during the three years previous' (to 1886) are as follows: one came on board a fishing smack at sea off Scarborough and was identified by A. Roberts (it is possible that this was the same bird as one claimed as a Little Owl which was captured on a fishing boat off Scarborough in November 1884, the details of which are published under that species, but Tengmalm's Owl is the more likely species to occur in such a situation); one was caught by some boys in an old quarry on Oliver's Mount, Scarborough, kept alive for nearly two years and finally preserved by J. Morley; and the third was trapped at Ayton Moor, 4 miles (6.4 km) from Scarborough, by a gamekeeper some time in 1885 and was in the possession of D. Young of Irton.

One was captured on a moor near Bickley on 7th November 1901, and went to the collection of Riley Fortune of Harrogate.

The latest occurrence of this owl in Yorkshire was in 1983, when, on 6th March, B.R. Spence was walking through the dunes at Spurn Point and heard the alarm calls of several Blackbirds, tits and Chaffinches coming from a clump of elderberry bushes. He investigated and found a Tengmalm's Owl sitting in one of the bushes. On his way back to the Warren area, he met C.E. Andrassy, P. Harrison, D. Proctor and Miss D. Walls and asked them to take notes on the bird. It was caught in a mist-net on the following day and stayed in the area until at least 27th March, when it was seen sitting out on top of a bush during the day, something it had not been seen to do before, and presumably preparing to migrate. It is possible that the owl had been in the area since January, as M. Rogers of Portland Bird Observatory and R. Lambert of Gibralter Point Bird Observatory, who were attending a Bird Observatories weekend at Spurn, reported seeing at that time a small owl at dusk in the point area which they had presumed to be a Little Owl. (See plates 92 and 93.)

This small owl, which breeds in the forests of northern and central Europe, as well as in Asia and North America, has become very rare as a wanderer to the British Isles in recent years. There are some 55 records, mostly before about 1918 with only six since 1959.

Nightjar
Caprimulgus europaeus

In Nelson's time, the Nightjar was 'nowhere very abundant, and decidedly local in its choice of breeding quarters'. Nelson mentioned the moorland fringes and the edges of woods on the slopes, at Sheffield, Barnsley, Huddersfield, Wakefield, Doncaster, Otley, Ripon and the upper valleys of the northern Pennines; the Nightjar also nested annually in the dales and on the North York Moors near Scarborough, Whitby and Pickering, in Wensleydale, Teesdale, Arkengarthdale, Swaledale and Sedbergh, the commons around York and the Cleveland Dales and also near Market Weighton, Cliff Wood, Holme-on-Spalding-Moor and at Scampston.

In 1952, Chislett more or less reiterated this situation, with some suggestion of a decrease in numbers.

The present breeding range is roughly the same, but some ground has been lost for various reasons; some areas planted with conifers have become unsuitable once the trees have grown, and other areas have been clear felled and turned over to agriculture. Most of the main sites, on the edges of moorland and on the lowland heaths, still hold breeding pairs. The moors around Doncaster at Hatfield and Thorne are among the county's strongholds, and during the last few years counts by M. Limbert and others at the former locality have located 30 singing males in 1977, 40 in 1978, 37 in 1979, 41 in 1980 and 25 in 1981. Counts on Thorne Moors have shown eight singing males in 1975, 16 pairs in 1976, 11 males in 1977, six in 1978 and ten in 1980. Adjacent areas hold a few pairs also.

The birch-covered commons at Skipwith and Allerthorpe have a few breeding pairs every year, and counts at the former since 1975 have shown that between two and five pairs have been present. Elsewhere, the only area where Nightjars

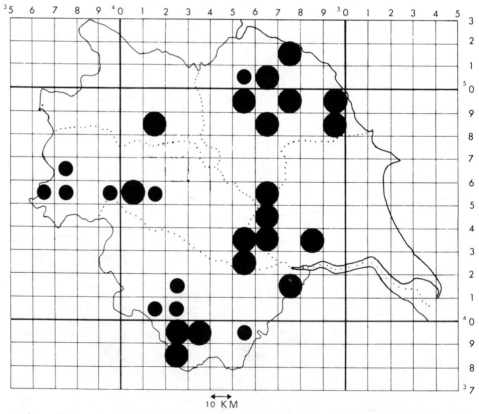

10 KM

Nightjar. Only on the North York Moors and on the lowland heaths around Hatfield and Thorne is this species well established. At most other sites its existence is precarious, and it is often forced to quit forestry areas when the trees become too tall.

breed in good numbers is on the North York Moors, where R. Leslie organised a survey in 1980 and 1981, the results of which showed that far more pairs were breeding there than had hitherto been realised: no fewer than 40 singing males were found at 33 sites in 1980 and 46 males at 25 sites in 1981. The area surveyed covered the whole of the North York Moors north of a line from Scarborough westwards to Thirsk and included the following areas, for which I have indicated the maximum number of pairs present in one or the other of the two survey years: Cropton Forest (11 pairs); Wykeham Forest (six pairs); Dalby Forest (four pairs); Newtondale (eight pairs); Langdale (seven pairs); Thirsk (two pairs); Bilsdale (one pair); Grosmont (one pair); and near Middlesbrough (one pair). Full details have been written up in *The Naturalist*, 1985, pp.23-8.

A singing male Nightjar may perform for a few nights at a particular locality and then move on, or may stay during the summer for one year only. In some areas, just one or two pairs hang on to their traditional sites for several years, before finally deserting when the areas become untenable. At Sawley High Moor, between Pateley Bridge and Ripon, where Miss M.R. Sanderson and Miss H.M. Jackson located seven pairs in 1965, between one and three pairs bred annually thereafter up to 1975; after lone singing males in 1975, 1976 and 1977, the site was finally deserted when the trees became too tall. Two singing males near Settle in June 1970 were the first records for the area.

Two broods are often reared and eggs may be found in August. Unfledged young were found at Thornthwaite on 2nd September 1889 (*The Naturalist*, 1889, p. 333).

Apart from the main breeding areas mentioned above, the species is very sparingly distributed in suitable habitat, but nevertheless widespread in the north, west and south of the county.

Away from the breeding areas, Nightjars are scarce and seldom seen, even on migration. It has occurred at Spurn in only seven years from 1952, single birds being usually involved; in 1963, one was seen on 5th, 9th and 12th September, and in 1970 one was seen on 1st June, another on 13th October and two on 14th October; one was caught there on 28th October 1976, one was found dead on 18th August 1979 and one was caught on 29th September 1979. One came aboard the Humber pilot cutter off Spurn on 14th September 1958, and a bird seen at Kilnsea on 5th June 1964 was found dead there the next day. One was seen at South Gare in early August 1970. In the same year, one was picked up still alive in a Scarborough garden on 15th September and taken to the Scarborough Museum, but it died shortly afterwards. One sang briefly at Fairburn Ings on 20th May 1972, and one spent some days on a garage roof at Kippax, near Leeds, in August 1976 before being found dead. A juvenile was found in a Doncaster garden on 11th September 1943 and one was at Elland Sewage-works on 5th August 1944. Also in 1944, a Nightjar haunted the grounds of a hospital at Walkley, Sheffield, on 1st September, spending the day on a skylight and seen flying at dusk. Most, if not all, of the September birds in places away from the breeding grounds refer to dispersing juveniles.

Most Nightjars have departed for their winter quarters in Africa by late September, and any after that are unusual. Nelson cited a bird at Easington on 23rd October 1878, and another, in a starved condition, at York in mid November 1889. A young bird ringed by R. Chislett near Ripon on 2nd July 1957 was found dead near Tadcaster on 2nd November 1957, and one ringed on Sawley High Moor on 26th July 1959 was found dead near Bayonne in France on 6th September 1963.

The species rarely arrives in Yorkshire before mid May, the earliest in recent years being one on Sawley High Moor on 8th May 1966. Although Chislett said that the Nightjar occurs in late April or May, there are only two records for April and none during the first week of May: a bird on 4th April 1869, quoted in *The*

Handbook of British Birds as having occurred in Yorkshire, was on an extraordinary date; the other concerned a female flushed at Spurn on 19th April 1948. Two birds at Spurn on 28th July 1897, included by Nelson in *The Birds of Yorkshire*, were unusual and may have been on an early return passage, One came on board a ship when 14 miles (22.4 km) off Whitby on 7th October 1833, and one alighted on a ship when 110 miles (176 km) east of Spurn in June 1897.

Superstitions connected with the Nightjar were prevalent in the remote Yorkshire dales in Nelson's time, and doubtless also are today. It was allegedly seen or heard only by the death-doomed in the Cleveland dales. In Nidderdale Nightjars were called 'Gobble Ratchets', and it was thought that they embodied the souls of unbaptised infants, 'doomed to wander forever in the air'. Other districts had varying ideas on the same theme. Vernacular names also vary from region to region, 'Goatsucker' being in general use. Night Hawk, Night Crow, Wheel Bird and Dor Hawk are just some of the names used for this strange and mysterious bird in various parts of the county.

Swift
Apus apus

Nelson's summary of the Swift's distribution as a breeding species in Yorkshire excluded only the manufacturing districts, where he said it was scarce. Today, it is as common in such districts as anywhere and makes use of the old factories and warehouses, which are most suitable for its needs.

The Swift does not arrive in force until early May, although there are records during the last week of April in almost every year. The earliest record in recent years was at Ilkley on 17th April 1949, but the majority of other records in that month are usually after 21st. Nelson mentions a curious incident on 5th April 1887 when several arrived at Spurn and remained all night on the lighthouse. It is difficult to imagine this event and it is possible the light keeper was mistaken.

Spectacular gatherings of feeding birds assemble over water when the wind is strong or cold or with drizzle, at any time from the arrival of the first main parties in early May throughout the breeding season in June and July. At such times, birds often fly low over tree-lined roads, where they find shelter, but are often killed by traffic. Such adverse weather must have prevailed in 1879, when large numbers of Swifts occurred on the coast at Redcar: on 20th August there were many thousands between the Teesmouth and Saltburn, flying at altitudes from 3 to 300 feet (0.9-91 m); at night, numbers roosted on the windowsills of sea-front houses and some entered rooms where windows had been left open. All except two or three had departed by next morning, but a second arrival occurred on 27th August when they were more numerous than ever, 'swarming like gnats in the air, and exciting considerable interest in the town as they flew along the esplanade and in the streets, where boys struck them down with whips and sticks' (*The Zoologist*, 1879, p. 423, and *The Field* of 6th and 13th September 1879). Gatherings of 1,000 to 2,000 are commonplace during these periods of adverse weather and any of the larger waters may attract them. During a spell of cold and wet weather in June 1977, an estimated 3,000 were feeding low over Hornsea Mere on 8th and 5,000 did so at Fairburn Ings from 13th to 15th.

During May, when the first waves of birds are arriving, steady streams of Swifts may be seen passing overhead and, if counted, often number several thousands. On 21st May 1977, 2,300 flew east-northeast over Wath Ings, and 1,500 were counted next day. Similar movements occur in every year at many places throughout the county.

In the autumn, when birds are pulling out, which they do from early August, similar movements can be witnessed. On 18th August 1979, 3,100 flew west over Swillington Ings, and large numbers are recorded annually. Swifts often fly ahead of storms, moving in large numbers to avoid them, and perpetual movement in one direction, suggesting migration, may often be the result of such meteorological avoidance. Whilst mist-netting Swifts at Knaresborough Ringing Station in dry windy weather, I have often caught birds with wet plumage indicating that they had encountered rain some distance away, and the same has been experienced by other ringers.

Southerly movements along the coast in spring and summer are most intriguing. They were known in Nelson's time, and writing in *The Birds of Yorkshire* he states that 'towards the end of June a north to south movement takes place along the coastline, reaching its height in the first half of July, and in most seasons gradually ceasing about the first week of August'. Visitors to the Spurn Peninsula cannot fail to notice these migrations, and almost every day from June to August streams of Swifts pass south along the road or over the beach, sometimes almost at ground level. Whence they come, or whither they go, we know not. The fact that many thousands of birds pass annually throughout the breeding season poses many questions. Birds that have flown northwards into the British Isles on their way to breeding areas in Europe, may turn south along the east coast before crossing over the sea to resume their journey, as evidenced by a bird ringed at Worsborough on 24th May 1966 which was in Denmark on 3rd July 1966. Some may be drawn from a huge reservoir of non-breeding birds which spend the summer roaming the countryside. It may well be that some of the same birds pass south on successive or on different days, and it would not be safe to assume that new birds are involved each day. Counts of up to 2,000 passing birds are made at Spurn on several days each year, and on some the movement may be of massive proportions as follows: 8,000 on 19th June 1962; 10,000 on 19th July 1969; 20,000 on 23rd June 1970, 8,000 on 28th June and again on 9th July 1970, and 5,000 on 11th and 13th July 1970; 12,000 on 16th July 1975; and 10,000 on 19th July 1978. Watchers at Flamborough Head counted 12,000 flying south on 11th July 1981, on which day 6,000 passed at Spurn.

Swifts start to desert their breeding colonies during the middle of August, and at this time parties of migrating birds are evident. Their departure may be very obvious, when large numbers pass over on just one or two days, after which the species is absent or very scarce. Adverse weather is often responsible for concentrating large numbers along a narrow front, most of which would otherwise pass through in less concentrated, and therefore less obvious, parties.

A few linger on into September, but individuals are by no means rare in that month. October Swifts may be looked for in every year and a few are usually to be seen. There are several later records, and some of those seen in late October, November and even in December may not be of British origin and very likely originate in the east. One at Knaresborough Ringing Station on 16th October 1976 had a very large white chin patch, a pale line along the centre of the underwing and the more flicking flight of the eastern race *pekinensis*. Two birds were seen over Harrogate on 16th November 1901; one at Keighley on 7th November 1920 (*Brit-*

ish Birds, 1921, p. 237); on 4th November 1950 a juvenile was picked up behind the door of a Huddersfield fish-and-chip shop in a weak condition, but flew off strongly when released on 6th November after being fed on the obligatory bread and milk!; one was at Spurn on 7th November 1963; one at Driffield on 1st November 1973; one at Ackworth on 4th November 1974; one at Spurn on 2nd November 1975; one at Scarborough on 2nd November 1976; one at Naburn on 5th November 1976; one at Bradford on 28th November 1984; and one at Spurn on 10th November 1984. An exceptionally late bird was at Whitby on 9th December 1979.

Many Swifts have been caught and ringed during the last 20 years since the mist-net was made available to bird-ringers. In the wet and windy conditions referred to above, sewage-farms are favourite places for Swifts to find insects and the birds are very easy to intercept with nets as they sweep low over the filter beds. They are long-lived birds and may be recaught in several successive years. A bird ringed at Ilkley on 28th June 1959 was shot at Leopoldville in the Congo on 26th January 1962; one ringed at Hackenthorpe on 19th July 1962 was found dead in Southern Rhodesia on 29th December 1962; one ringed at Worsborough Dale on 28th May 1979 was found dead in Malawi on 4th January 1982; and four others have been recovered in France (two), Spain and Denmark. A chick ringed in the nest in Norway on 25th July 1954 was found dead at Rossington on 25th August 1954, giving a good indication of how quickly the young birds leave their natal areas and start moving south to the winter quarters.

Swifts are prone to schizochroism, a condition which produces varying amounts of white feathers. These birds may cause identification problems, especially if the white feathers are present about the rump, when the bird may resemble one of the smaller white-rumped species. One at Ossett Sewage-farm on 27th June 1954 had a creamy-white belly; and, in 1975, aberrant birds occurred at Harrogate on 5th May, at Knaresborough Ringing Station on 22nd June (see plate 95), and at Scarborough on 8th June, the latter bird having a white tail. Another bird at Scarborough on 16th June 1978 had much white on the underparts and resembled an Alpine Swift when glimpsed briefly.

Although Swifts breed mainly in crevices and under roofs of buildings, several pairs breed in more natural rock sites as at Kilnsey Crag and the limestone crags along the Nidd gorge at Knaresborough. A pair nested in an old House Martin's nest under the eaves of the County School at Whitby in 1944. For details of the behaviour of Swifts at Masham in 1946, see *The Naturalist*, 1947, p. 9.

Alpine Swift
Apus melba

The 'White-bellied Swift' of Nelson occurred on seven occasions up to 1892, details of which were published in *The Birds of Yorkshire*: the first was obtained at Oughtibridge, near Sheffield, about the year 1869; one was seen on 2nd June 1870 at Hornsea by F. Boyes, who said the bird came within 10 yards of him; one was caught at Ripponden, near Halifax, in the autumn of 1872 and was preserved — how one catches an Alpine Swift is a mystery!; in 1800, one was seen at Scarborough on 17th April and afterwards, at intervals, for nearly a fortnight; a female was picked up in an exhausted state at Kirkburton, near Huddersfield, on 2nd June 1881. One was watched as it came in over the sea at Scarborough in the autumn of 1890; on reaching land, it dropped dead near a Mr Marshall of

Stockton-on-Tees, who took it to J. Morley who identified it (*The Field* for 18th October 1890). The last of Nelson's records concerned one taken on the moors at Langsett in 1892; the specimen was purchased by W.E. Brady and presented by him to the Barnsley Naturalists' Society on 15th May 1893.

Chislett knew of only two other records up to the publication of his *Yorkshire Birds* in 1952. The first record concerned ten swifts seen by G.F. Williams and G. Twist at Teesmouth on 25th July 1948 which were described as obviously larger than common Swifts and with white bellies; they hawked low over tipped ground for 20 minutes and Chislett considered that they could have been only of this species. It is difficult to imagine what else they could have been. The *Proceedings of the Whitby Naturalists' Society* for 1938 includes a note of an Alpine Swift, distinguished by its white chin and underparts, seen near Whitby, at Whitsuntide 1933, during a visit of the British Empire Naturalists' Society.

There have since been 14 records of this impressive swift as follows: one was seen by E.C. Sterne at Eccup Reservoir on 4th June 1960; one was at Spurn on 16th May 1965; one was seen by B.R. Spence at Spurn on 27th June 1967; one was at Kettleness on 18th April 1970; one was at Spurn on 2nd July 1972; one was seen by P.T. Treloar, J.L.C. Gandy and myself at Knaresborough Ringing Station on 27th May 1973; one was at Bempton on 13th May 1974; one was seen by G. Walker at Wheldrake Ings on 21st September 1975, and another was seen by C.H. Wear at Hornsea Mere on 26th August 1975; one was seen by Mrs J. Webb at Burniston, near Scarborough, on 14th June 1976, and another appeared around the Scarborough Castle Hill on 18th and 19th September 1976; one was seen by P.A. Lassey over Flamborough village on 1st July 1978; one was seen by S.C. Madge and several others at Fairburn Ings from 21st May to 1st June 1979; one was seen by P.A. Lassey and Miss Irene Smith at Bempton and Flamborough on 19th May 1979, and one was seen flying south at Mappleton by W.F. Curtis on 23rd May 1979; one was seen by R.G. Hawley over Hornsea Mere on 2nd September 1980, and another was seen by Mrs J. Webb at Scarborough on 6th September 1980; one was at Horbury Lagoons, near Wakefield, on 8th May 1983; several observers watched a bird at Fairburn Ings on 9th June 1983; P.A. Lassey saw one over Flamborough village on 10th July 1983, and B.R. Spence saw one flying south at Spurn on 19th July 1983; and G. Carr saw one near Staxton on 9th August 1984.

There are now over 340 British records of this species, which breeds in southern Eurasia, and northwest and east Africa.

Kingfisher
Alcedo atthis

The early naturalists' understanding of the facts was often far from the truth, and in Millar's *History of Doncaster* (1804) it is stated that 'The Kingfisher conveys the small fish upon which it preys to a place, generally the deserted hole of a Water rat, where it dissects the flesh from the bones of the fish, keeping them together to form a nest which consists of many thousand of these small bones.' Kingfishers generally excavate their own nesting holes, although they may adopt an existing one if the position suits, and the small bones found in the cavity are regurgitated in the form of pellets, which break down to form a base for the nest.

The Kingfisher was formerly persecuted by anglers and taxidermists, and T. Allis, in his report to the British Association at York in 1844, stated that it used to be very common near Huddersfield but snaring and catching with bird-lime had reduced these to rare birds. He also said that in autumn they assembled along the cloughs, or glens, about Halifax and one taxidermist caught more than 50 in one season by placing a net across the bottom of the clough and driving the birds down the stream.

In spite of such pressures, the Kingfisher was still regarded as common in the early part of the century in the valleys of the lower Wharfe and Nidd, and fairly common along rivers and streams in most parts of Yorkshire.

Although still widely distributed in almost every suitable part of the county, it is nowhere common. Most rivers, streams, and dykes near large sheets of water hold a pair during the summer months, although proof of successful breeding is often difficult to obtain. In 1968, records came from 30 sites in the northern part of the West Riding (vice-county 64) with breeding proved at only five of these, and in 1971 the figures were 60 and 13 respectively. In the southern part of the West Riding (vice-county 63) in 1981, birds were reported from 56 localities but breeding was proved at only six. In 1973, the Wharfedale Naturalists' Society undertook a survey along the River Wharfe and located ten breeding pairs between Buckden and Pool.

The species is scarce during the breeding season only in Holderness, in the southern part of the North York Moors and in the high barren Pennines, but it occurs along many upland streams and along the river valleys of the Pennine foothills. It is perhaps most at home along the slower-flowing rivers and canals of the flatter country adjacent to the hills and out into the vales.

The species suffers during severe weather, and, following the really hard winters of 1947 and 1962/63, the population was drastically reduced. Recovery was slow after the latter period and it did not return to full strength until at least 1970. Two broods are often reared and families are sometimes large, six or seven chicks being not unusual in some years.

Birds disperse after the breeding season and some move to the coast, especially in hard weather when they may seek food along the beach in rock pools and streams crossing the littoral part of the shore. There have been several records in recent years, at, or near, Spurn during the winter months, though mostly during September and October when birds are on the move, some of which may be immigrants. Nelson said that there was 'a considerable accession to the numbers of our resident birds, chiefly observable in August, September and October in the coastal districts'. On 4th July 1905, one was seen about 2 miles (3.2 km) off Redcar heading for the land, and on 7th April 1981 one landed on an oil rig off Spurn and later died. The latter was an immature bird and much paler on the underparts than Yorkshire breeding stock.

A bird ringed at Shipley on 28th June 1936 was recovered in the Pendle Forest area of Lancashire on 13th February 1937; one ringed on 28th May 1939 at Wilmslow in Cheshire was at Northallerton on 31st March 1941; an adult female ringed at Kilnhurst on 23rd April 1962 was found dead at Hexham, Northumberland, on 22nd August 1962; one ringed in Leicestershire on 20th September 1977 was retrapped at Wombwell, near Barnsley, on 11th July 1978 and later found dead there on 28th August 1978; and a male ringed at Hackenthorpe on 24th August 1981 was at Finham in the West Midlands on 8th November 1981. It is thus clear that many Yorkshire Kingfishers disperse in the autumn, and one of 15 caught at Knaresborough Ringing Station in the autumn of 1973 was retrapped

Plate 101. First-year male Red-spotted Bluethroat, caught at Knaresborough Ringing Station on 18th September 1971. The first inland record for Yorkshire. *Photo: D.N. Brown*

Plate 102. Siberian Stonechat at Flamborough Head in October 1981, showing the very pale underparts and rump typical of the eastern races. *Photo: P.A. Doherty*

Plate 103. Wheatear, a common breeding bird over much of the high ground in the west and north of the county. *Photo: W. Higham*

Plate 104. A cock Ring Ouzel at its nest on a Yorkshire heather moor. *Photo: W. Higham*

Plate 105. Blyth's Reed Warbler caught at Spurn Point on 28th May 1984. The third Yorkshire record. *Photo: G. Neal*

Plate 106. Booted Warbler, caught and ringed at Spurn Bird Observatory, where it remained from 5th to 7th September 1981. *Photo: D.M. Cottridge*

Plate 107. Icterine Warbler caught at Flamborough Head in August 1982, a regular early-autumn migrant along the Yorkshire coastline. *Photo: P.A. Lassey*

Plate 108. Desert Warbler, the first record for Yorkshire and only the second for the British Isles, at Spurn Bird Observatory from 20th to 24th October 1975. *Photo: K. Atkin*

Plate 109. The Spurn Desert Warbler, having been caught and ringed on 20th October 1975. *Photo: G. Neal*

Plate 110. Pallas's Warbler caught at Flamborough Head in October 1982, one of ten different individuals at that locality in what was a record year for the species in the British Isles. *Photo: P.A. Lassey*

Plate 111. Radde's Warbler which stayed at Spurn Bird Observatory from 14th to 16th October 1978. The first Yorkshire record. *Photo: J.W. Hartley*

Plate 112. B.R. Spence holding the 1978 Radde's Warbler for a party of birdwatchers who were fortunate enough to be visiting the observatory. *Photo: J.W. Hartley*

Plate 113. A male Red-backed Shrike caught at Spurn on 25th May 1984 showing a white wing patch, found only in the eastern populations. *Photo: J. Cudworth*

Plate 114. Serin caught at Spurn Bird Observatory on 7th November 1982. *Photo: C. Massingham*

Plate 115. Parrot Crossbill trapped at Spurn Bird Observatory on 11th October 1982. The bird was very weak and was found dead next day. *Photo: J. Cudworth*

Plate 116. Two Parrot Crossbill skins. Upper, the 1982 Spurn bird, a first-year female (see above); and lower, an adult female found dying at Tophill Low Reservoir on 26th October 1975. *Photo: M.F. Brown*

Plate 117. Song Sparrow caught and ringed at Spurn Bird Observatory on 18th May 1964. The first record for Yorkshire and only the second for Europe. *Photo: J. Cudworth*

Plate 118. White-throated Sparrow, caught and ringed at Spurn Bird Observatory on 12th May 1983. A new species for the county list. *Photo: T.M. Clegg*

Plate 119. Rustic Bunting which stayed at Flamborough Head from 21st to 23rd May 1978 and was caught and ringed. Only the third Yorkshire record. *Photo: P.A. Lassey*

by R. Spencer at Marsworth Reservoir in Hertfordshire on 21st August 1973. Between July and December 1975, 17 birds were caught and ringed at Knaresborough as they came to a pond stocked with small rudd.

In 1960, the warden of Ingleton Youth Hostel told E.C. Sterne that a Kingfisher regularly visited fat hung in a tree, from which it fed by hovering like a humming-bird. From late August to the end of October 1983, at Rudston, near Driffield, a Kingfisher used the top of a greenhouse as a vantage point from which to catch insects on the glass roof; it also flew to the lounge window of the nearby house, where it alighted on the sill and caught spiders, beetles, flies and moths. On one occasion it was seen to hover along the house wall, from which it picked insects. The owner of the greenhouse, Mr A.S. Ezard, said that the bird was there at dawn each day and still there when he returned from work each evening (*The Naturalist*, 1984, p. 78).

Nelson summarised the Kingfisher's status as 'Resident, generally but sparsely distributed. Occurs in the autumn as a migrant on the coast.' The same applies today, but the origin of the birds along the coast in autumn is not really known. That a few come across the North Sea I think there is little doubt, but some may be British birds moving south along the coastal strip.

Blue-tailed Bee-eater
Merops philippinus

Nelson included an account of the Blue-tailed Bee-eater as a footnote in his *The Birds of Yorkshire* and I repeat his comments in full:

'The only European example on record of the Blue-tailed Bee-eater (*Merops phillipensis*, L.), which is an inhabitant of India, Burma, and the Islands of the East, is the one mentioned by the late John Hancock (*Birds of Northumberland and Durham* 1874, p. 28), as having occurred in August 1862, near Seaton Snook, a place on the Durham side of the Teesmouth, by Thomas Hann of Byers Green. This passed into the possession of the Rev. T.M. Hick of Newburn. Whatever may be the facts relating to this episode, the occurrence is quite inexplicable. The locality where the bird was obtained is, however, actually on the Yorkshire side of the river, and therefore within the scope of the present work. Thomas Hann was well known to me, and to George Mussell, the Middlesbrough taxidermist. He called at Mussell's house in Middlesbrough on the day on which the bird was killed and detailed to him how he had been to the "Branch End," where he was sitting on a slag ball when the bird alighted near him and was shot. He subsequently told Mussell that he came by train from Eston, and that he was offered twelve shillings and sixpence for the specimen when he arrived at Middlesbrough station.

'The mention of slag proves the shooting to have been on the Yorkshire side, as that on the north side of the river is tipped from Messrs. Bell Bros.' Clarence Works, and I learn from Sir Hugh Bell that the tipping did not commence (except in the immediate vicinity of the works) until 1872 or 1873, and there was no slag at all at Seaton Snook until well on into the "seventies." The "Branch End" is on the Yorkshire side, near Bolckow, Vaughan & Co.'s works, where tipping was in progress before 1862.'

The record was not admitted to the British list by the editors of *The Handbook of*

British Birds, but no reasons were given as to why it was not considered acceptable. The chances of a live bee-eater being brought from the East at that time, when ships had to round the Cape, were very remote and it therefore seems unlikely that it was an escape. The Blue-tailed Bee-eater is now considered a superspecies with the Blue-cheeked Bee-eater *Merops superciliosus*, an example of which occurred on the Isles of Scilly in June 1951 and which was admitted to the British list. The breeding range of *philippinus* is from India through southeast Asia, and that of *superciliosus* from Ethiopia to South Africa and to northwest India. When P.J. Stead was researching for his *Birds of Teesmouth* (1964) during the early 1960s, he made extensive enquiries about the whereabouts of the specimen, which went eventually to the Hancock Museum in Newcastle, but the curator, G.W. Temperley, could not remember it. The specimen was examined by Hancock and there can be no doubt that the identity was correct.

Regarding the claim that the bird had been obtained on the Durham side of the estuary, it is clear that this was erroneous and possibly the result of Hann later giving that false locality in order to make the specimen more attractive to his Durham client, the Reverend Hick, a practice not unheard of in those days.

The details are published here for completeness, but without comment as to its rightful claim to be regarded as a Yorkshire record.

Bee-eater
Merops apiaster

The first occurrence of this species in Yorkshire was at Sheffield about 1849 and published by Morris in his *British Birds*, vol. 1, p. 313.

T. Stephenson, in a manuscript dated 1880, wrote that 'Wm. Lister of Glaisdale says, several years ago a stuffed one was in possession of the late William Keld Agar in Fryup.' No other details are given and I do not feel able to accept such a record as having been positively obtained in the county.

A male was captured near Beverley on 5th June 1880 about which Nelson states that 'although this bird was in full plumage, it was in very poor physical condition and it would seem that either the very cold weather, or its passage, had been too much for it'.

R. Richardson, the birdstuffer of Beverley, received a fine male Bee-eater from Filey which was stated to have been caught alive on 9th June 1880 in an exhausted state.

The fifth record published by Nelson is most interesting and deserves to be repeated in full: Mr G.W. Murdock, of Bentham, wrote to Nelson on 13th September 1905 to inform him that, on 9th of that month, James Wilcock of Asperlands, High Bentham, had been watching 'three small and beautiful birds which were quite new to him and that they were busy eating his bees. He described how one of them would take up its stand just at the mouth of the skip and with its hard bill stab a bee as it emerged, and promptly swallow it. He saw one bird take eight bees in that way and at least two other birds of a precisely similar build and colouration had been seen working in co-operation. Finally he managed to secure one, caught in the very act of seizing and swallowing bees, that he brought to me and it proved to be a male Bee-eater.'

No others had been seen in the county up to the publication of Chislett's *Yorkshire Birds* in 1952, but there have been several since: one flew south along the Spurn Peninsula on 18th June 1968; one was at Midhopestones, near Stocksbridge, on 6th September 1971; S.C. Madge saw one flying along Bempton clifftop on 17th May 1974; R.P. Council and B.R. Spence watched one flying south at Spurn on 25th June 1980 which paused to feed for a short while before continuing down the peninsula; the *British Birds* Rarities Committee declined to accept another heard calling over the same area on 20th July in the same year, as it was not seen; B.R. Spence saw another there on 14th May 1981; G. Smith watched one flying south along the River Derwent near Thorganby on 23rd May 1981; P. Smith saw three flying northwest over Parlington Park on 10th June 1981; one circled Flamborough Head, calling regularly in fog, for ten minutes on 22nd May 1981 which P.A. Lassey was able to recognise from his knowledge of the distinctive calls; one was at Hunmanby on 18th May 1982; M.E. Blunt and K. Denny saw one at Spurn on 20th May 1982; one was at Fairburn Ings on 29th-30th May 1983; and one was heard and later seen at Spurn on 8th June 1983.

There are now over 300 records of this species in the British Isles. It breeds in southern Europe, southwest Asia and northwest Africa and a few wander to the British Isles in almost every year.

Roller
Coracias garrulus

In *The Birds of Yorkshire*, Nelson listed 16 records involving 18 birds as follows: one was shot in Fixby Park, near Huddersfield, in 1824; one was killed at Seamer, near Scarborough, in 1832 and purchased for the Scarborough Museum; a second Scarborough example was obtained in 1833; an undated reference to one 'procured' near Whitby in 1839 probably concerns the one referred to in Ord's *History of Cleveland* as 'shot near Kildale by John Bell M.P. in the collection at Kildale Hall'; two are stated to have been obtained in 1842 as reported in Dr Lankester's *Askern*; one flew on board the Hamburgh steamer in May 1843 when 40 miles (64 km) off Flamborough Head; Allis reported one obtained at Hatfield about 1844 (actually in 1838), and one was recorded by Morris at Halifax about the same time. In July 1847, a pair was seen in a plantation called 'Forty Pence' near Skelton-in-Cleveland; one of these was subsequently killed and proved to be a female with eggs in the oviduct (*The Zoologist*, 1848, p. 1968), and the specimen was acquired by J. Hancock and referred to in his *Birds of Northumberland and Durham*, p. 28. One was obtained at Whitby in 1852, and one was shot at Bridlington in 1868; T. Boynton of Bridlington has a specimen which was formerly in the collection of W.W. Boulton of Beverley, but there is no date or location given for the record; one occurred at Bingley in July 1872; one was taken by R. Hay on the 'Haggs' at Whitby in June 1874; one was reported at Boltby, near Thirsk, on 5th June 1880 which had recently fed on a mouse, swallowed whole, and several beetles; H.T. Archer saw one on the banks of the River Wharfe near Ilkley at the end of July 1881; and Nelson examined an immature female from Acklam-in-Cleveland on 21st September 1901.

When Chislett published *Yorkshire Birds* in 1952, he could add only one other record. This concerned a bird shot by E. Scott, a gamekeeper, at Grinkle Park on 11th June 1931 which was subsequently inspected by W.S. Medlicott and published in *British Birds*, 1936, p. 326.

It was to be 37 years before another Roller was identified in Yorkshire, when one frequented Bretton Park, near Wakefield, from 2nd September to 6th October 1968. It was seen by very many people, including myself, as it sat on telegraph wires and dropped to the ground to catch insect prey.

Another was watched by R. Smith for 15 minutes on 15th July 1977 in Ripley Park, near Harrogate, as it perched on wires from which it dropped to feed in the traditional manner.

On 26th September 1982, B. Armitage saw a Roller in the distance at Blacktoft Sands. The *British Birds* Rarities Committee felt unable to accept the record because of the brevity and range of the sighting, although Armitage, a well-known and competent observer, was certain of his identification.

Yorkshire thus had its fair share of Rollers during the nineteenth century along with the rest of the British Isles, where in recent years occurrences have been fewer; even so, for only four to be recorded since 1901 in this extensive county is surprising.

Hoopoe
Upupa epops

The Tunstall manuscript of 1784 includes on page 63 the following reference to this species: 'Many Hoopoes were seen in Yorkshire in the end of last summer; one was sent to me, shot within a few miles of this place [Wycliffe-on-Tees] in September; another, about the same time from Holderness, where many were seen.'

J. Cordeaux, in his *Birds of the Humber District* (1899, p. 16), stated that 'fifty years ago it was known to have occurred annually at Flamborough in spring'. In 1836, a flock was noted at Saltburn and several were obtained. Nelson had knowledge of at least 70 individuals up to 1906, several of which had occurred inland, but the majority along the coast.

In his *Yorkshire Birds* (1952), Chislett said that 'If Nelson saw no reason to particularise his 58 records, neither do I the 31 that have reached me from 1906. Space is more profitably kept for species that have problems more important than not uncommon vagrancy.' That could have come only from the pen of Chislett. Twelve had occurred in spring and 18 in autumn from September to November, with one in Hull on 9th December 1943. The majority were along the coast but seven were seen inland.

Since 1951, there have been 80 Hoopoes recorded in the county, 43 of which have been seen along the coast and the remainder at inland localities. Spring is undoubtedly the best time to see a Yorkshire Hoopoe and, of the 80 recorded since 1951, 51 have occurred during April and May, two in June, three in July and 24 during August to October.

The Hoopoe breeds commonly in southern Europe and occasionally in the south of England, the majority of birds reaching Yorkshire being seen during the spring migration period, when they are returning from their winter quarters in Africa and overshoot into the British Isles.

Wryneck
Jynx torquilla

When Nelson wrote *The Birds of Yorkshire* at the beginning of the present century, the Wryneck was an extremely local summer visitor and was also seen occasionally near the coast during the spring and autumn migrations.

Marmaduke Tunstall, writing in 1784, stated that he once had a nest of young Wrynecks taken to him which seemed to take food very readily, frequently darting out their long tongues; they all died the next day.

This species formerly nested in the south and southwest of the West Riding and in the adjacent parts of the East Riding, where it frequented old timbered parks and woods. Denny described it as fairly abundant in the neighbourhood of Leeds in 1840, and Allis said that it was common near Doncaster in 1844. It was an annual visitor in spring near Sheffield and was recorded annually at Walton Hall. It was becoming scarce by Nelson's time and very soon thereafter ceased to breed. The only subsequent instances of its occurrence in the summer up to the 1950s are on 8th June 1909, when one was calling in Studley Park, near Ripon; and on 12th July 1946, when, according to Sir A.F. Phillip Christison, one near York had five or six young which flew into a tree where he was standing.

Since Chislett published *Yorkshire Birds* in 1952, there has been no evidence of breeding, but one was on Thorne Moor from 15th to 21st June 1974 and one called regularly at Potteric Carr from 5th to 13th July 1976.

In 1978, when more birds than usual passed along the coastal strip, two also occurred inland, one at Silkstone Common on 6th May and one at Ingbirchworth Reservoir on 27th May. There have been 31 other inland records, all of which have been during late August and September, with an occasional bird in early October. Five birds occurred inland in the autumn of 1974, and there was a remarkable passage in 1976 when, in addition to the coastal birds, records came from 12 inland localities. The first was on 22nd August at Potteric Carr, where one had been seen in July (see above), followed by one at Fairburn Ings on 27th; one was caught at Knaresborough Ringing Station on 28th and another, surprisingly, on 30th; one was seen at Harrogate on 29th, and one at Wintersett Reservoir on 30th; one was found dead at Rothwell on 31st; another was found dead at Carcroft on 1st September; one was seen at Lower Barden on 4th; one at Fairburn Ings on 13th; one at Harrogate on 26th; one at Langsett on 29th; and a late bird was at Doncaster on 9th October which died.

The spring passage in 1978 was the best ever recorded in the county. After two at Grimston on 30th April, birds were seen at many places, with ten at Flamborough on 1st May followed by 23 on 2nd May, seven on 3rd and eight on

6th, when four were also at Filey. Spurn had one to two birds on several dates from 30th April to 25th May, with five on 7th May.

In 1980, the autumn passage was also above average, with birds at several places, especially on 31st August when an obvious influx occurred with maximum numbers of eight at Flamborough and three at Spurn.

The species is now a passage migrant occurring along the coastline annually in both spring and autumn, most numerously during the latter period. Numbers fluctuate from year to year, but there have been only six years since 1960 in which fewer than ten birds have been recorded.

A Wryneck ringed at Spurn on 7th September 1958 was found dead in Sweden on 2nd July 1959.

Green Woodpecker
Picus viridis

Nelson's statement that the Green Woodpecker is the bird referred to as the 'Wood Weele' in the ballad of 'Robin Hood and Guy of Gisborne' in connection with Yorkshire establishes its ancient association with the county.

At the turn of the century it was most numerous in the Vales of York and Pickering, and in the latter area it preferred the woodlands of the many valleys running up into the North York Moors. Such is one of its favoured habitats today. The Green Woodpecker is not uncommon along the wooded scarps of the Hambleton Hills and the Pennines, and along the western slopes of the Wolds. Birds occur, and breed, well up the higher valleys, as in Langstrothdale, Littondale and in Bransdale. On 27th April 1974, seven were seen in the Langdale Valley, near Scarborough, including three together. Nelson knew of nesting trees close to the edge of the moors in some Cleveland dales. The birch woods in the south of the county about Hatfield and Thorne and those around York are other favoured breeding places. It is fairly generally distributed over much of the county, particularly in woodland where the wood ant occurs, being scarcest on the top of the chalk Wolds of the East Riding and also in Holderness. It is nowhere really common, but several pairs may be found in close proximity in the most popular nesting localities.

A survey undertaken by members of the Yorkshire Naturalists' Union in 1972 gave a total of 74 proven and probable breeding pairs, 42 of which were in the West Riding. The habitats recorded showed a marked preference for open parkland country with scattered timber. In the Settle area, B. Shorrock said of the species in 1977 and 1978 that it was 'as common as it ever will be'. Records of single birds came from 30 localities in Nidderdale in 1978.

After the severe winter of 1962/63, very few Green Woodpeckers were seen and many observers saw none at all in 1963. On 18th February 1963, at Huby, one seen to fall from a tree in a very weak condition later died. The increase was slow, and even in 1966 records were still very scarce.

Whether Green Woodpeckers move any great distance is not known. Nelson recorded one or two instances of the species' occurrence at Flamborough, where one was picked up in an exhausted state on 17th October 1894 and another in the autumn of 1903. W.J. Clarke saw one flying north over the sea at Scarborough among a flock of immature Herring Gulls on 15th January 1910, possibly having come from the woods on the cliffs at Knipe Point, Cayton Bay, where birds are seen every year, though breeding has not been proved.

416

It occurs rarely at Spurn, and there have been records in only six years since the first on 17th October 1952. The others were as follows: one flew south along the peninsula on 15th April 1960, having been seen earlier as it passed through the Warren area; single birds were seen on 21st April 1962 and 14th, 17th and 19th August 1962; 15th April 1965; 20th May 1967; and on 9th August 1984. One flew south along the beach at Tunstall on 15th November 1970. These birds could have been undertaking no more than local movement around the eastern part of the county.

In the absence of any proof of birds migrating to or from Yorkshire, the species remains more or less as summarised by Nelson in 1907: 'Resident, local, but fairly common where it occurs.'

Great Spotted Woodpecker
Dendrocopos major

Nelson's assessment of the status of this woodpecker as 'Resident, local, thinly distributed, although more general than the other Yorkshire species and observed as an autumn migrant on the coast' needs some amendment, as it cannot be termed thinly distributed today. When Chislett published *Yorkshire Birds* in 1952, he said that it was distributed more generally and more numerously than at the turn of the century.

Wherever trees occur, whether old mature woodland in the lowlands or younger timber in the dales and cloughs of the Pennines, the Great Spotted Woodpecker can be found. It is a familiar bird at feeding tables in suburbia during the winter months, and some pairs nest in close proximity to towns. In 1959, the keeper at Roundhay Park in Leeds knew of eight nests.

A survey organised by the Yorkshire Naturalists' Union in 1972 showed a total of 101 breeding pairs, 67 of which were in the West Riding. More pairs must surely have nested, but the relative distribution figures will represent the true picture. Mature broadleaved woodland was the most popular habitat, followed by more open parkland timber. Conifers were not favoured. In 1978, 16 pairs were located in the Barnsley area and 13 pairs were in the Doncaster district, nine of which were proved to breed.

Much damage to nesting boxes is often inflicted by Great Spotted Woodpeckers and young birds are often pulled out and eaten. Holes are usually bored through the sides of traditional tit-type nesting boxes, although nestlings may be taken through the entrance hole when this is large enough or after it has been enlarged by the woodpeckers. J.B. Hague described attacks on nesting boxes in a wood at Sprotborough, near Doncaster, during the years 1958 to 1960 when several had holes drilled through the sides or the entrance holes enlarged; both eggs and young were taken. On 1st May 1960, a male Great Spotted Woodpecker was found roosting in a box, the entrance hole of which had recently been enlarged (*The Naturalist*, 1967, pp. 115-16).

Natural nest sites vary both in height above the ground and in the choice of tree.

Chislett recorded a nest in a silver birch only 3 feet (91 cm) from the ground and another in the upper branches of a lofty beech.

Records along the coast in spring and autumn in every year include migrant birds from Scandinavia, and such are known to occur from birds trapped at Spurn and elsewhere. They have appeared in almost every month, most numerously in the autumn when several birds of the northern race *Dendrocopos major major* have been seen or trapped at Spurn, Grimston and Flamborough. At Whitby, on 20th September 1949, one was watched as it came in low over the sea and then rose to clear the pier and the east cliff. G.R. Bennett saw one flying south over the sea at Atwick on 21st October 1960; one came in over the sea at Flamborough on 26th September 1978; and birds often fly south along the Spurn Peninsula.

In 1968, the largest recorded influx occurred along the coast. No fewer than 17 birds were at Spurn on 15th September and 18 were caught and ringed there between 14th and 17th September. All belonged to the northern race. During the same period, there were two at Flamborough and one at Filey Brigg on 15th; two at Muston on 16th; two at Hornsea on 17th and eight on 18th; three near Kilnsea on 15th and five on 21st; five in the Scarborough area on 25th and three at Skeffling on 26th. All except one, which remained until it was killed by a car on 9th December, had left the Spurn Peninsula by 10th October. One trapped at Hornsea on 17th November was also of the northern race. A female, also of this race, caught at Spurn on 5th May 1969, was doubtless on its return journey. This influx was reported in many parts of eastern Britain from 9th August, the main arrival taking place during September. The migration was first noted in Finland, where many were caught and ringed, and at Revtangen in Norway, where 700 were seen on 7th September (*British Birds*, 1968, pp. 474 and 538). For full details of the Yorkshire influx see the *Spurn Bird Observatory Report* for 1968, pp. 52-6.

Another influx occurred in 1972 and H.O. Bunce saw 12 birds on the Flamborough Headland on 24th September; one was on Bempton clifftop the next day, and several appeared in the Hornsea area in November, one of which was trapped and proved to be of the northern race. The influx was also noted at Spurn from 4th September, and 14 birds were caught and ringed, all of which belonged to the northern race.

Seven birds flying north over Knaresborough Ringing Station in a loose flock on 11th October 1980 were unusual. During a year of coastal influx it would have been tempting to assume that they were immigrants, but none occurred at Spurn in that year and only one was seen at Flamborough, in October.

One ringed at Spurn on 15th September 1968 was found dead at Tuxford in Nottinghamshire on 26th December 1968, and one ringed on 20th October 1975 was retrapped near Cambridge on 1st January 1976. Both these birds were diagnosed as belonging to the northern race when trapped.

Birds of the British race have been recorded at Spurn, and these need not be of local origin; a young bird ringed at Sheffield on 26th June 1947 was recovered in Staffordshire on 25th December 1947, showing that some of our breeding birds move south in the winter.

Lesser Spotted Woodpecker
Dendrocopos minor

This small and elusive woodpecker is very local in Yorkshire, being almost confined to the area immediately east of the Pennines in a triangle drawn from Richmond in the north, southwards through Harrogate and Leeds to the Huddersfield, Barnsley and Sheffield areas and eastwards to York; outside this area it is very scarce as a breeding bird. Even in the most densely populated area west of the River Ouse to the Pennine dales, breeding is often very difficult to prove. The species is, however, located annually in the woodlands of this region during the summer, and

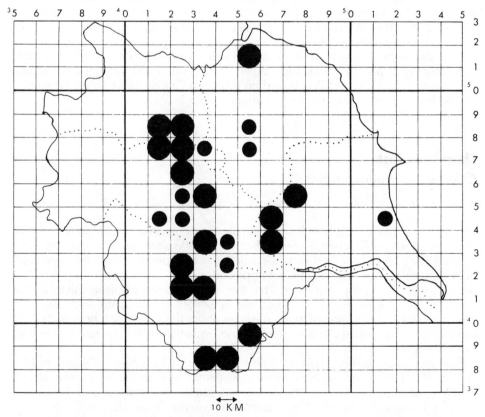

Lesser Spotted Woodpecker. Centred on the mature woodland in the middle of the county in a triangle drawn through Wensleydale in the north, York in the east and Sheffield in the south, this species is nowhere common and is very difficult to locate in the breeding season.

419

doubtless more pairs than are found breed successfully. It may occur similarly, if only sparingly, in other parts of the county.

Two or three pairs have bred in the Sedbergh area during recent years; an occasional pair has bred near Saltburn, and it has nested in Duncombe Park for many years. In the southeast of the county in Holderness, records are very few, except from Hornsea Mere where it probably breeds. In several years, no records are received for this area, and a similar situation exists in the northwestern part of the county. It becomes thinly distributed in the extreme south, and a pair which reared young near Worsborough in 1976 was the first proof of breeding in that area. In 1977, single pairs bred at Cusworth Park and at Sandal Beat, the first proof of breeding in the Doncaster area for over ten years. A bird seen on the Broomhead Estate on 11th March 1973 was the first record there for 25 years.

The species favours old timbers, and the open parklands around York, Leeds, Harewood, Bramham, Studley and at Bretton are regular breeding places.

Outside the nesting season, a Lesser Spotted Woodpecker may occur almost anywhere in the county, but most numerously within the breeding areas.

In the Yorkshire Naturalists' Union Ornithological Report for 1941, Chislett stated that a 'quite unmistakeable male' was seen at Hickleton, near Doncaster, on 26th February by the Reverend F.W. Bond and went on to remark that 'the species is not often recorded in Yorkshire'. Records thereafter, up to 1952 when *Yorkshire Birds* was published, enabled Chislett to say that during the last ten years it had been seen much more frequently than formerly, and an increase in keen observers during the last 30 years has resulted in a further increase in sightings. In 1979, records came from 40 widespread localities in the West Riding, although breeding was confirmed at only six of these.

It is hard to believe that there are more Lesser Spotted Woodpeckers now than during the early part of the century, especially in view of the large amount of old timber felled during World War II, and on this point I agree with Chislett, who concluded his chapter on the species in *Yorkshire Birds* in a similar vein.

Short-toed Lark
Calandrella brachydactyla

On 14th May 1955, J. Cudworth saw a small sandy-coloured lark in Clubley's Field at Spurn. When approached, it flew with three Skylarks and was noticeably smaller; it called three times, and Cudworth identified it as this species, which he knew well from visits to Europe. Although Chislett placed the record in square brackets, his reason for so doing was not clear. That the bird was seen no nearer than 60-70 yards (c. 60 m) is no reason for doubting its validity, which is the implication in *Yorkshire Birds*. I have spoken to the observer about the record and he is quite certain of the bird's identity; I have therefore no hesitation in accepting it as the first Yorkshire record.

The second occurrence was on 30th November 1958, when J. Cudworth, J.K. Fenton, R.C. Parkinson and N.H. Ward saw a small lark on the beach east of the Warren area at Spurn. Later in the day, it was caught in a mist-net by E.S. Skinner and a full plumage description was taken and entered in the daily logbook by P. Hope Jones. It was very grey on the upperparts and was diagnosed as belonging to the eastern race *longipennis*.

One frequented the fields north of the canal zone at Spurn from 13th to 18th September 1969 where it was watched by J. Cudworth, G.E. Dobbs and T.R.

Bradbury. Another was seen at the Spurn Chalk Bank from 13th to 18th June 1970 and caught on the first date, when it was identified as belonging to the greyish eastern race.

The next county record was also at Spurn, where A.O. Aitkan, J.R. Colman and R.A. Williams saw one with Skylarks in the fields north of the Warren Cottage on 21st September 1973.

In 1974, B.R. Spence caught one at Spurn on 9th May, and another stayed in the vicinity of Coatham Marsh, near Redcar, from 21st June to 14th August. The latter moulted during its stay and frequently dust-bathed on a local rubbish tip, which soiled its plumage and gave it an atypical appearance; it was seen by very many people, including D.G. Bell, D.J. Britton and G.L. Coates.

One seen at Spurn on 28th May 1977 by S.M. Lister, J.M. Turton and others was thought to belong to the reddish western race *brachydactyla.*

One was seen by N.A. Bell at Easington on 12th, 13th and 19th June 1982. In 1983, one was seen by S.M. Lister at the Easington Lagoons on 29th May, and one was found dead in the sand dunes at Spurn on 12th June by B.R. Spence. Although the corpse was badly flyblown, with many larvae in the orbits and belly region, it was sent to me for possible preservation, something I was able to achieve with care.

On 17th June 1984, J. Cudworth saw a small lark flying past him at the Narrow Neck at Spurn. He recognised it as of this species from the call, which it uttered as it flew south.

Lesser Short-toed Lark
Calandrella rufescens

At 14.30 hours on 14th November 1984, B.R. Spence was driving his car southwards along the Spurn Peninsula when a small bird was flushed from the side of the road. It landed behind the car, and, on pulling up, he saw it sitting at the edge of the road. On reversing to get a better view, he was surprised to find that he could draw right alongside it, and even more surprised to see that it was a very small lark, somewhat reminiscent of a Short-toed Lark, but very much darker and with a band of narrow streaks across its breast. The bird crouched at the side of the road for some 30 seconds, before walking off with a crouching gait as it stumbled through the sparse marram grass as though rather weak, before flying some 10 yards (9m) down the road, where Spence was able to draw his car alongside it as it stood briefly only about a yard away before walking off into the marram grass again. During these periods of very close observation, all the plumage details were well seen and the observer realised that it was in fact a Lesser Short-toed Lark, the first for Yorkshire and England; all the other records in these islands have been in Ireland in 1956 and 1958, when a total of 42 birds was seen on four dates.

Thinking that he could catch it with a hand-net, Spence returned to the observatory to collect one, but on his return only five minutes later the bird was not to be seen, and subsequent searching of the whole area during the afternoon and the next day failed to relocate it.

Full details have been submitted to the Yorkshire Naturalists' Union Reports Committee and will eventually be submitted to the *British Birds* Rarities Committee.

Crested Lark
Galerida cristata

Chislett square-bracketed a probable record of this species at Spurn on 11th April 1947 which was seen by H.G. Brownlow. The meagre details and the way in which they are given in *Yorkshire Birds* suggest that Brownlow was certain of his identification but Chislett had doubts. The absence of a filing system for field notes at the time of this record means that it can never be re-assessed and will remain inadequately documented and in doubt for ever.

I can now add the species positively to the Yorkshire list on the strength of a bird near Tunstall on the Holderness coast on 11th June 1972. A.W. Wallis first saw it in the morning, when it was running on bare ground among parked cars near the cliff-top and was fairly oblivious of the many nearby people; such are the habits of the species on the coast of Brittany. Later in the day he set a mist-net and managed to catch the bird, and a full description, including detailed measurements, was taken before it was ringed and released.

Although breeding just across the English Channel and a familiar bird on the out-skirts of Calais and Boulogne, the Crested Lark very seldom crosses to Britain.

Woodlark
Lullula arborea

The Woodlark has been lost to Yorkshire as a breeding species since the publication of Chislett's *Yorkshire Birds* in 1952. Nelson listed only Langwith and near York as breeding places during the early nineteenth century, and it was reported by R. Fortune to have nested on Harlow Moor at Harrogate in 1880. It was never common in the county, but a few pairs persisted in the East and West Ridings until the last pair managed to rear one young in 1958.

A pair reared three young on a conifer-planted heath adjoining tall oaks in the southern part of the North Riding in 1945 (*The Naturalist*, 1946, p. 17) and it bred there up to 1949. At least four pairs bred in 1949 and more were suspected of doing so. At one site in the East Riding, a bird was first heard on 25th February and display was seen on 13th May where the adults were seen feeding a juvenile on 14th May. Some miles away, a second pair bred and had four young in the nest on 10th April. A third pair had five eggs on 1st May and the fourth pair was feeding fledged young on 9th July. The sites were many miles apart and Chislett expressed hope that the species was in the process of becoming well established. One pair was successful in 1950. Five eggs in the Doncaster Museum were taken on Thorne Moors on 21st May 1950. In the following year, birds were singing in three areas, but no nests were found. F.C. Griffiths noted three pairs with young in South Yorkshire on 12th July 1952.

In 1955, J.S. Trimingham and R.J. Rhodes made detailed observations on a pair in the south of the county. The nest was found on 30th April, when it contained four eggs; it was sited in short grass, close to an isolated patch of dead bracken near the edge of a stony and sandy heath. Both adults were seen feeding young in the nest on 14th May, but on 19th the nest contained only three dead young and the fourth was found dead nearby; both adults were in the vicinity. The weather during the previous few days had been very severe, with cold winds, heavy rain, hail and sleet. A second nest was found on 30th May which was in longer grass than the first one and in a deeper depression, being well sheltered by a large grass tussock. The eggs were intact on 9th June, but the nest was empty when next visited on 27th, with evidence of successful fledging as three birds were flushed nearby. Singing Woodlarks were seen in two other nearby localities in 1955, and at one of these a family party of one adult and four juveniles was seen on 25th June and subsequently. For full details of the observations see *The Naturalist*, 1956, pp. 45-6.

In 1956, two pairs were thwarted on three occasions and produced 24 eggs from which one pair reared four young. Bad weather was again responsible for the failures. Nesting occurred in the East and West Ridings in 1957 and birds were seen at three localities in the former. One young bird, which was the only one to fledge from two broods in 1958, was the last Woodlark known to have been reared in Yorkshire.

An occasional bird sang in the breeding areas during the next few years, but nesting was never suspected. A bird which sang on Strensall Common on 1st June 1965 was not heard subsequently, and this was the last time the Woodlark's song was to be heard in the county. In 1959, one bird spent the whole of May near Sedbergh School but disappeared during early June.

Woodlarks have occurred at Spurn, mainly singly (two in 1950 and 1979), in 16 of the years since 1950 and mainly during March to May and from September to November. One was at South Gare on 18th September 1969; one was with Skylarks in the clifftop fields at Jackson's Bay, Scarborough, on 29th January 1976; two were there next day, and two again on 6th January 1979; one was at Flamborough on 13th October 1978; one flew south at Grimston on 16th October 1978; one was at Kilnsea on 2nd October 1983, and single birds were at Flamborough on 21st October and 31st December 1983.

Away from the coast there have been a few records in recent years: one flew west over Esholt on 14th May 1961; T.M. Clegg saw one at Hatfield on 29th January 1966; P.T. Treloar and C. Winn saw one at Fairburn Ings on 18th April 1971; one was seen by J.S. Armitage and other watchers near Wintersett Reservoir on 2nd November 1975 (*The Naturalist*, 1976, p. 107); one was at Fairburn Ings on 1st June 1976; P. Doherty heard one calling and saw it as it flew over Eccup Reservoir on 7th January 1977; one was at Stone Creek on 8th May 1983, and one was at Blacktoft Sands on 25th May 1983.

The Woodlark is now a scarce bird in Yorkshire, occurring only occasionally when single birds are recorded along the coast and very rarely inland. Whether the species will ever breed here again is doubtful.

Skylark
Alauda arvensis

There is no part of Yorkshire, be it on the high barren moors of the Pennines or on the coastal dunes of Holderness, where the Skylark is absent during the breeding season. Nelson described it as a generally and abundantly distributed resident and such it remains today.

Each autumn, the resident population is augmented by many thousands of birds from central and northern Europe. Nelson said that enormous bodies of immigrant Skylarks arrived on the east coast in autumn, individually outnumbering any other migrant, and during September and October, when the movement was at its height, a succession of straggling flocks could be seen passing southwards from daybreak to noon. He considered that the majority were British breeding birds, having moved to the coast preparatory to leaving southwards. He was in part correct, but the majority would have been immigrant birds. On 9th December 1878, with severe gales and snow showers, great flights passed Redcar from the east in company with Redwings and Fieldfares, and on 8th February 1902 Nelson witnessed what he referred to as 'an extraordinary migration' preceding a fortnight's intensely hard frost when huge flocks flew south from early morning to dusk.

Southerly movement occurs every autumn along the east coast and is most evident at Spurn, where the birds are channelled along the peninsula. From late September through October and into November, Skylarks are moving on most days, their numbers usually peaking during the second half of October when several hundreds may pass daily. On 4th and 5th February 1947, at the beginning of a long severe spell, G.R. Edwards counted flocks flying south at Spurn which he estimated were passing at the rate of 1,500 per hour. At the end of October 1971, larger numbers than usual passed through, with 3,500 on 27th, 10,000 on 28th, 9,000 on 29th, 640 on 30th and 1,421 on 31st. In 1975, the movement was again larger than usual and, having started in late September, it built up to 1,000 birds on 14th and 15th October; 1,500 on 21st; 2,000 on 22nd and 23rd; 3,000 on 24th; 1,050 on 28th; 1,000 on 30th; and 600 on 2nd November.

Large numbers inland are invariably connected with prolonged hard weather or snow cover, and straggling flocks may be encountered anywhere in the county as feeding parties shift their location. Sometimes, the movements may last for only a few hours and consist of small numbers of birds, but at times large flocks may be on the move for several days. A flock of 1,000 was on stubble at Staveley on 27th December 1962; 2,000 flew south over Kirk Ella, near Hull, during a period of snow cover on 31st January 1972; 2,000 were on stubble at Healaugh during cold weather on 1st December 1973, and 1,200 flew west over Knottingley on 3rd; 3,420 flew southwest over Knaresborough Ringing Station up to midday during snow showers on 25th January 1976, and 1,150 flew south in similar conditions on 28th December 1976; and 2,500 appeared at Hatfield Marina during snow cover on 10th February 1978.

Some Yorkshire-born Skylarks move south for the winter, but many stay through; in very severe winters, such as in 1947 and 1962, it is likely that all the birds pulled out and went south. A bird ringed at Portland Bill in Dorset on 24th January 1963 and recaught at Flamborough Head on 3rd November 1963 was probably newly arrived on the latter date on its way from northern Europe.

White or buff-coloured varieties were 'not uncommon' in Nelson's time and he saw a pure white bird in a migrating flock coming in over the sea, presumably at Redcar, on 9th October 1890. A bird with much white in its plumage was seen by G.H. Ainsworth and J. Lord at Spurn during April and early May and again in December 1946, and S.M. Lister saw a completely white individual among a flock of normal birds at Kilnsea on 13th November 1979.

A pure white Skylark, shot at Riccal about 1870 by Richard Pratt, a timber merchant and farmer, which I inspected in the Yorkshire Museum in September 1984, was not recorded by Nelson in *The Birds of Yorkshire*.

Shore Lark
Eremophila alpestris

In a communication to *The Zoologist* (1854, p. 4251), Thomas Allis wrote: 'I have a fine specimen of this rare bird, which was shot at Filey on the Yorkshire coast, in the early part of March 1853; a second was seen at the same time but was not obtained.' Nelson said that the honour of introducing the Shore Lark to the Yorkshire avifauna thus fell to Allis. He also stated in *The Birds of Yorkshire* that no species was more overlooked than the Shore Lark; and 'our earliest appraisals of its visits are chiefly due to speculative shots at small birds on the coast, which occasionally result in the Shore Lark falling to the gun, and being duly chronicled'.

The more experienced observers at the turn of the century, including Messrs Boyes, Cordeaux and Eagle Clarke, became aware of the species during the winter months and appreciated its annual occurrence. Numbers fluctuated annually then, as they do today, and, as for several other species, the old records infer that more visited the county than do now. In 1879/80, a large flock appeared near Kilnsea and 23 were obtained during the winter. Spurn became known as the chief habitat for the species in Yorkshire, mainly because, as Nelson said, it was regularly visited by the birdmen of the day, who published their findings in the ornithological journals, although the Teesmouth was equally good for the species. It was 'abundant' in the years 1883, 1889, 1890, 1891, 1894/95 and 1898/99, mainly during October and November. During the period November 1900 to February 1901, a flock of fully 200 frequented an area of reclaimed land at Teesmouth; nothing remotely approaching that number has occurred since.

In 1952, Chislett said in *Yorkshire Birds* that 'Winters in which the Shore Lark has definitely occurred on the Yorkshire coast have been so few in recent years that all can be cited.' The majority of records involved only a few birds in sporadic years from 1908, the first large flock being seen in the winter of 1948/49 when 18 frequented the shingle on the Humber Estuary opposite the Warren Cottage at Spurn. This flock remained throughout the winter and peaked at 29 birds. On 6th February, 28 were present and H.O. Bunce and Miss F.E. Crackles noted their food as the seeds of *Atroplex portulacoides* and *Suaeda maritima*.

From 1964, Shore Larks were recorded more frequently and more numerously, and some places along the coast became established as favourite winter haunts, some of which are still popular today. South Gare at Teesmouth, the clifftop fields at Filey and Bempton, the headland at Flamborough, the coastal fields and beach at Barmston and Fraisthorpe, and the beach at the Easington Lagoons attract good numbers almost annually.

Anywhere along the coast from the Tees to the Humber during the winter months, a Shore Lark may be encountered, with small parties occasionally and sometimes larger flocks at the above-mentioned places. Maximum counts during the last 20 years have been as follows. South Gare: 84 on 24th October 1971, 105 on 25th October 1971, 77 on 23rd November 1971, 40 on 28th December 1971 and 25 on 28th January 1973; Filey: 32 on 2nd February 1964 and 25 on 4th December 1965; Bempton: 25 on 3rd and 26th February 1973, 26 on 12th February 1974, 23 on 20th April 1974 and 25 on 21st December 1977; Flamborough: 24 on 20th December 1961 and 21 on 7th January 1962; Barmston/Fraisthorpe: 25 on 3rd December 1978, 42 on 7th January 1979, 24 on 11th March 1979 and 20 on 23rd December 1979; Easington Lagoons/Spurn: 13 in February 1975, 24 on 15th December 1976 and 14 on 18th November 1978. A flock of 40-50 birds frequented Bran Sands between 26th and 31st December 1972, and 17 were on Redcar jetty in October 1972.

Inland records are rare and there have been only four, three of which were at Fairburn Ings: the first was on 1st January 1960 (*The Naturalist*, 1960, p. 88); the second on 14th November 1971; and the third in 1977, seen by S.C. Madge on the slag heaps, on the unexpected date of 13th May. One was at Lower Gorple Reservoir on the Lancashire border on 12th December 1971 (*The Naturalist*, 1972, p. 134).

The first birds of autumn usually arrive during early October, earlier dates being 18th September 1895, when two were killed at Redcar; 28th September 1965, when one was at Spurn and another came in over the sea at Filey; and 29th September 1975, when one was at Spurn.

After the birds have arrived during October and assembled in small flocks along the coast, some often disperse at the turn of the year and fewer are seen during the early months. Most birds have departed by early April, but a few stay on; in 1962 one stayed at Spurn until 6th May; three were still at Bempton on 16th May 1972, and two were there on 9th May 1974.

The Shore Lark's status remains as Nelson summarised it: 'Winter visitant to the coast-line, irregular in numbers. . . .'

Sand Martin

Riparia riparia

The Sand Martin is usually the first of the swallow tribe to arrive in Yorkshire in the spring. The main influx usually occurs during the second week of April, but there are few years when a March Sand Martin is not recorded. The earliest dates have been 19th March 1966, when two were at Fairburn Ings; 13th March 1978, when one was at Denaby Ings, followed by five at Fairburn Ings on 16th; and on 12th March 1981, again at Fairburn Ings, with three at Knotford Nook Gravel-pit the next day and two at Wintersett Reservoir on 14th.

During the main arrival period in April, birds concentrate to feed over large sheets of water and at sewage-farms. If the weather is cold and damp, the concentrations of birds are often most spectacular and several hundreds, or even thousands, may be seen fluttering low over the water seeking shelter in the lee of banks or trees, or hawking low over sewage-farm filter beds, where bird-ringers have found them easy to catch in mist-nets. If the spring weather is warm and settled, the majority pass steadily through and large numbers are not so evident.

The traditional nesting site is along the banks of rivers, where they make their burrows, often in very large colonies, although other sites are regularly used. Gravel-pits provide excellent nesting faces, and small colonies have been recorded also in peat cuttings, moorland gullies, slag heaps, sea-cliffs and dunes, and even in sawdust heaps. A few pairs nest annually in ancient holes in the soft limestone crag behind the Mother Shipton Inn at Knaresborough, and a solitary pair nested in a drainpipe sticking out of a wall only 2 feet (61 cm) from the ground at Knaresborough in 1968, 1969 and 1970.

During the 1950s, J.A.S. Borrett and I embarked on an intensive ringing programme using a method of catching Sand Martins at colonies which we had developed, and which was later used in many parts of the country. The method was to fix a polythene bag onto a small cardboard tube and insert one into each hole of a breeding colony before dawn, the birds being easily caught as they came out at first light. The best time to carry out the operation was, we discovered, during early July when the fledged juveniles were still roosting in the colony, which they do for only a few days before moving on to seek reedbed roosting sites while on migration. By removing and replacing tubes, we took no fewer than 17 juveniles from one hole on one occasion, and catches of seven or eight from one hole were commonplace. In 1955, we ringed 1,301 birds working at four or five gravel-pits and some riverbank sites. Full details were published in *The Naturalist*, 1958, pp. 37-8. Many interesting inter-colony movements within a particular season and the return to the same or different colonies in subsequent years were noted. A juvenile ringed in its natal colony at Knaresborough on 10th July 1961 and retrapped at Littlebourne in Kent on 30th July 1961 illustrates how soon after leaving the nest the young birds begin their southward journey to the winter quarters in Africa. Another juvenile ringed at Castley on 6th July 1961 was retrapped at Romford in Essex only 12 days later. Many birds have been ringed at reedbed roosts, especially at Fairburn Ings, and there are several foreign recoveries in France and Spain in both spring and autumn.

Roosts in reedbeds and in willow bushes overhanging water, which they often share with Swallows while on migration, can be spectacular. The most impressive of all has been at Fairburn Ings where, from the late 1950s until the 1970s, large numbers assembled every autumn. The first large count was in 1956, when C. Winn estimated 13,000 Sand Martins to be present. In 1959, the peak autumn count was 30,000 birds on 19th August. A count of 70,000 on 28th August 1960 was completely overshadowed by an estimated 300,000 birds on 11th September 1960. The peak numbers in 1961 were 100,000 on 22nd August and 60,000 on 3rd September. Up to about 10,000 were regularly present during the 1960s, and 20,000 were there on 5th September 1974. Mist-netting at this spectacular roost was organised by C. Winn and D.J.R. Potter, who, between them, must have handled more Sand Martins and Swallows than anyone else in Britain at that time, and probably since.

Other large sheets of water with suitable reedbeds have attracted roosts over the years, notably Swillington Ings and Mickletown Ings. The extensive reedbeds at Blacktoft Sands also hold large numbers of roosting birds each autumn, and the species may settle in to roost, sometimes for only a few nights, at any sheet of water with appropriate cover.

Once September is drawing to a close, Sand Martins become scarce and, although a few can be found lingering on at large roosts of Swallows, or feeding over the larger sheets of water as they move southwards, the great majority will be nearing or will have crossed the south coast before the month is out. Migration is noted every autumn at Spurn Point, where birds fly south along the peninsula on several days during August and September with a few moving through in July and early October. A hundred or more often pass during the day, and in 1978 a total of 2,063 flew south on 22 September days, the maximum on one day being 600 on 11th.

Nelson recorded a party of 30 birds at Teesmouth on 22nd October 1907, a late date and one which has been extended on only a handful of occasions: one was at Spurn on 17th October 1949; three at Ilkley on 29th October 1961; one at Spurn on 29th October 1980; one at Spurn on 10th November 1977; one at Beal Bridge on 11th November 1964; and one at Spurn on 17th November 1969.

Birds with abnormal plumage are not rare, and Nelson recorded six examples of white or partly white individuals. A white bird spent the season of 1952 at a colony by the Wiske near Yafforth; in 1959, one was at Fairburn Ings on 22nd and 23rd July; one was at Masham from 21st to 24th August 1976, one was at Elland in the autumn and one was at Fairburn Ings from 26th to 28th November in the same year.

The number of Sand Martins visiting Yorkshire in 1984 was drastically low compared with most recent years. The paucity of birds was evident at national level and the true situation and probable causes will be revealed in due course when the details are written up elsewhere.

Swallow
Hirundo rustica

In a letter to John Ray dated 8th February 1675, Dr Martin Lister wrote thus: 'Dear Sir, ... one and the same Swallow, I have known, by the abstracting daily of her eggs, to have laid nineteen successively and then to have given over.' (*Correspondence of John Ray*, p. 117), thus, according to Nelson, establishing an association with Yorkshire of great antiquity.

The Swallow is one of the most familiar of Yorkshire's birds, being found during the summer months in every part of the county, where it breeds in a wide variety of places. Its nest may be built anywhere from inside the old concrete pillboxes among the dunes of Spurn Point to the old stone-built huts on the highest part of the Pennines. The presence of animals will usually induce a pair to build a nest in the same building, and, in addition to the most traditional sites in cow byres and other farm buildings, I have known them to build in suburban chicken huts. Some time during the 1960s, P.T. Treloar and I.B. Dobson noticed Swallows disappearing into the centre of a cornfield on Barnbow Common, near Leeds. On going to investigate, they found an old wartime concrete bunker, the roof of which was level with the ground, and into which the birds were entering through a hole, broken through the concrete in one corner; they were obviously nesting in what must have been a very dark situation. The Swallow is entirely dependent on man-made structures in which to build its nest, and I know of no completely 'natural' site. Chislett knew of none either, but mentioned an example of one that he had once found under an overhanging sod on a cliff face in Wales. Two, and sometimes three or even four broods are reared in a season, and young birds may still be in the nest as late as October. A pair reared four broods in the same stables at Goathland in 1944.

The first Swallows usually arrive during early April, and March birds are not common. Nelson cited only two such records: two birds near Pontefract on 30th March 1830, and a pair at Easby-in-Cleveland on 25th March 1897. In *Yorkshire Birds*, Chislett listed only five others, the earliest of which was 18th March 1945 at Hull. More March birds have occurred in recent years and there have been records in 16 of the years from 1952. The earliest was at Elland on 10th March 1959, the majority occurring during the last week of the month. In some years, an obvious early arrival takes place, and there were six March birds in 1958 and six again in

1981. An early bird often precedes the next by several days and the main arrival by a week or more. Although early-April Swallows are to be expected in every year, the main influx usually takes place during the second or third weeks of the month.

Like the other two species of hirundines, Swallows are affected by cold and wet weather during their spring arrival periods and such conditions will force many to seek food in the shelter of trees, especially those over water and at sewage-farms, where insects are plentiful. At Wintersett Reservoir, on 6th May 1951, 'thousands' were seen over the water during a cold northeaster. Such numbers are to be seen only if adverse weather coincides with a peak arrival period, otherwise large spring concentrations are not common. During a period of snow showers in late April 1981, 32 were found dead in a lake at Lingerfield, near Knaresborough.

In the autumn, similarly, bad weather will cause many birds to assemble and seek shelter while feeding.

When the autumn migration is under way, Swallows spend the night roosting in reedbeds, or among willows overhanging water, and some spectacular numbers have been recorded. The most famous roost was, and to a lesser extent still is, at Fairburn Ings where, during the late 1950s and subsequently, counts of 5,000 on 4th September 1958 and 15,000 on 19th August 1959 were later to be completely overshadowed in 1960, when 50,000 were gathered at the end of August and peaked at a staggering 700,000 on 11th September. C. Winn and D.J.R. Potter caught birds in mist-nets and ringed 2,373 during the autumn of that year. In 1961, after a count of 200,000 on 30th August and 250,000 on 3rd September, numbers fell to 5,000 by mid September, but an incredible estimate of one million birds re-appeared on 22nd and 23rd September, gradually decreasing thereafter, but up to 80,000 were still appearing nightly at the month end. Between 400,000 and 600,000 attended the roost during the autumn of 1963, and a peak count of one million birds was made on 10th September 1964. The roost still exists and 300,000 were present on 23rd September 1973, with around 10,000 in most recent years. An exceptional 200,000 which came into the roost on 16th September 1980 were probably forced down by a heavy thunderstorm. Mining subsidence has altered the nature of the reedbeds over the years and the location of the roost has changed from time to time.

Many other waters with suitable reedbeds or other tall emergent vegetation have held large roosts over the years. Sometimes these are of a temporary nature, and birds may roost in a particular place for just a few nights or during just one autumn. Other roosts, as at Fairburn, may become traditional and attract birds annually, provided that the conditions remain stable. Wheldrake Ings, Mickletown Ings, Potteric Carr, Sprotborough Flash, Broomhill Flash, Wath Ings, Wombwell Ings, Blacktoft Sands and several other localities have held roosts of between 10,000 and 15,000 Swallows in recent years, and 100,000 were present at a roost near Staveley during early September 1984.

The majority have left for their winter quarters by early October, but several pass through later and the sight of a November Swallow need occasion no surprise. There are several records during the last week of that month, mainly from the coast, but two were at Naburn Sewage-farm, near York, on 21st November 1978, and single birds were at Tinsley Sewage-farm and at Rotherham on 25th November 1980. Some of these birds could be from late broods, but those passing south along the coast during late October and into early November could be from northern Europe. There have been December Swallows in five recent years: at Great Ayton on 17th December 1955; Drighlington on 5th December 1959; Wilberfoss on 4th December 1961; and at Scarborough on 1st December 1964 and on 12th December 1968. Nelson mentioned one at Redcar on 3rd December 1846, three birds at Huddersfield on the strange date of 13th January 1831, and one at Halifax on 4th February 1862.

Each year, mainly during the autumn, spectacular numbers of Swallows migrate southwards along the coastline and are funnelled along the Spurn Peninsula, where they are counted by watchers stationed at the Narrow Neck. Southerly passage is not confined to the autumn, and in spring up to 1,000 to 2,000 birds may pass south on several May days. Such movements likely consist of birds which have overshot into Britain and are making their way back into Europe to continue their journey northwards to their breeding grounds in the Low Countries and beyond.

In the autumn, up to 20,000 birds have often been counted during the peak month of September as they pass along the peninsula, numbers fluctuating from day to day, and maximum daily counts have been 12,272 on 4th September 1971, 9,000 on 9th September 1974 and 9,400 on 13th September 1978. Birds continue to pass during October in every year and a few during early November.

Of the many Swallows ringed in Yorkshire over the years, several have been recovered in South Africa and at many places en route. It is unnecessary to list them all in detail, but some illustrate the speed of movement and are worth giving in full. A juvenile ringed at Fairburn Ings on 23rd September 1960 was in Spanish West Africa on 4th November 1960, and another ringed on 24th September 1960 was near Ladysmith in South Africa on 31st December 1960. One ringed at Wintersett Reservoir on 12th September 1981 was found dead at Everton in Bedfordshire the next day. It is interesting to note that two birds ringed on Gozo in the Maltese archipelago while on spring migration have been recovered in Yorkshire: one, a male ringed on 14th April 1974, was retrapped at Brough on 26th September 1974, and another male ringed on 14th April 1982 was retrapped near Skipton on 28th August 1982. A bird caught while roosting in a concrete pillbox at Spurn on 18th May 1956 was caught there again two years later.

Nelson said that white varieties occurred almost every year, and several have done so in recent years. White, or leucistic buff-coloured Swallows have occurred at Tadcaster in July 1959 and at Stainforth in August 1959; Armthorpe during August 1961; Scarborough in July 1976; Otley in June 1977, and flying south at Spurn on 3rd September 1977; and at Spurn, again flying south, on 21st August 1979. A white nestling was at Cawood in 1977, and a pure white bird was seen at Knaresborough in 1982.

The vast numbers of Swallows which go to roost in reedbeds in the autumn, and their sudden appearance over water in the spring, gave rise to the ancient belief that they hibernated in the mud at the bottom of ponds and lakes. At the turn of the century, Nelson said that 'the belief dies hard in the remote dales'. Old reports of supposed hibernation in more feasible places must be treated with some reserve. In mid winter 1880, some 20 Swallows were reputedly found inside an old tree that was cut down on Lord Feversham's estate at Helmsley, one of which showed signs of life but soon died. According to Pennant (vol. iv, pp. 13-14), several bushels-full of Swallows in a torpid state were found in a cliff at Whitby while men were digging out a fox. It is most difficult to imagine the circumstances which gave rise to such reports; even allowing for some exaggeration and embellishment, the instances are highly unlikely.

'Summer visitor, generally distributed, abundant, arrives in mid-April and departs at the end of September, a few remaining until October', is how Nelson summarised the Swallow's status in 1907. There is but little need to change it.

Red-rumped Swallow
Hirundo daurica

This species was added to the Yorkshire list of birds at Spurn on 3rd May 1964, when J. Cudworth, B.R.Spence and G.R. Wilkinson were at the Narrow Neck counting passing Swallows and a Red-rumped Swallow flew south.

On 13th May 1965, at the same place, G.R. Edwards, B.R. Spence and S.J. Weston had a similar experience to add the second record for the county. Another flew south along the peninsula on 3rd June 1967.

One was seen at Figham, near Beverley, on 16th April 1969 by the young son of F.M. Nethercoat and subsequently by H.T. James, M.G. Hodgson, T.W. Upton and others during its stay until 20th April.

On the evening of 27th April 1971, C. Winn and others saw one at Fairburn Ings which was still present the next morning. On 7th May 1974, P.J. Dunn and K. Sawyer watched one at Healaugh Pond, near Tadcaster. M. Francis saw one at Seamer Road Mere, Scarborough, on 10th May 1976.

In 1977, no fewer than five Red-rumped Swallows were reported, the first being seen by J. Adlard, R.G. Hawley and R.G. Sturman at Hornsea Mere on 30th April; two were seen by J.M. Baildon, J. Cudworth and D. Page at Spurn on 22nd October; another, or one of the same, was seen by D. Abbott, B. Banson and D. Ford, also at Spurn, on 25th October and another was seen there by J. Cudworth, R. Gilbert and K. Pearson on 13th November.

D. Braithwaite saw and sketched one at Naburn Sewage-farm, near York, on 16th and 17th May 1979, in which year another was seen by S.M. Lister at Spurn on 19th May and a third was watched by I. Forsyth and D.G. Hobson at Flamborough Head on 23rd June.

This south European species has extended its breeding range westwards during the last 20 years, and there are now some 90 records in the British Isles, mostly since 1968.

House Martin
Delichon urbica

The House Martin was said by Nelson to be decreasing in numbers in the manufacturing districts and in the neighbourhood of many large towns 'where whole colonies have deserted their breeding places owing to the prevalence of smoke and the destruction and usurpation of their nests by the ubiquitous House Sparrow'. There were some exceptions, and particularly in Harrogate the reverse was the case.

In 1952, when Chislett published his *Yorkshire Birds*, he said that 'the House Martin now occurs rather less frequently in the suburbs of the large towns than the Swallow'. There is no doubt that the Clean Air Act has helped the species, and today it nests fairly commonly in the centre of some large cities and towns, and new housing estates are sometimes colonised before their completion. Occupation at such sites may be for just one season, but at others a regular colony may be established. Unlike the Swallow, the House Martin breeds in many natural sites and the sea-cliffs at Flamborough and Bempton, Whitby, Boulby, Staithes (30 nests in 1965) and Saltburn all hold small colonies. Some inland crags, the most famous being perhaps Kilnsey Crag in Wharfedale, where 15 nests were counted in 1946, have held breeding colonies for many years. The Kilnsey colony is still there today, as is one at Malham Cove where 17 nests were seen in 1948.

Many types of man-made site are used, apart from the most typical under eaves of houses and other large buildings. There were 30 nests on a dutch barn at Helmsley in 1944, and six pairs built nests on a bridge buttress at Roundhill Reservoir in 1965. In upland situations, where tall buildings are few, nests may be built only a few feet from the ground, in contrast to the normal town situation. Two, or even three, broods are often reared and birds may be feeding young in the nest well into October. In 1942, two broods were being fed in nests on the Malet Lambert High School in Hull on 15th November, and a newly dead adult bird was found there on 23rd November.

Most areas are clear of birds by mid October, but a few linger on, or pass through, in every year up to mid November and sometimes later. Single birds were at Saltburn on 29th November 1953; at Spurn on 23rd November 1957; at Scarborough on 28th November 1960; at Hornsea Mere on 23rd December 1961; at Thirsk on 2nd December 1979; and at Whitby on 3rd December 1979. Nelson cited two December records: one at Whitby on 4th December 1888, and one at Redcar from 14th to 20th December 1900 which frequented his house.

The main spring arrival is usually during the third week of April, although a few appear during the first week in most years, these early ones often being isolated and preceding and main arrival by several days. March birds are rare and I know of only seven, one of which was listed by Nelson, in Wensleydale on 6th March 1879. The others were at Methley on 21st March 1947; at Scisset on 31st March 1954; at Ripley on 14th March 1957; at Fairburn Ings on 24th March 1957; at Harrogate on 27th March 1957; and at Lowthorpe on 26th March 1972.

Birds pass south along the coast in both spring and autumn, and the movement is particularly evident along the Spurn Peninsula, where on any day from early May through to early November birds may be seen moving through. During the spring of 1979, 3,768 birds flew south during May (on 19 days); 729 in June (on 14 days); 64 in July (on four days); 89 in August (on ten days) and on 21 days in September when 12,449 passed through, the maxima on any one day being 3,000 on 11th, 1,042 on 17th, 2,171 on 18th and 3,000 on 20th. Numbers were higher than usual in that year.

Two birds ringed at Harrogate have been recovered abroad: one ringed on 11th June 1958 was on Texel in the Netherlands on 15th June 1961; and the other, ringed on 30th May 1969, was at Murcia in Spain on 7th October 1969, being the first recovery of a British-ringed House Martin in that country. Evidence that some feeding birds assembled at Yorkshire waters in late spring are still on their way northward comes from two birds ringed here and recovered subsequently in Scotland: the first, ringed at Knaresborough Ringing Station on 17th May 1967, was retrapped at Elie in Fife on 12th August 1967; and the second, ringed at Wintersett Reservoir on 27th May 1979, was found dead at Falkirk on 8th June 1979. A bird ringed at Ilkley on 15th July 1961 was retrapped in the Somme in France on 8th May 1965.

A pure albino House Martin, complete with pink eyes, was at Patrington on 26th September 1880, and an all-white bird was seen by many people at Rievaulx during July and August 1959.

On 25th September 1980, P. Smith caught a bird at Wintersett Reservoir which he concluded was a hybrid House Martin x Swallow. The bird resembled a juvenile Swallow, but had a buffish throat and a white rump; the tail was more forked than a House Martin's, but lacked the white mirrors of a Swallow, and the legs were pinkish with traces of white feathers, the latter being a pure House Martin character.

It is difficult to know whether the status of the species has changed significantly since the nineteenth century. Supposed declines at the beginning of the twentieth century and during the 1940s, reported by Nelson and Chislett respectively, were, as the former assumed, probably due to atmospheric pollution, but an improvement in this respect in more recent years has doubtless allowed a return to former status. Marked variation in the size of some breeding colonies from year to year is probably no more than a normal seasonal trend in most cases.

Richard's Pipit
Anthus novaeseelandiae

Nelson considered that the circumstances connected with a Richard's Pipit which, according to D. Graham, the York taxidermist, had occurred on the coast in 1849 and was reported by him in *The Zoologist*, 1849, p. 2569, were 'not of a sufficiently reliable nature to warrant its inclusion in the Yorkshire list'. Chislett said that 'one or two suspected occurrences are insufficiently authenticated to warrant inclusion'.

The first acceptable record came in 1956, when J. Cudworth watched and identified one at Spurn on 15th November. It was later seen by J.K. Fenton, C. Winn and others during its stay until the year end.

On 10th November 1957, Cudworth again saw and heard a pipit at Spurn which he immediately recognised from his experience in the previous year. It remained in the area until 8th December and was seen by many people.

One was seen in the Easington Lagoons area on 1st November 1958 by W.C. Wakefield and D.J.R. Potter. Another occurred near the Crown and Anchor Inn at Kilnsea from 27th to 29th November which was seen by J. Cudworth, J.K. Fenton and P. Hope Jones, and caught and ringed on the latter date.

G.R. Bennett saw one at Atwick on 22nd October 1960; one stayed at Spurn from 21st October to 1st November 1961 which, after being identified by J. Cudworth and P.J. Mountford, was seen by many visitors to the observatory; a bird seen at Spurn on 9th and 10th November 1963 was found dead on 17th, and the specimen went to the City of Liverpool Museum; two were at Spurn on 23rd September 1964, one of which was still present the next day, and single birds occurred there on 18th September 1966 and on 1st and 2nd October 1966.

More than ever were recorded at Spurn in 1967, when, after one on 17th and 18th September, at least 11 individuals were seen between 4th October and 19th November, including four on 23rd October and four again on 10th November. Farther up the coast at Kilnsea, single birds were present from 7th October to 4th November, with three birds from 22nd to 28th October, and one was at Filey North Cliff on 12th November.

In 1968, at least 12 individual birds were seen at Spurn from 18th September to

8th November, and 1969 produced at least eight birds: five on 13th September; four on 15th September; singles on 17th and 18th September; one on 6th October; and one on 19th and 20th October. R.H. Appleby saw one at Filey on 31st October 1969.

Single birds were seen at Spurn on 12 dates between 27th September and 22nd November 1970, with two on 1st October, and another was seen by W.F. Curtis at Hornsea Mere on 2nd November.

Since then, birds have occurred at Spurn and Kilnsea as follows: one on 14th October 1971; one on 6th May 1973, being the first spring record for the county; singles flew south on 21st and 27th October 1974, on which latter date another was seen on the peninsula; one on 29th September 1975; one on 24th October 1976; one from 16th to 25th October 1977 was caught and ringed on 29th; one on 15th October 1980; one on 27th and 28th October 1981; one on 9th October 1983; one on 28th October 1984, with two on 29th and single birds on three November dates to 11th.

Away from the Spurn area, few Richard's Pipits are seen, but there are records as follows: one was seen by D.G. Bell and D.J. Britton at South Gare on 1st and 2nd May 1974; C.D.R. Heard and N.A. Bell saw two in the clifftop fields at Filey on 26th and 27th October 1975; one was seen by R.H. Appleby at Scarborough on 14th October 1975; P.J. Dunn saw one at Filey on 7th October 1981; R.G. Hawley and D. Bryan saw one at Hornsea Mere on 26th October 1981; two were at Flamborough on 6th October 1982, and one on 23rd-24th; one was near Cherry Cobb Sands on 16th October 1983; and one was at Flamborough on 22nd October 1983 and on 16th September 1984.

Tawny Pipit
Anthus campestris

A male Tawny Pipit was found at Barmston on 20th November 1869 by T. Boynton, in whose collection Nelson examined it (*The Zoologist*, 1870, pp. 2021, 2068 and 2100). The date is very late for this species, which normally occurs during September and early October, but in the absence of the specimen it is impossible to re-appraise the record.

At Spurn, on 23rd September 1946, G.H. Ainsworth and J. Lord watched a pipit with long yellow legs, long tail, greyish sides to the head, lightly streaked breast, and a dull brown back with darker striations which they identified as this species. Chislett placed the record in square brackets in the Yorkshire Naturalists' Union Report for that year, thus inferring some doubt, but published it in *Yorkshire Birds* without such reserve.

Chislett saw a pipit briefly on the Humber shore at Spurn on 31st October 1947 which he thought was of this species, but the bird flew before he had seen it well enough; the date was very late.

A record of two birds at Spurn on 23rd September 1949 which were thought to be Tawny Pipits is not sufficiently authenticated for acceptance. One at Spurn on 4th October 1954 was similarly unproven.

The second fully acceptable Yorkshire Tawny Pipit was to come in 1960, when one gave good views to several people at Spurn on 1st May; it frequented an area of bare sand which had been created by a fire in 1959.

The next was again at Spurn, on 15th May 1965, as was another on 14th and 15th June 1966. One was near the Spurn Warren on 6th June 1970, and another was present from 10th to 12th June 1971, being caught and ringed on the latter date.

S.C. Madge saw one at Bempton on 18th and 19th May 1974, and P.J. Dunn saw one at Filey on 7th August 1978. One occurred from 26th to 28th September 1981 near the lighthouse at Spurn, where it was seen by G.P. Catley, J. Cudworth and D.A. Robinson. B.R. Spence and others saw one at Spurn on 23rd and 24th May 1983.

Olive-backed Pipit
Anthus hodgsoni

This rare pipit from northern Russia and central and eastern Asia was added to the Yorkshire list of birds in 1981, when one occurred at Spurn Point on 24th October. It was caught and ringed, and it frequented the area just south of the Warren until being last seen on 1st November (see plate 96). Another bird occurred at Spurn from 22nd to 25th October 1982, and D.J. Britton watched another example of this very striking pipit in Locke Park, Redcar, on 13th October 1982.

One was caught and ringed at Flamborough Head by P.A. Lassey, and seen by other observers, on 26th September 1984 (see plate 97). It was last seen on 2nd October.

There are now about 34 records in the British Isles, all but one of which have occurred since 1958.

Tree Pipit
Anthus trivialis

Having spent the winter months in north tropical Africa, the Tree Pipit returns to Yorkshire in April, the majority arriving during the third week of that month. A few are seen during the second week in most years, but it is never generally distributed until nearer the month end. March birds are extremely rare, and there have been only seven records as follows: Riley Fortune saw 'several' near Harrogate on 18th March 1894; J.P. Utley saw one on 23rd March 1948 for which Chislett gives no locality; P. Young heard one in song at Leighton Reservoir on 28th March 1955; A. Pilkington saw one in the Dunsop Valley on 30th March 1958, and the same observer saw a small party among the young conifers at Stocks Reservoir and heard the song on 24th March 1959; two were at Redcar on 28th March 1967; and one was at Fulford, near York, on 30th March 1980. Those seen by Riley Fortune near Harrogate in 1894 were probably wrongly identified.

The Tree Pipit nests over much of the county wherever suitable habitat exists and is absent as a breeding species only in Holderness. Its preferred habitat is open scrubland, woodland and heathland at all altitudes, from the valley floors in the plains to the Pennine gills and cloughs. It is more sparingly distributed in some areas than others and it is not common in the northeast of the county, where it prefers the edges of the Cleveland Hills.

Most have deserted their breeding areas by mid September, but birds may be seen well into October, especially along the coast when migrants pass through.

Small numbers may be heard calling as they pass overhead along the coastline during September and early October, but numbers are never large. In 1958, a September 'rush' brought up to 50 birds to Spurn and birds were noted in some numbers on Filey clifftops and at Flamborough. In 1959, the autumn passage peaked at 48 birds which passed Spurn during a three-hour watch in the early morning of 22nd September. On 17th September 1960, 20 were at Redcar. Autumn passage in 1970 started in early September, when 20 passed south at Spurn on 5th and 30 the next day, with a few continuing to be seen up to 25th. In 1974, 36 flying south at Spurn on 9th September was by far the largest number of the autumn, no more than six being seen on any one day from 24th July to the end of September. Flamborough Head had 25 birds on 17th September 1976 and 15 were at Spurn on 22nd.

Spring passage is seldom evident and birds usually trickle through in small numbers, but in 1970 20 were at Spurn and ten were at Flamborough on 10th May. In 1978, the largest number ever recorded passing through the county occurred during late April and early May: the first were 13 at Grimston on 30th April, and 34 at Flamborough on 1st May increasing to 57 on 2nd, then gradually decreasing to 41 on 5th and 28 on 7th; Spurn had its peak count of 26 on 1st May.

The latest birds have been on 30th October 1960 at Spurn; 18th October 1964 at Hornsea Mere; 19th October 1966 inland at Sedbergh; 19th October 1969 at Spurn; and 26th October 1975 at Scarborough, when several other species of small passerines occurred.

Three Yorkshire-ringed Tree Pipits have been recovered abroad: one ringed near Ingleton in June 1931 was recovered near Bordeaux in France on 18th September 1932; a nestling ringed near Pateley Bridge on 22nd June 1958 was in Portugal on 21st September 1958; and a juvenile ringed at Knaresborough on 12th July 1975 was found dead in the Netherlands on 16th May 1976.

A bird ringed on 3rd May 1984 at Den Haan in the Netherlands was retrapped at Anchor Plain, near York, on 13th May 1984.

In Willughby's *Ornithology* (1678), the Tree Pipit was referred to as the Lesser Crested Lark, having been first found and described by Ralph Johnson of Greta Bridge.

Pechora Pipit
Anthus gustavi

This very rare pipit, which breeds in the tundras of northeast Russia and Siberia and winters in southern Asia, has occurred in the British Isles on only some 25 occasions up to 1984, one of which was in Yorkshire when on 26th September 1966 one was trapped at Spurn Point by B.R. Spence. It was also seen by G.W. Follows, M.E. Greenhalgh and several other observers during the day.

This was the first record away from Fair Isle, where all the other 16 birds up to the time of this occurrence had been seen.

Meadow Pipit
Anthus pratensis

It is doubtful whether the breeding status of the 'Titlark' has changed since Nelson wrote 'Resident; generally distributed; abundant in Summer, especially in moorland and marshy districts.'

There are few places in the county where the species is entirely absent during the breeding season, although in some lowland areas it is only thinly distributed. On the moorlands and their fringes, it is extremely common and one of the most characteristic birds of such habitat. It needs large open spaces in which to breed. Lowland commons or flat pastureland along the coast are favoured places, and it now breeds regularly on the overgrown banks and edges of gravel-pits.

There are few better visible migrant passerines than the Meadow Pipit, and movements along the Spurn Peninsula have been monitored for many years and often reach spectacular proportions. Such movement occurs every spring from late March until May and in the autumn from early August to early November. Spring passage is never so obvious as that in autumn and daily counts at that time are usually below 100 birds. Over 200, however, may pass on a few days, as in 1972, when 208 flew north on 2nd April and 422 on 7th; in 1975, 410 passed on 12th April, 200 on 13th and 264 on 15th. Some also pass southwards during the same periods, and 265 did so on 12th April. Similar movement is witnessed along the length of the coastline, especially at such vantage points as Flamborough Head and at Teesmouth. In 1961, D.R. Seaward counted birds flying north at Redcar during March: 1,387 passed in 105 minutes from dawn on 3rd, and this movement continued for most of the day. As stated, the passage in spring need not always be to the north; for instance in 1971, at Spurn, the only definite passage was between 16th and 19th April when 189 birds flew south on the first date and smaller numbers during the next three days.

Every year, from August until November, Meadow Pipits pass south along the Spurn Peninsula in numbers varying from day to day, but during the peak month of September there are few days when the numbers passing total less than 100. Over the years, J. Cudworth and others have counted birds almost daily during the autumn and the peak daily counts have been as follows: 6,000 on 17th September 1965 and again on 14th September 1966; 8,200 on 18th September 1967, with 4,500 on 27th and 3,000 on 4th October; 5,915 on 9th September 1974; 9,000 on 19th September 1979; and 9,407 on 18th September 1980. The total count during September 1978 was 30,600 birds; 45,373 passed south during September and October 1980, and 43,675 flew south during September 1983.

Although this movement can be seen almost anywhere along the coastline, nowhere are the birds so concentrated as they are along the narrow peninsula at Spurn Point, where coastal migrants and those moving eastwards along the Humber are funnelled into a great stream. In recent years, B.R. Spence, the Yorkshire Wildlife Trust warden, has lured passing birds down into the trapping areas by playing tape recordings of their song and has caught several thousands. During the last ten years, the average annual catch has been around 450 birds, with no fewer than 880 in 1980 and 1,523 in 1983, 413 of which were trapped on 13th September.

The autumn exodus from the breeding grounds is witnessed annually at several inland localities, and, in addition to birds passing overhead to the south, large numbers gather by the sides of reservoirs and gravel-pits. Watchers have reported daily counts of up to 400 birds, and occasionally more, at many localities, and concentrated watching during September will reveal migrating Meadow Pipits almost anywhere in the county, especially along the slopes of the hills. At Langsett, on 24th September 1980, 2,650 birds were counted as they flew southeast in four hours, and 800 passed similarly in four hours on 29th. Meadow Pipits passing over Chidswell on 3rd October 1965 totalled 600. On 26th September 1976, 500 flew south over Cockett Moss near Settle, and 500 flew west over Ilkley Moor on 21st September 1979.

During the spring period, migrants are less evident, but at Hutton Magna on 6th April 1979 1,200 flew west; and at Kirk Ella, on the north slope of the Wolds, 200 flew northwest on 17th April 1970, 120 on 24th and 150 on 30th (1,500 flew south at this latter locality on 11th September 1970). As in autumn, migrating birds during April assemble in loose flocks by the sides of reservoirs and other large sheets of water. Gatherings of 100 to 500 birds are not uncommon at such places, whether they be lowland flashes and gravel-pits or upland reservoirs adjacent to the moors on which some of the birds may eventually nest. Gouthwaite Reservoir in Upper Nidderdale is a popular place for such numbers to collect, and up to 300 and more occur there during April in most years. At Lofthouse, at the head of Nidderdale, 300 birds were flocked on 10th April 1978; whether they were all Yorkshire breeders is unlikely.

Although most Meadow Pipits move south during the autumn, some remain throughout the winter months and counts of up to 100 birds at some sewage-farms are quite normal during that period. The sewage-farms at Harrogate and Spofforth attract good numbers in most winters, and at Knostrop Sewage-farm 200 were present during February 1970. During a period of very cold weather in mid April 1978, B. Shorrock counted flocks of 200 and 300 birds near Settle on 13th.

Yorkshire-born Meadow Pipits have been proved to travel south in their first year of life, and recoveries of ringed birds have come from the Landes Département of France and from the Algarve in Portugal. Birds ringed at Spurn while on active migration, and therefore of unknown origin, have been recovered in France, Spain, Portugal, Italy (only the third recovery from that country), Morocco and Algeria (the first recovery from there). Recoveries in most of these areas of other birds ringed in various parts of the county are too numerous to list in detail.

Many of the Meadow Pipits passing through Yorkshire during the late spring are obviously different in size and colour, being larger and paler than the typical olive-coloured bird of the Yorkshire moorlands. These are on their way to breeding areas farther north, probably in Iceland and northern Europe.

Nelson mentioned the occurrence of a few all-white specimens and of a pied one from Dalton, near Huddersfield. A bird at Knotford Nook Gravel-pits on 2nd April 1972 had an all-white body and tail, with brown flecks on the mantle and flanks, brown wing feathers and an orange-coloured bill and legs.

Red-throated Pipit
Anthus cervinus

At 16.00 hours on 10th May 1970, H.O. Bunce and Miss J. Fairhurst saw a Red-throated Pipit in full summer plumage by a small pond on the Flamborough Headland, where they watched it as close as 30 yards (27 m) as it fed among the thick cover along the pond edge. The species thus entered the county list of birds, and has since been recorded on five other occasions.

The second example was caught and ringed at Spurn Bird Observatory on 21st September 1972 and examined by B.R. Spence, G.R. Edwards and T.J. Bennett. R.G. Hawley saw another in full summer plumage at Hornsea Mere on 1st June 1975.

The fourth record was of one, also in summer plumage, seen by D.G. Bell and D.J. Britton on Coatham Marsh on 15th and 16th May 1976. The fifth was at Spurn Point in 1977, when N.A. Bell, G.E. Dobbs and P. Higson watched one on 29th May. Another was seen at Spurn by B.A. Ryan on 19th May 1982.

There are now about 170 British records of this pipit, which breeds across north-ern Eurasia and spends the winter from tropical Africa to southeast Asia. The majority have been recorded since 1958.

Rock Pipit
Anthus spinoletta

'As may be expected this bird is strictly limited to the coast-line, and from no inland locality is there any report of its occurrence.' So wrote Nelson in 1907. When Chislett published *Yorkshire Birds* in 1952, he could cite no inland records either, but mentioned one or two which were referable to the central European race, colloquially known as the Water Pipit.

From about 1960, Rock Pipits began to be noticed at several inland places. In the Yorkshire Naturalists' Union Ornithological Report for 1962, Chislett, when referring to six records in October of that year, said 'These records, with others in recent years, suggest a small, regular passage in the eastern Pennine districts in October and November.' (*The Naturalist*, 1963, pp. 37-9). More were seen during subsequent years and it is now recorded annually at inland sites, usually by large sheets of water or at sewage-farms, and sometimes from up to ten localities in a year. Occurrences are usually of single birds and are mainly during the period October to April. One at Broomhill Flash on 13th July 1980 was unusual.

The Scandinavian Rock Pipit *Anthus spinoletta littoralis* is a regular passage migrant every spring through the eastern part of Yorkshire. When R.G. Hawley was the RSPB warden at Hornsea Mere during the 1970s, he noted small parties every spring. In 1975, up to 12 birds were seen from 18th March to 13th April, and small numbers are seen there annually; up to ten were present in mid April 1980. Single birds or small numbers also occur at Spurn, Flamborough, Bempton, Scarborough and elsewhere along the coastline, and into the Humber Estuary. A few have been seen at inland localities: S.M. Lister described one at Tadcaster on 6th April 1975 and one was caught at Stanley Sewage-farm on 4th December 1975; a bird in Langstrothdale on 11th April 1978 was considered to belong to this race, as was another at Hay-a-Park Gravel-pit, Knaresborough, on 15th April 1980.

The Water Pipit *Anthus spinoletta spinoletta*, which breeds in the high ground of Spain, France and eastwards to the Balkans, occurs occasionally in Yorkshire, although it is likely that some early records were referable to the Scandinavian race *littoralis*. Single Water Pipits were recorded at Wintersett Reservoir in 1967, 1970, 1973, 1975, 1977 (caught and ringed) and 1978, and there have been records from Fairburn Ings, Settle, Trent Falls, Hornsea Mere, Blackmoorfoot Reservoir, Elland, Ilkley Sewage-farm, Marley Sewage-farm, Knaresborough Ringing Station and Spurn. All have occurred between October and April, with a slight peak during March and April.

Southerly passage is recorded at Spurn every autumn from September to November, and will include both British and Scandinavian birds. The majority pass during October, and some counts in recent years have produced the following totals in that month: 163 in 1976 (45 on 16th); 279 in 1977 (50 on 10th); 253 in 1978 (46 on 12th); 95 in 1979 (31 on 29th); 105 in 1980 (31 on 13th); 208 in 1981 (24 on 12th); 130 in 1982 (23 on 3rd). A few also pass south during March and April.

Our resident Rock Pipits breed very sparingly along the rocky parts of the coast-line from Flamborough northwards to Boulby.

Yellow Wagtail
Motacilla flava

The breeding distribution of the Yellow Wagtail in Yorkshire includes more hill country than lowland pasture, which, as Chislett said in *Yorkshire Birds*, is the reverse of the general impression gained by many people from *The Handbook of British Birds*, which suggests that this is a bird only of low-lying country. Even the *Atlas of Breeding Birds in Britain and Ireland* published in 1976 said that it was invariably associated with water — not the rushing upland streams favoured by Grey Wagtails, but damp water meadows and marshy fields along river valleys and freshwater marshes along the coast. Not necessarily so in Yorkshire, where, among the dales and high moorlands of the Pennines from the south of the county north-wards to the valleys of the Tees, Swale and Ure, it is very numerous. Wensleydale, Wharfedale and Nidderdale are favoured localities, and the species is a common sight in the summer among the upland meadows alongside streams, rivers and reservoirs, where it is a familiar sight on dry-stone walls, especially when feeding young. In such areas, all three species of breeding wagtail may occur alongside each other in close proximity.

This is a scarce breeding bird in the Vale of Pickering, on the Wolds, and over much of the North York Moors, but in the southeast of the county, in Holderness, it is common in the generally expected habitat of damp water meadows and marshy ground alongside the Humber and the coast.

The Yellow Wagtail is a summer visitor, the vanguard arriving during early April, followed by the main influx from the third week of the month. The earliest records are 2nd April 1945 near York; 27th March 1957 at Filey; 29th and 30th March 1965 at Knaresborough Sewage-farm; 31st March 1968 at Fairburn Ings; 30th March 1969 at Redcar; 5th to 9th February 1975 at Hornsea Mere; and 25th March 1978 at Tophill Low Reservoir. In 1962, a female stayed from 27th January to 3rd February at Swinton, near Mexborough, where it fed on the refuse of a maggot farm. It was first seen by T. Grant, who informed R.J. Rhodes, and it was caught in a mist-net on 3rd February. This was the first winter record for Yorkshire apart from the 1975 Hornsea bird, and, so far as could be ascertained, only the fourth for the British Isles (*The Naturalist*, 1962, p. 44).

The very early arrivals are usually several days ahead of the next, and well ahead of the main arrival which, in some years, does not occur until towards the end of April. Spring passage is evident every year at this period at sewage-farms and by reservoirs, gravel-pits and any other large sheet of water, where gatherings of up to 50 birds are commonplace. Some larger concentrations have been as follows: 125 at Harrogate Sewage-farm on 29th April 1956; 100 at Gouthwaite Reservoir on 7th May 1957, 150 on 11th May 1957 and 150 on 4th May 1958; 100 at Wintersett Reservoir on 26th April 1970; 173 at Bolton-on-Swale Gravel-pit on 1st May 1976, 200 on 27th April 1978 and 170 on 29th April 1979; and 100 at Malham Tarn on 3rd May 1979. A general arrival is often evident at several different localities, where large numbers occur on the same or adjacent dates.

After the breeding season, birds start to collect together prior to their migration. At such times, several large assemblies may be seen at roosts, or feeding at sewage-farms and along the edges of large sheets of water. Birds collect at many such places during late July, August and early September, and the largest numbers have been as follows: a roost in the reedbeds at Fairburn Ings has had maximum counts of 100 on 10th September 1950, up to 300 between 15th August and 6th September 1959, 300 on 26th August 1961 and also during August 1962, 180 on 3rd September 1975 and 250 on 7th September 1976; Wintersett Reservoir had 200 at a roost on 7th August 1974, 150 roosting in corn on 14th August 1975, 300 on 21st August 1976 and 116 on 13th September 1976; Potteric Carr had a roost of 180 on 25th September 1964, 150 on 12th August 1979, 100 on 10th August 1981, and 500 on 4th September 1981, the largest gathering ever recorded in the county;

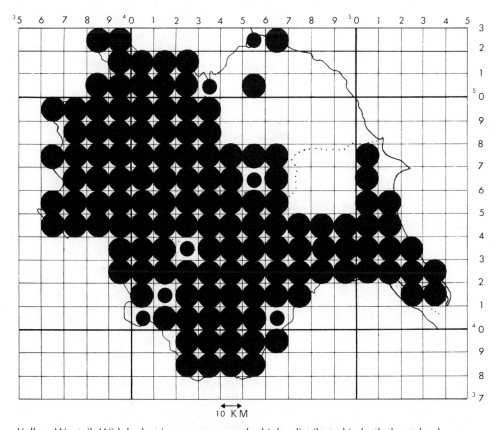

10 KM

Yellow Wagtail. Widely, but in some areas only thinly, distributed in both the upland pastures of the Pennines and the lowlands of the southeast, the latter being the traditional habitat in southern England. Absent only on the chalk Wolds and the North York Moors.

Dewsbury Sewage-farm had 200 on 24th August 1951; a roost at Gouthwaite Reservoir held 200 birds nightly between 5th and 10th September 1960, after a build-up from 100 birds during late July; Denaby Ings had 200 on 5th August 1978; and slightly smaller numbers have been recorded at Swillington Ings, Carlton Marsh and Wath Ings over the years.

On eight evenings from 7th to 20th September 1953, J. Cudworth counted 539 birds flying down the Calder Valley, no doubt on their way to a roost, with 143 on 17th September as the maximum in one evening. Small numbers pass down the Spurn Peninsula in the spring and rather more during the autumn.

Most inland areas are clear of birds by mid September, but a few always linger on into October and even November. October records are too numerous to list in detail and occur in most years, especially along the coastline when the birds involved are likely to be migrants from much farther north. November records have come from Wintersett Reservoir on 5th November 1959; Southfield Reservoir on 9th November 1964, and Adwick-le-Street Sewage-farm on 29th November 1964; two at Spurn Point on 1st November 1968; Fairburn Ings on 11th November 1972; Knaresborough Ringing Station in 1973, where a bird with a slightly drooping wing, but able to fly strongly, stayed from 22nd October to 11th November; and Tophill Low Reservoir on 20th November 1977, and Wheldrake Ings on 27th November 1977.

The Blue-headed Wagtail *Motacilla flava flava*, the race which breeds up to the coasts of western Europe, occurs in Yorkshire every year, mainly during the spring migration period from April to early June. Records have come from places too numerous to list in detail, both inland and along the coast. More occur in some years than others, and there may be from one to five records in a year. In 1979, a pair of birds showing the characters of this race nested successfully at Spurn, and a second pair probably did so. One pair bred in 1980 and reared two broods. A male was paired and had young near Grassington on 6th June 1949, and a male was paired to a normal female Yellow Wagtail on Allerthorpe Common in 1956.

Birds showing the characters of the race *Motacilla flava cinereocapilla*, known as the Ashy-headed Wagtail, which breeds in Italy, Sicily and Sardinia, have occurred in Yorkshire on seven occasions. The first was at Flamborough, when D.I.M. Wallace diagnosed a bird as belonging to this race on 19th May 1979; the second was at Blacktoft Sands between 15th and 17th April 1981; the third was at Coatham Marsh on 8th May 1981; single birds were at Blacktoft Sands from 13th to 16th May 1982, and at Flamborough on 22nd May 1982; at Thrybergh Reservoir on 17th April 1983, and at Filey on 2nd and 3rd June 1983.

Birds showing the characters of the race *Motacilla flava beema*, known as the Sykes's Wagtail, which breeds from southeast Russia to the Yenisei, occurred at Coatham Marsh on 15th May 1976; Saltburn on 5th May 1977; Knaresborough Ringing Station on 2nd and 13th May 1980; Bolton-on-Swale Gravel-pits on 9th May 1981; Withernsea on 16th May 1982; and at Flamborough on 6th May 1983.

A bird at Hay-a-Park Gravel-pit, Knaresborough, on 6th and 7th May 1980 was considered by R. Evison and P.T. Treloar to belong to the Spanish race *Motacilla flava iberiae*.

The Grey-headed Wagtail *Motacilla flava thunbergi*, which breeds in western Europe north of the range of the nominate *flava* and eastwards through Russia to northwest Siberia, has occurred several times in Yorkshire. The first was caught in a lark net at Halifax in the spring of 1901, and exhibited at a meeting of the British Ornithologists' Club on 20th May 1903 by W. Eagle Clarke (*BOC Bulletin* No. 98). The majority of the others have occurred singly at Spurn on the following dates: 10th May 1967; 6th June 1968; 7th May 1969; 9th May 1970; 18th and 19th May 1975, and from 29th to 31st May 1975; 4th and 29th May 1978; 31st May 1979; 19th May 1981 (two birds); and from 13th to 16th May 1982. One was in

Newtondale on 20th May 1973 which D.E. Murray and T.W. Upton identified as belonging to this race; R.G. Hawley saw one at Hornsea Mere on 17th and 18th May 1975; S.C. Madge and C. Winn saw one at Fairburn Ings on 10th May 1976; H.J. Whitehead saw one at Hornsea Mere on 15th May 1977; R. Evison and P.T. Treloar saw one at Staveley Lagoon on 13th May 1977; P.A. Lassey and Miss I. Smith saw one at Flamborough Head from 14th May to 3rd June 1978; R.G. Hawley and D.E. Murray saw one at Hornsea Mere from 13th to 15th May 1978 and again on 8th and 9th May 1979; H.J. Whitehead saw one at Flamborough on 20th May 1979; two were at Hornsea Mere and at Filey Brigg on 15th May 1982; and single birds were at Flamborough on 29th-30th May 1983 and on 26th June 1983.

A bird showing the characters of the race *Motacilla flava lutea*, which breeds on the Kirghiz Steppes, was identified by D.I.M. Wallace at Flamborough on 1st June 1982.

This morphologically unstable species may produce colour variants within a particular population, and birds showing characters of the more subtle races such as nominate *flava*, *cinereocapilla*, *iberiae*, and especially *beema*, need not necessarily have originated in the breeding areas of those subspecies, although most Blue-headed *flava* will undoubtedly be passage migrants from western Europe and the more characteristic *thunbergi* are unlikely to be the result of such variation. Hybridisation between individuals of different races, as recorded in Yorkshire between the British race *flavissima* and *flava*, is not uncommon, and this pairing often produces offspring which show characters of *beema*. For details of breeding by an apparent *beema* at Hatfield in 1976, see *The Naturalist*, 1978, p. 24.

All the races move southwards during the autumn for their winter quarters in Africa and India, and there are several recoveries of Yorkshire-ringed birds in France, Spain, Portugal and Morocco, and a few more interesting recoveries as follows: one ringed at Low Ellers Carr on 25th September 1964 was killed by a car in the Senegal on 14th December 1964; one ringed in the Senegal as an adult male on 20th March 1971 was retrapped at Knaresborough Ringing Station on 26th August 1973; one ringed as a juvenile at Knaresborough Ringing Station on 28th July 1973 was found dead at Susana, Guinea-Bissau, on 4th July 1974, being only the second recovery of a British-ringed Yellow Wagtail in that region; and one ringed at Doncaster on 22nd September 1977 was recovered in Algeria on 6th April 1978.

Citrine Wagtail
Motacilla citreola

The first and only recorded occurrence in Yorkshire of this rare wagtail, which breeds from northeast and southeast Russia, eastwards through Siberia and Mongolia to Amurland, south to Iran and the northwest Himalayas, was at Bolton-on-Swale Gravel-pit, where G.D. Moore saw one on 24th April 1978.

There are now about 36 British records of the Citrine Wagtail, which occurs here as a vagrant while undergoing its migration to and from the winter quarters in India and southeast Asia.

Grey Wagtail
Motacilla cinerea

The Grey Wagtail is the most specialised of the three breeding wagtails and is confined during the summer months to the hill country of the Pennines and the Cleveland Hills. Breeding pairs may be found by the side of upland streams and along the rivers as they flow eastwards into the plains, anywhere from Sheffield in the south to the Tees Valley, and eastwards through the Cleveland Hills and the dales of the North York Moors, thence down the coast to Scarborough.

In 1974, a pair nested at an altitude of 1,400 feet (427 m) on Cronkley Fell in Upper Teesdale. The lower reaches of the Nidd, the Wharfe and some other rivers have their breeding pairs but, once the plains are reached, the species will nest only rarely. In 1975, 21 breeding pairs were located in Nidderdale. It is absent as a breeding species in the East Riding, except for an occasional pair in the northwest of that area. A single pair which bred near Malton in 1973 was the first to do so for many years. Breeding occurred subsequently in each of the years to 1976, and two pairs bred in the same general area in 1980. A pair nested near Garrowby in 1981. The Grey Wagtail is also scarce during the breeding season in the flat carrlands of

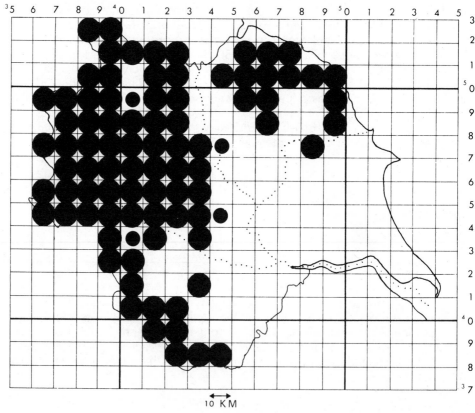

Grey Wagtail. Breeds along the upland streams of the Pennines and North York Moors and along some foothill rivers where rocky banks and weirs occur.

the south and along the lower parts of the Aire Valley.

The severe winter of 1962/63 reduced the population considerably and recovery was slow; it was to be the end of the decade before numbers were back to strength. Recovery after the hard winter of 1947 was quicker and numbers were almost normal by 1949.

During the last years of World War II, Grey Wagtails were regularly seen close to the centre of Sheffield, having followed the streams through built-up areas to the blitzed sites, which provided good open feeding areas.

At the end of the breeding season, birds wander away from the high ground and may be seen at lowland sewage-farms and along rivers, where they have been absent during the summer. A party of 15 Grey Wagtails was at Redmires Reservoir on 19th August 1975.

Small numbers fly south along the coast every autumn, usually during September, with fewer during October. R.H. Appleby counted ten birds flying south over Scarborough Castle Hill on 26th September 1975. In 1976, 42 birds passed at Spurn on 14 days during the period, and between 30 and 40 are counted there in most autumns, the maximum in one day being ten birds on 27th September 1977. Fewer are seen in spring.

During the winter months, especially in severe weather, solitary birds can often be seen in the centre of the larger towns, where they seek food by roadside pools and on flat roofs. The coastal towns also attract a few and the harbours and fish quays are favoured places. One bird picked at fish roes on a Hull fish quay in the winter of 1963.

Sewage-farm filter beds are popular places for feeding Grey Wagtails in winter, and away from these large numbers are scarce. Parties of up to six birds are regular at some, and Dewsbury Sewage-farm had 15 birds on 26th November 1950.

A Yorkshire-born Grey Wagtail ringed at Addingham in Wharfedale on 30th July 1964 was retrapped in Denbighshire on 21st May 1967. A bird ringed at Cholsey in Berkshire on 23rd December 1965 was retrapped at West Burton in Wensleydale on 24th June 1967, and a bird ringed at Mindelo in Portugal on 27th October 1954 was retrapped near Sheffield on 12th April 1957. The species would repay more ringing, especially of nestlings.

Nelson's summary of the Grey Wagtail's status, written in 1907, reads 'Resident; chiefly confined in summer to the moorland streams of the west, from Sheffield northward, and Cleveland; autumnal migrant in small numbers; more generally distributed in winter.' This needs little, if any, amendment today.

Pied Wagtail
Motacilla alba

This most familiar of wagtails is a common breeding bird over the whole of Yorkshire, from the lowlands to the tops of the high fells. Everywhere, where suitable habitat exists — and this may range from a small farm pond to a racing upland stream — the species can be found during the summer months. The nest site varies as much as the habitat and need not be close to water; the species is just as much at home among the dry-stone walls of the western dales as it is on sewage-farm filter beds in the plains. Nelson mentioned the chalk pits on the Wolds as frequently used nesting places, and the increase in gravel-pits in more recent times has provided the species with many and varied nest sites.

Every spring, migrating flocks of bright, clean males appear at sewage-farms and by the sides of the larger sheets of water, where they feed for short periods before moving on to breeding grounds farther north. These passing flocks vary in numbers from year to year and sometimes the birds trickle through with no obvious peak movement, unless the migration is temporarily halted by adverse weather, after which their sudden appearance may be spectacular. Counts of up to 50 birds are common during late March and April, with some larger numbers on record: Esholt Sewage-farm had 150 on 29th March 1966; 200 were at Knostrop Sewage-farm in February 1970; 105 were at Ben Rhydding Sewage-farm in March 1972; 100 were at Harrogate Sewage-farm on 28th March 1977; and 150 were at Settle Sewage-farm on 14th April 1977.

Autumn numbers are much larger, especially at roosts, which may form in a variety of situations; in willow bushes over water, reedbeds, large areas of dead willowherb, on ivy-covered walls or even on, or in, buildings and other man-made structures. In 1976, 200 birds roosted on the brewery building in Tadcaster, and the most spectacular roosts have been on the beams inside Ferry Bridge Power Station, where C. Winn and his colleagues attemped to catch some of the 2,000 to 2,500 birds which spent the night on the rafters during the mid 1960s; and at York Railway Station, where from 1975 to the present time large numbers have roosted on the roof girders. H.J. Whitehead first counted this roost in 1975, when there were 1,680 birds on 13th March; 1,020 on 18th March; 1,328 on 20th March; 947 on 8th November; and 875 on 23rd November. Up to 1,500 birds have been counted during the winter months in almost every year since then. In 1972, 35 birds roosted in a similar situation at Ilkley Railway Station.

Other large roosts, in more natural sites, have been at Sandall Beat, where between 400 and 600 were counted during the early 1970s; Sprotborough Flash, 600 on 28th October 1980; Potteric Carr, 300 on 4th November 1980; Hay-a-Park Gravel-pit, 400 in typha during October 1974; and up to 100 to 200 birds at several other places too numerous to list. Other interesting roost sites were a sugar-beet field at West Tanfield, where 200 roosted in September 1975; and a maize field near Ripon, where 200 roosted in August 1976. On 6th December 1981, I saw 100 birds going to roost among the ivy growing on the front of the Golden Lion Hotel in Thirsk market place. In April 1982 S. Cochrane found about 80 birds roosting in a strip of larch trees about 10 yards wide and 200 yards long (9 m × 183 m) in the middle of Wykeham Forest. The trees had been planted as seedlings and had never been thinned, producing a dense block of spindly trees 3-4 m tall. The roost was still in use in the spring of 1983, and in October 1983, on 28th, a total of 192 birds, the maximum counted, was present all of which arrived from the south-east.

Many Pied Wagtails leave Yorkshire during the winter months, when large concentrations away from roosts are scarce. A few are usually present at sewage-farms, where food is plentiful, but the numbers are usually low. Roosts attract birds from a wide area, and flight-lines are often evident during the evenings; birds often assemble in one place during the early evening before finally moving off to the roost, which may be some distance away. At Knaresborough Sewage-farm in 1972, good numbers gathered on the filter beds and, as they flew off in small groups, were counted as follows: 195 on 15th September, 274 on 16th September, 454 on 18th September, 169 on 19th September, 111 on 21st September and 120 on 22nd September. On 20th October 1946, just before dusk, 1,000 birds moved south-southeast over Swillington Ings, and on 11th October 1947 three waves of birds, each numbering about 200, flew over similarly. On 28th August 1974, F.A. Wardman counted 260 birds in 20 minutes as they flew over Ilkley to a roost on the famous moor.

The species is very fond of feeding on mown grassland. Lawns, sports fields and such places as the Harrogate Stray are regularly frequented, especially during the autumn, when several birds, both young and old, may be seen running with frequent rushes, often quite oblivious of nearby traffic, as they chase insects.

Small numbers of birds move south along the coastline and eastwards along the Humber shore during spring and autumn, especially during the latter period, and are most obvious along the Spurn Peninsula, where they are funnelled into a stream as they pass the Narrow Neck. Numbers are never large, but up to 20 or 30 may pass on some days and in most years some birds pass on every day from August to October.

There are many recoveries of Yorkshire-ringed Pied Wagtails, which shed some light on their winter quarters. Birds ringed as nestlings or juveniles have been recovered in France, Portugal, Spain and Morocco, and birds ringed during the autumn and winter months have been recovered in France and Portugal.

An adult Pied Wagtail, ringed at Reading in Berkshire on 1st February 1970, was retrapped at Denholme, Bradford, on 5th July 1970 and again at Reading on 25th February 1973; whether it was on its home ground when at Denholme or on migration from farther north would be interesting to know. A bird ringed on Fair Isle on 22nd April 1963, and found dead near Loftus on 8th May in the same year, had doubtless overshot too far to the north and had corrected its mistake to return to its presumed breeding area in Yorkshire. One ringed at the Ferrybridge Power Station roost on 5th February 1964 was recaught while roosting in a factory at Elgin, Morayshire, on 27th June 1967.

The nominate race *Motacilla alba alba*, known colloquially as the White Wagtail, which breeds in southeast Greenland, Iceland and Continental Europe eastwards to the Urals, Asia Minor and Syria, occurs in Yorkshire every year on passage. The movement is widespread across the width of the county, and at any time from mid March to mid May examples of this race can be seen with migrating flocks of Pied Wagtails, when the pale grey mantles of the males are easy to distinguish from the jet-black mantles of the British *yarrellii* males. First-year female Pied Wagtails can be very pale and these may lead to thoughts of Whites; the grey, instead of black, rump should always be looked for. Numbers vary annually depending on the strength of the general wagtail passage. The majority are recorded in spring, when they are most obvious, but some undoubtedly pass through the county in autumn, when they are difficult to separate from young female Pied Wagtails.

It is inevitable that such a well-known species should attract a variety of local names. Nelson listed several, including the familiar Willy Wagtail; Seed Bird, used in Wharfedale from its habit of following the plough; Peggy Dish-wash in the North Riding; and Bessie Ducker at Huddersfield. Some of these names are still in use in the more remote parts of the county.

Waxwing
Bombycilla garrulus

The Waxwing breeds in Fenno-Scandia eastwards across northern Eurasia to Kamchatka, north to the tree-line, and also in North America. Its movements are very erratic and usually linked to the availability of its food, the severity of the winter, or both.

It has attracted the attentions of countrymen for many years and some interesting accounts of occurrences in early times are given by Nelson in *The Birds of Yorkshire*. The first example ever to be recorded in the British Isles was referred to in a letter to John Ray from Dr Martin Lister, who said 'One or two were shot at York in January 1680 (or, to use the new style, 1681). His figure, though crude, sufficiently shews the species, to which he gave the name of Silk-tail.' Another reference was made by Ralph Johnson of Greta Bridge, who, in a letter to Ray dated 7th May 1686, described two birds which had been killed in March 1685, saying that 'they came near us in great flocks, like Fieldfare, and fed upon haws as they do'. A letter to Ray from Thoresby of Leeds, dated 27th April 1703, mentioned a third visitation and said 'I am tempted that the German Silk-tail is become natural to us, there being no less than three killed nigh this town the last winter.' The Waxwing was abundant during the winter of 1828/29 and again in 1834/35 and 1849/50, numerous references being published in *The Zoologist* for 1850. In the winter of 1863/64, large flights appeared on the coast, and at Acklam, near Middlesbrough, 11 birds were shot by George Mussell, Nelson's taxidermist, who ate the bodies and found them to be excellent food (*The Zoologist*, 1864). The next great arrival was in December 1866 and January 1867, when many were shot along the coast and several others inland. Henry Seebohm met with a flock in Glossop Road, Sheffield, and several were killed at other inland localities.

One shot at Scarborough had wax tips to its tail feathers as well as on the wing feathers, as had a bird found dead in Harrogate on 5th March 1963 which Major C. Worrin brought to me for preservation; it was a fine male and one of the few I have seen with wax on the tail tips.

The most spectacular invasion in recent years was during the winter of 1946/47, which was one of the most severe periods of modern times when deep snow covered the landscape from January to March, and birds occurred all along the east coast of Scotland and England. The first Yorkshire bird occurred at Scarborough on 9th November, with 30 at Middlesbrough on 13th increasing to 100 during the month. A flock of 100 was seen in Holderness Road, Hull, by G.H. Ainsworth and birds were scattered all over the county. A flock of 60 was seen by Lord Bolton in Wensleydale and 20 were seen between Skipton and Grassington. The last was a bird at Hull on 15th March, when the thaw began; none appeared in the following winter.

During December 1958, good numbers occurred along the coast, with 30 at Cloughton on 26th December and 200 at Ayton for three days from 28th

December. Other large flocks were seen at Thornton-le-Dale and Pickering, as well as smaller numbers elsewhere, and 150 were at Runswick Bay on 6th January 1959 (*The Naturalist*, 1960, pp. 125-6).

Many birds came in during the winter of 1963/64, and were widespread over much of the county. For full details of this influx, see *The Naturalist*, 1965, pp. 83-7, and 1966, p. 3.

More arrived in the autumn of 1965, the forerunners of which were two at Spurn on 12th October; many followed during November and December. After small parties during late October, 400 birds appeared in Scarborough and fed on the berries of service trees. Birds quickly spread to inland localities and were recorded from most parts of the county, except the extreme northwest, during the winter. There was a flock of 30 at York on 29th October; 35 at Driffield on 8th November; 300 at Middlesbrough on 10th November; 50 near Hull on 14th November; 300 west of Hull on 14th November; and flocks of between 20 and 30 birds at Knaresborough, Bingley, Skipton, Bentley Colliery and Sheffield up to the year end. Numbers began to decline during early 1966 as they departed northwards, and the last to be seen were between two and four birds at a Halifax bird table from 10th to 25th April.

A large influx occurred in the autumn of 1970. The first indication of what was to follow was a flock of 20 birds at Spurn on 13th October, whereafter many more came in, with a huge arrival during the first week of November from Flamborough Head northwards to the Tees Estuary. Over 300 birds were in North Lees Avenue, Scarborough, during the morning of 7th, most of which soon dispersed, and parties of three to 100 birds were reported in other areas of the town. A flock of 100 was in Albert Park, Middlesbrough, during the same period. Inland, there were 70 at Guisborough; 43 at Hull; two flocks each of 40 birds near Harrogate; 50 at Studley Roger; 25 at Otley; 50 at Burley; 20 at Ilkley; and up to 20 birds at six places in the Huddersfield and Bradford areas. Smaller flocks occurred at many other localities and were seen into 1971, mainly during the first two months (*The Naturalist*, 1971, p. 69).

Several flocks of between 50 and 80 birds occurred in 1974, and there were some large gatherings in 1975 also, with a relatively large flock of 180 at Mickle Ings, near Otley, on 1st January.

Although Waxwings occur in Yorkshire every year, in some there are very few, as in 1969 when there were only four records involving under ten birds.

Late spring Waxwings are scarce, as the majority leave early, but there have been a few lingering individuals. One bird was at Harrogate as late as 13th May 1971, and there were three late records in 1977: one at Boston Spa on 28th April, one at Harrogate on 22nd May and one at Knaresborough on 29th May.

In 1978, a relatively poor year for Waxwings, in the same Knaresborough garden as the May 1977 bird, two birds were seen by F. Symonds on 5th July, a quite exceptional date for a British Waxwing.

The species is well known for its confiding nature and flocks often feed in the centre of towns, where ornamental trees and shrubs provide berries, when they may be completely oblivious of nearby people and traffic. Cotoneaster berries are a favourite food and birds often feed on these just a few inches from windows through which people watch. Rosehips, berries of the rowan and hawthorn and fruits of cherry, crab-apple and elderberry are all taken, whether on the trees or fallen. Feeding flocks indulge in regular drinking, and fly down from the tree to roadside puddles or river banks where bird-ringers are able to catch them in mist-nets during this activity.

A bird ringed at Oulu, in Finland, on 11th October 1963 was found dead near Otley on 6th December 1963, and one ringed at Rogaland in Norway on 12th November 1973 was found dead at Middlesbrough on 3rd December 1973. Two others, ringed in Yorkshire, have been recovered within the county during the same winter, and one ringed at Low Hauxley in Northumberland on 21st November 1965 was found dead at Thorne, near Doncaster, on 10th December 1965.

Dipper
Cinclus cinclus

The earliest reference to the Dipper as a Yorkshire bird appears to have been in Willughby's *Ornithology*, 1678, p. 149, where it is stated that one was shot on the River Rivelin, near Sheffield.

It is a common breeding bird along the length of the Yorkshire Pennines, in the Hambleton and Cleveland Hills and over the North York Moors. An occasional pair nests in the northern part of the Wolds. It prefers fast-running water and occurs well down the river valleys until they enter the plains, where the slow, deeper water is unsuitable for its specialised feeding habits. It is absent during the nesting season in the Vale of Mowbray corridor between the Hambleton Hills and the Northern Pennines, over most of the East Riding, and in the flat land east of Doncaster and Sheffield. A pair nests each year within 100 yards of the beach on Scalby Beck, where the Dippers can be seen regularly from the bridge which crosses at its mouth, and birds can also be seen at the top of the waterfall where Hayburn Wyke Beck tumbles to the beach.

The Sedbergh School Ornithological Society has studied the Dipper in the fells of the northwest. In 1953, 25 pairs bred along a 15-mile (24-km) stretch of river and 12 pairs on the becks of the open fells, where territories were longer. Of 23 nests, 14 were used for a second brood. Some nests were robbed, but of 88 eggs produced 67 percent hatched and the resulting young fledged successfully. Another census in 1958 within a 2½-mile (4-km) radius of Sedbergh produced 20 nests in which 117 eggs were laid and 79 young fledged successfully. In 1965, no fewer than 114 young were ringed from 65 nests. For very full details of the breeding cycle during a similar survey in 1957, see *The Naturalist*, 1961, pp. 45-9.

Outside the breeding season, an occasional Dipper may be found in the southeastern part of the county wherever water exists and occasionally along the coastline, but such records are scarce.

Nests are usually sited on some ledge overhanging water, whether it be a natural low cliff, stone wall or tree root. Occasionally the birds may build on top of a large overhanging branch, and not infrequently under bridges if a suitable cavity or ledge provides enough support for the nest. Chislett mentioned a nest built in an old petrol tin lodged above a small waterfall near Masham in 1946. In 1901, a nest was built behind the Dropping Well at Knaresborough, where the birds had to fly through the falling water each time they visited it. On 23rd May 1969, M. Greenhalgh found a nest situated 12 feet (3.7 m) down in the vertical shaft of a pothole. It was attached to the rock face and the adults were removing faecal sacs, indicating the presence of young, which on leaving the nest for the first time would have had to fly directly upwards for the 12 feet, or fall about 200 feet (60 m) to the bottom of the pothole (*The Naturalist*, 1969, p. 84). On 23rd March 1975, G. Thrussel watched two Dippers perched in the top of a tree near the River Nidd at Ripley. After perching for a while, they flew off and then returned through the wood in what seemed to be a nuptial flight. They eventually came together and dropped to the ground in a tangle of wings and feathers only a few yards from the observer (*The Naturalist*, 1975, p. 100).

The Black-bellied Dipper *Cinclus cinclus cinclus*, known in Nelson's time as *Cinclus melanogaster*, and which breeds mainly in Scandinavia, has occurred in Yorkshire on some six occasions. Having questioned the validity of the specific rank afforded to this form at the beginning of the present century and saying that the American trinomial system could well be applied to it (how right he was), Nelson listed four examples, the first of which was procured in a drain at Welwick on 24th October 1874 and recorded by F.Boyes in *The Zoologist*, 1877, p. 53; the specimen went to the Yorkshire Museum. The second was also recorded by Boyes, in *The Zoologist*, 1876, p. 4871, as having been obtained on the River Hull at Beverley on 29th October 1875. One was taken at Flotmanby, near Filey, on 8th December 1875 (*The Field*, January 1876, p. 22), and J.H. Gurney had a specimen in his collection which was taken at Bridlington.

On the morning of 11th November 1962, one was seen at Worsborough Reservoir, near Barnsley, by Mr and Mrs T.M. Clegg and a party of birdwatchers from Sheffield. Later in the day, it was seen by D.J. Standring and was eventually caught in a mist-net by A. Archer during the late afternoon. It remained in the area until

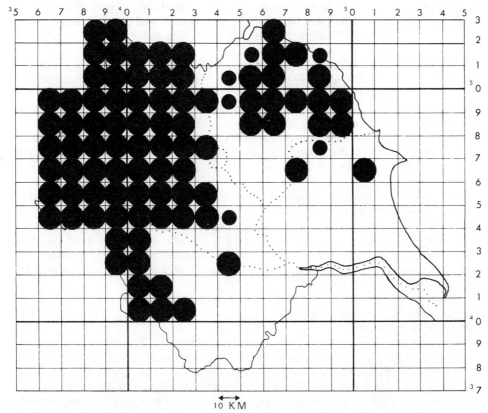

Dipper. A familiar bird along all the moorland streams and the faster-flowing parts of the rivers as they leave the valleys.

27th February 1963 and frequented the stream immediately below the reservoir outflow (*The Naturalist*, 1964, p. 48).

On 29th March 1977, S. Rooke identified a bird by a small pond near Bempton as belonging to this race. It stayed until 9th April.

A young Dipper ringed at Dunsop Bridge, Slaidburn, on 12th May 1964 was retrapped at Askwith, near Otley, on 23rd May 1965.

Wren
Troglodytes troglodytes

The Wren is one of the most widespread and common breeding birds in Yorkshire and may be encountered in every type of habitat, including the highest of the Pennine gills, where it will scold from the long heather or small windswept bushes. It also breeds along the coastline, and in 1978 S. Rooke located ten pairs along the Bempton Cliffs. A survey at Askham Bog in 1977 and 1978, as part of the British Trust for Ornithology Common Bird Census, revealed 53 and 62 pairs respectively. After the severe weather during the early part of 1979, numbers were reduced in most areas and only 23 pairs nested there.

During very cold weather, several Wrens may roost together, and at Aberford on 20th February 1979 no fewer than 20 were seen to enter a nesting box, where they spent the night; at Spurn, seven birds entered two nesting boxes on 2nd January. Nests are sometimes built during the winter, or newly erected nesting boxes lined, to provide roosting places. In November 1942, five birds roosted in an old House Martin's nest on Duncombe Park House, the last 100 yards of approach being flown entirely in the open. The population was severely reduced during the very prolonged and severe winter of 1962/63, but recovery was complete by 1966.

The choice of nest site is wide and some interesting ones have been recorded in Yorkshire. In 1948, a pair built inside the old nest of a Dipper near Loftus, and in June 1975 a pair had a nest with young deep inside a Sand Martin's burrow at Mowthorpe, near Scarborough. The species is equally at home in a nest built in some outbuilding in suburbia as it is in a lonely moorland gully. In 1979, a nest with two eggs was found at Scarborough in the middle of a plant of purple-sprouting broccoli, but the birds deserted.

On 28th September 1959, a Wren was disturbed by a rat on the canal bank at Bingley, whereupon it flopped into the water, floated with outstretched wings and propelled itself to land.

Although the species is basically sedentary, an influx is noted every autumn along the coast, especially at Spurn where birds appear during September and October, when they often number up to 20 or more in a day. Up to 40 were present on several dates between 9th and 17th October 1974, and 38 were at South Gare on 5th October. The origin of these birds is not clear and their movements not fully understood; that they are of more than local origin is proven by ringing. A Wren ringed at Gibralter Point in Lincolnshire on 23rd October 1967 was found dead at Grassington on 20th June 1968, and another ringed at Gibralter Point on 10th October 1980 was found dead at Auckley, near Doncaster, on 30th July 1981. One ringed at South Gare on 9th October 1974 was retrapped at Spurn five days later, providing excellent proof of southerly movement. Three birds ringed in July have provided interesting recoveries: one ringed at Low Hauxley in Northumberland on 31st July 1973 was found dead near Huddersfield on 17th November 1973; one ringed at Grimston, near Withernsea, on 19th July 1975 was found dead at Esher in Surrey on 10th February 1976; and one ringed at Wilton, near Redcar, on 30th July 1978 was retrapped near Retford in Nottinghamshire on 23rd October 1978. A bird ringed at Walberswick in Suffolk on 26th October 1957 was retrapped at Huntington, near York, on 8th June 1959; one ringed at Adwick-le-Street, near Doncaster, on 1st November 1971 was recovered at Norwich in Norfolk on 2nd June 1973; one ringed at Reculver in Kent on 20th October 1973 was retrapped at Potteric Carr, near Doncaster, on 21st April 1974; and one ringed at York on 14th August 1983 was found dead in Suffolk on 9th February 1984. Clearly, some birds move long distances from their breeding grounds in the autumn, and recoveries indicate that some make the return journey.

Nelson was aware of the autumn influx along the coast, reporting that they were 'very abundant' at Spurn in October 1870. A migration was evident at Flamborough from July to October 1881 and movement during the first of those months, most likely consisting of birds with an origin farther north or west in Britain, is known today, as evidenced by the ringing recoveries above. In October 1899, Wrens 'swarmed' on the sandhills at Redcar, where they remained for just a day or two. Nelson also said that 'their occurrence on vessels in the North Sea is by no means uncommon', but no such instances have come to my notice in recent years.

A white-headed Wren was seen regularly by a gamekeeper at Lindley in 1957.

Dunnock
Prunella modularis

In a letter to John Ray, dated 8th February 1675, Dr Martin Lister said 'The *Currucca* or Hedge Sparrow, which I have often seen, lays sea-green or pale-blue eggs, which neatly emptied and wired, fair ladies wear at their ears for pendants.'

Although distributed all over the county during the breeding season, it is not particularly abundant on the high open ground where hedges and small plantations are absent, but even the smallest area of bushes in such localities will have its breeding pair. It is most familiar as a bird of gardens, even in the larger towns, where its shuffling and unobtrusive presence is well known.

Chislett had found its nest in heather, and on 15th June 1922 E.A. Wallis, father of A.J. Wallis of Scarborough, found a nest with young on an open moor on the Hambleton Hills, a mile from any cultivated ground. A pair bred in juniper scrub at an altitude of 1,750 feet (533 m) on Cronkley Fell in Upper Teesdale in 1974.

The Dunnock acts as a common host for the Cuckoo in lowland areas, and there are several instances of young Cuckoos being reared in small suburban gardens.

Every autumn, Dunnocks appear along the coast, sometimes in large numbers, and Nelson cited several years in which it appeared at Spurn. It was 'very abundant' there on 17th October 1880; in 1882 'great numbers' occurred, and on 8th October its appearance coincided with enormous flights which crossed Heligoland during the period 6th to 8th October. The years 1884, 1892, 1894 and 1898 were also years of much immigration.

In more recent years, there has been almost annual evidence of immigration along the coastline, especially along the Spurn Peninsula; in 1967, the mid September influx peaked at 77 birds on 20th; a considerable increase occurred there on 3rd September 1971, and 24 flew north at the Narrow Neck during the morning of 25th, when there was much excited calling from birds assembled at the point. An obvious increase was noted at Knaresborough Ringing Station during late September 1971, and birds were seen flying around very high over the area on 22nd and 30th and on 1st and 2nd October; 29 new birds were caught and ringed during the period 19th September to 5th October. At Swillington Ings, 20 birds, seen by J. Ward during early October, increased to 100 by 31st.

In October 1973, R.H. Appleby counted up to 50 birds daily on the Scarborough Castle Hill during the period 3rd to 9th, and the species was 'very numerous' there on 9th October 1975 together with other migrants.

Several Dunnocks caught at Spurn during an influx on 27th October 1976 showed the characters of the Continental race *Prunella modularis modularis*, one of the few occurrences when such taxonomic evidence of origin has been noted. This race was doubtless included in the following records. In 1978, Spurn had 70 birds on 8th October and 50 on 9th, and 45 were seen by A.W. Wallis at Grimston on 13th. Passage at Filey, Flamborough and Spurn in late September and October 1980 produced a maximum daily count of 35 at Flamborough, where there were 40 also on 3rd and 12th October 1981, and peaks of over 50 at Spurn on 30th August, 16th September and 14th October. Evidence of Continental origin was provided by a bird ringed at Spurn on 3rd April 1958 which was found dead in Schleswig-Holstein in Germany on 14th January 1959. A bird ringed at Red Hill in Warwickshire on 10th December 1967 was at Hovingham, near Malton, on 19th April 1968; and one ringed at Low Hauxley in Northumberland on 25th May 1981 was at West Ayton on 21st March 1982.

It is obvious from the excited and restless behaviour of Dunnocks at inland localities during September and October that some move out, probably to the coast or southwards. Those occurring at coastal watchpoints certainly include birds from across the sea, but some Yorkshire birds and some from elsewhere in Britain will doubtless be included, although the great majority are sedentary.

Very severe weather affected the Dunnock population in 1962/63, but the reduction was not general; some observers considered the numbers to be normal, while others detected a substantial decrease. The hard winter of 1978/79 also reduced the population in some areas: only four pairs bred at Askham Bog compared with 32 in 1978; and only 12 birds were caught and ringed at Knaresborough Ringing Station in 1979 compared with 75 in 1980, by which time most areas had recovered.

Birds with abnormal plumage have been recorded on a few occasions. Nelson mentioned 'pale-buff' varieties, an albino from Leeds which went to the Leeds Museum and an entirely black example which was obtained at Almondbury Bank, near Huddersfield, on 14th May 1865. 'Cream-coloured' birds were seen at Scarborough and Selby in January 1897 and 'white' birds at Selby in 1890 and Beverley in 1900. In more recent years, a bird with pigeon-grey plumage was seen by the Reverend K. Ilderton at Harrogate on 31st July 1948. A bird at Mexborough Ings on 1st January 1955 had white wings and outer tail feathers. One with a pure white crown frequented a garden at Burley-in-Wharfedale from October to December 1974.

Although considered to be mainly an insectivorous bird, the Dunnock will readily take seed, especially that which has fallen from bird tables, underneath which it spends much time. It will also eat whole grain in poultry runs and farm-yards, and I have caught several at Knaresborough Ringing Station in traps baited for finches with wheat.

The species is perhaps better known to countrymen as the Hedge Sparrow, and it has attracted several other names in various parts of the county. Dicky Dunnock is in general use, and Cuddy was a common name for it in my youth.

Alpine Accentor
Prunella collaris

During the winter of 1862/63, Mr Alfred Roberts, the Scarborough taxidermist, was offered a string of larks and other small birds by a poor man who had collected them in the area, and among which was an Alpine Accentor. The preserved specimen was purchased by W.W. Boulton of Beverley and later went to the collection of J.H. Gurney of Keswick Hall, Norwich, where William Eagle Clarke inspected it.

There are now about 30 British records of this montane species, which breeds in the mountains of southern and eastern Europe to the Himalayas and beyond, but the above record remains the only one for Yorkshire.

Rufous Bush Robin
Cercotrichas galactotes

While on a visit to Flamborough on 5th October 1972, Mr and Mrs K. Allsopp of Norfolk were fortunate enough to see an example of this species. It was still there the next day and was watched by D.J. Britton and A.J. Wallis, who successfully photographed it as it fed on the short turf (*British Birds*, 1973, p. 346).

This rare visitor from southern Europe, southwest Asia and North Africa was an addition to the Yorkshire list of bird species and only the tenth for the British Isles.

Robin
Erithacus rubecula

It is doubtful if there is a garden in Yorkshire that has not been visited by a Robin at some time or other. This popular and very well-known bird is most confiding and shows little fear of man in the built-up areas where it chooses to make its home. Those birds which nest away from habitation, in woodland, the true home of the species, are less confiding and quite shy and retiring. Only above the tree-limits on the very high ground of the moors and fells along the Pennines is it absent.

Every autumn, during late September or early October, immigrant Robins come across the North Sea, and in some years the numbers are very large and spectacular. Some stay in Yorkshire and others continue their journey to spend the winter farther south in Britain or in France, Iberia and beyond.

Over the years, there have been some large immigrations and Nelson listed several in *The Birds of Yorkshire*. The largest numbers to reach Yorkshire in recent years occurred in the first week of October 1951, when they were seen all along the coastline from the Tees to the Humber. At Teesmouth, 'hundreds' were present during the first few days of the month; 50 were at Cayton Bay on 2nd October and large numbers were at Robin Hood's Bay. At Spurn, the birds were more concentrated and obvious, with counts of 300 on 1st October; 500 on 2nd and 3rd; 300 on 4th and 5th and 100 on 8th, after which numbers fell as birds moved on. Some 600 were caught and ringed during the week, suggesting that the daily sightings were underestimated.

The Continental Robin *Erithacus rubecula rubecula*, which breeds over the whole of Europe, is much yellower on the breast and greyer on the back than the British race, features that can be noticed in the field. The presence of this race was confirmed at Spurn in 1909 by H.F. Witherby, and modern trapping techniques now enable ringers to handle and so diagnose birds every year. On 19th October 1975, 200 were at Spurn and 100 were at Filey, with 20 at Hornsea Mere on 20th and others in evidence at several coastal localities.

A large arrival of Continental Robins took place along the coast during late September and October 1976, when they appeared at Flamborough Head on 11th September and notable arrivals occurred on 17th, 18th and 26th; a second arrival was noted between 25th and 30th October. Spurn had spectacular numbers during the same periods, with 70 on 18th September; 70 to 150 during the period 25th to 27th; 250 on 1st October, most of which dispersed by the middle of the month, but were followed by a big influx on 27th when 300 appeared, increasing to 600 on 28th, 1,000 on 29th and 600 on 30th, whereafter numbers quickly dropped and only 100 remained on 1st November. Other coastal places had large numbers and the movement must have been on a very large scale. Another influx occurred in the autumn of 1979, when counts of 100 to 300 were made at several places along the coast with a maximum count at Spurn of 500 on 1st October. Some birds penetrate to inland localities: over 50 were at Fairburn Ings during late October 1976, some of which, if not all, would have been immigrants; ringing recoveries prove the occurrence of such at inland sites (see below).

Several Yorkshire-ringed Robins have been recovered abroad. Most have concerned birds ringed at Spurn and have come from France, Spain, Portugal, the Balearic Islands, Belgium, the Netherlands, Germany, Italy and Norway. Of the 20 recovered, 17 were ringed in October and three in April, the latter birds being on their return journey. One ringed at Spurn on 1st October 1951 was recovered in Italy on 12th November 1951, and another ringed there on 23rd October 1949 was in central Norway on 7th April 1951. One ringed at Falsterbo, in Sweden, on 24th October 1961 was recovered near Pocklington on 2nd April 1962, and one ringed in Finland on 8th May 1976 was at Melsonby, near Scotch Corner, on 13th December 1976. Speed of movement was indicated by a bird ringed on the Isle of May on 16th October and retrapped at Spurn two days later. An immigrant ringed at Spurn on 9th October 1956 was at Rotherham on 20th February 1957, and another ringed on 2nd October 1979 was found dead at Sheffield on 7th October 1979, proving that some of the winter Robins which appear inland need not necessarily be Yorkshire-bred. Birds recovered abroad, either in their winter quarters or en route, thus include some ringed in Yorkshire on their southward journey in the autumn and others on their northward journey in early spring.

A bird trapped at South Landing on Flamborough Head on 8th April 1978 was slaty blue-grey on the upperparts with a very pale orange breast and a strikingly white belly. The blue-grey of the mantle was much more intense than the greyer colour of the nominate race and P.A. Lassey is of the opinion that this bird could have been referable to the race *Erithacus rubecula tataricus*, which breeds to the north and east of nominate *rubecula*. It stayed in the area for three weeks and was very skulking, behaviour which is exhibited by the immigrant Continental birds along the coast. At least two other Robins showing the very 'blue' upperparts have been seen at this locality.

The variety of nesting sites used by the Robin is well known, those provided by man particularly so. Natural sites are less familiar and are usually in bank sides, on the ground or among tree roots and fallen timber in thick woodland, which is the primitive habitat of the species. A pair at Haxby, near York, built an open nest in a small box bush in both 1950 and 1953, and a young Cuckoo was reared by a pair of Robins there in 1948.

Birds with abnormal plumage are scarce and only one example has been seen in recent years. It concerned a bird with white wings and tail which A. Gordon saw in Bransdale in 1955. Nelson mentioned a white bird in the Tunstall Museum; a juvenile from Knaresborough which had white wing and tail feathers; pale leucistic specimens from Beverley and Patrington; and a few others with white or pale feathers. A pure albino caught at Sedbergh in 1897 was kept alive for two years.

For details of a Robin seen diving regularly into swarms of whirligig beetles at Wike, near Leeds, in 1967, see *The Naturalist*, 1976, p. 76.

The Robin's status is probably unchanged since Nelson wrote in 1907 'Resident, widely distributed and abundant. A regular spring and autumn migrant.'

See also under Bluethroat on page 461.

Thrush Nightingale
Luscinia luscinia

In the evening of 16th May 1967, in Locke Park, Redcar, S.C. Norman and W. Norman watched a bird which they thought was this species because of the lack of rufous in the tail and the dingy breast. It appeared to be very tired and often stumbled and fell over as it fed on the ground among rose bushes. Early next morning, the bird was found dead by S.C. Norman and W.I. Boustead, on the ground near to where it had been seen the previous evening, and the corpse was presented to me for preservation. It was indeed a 'Sprosser', the first for Yorkshire, the eighth for Britain and only the third record outside Fair Isle. It was a female and weighed only 15.75 g, just half the weight of two birds caught in Northumberland in 1965, and so beyond the point of no return, having completely expended its reserves of energy (see plate 100).

The second Yorkshire example occurred at Spurn, when one was caught and ringed on 5th June 1971 and examined in the hand by J. Cudworth and B.R. Spence.

A male occurred on 5th June 1983 at Flamborough Head, where it was watched by A.M. Allport, D.G. Hobson, P.A. Lassey and J.C. Lamplough.

In 1984, there was an unprecedented series of records at Spurn Bird Observatory, starting with one on 23rd May which stayed until 29th. It was caught on the first date and seen in the hand by J. Cudworth, B.R. Spence and G. Thomas, and subsequently in the field by very many observers. Another sang regularly on 25th and 26th May and was seen by J. Cudworth, Mr and Mrs C. Massingham and others, and a third, caught in the Warren trap on 30th May by B.R. Spence, stayed until 2nd June.

Nightingale
Luscinia megarhynchos

In 1766, Pennant wrote of the Nightingale in *British Zoology* (first ed., 1766, p. 100) that 'it is not found in North Wales, or in any of the English counties north of it, except Yorkshire, where they are met with in great plenty about Doncaster'. In his report to the British Association at York in 1844, Thomas Allis said that it bred every year in the wood at Cawood, near York; near Huddersfield; at Cinderfield Dyke Wood in Bradley; that a few pairs could be found near Barnsley every year; it was occasionally heard near Sheffield; occurred at Walton Hall and Bramham Park; and was common near Doncaster in Edlington and other woods.

Nelson devoted no fewer than 17 pages to this exciting species in *The Birds of Yorkshire* in 1907. Towards the end of the nineteenth century, odd pairs of Nightingales bred farther north than known to Allis, and single pairs nested in Gibbet Wood at Staveley, near Boroughbridge, in 1870; a pair reared young in the rectory garden at Staveley in 1881 and a pair bred in the nearby Loftus Fox Covert in 1883.

At the beginning of the present century, the species occurred fairly regularly in

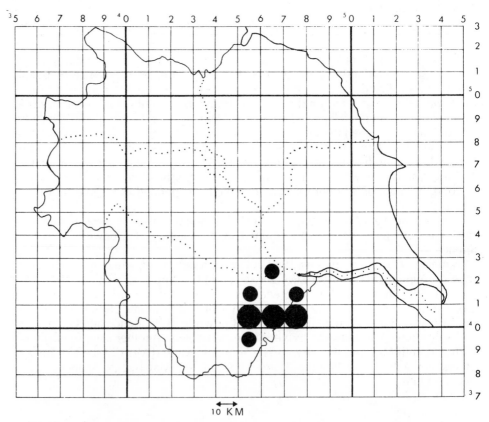

10 KM

Nightingale. A small breeding population persists in the heathland of the south around Hatfield and Thorne.

the lowlands of the southern and southeastern parts of the county circumscribed by a line drawn from Barnsley northwards to Leeds and Harrogate, then eastwards through York, Beverley and to the coast at Hornsea. Nelson wrote in great detail about the distribution in each part of this area and gave the names of every wood or copse and the years in which the bird had occurred or nested, this discourse accounting for 13 of his 17 pages.

Today, the Nightingale still breeds in the county but only in a limited area in the southern part. In 1952, a pair nested near Kippax, and birds sang at Kirkbymoorside and at Wass during most of May and two did so at Roche Abbey. There were a few other records during the 1950s, at Skipwith, Allerthorpe, and Ampleforth College, but by the next decade most had ceased to appear. The Yorkshire breeding population is now confined to a few small areas east of Doncaster where, in 1958, nine singing males were at one locality and seven in another.

Occasionally, a Nightingale will sing for a few days well away from the southern breeding area and in recent years such birds have been heard at Fairburn Ings on 28th April 1971; near Knaresborough in mid May 1973; near York in May 1975; at Harrogate on 28th May 1977; in Bishops Wood, Selby, where two sang in May and June 1980, and again at Harrogate on 19th May 1980; in Bishops Wood on 4th June 1981; and at Naburn, near York, on 18th May 1981.

Migrant birds have occurred at Spurn and Flamborough in several recent years, mainly during the spring and usually single birds, some of which have been caught and ringed. Several occurred in 1977, when one was at Hornsea Mere on 1st May, singles were at Bempton on 6th and 29th May, and three were at Spurn on 28th May. Birds passing along the coast in May often sing and disclose their presence, which would otherwise often go unrecorded.

It is possible that a few sightings of silent Nightingales along the coast in spring have referred to the Thrush Nightingale.

The present status is that of a summer visitor, breeding in very small numbers in a restricted area in the south of the county, with small numbers passing along the coast in spring and occasionally in autumn and a few isolated records of transient birds from inland localities.

Bluethroat
Luscinia svecica

Of the two races of Bluethroat which visit Yorkshire, the Red-spotted *Luscinia svecica svecica* is by far the commoner. Nelson said that the Spurn promontory appeared to be the only district where it could be said to have been actually obtained, and where no fewer than six examples had been procured.

The first record for the county was on 11th September 1882, when W. Eagle Clarke saw two birds near the Spurn lighthouse, one of which was shot (not by Clarke) and sent to Henry Seebohm. The occurrences of 13 others up to 1903 were detailed by Nelson in *The Birds of Yorkshire* and he said that it was probably a regular autumn migrant which was overlooked. He was quite correct in this assumption, for we now know it as an almost annual passage migrant along the Yorkshire seaboard. Chislett listed records in only seven years up to 1952, but it has occurred in every year since then except for 1961.

Numbers vary from year to year; in several, only one bird has been recorded, in others up to ten. The most seen were in 1969, when there were four in the spring and at least 16 birds along the coast during the autumn, and in 1984, when there were at least 15 different birds at Flamborough in the spring.

The majority, about 150, have occurred in the autumn, mainly during September and October, and about 65 have been noted during April and May. Most have been on the Spurn Peninsula, but Flamborough, Bempton, Filey, Scarborough, Teesmouth, and doubtless other places, too, have all had their Bluethroats.

There have been only three inland records of the Red-spotted race, the first being caught at Knaresborough Ringing Station at dawn on 18th September 1971 (see plate 101); one was seen at Fairburn Ings on 12th and 13th October 1975, and one at Hebden Bridge, near Halifax, on 28th May 1984 by T.I. Corbett and R.J. Hirst. The Red-spotted race breeds across northern Europe from Scandinavia to Alaska, and birds visiting the Yorkshire coast are from the western population on their journey to the wintering grounds in the Mediterranean area and into Africa.

The White-spotted race *Luscinia svecica cyanecula* breeds across Europe south of the range of the Red-spotted race, to France and the Balkans eastwards to Asia.

The first occurrence in the county makes interesting reading and I quote from Nelson's *The Birds of Yorkshire*:

'The first known instance of the visitation of this rare migrant to Yorkshire, and to Britain, is that communicated by the late Alfred Roberts of Scarborough. Writing to Mr. W. Eagle Clarke on 1st January 1880, he stated that "a fine female specimen of the Blue-throated Warbler was found dead under the telegraph wires, near Scarborough, by the late John Young, gamekeeper to Lord Londesborough (April 1876). The ovary contained eggs in a forward state. It had a white satiny spot in the centre of the blue throat. The specimen is in the possession of Mrs. Young".'

The example was recorded at the time by the Reverend Julian G. Tuck in *The Zoologist*, 1876, p. 4956, and in *The Field* of 6th May 1876 thus:

'I have much pleasure in recording for the first time in Yorkshire, the occurrence of the Bluethroat, or Blue-throated Warbler. A specimen of this rare little bird which had been picked up dead under the telegraph wires at Seamer, near Scarborough, was taken to Mr. Roberts of Scarborough, on the 12th April. Its head and neck had been considerably damaged from coming in contact with the wires; in addition to which, the man who found it kept it several days, and then carried it to Scarborough in his pocket. Mr. Roberts thought, when he first saw it, that it would be impossible to mount it, but with skilful handling and great patience he has now managed to make it into a very presentable specimen. It is a female bird, in good plumage, and Mr. Roberts told me it contained well developed eggs. The occurrence of this specimen is the more interesting as it is an example of the type which possesses a white spot in the centre of the blue on the throat. (Cf. Yarrell, *British Birds*, 4th Edition, Volume I, p. 323).'

Nelson eventually traced the bird to Mr D. Young, son of the original owner, at Blankney in Lincolnshire, from whom he borrowed it and exhibited it at a meeting of the British Ornithologists' Club in October 1907.

There have since been five other Yorkshire records of this race. The first occurred at Spurn on 6th April 1958, when it was caught and ringed by E.S. Skinner (*The Naturalist*, 1959, pp. 96-8); one was seen at Spurn from 10th to 13th April 1966; a male appeared in the garden of P.D. Kirk, a keen birdwatcher, at Normanton on 25th May 1974; one was at Bempton on 8th June 1975; and a male sang regularly at Blacktoft Sands between 12th and 19th May 1981.

In conclusion, I must draw attention to a record which appeared in *The Naturalist*, 1926, pp. 86-7 and 172, concerning a bird at Scarborough. I quote from Chislett's *Yorkshire Birds*:

'On November 15th 1925, the late W.J. Clarke, at that time Y.N.U. recorder for birds for the North Riding, noticed a small bird skulking in the privet hedge of his Scarborough garden and soon saw it was a Red-spotted Bluethroat. The bird remained in the neighbourhood until April 15th, 1926, although not always in the same garden. Between January 14th and April 4th it appeared almost every day and became very tame, coming fearlessly into the kitchen and eating crumbs off the oilcloth, within four or five feet of the occupants of the room. "It frequently foraged off the lawn and appeared to stand and listen for its prey, suddenly making a little run forward or sideways, and plunging its beak into the ground would draw out a leather-jacket or earthworm. The latter were not swallowed unless very small, even a moderately sized one was thrown to one side. About the middle of March the bird began to moult, the operation being not completed when it left, but the blue of the band on the chest had become considerably brighter." The story was not yet finished, for a Bluethroat, probably the same bird, reappeared on February 1st, 1927, and remained until April 30th.'

A photograph of this bird appears in *The Naturalist* (see reference above) and clearly shows a perfectly normal Robin. Even the bird's habit of entering the kitchen and eating crumbs from the lino smacks of that species, and it is difficult to imagine how someone of Clarke's experience could have been fooled. The notes published at the time say that details of the bird were sent to Riley Fortune, who agreed that it was a Blue-throated Warbler. The most likely explanation is that the bird's plumage was aberrant in that the blue-grey of the lower breast was exaggerated and perhaps there was some blue on the actual breast, but the bird resembled a Bluethroat in no other way and should never have suggested one. I am grateful to J. Cudworth for drawing my attention to the photograph and, while I was having lunch with him in my local wine-bar recently, we showed the photograph to a young waitress and asked what she thought it was. 'I'm no expert' she replied, 'but it looks like a Robin Redbreast to me.' Indeed it does and it is surprising that the mistake has not been spotted before.

Black Redstart
Phoenicurus ochruros

At the turn of the century, the Black Redstart was described by Nelson as an 'Irregular visitant on the coast in spring and autumn; very rare indeed.' I suspect that the last part of this assessment should have read 'very rare inland', as the details published in *The Birds of Yorkshire* do not indicate the rarity implied in that statement; only two inland records were published, however. In *Yorkshire Birds*, Chislett quoted the same assessment and amended it to 'inland' without qualifying the change — perhaps he read it as 'inland'.

Today, it is a regular passage migrant along the coastline in spring and autumn, and inland occurrences are not rare, especially in the south of the county, where birds have been seen fairly regularly in recent years at up to six localities annually and at ten places in 1976. A bird sang from blitzed buildings in Hull from 21st June to 9th July 1949, and on 10th July G.H. Ainsworth saw two birds fly from a high crevice near the High Street but these were not seen again. Later in the autumn, on 25th September, E.M. Nicholson heard two males singing in the same area, one of them delivering its song 13 times in a minute. Singing males occurred annually thereafter, and in May 1952 single birds frequented the area of the Market Place and near the Railway Station, but there was no proof of nesting.

In 1958, a male in full breeding dress was at Sheffield on 18th June. The species was noted in this area again in 1975, when one pair reared two broods and another female deserted three infertile eggs. Males sang at two other nearby localities in the same year. In 1976, two pairs reared young, a third pair occupied territory and other singing males were recorded. At least five pairs were present in the city area in 1977 and breeding has occurred in every year since then, with no fewer than nine pairs in 1979. D. Herringshaw has monitored this very welcome addition to the Yorkshire list of breeding birds in its only regular locality.

A pair nested successfully on the cliffs at Flamborough in 1972 and fledged four young. In 1973, a pair bred in the vent pipe of a tugboat in a Hull dry dock and reared six young, which fledged on 22nd and 23rd June. In 1978, a pair bred in Goole Docks, where young were being fed in June. A male sang in the centre of Huddersfield from 12th to 26th June 1978, with a second bird on 14th June and 6th July, and one sang there from 12th to 21st June 1979. A pair nested and reared young at Thorpe Marsh, near Doncaster, in 1980 and 1981, and a pair reared three young near Filey in 1983.

Most of the relatively numerous inland birds away from the south of the county occur in April and during the autumn, and records come from widespread localities. One was in Sheffield on the very early date of 20th February 1978.

Along the coast, the Black Redstart is a well-known migrant, appearing during late March and passing through during April and early May, with a few birds in evidence up to June in some years. The first birds of autumn usually appear during the second half of September and continue to pass through until, and during, November. One stayed in the Kilnsea area from 7th November 1975 to 1st January 1976. Numbers passing are never large, and only at Spurn have daily counts ever reached double figures as birds bottle-up along the peninsula. Counts of ten or more have been made in only six years, as follows: ten on 16th April 1966; 15 on 19th October 1968; 13 in April 1973; 20 on 16th October 1974, with 15 still present on 20th; 12 in late October 1970; and ten on 14th October 1980.

The species has a very wide breeding distribution from northwest Africa through Iberia and southern England into southern Scandinavia, and eastwards across Continental Europe. The majority spend the winter in North Africa.

The recovery of four ringed Black Redstarts sheds some light on the origin of those passing through Yorkshire. A young bird ringed in Germany on 15th July 1951 was retrapped at Spurn on 27th October 1951; a female ringed at Spurn on 5th April 1958 was found breeding in Germany on 7th May 1958; one ringed at Spurn on 26th October 1971 was found dead in France on 26th November 1972; and a young bird ringed in West Germany on 26th July 1975 was retrapped at Spurn on 1st April 1978.

Save for regular breeding by a few pairs in the extreme south of the county in recent years, which, as in the London area and elsewhere in the south, was almost certainly prompted by the very suitable habitat created by extensive bombing of the larger cities during World War II, the status of the Black Redstart has probably changed but little since Nelson's time.

Redstart
Phoenicurus phoenicurus

The handsome Redstart breeds over much of Yorkshire and is scarce only in the East Riding, particularly in Holderness and along the Vale of Mowbray corridor between the Pennines and the Hambleton Hills. It is most numerous in the wooded gills and cloughs of the Pennines, where it nests up to the heather-line and even out onto the more open upland areas where a few stunted trees provide the habitat necessary, and where it is equally at home in a dry-stone wall as in an old mossy stump along a wooded stream in the foothills. It breeds also in the woods on the flatter country in the plains, though more sparingly than in the hill country.

The first Redstarts of spring usually occur towards the end of the first week of April, but the main influx is not usually until the third week of that month. A bird at Harewood on 31st March 1956 was exceptionally early and well ahead of the next on 14th April. One occurred at Spurn on 31st March 1968.

Passage along the east coast in spring is not often very evident, but small numbers pass every year. A count of 40 Redstarts at Hornsea on 24th April 1971 was the most ever recorded at that season; Spurn had eight on the same day and 12 on 25th.

Autumn passage is much more noticeable, and in some years large numbers occur. A few birds appear during late August, but the main movement is during September and early October, when they may be seen anywhere along the coast-line in small numbers, and in large concentrations on the prominences at South Gare, Scarborough Castle Hill, Filey Brigg, Flamborough Head and Spurn Point, especially when the weather conditions bring the large 'falls' of migrants with easterly winds and rain or mist.

Larger numbers than usual occurred at Spurn in 1957, when the highest daily count was 150 on 21st September. In 1963, 200 appeared on 1st September and the species was very numerous at Flamborough. The most exceptional year was 1969, when a very large fall of migrants occurred during the night of 16th September; next morning, there were no fewer than 1,000 Redstarts at South Gare, 400 at Hornsea Mere and 150 at Spurn, where the numbers increased to 300 the next day, when 520 were also at Scarborough. A second, smaller, wave of birds appeared on 13th and 14th October, when Spurn had 14 birds and a few were seen at other coastal places. Two distinct arrivals occur in most years, sometimes only a few days apart.

In most recent years, the maximum daily counts at Spurn and Flamborough have not exceeded 30-40 birds, except in 1976 when 100 were at Flamborough on 17th September and up to 80 were at Spurn during mid October. A few birds continue to move along the coast up to the end of October and sometimes in early November, the latest being one at Spurn on 13th November 1967 and another on 16th November 1984.

Most inland breeding areas are clear of Redstarts by the end of August, and later birds are probably on passage through the county, when their appearance is often coincident with movement along the coast. A bird was in Kirkstall Road, Leeds, on 4th November 1970 and an exceptionally late individual was at Fairburn Ings on 29th December 1975.

Ringing recoveries shed light on the origins and destinations of the Redstarts which arrive along the east coast every autumn on their journey to the winter quarters in central Africa, and also on those of birds bred in Yorkshire. Three Redstarts ringed as nestlings in June have been recovered in Spain and Portugal, and five ringed while on autumn passage at Spurn have been recovered in Spain (four) and Italy (one). A female ringed at Spurn on 10th June 1964 and found dead at Navarra in Spain on 24th September in the same year poses the question of which way the bird was travelling when ringed at Spurn. Another female ringed at South Gare on 17th September 1969 was recovered in Morocco on 16th October 1969, being only the sixth recovery of a Redstart in that country. A male ringed in Finland on 18th September 1976 was retrapped at Spurn on 4th October 1976, and a female ringed on Öland in Sweden on 23rd September 1979 was at Spurn on 1st October 1979.

A female at Flamborough on 4th October 1976 was very pale greyish-brown above and white below, with a distinct whitish wing panel formed by the edges of the secondary feathers. S.C. Madge considered that it might have been an example of the eastern race *Phoenicurus phoenicurus samamiscus*.

On 2nd July 1944, a true albino was killed by a car near Helmsley, and a few hours later A. Gordon saw another albino near the same place. They were doubt-less juveniles from the same brood and the dead specimen went to the Yorkshire Museum.

The Redstart is thus a fairly common summer visitor to Yorkshire, being most numerous about the hilly parts of the county, and occurs along the coast at times of migration in both spring and autumn, mainly during the latter period.

Whinchat
Saxicola rubetra

The Whinchat was described by Nelson as a 'Summer visitant, common and gener-ally distributed.' Areas of intensive cultivation are not favoured by the species and there are undoubtedly fewer Whinchats now than at the beginning of the present century. It is a familiar bird on some of the higher ground where young forestry exists, such as in Langstrothdale and most other similar localities along the Pennines and on the North York Moors, and is equally at home among the scrub-covered land in the plains and about the carrlands in the south of the county. It is relatively scarce in much of Holderness and on the flat farmland around York and in the Vale of Pickering. A pair nested at Bubwith on the Lower Derwent in 1979, and a pair attempted to do so at Spurn in 1980 for the first time since the observatory was established in 1946.

The main arrival period is during the third week of April, although a few birds are seen earlier in some years. In *Yorkshire Birds*, Chislett listed one on 16th April 1943 as the earliest of which he had note, but omitted a bird at Meltham, near Huddersfield, on 11th April 1949 which he published in the county bird report for that year. Better coverage in recent years has revealed a few earlier records, but such are still scarce before about 16th. Single birds were at Harthill Reservoir on 7th April 1974, Thorne Moor on 8th April 1977, Scalby on 9th April 1975, Hornsea on 10th April 1971 and at Spurn on 11th April 1972. Nelson saw two birds on the Redcar sandhills on the exceptionally early date of 28th March 1906.

Most breeding areas are deserted by the third week of September, but some birds linger on, and a few appear at inland localities on late dates which could be associated with coastal passage. There are several inland records during early October and some later ones have been at Fairburn Ings on 25th October 1959,

Huddersfield on 26th October 1968 and Meltham Wood on 27th October 1974. A Whinchat stayed at Selby from 5th November until 11th December 1975, being caught and ringed by P. Reid on 8th November. One was seen on Thorne Moor on 6th November 1979.

Small parties of up to five or six birds, and sometimes more, often appear at sewage-farms or at gravel-pits and other suitably rough ground during the autumn. Most are juveniles and likely dispersing family parties from higher ground; 20 were counted at Cawood Ings on 20th September 1970.

Autumn passage along the coast may be witnessed from mid August until early October, when small numbers are to be seen from the Teesmouth to Spurn. Most of the regularly watched sites at South Gare, Filey, Flamborough and Spurn record good numbers during late August and September, the latter locality often having relatively large numbers as birds concentrate along the peninsula. The maximum counts there in recent years have been as follows: 75 on 9th September 1958, 50 on 8th September 1959, 70 on 30th August 1966, 50 on 17th September 1969, 50 on 25th August 1971 and 90 on 30th August 1974. In 1980, 57 were at Flamborough Head on 4th September, 78 on 8th, then fewer until a new influx of 50 occurred on 19th, illustrating the fact that, as with some other passage migrants, Whinchats often come in two distinct waves.

Whinchats ringed on migration at Spurn in September (one) and October (three), which probably originated in northern Europe, have been recovered in Spain and Portugal, and one ringed in May 1973 was shot in Spain in October 1974. Three birds ringed as nestlings near Ingleton in June of the years 1914, 1925 and 1931 were recovered in the autumn of the same years in Portugal.

In Rennie's *Field Naturalist* of November 1833, p. 467, is a reference to Whinchats coming on board a vessel some 10 miles (16 km) off the Yorkshire coast opposite Redcliff.

Stonechat
Saxicola torquata

Nelson's summary of the status of this erratic species applies equally well today, except that there are fewer birds than formerly. 'Resident; also summer visitant; locally distributed. The majority leave in autumn, only a few remaining, chiefly near the coast' is how he described it in 1907.

There was no evidence of abundance shown in *The Birds of Yorkshire* and Nelson said that, although the Stonechat was frequently spoken of as a common Yorkshire bird, it could not be considered abundant anywhere and that it was an erratic and puzzling species. Being very much aware of the bird's fluctuating status, he published details of its breeding areas and numbers in some detail. It nested, until 1880, on the 'wild wastes and commons' bordering the moors near Sheffield and also about Huddersfield. In the extreme northwest of the West Riding, it nested near Craven, Settle and Malham and was a fairly common summer visitor in the Clapham area. Three nests with eggs were found on the banks of the River Wharfe near Ilkley in May 1871. A few pairs bred around Leeds, as at Adel Moor, where single pairs nested in 1900 and 1901.

In the Allen manuscript of 1791, it was said to be 'common in summer on the heaths' of the East Riding. Nelson said that a few pairs bred near Scarborough and Whitby and on the Goathland Moors, and he described it as 'numerous' in a certain valley 7-8 miles (c. 12 km) west of Helmsley, which would have been on the edge of the Hambleton Hills. At Hawes it was described as being 'fairly abundant', and it also nested regularly near Sedbergh. In Upper Teesdale and in Cleveland, the Stonechat was scarce, with very few breeding pairs. A few other areas were mentioned as having an occasional breeding pair.

Clearly, there were more breeding Stonechats at the end of the nineteenth century than there are now, and the decrease is not apparently recent as none of Chislett's correspondents were able to describe the Stonechat as other than 'scarce' or 'rare' and breeding records were very few during the early part of the present century. Chislett listed all the breeding records between 1906 and 1950, during which period one, and occasionally two, pairs nested in about 18 of those years, and mainly during the period 1929 to 1950, which probably reflected as much as anything else the mobility of observers through improved transport.

A pair feeding young near Gouthwaite Reservoir in June 1952 marked the end of a run of breeding, after which time none was known to nest until 1966, when single pairs did so at Harrogate and near Leeds; at the latter locality breeding also occurred in 1967. Single pairs bred on Ellerby Moor and Sawley Moor in 1968. One pair at Yateholme in 1972 was the next proven record, after which a run of breeding occurred similar to that during the 1940s and 1950s. After single pairs on Rombald's Moor and in Ribblesdale in 1973, breeding occurred in 1974 at four sites in the southwest and at Jugger Howe, near Scarborough. An increase followed in 1975, when eight pairs bred in the western part of the county, mainly in the southwest; two broods were reared by a pair on Barden Moor, where F.A. Wardman had seen nine males and six females on 2nd February; two pairs bred on Ilkley Moor; and a recently fledged juvenile was at Filey on 19th July. Six pairs bred in the west in 1976 and one pair had three juveniles at Scalby Mills in June. Breeding in 1977 occurred at Scammonden, near Halifax (two pairs), and in three places in the Settle area at Swarth Moor, Whelpstone Crag and Sandy Dyke. A juvenile near the Warren Cottage at Spurn on 19th June 1977 was a most interesting record as none was known to have bred in the area.

The species is primarily a bird of the West Country and thus Yorkshire is not likely to have any permanent increase in its breeding population.

During the non-breeding season, the Stonechat is more in evidence and single birds, or sometimes two, may be seen both inland and on the coast at any time from August to April. The majority are along the Pennine foothills or on the coastal strip, where there is some suggestion of passage. On 23rd October 1976, two were seen flying in over the sea at Filey with immigrant thrushes. In 1974, Spurn had 11 on 28th September, 18 on 29th, 13 on 30th, 15 on 5th October, 19 on 8th, 12 on 19th and ten on 2nd November, and there were up to ten birds along the beach area at Great Cowden, near Hornsea, during October to December. More than usual occurred along the coast in 1975, the first of the influx being five birds at Flamborough on 20th October, followed by eight at Filey on 21st. Spurn had several birds during the same period, with 15 on 27th October and eight to nine during the period 20th to 22nd December. Coincident with this coastal influx were several inland records, some of which were the first Stonechats for 20 years in some areas.

Gatherings of more than just a few Stonechats are very rare inland; nine at Tophill Low Reservoir on 27th February 1972, seven near York on 22nd September 1977, and an unprecedented record of 15 birds on Barden Moor on 2nd February 1975 (see above) are especially worthy of note.

It is clear that several Stonechats spend the winter in Yorkshire and there are several records during that period in most years. The species has a wide, but discontinuous distribution, throughout Europe from Iberia eastwards through southern Russia and Asia Minor, in northeastern Russia across Asia and Japan, throughout the Himalayas and Burma, and also in Africa.

During the last ten years, there have been several records of Stonechats showing the characters of the races from the Continent and from farther east. The first concerned a bird which stayed at Wintersett Reservoir from 19th to 24th October 1976 and which J.S. Armitage caught and ringed on 22nd, when he diagnosed it as belonging to one of the eastern races *Saxicola torquata maura* or *S.t. stejnegeri* from northeast Russia and western Asia. Other examples from this region have been recorded at Flamborough on 1st May 1978, 25th May 1978, 18th and 19th October and from 21st to 31st October 1981 (see plate 102), from 13th to 23rd October 1982 and from 8th to 10th June 1984; and at Spurn on 25th October 1980, 2nd November 1980, and during November and December 1984. Examples of the Continental race *Saxicola torquata rubicola* have occurred at Spurn on 20th and 21st March 1976, 2nd April 1977 and 14th and 15th April 1979; and at Flamborough on 29th and 30th March 1980.

Wheatear
Oenanthe oenanthe

The earliest published reference to the Wheatear as a Yorkshire bird was by E. Blyth, who stated that, on 17th September 1837, when on a voyage northward from London, and about 10 miles (16 km) from Redcliff, Cayton Bay, on the Yorkshire coast, several Wheatears alighted on the vessel; they all left on the first night after their appearance (Rennie's *Field Naturalist*, November 1837, p. 467).

In 1844, Thomas Allis said that it was becoming scarcer than it was formerly, a process which Chislett considered had no doubt continued to some extent. It is, however, still a fairly common breeding bird over much of the high ground of the Pennines from Sheffield in the south to Upper Teesdale in the north, and also on the hills of the northeast in Cleveland and to a lesser extent on the North York Moors, and wherever stony ground occurs a pair or two can usually be found. It is scarce on the chalk Wolds, where an occasional pair may linger into the summer and where H.O. Bunce located four breeding pairs in the vicinity of Millington, near Pocklington, in 1957. A male spent the summer of 1980 on Coatham Marsh, and a pair reared young at Wilton in Teesmouth in 1982. At Flamborough on 17th July 1977, D.I.M. Wallace saw a 'fluffy' juvenile but there was no sign of any adult birds. In the following year, another very young juvenile appeared on 9th July which the same observer could only conclude was of local origin. In 1979, a pair of birds held territory in the same area and both were watched entering a nesting hole; the male performed song flights up to the end of May and a juvenile was seen on 12th July. S.M. Lister watched a pair at Kilnsea, near Spurn, on 11th June 1978, the male of which performed distraction display, but subsequent visits revealed no proof of successful breeding. Chislett mentioned seeing in 1938 a female enter a rabbit hole, carrying a feather, on Hatfield Chase, where a few pairs used to breed. Although an occasional pair may nest by the side of a gravel-pit or on similarly rough ground in relatively low country or along the coast, the Wheatear is most typically a bird of the barren Yorkshire moors, where it frequents the dry-stone walls and rocky outcrops.

One of the earliest migrants to arrive, there are very few years when the Wheatear has not made an appearance before the middle of March. The earliest have been at Sedbergh on 2nd March 1959; at Eccup Moor on 2nd March 1966; and an exceptionally early bird at Malham on 25th February 1968 which was well ahead of the next, at Middleton Moor on 13th March. In 1957, there were no fewer than 45 records of Wheatears in March, the first being seen by C.E. Andrassy at Fairburn Ings on 3rd. In contrast, only one March bird was seen in 1975, at Houndkirk Moor on 30th.

Although the forerunners occur in March, the main arrival does not usually take place until early April. Large numbers also pass along the coast during that month, and into May, and the major watchpoints at Spurn, Flamborough, Filey, Scarborough and South Gare usually record concentrations of up to 30-40 birds in most years and more in some. On 7th May 1976, 200 Wheatears were counted between South Gare Breakwater and Redcar, and 176 were at Flamborough on 12th April 1980. In 1978, a notable spring passage occurred, when birds were evident all along the coastline: Spurn had 38 on 1st May, on which date 55 were at Filey; 60 were at Flamborough on 2nd, increasing to 75 on 3rd and 120 by 7th; and 34 were on Hollym Carrs on 8th. Birds were in the area throughout the first half of May, before they all moved on.

Large numbers on passage at inland sites are not common, but in 1977 22 were at Wath Ings during the morning of 30th April, increasing to 50 in the afternoon, and these were still present the next day.

Passage during the autumn is much more noticeable and some large numbers are often seen. Birds pass along the coast from early July until October, the main period being during September. When such migration is in progress, Wheatears· may be seen anywhere along the coast from the Tees to the·Humber in numbers varying from year to year. Peak counts have been 250 at Spurn from 3rd to 9th September 1958; 160 there from 1st to 5th September 1963, when exceptional

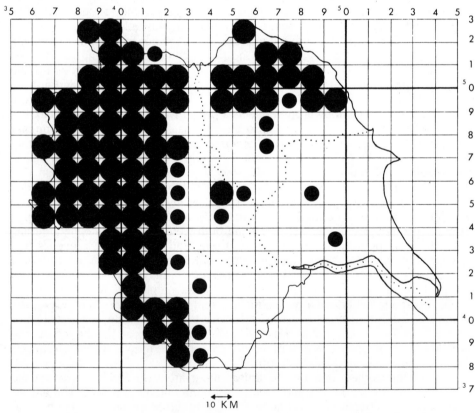

Wheatear. Generally distributed on the high ground of the Pennines and North York Moors, with a tendency in recent years for an occasional pair to breed at lowland gravel-pits.

numbers were also at Flamborough and Bempton; 250 at Spurn on 29th August 1966; and 200 at Hornsea on 16th September 1969, in which year the migration was also noted in strength at Spurn (100 birds on 17th and 150 next day), at Scarborough (200 on 18th) and at South Gare (200 on 17th).

Nelson referred to '. . . a large race or variety, of a richer buff colour and with longer legs, which is more arboreal in habits than the ordinary form, that occasionally passes through in spring'. Great numbers were seen at Spurn and Flamborough in 1893, and it was noted on the high moors near Bradford after the nesting birds had arrived. Such is the description and habit of the Greenland Wheatear *Oenanthe oenanthe leucorrhoa*, which we now recognise every year in both spring and autumn. Birds about lowland fields in May are usually of this race, as are those passing late in the spring along the coastline. Such birds passed almost daily at Spurn during May 1979, and 26 were at Flamborough on 10th May 1981. Fewer are detected during the autumn. A bird found dead at Paull on 4th May 1959 was sent by B.S. Pashby to A. Hazelwood of the Bolton Museum, who ascribed it to the race *Oenanthe oenanthe schioleri*, which breeds in Iceland and the Faeroes. A male which I received from Spurn on 15th September 1965 was also of this race.

Most breeding areas are deserted by the middle of August, but some birds linger on into September and the species may be seen on passage at inland sites throughout October and sometimes into November. Single birds were at Topcliffe on 24th November 1960, at Oxenhope Moor on 7th November 1970 and at Royd Moor on 10th November 1979.

Along the coast, November birds are more frequent. They have occurred in 14 years between 1957 and 1984, the latest being on 29th at Filey Brigg.

Recoveries of ringed birds have revealed nothing new about the routes taken by the Wheatear to its winter quarters on the African savannas. A young bird ringed in June 1924 was recovered in France in September 1924; a migrant ringed at Spurn on 7th September 1956 was in Spain on 8th September 1957; a nestling ringed at Appletreewick on 7th June 1965 was at Cadiz in Spain on 7th September 1965; and a migrant ringed at Spurn on 21st May 1973 was shot in Morocco on 4th October 1973.

A leucistic bird was seen at Wath Ings on 31st August 1975, and Nelson listed several examples of birds with abnormal plumage.

The proliferation of unsuspecting birdwatchers still roaming the moors, eagerly hoping for the sight of an early Wheatear in spring, belies the belief in some parts of North Yorkshire that to see or hear one foretells the death of the observer.

Black-eared Wheatear
Oenanthe hispanica

H.B. Hewetson saw a bird at Spurn on 18th September 1892 which he identified as this species (*The Zoologist*, 1892, p. 424, 1895, p. 57; and *The Naturalist*, 1893, p. 7, 1897, p. 201). J. Cordeaux published the record in his *Birds of the Humber District* (1899, p. 2) and it was included in *The Handbook* under the western race *Oenanthe hispanica hispanica*.

On 6th June 1915, W.S. Medlicott watched a male wheatear on the Cleveland Hills at ranges down to 15 yards for three hours. It was almost pure white except for black wings, throat and central tail feathers. The bird sang a shorter, sweeter and more guttural song than the common Wheatear and was more active and restless. Medlicott examined skins in the South Kensington Museum and said that one or two were exactly like the bird he saw (*British Birds,*1915, pp. 122-3). This record was included in *The Handbook* under the eastern race *Oenanthe hispanica melanoleuca.*

Desert Wheatear
Oenanthe deserti

Five examples of this rare bird have occurred in Yorkshire, the first being in 1885 when one was obtained between Easington and Kilnsea on 17th October. The specimen was identified by William Eagle Clarke and exhibited by H.E. Dresser at a meeting of the Zoological Society. The specimen, a female, was in the collection of J.H. Gurney, and was subsequently ascribed to the western race *Oenanthe deserti homochroa* (*Proceedings of the Zoological Society*, 1885, pp. 835-6; and *The Ibis*, 1886, p. 100).

A Desert Wheatear frequented the area around Gorple Reservoir, near Halifax, from 12th November 1949 to 22nd January 1950. It was first reported by J. Crossley, the reservoir keeper, and was subsequently seen by C.A. Mitchell, P. Andrews and R. Crossley, three young members of the Halifax Scientific Society. They made detailed notes and sketches, from which G.R. Edwards was able to say that it was one of the races of the Desert Wheatear. On 9th January 1950, Edwards, together with R.F. Dickens and P.E. Davis, managed to catch it in a trap baited with worms and took notes of its plumage and photographed it in the hand. Owing to the grimy state of its plumage, it was not possible to determine the race to which it belonged. During its stay, it was watched by several people, including R.S.R. Fitter and P.A.D. Hollom — a well-twitched bird indeed. (*British Birds*, 43, pp. 179-83 and plates 34-36)

The third Yorkshire record came from the same locality as the first: the Humber bank between Easington and Kilnsea, where, on 16th April 1962, following two days of strong northeasterly winds, G.R. Naylor saw an unfamiliar wheatear and observed it for 20 minutes. From his field notes and sketches, he eventually identified it as a Desert Wheatear and summoned P.J. Mountford, then the warden at the Spurn Bird Observatory, G.R. Edwards and R.F. Dickens, who all saw the bird and agreed on its identity. It was identified as belonging to the western race *homochroa*, which breeds from the Nile, westwards across North Africa to Morocco. It remained in the area until 19th April, and was seen by many people and photographed by J.C.H. Leeson. (*The Naturalist*, 1962, p. 146)

On 29th November 1974, a wheatear was seen on the beach at Fraisthorpe, south of Bridlington, and subsequently identified as a Desert Wheatear by G. Brown, R.G. Hawley and D.I.M. Wallace. It remained in the area for the next three days, but could be found only during the early mornings.

J.C. Lamplough watched one at Flamborough Head for 20 minutes on 3rd May 1984, and later for an hour with G.A. Speck. This record has not yet been submitted to the *British Birds* Rarities Committee for consideration.

Rock Thrush

Monticola saxatilis

In June 1852, a Mr T. Bedlington of Middlesbrough followed a bird which he did not know along the clifftops for about 2 miles (3.2 km) and often got within a dozen yards of it by creeping behind hedges. It was thrush-like in its movements, but slightly smaller in size. He was able to identify it 'in a moment' after seeing the coloured figure in Morris's *British Birds*. Nelson concluded his chapter on the event that, with such a showy species, there could be no reasonable doubt as to Bedlington's identification. Chislett agreed with this, but the editors of *The Handbook of British Birds* square bracketed 'one said to have been seen near Whitby'. Such an ancient record can never really be proved, or discounted, in the absence of the specimen but, if one takes all the available details into account, it is possible to form an opinion: the time of year was correct, eight of the ten British records having occurred during May and June; and, as stated by Nelson and Chislett, this conspicuous and colourful species would be easy to identify from a coloured plate, after being fairly closely watched over 2 miles.

A second example occurred on 17th May 1969, at Knowlson's Drop on Sutton Bank crags, near Thirsk. C.F. Clapham watched the bird in the morning and was able to get excellent views through binoculars as it perched on bushes and then on the actual cliff face, from where it made sallies to catch flying insects. He returned in the evening and relocated it, again having good views as it flew about the cliff face, before finally disappearing over the top. It was a male in perfect plumage and was the tenth British record. Another male had been seen at Salthouse Heath in Norfolk ten days previously. The habitat at Sutton Bank is absolutely perfect for this species, and very reminiscent of the crags and slopes where I have watched it in the French Alps and in Yugoslavia.

On 3rd May 1984, a male was located at 19.30 hours near the caravan site at Kilnsea by V. Grantham. It was caught the next day and examined in the hand by B.R. Spence, G. Thomas and Grantham, and was later seen in the field by about 30 other observers.

White's Thrush

Zoothera dauma

Nelson cites six records of this species, one of which, from near Huddersfield in 1864, he suggests is not a genuine Yorkshire specimen.

The first generally, if not wholeheartedly, accepted example, which Canon Atkinson claims to have watched on his lawn at Danby-in-Cleveland in the spring of 1870 and detailed in *Forty Years in a Moorland Parish*, p. 328, must remain in some doubt. It is one of only two of the 33 British records that have occurred outside the period September to January and, although Professor Alfred Newton, in his edition of Yarrell, said 'this well-known observer is hardly likely to have been mistaken', there is no real evidence on which to evaluate the claim. In my opinion the record is too much out of character, both in temporal and in behavioural terms, to be acceptable; perhaps it was simply a Mistle Thrush, which a large spotted thrush on a lawn in spring is most likely to be.

Four others have occurred. One hit wires at Whitby in November 1878 and the specimen went to the Whitby Museum; one was shot in November 1881 near Withernsea and went to the Yorkshire Museum; one was obtained near Pocklington in early January 1882 (*The Zoologist*, 1882, p. 74); and one was 'taken' at Halifax in December 1902 and sent to the Halifax Museum. A photograph of the last bird appears in Nelson's *The Birds of Yorkshire*, opposite page 12.

The only record in recent times occurred at Felixkirk, near Thirsk, on 18th December 1976, when a bird was seen with Fieldfares by B. Lavery. It fed on short grass with the other thrushes and spent some time sheltering under the surrounding hedges. Full details were supplied and the record was accepted by both the Yorkshire Naturalists' Union and *British Birds* Rarities Committees.

Ring Ouzel
Turdus torquatus

It is doubtful if the status of the Ring Ouzel has changed at all since Nelson wrote in 1907 'Summer visitant, locally distributed; also a transient visitant in spring and autumn.' Chislett commented that the increased disturbance on the lonely moors by hikers and others was not to the species' liking and there may have been some reduction in numbers. Such intrusion on the birds' privacy is usually of a brief nature and I doubt if it has made any significant difference.

The earliest reference to the species in connection with Yorkshire was made by Martin Lister of York in a letter to John Ray dated 2nd July 1676, where he said: 'As to that question of a Heath Throstle, I find that the Ring Ousel is so called with us in Craven, where there is everywhere on the moors, plenty of them.'

In the early part of the present century, William Talbot found 13 nests during a walk from Hebden Bridge to Todmorden, a distance of about 2 miles (3.2 km); G.R. Edwards found 13 nests in the Halifax area in 1944, and J.P. Utley found 16 pairs in one area of Swaledale in 1945. A survey of 13 square miles (34 km²) of the Howgill Fells in 1937 revealed a total of 18 pairs. An apparently authentic record of one nesting in a peat drain on the low-lying Thorne Moor was published in *The Zoologist*, 1843, p. 144.

The first Ring Ouzels usually appear on the moors during the third week of March, but the main influx is often not until early April. In some years, the first bird is recorded during the second week of March, and some earlier individuals are seen in some years. One was seen on Barden Moor on 22nd February 1959, and Miss M. Dalby saw two on Burley Moor on 15th February 1965. A bird at Crosshills, near Keighley, from 18th to 20th January 1977 was quite exceptional. One was at South Gare on 3rd March 1960. The Ring Ouzel does not often occur in lowland areas during the spring arrival period, except along the coast, and the birds make straight for the upland breeding areas. During the autumn, however, a few single birds are located at lowland sites during September and October.

Moorland flocks are scarce, and 25 on Moughton Fell on 25th August 1980 and 45 on Ilkley Moor on 17th September 1980 are interesting records. These were no doubt birds of local origin collecting together prior to migration.

Most birds have left the moors by mid September, although a few linger on or call in at Yorkshire moorlands on their migration from farther north. October records are not unusual and occur in most years, with an occasional bird in November. Single Ring Ouzels were at Osset on 15th November 1965 and on 5th November 1979; Baildon on 15th November 1966; Fairburn Ings on 19th November 1967; North Rigton on 6th November 1976; Lower Barden Moor from 27th November to 4th December 1976; and Burbage Moor from 16th November to 9th December 1979; one was in Colsterdale on 6th December 1982. Nelson mentioned three winter records: at Holmfirth on 25th December 1855, at Oxenhope on 2nd February 1856 and at Leeds in December 1881.

Migrants pass along the coast in fluctuating numbers during both spring and autumn. In 1976, six Ring Ouzels were seen flying in over the sea at Filey on 23rd October and birds were in evidence at other coastal places during the next few days, with an exceptional count of 61 at Flamborough on 30th October. In early May 1978, an unusually heavy passage occurred, with 18 at Flamborough on 1st and 52 the next day; most departed overnight and only 15 remained on 3rd. The species was also more in evidence than usual at Spurn during the same period. A bird at Filey on 24th August 1970 was unusually early for one to be wandering on the coast, whatever its origin.

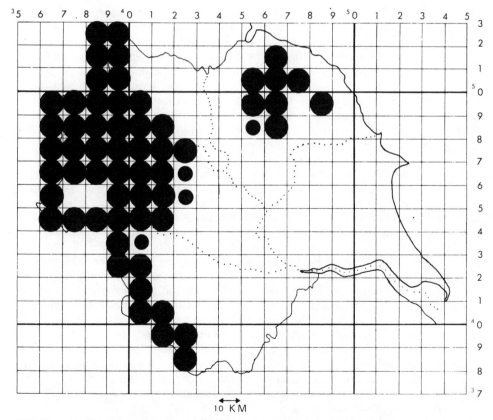

Ring Ouzel. A characteristic, albeit a shy bird of moorland gills and cloughs of the Pennines and North York Moors. The two blank squares in the west contain Stocks Reservoir in the Forest of Bowland and the wide pastureland of the Ribble Valley.

Late individuals are seen along the coast in most years. There have been several records up to 10th November, and a very late individual was at Spurn on 23rd November 1969. One at East Park, Hull, on 3rd December 1969 was doubtless an immigrant too.

One ringed in Belgium on 27th April 1978 and retrapped at Spurn on 30th April in the same year was the first foreign-ringed Ring Ouzel to be recovered in Britain. There are several recoveries abroad of Ring Ouzels ringed in Yorkshire, both as nestlings and as migrants. Seven ringed as nestlings have been recovered on migration in Spain and France, and six migrants ringed at Spurn during the spring and autumn passage periods have been recovered in Spain, France, Italy and Morocco, the last two being only the third recoveries in those countries at the time.

The Heath Throstle, as the Ring Ouzel was known in the Craven district during the seventeenth century, is one of the most familiar birds of the barren Yorkshire moorlands, although its shy and retiring manner often prevents its detection by the casual observer.

Blackbird

Turdus merula

The Blackbird is a common resident over the whole of Yorkshire. Large numbers of immigrants arrive along the coastline every autumn from late September to November, many of which eventually pass through to winter in France and Spain, but some spend the winter months in the county. In some years, many thousands arrive along our seaboard, and at migrational focal points, such as at Spurn, Flamborough, Filey and Teesmouth, the arrivals are often spectacular as birds drop from the sky to rest and feed in the coastal bushes, or are seen struggling in low over the sea. Much migration is undertaken during the hours of darkness, when their thin calls may be heard overhead, especially in foggy conditions, after which a dawn inspection of the area will often reveal the coastal bushes to be 'heaving' with birds.

The peak period of arrival is during October, when up to 1,000 Blackbirds have been counted, or estimated, on the Spurn Peninsula on some days. The largest influx on record occurred in 1961: after an arrival on 20th October, when Spurn had 1,000 birds and smaller numbers were evident at other coastal places, tremendous numbers came in on 5th November. Bird-ringers at Spurn caught 647 Blackbirds during the day and immigration was in progress from dawn till dusk, the estimated number involved being calculated at between 15,000 and 19,000. The migrants quickly dispersed inland and an increase was noted at several places on the Wolds and elsewhere. Farther north at Redcar, the first wave was noted on 22nd October; D.R. Seaward described the events there as the largest influx he had ever witnessed and said 'During the first part of the morning, which was grey but with high cloud cover, birds were passing over very high as occasionally a flock of mixed thrushes would drop into the fox covert. About 1100 hours, the cloud lowered and rain started. In the next hour, about 800 Blackbirds came in off the sea on a mile front. This continued for another hour and then decreased as the weather improved.' Such is the setting for the best arrivals to take place and when they are seen to advantage.

At Spurn, on 7th October 1977, 1,000 Blackbirds arrived, 600 of which flew straight inland without stopping. The most spectacular 'falls' occur during misty or rainy conditions, which force the birds down as soon as they see the coast from

474

dawn onwards. On 19th November 1972, such conditions prevailed and large numbers dropped in along the coastline. At Scarborough, R.H. Appleby reported that they were 'falling like leaves from a full overcast sky, in rain with a gale-force south wind ... 30 dropped, then 40 ... the harbour area was covered with them'. Many inland localities have a noticeable increase during the days following such large arrivals. For details of 282 birds caught at Spurn on 6th November 1954 during a period of thrush immigration, see *The Naturalist*, 1955, pp. 3-4.

In spring, returning migrants are less evident along the coast, but occur from March to May in small numbers. I have watched Blackbirds at Knaresborough Ringing Station on some early April evenings fly high into the sky and head off eastwards, and have been convinced that these are Continental birds leaving for the coast and thence onward. Coastal observers note this behaviour regularly during the spring.

There are many foreign recoveries of Blackbirds ringed in Yorkshire, and several recoveries in the county of birds ringed abroad. All the birds recovered abroad were presumed winter visitors, ringed here during the non-breeding season. They have been recovered in Finland, Norway, Sweden, Denmark, Belgium, Holland, France, Spain, Germany, Poland (one), Latvia (one) and Italy (one), the last being only the second recovery of a British-ringed Blackbird from that country at the time. One ringed at Thornaby-on-Tees on 1st March 1955 was recovered at Kalningrad in the USSR on 13th April 1955.

Recoveries showing speed of movement came from birds ringed at Spurn on 6th November 1954 and found dead in Germany on 10th November 1954; at Huddersfield on 19th March 1972 and retrapped in Norway on 26th March 1972; and at Spurn on 30th April 1974 and retrapped in Norway on 6th May 1974.

There are several recoveries in Yorkshire during the autumn and winter months of birds ringed abroad as nestlings or as adults on the breeding grounds in Germany, Holland, Denmark, Sweden and Finland.

Ringing has shown that some Blackbirds live for up to seven or eight years. One ringed at Heslington, near York, on 11th May 1933 was found dead there in 1948, having reached an exceptional age.

During the winter months, Blackbirds roost communally, sometimes in large numbers. In 1962, for example, at Farnley Park, near Leeds, 656 were counted as they entered a roost, and in the same year a roost at Newmillerdam built up during November until it held 'hundreds' each night in December. A roost at Primrose Valley, near Filey, had 300 birds on 7th December 1975. A large stand of rhododendrons at Creskeld Hall, near Leeds, held a roost of 500 birds during January to March 1975. The largest roost on record in Yorkshire was at Otley Plantation, near Leeds, from October 1974 to March 1975, when up to 3,000 Blackbirds attended nightly. In 1981, 700 roosted in the grounds of York University during January and 400 during December, and near Headingley 500 birds were also present during January and February.

Large concentrations away from such roosts are scarce, but two are worthy of mention. P.V. Irving counted 150 on a freshly manured field near Knaresborough on 22nd December 1975, and E.C. Sterne saw 100 males in a field near Gouthwaite Reservoir on 22nd February 1958.

At Goldsborough Dam, near Knaresborough, on 29th June 1952, I watched a juvenile Blackbird catching minnows in shallow water in the River Nidd. It caught them as they moved over a flat mossy stone and swallowed 11 in 15 minutes. An adult Song Thrush also caught two, which it carried to a wall and bashed before swallowing. A similar incident was witnessed at Ramsgill in Upper Nidderdale in 1949, when a Blackbird alighted on a stone in the river and caught a minnow.

Blackbirds with abnormal plumage are seen regularly and too numerously to be detailed. Nelson listed several pied and pure white specimens. In more recent years pure white birds, often with dark eyes indicating that they are not true albinos, have been recorded from several parts of the county. Piebald specimens are relatively common, especially in suburbia, some birds having just one or two white feathers.

The Blackbird is by nature a forest bird that has adapted to the ever-increasing suburban environment with some advantage; many males, however, are killed by traffic during the spring, when rivals chase each other across busy roads. It is undoubtedly one of the most familiar birds of the Yorkshire countryside. It can be found breeding in all habitats from large city parks or factory buildings to the remotest gills or cloughs along the Pennines, where it may share its territory with the Ring Ouzel.

Eye-browed Thrush
Turdus obscurus

On 16th April 1981, A. Johnson saw an unusual thrush with several Redwings in a paddock at Aldborough in the East Riding. He suspected that it was an Eye-browed Thrush, and on the following day he discussed the bird with B. Porter while the two men were fishing on the beach; after going to see it, Porter agreed with Johnson about its identity. They phoned J.E.S. Walker at Hornsea and told him of their find. During the next few days, it was seen every time they passed the paddock, and Johnson got as near as 10 feet (3 m) from it while feeding his geese.

They phoned Walker again and he eventually went to the site and was able to take several photographs of the bird, which unfortunately did not come out. I. Procter and W.F. Curtis were contacted, but the thrush was not there when they looked for it in the afternoon of 23rd. D.I.M. Wallace visited the paddock that evening and was fortunate enough to locate it, again feeding with Redwings; he made several sketches during the hour that he watched.

The weather on that last evening was very clear before a blizzard, and the bird was not seen again. It was a new species for the Yorkshire list of birds and only the fifth for the British Isles; another one occurred at Newburgh in Grampian on 27th May in the same year.

The species breeds from Siberia eastwards into Asia, and winters in Burma, China, Malaya and across the Philippines to Indonesia.

Fieldfare
Turdus pilaris

Every autumn, from the second week of August, but mainly from the middle of October, large numbers of Fieldfares visit Yorkshire from northern Europe, when flocks may be seen heading purposefully westwards over the county. Numbers vary annually, some years producing spectacular flocks and others having only moderate numbers which trickle through less obviously. The most marked arrivals occur during periods of easterly winds, and the weather dictates whether they come across at leisure and pass straight over the coast, or struggle in low above the sea and are forced to seek rest and shelter in the coastal bushes. The sea buckthorn along the Spurn Peninsula often plays host to hordes of tired Fieldfares, which may feed on the berries for several days before moving on.

The largest immigration ever witnessed in the county occurred in 1972. A few birds arrived early, and one was seen at Spurn from 22nd to 25th July with up to six from 27th July to the end of August. Three birds were seen at Gouthwaite Reservoir on 2nd August, and one at Seamer Gravel-pit and two at Hornsea Mere on 28th. Spurn then had Fieldfares almost daily during September, and a flock of 40 passed over Gouthwaite Reservoir on 2nd of that month. This vanguard was to herald a most spectacular movement of Fieldfares. The first ones occurred on 12th October, with a fairly heavy movement during the weekend of 14th/15th when 2,200 passed over Swinsty Reservoir on 15th and several flocks of up to 900 were seen in the south of the county. This early movement was to be completely overshadowed by a great influx on 21st and 22nd; during that weekend, but mainly on the first date, huge flocks passed westward over most of the county, but strangely were not seen by observers along the coast. Such large numbers could not have come in unde- tected and it is difficult to understand why they were not noted at coastal points, as the movement was in evidence over the whole length of the county from Teesdale to the Doncaster area. At Gouthwaite Reservoir in Upper Nidderdale, P.J. Carlton watched from 08.00 hours to 17.00 hours and estimated that 16,000 birds passed westward; and at Knaresborough Ringing Station, where the observation tower was manned from dawn till dusk, no fewer than 23,880 were counted on a mile-wide front, the last flock, of 500 birds, passing just on dark. The movement was still in progress on the following day, but at reduced strength, and 9,000 passed over the Knaresborough tower. A second influx took place in early November, and, in con- trast, the largest numbers were seen along the coast at Spurn, where 13,000 came in over the sea on 4th and continued westward without stopping. Several inland observers recorded this second movement, the largest counts being on 5th, when there were maximum counts of 3,000 over Knaresborough Ringing Station, 1,486 over Swillington Ings and 2,360 over Thorne Moor. Large numbers were not much in evidence in Yorkshire during the winter months, suggesting that the majority had continued westward, probably into Ireland.

To list flock sizes in other years is not necessary, except to say that daily counts along the coast when birds are arriving may reach up to 1,000 or 2,000 on several days in October and November. Similarly large gatherings can be seen over much of the county during the same periods when they feed along the hawthorn hedges or on pastureland. Such inland concentrations are often of a temporary nature before the flocks move on. Severe weather, especially if there is snow cover, forces many Fieldfares to move as they search for food, and large straggling flocks are a common sight at such times.

A return movement takes place each spring. During April and early May, flocks pass through the county, but never in such numbers as are witnessed during their arrival in the autumn. Although the majority have left Yorkshire by mid May, some stragglers are seen into early June, both along the coast and inland. Single birds were at Spurn on 21st June 1967 and on 10th and 24th June 1972; Great Cowden, near Hornsea, on 24th June and up to 7th July 1969; South Cave on 16th June 1973; in the Rivelin Valley on 14th June 1975; and at Howell Wood on 18th June 1980.

Single birds on Thorne Moor on 20th July 1968 and 7th July 1973, near Sheffield on 24th July 1973 and at Tophill Low Reservoir on 28th July 1978 may have been connected with the occasional breeding attempts in the southwest of the county in some recent years. A pair of Fieldfares spent the summer on the moors of the southwest in 1974, and again in 1976 when they successfully reared young. A pair summered in the Washburn Valley in 1978, but breeding was not proved, and it is possible that a pair bred near Huddersfield in 1982 and 1983.

The Fieldfare roosts on high ground in long heather or in young conifer plantations, and large numbers assemble at such places, especially during the periods of arrival and departure.

A Fieldfare ringed at Ossett on 29th December 1961 was recovered in France on 2nd January 1962; and three birds ringed at Spurn in August, November and January have been recovered in Austria (January), Greece (February) and Yugoslavia (January), the last being only the second recovery of a British-ringed Fieldfare in that country. One ringed at Middlestown, near Huddersfield, on 11th February 1967 was in Greece in 1974. Nine birds ringed during the breeding season in Norway (four), Sweden (three) and Finland (two) have been recovered in Yorkshire during the autumn and winter months. A bird ringed at Rossington on 23rd February 1963 was shot at Stockholm on 18th May 1965.

Nelson knew of several pied specimens, and a light buff-coloured Fieldfare was seen at Wakefield in 1873. A bird at Knaresborough Ringing Station on 11th April 1975 had all-white wing-coverts and underparts, and another almost all-white individual was at Hunmanby on 26th October 1973. One at Flamborough on 26th October 1980 had the head and body heavily marked with white.

This handsome thrush was known as a Yorkshire bird as long ago as the fourteenth century, for, in the ordinances as to the price of food in the City of York in the year 1393, it is recorded that the 'price for twelve Fieldfares be twopence'.

Song Thrush
Turdus philomelos

Chislett commented in *Yorkshire Birds* that the opinion was held generally that the Song Thrush was less numerous in Yorkshire at that time (1952) than at the turn of the century when Nelson published *The Birds of Yorkshire*. Whether or not this was true, there was certainly nothing in Nelson's chapter on the species to suggest a greater abundance than we know today. It is, however, likely that the removal of hedgerows and scrubland over the years has robbed the species of much suitable breeding habitat, but it is still a relatively common bird and can be found nesting everywhere in the county in habitats as varied as lonely moorland gullies to busy suburban parks.

Many Yorkshire Song Thrushes leave the county during the winter months, especially those which nest in the upper dales. Many spend the winter in the West Country and in Ireland and their return to the breeding areas in early spring, when they suddenly re-appear and take up territory, is very noticeable.

Every autumn, usually from late September, many Song Thrushes come across the North Sea into Britain and their arrival is often very evident along the coastline. The main period of influx is usually during mid October, when many thrushes arrive, including Blackbirds, Fieldfares and Redwings. Several hundreds may be seen in most years, especially at the migrational focal points at Spurn, Flamborough and South Gare. One of the largest arrivals in recent years was in 1966, when 'thousands' crossed the northern part of the coast and 2,000 came in at South Gare on both 15th and 17th October; in 1970, S.C. Norman counted 1,100 at that locality on 12th and 13th October. There were two distinct waves of immigration in 1979, the first occurring on 30th September when 500 were at Grimston and 300 were at Spurn; the second, and much larger, influx started on 13th October, when counts along the coast showed 150 birds on Scarborough Castle Hill, 300 at Filey, 800 at Flamborough and 1,500 at Grimston. Spurn did not have large numbers and the maximum during the period was 60 on 17th October.

Inland localities often reflect the coastal numbers. In 1976, 150 were at Gouthwaite Reservoir on 3rd October and 300 were at Fairburn Ings on 2nd November. In October 1980, 60 appeared at Knaresborough Ringing Station on 18th, 150 were at Wentworth on 22nd and 50 were at Ossett Spa Sewage-farm on 31st.

During the spring, when birds are returning to their Scandinavian and west European breeding areas, some coastal movement is noted, but never on a large scale. Flamborough Head had 250 Song Thrushes on 16th April 1977 and Spurn had 100 on 17th April 1978, but numbers are usually fewer. It is likely that birds pass eastwards straight over the coast at night, having set off from inland localities during the evenings.

On 1st January 1979, 200 Song Thrushes were counted as they flew south along the Spurn Peninsula, no doubt having been forced out of Holderness by the very severe weather which prevailed at the time.

There are many recoveries of ringed Song Thrushes, both abroad and in Yorkshire. Birds ringed as nestlings have been recovered in France between October and January; others have been recovered to the west of Yorkshire and in Ireland. Several birds caught and ringed while on migration at Spurn Bird Observatory have subsequently been recovered between October and February in France, Spain and Portugal.

The much greyer back and whiter underparts with smaller spots, characters typical of the Continental race *Turdus philomelos philomelos* which breeds across the whole of Europe from Fenno-Scandia eastwards into Siberia, and across Asia Minor to Iran, can be seen on many coastal birds during the spring and autumn migration periods. Such characters were noted on 100 birds at Flamborough on 2nd May 1978, and several dead specimens from both coastal and inland localities have been so diagnosed over the years.

A Song Thrush ringed at Huddersfield on 7th January 1960 was retrapped there on 13th February and found dead on 13th May; it was sent to A. Hazelwood at the Bolton Museum, who identified it as an example of the Hebridean race *Turdus philomelos hebridensis* in breeding condition. In early March 1963, I found a dead Song Thrush on the road at Harrogate which E. Gorton of the Bolton Museum concluded was also an example of the Hebridean race.

Plumage aberration is relatively frequent in this species. Nelson mentioned two leucistic examples, and in 1966 one was at Ilkley in February. A pure white bird with dark eyes was at Baildon during the same autumn; other dark-eyed white birds were at Ilkley during March 1970 and at Gouthwaite Reservoir on 18th March 1973.

Between early March and the end of July 1980, a pair of Song Thrushes tried unsuccessfully to nest five times in a garden at Burley-in-Wharfedale and eventually managed to rear a brood at the sixth attempt. The first nest was located on 7th March when it held four eggs, but these were taken by a Magpie when they were almost ready to hatch. The second nest was built in a nearby clematis, but strong winds in April tilted the nest over. The third clutch of four eggs was laid in the first nest, in a small conifer, but a cat disturbed the sitting bird and the nest was deserted. A fourth nest was immediately built in a privet hedge and, on 15th May, there were two chicks in this nest, both pure albinos with pink eyes. Both were taken by Magpies, and within two days a fifth nest was being built in a beech hedge and was completed on 20th May. When the occupants of the house, Bob and Freda Draper, returned from holiday some two weeks later, there were two chicks in the nest, one normal and the other an albino. Netting was placed over the hedge to protect the nest from Magpies, and both young eventually fledged on 19th June. Their first night out of the nest coincided with strong winds and driving rain, and both were found dead the next day. Meanwhile, a sixth nest was being built near to the last and it contained three eggs only three days after the previous young had died. A fourth egg was laid on 8th July and four chicks resulted, three of which were normal and the other an albino. They all fledged successfully on 20th July, the albino bird being seen in the area during the next three weeks before it disappeared. There can be few more persistent Song Thrushes! It is interesting to note that a pair of Robins took over the tilted nest in the clematis and built a nest in it. I am grateful to Mrs Freda Draper for supplying the above information.

Although still a common bird throughout the county, the Song Thrush is perhaps less numerous than formerly, although the true situation is often very difficult to determine.

Redwing
Turdus iliacus

The Redwing is a winter visitor to Yorkshire in numbers varying from year to year. The first birds normally arrive during the second week of September, but the main influx is often not until a month later. The earliest arrival dates on record are 27th August 1941, when J.P. Utley saw a party of 20 near Holmfirth; 31st August 1957, when C.A. Andrassy saw one at Spurn, where there were other August records on 28th August 1973 and 30 August 1977; one at Shirecliffe on 27th August 1981; and a freshly dead bird found by E.E. Jackson at Leighton Reservoir on the very early date of 12th August 1959.

Redwings figure prominently in the large thrush immigrations every autumn, when their thin calls may be heard overhead during the night, especially in foggy or rainy conditions. Along the coast they are very obvious, often being oblivious of man if they have had a bad crossing and are tired. Many hundreds perish every year and it is the least able of the thrushes to cope with severe weather. G.R. Bennett counted 133 dead Redwings on the beach at Hornsea on 1st October 1960, and 145 the next day during a period of very strong winds. On 14th January 1962, 30 were found dead at Flamborough.

During very severe weather in December 1878, there was an immense immigration on the Cleveland coast. A heavy snowstorm with a northerly gale started on 9th December, on which date flocks of Redwings, with Fieldfares and other small birds, passed continuously all day in a northwesterly direction. The movement continued 'without intermission' during the daylight hours until 12th December, when the species became fewer and Fieldfares predominated until 21st, when migration stopped. Thousands succumbed, or were so hungered that they entered the city centres of Leeds and other large towns where they searched for food along the busy streets. At Flamborough, they resorted to the shore at low water, where they searched for food among the seaweed and around discarded fish; when the tide rose they sheltered at the base of the cliffs, where scores perished.

In more recent times, there have been many large arrivals, some of which have been most spectacular. In 1967, the main arrival date was 17th October, when 2,000 were at Spurn and 'hundreds' were seen inland at Huddersfield and Doncaster. As often happens, a second influx occurred in early November, when 4,000 Redwings came in at Spurn. After a count of 1,000 there on 12th October 1969, flocks of up to 250 were seen at several places inland and, again, a second arrival occurred on 28th October, when no fewer than 10,000 were seen at Spurn, most of which continued westwards without dropping in. A most spectacular migration occurred in 1971 when, on 13th October, S.G. Wilson counted 15,000 flying northwest over Kirk Ella, near Hull, on the eastern slope of the Wolds. Next day 3,000 were seen, and 5,000 more on 15th. The usual second arrival came on 22nd October, when 5,000 were at Hornsea, and 1,400 came in low over the sea at Filey on 23rd; Wilson watched at Kirk Ella on 25th and 26th and counted 1,000 and 2,000 birds respectively. On 23rd October 1976, at Spurn, 4,500 came in and continued westwards; 5,000 were present on the peninsula on 27th and 2,000 were grounded there on 28th.

A large immigration occurred on 7th October 1977 (see also Song Thrush) and Spurn had 5,000 birds, 4,700 of which passed straight overhead to the west. Strong easterly winds on 6th, followed by coastal fog, provided the right conditions to force birds down on their arrival; it was estimated that 13,000 were scattered along the clifftops between Atwick and Skipsea and many hundreds more were near Atwick Gap, with 1,800 near Hornsea, 5,000 at Burniston and smaller numbers all along the coast northwards to Teesmouth. As the fog lifted, more birds were seen coming in but continuing westwards without stopping. The influx was noted at many inland localities during the next few days and 1,000 were at Leighton Reservoir on 8th, with 2,000 near Ripon and 1,000 over Knaresborough Ringing Station on 9th.

The general pattern is the same every autumn, with the main arrival period usually being dictated by easterly winds any time during October and early November. The year 1979 was no exception and, after a good influx during 29th-30th September, a second and larger one occurred on 13th October, when 1,500 were at Spurn, 1,900 at Grimston, 6,000 at Flamborough, 600 at Filey, 3,000 on Scarborough Castle Hill, and many more all along the cliffs from Spurn to Teesmouth. Flocks inland at the year end included 2,500 in the Rivelin Valley on 5th December and 500 at Wintersett Reservoir on 17th.

The Redwing is thus very evident in the county in October and during the following weeks, as thousands of birds arrive and disperse over the countryside to feed with other thrushes along hawthorn hedges and on grassland. During periods of severe weather, especially if there is snow cover, they resort to suburbia where they feed in gardens, on grass verges and in orchards.

A return movement takes place during April, when flocks can be seen heading eastwards or assembling on pastureland prior to departing. Most have gone by mid April, but some inevitably linger on and there are several records during May with occasional individuals into June, especially along the coast. Late birds have been at Spurn on 25th June 1973, 11th June 1975 and 8th June 1980. In 1967, one was there on three dates in July. One sang vigorously at Fairburn Ings on 9th May 1978, and such songsters can occasionally be heard among migrating flocks as they stop to feed during April and early May.

The Redwing has provided some very exciting ringing recoveries. Four birds ringed while on migration at Spurn during October and November have been recovered in France (three) and Sardinia (one), this last being only the third recovery of a British-ringed Redwing from that island. One ringed at Sedbergh on 13th January 1961 was shot in Italy on 10th October 1961; one ringed at Ossett on 12th October 1963 was shot at Genoa in Italy on 25th October 1964; one ringed at Skelton, near York, on 4th February 1973 was found dead in the Lebanon on 23rd January 1974; a Redwing ringed at Adwick-le-Street on 31st October 1971 was recovered near Smolensk in the USSR on 13th April 1972; and a juvenile ringed at Wintersett Reservoir on 20th October 1974 was recovered at Sverdlousk in the USSR, being only the third recovery from east of the Urals. Two birds ringed as nestlings in Finland have been recovered in Yorkshire: one at Middlesbrough in January 1963 and the other at Hessle, near Hull, in January 1968.

A Redwing roost in rhododendrons at Stainborough Castle, near Barnsley, in

January 1978 held 4,000 birds; a roost in the Harrogate pine woods held 1,000 birds, also in January 1978; another at Bramhall, near Sheffield, held 1,000 birds in early November 1981; and one at Esholt held 1,200 birds in November and December 1969.

The presence of the larger and darker Iceland Redwing *Turdus iliacus coburni* has been suspected on several occasions, as in 1949 when G.R. Edwards saw several very dark individuals at Spurn on 10th November, one having been caught and ringed on 9th. Single birds caught at Spurn on 6th and 10th November 1970 were also considered to belong to this race.

Mistle Thrush
Turdus viscivorus

In *The Birds of Yorkshire*, Nelson said that 'flocks of immigrant Mistle Thrushes arrive on our coasts in the autumn from northern Europe, where the bird is to some extent a summer visitant'. He listed 'flocks' coming in at Redcar on 4th October 1884 and 'a great rush' at Teesmouth on 11th October 1885. Surely these were Fieldfares, for we have no evidence whatsoever of definite immigration during the present century. Nelson also said that they were less noticed at the light stations than other thrushes, being frequently confused with Fieldfares, both species being 'indifferently designated as large grey thrushes'.

Three birds, calling as they flew over West Cliff at Whitby from the north on 3rd November 1949, 'seemed to have come in from the sea' but they are just as likely to have been simply moving down the coast on a local flight. On 12th October 1952, one was with migrant Song Thrushes on Filey clifftop, but again there is absolutely no proof that it arrived with them. On 26th November 1955, three circled the Spurn lighthouse before flying to the southwest. In the same year, on 9th October, a day of much migration, four coasted northwest at Redcar, again offering no proof of their origin. Seven moved north at Spurn on 15th February 1958 and 18 were at Flamborough on 13th September 1959, both parties most likely being wanderers of fairly local origin, as would be the case with 11 others at Flamborough on 10th September 1961.

Some large concentrations occur during the late summer and autumn. Those near the coast could well become mixed up with flocks of Fieldfares and other thrushes during the latter period, giving rise to thoughts of immigration.

According to Nelson, the severe winters of 1878/79 and 1879/80 reduced the numbers considerably, but after two or three years they had recovered. In the winter of 1894/95, 'they perished in thousands and were almost exterminated in the East Riding'. It is more than likely that these incidents also referred to Fieldfares, which countrymen seem to have misidentified. Although flocks do occur during the autumn, large numbers as indicated by Nelson never persist throughout the winter months. Chislett mentioned a flock of 60-70 birds in Thornton-le-Dale on 30th September 1944 which was the only large gathering known to him. In more recent years, such flocks have been recorded annually and assemblies of between 20 and 50 birds may be seen in most years, mainly during September, with some larger flocks recorded in some years. K. Dawson saw 200 Mistle Thrushes feeding on rowan berries in Washburndale on 9th August 1953, the largest gathering ever recorded in the county and approached only by 180 birds at Norton, near Sheffield, on 12th September 1979. On 5th August 1958, A. Frudd counted three flocks of 40, 82 and 35 as they flew down the valley at Denholme, near Bradford.

Chislett said of a flock of 80 in Hornby Park on 29th September 1959 that 'thoughts of Fieldfare are inevitable'; perhaps not, in the light of modern knowledge.

Records of other flocks in excess of 50 birds are as follows: 60 at Thornhill, near Dewsbury, on 9th August 1966; 67 at Gouthwaite Reservoir on 16th September 1972; 60 at Ogden Beck on 24th September 1972, and 60 at Wintersett Reservoir on 21st October 1972; 74 feeding on bilberries on Broomhead Moor on 7th August 1977, and 64 at Wortley Park, near Leeds, on 14th October 1977; 75 at Elsecar on 8th September 1979 and 71 at Hooton Pagnell on 9th September 1979, in which year there were flocks of 50 at Swinithwaite in Wensleydale on 13th August, at Wyke, near Bradford, on 20th August, at Redmires on 5th October and at Bentley Tilts, near Doncaster, on 13th October, and the 108 at Sheffield on 12th September (see above). In 1981, 84 birds were on Lodge Moor on 24th September.

Spring flocks are rare, and 60 at Fadmoor, near Kirkbymoorside, on 12th April 1971 is the only one of note.

Yorkshire-ringed Mistle Thrushes have not moved very far: a nestling ringed at York on 17th June 1939 was at Doncaster on 6th February 1941; one ringed at Shipley on 12th April 1935 was recovered at Bolton in Lancashire on 14th March 1936; and a bird ringed at Spurn on 18th February 1959 was found dead at Headingley on 2nd March 1960. A nestling ringed at Kentmere in Westmorland on 30th April 1957 was retrapped at Apperley Bridge on 9th February 1958, and one ringed at Skelton in Cumberland on 10th December 1967 was found dead at Boston Spa on 15th May 1968. One ringed near Ramsgate in Kent on 16th December 1979 and found dead at Great Ayton on 21st December 1981 is a most interesting recovery; was it a Yorkshire bird that had moved south during the hard winter of 1979?

A cream-coloured Mistle Thrush was caught alive by a boy near Cayton in 1943; it subsequently died and the skin is preserved in the York Museum. One at Flockton Moor, near Wakefield, on 10th November 1953 was uniformly white, tinged with grey, and one near Sleights in the same year had a white crescent across the breast.

The 'Stormcock' breeds throughout Yorkshire. It is a familiar bird of the upland areas, where it frequents lone trees on the moor edges and in the gills and cloughs, and is equally at home in town centres, where small parks or tree-lined roads offer the required habitat.

Cetti's Warbler
Cettia cetti

In his garden by the side of Hornsea Mere, Dr J.E.S. Walker trapped a Cetti's Warbler in a mist-net on 2nd November 1972 which he showed to G. Bird. From the state of its plumage it was considered to be a bird of the year, and after being ringed and released it was not seen again. It was a new bird for the Yorkshire list (*The Naturalist*, 1973, pp. 89-90).

On 5th November 1977, R.G. Hawley watched a Cetti's Warbler along a drain at the Wassand end of Hornsea Mere. He saw it again on 25th, after which, although it had doubtless been in the area during the interim, it was not seen again.

One was at Blacktoft Sands from 26th September to 1st October 1982.

This species has spread northwestwards in Europe during recent years, and since about 1971 breeding has occurred in several counties in southern England.

Grasshopper Warbler
Locustella naevia

Nelson's assessment of the status of this skulking species needs absolutely no amendment some 75 years on. He wrote 'Summer visitant; local; thinly distributed, and varying in numbers in different years.'

Its erratic appearance and annual variation in numbers is well known to most birdwatchers and its reeling song is also very familiar. Only on the high moorlands of the Pennines and on much of the chalk Wolds is it reluctant to take up territory. In any other locality, the species may settle down to nest, or sing for a few days in spring before apparently moving on. Scrubland and other rank vegetation is favoured, especially that with an aquatic association. Some individuals colonise developing habitat for a few years before it changes and becomes unsuitable; young forestry plantations are a good example of this habitat.

That more pairs nest successfully than are ever located is certain, although the presence of a reeling bird does not necessarily mean that breeding is taking place. These birds sing while on migration, as do other species, but they usually do so in habitat which appears to be perfectly suitable for nesting and this complicates the true situation.

More Grasshopper Warblers were evident in 1977 than for several years previously. Blacktoft Sands had eight singing males, a total which was double that normally recorded; eight sang on Thorne Moor and five at Mickletown Ings, and observers in the York and Harrogate areas registered more than usual. In contrast, and perhaps illustrating the difficulty in assessing the true status, several people in the Leeds area considered it to be scarce and Fairburn Ings had a 'poor season'. Such variation of impressions is typical in most years.

The first main spring arrival usually takes place during the second half of April and earlier birds are not common. The earliest on record is one at Ben Rhydding Sewage-farm which L.G. Dewdney reported on 9th April 1961; one was at Spurn on 10th April 1966; one at Roche Abbey on 12th April 1952; one at Potteric Carr on 13th April 1979; and single birds at Spurn and Worsborough Reservoir on 13th April 1980.

Very few migrant Grasshopper Warblers are recorded along the coast and, although some pass through Spurn Point, and doubtless through other coastal places, numbers are never more than single figures on any one day. In 1969, a few passed through daily from 24th April to 14th May, with seven on 28th April and 3rd May. Four birds on 7th May 1972 was the maximum in that year, since when very few have been recorded, some years producing only two records of single birds.

Of four reeling males near Guisborough on 13th April 1960, one came and sang only an arm's length from D.G. Bell and remained for over an hour. In one of the intervals during its song, it dozed off; on being gently touched, it immediately burst into song again.

The Grasshopper Warbler is thus a most erratic species, both in numbers and in distribution, and birds may be present or absent in one year where the reverse has applied for several previous years.

River Warbler
Locustella fluviatilis

At 06.50 hours on 24th August 1981, a small bird was found caught in a mist-net at the Spurn Bird Observatory Warren area. It was obviously something new and the observers, B.R. Spence, B. Banson and M.V. Sneary, examined it in detail and identified it as a River Warbler, the first for Yorkshire. After being seen in the hand by several other observers, it was released near the canal zone in the hope that it could be watched there, but in typical fashion it skulked into cover and was not seen again.

This was only the sixth record for the British Isles, the others being recorded singly on Fair Isle in 1961, 1969 and 1981; on Bardsey in 1969; and in Norfolk in 1981.

The species breeds from the Baltic, East Germany and the Balkans, eastwards across central and southern Russia to western Siberia, and winters mainly in East Africa.

Savi's Warbler
Locustella luscinioides

The first record of this species in Yorkshire was at Knaresborough Ringing Station, when, on the evening of 14th May 1969, Jean Brown heard a short burst of reeling song from a patch of thick undergrowth. It had been raining heavily with a severe thunderstorm just prior to this, and other people present were sitting in the ringing laboratory. D. Brown and R. Evison were summoned and heard four more bursts of song but were unable to see the bird; as the light was failing, they left the area until the following morning. Evison suspected that the bird was a Savi's Warbler and was at the ringing station at 05.00 hours next morning when he heard the song again and saw the bird, which was sitting in full view among broken reed-mace stems and willow scrub. Through binoculars, it was seen to resemble a Reed Warbler in general coloration, being completely unstreaked. The song was a low-pitched reel delivered in short bursts of about three to five seconds. It was singing next to a furled mist-net, one end of which Evison managed to lower without disturbing the bird; while he was lowering the other end, it flew straight into the net and rolled out. I arrived at 06.00 hours and heard the bird singing within 6 feet (1.8 m) of me in a dense tangle of bramble about 50 yards upriver. The occurrence coincided with the arrival of a Savi's Warbler at Cley in Norfolk on 16th May and single birds at three localities in Kent and in one other county on the same date. (*The Naturalist*, 1970, p. 6)

The second record came from Fairburn Ings, where one sang from 8th July to early August 1971. It was seen and heard by several observers, including Dr J.D. Pickup and C. Winn.

Another was heard and seen at Hornsea Mere on 16th and 17th August 1973 by D.T. Ireland and S.C. Madge.

In 1977, there were several records during late April and in May in several

English counties. Yorkshire had six birds as follows: one at Tophill Low Reservoir from 30th April to 30th May, with a second bird on 25th May, both of which were seen by many observers including D. Bryan, N.A. Bell and G.E. Dobbs; one was seen by P.A. Lassey, Miss I. Smith and D.I.M. Wallace in Dane's Dyke at Flamborough from 15th to 19th May; one was seen at Hornsea Mere by R.G. Hawley on 17th May which stayed until 23rd; and one sang at Blacktoft Sands from 12th May to 2nd July, with a second bird present from 16th May to 14th June. This series of records was quite exceptional.

P.A. Lassey and Miss I. Smith saw and heard one at Flamborough on 6th May 1978. One caught at Hornsea Mere by J.E.S. Walker on 16th May 1979 was also seen by W.F. Curtis. One at Blacktoft Sands from 8th to 15th July 1980 was seen by A. Grieve and several other observers.

One appeared on 23rd May 1984 in the canal zone at Spurn, where it stayed until 30th. It was caught and ringed on the first date and examined in the hand by J. Cudworth, B.R. Spence and G. Thomas, and was subsequently seen in the field by many observers.

That there should now be 13 records of this species since it first entered the county list in 1969 is remarkable. It breeds from Iberia eastwards across southern Europe and in southwest Asia, and winters in tropical and northeast Africa. The species formerly nested in the fens of East Anglia until the middle of the nineteenth century, and very small numbers have done so again in southern England since about 1960.

Aquatic Warbler
Acrocephalus paludicola

On 16th November 1967, two schoolboys found a dying bird near the roadside at Airey Hill, Whitby, and took it to B. Fewster, where it died shortly afterwards. He identified it as an Aquatic Warbler and injected the specimen with formalin. I saw it shortly afterwards and prepared a description for submission to the *British Birds* Rarities Committee. It was a young bird of the year, and the corpse was lodged at the Whitby Museum in Pannett Park but is now lost. Full details of this new bird for the Yorkshire list were published in *The Naturalist*, 1968, p. 84.

The second record came from Spurn on 12th August 1973, when J. Cudworth saw a bird at the Narrow Neck. It was subsequently caught and full details were taken at the Warren ringing laboratory. Several people had the opportunity to see it before it was released back at the Narrow Neck.

On 9th May 1975, one was watched by B. Banson, J. Cudworth, B.R. Spence and others at close range among the reeds along the canal zone at Spurn; it was later caught and ringed. It stayed in the area for the next two days.

One was located, again on the canal zone at Spurn, by G. Neal on 22nd September 1976, when he had good views of the bird as it perched on a stem of *Phragmites*. He returned to the observatory to inform the others present, and B.R. Spence set a mist-net and caught the bird at 17.00 hours. It was released in the same area, where it remained during the next two days and was seen by many people, including J.M. Bayldon, M. Ibbotson and N. Money.

The canal zone at Spurn was to provide yet another Aquatic Warbler in 1977, when one was seen during the morning of 21st August by B. Banson, J.C. Lidgate and others. It was caught in the afternoon, and after being released stayed in the area during the next day.

On the morning of 18th August 1981, G. Speight found one at Spurn, again on the canal zone. It was seen later by D. Page, J.M. Turton, L.J. Degnam and N. Whitehouse, who were fortunate enough to locate a second bird nearby and subsequently watch them both together.

Another Aquatic Warbler was seen at Kilnsea on 10th August 1983 by G.R. Welch and his wife.

The Aquatic Warbler breeds locally across Europe to central Russia and into Hungary and the Caspian region, and is thought to winter in tropical Africa. It is a rare bird in northern Britain, although several are trapped in the southern counties each year, mostly during August and September.

Sedge Warbler
Acrocephalus schoenobaenus

Since Nelson summarised the status of this species in 1907 as 'Summer visitant; common and generally distributed', the Sedge Warbler has changed perhaps only slightly in regard to its numbers, for it is still a generally distributed summer visitor, absent as a breeding species only on the high barren moorlands of the Pennines and the North York Moors and in the dry parts of the Wolds.

Any overgrown area, especially near water, will attract a breeding pair and some of the larger ings and reservoirs have many pairs about their margins. During recent years, breeding pairs have been counted at several major waters as follows: Blacktoft Sands, 50 pairs in 1976, 60 pairs in 1979, 70 pairs in 1980 and 65 pairs in 1981; Fairburn Ings, 50 pairs in 1976, 40 pairs in 1977 after there had been 80 singing males in the spring, 35 pairs in 1978, 34 pairs in 1980 and 29 pairs in 1981; Wintersett Reservoir, 45 pairs in 1976, 26 pairs in 1980 and 25 pairs in 1981; Potteric Carr, 35 pairs in 1981; Mickletown Ings, 36 singing males in 1977, 26 in 1980 and 22 in 1981; Thorne Moors, 45 singing males in 1977; and Wheldrake Ings, 24 pairs in 1981. In 1971, D.T. Ireland, the RSPB warden at Hornsea Mere, estimated a breeding population there of 250 pairs.

Away from such areas, small populations of breeding pairs occur at many suitable places by rivers or overgrown sewage-farms, and smaller numbers breed away from obvious water along the edges of cornfields or root crops.

The first main arrival takes place during the third week of April in most years, earlier birds being quite scarce. The earliest on record was seen by J.A. Booker at Wintersett Reservoir on 8th April 1961, and other early birds have been on 10th April 1966 at Spurn; 13th April 1979 at Blacktoft Sands; and again on 13th April in 1980 at both Tophill Low Reservoir and Blacktoft Sands.

The breeding areas are usually clear of birds by the end of September, but a few individuals linger at the larger colonies and there are several October records: single birds were at Hornsea Mere on 21st October 1961, 18th October 1964 and 12th October 1973; one was at Blacktoft Sands on 19th October 1981; one was at Batley on 11th October 1967; one was at Flamborough on 20th October 1981, and one was at Spurn on the same date. Migration along the coast is never very evident, but a few pass during May and in the autumn, the late birds in October undoubtedly having crossed the North Sea.

There are no records in Yorkshire of Sedge Warblers ringed abroad, but four birds ringed here have been recovered in France as follows: a juvenile ringed at Sprotborough Flash on 6th August 1962 was found dead in the Côtes du Nord on 26th August 1962; a juvenile ringed at Adwick-le-Street Sewage-farm on 1st August

1964 was found dead in the same region of France at the end of August 1964; another ringed at Sprotborough Flash on 5th June 1965 was at Manche on 23rd April 1966; and one ringed at Armthorpe on 21st August 1969 was in the Charente-Maritime district on 8th September 1969. A juvenile ringed at Fairburn Ings on 12th August 1970 was recaught at St Ouen, Jersey, on 7th May 1972.

There have been several recoveries within the British Isles involving birds ringed in Yorkshire, and of others ringed elsewhere in Britain and recovered here. A nestling ringed at Driffield on 11th June 1949 was at Sidcup, Kent, in August 1949; a juvenile ringed at Adwick-le-Street on 27th July 1963 was in Essex on 5th August 1963; one ringed at Old Denaby on 8th August 1966 was retrapped at Chichester in Sussex on 16th August 1966; one ringed at Hornsea Mere on 27th July 1967 was retrapped at Sandwich Bay in Kent on 6th August 1967; one ringed at Swillington Ings on 6th September 1967 was at Egham in Surrey only six days later; and one ringed at Sprotborough Flash on 21st August 1968 was retrapped at Sittingbourne in Kent on 3rd September 1968.

Three birds have been recovered in Yorkshire, having been ringed elsewhere in Britain: one ringed in Kent on 29th July 1967 was retrapped at Fairburn Ings on 29th August 1968; one ringed in Devon on 5th September 1971 was retrapped at Wilton, near Redcar, on 6th May 1973; and one ringed on the Isle of Canna in Inverness on 11th July 1976 was retrapped at Selby on 10th August 1976.

Blyth's Reed Warbler
Acrocephalus dumetorum

On 20th September 1912, an example of this very rare visitor to the British Isles was seen feeding in sea buckthorn near the lighthouse at Spurn, where it was eventually shot by J.K. Stanford and identified by E. Hartert and N.F. Ticehurst (*British Birds*, 1912, p. 217).

Another one occurred in Yorkshire on 30th August 1975, when R.H. Appleby watched a bird at Filey Brigg of which he took detailed notes and made sketches. These were submitted to the Yorkshire Naturalists' Union and *British Birds* Rarities Committees, being accepted by both.

A third bird appeared at Spurn Bird Observatory on 28th May 1984. It was first heard singing by B.R. Spence and seen briefly by N.A. Bell and G. Neal before being caught in a mist-net. It was seen in the hand by many observers at the Warren, and later by many more after its release (see plate 105).

The species breeds across northern Europe into Siberia, Afghanistan and Mongolia and spends the winter months in India.

Marsh Warbler
Acrocephalus palustris

This species did not enter the Yorkshire list of birds until 1928, when E.A. Wallis and T.N. Roberts saw and heard one at close quarters on 10th June and for some days afterwards at Scarborough Mere. Eagle Clarke, having discussed the record with Wallis, gave details to Chislett and said that he had identified the song, having had experience of the species abroad (*The Naturalist*, 1929, p. 78).

On 29th June 1933, T.N. Roberts identified another Marsh Warbler which he watched for some time near Scarborough (*The Naturalist*, 1934, p. 19).

There have been several acceptable records since the publication of *Yorkshire Birds* in 1952. One was in full song at Spurn on 4th June 1963 and was watched at close range by J. Cudworth and others, and a bird of the year was trapped at Flamborough on 21st September 1963 by Miss M.R. Sanderson and A.F.G. Walker, who took detailed notes and measurements. Most of the recent records have occurred at Spurn Point, as follows: one sang all day on 2nd June 1970; one was in full song on 12th June 1971; one was caught and ringed by B.R. Spence and P. Delaloye on 13th September 1972; one was caught by B.R. Spence on 25th May 1974; one was caught on 4th June 1977; one occurred from 26th to 28th June 1980; and one was singing at the Point dunes on 3rd June 1982. Elsewhere, one was at Birdwell, near Barnsley, on 22nd and 23rd June 1980 where it was watched by A.G. Blunt and J.D.H. Brown; one was seen at Filey Brigg from 7th to 10th October 1982 by P.J. Dunn and H.J. Whitehead; and one was seen and heard at Wintersett Reservoir by S. Denny and P. Bradley on 12th June 1984.

Mist-netting at Flamborough Head by P.A. Lassey and his colleagues has produced good results, including several Marsh Warblers. In 1976, one was caught on 13th August, another on 17th August and two on 27th, one of which remained until 29th, and another occurred on 17th September; all were birds of the year. M. Francis saw and heard one singing at Wheatcroft, near Scarborough, on 11th June 1978. J. Harriman and D. Suddaby watched a bird at Flamborough, in full song, on 8th June 1980. In 1984, two were at Spurn on 3rd and 4th June and one at Flamborough on 18th June.

There have been several sight records at Flamborough of birds identified as Marsh Warblers by experienced observers, the first being seen by D.I.M. Wallace on 10th September 1972 with another on 20th and 21st September. P.A. Lassey and D.I.M. Wallace saw birds on 28th, 29th and 30th August and on 23rd October 1976, the year in which five birds were caught there, and another was seen on 3rd and 5th October by S.L. James.

This species is very difficult to tell apart from the Reed Warbler and great care must be exercised when identifying it. A bird at Hay-a-Park Gravel-pit at Knaresborough in 1983 in a small Reed Warbler colony had a very varied song, full of mimicry and including loud sweet notes. It gave rise to thoughts of Marsh Warbler, especially as it was somewhat colder in colour than its neighbours, but it was concluded to be a Reed Warbler with a most unusual song. P.T. Treloar studied the bird closely and recorded the mimicry of 21 species, including the scream of a Swift, the alarm notes of Swallows and Sand Martins and calls of Oystercatcher and Common Sandpiper as well as Blue Tit, finches and wagtails. A tape recording of its performance was sent to Miss F. Dowsett-Lemaire, who has studied the song of Marsh Warbler; she agreed with most of the claimed species mimicked and added Nightingale and Bee-eater. She also agreed that the bird was a Reed Warbler, though not a typical dual performer. The song of the Marsh Warbler, and probably that of some Reed Warblers, is thought to be learned by an individual mainly from hearing other songsters around it in the natal colony and while on the first migration.

The Marsh Warbler breeds very sparingly in parts of southern England, but is relatively common in the adjacent Continent, north to southern Sweden and Finland, and eastwards to the Urals, and winters in East Africa. It is very likely that some passage birds are overlooked.

Reed Warbler
Acrocephalus scirpaceus

Nelson said of the Reed Warbler that 'it is to be feared its numbers are decreasing, owing chiefly to the drainage of its accustomed haunts'. There can be little doubt that the species was once very common in the undrained levels of the East Riding and in the south of the county on the carrlands of Hatfield and Thorne. It is in these areas that it can be found today, breeding fairly commonly in the larger tracts of *Phragmites*, and less so in reed-filled dykes and by the sides of established reservoirs and gravel-pits. The reedbeds at Hornsea Mere hold many birds, and an estimate by the RSPB warden in 1971 gave a figure of 650 pairs. Blacktoft Sands is undoubtedly one of the county's strongholds, and counts in recent years have shown 200 pairs in 1974, 450 pairs in 1978 and about 400 pairs annually since 1979. All the reedbeds along the Humber hold breeding pairs, as do most of the dykes in Holderness. In the southeastern corner of the county, any suitable habitat, which really means the presence of *Phragmites* although nests are often built in adjacent willowherb and other vegetation, will hold breeding pairs and the species is spreading into newly formed habitat at gravel-pits and reservoirs on the edge of its range. A small bed of *Phragmites* at Hay-a-Park Gravel-pit, near Knaresborough, has held a few pairs since 1980, and small numbers nest in the Derwent Valley and in other areas near York.

According to Nelson, it was formerly common near Knaresborough and at several other places on the edge of its present range, and it was at one time frequent at Scarborough Mere until an increase in water level and increased leisure activity resulted in the loss of reeds. Odd pairs have persisted at this latter site up to the present time, the last successful breeding being in 1977 and 1981, in which year three singing males were present.

The subsidence flashes at Fairburn, Mickletown and Swillington Ings each hold from ten to 20 pairs annually, the population at the first locality in 1978 being judged to be down by 50 percent when only 12 pairs nested. In contrast, Potteric Carr had an estimated 100 pairs in that year, and 60 pairs bred there in 1979 followed by a drastic reduction in 1981 when only 20 pairs bred. Wintersett and Worsborough Reservoirs held 12 and ten pairs respectively in 1980.

In 1973, the Yorkshire Naturalists' Union organised a survey of all the Reed Warbler breeding sites in the county. The enquiry was conducted over the three years 1974 to 1976, and during that period 85 sites were located or confirmed, holding a minimum of 1,450 breeding pairs, the majority of which, almost 50 percent, were at Hornsea Mere and Blacktoft Sands.

A newly flooded area adjacent to Tophill Low Reservoir, in which the dominant vegetation was *Phalaris arundinacea*, rosebay willowherb and meadowsweet, held 16 pairs during the summer of 1975, having been flooded for the first time in the spring of that year. Other reedbeds along the Humber also held many pairs, and those between Faxfleet and Brough had about 200 pairs in each of the three years.

The survey showed that 86 percent of the breeding pairs were in *Phragmites* beds or vegetation dominated by this plant. It should be remembered, however, that the three main sites, at Hornsea Mere, Blacktoft Sands and the linear reedbeds along the Humber, hold over 65 percent of the estimated county population, and of the remainder only about 7.5 percent were breeding in areas where there was no *Phragmites* at all.

The first birds of spring may appear during the second week of April, but the main arrival is not usually until the last week of the month. In 1972, the general arrival was late and the first Reed Warbler was not seen until 2nd May at Hornsea Mere. The earliest bird of which I have note was at Denaby Ings on 13th April 1976, a year in which the next bird was not until 28th April. Other early records are 16th April at Hornsea Mere and 15th April 1981 at Tophill Low Reservoir.

Birds often linger at their breeding places into early October and others pass along the coast in that month. One at Worsborough Reservoir on 12th October 1980 was late for an inland site, but the latest records for the county concern two birds at Potteric Carr on 31st October 1975 and one caught at Wintersett Reservoir on 7th November 1982. Birds have been recorded at Blacktoft Sands and Hornsea Mere up to 19th October, and at Spurn and Flamborough up to 20th.

A Reed Warbler travelling northwards, presumably to its Yorkshire breeding quarters, was ringed at Gillingham in Norfolk on 15th June 1980 and retrapped at Hornsea Mere two days later. A juvenile ringed at Sandwich Bay in Kent on 9th September 1966 was very probably a Yorkshire-bred bird moving south to its winter quarters in Africa, as it was caught again at Brough on the Humber on 26th August 1967.

One ringed at Spurn on 8th October 1955 had reached Lisbon in Portugal by 13th, when it was shot. A juvenile ringed at Fairburn Ings on 3rd September 1964 was recovered in the Gironde area of France on 3rd October 1964, and another juvenile ringed at Hornsea on 20th August 1967 was shot in France on 11th September 1967.

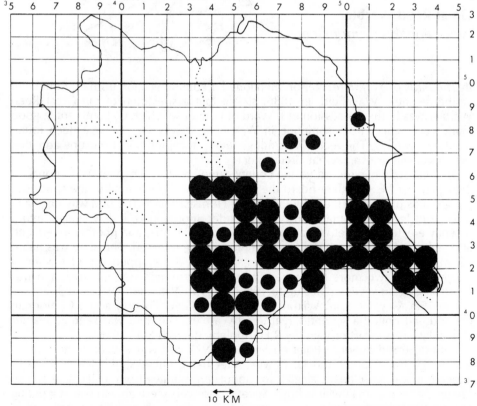

10 KM

Reed Warbler. Restricted almost entirely to the *Phragmites* beds in the southeast, this species has spread westwards in recent years and colonised gravel-pits and lakes where this plant predominates.

The Reed Warbler has apparently increased as a breeding species since Nelson wrote 'Summer visitant; very locally distributed', but the trend seems likely to be a return, at least in part, to an earlier status.

On 24th September 1977, A. Amery, B. Walker and other members of a Manchester group who were visiting the Spurn Bird Observatory found an unusual warbler which looked very pale and which J. Cudworth and B.R. Spence eventually caught in a mist-net. It was taken back to the ringing hut and a full description of its plumage and details of its measurements were taken. The whole of the upperparts were sandy-brown, except for the rump which was orange-rufous; the underparts were white with a pale sandy wash on the flanks. D. Proctor and P. Harrison, who had caught and ringed 70 Reed Warblers in the West Riding during the summer, commented that the bird was quite unlike any of these. Its characters fitted those of the eastern race *Acrocephalus scirpaceus fuscus*, which breeds in eastern Russia (*Spurn Bird Observatory Report*, 1977, p. 48). A bird caught at Spurn on 3rd June 1984 was also ascribed to this race.

Great Reed Warbler
Acrocephalus arundinaceus

In *The Birds of Yorkshire*, Nelson mentioned a communication from G. Roberts of Lofthouse, near Wakefield, in 1886, stating that a specimen of the Great Reed Warbler was in the possession of J. Ward of Lofthouse which G. Lumb got 'a good many years since' from someone in Wakefield; it was said to have been found dead near Methly. The record was not generally accepted and it must be admitted that the details are somewhat circumspect.

The first authentic record for the county came in 1971, when, at 04.10 hours on 29th May, Dr J.E.S. Walker heard the deep, harsh croaking song of the species in the grounds of Grebe House by the side of Hornsea Mere. The bird was singing in a patch of lesser reed-mace and, as the finder approached, it flew straight into a recently erected mist-net. It was examined in detail, ringed and photographed, and also seen by D.T. Ireland and G. Bird before being released. The song was heard again on the following day by Ireland, and it was retrapped on 31st when it weighed 38 g, two more than when first caught. It remained in the area, and was heard singing on several dates up to 19th June (*The Naturalist*, 1973, p. 89).

On 19th May 1973, at Wilton, near Redcar, G.W. Follows and S.C. Norman trapped and ringed a second Great Reed Warbler. The third was seen at Seamer Gravel Pits, near Scarborough, by R.H. Appleby on 16th May 1976.

One occurred at Spurn Point on 3rd June 1977 and was caught in the Warren trap by D. Barraclough and D. Bower. After being ringed and released by B.R. Spence, it was later heard singing for about ten minutes from a patch of sparse *Phragmites* and a small willow bush. Several observers were able to watch it during most of the following day.

In 1984, two birds occurred, both on 19th May. The first was at Knaresborough Ringing Station when, at 08.30 hours, R. Evison heard a snatch of *Acrocephalus* song while setting mist-nets around a small pond with *Phragmites* where a few passage Reed Warblers have been caught over the years. The song was not heard again until 11.00 hours, when P.T. Treloar and I located the bird among willow and hawthorn bushes on the opposite bank of the River Nidd. It was eventually seen well as it sat out in bright sunlight and made several flycatching sallies over the river, and during the day it was also seen by several people including D.R.J. Watkins, J.L.C. Gandy and Miss A. Mettam. It sang vigorously for short periods of up to ten minutes and was then often silent for up to an hour or more, being last seen and heard at 18.00 hours.

The second bird in 1984 was at Saltmarsh Delph, near Blacktoft Sands, when one appeared during the morning of 19th May and was seen and heard by many observers during its long stay into June.

Olivaceous Warbler
Hippolais pallida

At 11.30 hours on 22nd October 1976, Miss Irene Smith located a very pale grey-ish warbler feeding at the edge of a plantation at the Flamborough South Landing. P.A. Lassey was informed and the two observers watched it for periods totalling over an hour, during which time they took detailed notes on the bird's behaviour and plumage and identified it as an Olivaceous Warbler. It usually fed low down in cover, but would occasionally fly into some taller mature sycamores and was heavy and clumsy while moving about, feeding on both insects and berries.

The species breeds across southern Europe eastwards to Asia and winters in tropical Africa. There are only 13 records for the British Isles, this being the first for Yorkshire.

Booted Warbler
Hippolais caligata

This eastern warbler, which breeds from northwest Russia eastwards across south-ern Siberia to Mongolia, and south to Iran, entered the Yorkshire list of birds in 1978 when one was seen in Beacon Lane, Kilnsea, near Spurn, on 9th September by J.S. George, D. Hursthouse and M.J. Stoyle. It was watched for about an hour, but the views obtained did not enable the observers to be certain of its identity, although they knew that it was a rare warbler. B.R. Spence arrived and set a mist-net, in which the bird was caught almost immediately. It was taken back to the Spurn Bird Observatory, where it was positively identified, ringed and later released at the Warren.

A second Booted Warbler was seen among the sea buckthorn at the Spurn

Narrow Neck by B.R. Spence and B. Banson on 5th September 1981. Several observers saw it before it was eventually caught and taken to the observatory for ringing. It was an adult. After a full description had been taken, it was released at the Warren, where it stayed for the next two days and was watched by very many people from all over the country. Some excellent photographs were taken of the bird in the hand and in the field by B. Banson, G. Neal and D.M. Cottridge (see plate 106).

One was located among brambles on the south side of the Scarborough Castle Hill on 11th October 1982 by R.H. Appleby, M. Williams and M. Marshall. It stayed for the next two days.

Icterine Warbler
Hippolais icterina

Nelson knew the Icterine Warbler as an extremely rare summer visitor from Continental Europe. He knew of only eight records in the British Isles, one of which was a Yorkshire specimen. The bird in question occurred at Easington, near Spurn, and the information was communicated to Nelson by John Cordeaux, who had received from P. Loten of Easington a dead example which had been killed by some boys with a catapult on 28th May 1891. Loten skinned it thinking that it was a Wood Warbler, but had some doubts. The specimen was sent to W. Eagle Clarke and purchased for the Royal Scottish Museum. (*The Zoologist*, 1891, p. 308; and *The Naturalist*, 1891, p. 241, and 1897, p. 201)

Eagle Clarke and T. Laidlow watched another in the Warren garden at Spurn in September 1897.

One was caught in the Spurn Warren trap on 4th September 1947 by Miss E. Crackles and G.H. Ainsworth. Another which frequented the Spurn 'wire dump' area from 25th to 27th August 1950 was seen by H.O. Bunce, W.A. Butterfield and others, and another was seen there on 11th September 1950 by R.F. Dickens and P.E. Davis. On 3rd September 1951, D.B. Isles, G. Harrison and I caught an Icterine Warbler in the Spurn Warren trap; it was a new bird for all three of us.

From 1954, the species has been recorded more frequently, both in spring and autumn, as the number of observers has increased and more trapping has been done. All the autumn birds have occurred between mid August and mid September, mostly singly but two or three on occasions and more in some exceptional years. On 24th August 1971, for instance, eight were on the Spurn Peninsula, an unprecedented number at the time.

There were several records in 1977, with an influx of birds during August, the first being at Spurn on 14th whereafter one to three were seen there up to 23rd with four on 19th. At Flamborough, the first was seen on 15th August, with a good series of records thereafter when birds were present almost daily to 23rd, maxima being six on 19th, eight on 21st and 14 on 22nd. Single birds were seen at Kilnsea, Easington, Hornsea, Dane's Dyke at Flamborough, Filey and Scarborough Castle Hill during the same period and in late September. At least four birds, and probably six, were at South Gare between 15th and 20th August. Six birds were at Flamborough on 8th August 1981.

The first spring record was in 1964 and odd Icterine Warblers have since occurred and stayed for a few days at this time of the year, some of which have been in song. These have been recorded in most years since 1970, and mainly at Spurn during late May and early June. One sang in Kilnsea churchyard from 21st to

23rd June 1970. In 1977, single birds were at Spurn on 27th May and 13th June, with two on 28th May.

Inland birds are scarce, but a few have been seen in recent years. On 6th September 1959, W.C. Wakefield saw and described one at Fairburn Ings; one was seen at Fockerby, near Goole, on 30th August 1974; one sang vigorously in a wooded ravine near Scarborough from 2nd to 14th July 1975 which was seen by several observers as it moved about the leaf canopy, and its song was tape recorded; one was in full song near Settle on 13th May 1976; one was seen at Harrogate Sewage-farm by Mrs J. Hall on 15th September 1978 as it fed in an apple tree; one was seen at Wilsic, south of Doncaster, on 14th August 1982 by K. Rotherham; and P.T. Treloar watched one at Knaresborough Ringing Station on 3rd September 1983 as it moved around the area with a mixed party of tits and other warblers.

The Icterine Warbler is now recorded far more frequently than during Nelson's time, and indeed up to the early 1950s, when birds were very likely being overlooked. It is now a regular autumn passage migrant along the coast between mid August and mid September, with a few records in spring in most years, and may be seen anywhere from South Gare to Spurn Point. There are six inland records, and the singing birds prompted a statement which I made in the Yorkshire Naturalists' Union Annual Ornithological Report for 1975 saying that 'I consider this species a likely candidate for future colonisation as a breeding bird', an event which I was to learn subsequently had already taken place in 1970, when a nest with eggs was found in the west of the county. The details supplied by the finder are as follows:

'On 31st May 1970, I had the good fortune to find the nest of the Icterine Warbler and the following details are from my field notes. My friend and I took a young boy, aged fourteen, out bird-watching at the request of his father. While walking down the side of a beck and on passing a small clump of ash trees, my attention was suddenly roused by hearing a bird singing whose notes were new to me. The call came from a small bird which at first I thought was a Wood Warbler; by this time the bird was calling in alarm — a loud harsh note.

We hid ourselves and observed the bird which was joined by its mate and I could see clearly through my binoculars that it was not a Wood Warbler; the bill was large for the size of the bird. I knew that it was a warbler, but confess I was completely confused as to the exact species. After about five minutes, I observed one of the birds alight upon a small nest in the fork of an ash tree about ten yards away, which was just five feet from the foot of the tree on a steep slope. The nest was deep-cupped and similar to the nest of a Chaffinch; the lining was of very fine grass and hair with bits of beech bark on the outside. It contained two pink eggs with black spots; the shell of the eggs being pink which was not the yolk showing through.

By this time I had decided that the nest belonged to a pair of Icterine Warblers and later confirmed this with my books. My next visit, with my colleague, was six days later and we found that the nest had disappeared. I am certain the young boy had taken the nest and a year later, his father told me that his son had taken some pink eggs from a deserted nest.'

The observer is well known to a prominent Yorkshire ornithologist who vouches for his countryside experience and reliability.

That it will nest again in the county, if it has not already done so, is more than probable.

Melodious Warbler
Hippolais polyglotta

This scarce passage migrant has occurred in Yorkshire on only four occasions.

The first was on 26th May 1979, when D.I.M. Wallace located one at Flamborough which was later caught in the Old Fall hedge and ringed by P.A. Lassey and Miss I. Smith.

The second was also at Flamborough, on 14th and 15th May 1981. It was watched by A. Grieve, D.G. Hobson and J. Harriman, and eventually caught and ringed.

P.A. Lassey recorded a third at Flamborough on 28th May 1983, and another appeared there on 4th and 5th September, when it was seen by A.M. Allport and others.

Marmora's Warbler
Sylvia sarda

In the late evening of 15th May 1982, J. Lunn received a telephone call from G. Lee of Barnsley, informing him that a small warbler that he had watched during the day on the Pennines near Langsett was almost certainly a Marmora's Warbler. Next morning, Lunn located the bird and watched it for approximately 35 minutes before losing sight of it. Later in the morning it was relocated about 500 yards (457 m) down the valley by other observers who had come to see it. During its stay until last seen on 24th July, it was watched by many hundreds of observers from all over the country who had gathered to see this first record for Yorkshire and the British Isles.

The actual locality was Mickleden Clough, a steep-sided gritstone valley high in the southern Pennines. Mickleden Beck, a small, fast-flowing stream, runs in the valley bottom, where the vegetation is dominated by grasses and wet flushes. In contrast, the valley sides are mainly heather, bilberry, cowberry and bracken. The bird frequented the steep east side of the valley, being only occasionally seen in the valley bottom, and preferred an area consisting almost entirely of low heather and bilberry interspersed with grass patches and bracken. The best views were obtained when it perched on top of the heather and sang, which it did regularly. The display was very striking and reminiscent of a Whitethroat, with a steady ascent to about 20 feet (6 m) above the heather with trailing legs and continuous singing, followed by a very steep undulating dive to alight at a spot which was usually farther down the slope from the point of take-off. During its stay, the bird was seen to carry nesting material, which consisted of grasses and cobwebs.

The Marmora's Warbler is confined to the Mediterranean, and there are two recognised races, one occupying Corsica, Sardinia and Sicily and the other being found only on the Balearic Islands. The latter race is very sedentary but the nominate race is known to wander, with records from the Mediterranean coasts of Spain, France and Italy, and it is from this population that the Yorkshire bird was presumed to have originated.

I am grateful to J. Lunn for the very detailed information which he put at my disposal. The event is recorded in full in *British Birds*, 1985, pp. 475-81.

Dartford Warbler
Sylvia undata

In *The Handbook of Yorkshire Vertebrata* by Clarke and Roebuck (1881, p. 21), the following appears under the heading of Dartford Warbler:

'Casual visitant, observed in one locality only — the Rivelin Valley — in the extreme south. Here Mr. Charles Dixon, who is well acquainted with the bird, has several times seen it in the gorse coverts, and in one solitary instance he found a nest with five eggs, observing the sitting bird from a distance of only a few feet. Hitherto, Melbourne in Derbyshire has been considered the most northerly locality in which it has occurred.'

Nelson dismissed this claim, saying that 'No faith is to be placed in [it].'

This southern species did, however, enter the Yorkshire list of birds in 1977, when one was seen by C. Gorman at Carlton Marsh, near Pontefract, at 17.00 hours on 23rd March. The observer was sitting in the shelter of a bank, when a small bird flitted through the dead stems of some *Glyceria maxima*. It was climbing up and down the grass stems and offering only very brief views, but a cocked tail was eventually seen and the observer realised that the bird was something new to him. Gradually, better views were obtained and eventually the dark red breast with small white spots, and the red eyes, were seen, enabling the identification as a male Dartford Warbler. Gorman contacted P.B. Wordsworth, who went to the site, and within minutes the two observers were able to watch it again. It was caught in a mist-net set by Wordsworth and was ringed and photographed before being released.

It stayed in the area for the next 12 days and spent much of its time in a patch of dead great willowherb, where it was seen by many people who came to see this rarity.

The Dartford Warbler breeds in southern England and from western France, Iberia and Morocco eastwards to Italy, Sicily and Tunisia and is mainly sedentary. The origin of the Yorkshire bird can only be conjectured.

Subalpine Warbler
Sylvia cantillans

This small warbler, which breeds mainly in the Mediterranean basin, was first recorded in Yorkshire on 9th May 1968, when a male was caught and ringed at Spurn Bird Observatory. Later in the same year, on 27th August, a female was caught. Remarkably, a third bird was caught at the Point on 21st October which, after being ringed, was released at the Warren. During the next few days, it gradually worked its way down the peninsula, being seen on 26th just south of the 'wire dump' area, where it remained until being last seen on 31st. This individual was originally identified as a first-year Spectacled Warbler *Sylvia conspicillata*, but was re-assessed in the light of recently appreciated criteria which are now known to separate these two very similar species in juvenile plumage.

On 23rd September 1976, M. Francis and F.A. Whitford found and identified a Subalpine Warbler on the Scarborough Castle Hill. It was still present the next day and was seen by several other observers.

A bird was heard singing among the sea buckthorn at Spurn on 22nd May 1977 by D. Page, P. Greaves and J. Palmer, who suspected that it was this species and waited for it to show itself. After almost an hour, the bird finally came out of cover and perched in the open only 10 feet (3 m) from the observers. It quickly dived back into the buckthorn, but the views it afforded were sufficient to allow the identification as a male of this species.

A female was trapped at Lovell Hill, Redcar, on 28th May 1978 by S.C. Norman.

Spurn Point was to have yet another, when one was caught and ringed on 9th May 1980. In the afternoon, B.R. Spence was looking for a Bluethroat which had been seen earlier in the day in the canal zone when he saw a small warbler feeding in a hawthorn hedge. He had very good views and immediately recognised it as a male Subalpine Warbler. Two mist-nets were erected and the bird was caught at 17.30 hours. It was taken back to the observatory for ringing, and when released flew off, gaining height, and left to the northwest until lost to view.

A male was seen at South Gare, Teesmouth, by A. Cruikshanks and others on 30th September 1983.

Sardinian Warbler
Sylvia melanocephala

This common Mediterranean scrub warbler entered the Yorkshire list of birds on 4th June 1982, when B.R. Spence caught one at the Spurn Bird Observatory. It was not seen until being found in the holding area of the Warren trap and the bird, a male, stayed in the area until 6th June.

There are only 12 British records of this small attractive warbler, most of which have been at coastal sites.

Desert Warbler
Sylvia nana

On 20th October 1975, an example of this small warbler was seen at Spurn Point. The appearance of this very rare species was totally unexpected, but came in a year when another occurred in Essex in November and one in Finland in October. The Spurn bird was first seen by I. Corbett, M. Mills and B.R. Spence, and was caught and ringed on the first day of its four-day stay. It frequented an area of rough upper beach with isolated buckthorn bushes, and often fed among a pile of old bricks. When feeding on the open beach, it hopped with its tail cocked and would often hop into cover and out of sight.

During its stay, it was viewed by very many people from all over the country, and some excellent photographs were taken by J. Seeviour, G. Neal, K. Atkin and others (see plates 108 and 109).

This was a new record for the county and only the second for the British Isles. It was diagnosed as belonging to the nominate race *Sylvia nana nana*, which breeds in central Asia.

A second Desert Warbler was seen at Flamborough Head on 24th October 1981 by A.M. Allport, D.G. Hobson and P.A. Lassey. Full details were taken but these have not yet been submitted to the *British Birds* Rarities Committee.

Orphean Warbler
Sylvia hortensis

On 6th July 1848, two birds were seen in a small plantation near Wetherby, one of which was shot and proved to be a female Orphean Warbler; from the state of its plumage, it was thought to have been nesting. It was the first record for the British Isles, and the species was added to the national list on the strength of this occurrence.

D. Graham, the York taxidermist, on hearing that a rare bird had been shot, went to Wetherby and obtained the specimen for Sir William Milner. There is absolutely no proof that the bird was nesting as suggested by Milner's comment that 'it had the appearance of having been engaged in incubation from the state of its plumage'.

The mounted specimen went eventually to the Leeds Museum, where it resides at the present time. I am grateful to A. Norris, who examined it at my request and confirmed the details on the label and also the fact that it was indeed very badly mounted as stated by Nelson, who said 'it was unfortunately very ill set up by the man who obtained it'.

The Orphean Warbler breeds in northwest Africa, throughout Spain, in southern and eastern France and Switzerland, and across southern Europe to the Balkans and as far as northwest India. There are only five accepted records for the British Isles.

Barred Warbler
Sylvia nisoria

'Rare autumn visitant on migration southward, from Northern Europe' is how Nelson described the status of this species in *The Birds of Yorkshire* and he listed only four records, the first of which concerned a female shot at Spurn on 28th August 1884 in an elder hedge near a potato garden on the sandhills. The specimen was exhibited at a meeting of The Zoological Society on 4th November 1884. (*The Zoologist*, 1884, p. 489, and *The Naturalist*, 1884, p. 91).

The second was also shot at Spurn, on 19th October 1892, by G.W. Jalland of Hull, who thought that it might be a Bluethroat; I wonder if he was disappointed! The specimen was acquired by Eagle Clarke for the Royal Scottish Museum (*The Zoologist*, 1892, p. 424, and *The Naturalist*, 1893, p. 14).

The third was shot at Kilnsea by G.E. Clubley on 13th November 1893. It went to the collection of J.H. Gurney (*The Zoologist*, 1894, p. 58, and *The Naturalist*, 1894, p. 15).

The fourth bird, an immature female, was shot in a garden at Skirlaugh on 3rd September 1894 (*The Zoologist*, 1895, p. 57; and *The Naturalist*, 1891, p. 196, and 1897, p. 201).

J.K. Stanford shot two Barred Warblers in 1912, one on 10th September and the other on 14th September, which Chislett published as being 'near Spurn'. In a letter to B.S. Pashby dated 18th June 1968, Stanford said that both birds were in fact shot in the Warren Cottage garden on the Spurn Peninsula.

Spurn was not very well watched for several years after this time, and the next Barred Warbler was not until 21st August 1938 when R.M. Garnett saw one near Kilnsea. It stayed in the area until 9th September, on which date it was also seen by R. Chislett.

Once the Spurn Bird Observatory was operating, from 1946, many small birds were caught in the traps and Barred Warblers featured in 1946, 1948, 1949, 1950 and 1952, in which latter year Chislett published *Yorkshire Birds*. They have occurred annually since then.

Small numbers occur in most years with above average numbers in some. Seven individuals were seen at Spurn in 1968 and nine in 1969. Good numbers occurred in 1971 when, after one bird on 19th August, there were seven on 24th August and one to two birds thereafter on several dates to 24th October. The following year was also above average, with five on 29th August, six on 4th September, five on 19th September, and singles on several intervening dates and on others up to 21st October. Flamborough also had five Barred Warblers on 20th August and single birds on other dates.

The three years 1975, 1976 and 1977 produced more records than usual, when up to four or five birds were seen at Spurn and Flamborough in each autumn and six were at Flamborough on 30th August 1976. Other coastal watchpoints had individuals during the same periods.

There have been six inland records. The first was in 1956 when, on 4th September, just before a storm, in his garden at Masham, R. Chislett saw an obviously tired bird perched on some raspberry canes over which he had built a netting funnel trap into which the bird was easily driven. It was still there next morning, when it appeared much more lively. It is interesting to note that this was the only Barred Warbler recorded in Yorkshire that year. The next was caught in a mist-net at Settle on 8th October 1966 by J.G. Ireland, F.J. Roberts and B. Shorrock and it stayed in the area until 10th. One was seen by A. Grieve at Whitgift, near Goole in the Upper Humber, on 29th August 1975, the day after one had been caught and ringed at Wintersett Reservoir by J.S. Armitage, D.F. Faulkner, P. Smith and G.J. Speight (*The Naturalist*, 1976, p. 76); occurrences along the coast were numerous at this time. The fifth inland record was at Sprotborough Flash, where a juvenile was caught and ringed on 20th August 1978 by R.J. Rhodes and K.H. Pearson, and finally one was caught at Anchor Plain, near York, on 4th September 1983.

The main time of arrival for coastal passage Barred Warblers is from mid August, with a second influx often taking place in late September and early October. The earliest date on record is 31st July, when two birds were at Spurn, one of which was caught by J. Cudworth; the next was on 9th August 1981 at Flamborough.

Some birds pass through well into October and there are records up to the end of that month and a few in early November. Two of the latter concerned birds retrapped at Spurn on 2nd and 3rd November 1974 which had been ringed there on 16th and 10th October respectively, illustrating the fact that some individuals do not move straight through. The latest record involved a bird seen by W. Norman and W.I. Boustead in Locke Park, Redcar, on 7th November 1970.

Anywhere from South Gare to Spurn, from mid August to mid October, especially when easterly winds prevail, a solitary Barred Warbler may be seen in the coastal bushes and sometimes more on the prominent headlands at Flamborough and Spurn.

Lesser Whitethroat
Sylvia curruca

The earliest Yorkshire reference to the Lesser Whitethroat was contained in *Loudon's Magazine* for July 1832, where it was stated that it occurred in Wensleydale. Nelson said that it was more abundant than the Whitethroat near York; that it was fairly abundant near Bedale; and that it nested near Malham and in the Nidd Valley, where it was found up to 1,000 feet (305 m) elevation on the edges of the moors.

Its discontinuous distribution has probably changed but little over the years, for today it is by no means generally spread over the county. It is most widely distributed in the south and in Holderness, and in most of the Pennine dales, but is absent or only very thinly represented over much of the Pennine, North York Moors and Wolds areas and also in the Vales of York and Pickering and on the flat land northwards from York through Thirsk, Northallerton and Richmond.

It was considered to be relatively scarce during the 1950s, but comments during the early 1970s suggested a return to what was thought to be a normal population.

The main period of arrival of this summer visitor is during the last week of April and early May, but a few birds put in an earlier appearance in most years. The earliest on record was a bird at Almholme on 2nd April 1976, and there were two early April records in 1962 when two birds were seen at Staithes on 3rd and one was seen at Harrogate by P.J. Carlton and A.F.G. Walker on the same date. G.K. Yeates saw one at Otley on 4th April 1948, and other early birds have been at Scalby on 7th April 1975, at Redcar on 10th April 1967 and at Spurn on 16th April 1961. Spring passage along the coast is not usually very evident, but in 1981 larger numbers than usual were recorded as follows: 40 at Spurn on 9th May, with 50 next day and 25 on 11th, and 13 at Filey and 48 at Flamborough on 10th.

Most birds have usually deserted their inland breeding areas by early September and later ones are very likely passing through from farther north. Single Lesser Whitethroats at Huddersfield on 27th October 1973 and at Knaresborough Ringing Station on 29th October 1974 are the latest on record at inland sites.

On the coast, some pass through well into October and several individuals of the eastern race *Sylvia curruca blythi*, which breeds in western Siberia, the Kirghiz Steppes and Mongolia, have been recorded. Records up to the middle of October are not unusual, with some later ones in most years, the latest of which have been on 30th October 1971 and on 31st October 1978 at Spurn. Individuals diagnosed as belonging to the race *blythi* were at Spurn on 29th October 1948; 9th October 1949; 26th September 1965; 7th October 1966; 28th October 1971; 19th October 1972; 23rd October to 2nd November 1981; and on 11th and 12th October 1982; most were trapped. A bird at Scarborough on 19th October 1975 was smaller than normal Lesser Whitethroats, with sandy-brown on the upperparts and indistinctly dark ear-coverts, and was considered by R.H. Appleby to belong to this race, as was one at Flamborough on 8th October 1977, another on 1st October 1978 and single birds on 10th and 16th October 1982. It is likely that several birds passing along the coast during October belong to this eastern race.

A bird at Knaresborough Ringing Station on 4th October 1984 was pale sandy-brown on the upperparts, including the crown, with indistinct ear-coverts, a white eye-stripe and throat and buffish flanks, and was more akin to the race *Sylvia curruca minula* in that it completely lacked any grey on the head. R. Evison and I watched it on and off for over an hour as it fed in the uppermost branches of a sycamore, level with our observation point on the tower.

According to Nelson, Lesser Whitethroats 'abounded' at Spurn on 3rd September 1881, but nothing to justify that comment has happened since.

A Lesser Whitethroat ringed at Südbaden in Germany on 3rd September 1969 was retrapped at Hornsea Mere on 10th May 1970; and another ringed at Hornsea Mere on 11th September 1971 was retrapped at Niedersachsen in West Germany on 9th September 1974, being the first recovery of a British-ringed Lesser Whitethroat in that country. One ringed at Spurn on 30th April 1966 was found dead at Attleborough in Norfolk on 13th May 1966, indicating a corrected

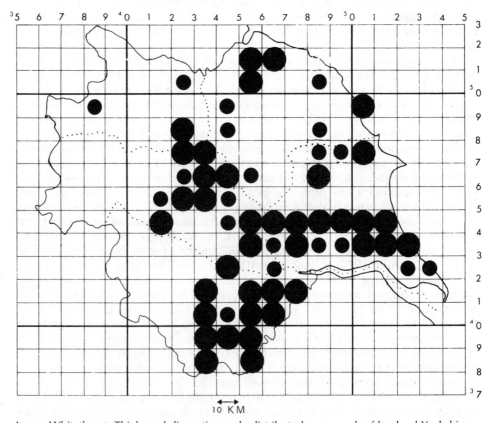

Lesser Whitethroat. Thinly and discontinuously distributed over much of lowland Yorkshire.

migrational overshoot. A juvenile ringed at Doncaster on 24th August 1971 was retrapped while breeding in East Lothian on 22nd June 1976, having reached a ripe old age for a small warbler. One must assume that it was born in that region in 1971 and was on passage when caught at Doncaster.

Nelson's assessment of this species' status at the beginning of the century as 'Summer visitant, generally but thinly distributed' needs some amendment since the species is no longer 'generally' distributed, as can be seen from the breeding distribution map. It perhaps never really was.

Whitethroat
Sylvia communis

In a letter to John Ray dated 29th March 1672, Ralph Johnson of Brignall, near Greta Bridge, wrote thus: 'Honoured Sir ... It is like enough our Whitethoat *Curruca cinerea* is of the Ficedulae, for it is her manner with us to fall upon a ripe cherry, whose skin when she hath broken with a chirp she invites her young brood, who devour it in a moment.' Thus the Whitethroat became chronicled in connection with Yorkshire.

Nelson referred to it as 'Summer visitant, common, and generally distributed' and Allis had previously said that it was abundant when he gave his report to The British Association at York in 1844. In 1952, Chislett considered that Nelson's assessment still described its status, but today, although fairly generally distributed, it is by no means abundant, nor is it even common anywhere.

When the British Trust for Ornithology organised the Atlas of Breeding Birds Survey during the years 1968 to 1972, the Whitethroat was reported in every 10-kilometre square in Yorkshire, but its distribution in each was not adequately portrayed by the overall impression of the results. After a bumper season in 1968, the Whitethroat population crashed in the wintering grounds in Africa and it was absent from many breeding areas for a few years thereafter; this was not, however, indicated on the breeding distribution maps, which had regard for the status over the five years of the survey, and the paucity after 1968 was thus lost. Two breeding sites in the Hatfield area, for instance, which normally held up to 16 pairs, had only three pairs in 1969. The most obvious effects of the population crash were detected by ringers: at Knaresborough Ringing Station, where a programme of constant-effort trapping had been operating since about 1955, only 12 Whitethroats were caught in 1969 after 274 had been ringed in 1968; only 30 percent of an average year's catch was ringed at Hornsea, and many other ringers noted the dramatic decline. During the early 1970s, the breeding population was still well below that of 1968 and B. Shorrock saw only one Whitethroat in the Settle area all summer in 1973. Some observers reported a slight improvement in 1974, but ringing figures at Knaresborough Ringing Station did not improve and the totals for the years 1969 to 1975 were 12, 46, 22, 37, 28, 27 and 23. It should be noted, however, that the population in 1968 was well above normal and it is perhaps unwise to make direct comparisons, although more were certainly trapped annually during the early 1960s.

By 1976, several observers were able to claim a noticeable increase, with 40 pairs located at 12 sites in the Barnsley area, 16 pairs at 11 sites in the Huddersfield area and 47 pairs in the Doncaster district. A general increase was also noted in the Lower Derwent area, the Scarborough district and on Thorne Moors. In that year also, 52 Whitethroats ringed at Knaresborough exceeded the numbers of trapped

Lesser Whitethroats for the first time since 1968. In 1977, 46 pairs were plotted at ten sites in the Barnsley area and the general status was back to normal by this time.

The first Whitethroats usually appear during the third week of April, but the main arrival is during the last week of the month, and in some years not until early May. Some early birds are seen in most years and are often in isolation, being well ahead of the next and more normal first arrivals around 14th or 15th. Early ones have been at Newsome on 3rd April 1901; in the Vale of Pickering on 8th April 1941; an exceptionally early bird sang and was seen in the Vale of Mowbray by D. and J.P. Utley on 18th, 20th and 24th March 1948; one was at Burnsall on 10th April 1949; one at Spurn on 6th April and another at Welton Water on 8th April 1961, in which year the next was not until 15th at Knaresborough; one at Fairburn Ings on 11th April 1977 preceded the next, at Tinsley Sewage-farm, by nine days; and one was at Spurn on 10th April 1981.

Coastal passage during the spring migration period is never very evident, but a marked movement is noted in some years, especially at Spurn where the maximum daily counts have been 40 on 30th April 1955; 35-40 during the period 21st to 23rd May 1956; 35 on 26th May 1957; 35 on 18th May 1958; 22 on 22nd April and 40 on 28th April 1968; 17 on 18th May 1974; 25 on 13th May 1979; and 50 on 11th May 1980.

Autumn passage at the coastal watchpoints is more apparent than during the spring, but the maximum daily counts seldom exceed 20 birds. Exceptions have been: at Spurn, 35 on 25th August 1956, 60 on 31st August 1961, 40 on 29th August 1963, and 40 on 12th and 20th August 1979; 26 at Grimston on 17th August 1979; and 25 at Flamborough on 8th September 1979.

Most inland areas have been deserted by the third week of September, but some birds linger on, or pass through from farther north during the last week, and very late birds have been on Thorne Moors on 1st October 1972 and at Harrogate Sewage-farm on 15th October 1980. Birds pass along the coast in late September and early October in every year, with later ones being on 30th October 1947 at Spurn; 28th October 1963 at Spurn; 30th October 1972 at Hornsea Mere; 31st October 1973 at Spurn; 14th October 1974 at Scalby Mills; 19th October 1975, when two were on Scarborough Castle Hill; 18th October 1978 at Easington; and 26th October 1979 at Flamborough. On 11th November 1968, one was at Spurn which, although it could fly, appeared to have a slightly damaged wing.

Birds ringed during the autumn migration period at Spurn have been recovered in France and Portugal; and single birds ringed at Redcar, Adwick-le-Street and Swillington in autumn have been recovered in Spain. All but one of these recoveries were during the same autumn of ringing. The French recovery was only 13 days after being ringed at Spurn. A bird ringed at Spurn on 23rd May 1960 was found dead in Northampton on 14th May 1961; a juvenile ringed at Spurn on 27th August 1966 was at Wells in Somerset on 17th May 1967; one ringed at South Cave on 8th September 1967 was in Northampton on 12th May 1968. One ringed at Dungeness in Kent on 7th May 1964 was found dead at Guisborough on 8th August 1965, and one ringed at Falsterbo in Sweden on 20th September 1982 was found dead at Cottingham on 10th October 1982.

The Whitethroat has attracted many local names over the years and Nelson listed no fewer than 15, perhaps the most popular being Peggy Whitethroat and Nettle Creeper, both of which are still commonly used by countrymen today.

Garden Warbler
Sylvia borin

There are few places in Yorkshire where, if suitable habitat in the form of dense thickets and understory exists, the Garden Warbler cannot be heard during the summer months. Nelson considered it more abundant in the south and middle of the county than farther north and perhaps this is the case today to some extent, being governed by the scarcity of habitat on much of the northern Pennines and North York Moors, although new conifer plantations on the high ground which allow the growth of deciduous trees about their margins are often frequented.

The Garden Warbler arrives in Yorkshire during the last week of April and in early May, some earlier ones being seen in several years. One at Methley on 7th April 1948 was the earliest recorded for the county.

Spring passage along the coast never involves many of these birds, and 22 at Flamborough on 18th May 1977 is the largest daily count at that period.

In autumn, most birds depart before mid September but, as with other species of warblers, a few remain, or pass through, during the end of that month and into October. Inland stragglers have been recorded at Knaresborough Ringing Station on 25th September 1971 and 26th September 1974; at Wintersett Reservoir on 28th September 1980; and one hit a window and was killed in the centre of Sheffield on 31st October 1979.

Coastal migration in autumn varies numerically from year to year, and the maximum daily counts have been as follows: 30 at South Gare on 1st September 1965; 100 at Spurn on 3rd September 1965, with 50 on 4th and 44 on 5th; 30 at Spurn on 19th September 1969; up to 60 at Spurn between 22nd and 26th August 1971; 45 at Flamborough on 29th August 1976, and 25 on 13th September 1976; a larger movement than usual took place in August 1977, when there were between ten and 35 at Spurn from 19th to 23rd, 14 at Filey on 20th and 16 next day, and 12 at Flamborough on 17th, 45 on 20th, 40 on 21st and 50 on 22nd.

Late birds pass along the coast, or arrive from over the sea to make a landfall at coastal headlands, from South Gare to Spurn. October records occur annually, some individuals being seen up to the end of that month, with a few in November all of which have been at Spurn as follows: one on 6th November 1954; one on 9th November 1965; one on 17th and 18th November 1967; three on 4th November 1968, one of which stayed until 12th, and another was found dead on the road on 16th; one on 10th November 1971; two on 5th and 6th November 1972; and one on 13th November 1984. One was seen at the Point at Spurn on 26th November and 29th December 1966, and again on 5th January 1967.

A bird ringed at Spurn on 21st August 1954 was retrapped on the island of Heligoland on 16th May 1955; one ringed at Redcar on 3rd September 1965 was retrapped at Finistère in France only 12 days later; one ringed at Ilkley on 25th July 1964 was shot at Guadalajara in Spain on 26th August 1965; and one ringed at Adel, near Leeds, on 8th August 1964 was found dead near Lisbon in Portugal on 6th October 1965. Three birds ringed in Belgium, two in August 1979 and one in August 1980, were retrapped at Wintersett Reservoir on 25th August 1979, at Grimston on 4th September 1979 and at Ingleby Greenhow on 31st May 1981 respectively.

In *The Birds of Yorkshire*, Nelson said that the species' partiality for cherries was alluded to in Rennie's *Field Naturalist* (February 1833) as follows:

'I have never seen the Pettychaps in Yorkshire until the cherries are ripe, when they immediately make their appearance and attack the Kentish cherry particularly, being so greedy that I have often taken them with a fishing rod tipped with birdlime while they were pecking at the fruit. If they finish the cherries in the morning they are gone before noon ... in Yorkshire they do not even wait for the late cherries. ...'

Blackcap
Sylvia atricapilla

Nelson considered the Blackcap to be scarcer than it is today for he said of it: 'Summer visitant, somewhat irregularly distributed, and not very numerous. Has occasionally occurred in winter.' Allis, in his report given to the British Association at York in 1844, had said that it was frequently met with in most parts of the county. Today, it is certainly more numerous than the Garden Warbler and occurs in almost every suitable part of the county, requiring, along with the last species, thick deciduous cover from which its song emanates from early April.

The tendency in recent years for several to stay throughout the winter months has somewhat complicated the dates of first arrival of migrants, but the main influx is not usually until the third week of April, although several birds appear during late March and early April in most years where none has wintered. Records of Blackcaps staying throughout the winter, or at least being recorded during the months of December, January and February, have occurred in 25 of the years since 1940, and annually from 1966 since when birds have done so with increasing frequency. Reports came from between three and nine localities each year up to 1975, in which year there were records from 17 different places; 13 in 1976; 16 in 1977; 15 in 1978, and around that number annually to the present time. More than usual occurred in 1983, when 44 birds were recorded from 30 localities in vice-county 64 during January to March and birds were also more numerous in other parts of the county. Birds seen during November, even at inland localities, could still be on migration from farther north and have not been included in these wintering figures.

Most inland areas are clear of birds by the end of September, but some are evident during October and early November. Along the coast, Blackcaps may still be passing in late November and a few have been recorded in December. One to two Blackcaps have been recorded at Spurn during the latter month in almost every year from the mid 1960s, since when the observatory has been manned more regularly. It is possible that some inland wintering birds are derived from these late presumed immigrants from north and west Europe.

Passage along the coast in autumn usually peaks during late September and October, although small numbers of Blackcaps are moving from August in most years. Up to 30 birds may be seen on some days during the period, and maximum daily counts in excess of that number have been at Spurn as follows: 80 on 8th October 1974, of which 64 were caught and ringed and 40 remained next day; 40 on 4th October 1976; 48 on 6th October 1982, with 51 on 9th, 90 on 11th, 78 of which were caught and ringed, and 50 on 21st.

There are many recoveries of Blackcaps ringed in Yorkshire and of others ringed abroad and recorded here. Ten birds ringed at Spurn, Hornsea and South Gare during September to November have been recovered in Spain (three), Portugal (two), Greece (one), the Lebanon (one), Cyprus (one) and Norway (two), the ones from Greece, Cyprus and one from Norway being the first recoveries of British-ringed Blackcaps in those countries. All except two were recovered between late October and March, the exceptions being the one in Lebanon on 2nd May 1973 and one in Norway on 29th June 1981, the latter being no doubt in its breeding area. Six birds ringed at inland sites in April, June, July and September have been recovered in Spain (three), Italy (one), Morocco (one) and Algeria (one). One ringed in Morocco on 14th January 1970 was retrapped at Spurn on 3rd May 1970; one ringed in Norway on 26th October 1976 was retrapped at Hornsea only seven days later on 2nd November; and one ringed in West Germany on 18th June 1978 had moved westwards, probably to spend the winter, and was retrapped at Spurn on 7th October. One ringed in Hertfordshire on 15th July 1967 had moved north to Spurn, where it was retrapped on 4th November; and one ringed at Wintersett Reservoir on 9th May 1979 was in Strathclyde ten days later, and obviously on migration when caught at Wintersett.

Summer visitor, common and generally distributed, also passage migrant along the coast with several staying throughout the winter, summarises the Blackcap's status today.

Greenish Warbler
Phylloscopus trochiloides

The first Yorkshire record of this species, which was only the second for the British Isles, occurred on 21st August 1949 when a small *Phylloscopus* warbler was driven into the Warren trap at Spurn Bird Observatory by G.H. Ainsworth after he had watched it feeding among the leaves of sycamore trees beside the Warren Cottage. It was examined in detail and also seen by H.O. Bunce, D.F. Walker and C. Milner, as well as by two well-known entomologists, W.D. Hincks and Dr Butler.

On 20th April 1957, J.K. Fenton and his wife, together with A. Archer, caught a small warbler, which had a single conspicuous wingbar and dark legs, in the Heligoland trap at the Spurn Chalk Bank which they thought was this species. The bird escaped, however, while being taken back to the observatory for examination and ringing.

Two Greenish Warblers occurred at Spurn in 1960, the first being caught on 4th June and the other on 4th September. One was caught at Spurn on 25th June 1967. One was seen near the Easington Lagoons on 28th August 1968 and later caught and ringed at the Spurn Bird Observatory, where it was released and where it stayed until 1st September.

One caught at Spurn by B.R. Spence, C. Guy and G. Finikin on 8th September 1971 was still there the next day. In 1973, a bird was seen in Locke Park, Redcar, on 23rd and 24th August, by A.J. Wheeldon and others. One stayed from 1st to 5th September 1974 in Kilnsea, where it was watched by S.C. Madge and B. Banson. One sang at Bempton at 06.30 hours on 6th June 1975, being last seen by S.C. Madge and R.G. Hawley at 11.00 hours, and another was seen on Scarborough Castle Hill by R.H. Appleby on 18th October 1975. One which occurred at Flamborough from 21st to 23rd August 1979 was seen by A. Grieve, P.A. Lassey and Miss I. Smith, and another was seen there on 8th August 1981 by P.A. Lassey and D.G. Hobson.

Two were caught and ringed at Spurn Bird Observatory by B. Banson and B.R. Spence on 6th September 1982, one remaining until 8th and the other until 9th. One was seen at Flamborough on 6th May 1983 by D.I.M. Wallace.

There are now about 126 records of this species in the British Isles, most of which have been recorded since 1958. It breeds from Finland and the Baltic States eastwards across central Russia and Siberia, south to the Ukraine, northern Afghanistan, Mongolia, Manchuria and through the Himalayas to central China, and spends the winter mainly in India and Indo-China.

Single birds seen at Redcar on 20th October 1961 and from 6th to 13th November 1966, and at Kilnsea on 19th October 1968, are no longer considered acceptable and were probably eastern Chiffchaffs showing a pale wingbar (*British Birds*, 1985, p. 450).

Arctic Warbler
Phylloscopus borealis

There have been five Yorkshire records of this northern warbler, the first being caught and ringed at Spurn Bird Observatory on 5th September 1964 by J. Cudworth, J.R. Mullins and B.R. Spence.

The second was also at Spurn, where it was caught on 12th October 1966. J.E.S. Walker caught the third in 1969 in his Hornsea garden, where the bird was present from 12th to 14th November.

In 1981, an Arctic Warbler was located in Kilnsea on 2nd September and was caught on 3rd. It stayed in the area until 6th September and was seen by many observers.

One at Flamborough on 4th September 1983 was watched by A.M. Allport, D.G. Hobson, P.A. Lassey and D.I.M. Wallace.

There are now about 136 British records of this species, which breeds from Arctic Scandinavia to Alaska and into Asia and which winters mainly in the Oriental Region, east of India.

Pallas's Warbler
Phylloscopus proregulus

On 22nd October 1960, P.H.G. Wolstenholme and J.M. Butterworth watched a Pallas's Warbler near the Narrow Neck on Spurn Peninsula. The same observers located it again the next morning, and it was eventually caught in the Heligoland trap at Chalk Bank where it was examined in detail and ringed. Several people staying at the observatory saw the bird, which was the first county record of this species (*British Birds*, 1961, pp. 364-5, and *The Naturalist*, 1962, p. 39).

The second county record was also at Spurn, on 3rd November 1963. In 1965, one was trapped there on 24th October where it remained until 28th, and another was present on 11th November which was caught the next day and stayed until

13th. One was at the Point on 19th October 1968, a second bird was present on 20th, and a third was caught on 26th which stayed until 28th; one was at Flamborough on 27th October in the same year. Single birds were at Spurn on 7th November 1970 and on 26th October 1971.

In 1975, several Pallas's Warblers came into Britain, along with more Yellow-browed Warblers than usual, and Yorkshire claimed six Pallas's records. The first was at Spurn on 14th October, when it was caught and ringed, after which it stayed in the area until 17th; a second bird was caught on 18th and a third on 19th, the latter staying until 22nd. One was in Dane's Dyke at Flamborough on 10th November, a second bird was located by D.I.M. Wallace and P.A. Lassey at the Flamborough South Landing later in the day, and R.H. Appleby saw one at Cornelian Bay, Scarborough, on 15th.

In 1976, three birds were recorded: one caught at Spurn on 23rd October stayed throughout the next day; a second was caught on 25th, and another occurred on 7th and 8th November. B. Banson, J. Cudworth, J.E. Dale and B.R. Spence were involved.

A bird caught by M.L. Denton at Blackmoorfoot Reservoir on 12th October 1977 was quite unexpected and the only one seen in Yorkshire that year, illustrating the value of watching at one site regularly over the years. It was also seen by Mr and Mrs J.E. Dale, P.D. Bell and S. Hey.

One was caught at Spurn on 11th October 1979 by A. Crawthorne, B.R. Spence and R. Spencer, and two birds present on 14th were seen by D.E. Murray, B.G. Pepper and G. Smith. One was seen by D.G. Hobson, P.A. Lassey and Miss I. Smith at Flamborough on 27th October; and another bird, located about 2 miles (3.2 km) away on 28th and 29th, was caught on the first date when it was seen by D.G. Hobson, P.A. Lassey and S.C. Madge.

In 1980, two Pallas's Warblers were caught at Spurn on 17th October by J.W. Hartley, B.R. Spence and R. Spencer, both birds being still there the next day when another was reported by J.M. Bayldon, J. Cudworth and N.P. Whitehouse; a fourth appeared on 19th which was seen by P.F. Berry, A.J. Hinchcliffe and P.D. Yates, and another was trapped by B. Banson and B.R. Spence on 31st October. One was seen by C. and R. Hopper and R. Walton at Scarborough on 1st November, and another was seen at Flamborough Head on 15th November by P.A. Lassey and Miss I. Smith.

Four birds occurred in 1981. One was in Beacon Lane at Kilnsea from 18th to 21st October where it was watched by A.S. Butler, J.E. Dale and several others; one was also at the Spurn Warren on 18th which remained until 20th and was seen by P.A. Doherty, J. Cudworth and others; two were on the Spurn Peninsula towards the lighthouse on 18th October which were seen by B. McCarthy and A.J. Harrop; and one was seen by A. Grieve at Easington on 20th October.

In 1982, record numbers were reported in the British Isles and Yorkshire had at least 19 individuals. The first was at Spurn on 9th October, whereafter single birds occurred there on nine dates to 28th; one was at Filey on 10th October and one on Scarborough Castle Hill on 11th. Ten different birds were at Flamborough from 10th October to 9th November, with two on 16th October. The Flamborough birds, which have not yet been submitted to the *British Birds* Rarities Committee, were seen by many birdwatchers (see plate 110).

The Pallas's Warbler breeds in Asia south to the Afghanistan border and the Himalayas, to central China, and winters from northern India to southern China.

Yellow-browed Warbler
Phylloscopus inornatus

Of the four examples mentioned by Nelson in *The Birds of Yorkshire*, three were cited in *The Handbook of British Birds* together with two more which were shot near Spurn on 28th and 30th September 1908 by A.R. Gale and H.F. Witherby respectively. The next record came from Spurn Bird Observatory in 1948, when one was caught on 7th October. In the following year, one was caught there on 6th October by Mrs Chislett and E. Holmes and a second bird was seen near Kilnsea later the same day by E.R. Parrinder and I.J. Ferguson-Lees.

In 1952, in the company of W.H. Jowsey and Miss A. Mason, I watched one in the dead uppermost branches of a sycamore at Knaresborough Ringing Station on 28th September; it was the first inland record for the county. On the following day, R. Chislett caught one at Spurn. One was caught at Spurn on 11th October 1955 and was seen during the next two days. The year 1958 produced two records, also at Spurn, where one was caught on 29th October and another was present from 25th to 27th November.

The species has occurred in every year since 1960, with Spurn being the most regular locality.

More records than usual occurred in 1972, with single birds at Kilnsea on 28th and 29th September; Spurn on 30th September, 7th October and from 21st to 25th October; Flamborough on 30th September and on 14th and 15th October; Redcar Fox Covert on 4th October; and South Gare from 6th to 8th October.

A bird found dead on Scarborough Castle Hill on 1st October 1974 had blowfly larvae in its head area, but I managed to preserve the skin which is now in my collection.

Exceptional numbers were seen in 1975, when Yellow-browed Warblers occurred from 9th October to 14th November at several coastal localities. A 'fall' of immigrant passerines on the first date produced three Yellow-browed Warblers on Scarborough Castle Hill and four at Spurn, with single birds at Filey and in Dane's Dyke at Flamborough the next day; three were at Flamborough South Landing on 12th and three were in Dane's Dyke on 15th, with one or two remaining at these two localities until the end of the month, the latest being one at each place on 14th November; three were at Ravenscar on 12th October, and single birds at Seamer Road Mere on 13th and on Scarborough Castle Hill on 24th and 25th; Spurn had one on 17th and two on 19th, on which date one was also at Kilnsea; one was in Locke Park, Redcar, on 11th, with two next day and another on 15th; and one was at South Gare on 15th.

Between five and ten birds occurred each autumn of the years 1976 to 1980 and more than usual in 1981, when there were two at Flamborough on 3rd October, one on 4th and 17th, then seven on 18th, three on 19th, two on 25th and single birds on 31st and on 1st, 7th and 30th November; one was at Kilnsea on 18th October, one from 18th to 20th and another from 21st to 25th, with other single birds on 19th and 22nd; and one was on Scarborough Castle Hill on 24th October.

At least 12 individual birds were at Flamborough in 1982, between 3rd October and 12th November, including four on 8th October and three on 16th and 23rd. One was at Grimston on 5th October, and from one to four birds were in the Spurn/Kilnsea area from 6th to 14th October.

510

Fewer occurred in 1983: Flamborough had singles on 29th September and on 16th-17th October, with two on 11th November; one was at Easington from 22nd to 24th October, and one was trapped in Errington Woods, Marske, on 1st October.

In 1984, from one to four occurred on several dates in the Spurn/Kilnsea area between 23rd September and 11th October, with seven on 26th September. Details from other localities are not to hand at the time of writing.

Inland records are scarce, but there were two in 1980, the first being seen by Mrs J. Hall at Harrogate Sewage-farm on 15th October and the other by P. Harrison and D. Proctor in Bretton Park on 2nd November. P.T. Treloar saw one at Knaresborough Ringing Station on 23rd October 1983.

Nelson's status comment of 'Accidental visitant in autumn from Asia, of rare occurrence' needs some amendment, for it is now more accurately termed a rare autumn passage migrant of annual occurrence in small numbers along the coast, with an occasional record inland.

The Yellow-browed Warbler breeds across Siberia, south to Afghanistan, the northwest Himalayas and northern Mongolia, and winters from Afghanistan and India to Malaysia and southern China.

Radde's Warbler
Phylloscopus schwarzi

This small warbler, which breeds in Siberia south to Manchuria and Korea, and winters from Burma to Indo-China, has occurred in the British Isles on about 46 occasions. Five of these birds have been recorded on the Yorkshire coast.

The first was at Spurn Point, where a bird remained from 14th to 16th October 1978 and was caught and ringed on the first date. J. Adlard, B.R. Spence and R. Sturman took detailed notes of this new county species, and it was photographed in the hand by J.W. Hartley and others (see plates 111 and 112).

Four Radde's Warblers occurred in 1982, the first being at Flamborough Head on 11th October. It stayed until 13th, when a second bird appeared which stayed until 15th, when it was caught and ringed by P.A. Lassey, D.G. Hobson and P.A. Doherty. The third was also at Flamborough, where it was seen by J.M. Pearson, P.A. Lassey and others on 17th. One was trapped at Spurn on 30th October by J. Cudworth and C.J. Mackenzie-Grieve. The Flamborough birds have not yet been submitted to the *British Birds* Rarities Committee.

Dusky Warbler
Phylloscopus fuscatus

On 26th October 1965, a Dusky Warbler was seen at Spurn Bird Observatory and caught and ringed the next day. It was seen by C. Bower, C.W. Holt, B.R. Spence and M. Densley who photographed it in the hand, the resulting colour slides being shown at the spring meeting of the Yorkshire Naturalists' Union Ornithological Section at Leeds in March 1966. This was only the fourth British record of this eastern warbler, which normally winters in India, Burma and China.

The second county record, which was the fourteenth for Britain, was also at Spurn Point on 7th November 1970. While R.G. Hawley was sitting near the old parade ground in the Point camp area, a small dark warbler with an unusual call note flew past him into some bushes, where he had close views of it and was able to make detailed notes in the company of P.H.G. Wolstenholme.

One occurred at Flamborough Head from 26th September to 4th October 1976. It was caught and ringed on the first date by P.A. Lassey and D.I.M. Wallace.

Bonelli's Warbler
Phylloscopus bonelli

The Bonelli's Warbler entered the Yorkshire list of birds on 15th October 1970, when one was caught at Spurn Bird Observatory. It was considered to belong to the eastern race *Phylloscopus bonelli orientalis*, which breeds in Europe eastwards from the Balkans and Poland.

A second example was trapped at Wilton, near Redcar, on 20th August 1972 by S.C. and W. Norman, and another was seen at Spurn later in the month on 29th and 30th August by J.C. Lidgate and B.R. Spence.

In 1976, one was singing in Kilnsea churchyard on 30th May which G.E. Dobbs and M. Hollingworth saw and recognised as this species, and another was seen at Flamborough by C.D.R. Heard and others from 2nd to 9th October 1976.

Details of one seen by D.I.M. Wallace at Holme-on-Spalding-Moor on 21st May 1983 have not yet been submitted.

The species breeds from northwest Africa, Iberia and France, eastwards through southern Europe and Asia Minor to the Near East, and northwards to southern Germany. It spends the winter in tropical Africa.

Wood Warbler
Phylloscopus sibilatrix

The Wood Warbler was known in connection with Yorkshire as early as 1676, when Willughby mentioned it in his *Ornithology*. Although Nelson referred to it as being common in a few places in the East Riding, it no longer breeds there, and away from the hanging woodlands of the Pennine foothills and the slopes of the North York Moors it is very scarce. Nelson also said that one of its favourite haunts was Rudding Park, near Harrogate, but none nests there today. In 1971, six singing males were in woodland near Doncaster and five pairs probably bred, a most unusual occurrence for that district. Wherever deciduous woods occur in the areas mentioned, especially those with beech, the Wood Warbler can be found in small numbers.

The first migrants to arrive usually make their appearance during the third week of April, but the main influx and general arrival is often not until early May. Birds before mid April are scarce, and there have been only a handful, as follows: one near Barnsley on 8th April 1879; three in Bolton Abbey Woods on 10th April 1957; two in Haw Park on 9th April 1960; one near Redcar on 11th April 1963; one at Knotford Nook on 5th April 1980; and one at Lindley Reservoir on 10th April 1980.

Most birds have departed from their breeding haunts before the end of August and later ones are few. Some pass along the coast well after the Yorkshire breeders have pulled out and doubtless come from farther afield; a few occur in most autumns, with an occasional one during the spring. Most pass through during August and September, late birds being at Spurn on 26th September 1940, 17th September 1968 and 27th September 1973, with one in East Park, Hull, on 21st September 1969 and two on Scarborough Castle Hill on 26th September 1976.

In 1978, more passed along the coast in spring than is usual: ten were at Hornsea Mere on 6th May, six on 7th and single birds on seven dates to 21st; three were at Flamborough on 5th May; single birds were at Grimston on 20th; and at Flamborough on 21st, with two there on 22nd; two were are Seamer on 6th and three in Duncombe Park, Helmsley, on the same date; and one was at Spurn on 16th May.

On 15th September 1972, a strange-looking individual appeared at Spurn which had a greyish wash on the upperparts, especially on the crown, hindneck and wing-coverts, and the yellow of the upper breast was also rather pale, giving the bird a very washed-out look. It stayed until 21st October, which in itself was an unusual event.

The Wood Warbler is a summer visitor to the deciduous woodlands in the hill country, especially in the valleys on the eastern slopes of the Pennines and North York Moors, and occasionally though rarely in woodland on the plains. It is very scarce away from its breeding haunts, and passage along the coast involves very few birds, most of which probably originate from farther north and in Europe.

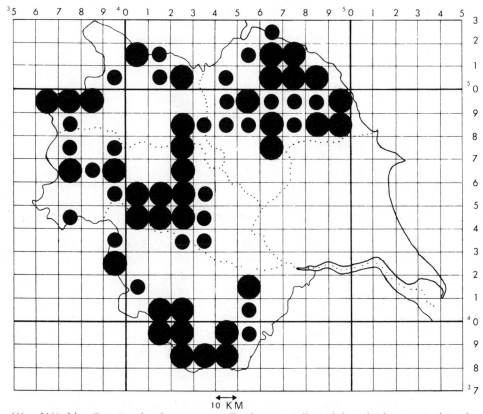

Wood Warbler. Restricted to hanging woodlands, especially with beech, this species breeds mainly on the eastern slopes of the Pennines and North York Moors.

Chiffchaff
Phylloscopus collybita

The Chiffchaff is distributed over much of Yorkshire during the summer months, but only sparsely, and always in fairly mature timber. Chislett said that in hedgerows, a common habitat in southern England, it is rarely seen or heard, and the same is true at the present time. It does not penetrate to the upper parts of the western dales but is well represented in the wooded parts of the lower areas and onto the plains, although it becomes thinly scattered in the East Riding. It is perhaps most common in the central and southwestern parts of the county.

It will breed in large suburban gardens if large trees exist. A pair did so in my neighbour's garden some years ago, building its nest in a lonicera bush about 2 feet (60 cm) from the ground and complete with a characteristic entrance ramp.

The Chiffchaff is always an early bird in the spring and a few have overwintered in recent years. The arrival dates of the first migrants are often clouded by the presence of these wintering individuals, but the main influx is usually during the first week of April, with forerunners being seen from mid March in several years. Single birds at Sedbergh on 9th March 1953 and at Adwick-le-Street, near Doncaster, on 5th and 6th March 1960 may have been newly arrived in those areas from farther south in England or from abroad; it is impossible to say.

A few have been recorded at inland localities during every winter since 1965, with birds at 12 localities in 1974 and at ten in 1975. Birds pass along the coast during October and into November, several of which are diagnosed as belonging to one or other of the two races *Phylloscopus collybita abietinus*, which breeds from Scandinavia and west Russia south to Iran, and *Phylloscopus collybita tristis*, which breeds in northern Siberia and south to Lake Baikal. Both are characterised by being greyer on the upperparts, and individuals of the latter race, especially, often have a pale wingbar. Nelson recorded several examples shot at Easington and Spurn on 17th October 1896 which were sent to H.E. Dresser, who ascribed them to one of the two eastern forms (*The Naturalist*, 1897, p. 17).

Passage along the coast never involves large numbers. The only indication of anything other than a trickle of birds is a comment in the county bird report for 1965 that 'hundreds' of *Phylloscopus* warblers, many of which would have been of this species, were in the area of South Gare on 1st October, a year in which Spurn had very few.

Birds often sing while on migration, and the familiar song of the Chiffchaff can be heard during September and October from solitary birds as they move through the county.

There are few ringing recoveries, though two of these concern birds ringed abroad and recovered in Yorkshire: a juvenile ringed in Madrid, Spain, on 26th November 1976 was caught at Wilton, near Redcar, on 23rd April 1978; and one ringed at Falsterbo in Sweden on 16th October 1981 was retrapped at Spurn on 8th October 1982. A Chiffchaff ringed at Brighouse on 7th September 1966 was retrapped at Dungeness in Kent 14 days later. One ringed at Bamburgh in Northumberland on 28th May 1967 was retrapped at Spurn on 23rd June 1967, a most peculiar date for a bird to be moving south — which overshooting spring migrants often do in order to get back into Europe. One ringed at Lewes in Sussex on 15th September 1978 was retrapped at Allerton Park, near Knaresborough, on 12th May 1979.

Nelson described the status of the Chiffchaff as 'Summer visitant; common, and generally distributed in wooded localities of the eastern and central districts; less numerous in the south-west and rare or exceptional in the north-west.' It is not so common in the eastern parts as implied by that assessment, but otherwise the comment holds true today.

Willow Warbler
Phylloscopus trochilus

The earliest allusion to this species in Yorkshire was contained in a letter dated 16th August 1799 from Charles Fothergill to William Fothergill stating that he had seen and shot several Willow Warblers in Askham Bogs, near York (Morris's *Naturalist*, 1854, iv, p. 167).

The species is commonly and generally distributed over the whole county, even onto the high moorlands where forestry plantations have been colonised. The main arrival of migrants is usually from mid April, but birds are recorded before the end of the first week of that month in every year, the earliest known to Chislett being on 30th March 1946 at Bretton, on 31st March 1946 at Masham and on 1st April 1946 at Scotton. Since that time there have been several March records, the earliest being on 25th March 1956, when P.J. Stead saw one at Gouthwaite Reservoir; 25th March 1963, when two were singing at Eccup Reservoir; and 24th March 1977, when one was at Potteric Carr, with one at Grantley near Ripon, the next day. Other late-March birds have occurred in 14 of the years since 1955, mainly only one record annually, but there were four in 1963 and four again in 1971.

Passage along the coast during the spring migration period never involves many birds, but small numbers, seldom exceeding 20 or 30 on any one day, are often seen: maxima have been 80 in Locke Park, Redcar, on 4th May 1970; 80 at Flamborough on 10th May 1980; 60 at South Gare on 8th May 1981; and 55 at Spurn on 11th May 1982. At this period, birds of the northern race *Phylloscopus trochilus acredula*, which breeds from Scandinavia eastwards to western Siberia and south to the Ukraine and the Kirghiz Steppes, have been recorded, or suspected, in several years. In 1970, one caught at Spurn on 30th April was ascribed to this race, as were four on 16th May and three on 24th May; most of the 40 seen at Spurn on 17th April 1977 were thought to be of this race, 12 of which were caught on 30th April. One caught inland at Adwick-le-Street Sewage-farm on 16th April 1971 was also considered to belong to this race, as was another at Spurn on 4th May.

In 1972, S.G. Wilson regularly watched a wood near Market Weighton and recorded a marked passage of Willow Warblers. After two birds on 12th April, 26 appeared on 16th, with 100 on 29th and no fewer than 300 on 30th.

Passage was noted at Fairburn Ings on 1st May 1979, when 60 birds were present. In 1977, the main arrival was very marked and occurred between 15th and 20th April, after which 43 singing males were on Thorne Moor on 23rd, 45 at Wintersett Reservoir on 24th and 59 in the Coxley Valley on 25th; the breeding population at Askham Bog in 1977 was 70 pairs.

Autumn passage starts in July, and is more evident than that during the spring. Some large numbers sometimes occur, especially when the weather conditions are favourable, with easterly winds to bring migrants over from the Continent. Daily maxima have been 100 at Flamborough on 23rd August 1976; 285 at Grimston on 25th August 1978; a large arrival on 19th August 1979, when 120 were at Spurn,

300 at Grimston, 70 at Flamborough and 85 at Filey, with 140 at Spurn on 20th and 115 still present there on 24th; and in 1980, when 90 were at Spurn on 23rd August, and 20 were at Filey and 60 at Flamborough on 31st.

Some stragglers pass along the coast into October, and have been seen up to 20th in most years. There have been a few during early November, as follows: one at Spurn on 3rd and 4th November 1946, in which year one was also seen by J.P. Utley in Lower Teesdale; one at Spurn on 3rd November 1963; and one in Locke Park, Redcar, on 11th November 1982.

Most birds have departed from their breeding haunts before mid September, but some linger on, or pass through, after this time; Willow Warblers in early October are not rare. Later ones include two in Roundhay Park, Leeds, on 9th November 1957, one of which was caught; and other late dates are 18th October 1959 at Ewden Bank; 18th December 1960, when a pale-legged *Phylloscopus* was in Hornby Park, near Northallerton; 16th October 1960, when G.R. Bennett saw and heard one singing at Hornsea Mere; 21st October 1961, when one was at Knaresborough Ringing Station and another at Redcar; one sang at Lindley Reservoir on 17th October 1974; one sang at Adel on 24th October 1976; one was caught at Hackenthorpe on 14th November 1976; single birds were at Adel Dam on 30th October 1977 and at Fairburn Ings on 20th November 1977; and two were in Scabba Wood, near Doncaster, on 25th October 1981. One at Scotton Banks, Knaresborough, on 15th December 1954 was seen and heard by Mrs G. Clarkson, who reported the occurrence to R. Chislett.

Willow Warblers pass through several inland sites during the autumn from mid July to the end of August, and ringers have intercepted many during this period. At Knaresborough Ringing Station, 527 were caught in 1973 and 400 in 1976. Similarly large numbers have been caught at Wintersett Reservoir and at other stations.

Ringing recoveries have been fairly numerous and to list them individually is unnecessary. They have come from France, Spain, Portugal, Morocco and Algeria. Speed of movement is illustrated by one ringed at Keyingham, near Hull, on 4th September 1953 which was at Toledo in Spain on 11th October 1953; one ringed at Spurn on 22nd August 1963 which was in Portugal on 11th September 1963; one ringed as a juvenile at Adwick-le-Street, near Doncaster, on 27th July 1963 which was shot at Pamplona in Spain on 26th August 1963; and a juvenile ringed at South Gare on 6th August 1974 which was found dead in Essex 12 days later. Several individuals have been retrapped in subsequent years at their place of ringing, and have included birds that have made the annual journey to the wintering grounds in tropical Africa up to five times.

The nest, although traditionally built on the ground, is sometimes built above it. In July 1949, R.M. Garnett found one 15 feet (4.6 m) up in a Virginia creeper against a house wall in Malton. A.F.G. Walker found one near Ramsgill in Upper Nidderdale in 1955 built 4½ feet (1.4 m) off the ground in a hawthorn hedge, and a nest at Knaresborough Ringing Station in 1975 was built into the top of a 4-feet (1.2-m) high bramble bush under which a feral cat had four kittens for a short while! A nest at Danby-in-Cleveland on 18th June 1976 contained one egg and a good-sized adder.

Nelson described the Willow Warbler as an abundant and generally distributed summer visitor. Such it remains today, and we now know it to be also a passage migrant to and from northern Europe.

Goldcrest
Regulus regulus

This, the smallest of British birds, is a resident in Yorkshire, and also a passage migrant, often in very large numbers. During the breeding season, it is fairly well distributed over most of the county and is absent only in treeless districts. Wherever suitable timber exists, in the former either of mature woodland or of dense stands of pine or spruce, their thin calls may be heard during the summer months. The planting of conifers on otherwise barren moorland has doubtless benefited the species, both during the breeding season and in the winter months. Suburban gardens and parks are used for nesting so long as the timber is mature and preferably mixed with some conifers.

Each autumn, waves of Goldcrests cross the North Sea and come to the British Isles, many hundreds occurring along the Yorkshire coast in some years. Nelson said that they 'generally arrive simultaneously with the Short-eared Owl and Woodcock, hence one of their local names — "Woodcock Pilot". In 1881 they appeared on 5th September, fully a month in advance of the time when they may usually be expected, being observed at Spurn and also at Redcar, where they sometimes come into fishermen's cottages, and remain as long as there are sufficient flies to support them.'

The fishermen at that time reported that Goldcrests frequently alighted on the smacks in the North Sea and in foggy weather hundreds perished. When Edward Blyth was sailing from Scotland to London in 1833, a flock landed on the ship when 14 miles (22.4 km) off Whitby.

In some years, according to Nelson, they occurred on the sandhills at Spurn in hundreds about the middle of October, some being so exhausted that they could easily have been caught in a butterfly net. In 1882, a 'great rush' occurred and they covered the whole length of the coast, the migration lasting for 92 days from 6th August. They arrived at Spurn daily during October until the hedges and the grass on the sand dunes positively swarmed with them, and on the sandhills near Redcar a huge flock like a swarm of bees came directly in over the sea and settled among the hedgerows where Nelson was watching for wildfowl. Other large invasions occurred in 1892, 1898 and 1906.

The story of Goldcrests arriving on the backs of Short-eared Owls may have some truth in it and should certainly not be mocked out of hand. Nelson mentioned an incident on 16th October 1881 when a contractor working on the Tees Breakwater saw a Short-eared Owl 'flopping' across the sea and, as it drew near, saw a small object between its shoulders; it landed near where he was standing, and a small bird flew off its back which was caught by one of his men and proved to be a Goldcrest. Hitch-hiking in this way is not impossible and a small bird, especially a Goldcrest, could so land on the back of a slowly flying bird as a last resort, during the long and hazardous crossing of the North Sea. The phenomenon has been known for many years to travellers in the East and also in America.

We now know that the Goldcrest arrives on the east coast any time from late August to October and early November, in numbers varying annually, depending on the strength and direction of the wind at the peak migration times. In 1948, they first occurred at Spurn on 7th October, and on the morning of 30th 'appeared in every bush along the promontory' and about 60 birds entered the Warren trap. A coasting ship that was piloted into the Humber on 29th October was 'covered with

Goldcrests' that had come aboard between Whitby and Flamborough; as she entered the river, the birds left and flew south into Lincolnshire. Inland areas had more Goldcrests than usual during the ensuing weeks.

In 1959, migrants appeared on 29th August and others arrived daily during September, with a large arrival on 10th October when they were all over the peninsula and 800 were estimated to be present; 76 were caught and ringed. Other coastal areas had large numbers, too: 120 were at Flamborough on 7th October with 'fantastic numbers' on 11th; 350-400 were at Filey Brigg, also on 11th; 200 were on Scarborough Castle Hill on 17th; and a 'huge influx' occurred on 10th at Redcar, where they remained numerous until 20th.

Other years of above average numbers were 1961; 1965; 1971, in which year 200 were at Grimston Wood, near Withernsea, in early September and 225 were at Spurn on 26th October; and 1973, when Spurn had 120 on 4th and 5th October, 100 were in Filey Ravine on 5th and 150 were on Scarborough Castle Hill on the same date, while later in the month 550 were at Spurn on 19th October and many others were seen all along the coast. These figures were overshadowed by an enormous influx during late September and October 1975. At Spurn, 65 birds occurred on 28th September and treble figures were counted from 10th to 22nd October, 810 on 11th being the daily maximum. No fewer than 1,063 were ringed during the 13 days, including 308 on 11th. Numbers dropped quickly thereafter and only nine birds remained at the end of October. On 9th, a day of easterly winds, fog and drizzle, many arrived on Scarborough Castle Hill, where R.H. Appleby estimated at least 800 to be present; 300 were at Flamborough on 11th, with 450 the next day. Goldcrests were recorded along the whole length of the coastline from Teesmouth to Spurn, and many thousands must have come in. Flamborough Head had 300 birds on 29th October 1976, after smaller numbers had been present from mid September. No fewer than 760 were at Flamborough on 30th September 1983 and 2,000 on 1st October. Such is the situation in most years, but numbers are not always so spectacular. Inland observers often record larger numbers coincident with arrivals on the coast.

In the spring of 1960, more Goldcrests than usual occurred along the coast as birds prepared to leave for their breeding grounds in northern Europe.

The autumn immigrants are slightly larger than the British resident population and are brighter green on the back. This is obvious in skins, and several that I have received from the coast have been so coloured. The Continental population breeds from Scandinavia eastwards to Asia.

The resident birds suffer badly during very severe weather, and after hard winters in 1947, 1962 and 1978 numbers were well down. Recovery is sometimes slow, but, as with most other small birds, is apparently often complete after only one or two seasons in some cases.

Of the many Goldcrests ringed, several have been recovered abroad in Germany, Denmark, Switzerland and France in spring, after being ringed at Spurn during the autumn. Two birds ringed in Finland in September 1973 were retrapped at Spurn in October of the same year and were the first recoveries of Finnish-ringed Goldcrests in Britain. One ringed at Grimston on 22nd April 1973 was found dead in Denmark on 25th May 1973. One ringed at Spurn on 10th October 1973 was retrapped in Essex 15 days later. One ringed on Fair Isle on 5th October 1973 was found dead near Doncaster on 1st January 1974.

The status of the Goldcrest remains as Nelson described it in 1907: 'Resident; generally distributed in suitable localities. A great influx of winter visitants and birds of passage in autumn.'

Firecrest
Regulus ignicapillus

Conforming to almost the same pattern as the two eastern *Phylloscopus* warblers, Yellow-browed and Pallas's, the Firecrest now occurs annually in Yorkshire. Nelson could record only six reliable instances of its occurrence in the county and, surprisingly, Chislett could add only two during the 45 years which he reviewed in 1952.

Nelson's six records were: one mentioned by Allis in 1844 which occurred at Woodend, near Thirsk; one found exhausted in a plantation at Armitage Bridge, near Huddersfield, on 3rd September 1814; one in Endcliff Woods, near Sheffield, in 1878; one shot at Clifton, near York, in December 1880; one killed by a boy at Easington on 4th November 1889; and the last at Spurn on 15th October 1892. It is curious that the first four records are from inland sites, the exception today.

Chislett's two additions concerned one shot by J.K. Stanford in the Warren Cottage garden at Spurn on 28th September 1912 following a large influx of Goldcrests on 24th and 25th; and one at Spurn on 23rd October 1938, among numerous Goldcrests, which was watched by G.H. Ainsworth and J. Lord.

Since 1956, Firecrests have occurred in all but two years, with 23 records coming from inland localities. The first record since Ainsworth and Lord's bird in 1938 was of one seen in Beacon Lane, Kilnsea, by J.A.S. Borrett and myself and later by D.A. Rushforth on 16th October 1956. Another was seen at Spurn on 19th April 1958 by E.S. Skinner, C. Winn and several others. Four were seen in 1959, two at Flamborough on 13th September, another caught there on 15th November and one at Marske on 22nd November.

The first inland record of this period was of one at Coxley in the West Riding on 13th March 1960 which was seen by A. Frudd and R. Wills. Spurn had Firecrests in the same year: one from 9th to 11th April; one on 1st and 2nd October; and another from 20th to 25th October, with two on 21st. There was only one record in 1961, at Spurn on 9th April. There were four records at Spurn in the autumn of 1962, and another inland at Eccup Reservoir on 15th November which was seen by G.R. Naylor. Single birds occurred in 1963, 1964, 1965 and 1967, with two in 1966 and three in 1969 and 1970, at Spurn, South Gare and Jackson's Bay near Scarborough, mostly at the former locality.

One occurred inland at Fairburn Ings on 22nd November 1969 and remained in the area until 15th February 1970. It was caught and ringed during its stay and was seen by very many observers.

In 1971, more were recorded at Spurn than ever before, with single birds on 11th and 23rd September; one to six birds from 26th to 31st October and one on 3rd and 6th November. One was in Locke Park, Redcar, on 25th April of the same year.

Even more were recorded in 1972. After one was shot at Driffield on 5th January and one sang at Spurn on 8th and 9th May, there was an influx in October when birds were seen at five coastal localities. Spurn had the most, with one on 1st, seven on 2nd, eight on 3rd, three on 4th and singles on 5th, 6th, 11th and 14th; 11 were caught and ringed. In addition, there were two at South Gare on 3rd and 4th October and one on 5th; one at Flamborough on 1st and 4th; and one at Hornsea on 3rd which was caught and ringed, as was one of the South Gare birds.

There were single birds at Spurn on 5th, 17th and 25th April, 14th May and 16th September 1973, and the species was recorded at four other places during the autumn: one at Bempton on 25th August; two at Flamborough on 25th and 26th September; one at Brough Haven on 21st September; and one at Fairburn Ings on 10th November which was seen by P.D. Kirk, C. Winn and others.

In 1974, single birds were at Spurn on 12th and 13th May and on 3rd, 23rd-24th and 26th October, and again on 10th November. One was at Ravenscar on 15th October, and two occurred inland: one at Broomhead Reservoir, seen by D. Herringshaw and D. Gosney on 26th October, and one in the Porter Valley, Sheffield, on 17th November.

A remarkable number of inland records occurred in 1975, with single birds at Dale Dike Reservoir, near Sheffield, on 23rd February; Thorne Moor on 29th March; Swillington on 1st April; near Ripon on 10th May, in song; Wyming Brook, near Sheffield, on 30th August; Dore, near Sheffield, on 11th September; Blackmoorfoot Reservoir on 18th October, which was caught and ringed; Crookesmoor, near Sheffield, on 24th October; Langsett on 2nd November; and Headingley on 27th November: a quite unprecedented series of records. Coastal birds were also numerous, with singles at Hornsea Mere on 16th and 18th March and again on 28th November; Bempton on 23rd March, 18th to 20th April and two on 27th April; Ravenscar on 12th October; and Spurn, where there was one on 7th April, two on 14th, two on 20th and two on 27th; one was in Kilnsea churchyard on 21st October and single birds were there on 22nd October and 22nd November.

In contrast, 1976 produced relatively few Firecrests, six along the coast in spring being no doubt connected with the previous autumn influx. The only three in autumn were two at Spurn and one at Flamborough.

M.L. Denton caught and ringed two birds at Blackmoorfoot Reservoir in 1977, one on 25th March and the other on 15th April. Seven birds occurred on the coast in that year, including one at Flamborough on 4th January and one at Spurn on 17th April, the others being in the autumn.

Another inland bird was seen in 1978, at Askham Bog, by D. Braithwaite on 11th April. Only three others occurred: at Flamborough on 29th March and from 15th to 21st October; and at Burniston on 23rd April.

There were eight records in the spring of 1979, including one in song at Hornsea Mere on 17th and 18th April. An influx in autumn brought several birds, all in October: one was at Filey on 1st and 2nd; one at Scarborough on 1st; one at Flamborough on 22nd, two on 24th, five on 26th, one on 27th and three on 28th; further singles at Filey, on 24th and 26th October; one at Grimston on the Holderness coast on 27th; and one at Kilnsea on 7th, with two on 26th and 27th.

Even larger numbers were seen in 1980. One was at Low Dalby on 19th February; single birds were at Spurn on 29th March, 3rd April, 9th, 12th, 26th and 27th May; and one was at Flamborough on 4th and 6th April. In the autumn, single birds were at Filey on 1st and 12th September, 15th October and 2nd November. Flamborough had single birds on 28th September and 12th October, then three on 1st November with at least 11 on 2nd, three on 3rd, two on 5th, five on 7th, three on 8th and 10th, six on 15th, seven on 16th and finally two on 22nd. Four at Spurn on 1st November were joined by a fifth on 3rd, and up to two were present up to 7th with five again on 8th; of these, one remained to the end of the year and another to at least 23rd November; three more appeared on 17th November, two of which were still there on 23rd, and another was seen on 30th. J.I. Martin watched one inland at Broomhead Reservoir on 2nd November.

In 1981, there were records of 12 Firecrests along the coast between January and May and of ten in autumn between 5th September and 11th November. One occurred inland at Edgerton, near Huddersfield, on 14th February; one at Lindley Wood Reservoir, near Otley, on 4th and 5th April; and one at Sawdon, near Scarborough, on 6th April.

There were at least 17 birds along the coast during January to April 1982 and from September to November, including three at Flamborough on 7th October. One was at Kilnsea on 1st June. There were also eight inland records: at the Botanical Gardens in Sheffield from 3rd to 5th January; at Harrogate Golf Course on 19th August; at Lodge Moor on 4th October; near Everingham on 31st October; at Langsett on 6th November; at Ingbirchworth on 7th November; and at Woolley Wood, near Sheffield, on 9th and 10th November.

In 1983, there were records from six coastal places on several dates between 26th March and 24th May, and in the autumn Flamborough had one to two birds on five dates between 2nd October and 14th November. There were four inland records: one at Bessacar, near Doncaster, from 9th to 14th April; one in Woolley Wood, near Sheffield, on 15th March and 25th April; one on the Anchor Plain, near York, on 20th November; and one at Thorpe Marsh on 26th December.

The status of the Firecrest has certainly changed during the last 25 years. It can no longer be regarded as a 'rare autumn visitant', which it was described as by Nelson on the strength of his six records, and which it remained until 1956. Since then, it has become an annual autumn and winter visitor in small numbers.

Spotted Flycatcher
Muscicapa striata

This summer visitor is generally distributed over the whole of Yorkshire, and it may be found breeding in almost any locality ranging from thick woodland in the low-lands to the gullies of the Pennines and North York Moors and among suburban development where some mature trees exist. The ancient name of 'Beam Bird', mentioned by Pennant, was adjoined to it from its habit of nesting on the ends of beams in outbuildings and other man-made structures.

It is not an early migrant and the main influx does not usually occur until well into May. April birds have been recorded in a few years, and Nelson mentioned one on 9th April at Skipton but did not give the year. In his *Yorkshire Birds*, Chislett mentioned one seen by H.B. Booth on 26th April 1922 at Bolton Abbey and said there was no recent record before early May, but in the Yorkshire Naturalists' Report for 1948 he published one at Coniston Cold on 25th April. There have been April records in 16 of the years since 1948, mainly during the last week of the month, the earliest being on 16th at Addingham in 1976, seen by F.A. Wardman, and on 18th at Cawthorne in 1967.

Most breeding areas have been deserted by mid September, but some birds are seen to the month end in most years and a few into early October. The latest county records are of one seen by P.J. Carlton in the Vicarage garden at Gouthwaite Reservoir on 2nd November 1975; one seen by S.M. Lister at Hornsea on 6th November 1982; and one at Spurn on 10th November 1984.

Passage along the coast is never very heavy and rarely involves more than single figures on any one day. Exceptions were on 2nd September 1963, when 50 were on the Spurn Peninsula; on 31st August 1977, when counts in two different areas of

Hornsea Mere by R.G. Hawley, I.G. Howard and W.F. Curtis recorded 35 and 20 birds; and on 25th August 1978, when 22 were counted at Grimston by A.W. Wallis and where there were 49 the next day.

A few late birds pass along the coast up to mid October, some later ones being on 18th October 1959 on Scarborough Castle Hill; and single birds at Spurn on 29th October 1966 and 20th October 1968, with two on 24th October 1983.

A nestling ringed at Knaresborough on 27th May 1957 was recovered at Cordoba in Spain on 2nd October 1957; one ringed at Maltby on 1st August 1965 was shot in France on 3rd September 1965; and one ringed as a nestling at Knaresborough on 5th August 1967 was retrapped near Billingham in Durham on 30th June 1968. Two birds ringed abroad have been recovered in Yorkshire: one ringed on the island of Heligoland on 14th June 1961 was retrapped at Spurn Bird Observatory on 15th July 1962; and one ringed at Finistère in France on 2nd September 1961 was found dead at Middlesbrough on 18th June 1962.

Red-breasted Flycatcher
Ficedula parva

'Accidental summer visitor from the European Continent, of extremely rare occurrence' is how Nelson described the status of this species in 1907. At that time, only one example was known from Yorkshire, which was the seventh record for Britain. It was obtained by J. Morley of Scarborough on 23rd October 1889 in a wood among beech trees. 'It was observed to fly from its perch at intervals, after flies, the white feathers in its tail being then very conspicuous. The wood was swarming with Golden-crested Wrens, and also Woodcock which had evidently just arrived.' The specimen was sent to London for comparison and where its identity was fully established, and it was exhibited by J.H. Gurney at a meeting of the Zoological Society. The stuffed bird went to the collection of Sir Vauncey Crewe at Caulke Abbey in Derbyshire. Nelson's reasons for declaring the status as 'Accidental summer visitor' on the strength of this one occurrence in October are difficult to understand.

Of the 12 records listed by Chislett, all but five birds were seen between 1946 and 1950. These were two seen at Beverley on 4th June 1907 — a strange date; one at Hull Bank House on 20th May 1907 (*The Naturalist*, 1907, p. 291); one shot by J.K. Stanford at Spurn on 24th September 1912; and one seen by G.H. Ainsworth at Spurn on 24th September 1938.

The establishment of the Spurn Bird Observatory in 1946 revealed that the species occurred almost annually along the coast, and the first spring record of the period came on 10th May 1947 when G.H. Ainsworth saw a male in full plumage. Later in the same year, three were caught in the Warren trap on 26th September. With the exception of 1951, 1953 and 1962, there have been records in every year, usually during late September and early October. On 29th August 1957, G.H. Ainsworth and R. Chislett saw a Pied Flycatcher and a Red-breasted Flycatcher, the latter complete with red throat, on wires near the Spurn Warren. On 12th October that year, a bird seen near Huddersfield was described to E.C.J. Swabey as Robin-like, with pink throat and breast, and having a dark tail with white patches on either side of the base; it hawked for flies from a tree stump. The bird had gone when Swabey arrived, but the description fits the species well and the date is convincing. Chislett placed the record in square brackets in the Yorkshire Naturalists' Union Ornithological Report for that year.

One at Spurn on 26th August 1960 was early, but in 1965 one was there from 14th to 16th August. One was at Spurn on 29th August and one at Hornsea on 31st August 1972, and one was at Flamborough on 19th August 1977. The first birds of autumn, however, do not usually appear until early September, and migration peaks during the latter half of that month and during early October. One at Flamborough from 5th to 8th November 1980 is the latest county record. Only one or two birds are annually seen on any one day, and there have been only two years, 1976 and 1980, when relatively large numbers have occurred. In 1976, birds were recorded from 22nd August to 23rd October at Spurn, Flamborough, Filey, Mappleton, Scarborough, Scalby and South Gare; maximum daily counts were four birds at Flamborough on 26th-27th September, three at Kilnsea on 23rd September, and three at Scarborough Castle Hill from 17th to 26th September. In 1980, after one at Scarborough on 20th September and another on 21st, there were birds at Spurn on several dates, with four on 11th October and three on 18th, and three at Flamborough on 12th October.

Spring records are few and, apart from those mentioned above, there have been only four others, all at Spurn as follows: a female on 23rd May 1959, one on 15th May 1960, a female on 6th June 1965 and one on 26th May 1980.

Inland records are scarce, and in addition to the 1957 Huddersfield bird there have been only three others: one was seen at Gateforth, near Knottingley, by B. Baxter, P.T. Treloar and C. Winn in May 1971; a male in full plumage was seen by T.M. Clegg on 27th May 1975 on Skipwith Common, where it fed actively for an hour and was seen again the next day by B. Cockerill; one at Bradfield, west of Sheffield, on 18th October 1981 was seen by D. Gosney and P.J. Freeman.

Thus, at any time from late August to early November, a Red-breasted Flycatcher may be seen along the coastline during times of passerine immigration, and there is always the chance of seeing one at an inland locality.

Pied Flycatcher
Ficedula hypoleuca

Nelson claimed Yorkshire as one of the chief headquarters of this species in Britain. In England, yes, but he apparently had no regard for Wales, where it is widely distributed in the hanging woodlands. During the summer months Pied Flycatchers can be found in many of the valleys along the eastern edge of the northern Pennines and the North York Moors, albeit only thinly.

Its presence is best detected by the thin song which is delivered from the canopy by this otherwise very inconspicuous species. Chislett considered that Nelson's informants lacked the power to detect birds by that means, as he claimed that it was declining in the Masham area where Chislett found it to be 'fairly common'.

The provision of nesting boxes is an undoubted asset to Pied Flycatchers and they are regularly used. Mature forestry plantations which are completely lacking in natural holes have been successfully colonised through the provision of boxes, as at Cropton and Dalby. In 1975 and 1976, up to 20 pairs bred in Duncombe Park and ten in Sleightholmedale, mainly in nesting boxes provided by G.W. Follows. In 1981, 24 pairs utilised boxes along the River Greta. B. Shorrock reported that a pair bred in a box at Malham Tarn in 1977, being only the second breeding record for the area, the first being at Clapham in 1954. Clearly, the scarcity of natural nesting sites is a limiting factor and the provision of boxes is a worthwhile task.

The normal arrival of the first summer visitors is usually during early May, but April birds occur in most years. The earliest have been on 15th April 1949 at Bolton Abbey; 12th April 1952 at Ripley; 14th April 1952 at Masham; and 14th April 1960 at Oakley.

Coastal passage in autumn is often very evident, especially at times of easterly winds when the Pied Flycatcher is one of the most characteristic of 'fall' migrants. Anywhere along the coast, but particularly at Flamborough and Spurn, small numbers occur every year, with larger numbers in some. The largest falls at Spurn have been as follows: 100 on 1st September 1963 and 300 on 2nd; 100 on 3rd September 1968; 100 on 28th August 1966 and 200 the next day, with a second influx of 100 on 18th September; 300 on 24th August 1971; and 250 on 30th August 1974. A 'tremendous influx' occurred at Flamborough from midday on 1st September 1963 (see Spurn above). A few birds pass through during early October, with later ones being seen on 22nd October 1950 at Spurn; 24th October 1971 at Spurn; 13th November 1976, when S.L. James caught one at Paull; 22nd October 1979 at Spurn; and 25th October 1981 and 7th November 1981, both at Flamborough.

Five Pied Flycatchers ringed at Spurn have been recovered abroad as follows: one ringed on 21st August 1951 was in northern Portugal on 12th September 1951; one ringed on 1st September 1963 had reached Ushant in northern France by 8th; one ringed on 2nd September 1963 was in Portugal on 17th September 1964; one ringed on 30th September 1966 was in Portugal on 16th October 1966; and one ringed on 15th August 1965 was retrapped on the island of Heligoland on 20th

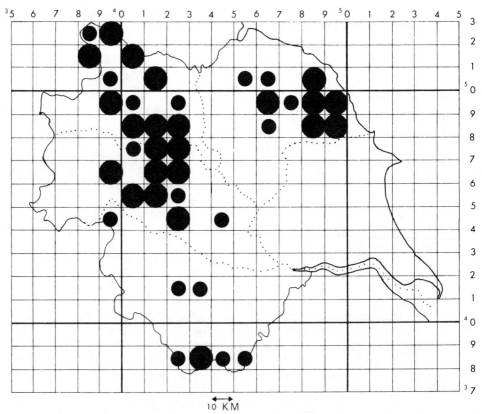

Pied Flycatcher. Restricted mainly to hanging oak and beech woodland on the eastern slopes of the Pennines and North York Moors.

May 1968, being the first British-ringed Pied Flycatcher to be recovered there.

Two birds from abroad have been recovered at Spurn: one ringed on the East Frisian Islands on 1st September 1962 was retrapped on 14th September 1962, and one ringed in Finland on 10th September 1970 was retrapped on 24th September 1970. A bird ringed at South Gare on 16th September 1973 was shot at Vizcaya in Spain on 20th September 1973, having wasted no time in getting there. A nestling ringed at Ripley on 12th June 1954 was in Merioneth on 14th May 1956.

Nelson's assessment of this species' status in 1907 as 'Summer visitant, very local in its distribution; fairly numerous in some districts; is noticed on the coast on both the vernal and autumnal migrations' needs little amendment today.

Bearded Tit
Panurus biarmicus

In Nelson's time, around the turn of the century, the Bearded Tit was a rare bird in Yorkshire and he knew it only as a 'Casual visitant; of very rare occurrence.' According to M. Booth of Killerby, writing in *The Zoologist*, 1845, p. 1135, a 'fine male' was seen near Kirkheaton Hospital 'three or four years ago'. Charles Waterton said that a pair once built a nest by the side of the lake at Walton Hall (*The Ibis*, 1865) and the species was also reported to have occurred at Scarthingwell. Nelson considered that only Waterton's claim was valid.

On 28th June 1901, a Mr K. McLean claimed to have seen a pair and three young ones at Hornsea Mere. He reported the incident in *The Naturalist*, 1901, p. 230, saying that, after hearing an unfamiliar soft musical 'tweet' among the rushes, he climbed a stunted tree and after a while was rewarded by seeing the birds, which he watched for ten minutes or so.

On 11th April 1911, W.H. St Quintin released six pairs and two extra males at Hornsea Mere. The experiment was monitored with much interest, and young were seen with one pair on 26th June. In 1912, three pairs were seen feeding young at nests in late April, and by 10th May the colony appeared to be well established, H.B. Booth optimistically declaring that it 'should contain 50 or 60 birds at the end of the season'. At least six, probably seven, first broods were reared according to G. Bolam, who said that 'probably as many second broods hatched before I left'. Alas, in 1914, E.W. Wade reported only one pair, and in November of that year W.H. St Quintin stated to a meeting of the Yorkshire Naturalists' Union Vertebrate Section that the experiment had apparently failed. The last bird, a male, was seen on 30th September 1916 when flushed by a dog. Details of these happenings were published in *The Naturalist* for the years 1911 to 1917.

The only other record known to Chislett concerned two males and a female in the reeds near the River Leven at Ingleby Barwick, near Yarm, on 6th and 7th December 1948.

On 17th October 1959, R.F. Dickens and D.A. Rushforth saw six Bearded Tits fly into a small reedbed near the Spurn Warren and a drive through the reeds revealed 11 birds, six of which were caught in a mist-net and ringed. They eventually towered upwards and circled at 100 feet (30 m), which Chislett considered 'might possibly indicate recent arrival with migrational urge still active'. Seven were seen during the next two days, and on 20th three flew down the peninsula in the early morning (*The Naturalist*, 1960, p. 4). During the same period, on 18th October, three were seen at Hornsea Mere by G.R. Bennett and M.K. Taylor.

Since that time the species has occurred in every year except 1963 and 1967. During the early 1960s up to five birds were seen annually at Blacktoft Sands, and in late October 1965 up to 21 were present. It is of course likely that birds visited this area in previous years but were not recorded. A few birds were being seen in various other parts of south Holderness during the period up to 1970, and on 27th July 1968 H.O. Bunce saw two well-grown young at Blacktoft. One was seen at Fairburn Ings by C. Winn on 31st August 1969.

In October 1971, an important movement occurred, with birds recorded at several coastal localities and at a few places inland. On 9th and 10th October, about 30 were in the Easington Lagoons area; two were on Broomfleet Island on 10th, 30 on 28th October and 3rd November, with fewer — up to 20 — on 22nd December; 30 were at Spurn on 9th October, with three remaining on 31st; 18 were at Hornsea Mere on 20th November and into December; four were at Trent Falls on 2nd October; three at Low Ellers Carr on 10th October, with 15 on 17th, and fewer to 19th March 1972; four at Almholme on 31st October; and one at Lindley Reservoir on 3rd November. Such numbers were quite unprecedented, but heralded a remarkable increase in the numbers visiting and staying in Yorkshire. In 1972, small parties were seen at most suitable places in Holderness, at Hornsea Mere and at some inland localities, Low Ellers Carr having 15 birds again on 5th November.

In 1973, no fewer than 80 were at Hornsea Mere on 12th October, most of which left next day; one of these birds had been ringed in Norfolk. Remarkable numbers were recorded by A. Chapman at Broomfleet Island from 22nd September, with 23 on 25th; 37 on 4th October, 53 on 7th, 81 on 29th, 30 on 30th; 150 on 27th November, 100 on 29th and 30th; 109 on 2nd December and 23 on 9th December. Two were at Adel Dam, Leeds, from 14th to 17th October and two at Fairburn Ings on 28th. Two males, each wearing a blue colour ring and a metal BTO ring, were seen at Worsborough Reservoir from 5th to 11th November and later moved to Wintersett, where they were seen on 16th and caught on 18th; one had been ringed at Minsmere in Suffolk on 18th September 1973. They then moved to Nostell Dam on 25th January where they remained until 16th December.

The events in 1974 were again quite remarkable. Regular counts along the frontage of Broomfleet Island showed up to 18 Bearded Tits to be present on most days during January and early February, a male on 1st June and a female on 30th June, with three young seen on 5th July and two small parties on 11th August; large numbers appeared in mid September and, after 17 birds on 14th, there were 150 on 18th, 200 on 30th, 100 on 11th October, 200 from 13th to 31st October, 180 on 3rd November, 100 on 4th and 40 on 1st December. Blacktoft Sands had 200 in January, 120 in February and an influx in mid March, when 200 suddenly appeared; at least 150 birds were paired in April and 60 pairs were located in May. The first broods fledged there from the third week of May and second broods at the end of June; a few third broods appeared in early August, and the last newly fledged youngster was seen on 16th September. As many as 700 birds were present at Blacktoft in early September, with much irruptive behaviour from 11th, increasing in intensity during October; 300 had departed by mid November and up to 250 remained throughout the winter. Hornsea Mere had birds from 9th October to mid November, with 18 on 15th October and 12 on 25th as maxima. A party of seven birds was in a small *Typha* bed at Hay-a-Park Gravel-pit, near

Knaresborough, from 8th to 17th October; all were caught and ringed and one was retrapped at Adlingfleet, near Goole, on 31st October. From one to four birds occurred at Fairburn Ings, Mickletown Ings and Filey during the same period, and seven were at Spurn during October and November.

Blacktoft Sands is now the favoured haunt of this species and large numbers occur every year. The maximum annual counts have been as follows: 350 during January/February 1976; 800 in October and early November 1976, when about half departed, but the numbers were maintained by birds from elsewhere and increased to 500 in late November, with 400 in December; 350 in January 1977, and a staggering 1,000 to 1,200 birds in September and early October, with irruptive behaviour in late September and early October after which 500 remained until December; 400 in January 1978 and 300 in early February, after which the breeding success was not good owing to cold and wet weather, the maximum in autumn being 600.

The weather during February 1979 was very cold, and the population at Blacktoft was reduced from 350 birds in early January to 40 by the end of March. Some new arrivals augmented the stock, and 25 pairs were present for the first brood period. These had poor success in a cold, wet spring and second broods did only marginally better, resulting in a peak of only 200 birds in August and September. It was also cold and wet in 1980 and the later breeding was relatively poor after successful first broods. Nevertheless, 500 birds were present in late September. The peak in 1981 was 600 birds in late September; 200 of these remained in December, and survived despite a cold period at the year end, leaving 120 birds in the early months of 1982, in which year about 70 pairs nested and 700 were present in September.

It was inevitable that these large numbers would be reflected elsewhere in the county, especially during the late autumn when the Blacktoft birds were erupting, and several inland waters had small numbers. During the years since 1975, the species has been recorded at Wath Ings, Potteric Carr, Castleford, Fairburn Ings, Mickletown Ings, Allerton Park, Knaresborough Ringing Station, the York area, Ben Rhydding and Wheldrake Ings.

Ringing recoveries have shown some interesting results. Four birds ringed at Spurn on 3rd November 1972 were all retrapped at Hornsea Mere the next day; one ringed at Ousefleet on 9th August 1977 was retrapped at Ashton in Lancashire on 13th August 1978; one ringed at Walberswick in Suffolk on 15th September 1977 was retrapped at Adlingfleet on 15th July 1978; and one ringed at Ousefleet on 29th August 1981 was in Shropshire on 19th December 1981. Recoveries of some of the many birds ringed in the Upper Humber have proved a two-way link between Blacktoft Sands and Leighton Moss in Lancashire, or Norfolk, some birds returning to the former locality after being retrapped at one of the other sites during the interim. Full details of the movements deserve publication in either *The Naturalist* or *Bird Study*.

It would seem that the Bearded Tit is now well established as a breeding species in the vast reedbeds at Blacktoft Sands and in similar habitat elsewhere along the Humber shore, and it is possible that small reedbeeds farther inland will be colonised by a few pairs.

There are few species that have made their mark so spectacularly in the county and in so short a time, and the Bearded Tit can now be termed a resident breeding species with autumn eruptions providing records in several parts of the county.

Long-tailed Tit
Aegithalos caudatus

Anywhere in Yorkshire, from the coastal regions, across the plains and through the vales to the foothills of the Pennines, on the North York Moors and the chalk Wolds, so long as suitable habitat exists, the Long-tailed Tit can be found in the breeding season. It is nowhere common and is inevitably more thinly distributed in some areas than in others, depending on the vegetation, but only in the treeless uplands is it completely absent. It is fond of gorse and low scrub, but will also build its nest in hedgerows, mature woodland and in conifer plantations. The nest may be well concealed in a bramble bush or completely in the open in the fork of some tree, where it is sometimes even more difficult to detect. On 16th March 1946, for example, a pair was constructing a nest 30 feet (9 m) from the ground in the fork of an ash tree at Masham. Nest building commences early in the year and is well under way by the end of March in most years; a pair building in a yew tree at Thornton-le-Dale on 12th February 1948 was particularly early.

Severe weather affects this delicate species. Following the hard winters of 1962/63 and 1978/79, the numbers were much reduced in many areas, but recovery was quick.

Wandering flocks in late summer and autumn often number from 20 to 40 birds, with larger ones occasionally. Up to 50 have been seen regularly by P.J. Carlton at Lindley Wood Reservoir in the Washburn Valley, with 60 on 17th October 1973, again on 7th November 1974 and in February and October 1975. S.M. Lister saw 63 in alder trees at Ramsgill in Upper Nidderdale on 7th February 1976; 60 were at Askham Bog during October to December 1978; 70 were at Thorpe Marsh on 22nd October 1980; and 80 were at Skipwith on 12th December 1982. Several flocks of up to 30 birds in Black Wood, near York, on 28th October 1977 were estimated by T.E. Dixon and E.B. Blake to total 200 individuals.

Long-tailed Tits have often occurred along the Spurn Peninsula, but there is no direct evidence of immigration. Several birds along the clifftop at Grimston in October 1978, including a party of 20 on 10th, were thought by A.W. Wallis to be possible migrants; 16 appeared at Spurn on the same day. On 7th January 1962, G.R. Bennett saw seven birds flying in over the sea at Flamborough, but these may have been of local origin having flown a little way offshore before coming in again.

Most ringing recoveries for this species have shown only relatively short movements, but there are three which are worthy of mention: a juvenile ringed at Armthorpe, near Doncaster, on 5th July 1964 was found dead at Retford in Nottinghamshire on 30th March 1968, having survived for a fair span; two birds ringed near Wragby in Lincolnshire on 7th October 1973 were still together when retrapped at Withernsea on 27th October 1973; and one ringed in Northampton on 22nd September 1974 was found dead at Kiveton Park, Sheffield, in 1975.

The white-headed race *Aegithalos caudatus caudatus*, which breeds from Scandinavia eastwards to the Urals and south to Poland and the Ukraine, has occurred only once in Yorkshire. The bird was mentioned by Nelson as having been seen in the company of birds of the British race at Kirkham Abbey on 18th March 1905 (*The Zoologist*, 1906, p. 149). A very interesting sequel came in 1984, when H.G. Alexander, at the age of 95 and living in America, wrote to his nephew Micahel Rowntree concerning a bird seen during a Bootham School Natural History Society excursion to Kirkham Abbey on 18th March 1905 as follows:

'In a patch of woodland near the river, I came on a party of Long-tailed Tits. Suddenly, in a tree quite close, I saw one with a pure white head. I had no binocular, but I did not need one; the bird must have been within ten yards for about half-a-minute. My impression is that I sent the record to *The Zoologist*. What I would like to know is, did the author of *The Birds of Yorkshire* (Nelson) accept it? Witherby, in *The Handbook*, practically only admits the two or three "specimens" of the Continental race; but his "others recorded as seen" might or might not include mine if it is in Nelson.' (*British Birds*, 1984, p. 221)

It is perhaps strange that there have been no other records of this race.

The vernacular names given to this species in Yorkshire are numerous, the most regularly used by countrymen being Bottle Tit. According to Nelson, Featherpoke was a term used in the North and East Ridings, but I knew it as such in the 1930s and 1940s in Nidderdale where Nelson said it was known as the Miller's Thumb.

Marsh Tit
Parus palustris

Records of this species at the beginning of the present century included the Willow Tit. Although the latter had been separated as a distinct species in 1897, the fact was not well known for some years and it was not immediately accepted by some older ornithologists.

The Marsh Tit's status today is that of a fairly general but thinly distributed resident, being most numerous in the wooded parts of the dales running up into the northern Pennines and in the Hambleton and Cleveland Hills. It is scarce in the southern Pennines and in the eastern part of the East Riding. A bird at Grimston on 21st September 1978 was, according to A.W. Wallis, only the second he had seen there in eight years.

In 1955, J.A.S. Borrett and I caught a Marsh Tit which was nesting in an old burrow at the edge of an active Sand Martin colony near Bedale.

From the early 1970s, there appeared to be a decline in numbers and several observers reported a marked reduction. It is still relatively scarce in some areas. At Knaresborough Ringing Station, trapping figures during the early 1970s showed it to be outnumbered three-to-one by the Willow Tit, and at Wintersett Reservoir no Marsh Tits, but 28 Willow Tits, were trapped in 1974.

While M.H. Ness was photographing regularly in Raincliffe Woods near Scarborough during January to March 1960, he saw 20 Marsh Tits together on one occasion. D.T. Ireland, while acting as warden for the RSPB at Hornsea Mere, reported the presence of 50 Marsh Tits on 12th October 1971; none was seen at Spurn during that period, indicating that the Hornsea birds were of local origin and resident in the area. Such flocks are unusual.

Five pairs bred at Askham Bog in 1979; 14 birds were seen in Studley Park on 3rd February 1979; and 12 pairs bred in Bramham Park in 1982.

It is difficult to assess the true situation regarding the population of this apparently fluctuating species without carefully censused figures, but it does seem to have declined in some areas in recent years.

Willow Tit
Parus montanus

As stated under the last species, the Willow Tit was not separated as a distinct species until 1897 and it was several years before enough was known of it for records
to be forthcoming; some of the older naturalists did not accept the species for
several years. When Nelson published *The Birds of Yorkshire* in 1907, he made no
mention of it.

It is a lover of low-lying and marshy land, especially with birch and alder, in the
decaying stumps of which it excavates its nest hole. Chislett considered the species
to be commoner on Hatfield Chase and Thorne Waste than anywhere else in the
county. He said that it was rare on the Wolds except at the southern end, but the
British Trust for Ornithology breeding birds survey (1968-72) showed it to occur in
most suitable habitat over most of the area. No breeding records came from the
North York Moors, however, and it was scarce in southern Holderness. For details
of the distribution in Yorkshire during the 1940s, see *The Naturalist*, 1945, p. 127.

In 1973, F.A. Wardman counted 25 pairs in an 8-mile (12.8-km) stretch of the
Washburn Valley from Leathley to Thruscross compared with ten pairs in 1963. In

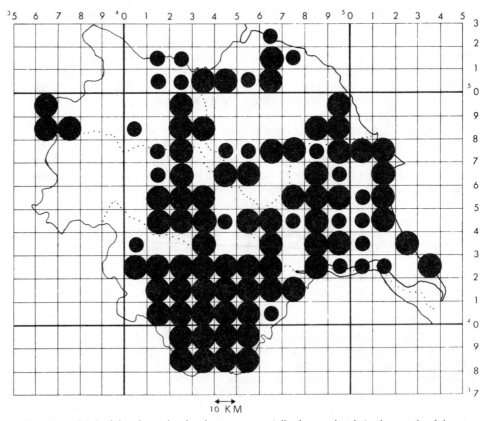

Willow Tit. A bird of the damp lowland areas, especially the carrlands in the south of the
county. Absent from the Pennines and the higher parts of the North York Moors.

1981, 20 pairs bred at Potteric Carr and single pairs at 20 other localities in the lowland parts of vice-county 63.

It is rare to find more than a few of these tits together. Those flocks that are seen consist mainly of family parties in late summer, but 19 were on Hatfield Moor on 4th October 1981 and an unprecedented 74 were counted on Dunnington Common on 11th January 1982. A few occur on the Spurn Peninsula in most years, often during the summer months. These are doubtless wandering birds from Holderness, and there is no real evidence of immigration.

Four examples showing characters of the northern race *Parus montanus borealis*, which breeds from Scandinavia eastwards to Siberia, have been seen in Yorkshire. The first was on Thorne Moors, where C.D.R. Heard watched one on 8th February 1975 (*The Naturalist*, 1981, p. 75); the second was seen by K.R. Mudd and others at Fairburn Ings on 13th May 1978; and there were two on Skipwith Common on 24th December 1981 which T.E. Dixon and E.B. Blake described in detail. That this strikingly large and paler race has not been seen along the coast is strange.

Crested Tit
Parus cristatus

According to Nelson in *The Birds of Yorkshire*, the Crested Tit was first mentioned in connection with the county by W. Lewin who, in 1797, remarked that 'It had been killed in Scotland and Yorkshire', and Thomas Allis in his report to the British Association at York in 1844 said that his friend J. Heppenstall had told him that one was seen in a garden at Thorne. It is impossible to evaluate these less than satisfactory records.

The only authentic record concerns a bird which was obtained near Whitby in March 1872. The specimen went to the Whitby Museum (*The Zoologist*, 1872, p. 3021) and the editors of *The Handbook* admitted the bird as the first and only record of the Northern Crested Tit *Parus cristatus cristatus* in the British Isles.

Three others have been recorded, none of which is sufficiently authenticated to justify a place on the county list, as follows: one was reported as being taken at Thirsk 'many years ago' (Lee, MS, 1880) but the specimen was not examined, and single birds were mentioned in *The Vertebrate Fauna of Yorkshire* (p. 24) and *The Naturalist*, 1888, p. 15, as having occurred near Bradford in March 1820 and at Keighley in August 1887 respectively without satisfactory supporting details.

Coal Tit
Parus ater

The Coal Tit was known in connection with Yorkshire as long ago as 1720 when a letter to Walter Moyle, 'a Cornishman and ornithologist of eminence', written by a Dr Sherard on 10th May in that year, referred to a *Parus ater* from Yorkshire that he had received (*The Works of Walter Moyle, Esq.*, 1726).

Nelson said that it was a common resident and was generally distributed except in the remote southwest and northwest parts of the West Riding, where it was local during the breeding season. Today, the Coal Tit is generally distributed, if only very thinly in some areas, over most of the county but is absent in some parts of Holderness. The extensive forestry on the high ground of the once barren moorlands along the Pennines and North York Moors have suited the species well and, although some plantations existed at the beginning of the present century, it can now be found breeding commonly where no trees stood in Nelson's time. Obviously absent from the high and barren fells of the northwest, continuing afforestation will attract it to those regions in time. It prefers the presence of at least a few conifers among the deciduous woodlands in which it breeds at lower elevations.

In autumn, wandering birds can be found in areas where none has nested; suburban gardens attract it, often in the company of Goldcrests which probably emanate from the same breeding woods. In the Yorkshire Naturalists' Union Report for 1957, Chislett said 'It is quite unusual for this species to appear in suburban gardens as at Roundhay in October ... and at Doncaster and elsewhere.' Not so today.

Some relatively large flocks occur during the autumn in some years, often consorting with other tit species. At Hornsea Mere in 1971, D.T. Ireland reported a sudden increase in the numbers present, to 75 birds on 13th October; P. Smith saw 14 at Newmillerdam on 3rd January 1972; 50 were among a mixed party of tits at Frickley Park during January 1975; 20-30 were in Harewood Park during July 1977 and September 1978; 25 were at Eccup Reservoir during the autumn of 1977; T.E. Dixon and E.B. Blake estimated a total of 100 birds in Black Wood, near York, during the period October 1977 to January 1978; 65 were in King's Moor Plantation on 2nd September 1978; 30 were in Bishop's Wood, Selby, on 29th October 1978; a total of 39 birds moved west to southwest at Redmires Reservoir on 13th and 14th October 1981; and there was a phenomenal count of 150 Coal Tits on Otley Chevin on 23rd December 1982, during a period of severe weather. At Tophill Low Reservoir, 30 birds on 29th October 1982 were away from their normal range.

A bird showing the characters of the Continental race *Parus ater ater* was caught at Spurn Bird Observatory on 24th October 1972; and single birds considered to be of this race were seen at Flamborough on 2nd November and 15th-16th November 1980, with 'several' in October 1982. J. Cordeaux claimed that this race was an occasional straggler to our coastline in autumn (*The Naturalist*, 1896, p. 8, and 1899, p. 24), but Nelson said that he was not aware of any evidence in support of that statement.

Coastal movements do in fact occur in some years and suggest immigration. The first such influx was noted in 1957, a year in which there was a sizeable movement of tits along the coast, and a flock of 15 appeared at Redcar on 18th October; 13 were at Spurn on 1st November, with 30 on 17th, 120 on 18th, 50 on 19th, and smaller numbers evident on the intervening dates; and B.S. Pashby saw 24 in bushes at Welton Water on 27th October. A few are seen along the coast in most autumns, and on 29th September 1961 G.R. Bennett saw two birds flying in over the sea at Atwick.

A nestling ringed at Bakewell in Derbyshire on 14th June 1966 was found dead at Rillington, near Malton, on 2nd January 1967; and a young bird ringed at Warsop in Nottinghamshire on 6th August 1977 was found dead at Sigglesthorne, near Hornsea, on 13th February 1978.

Blue Tit
Parus caeruleus

This familiar tit is common everywhere in Yorkshire and it can be found in the breeding season from the coast, westwards across the vales and plains to the Pennines and on the North York Moors, where it penetrates up the valleys to the highest parts so long as there are a few trees. It is no less frequent in suburbia, and even large cities have their breeding Blue Tits. The incidence in towns and cities is aided by the provision of nesting boxes, a most valuable substitute for natural holes, which are scarce in the over-tidy countryside. Competition with Great Tits and Tree Sparrows for the occupancy of nesting boxes is not unusual, and I have recorded instances of mixed clutches of eggs at Knaresborough Ringing Station. Tree Sparrows appear to be fairly easily evicted by Blue Tits, and a pair of the latter reared five young Tree Sparrows near Doncaster in 1959 (*The Naturalist*, 1960, pp. 107-8).

Both Nelson and Chislett devoted most of their chapters on the species to its coastal appearances and migration. The former said that 'Great arrivals take place on the east coast in the autumn, generally accompanied by their larger relative, the Great Tit', and he went on to say that, from mid September to mid November, the hedgerows near the coast 'swarm with these little clean-coloured individuals'. There is no doubt that in some years bright, clean Blue Tits can be seen along the coast, but no incident to justify the term 'swarm' has happened in recent years. The most spectacular arrival in more modern times was in 1957, when large numbers were recorded along the coast from Teesmouth to Spurn. At Redcar, D.R. Seaward noted 'bright clean birds' visiting his garden in early October and realised that a movement was taking place when 64 passed through a nearby fox covert between 07.45 hours and 08.15 hours, with others passing through his garden all morning; about 100 tits, most of which were of this species, passed through the covert in just over two hours on 17th, and a further 21 passed through his garden on 21st October, after 100 had been seen in Zetland Park, Redcar, a few days earlier. Six were on the South Gare on 27th October. In the Helmsley area, Adam Gordon spoke of a 'great invasion'. On 13th October, B.S. Pashby counted 41 birds flying west along the Humber bank at North Ferriby between 06.15 hours and 09.00 hours, and 12 of these flew south over the Humber. Larger numbers than usual appeared at Flamborough in late October and November. At Spurn, where the most continuous observations were carried out, the first indication of an influx was 12 birds on 16th September, with 65 on 1st October, 50 on 6th, 80 on 7th, 42 on 8th, 80 on 15th, 12 on 17th and 18th, 150 on 19th and 24 on 20th. Of those caught and ringed, racial determination was not considered possible, this being difficult in the absence of direct comparison with a series of skins. On 1st October, the 65 birds recorded were flying northward; on 6th, two parties of 17 and 22 birds flew south to the Point and then turned back. Most of the daily counts were of birds flying south past the Narrow Neck, but on some days birds were wandering about the Peninsula in both directions, a few heading out over the Humber.

That some of these Blue Tits were of Continental origin is perhaps indicated by Nelson's report of a 'great influx' during the last half of October 1878 which corresponded with a similar one at Heligoland (*The Zoologist*, 1879, p. 44); by the recovery at Tourcoing, Nord, France, on 12th April 1958 of one ringed at Spurn on 6th April 1958; and by one ringed in East Flanders, Belgium, on 28th July 1957 being found dead at Thirsk in February 1958.

There is some evidence of movement in most autumns, but usually only small numbers are involved. Relatively larger movements have occurred in a few years: in 1970 there were more than usual at Spurn in late September, with up to 31 birds as the highest daily count, and in 1971 there were counts of 30 on 27th September and 34 on 2nd October, and similar peak numbers have occurred in several years to the present time. There were up to 80 on Scarborough Castle Hill between 3rd and 9th October 1973, during which period Spurn recorded its highest number of 34. A notable influx occurred in 1975, when there were 20 at Filey on 6th September and several parties on Scarborough Castle Hill on 21st September; the species was much in evidence again at Filey and Scarborough on 27th September; Spurn had 25 birds on 30th September; and at least 300 appeared on Scarborough Castle Hill on 9th October, when others were seen all along the coast from Filey to Ravenscar. The birds were very bright and clean-looking. Smaller numbers have occurred every autumn since that time, with the most in 1979 when Spurn had 50 on 24th September, 33 of which flew south at the Narrow Neck; 70 on 27th, 64 of which flew south; 20 on 18th October and smaller numbers to early November. Scarborough Castle Hill had 300 on 13th October and 150 on 27th October.

There was an influx at Flamborough on 2nd and 3rd November 1980 when 120 birds were present, but large numbers were not noted elsewhere, the peak at Spurn being 40 during August.

Some large concentrations occur at inland localities during the autumn and winter months, when flocks of up to 50 birds are seen regularly. In 1971, up to 100 occurred in Bretton Park on several dates during February and March and 100 were there on 1st January 1981; 100 were seen in the late evening at Creskeld Hall on 30th January 1977, and 80 were feeding on beech mast in the grounds of Conyngham Hall at Knaresborough on the same date; 60 were in a plantation at Tophill Low Reservoir on 6th December 1978 where there were 120 on 29th October 1982; 100 were at Blacktoft Sands in early December 1981; 190 were near Otley between 22nd and 28th December 1982 and 160 were at Arthington Hall on 29th December 1982.

Several Yorkshire-ringed Blue Tits have travelled good distances within the British Isles: one ringed at Middlesbrough on 11th January 1958 was near Eastbourne in Sussex on 14th December 1958; one ringed at Giggleswick on 23rd January 1958 was in Essex on 20th April 1958; one ringed at Ackworth on 18th February 1958 was in Worcestershire on 7th April 1958; and one ringed at Doncaster on 1st March 1958 was near Cheadle in Staffordshire on 25th April 1958. These birds were doubtless part of the great immigration in October 1957, referred to above.

A Blue Tit ringed at Stewkley in Buckinghamshire on 8th April 1958 was near Maltby on 21st October 1959; a juvenile ringed at Knaresborough Ringing Station on 2nd July 1972 was retrapped at Botley in Oxfordshire on 26th February 1978; and a juvenile ringed at Tring in Hertfordshire on 21st July 1977 was retrapped at Selby on 25th February 1978.

It is inevitable that such a familiar bird should attract several local names, and Nelson listed some which are still in use by countrymen in Yorkshire today, Billy Bluecap being perhaps the most familiar.

Great Tit
Parus major

The Great Tit is distributed over the whole county except for the higher treeless moorlands of the Pennines. Only a complete lack of nesting sites precludes it from such habitat, for it may be found along the gills and cloughs and in isolated stands of timber or old buildings where such occur in the upland country. Nest sites are varied but usually in holes in trees, masonry or nesting boxes. Nelson published a photograph of one in an open nest of the Song Thrush in a clump of woodbine near Harrogate in 1902; W.H. St Quintin reported one at Scampston built in an old Blackbird's nest; and a pair nested in a squirrel's drey at Eccup Reservoir in 1977.

There is some evidence of migration along the coast in autumn, but there have been no large numbers in recent years to equal those referred to by Nelson in *The Birds of Yorkshire*. He said that unusual numbers appeared in late October 1878 and that the species was very abundant after a severe storm on 30th October, in company with Blue Tits and Wrens, both at Spurn and at Teesmouth, the movement coinciding with a similar one on the island of Heligoland. He mentioned 1883, 1884, 1886, 1889 and 1901 as years in which a distinct increase in numbers was noted along the coast. Speaking of its frequent autumn appearances at Spurn, Nelson said that the birds were 'cleaner and brighter looking than the residents' and that some had been known to alight on vessels in the North Sea during migration.

Great Tits are evident along the coast in every autumn, but whether these are wandering birds of fairly local origin or immigrants is not known for certain; the former are most likely. The large tit influx in October 1957 (see also Blue Tit) included some Great Tits: at Spurn, 40 appeared on 19th October, 30 of which remained the next day. On 13th October 1979, R.H. Appleby counted 30 Great Tits with 300 Blue Tits on Scarborough Castle Hill; very few were seen at Spurn during the period. Evidence of arrival from over the sea came in 1961, when G.R. Bennett watched three birds flying in at Atwick and D.R. Seaward saw two coming in at Redcar the next day.

Birds along the coast in autumn need not be immigrants, as evidenced by a Great Tit ringed at York on 7th November 1932 which was recovered at Scarborough on 25th December 1933. One ringed at Sedbergh on 9th March 1952 was at Cottingham, near Hull, on 6th April 1952. A female ringed at Ramsbottom in Lancashire on 27th February 1981 was retrapped at Grosmont, Whitby, on 21st March 1982.

Large gatherings inland are scarce, but assemblies of up to 20 to 30 birds have been recorded in woodland during the autumn and winter months. A. Frudd caught and ringed 30 in Bretton Park on 2nd January 1965, and flocks of 50 and 30 birds were seen there on 25th February; 100 were counted there on 14th

December 1980, 50 of which were still present in early January 1981. In 1982, there were flocks of 80 birds at Fountains Abbey on 6th March; 72 at Hall Dike, Huddersfield, on 4th December; and 57 at Arthington Hall on 29th December.

Nuthatch
Sitta europaea

The Nuthatch was mentioned in connection with Yorkshire in 1678, in a letter from Ralph Johnson of Greta Bridge to John Ray:

> 'The Nuthatch or Nut Jobber — *Picus cinereus* — She hath not a long tongue as the other [the Woodpecker kind] because she feeds not on Cossi as they do, but on other insects, and especially on nut-kernels. It is a pretty sight to see her fetch a nut out of her hoard, place it in a chink and then stand over it with her head downward, strike it with all her might, and breaking the shell, catch up the kernel. The motion is rather down than up trees; nor hath she two hind toes, but the inner toe is separated a little from the middle, and falls somewhat across (as in the Owl kind) whereby she can support herself in any motion. Her voice is very shrill, Mr Johnson.' (Willughby's *Ornithology*, 1678, p. 23)

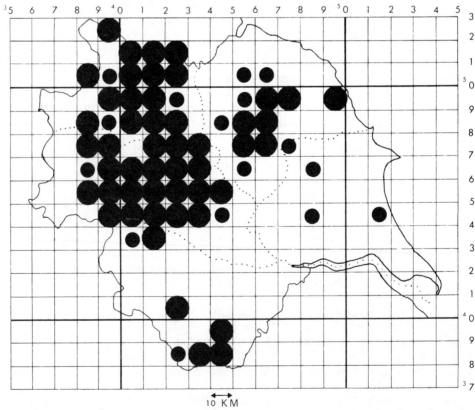

Nuthatch. A preference for mature hanging woodland restricts this species to the valleys of the Pennines and North York Moors. Open parkland with old timber in the eastern vales holds very few pairs.

Nelson knew the Nuthatch as an irregularly distributed species which was nowhere common. He described places where it is still a familiar bird, but spoke of diminishing numbers in some areas. There has doubtless been a general reduction in numbers as a result of the disappearance of timber over the years, but the general areas of distribution have probably changed but little since the beginning of the century. It is most numerous in the northwest, where it frequents the hanging woodland in the valleys and slopes of the Pennines, and also on the North York Moors where such habitat exists. There is evidence of an increase in the Sheffield area in recent years, with reports coming from 20 localities in 1981 including at least three pairs in Graves Park; a pair bred in Woolley Wood in 1982, in which year ten birds were seen in Eccleshall Woods in March. It is very scarce in the East Riding and absent in the open flat carrlands of the south around December.

A bird at Hornsea on 31st August 1961 was described in the Yorkshire Naturalists' Union Ornithological Report for 1961 as 'a most unexpected and interesting record'. Two were seen there on 1st and 2nd September 1966, and a pair almost certainly nested in 1970 but actual proof was lacking. A pair with three newly fledged young at Birdsall, south of Malton, on 23rd June 1974 was the first actual proof of nesting in vice-county 61 for 20 years. The birds were present in 1975, but breeding has not been proved since.

The longest journey ever made by a British-ringed Nuthatch concerned a bird ringed at Arthington, near Otley, on 29th December 1982 which was found dead at Catterick on 29th April 1983, having travelled 33 miles (53 km).

Treecreeper
Certhia familiaris

Chislett's statement in *Yorkshire Birds* that the Treecreeper had probably increased in numbers since Nelson published *The Birds of Yorkshire* in 1907, apparently based in part on his observations around Masham, where it was 'quite numerous', was probably a reflection of more observers rather than a genuine increase. One would assume that the diminishing amount of old timber over the years has in fact reduced its numbers, although it is still a widely distributed species in Yorkshire.

Wherever suitable stands of timber exist, from the coastal woods to the wooded gills and cloughs of the Pennines and the North York Moors, a pair of Treecreepers can be found during the summer months. The hard winters of 1946/47 and 1962/63 reduced the population considerably but, as with most other species, recovery was complete in just a few years.

Natural nesting sites must be scarcer now than formerly and artificial sites are readily utilised. In 1943, A. Whitaker knew of six nests in the Sheffield area, three of which were behind pieces of bark that he had fixed in suitable places. Nests may be built in crevices in masonry; one at Esholt in 1948 was so placed, and Nelson recorded that this type of site was used commonly in the Halifax area.

One fed regularly on dripping spread on the bark of a tree at Knaresborough Ringing Station in the winter of 1975/76.

Nelson mentioned a few records from Spurn and suggested that the birds could have crossed the North Sea, and several Treecreepers on the coastline in more recent years have been diagnosed as belonging to the northern race *Certhia familiaris familiaris*. One caught at Spurn on 6th October 1959 later died and was identified by A. Hazelwood of the Bolton Museum as belonging to this race (*The Naturalist*, 1960, p. 3), as was another caught on 24th October 1982, on which date a Continental Coal Tit was also caught. One at Flamborough on 8th October 1977 was very pale above and pure white below and was considered to belong to this race, as was most likely the case with five birds on Filey Brigg on 8th October in the same year.

One caught at Spurn on 18th September 1983 was recovered at Garston, Merseyside, on 3rd October 1983, having travelled a distance of 125 miles (200 km).

Short-toed Treecreeper
Certhia brachydactyla

An example of this species was caught and ringed by C. Carter at Hornsea on 26th October 1970. It was the first accepted record for the county and only the second for the British Isles.

The Short-toed Treecreeper breeds over much of Europe as far as the English Channel, but rarely crosses into England.

Penduline Tit
Remiz pendulinus

The first British record of the Penduline Tit occurred at Spurn on 22nd October 1966. It was first seen by R.J. Raines and A.A. Bell in an isolated elderberry bush among sea buckthorn just south of the Warren Cottage. After being positively ident-ified and notes being made, other observers were contacted, but ten minutes later the bird had disappeared. On 28th October, in the buckthorn area north of the Kilnsea Beacon some 3 km north of the original site, B. Banson, M. Densley and S.J. Kenyon located what was obviously the same bird in a patch of *Phragmites*. Further notes were made by the finders, and later by B.R. Spence and C. Winn, and an unsuccessful attempt was made to catch it in a mist-net. About this time, Penduline Tits were extending their range westwards and were breeding in Denmark (*British Birds*, 1967, pp. 517-20).

On 25th November 1981, two birds appeared at Blacktoft Sands, where they stayed until at least 4th January 1982 and were seen by A. Grieve, D. Hursthouse, D. Morton and many others. They fed by pecking at the reed stems in the manner of Blue Tits and also fed low down in the reeds like Bearded Tits, with which they often associated. The female was wearing a ring on the left leg. From the shape of the black eye-mask, both birds were considered to be in their first year. They sur-vived a period of severe weather during mid December, but their ultimate fate is unknown.

Golden Oriole
Oriolus oriolus

In *The Birds of Yorkshire*, Nelson listed records of 14 Golden Orioles up to 1903, the first being a bird killed in the spring of 1834 near the Spurn lighthouse. The specimen went to the Yorkshire Museum. Of the other records, eight had been 'obtained' near the coast and the other six either seen or shot at inland localities.

Chislett listed records in seven years between 1911 and 1949. In most of these years there was but a single record, but in 1945 W.S. Medlicott heard a male singing from the thick foliage of a young birch at Goathland at 30 yards' (27 m) range; a female was seen near Hutton-le-Hole on 6th June and a male was seen about a quarter-of-a-mile (0.4 km) away, also on 6th June.

In 1947, a male was seen near Sleights on 5th and 6th May by Medlicott, R.M. Garnett and C.E.A. Burnham, and a female was seen by the latter observer at Robin Hood's Bay on 11th May. In the same year, an emaciated male was picked up dead near Settle on 6th May which was sent to the Leeds Museum, and a male was near Paull-on-Humber during the first week of May.

Birds have been seen or heard in 18 of the years from 1950 to 1984, and all have been between late April and early July except for one at Spurn on 25th September 1969. In spring, a male Golden Oriole may sing briefly at some inland locality before moving on and such have been recorded at Snainton, Market Weighton (1965 and 1972), Fairburn Ings (1967, 1970 and 1981), Helmsley, Otley, Guisborough, Selby, Ousefleet, Bolton Abbey, Strensall Common, Lindley Moor Wood, Denaby Ings, Doncaster, Worsborough Reservoir and at Aughton. Birds have stayed for a few days at some of these localities.

The tendency in recent years for one or two Golden Orioles to linger in suitable habitat may lead to a breeding attempt, if this has not already taken place.

Nelson's status assessment as 'Accidental visitant, of very rare occurrence, during the spring and autumn migrations' was based on only two records during the latter period, both in August, at Wakefield and Bingley. It is now almost annual during the spring and early summer in very small numbers.

Isabelline Shrike
Lanius isabellinus

P.A. Lassey watched an example of this eastern shrike at Flamborough on 25th August 1983 which he ascribed to the race *phoenicuroides*.

It was a new species for the Yorkshire list and full details were submitted to the Yorkshire Naturalists' Union Records Committee.

Red-backed Shrike
Lanius collurio

The Red-backed Shrike formerly bred in Yorkshire, but ceased to do so during the 1930s. A pair summered regularly at Brambles Farm, near Middlesbrough, during the early 1930s and may have bred, but proof was not forthcoming.

Nelson's breeding records came from near York, Leeds, Barnsley, Huddersfield, Sheffield, Swillington, Easington, Scarborough and Redcar. He also knew the species as a breeding bird near Sedbergh, where it persisted until 1934 when the last known nest was found at Hebblethwaite Hall. It was never common in the county and old records of its status vary: H. Denny stated that it was not uncommon near Leeds, and it was said to be an almost annual visitor near Huddersfield; a record in Nidderdale on 1st July 1879 was the only one in that area at the time; and most other accounts at the end of the nineteenth century concerned single birds or odd pairs, which were often shot, in various parts of the county.

In *Yorkshire Birds*, Chislett said that 'Between 1907 and 1946, occurrences of the Red-backed Shrike in Yorkshire were very few.' A pair was seen in June 1910 near Hornsea Mere; a male was near Hull for ten days in June 1941; a male was at Healaugh on 24th June 1944; and a male was seen frequently from May to August 1944 near Hutton-le-Hole. That one or two pairs succeeded in nesting after 1934 is probable.

The establishment of the Spurn Bird Observatory in 1946 revealed that the species occurred almost annually as a passage migrant, mainly during the autumn, and regular watching at other coastal points in more recent years has shown it to occur along the length of the county from Spurn to Teesmouth. Passage birds appear during May and early June and from late July to early October, August and September being the main months of occurrence. One or two birds at any one locality are usual, with three occasionally, and some may linger for several days in one place before moving on. The most spectacular movement occurred in the autumn of 1977, when relatively large numbers were reported from every regularly watched locality from the Tees to the Humber. Spurn had 12 birds on 19th August followed by 20 on 20th, on which date 21 were at Flamborough Head. Seven were at Filey on 21st, when Spurn and Flamborough had the remnants of the initial influx, followed by what appeared to be a second wave on 27th when 25 birds were at Flamborough. The species was evident throughout the month and 11 were at Bempton on 29th. Watchers at Teesmouth recorded fewer Red-backed Shrikes, but more than usual were present there during the period. A few were seen during September and the last was at Spurn on 9th October.

Very few penetrate to inland localities and there have been records of single birds in ten of the last 30 years. A male was on Bentley Common, near Doncaster, on 8th August 1955; one was at an altitude of 700 feet (214 m) at Stanghow, near Skelton, on 3rd August 1957; one was near Harrogate on 8th and 9th October 1963; one was on Thorne Moor on 14th September 1974 and another on 5th August 1975; a juvenile was at Normanton from 18th to 21st September 1974; four occurred in 1977 (see coastal influx), at Harrogate on 27th May, Fairburn Ings on 28th August and 13th September, and Castleford on 14th September; a male was on Denaby Ings on 25th May 1978, in which year one was also near Richmond on 10th August; a female was at Strines Reservoir, near Sheffield, from 12th to 17th June 1980; one was at York University on 2nd September 1981, in which year another was at Heworth Golf Course on 7th August and one was at Bramhope, Leeds, from 18th to 20th October; a very late bird was at Fairburn Ings on 13th November 1982; and one was at Coxley, near Wakefield, from 8th to 10th June 1983.

Most of these inland occurrences are complementary to the coastal passage, especially the three in August and September 1977.

Nelson's summary of this species' status as 'Bird of passage, of rare occurrence, has occasionally stayed to nest' needs some amendment, for it is now an annual passage migrant along the coastline in both spring and autumn, mainly during the latter period. No longer do any stay to nest.

Lesser Grey Shrike
Lanius minor

The ninth British occurrence of this species was recorded by Nelson when one was shot at Sleights, near Whitby, on 20th September 1905. The bird was sent to W. Eagle Clarke, who identified it as a bird of the year, and the specimen went to the Whitby Museum (*The Naturalist*, 1906, p. 70).

In *Yorkshire Birds*, Chislett published the following note:

'Mr. and Mrs. A.C. Hoyle inspected a male Lesser Grey Shrike in a tree top in the Norwoods, Roche Abbey, near Maltby on 3rd February 1952. As they watched through ×10.5 binoculars the bird flew to some pylon wires about 20 yards distant, where in good light the following features were noticed; breast white with a distinct rosy tinge on the lower part, black band through eyes joined across forehead, white patch on black wings. Long black tail and grey back, size about as Hawfinch apart from tail. The bird had been seen on 26th January and was seen again on 16th March by the same observers with R. Bramhill, who agreed as to its identity. I (R.C.) was unable to find the bird on 10th February but knowing all the observers and having discussed the matter with them, I have no doubt of the accuracy of the record.'

This species is a summer visitor to Europe, wintering in Africa south of the equator. The British records, most of which have occurred since 1955, have fallen mainly during the periods May-June and September-October and all between April and November. For one to be in Yorkshire during January to March is very unusual and, in spite of Chislett's confidence in the record, I cannot help feeling that a mistake was made. Adult examples of the Great Grey Shrike can have their breasts faintly tinged with pink, and unless the observer is completely familiar with what is meant by the black eye-stripes being joined across the forehead then it is possible to imagine that they are so joined in the Great Grey, especially if the bird is viewed from a low angle.

Seven have occurred during the period of my review, the first being at Spurn when J.S. Armitage and A.R. Hall watched one sitting on top of the Heligoland trap at Chalk Bank on 12th May 1959. Full details were entered in the observatory log-book and included 'black forehead continuing past eyes and over ear coverts and a pink flush on the breast'.

On 4th July 1961, at Eastfield, near Scarborough, R.H. Appleby saw a bird on the telegraph wires which he identified as this species. It remained in the area until 27th August and was seen by several observers, including P.J. Stead and A.J. Wallis.

One was at Spurn on 27th August 1966 and seen by B. Banson, P.R. Edwards and B.R. Spence, and another was there from 11th to 15th June 1970 which was trapped and ringed by B.R. Spence and N. Tiersley.

A male was seen at Hornsea Mere by R.G. Hawley and I.G. Howard on 23rd May 1976. One which stayed at Sammy's Point, near Easington, from 30th August to 8th September 1981 was seen by several observers, including J. Cudworth, B.G. Pepper and J.M. Turton. One was reported by J.C. Lamplough at Flamborough on 18th May 1982.

There are now about 120 records of this western and central European breeding bird in the British Isles, mostly from 1955, since when it has occurred almost annually.

Great Grey Shrike
Lanius excubitor

This winter visitor was mentioned in connection with Yorkshire in 1713, when in Ray's *Synopsis* it was referred to under the name of 'The Greater Butcher Bird'.

The first Yorkshire specimen known to Nelson was a female in the Burton Agnes collection which was labelled 'shot near Malton in 1836'.

We know the species as an annual visitor in autumn, when small numbers arrive along the coastline and penetrate to widely scattered inland localities. Anywhere in Yorkshire, from the coastal hedgerows to the moorland edges along the Pennines, a solitary Great Grey Strike may take up winter residence. Relatively open bushy country is preferred, but hedgerows in large areas of arable or pastureland are just as likely to attract the species.

It usually makes its appearance about mid October, and September records are scarce, the earliest bird of which I have note being on 16th September 1972 when G.W. Follows saw one at Redcar Fox Covert. Other early records have been as follows: 22nd September 1970 at Spurn, 23rd September 1967 at Filey, and three birds at Flamborough on 27th September 1976.

Most birds have left by April, but there are a few records into early May, the latest being near York on 6th May 1976. In 1954 and 1956, however, there was an unprecedented series of late records up to early June. In 1954, one was seen near Barnard Castle on 4th June by J.P. Utley, one was seen near Middleton-in-Teesdale on 5th June by N. Harmby, and a third was seen on Danby Rigg on 11th June by Misses M.A. Hoare and I. Lemon. In 1956, one was seen on 22nd May at Gillamoor by Miss M.A. Hoare and one was seen at Rylstone on 3rd June by E.C. Sterne.

The record of a bird seen at Alwoodley by F.M. Firth on 28th June 1942, at first thought to be a Lesser Grey Shrike but eventually claimed as a probable Great Grey, is most unsatisfactory.

There has been no large immigration in recent years to match the 20 birds at Kilnsea on 15th October 1892 reported by Nelson in *The Birds of Yorkshire*. Nelson had a specimen in his collection which was brought in on 25th October 1891 by a pilot, who had captured it when 3 miles (4.8 km) out to sea as it rested on the sheet of his coble. It lived for several days, feeding on small birds. Nelson mentioned a young bird of the year at Kilnsea on 26th August 1877, which was recorded in *The Field*, 1877, p. 281, as being unprecedentedly early; it was three weeks ahead of the next — and very early — bird at Redcar on 16th September 1972, and one wonders whether it was a Lesser Grey Shrike.

A Great Grey Strike ringed at Spurn Bird Observatory on 8th October 1966 was found dead at Crowland in Lincolnshire 28 days later.

Nelson's summary in 1907 as 'Winter visitant, in limited numbers, chiefly on the coast-line; remains throughout winter, departing in spring' needs no amendment today.

Woodchat Shrike
Lanius senator

Nelson referred to six occurrences of this south European shrike, some of which are most unsatisfactory. Chislett published details of only two of these birds, and said 'five other occurrences are given with but little detail'. There were in fact only four other records.

The two acceptable records mentioned in *Yorkshire Birds* were of a male shot at Hackness near Scarborough in June 1881 which went to the collection of R. Chase of Birmingham (*The Zoologist*, 1892, p. 347); and of a male which was watched on 9th May 1903 on a large furze bush on the middle cliff at Reighton by C.G. Danford of Reighton Hall, who was familiar with the bird, having seen it often in Hungary (*The Naturalist*, 1903, p. 262).

The other records mentioned by Nelson are as follows: Yarrell, in his first edition of *British Birds* (1843), stated that 'a few years ago, Mr. Leadbitter received a specimen which had been killed in Yorkshire'; 'According to the late A. Roberts of Scarborough, Mr. Alwin S. Bell obtained two young birds in the Castle Holmes, Scarborough in the year 1860 or 1861, but he (Mr. Bell) only succeeded in preserving one of them owing to their being so very fat.' It is very unlikely that two young Woodchats would occur together and doubtful that they would be 'so very fat' if they had; this record cannot be accepted as definite in my view. The third reads 'The late J. Varley of Almondbury, near Huddersfield reported in 1879 that when he was a bird-nester he saw two Woodchats brought in to be preserved by a bird-stuffer.' Again, the account of two birds is most disturbing and, as with several old records where 'a pair' is said to have occurred, one cannot help being suspicious. The fourth record also concerned two birds which J.B. Hewitson saw at Easington on 8th September 1896 and reported to J. Cordeaux. The latter added that Hewitson knew the bird well, having seen it in Morocco.

Since the last acceptable record in 1903, there have been 17 others in the county, details of which are as follows.

The first was on 13th May 1952, when one was caught in the Warren trap at the Spurn Bird Observatory by J.A. Chadwick and J.B. Nelson; it was also inspected by

W.F. Fearnley, Mrs O.M. Pennock and G.H. Ainsworth. P.J. Mountford, the warden of Spurn Bird Observatory at the time, saw a Woodchat there on 31st May 1961, and a male was also there from 20th September to 13th October 1963 which was trapped on 22nd September, when it was aged as a second-year bird. Another occurred at Spurn on 7th June 1964 and stayed until 29th, and a male was present there on 5th June 1965. In 1966, J.K. Fenton and B.R. Spence saw a female at Spurn on 28th May, and one was seen on Irton Moor, Scarborough, on 7th June by P. Robson.

H.T. James of Beverley saw one near Pocklington on 27th May 1968; P.S. Elsworth saw one near East Cowton on 10th June 1969; A.W. Wallis saw one near Tunstall, north of Withernsea, on 6th and 7th May 1972; an immature was seen by B. Banson, J. Fitzharris and B.R. Spence near Easington on 29th and 30th August 1973; one was at Dunsville, near Doncaster, on 28th May 1978 where it was watched by Miss K.J. Martin and S. Wildman; one was seen in a garden at Rimswell, near Withernsea, on 28th May 1979, identified from the painting in *Thorburn's Birds* by the finders, and subsequently seen and confirmed by B.R. Spence; one was seen at Spurn on 14th July 1980 by R.P. Council and B.R. Spence; an adult was seen at Welton Water on 12th June 1981 by N.P. Senior; one was seen near Easington on 15th and 16th May 1983 by J. Metcalfe; and one was at Spurn on 11th May 1984.

The Woodchat Shrike, which breeds from central Europe eastwards to southeast Asia and also in North Africa, has occurred in the British Isles on about 466 occasions and has been recorded annually since the mid 1950s.

Jay
Garrulus glandarius

Nelson's opening words in his chapter on this species in 1907 apply equally well today:

> 'This handsome woodland bird shares, with the hawk and crow families, the unenviable notoriety of figuring in the keeper's "Black List", and is consequently subject to incessant persecution wherever it ventures to show itself in a game preserving neighbourhood.'

A few years prior to 1907, according to Nelson, no fewer than 24 were procured in one day in Bramham Woods. He went on to say that horticulturists, as well as gamekeepers, were its enemy as it fed on peas and cherries, and it was becoming scarce in most parts of the county at the turn of the century.

In spite of persecution over the years, Jays still manage to nest over much of Yorkshire, and the Breeding Birds Survey organised by the British Trust for Ornithology during the years 1968-72 showed that breeding pairs could be found in most areas except some of the eastern parts of the East Riding and the higher parts of the Pennines, the North York Moors and the Wolds. The species has increased in the woodlands around Hornsea in recent years. It is, however, very thinly distributed over much of its range, and there are large tracts of deciduous woodland without the species as a result of the attentions of gamekeepers. It does relatively well in large suburban parks and gardens, and many of the conifer plantations, which are now so much a feature in many areas, are providing sanctuary.

There was an undoubted increase in the resident population during the years of

World War II, when most gamekeepers were being trained to shoot larger quarry. Extensive felling of large timber to service the war effort caused birds to wander and colonise new areas at that time. The Jay is common on the heathland at Hatfield and Thorne in the south of the county, and counts in recent years have shown figures of 68 on 19th October and 56 on 26th October 1980, with similarly high numbers in 1981 and 1982. Some of the woodlands of vice-county 63 in the southwest hold good numbers, and there have been counts of 20 to 30 birds at Wintersett Reservoir, the Rivelin Valley, Yateholme and in Bretton Park.

The Jay is an extremely secretive species and it is most often detected by its single, harsh call, sometimes the only indication of its presence; one can never guarantee the sight of a bird, even in woodland where it is known to be present.

That Jays come across the North Sea to Britain is a well-known fact. In early October 1882, Gätke reported 'thousands upon thousands' migrating over Heligoland and the species was subsequently much in evidence in Yorkshire's coastal woodlands. On 5th October 1941, five birds seen flying very high in a southwesterly direction over Goathland Moor by W.S. Medlicott were probably immigrants. A bird shot at Pallathorpe on 17th March 1947 was sent to the Yorkshire Museum and identified by R. Wagstaffe as an example of the Continental race *Garrulus glandarius glandarius*, being very grey on the mantle and lacking any deep vinous tinge (*British Birds*, 1947, p. 211). On 20th February 1948, in Dalby Forest, M.F.M. Meiklejohn and A.J. Wallis watched 20 Jays from a vantage point above the birds and noted very grey mantles. Two flocks, each of about 30 individuals, were seen flying high to the south over the River Humber near Hessle on 22nd April 1948. The two flocks were about an hour apart and were followed by a few stragglers. It is very likely that they were returning Continental birds, as was one flying in over the sea to continue directly inland at Tunstall on 19th April 1970, having probably thought twice about setting out to cross the North Sea on its return migration.

On 14th and 15th October 1972, five and four Jays respectively flew northeast over Knaresborough Ringing Station; Redwings and Bramblings were arriving in large numbers also, but there was no evidence of any immigration of Jays from the coastal areas.

A remarkable invasion occurred in early October 1983, when many thousands of Jays came into Britain. Yorkshire's first birds occurred at Spurn on 11th, when 15 were seen, followed by 30 on 17th, 39 on 19th and a few more up to 31st. The increase was also noted at many inland localities as birds dispersed and spread westwards. One bird ringed at Spurn on 18th October 1983 was recovered at Grimsby on 17th April 1984. Two other recoveries in 1983 did not relate to Continental birds: one ringed as a nestling in Buckinghamshire on 11th June 1983 was recovered at Warter, 212 miles (339 km) north, on 29th October 1983; and a juvenile ringed at Warsop in Nottinghamshire on 16th July 1983 was found dead at Buttercrambe, 58 miles (93 km) north, on about 29th November 1983: probably indicating a restlessness in the Jay population generally in that year. One ringed at Denaby Ings on 30th October 1966 and recovered at Southowram, Halifax, on 12th October 1972 had moved a distance of 27 miles (43 km).

On 15th June 1975, at Runswick Bay, A.J. Wallis watched a Jay chase a Willow Warbler, force it to the ground and pick it up. F.A. Wardman saw one eat a slow-worm at Lindley on 19th June 1975.

Nelson recorded several white examples, at Doncaster, York (three) and near Selby.

An old superstition in the Cleveland Dales supposed that, if the call of the Jay was heard after that of the owl, then the former was talking with the 'restless dead'.

The Jay is, as Nelson described it, 'a handsome woodland bird' and its cunning ways will ensure its place in the Yorkshire countryside in spite of much opposition.

Magpie
Pica pica

What has been said of the Jay in relation to its distribution, and persecution by man, can be applied equally well to the Magpie. Being of a more bold and confiding nature, however, the latter has now invaded suburbia, where benefit is derived from the lack of pressure from gamekeepers and shooters. In his *Yorkshire Birds*, Chislett said that the Magpie was probably more numerous in 1952 than it was at the beginning of the century when Nelson wrote 'Resident, decreasing in numbers, but still fairly common.' It is possibly even commoner today. There are few large cities that do not have a good population of Magpies in their large gardens and parks, and any motorway journey through such suburbs, whether they be residential or industrial, will provide many sightings.

A survey of Magpies within a 5-mile (8-km) radius of the centre of Sheffield, at least half of which area was at the time built-up, was organised by L. Carr in 1946 and revealed 258 nests, built mainly in hawthorn trees. A further study was organised by the Sheffield Bird Study Group in 1976 and 1977, and in the former year 93 of the 100 1-km squares centred on the city were surveyed by 51 observers who located 381 nests. Density ranged from one to 12 nests per square, with an average of four. Only 11 squares were without Magpies, and these were either heavily industrial or with little or no vegetation. For details of the interim report of this survey, see *The Magpie* (journal of the Sheffield Bird Study Group), No. 1, pp. 4-6. K. Clarkson has studied Magpies in the Rivelin Valley, part of the Sheffield area study, and has shown that the area has a relatively high breeding density.

Some large numbers have been counted entering roosts. The first such was monitored near Northallerton during 1942 by J.P. Utley, who spent up to three-and-a-half hours watching the birds arrive on seven dates between 30th March and 15th November and estimated that 200 to 250 birds used the coppice (*British Birds*, 1942/43, pp. 159-60). During the hard weather in February 1947, up to 300 roosted with Starlings in a covert near Nunthorpe. Roost gatherings in more recent years have numbered between 50 and 80 birds at several places, notably Melton, Farnley Park, Arthington, Cottingley, Ardsley Reservoir, Worsborough, the Ewden Valley and at several places near Leeds. Larger roosts are established and occur annually at Ogden Reservoir, where 100 were counted on 18th December 1976; Blackmoorfoot Reservoir, where 120 were seen on 20th December 1977 and 130 on 2nd February 1981; 110 were in Hall Dyke Wood, near Huddersfield, on 23rd January 1977; 119 in Dane's Dyke, Flamborough, in December 1980; and the Rivelin Valley, near Sheffield, where up to 120 were gathered during January 1980.

Although the traditional nest site is in the thick tangle of a hawthorn bush or high in the top of an ash, some interesting variations are on record. In 1946, a pair built its nest in a pile of barbed wire on the Spurn Peninsula. In 1979, a pair successfully reared young in a nest built on the girders of a transformer at Tinsley, near Sheffield; the nest had no roof and the sitting bird could easily be seen.

Plumage variants are not common in this species. Nelson, who listed such details in *The Birds of Yorkshire*, cited two leucistic birds in which the black feathers were replaced by grey in one and rusty-brown in the other; he also mentioned an albino, caught at Kirkbymoorside on 4th June 1904. Two birds shot near Danby-in-Cleveland and sent to the Leeds Museum had the black parts replaced by a light cinnamon colour.

The Magpie features often in Yorkshire folklore, and is part of the famous verses on 'The Yorkshireman's Coat of Arms' thus:

'A flea, a fly,
A flitch of bacon,
and a chattering Magpie'

to which last subject is attached:

'A Magpie can talk for a terrible span,
An' so an' all can a Yorkshireman.'

Its local names are many and Nelson quoted no fewer than 23, some of which were variants on the same theme, i.e. Pianate, Pyenate or Pynot used in the West Riding, and Pianot or Pyet used in Swaledale. The general term used by most countryfolk, is of course, 'Maggie'.

A juvenile ringed at Knaresborough Ringing Station on 19th July 1963 was shot at Sessay, near Thirsk, on 9th April 1964, having travelled 13 miles (20.8 km), but most recoveries of Yorkshire-ringed Magpies show only local movement.

On 17th September 1984, A.J. Wallis witnessed a Magpie 'parliament' near Tofta Farm in Staintondale. Some 14 birds were jumping about a grass field, forming a rough circle, and one or two at a time would suddenly make an aggressive attack on something which was hidden from view behind a large tuft of grass. In a lull in these attacks another Magpie appeared from behind the tuft and immediately the attacks began again, preventing it from getting away. Eventually all the others birds flew off and the one bird remained, standing with its feathers disarranged, panting for breath and seemingly unable to fly. It was not possible to approach the bird, and whether or not it died from the attacks to which it had been subjected is not known.

Nutcracker
Nucifraga caryocatactes

Five instances of the Nutcracker's occurrence in Yorkshire were published by Nelson, the first being at Campsall, near Doncaster, where one was said to have occurred on the authority of Neville Wood and mentioned in Lankester's *Askern*, 1842, p. 70.

One was obtained at Wakefield in the autumn of 1865 and purchased by J.E. Harting from G. Lumb, who had it in the flesh (Harting's *Handbook*, second ed., p. 388). T. Boynton of Bridlington had a specimen which was procured in Boynton Woods. One was said to have been killed at Dungeon Wood, Huddersfield, in 1870 and preserved by S.L. Mosley, from whom it was bought by the Reverend G.D. Armitage. Mosley subsequently stated that he never possessed such a specimen (*The Naturalist*, 1909, p. 127). One was killed by a keeper at Ilkley on 5th

January 1901 and bought by A. Page on the same day (*The Ibis*, 1901, p. 737).

The next record, published by Chislett in *Yorkshire Birds*, was on 23rd March 1943 when J.P. Utley saw a Jay-sized bird with a white-spotted brown body, black tail with a narrow white bar at the tip, and broad bluish-black wings. The bird flew in front of the car in which Utley was being driven to Great Smeaton.

On 27th April 1951, from his bedroom window, Ken Dawson saw two Nutcrackers sitting on a chimney of the house opposite in Morley Place, Beeston, Leeds. The birds remained for ten minutes before flying off and were watched at a range of about 50 feet (15 m) through ×10 binoculars. Dawson's notes included: about 1 foot (30 cm) in length, bills long and slender, plumage chocolate-brown, heavily streaked and spotted with white on breast, mantle and head except for the crown. The undertail-coverts were white and the short tail was very dark brown or black with white tips to the feathers. The wings were black with a sheen and were very broad. There was a patch of greyish feathers around the base of the bill on one bird only. Though there can be no doubt that the birds were Nutcrackers, their origin is difficult to imagine in view of the suburban location and in a year when there was no marked influx into the country (*British Birds*, 1952, p. 68).

Chislett published details under this species of a bird seen in a garden at Scotton, near Knaresborough, by a Mrs E.K. Phillips during April 1951. She noticed 'speckled appearance and white edge extending up sides of tail'. The bird was seen again in May, and in the middle of that month two birds were watched for three hours as they fed a young bird on the top of a weeping ornamental cherry tree. They called 'kerr-kerr' and 'yark-yark'. After consulting *The Handbook*, she concluded that they must have been Nutcrackers. Chislett saw Mr and Mrs Phillips on 19th June, and it was evident that they had seen something unusual to them. He says: 'it is a pity that confirmation was not sought in April or May, for I could not rid myself of the suspicion that a mistake had been made'. If confirmation had been sought, in my opinion it would have revealed Mistle Thrushes. What is perfectly clear is that the incident should not be considered as even a probable record of breeding Nutcrackers.

On 6th September 1952, in Wadworth Wood, near Doncaster, R. Bramhill heard an unfamiliar call which he traced to a bird in a small tree. When he imitated the call, the bird flew towards him and passed over at about 8 feet (2.4 m). It was Jackdaw-sized with rounded wings, rich brown in colour, heavily spotted with white on breast and back, with a dark tail edged white. It was present until 10th September.

At Eccup Reservoir on 1st November 1955, A. Walker saw three birds fly out of a plantation. They showed conspicuous white undertail-coverts, and white edges and tips to the black tail. One settled on a tree, and the mottled brown plumage with black wings was clearly seen through binoculars at 20 yards' (18 m) range.

In 1968, a remarkable invasion took place and about 315 were recorded in Britain. There were at least ten records in Yorkshire, as follows. Spurn Bird Observatory had single birds on 22nd August, 24th September and 14th October, all of which flew south and were seen by B.G. Pepper, B.R. Spence, A.W. Wallis and several others. One was in Sewerby Park, Bridlington, from 25th September to 3rd November, and was watched by H.O. Bunce, P. Robson, A.J. Wallis and myself among many other birdwatchers. Two were at Flamborough on 17th October and one from 18th October to 17th November, when it was found emaciated and later died. Up to three birds were in Wykeham Forest from 7th October to the end of November which R.H. Appleby and A.J. Wallis saw several times; two of these stayed over into 1969 and were seen from 25th February until at least 4th May. One was seen in a Barnsley garden by R.L. Kaye on 7th February 1969.

All the British records were reviewed by J.N Hollyer in *British Birds*, 1970, pp. 353-73, and were considered to belong to the slender-billed race *macrorhynchus*.

This species is a very irregular visitor to the British Isles and occurrences are usually a result of irruptive migrations of the slender-billed form, which breeds in northeast Russia, Siberia, northern Mongolia and Manchuria. The thick-billed race from central Europe is normally sedentary, but a few have wandered to the British Isles.

Chough
Pyrrhocorax pyrrhocorax

There is fairly strong evidence to show that the Chough once nested on the high sea-cliffs of Yorkshire. A Mr McLean reported to Nelson that an old man who worked in the alum works at Boulby in the early part of the nineteenth century remembered 'Red-legged Daws' on the cliffs there. These cliffs are the highest in England and reach a height of 600 feet (180 m), an ideal habitat for this species. Canon Atkinson stated that until about 1861 it was known to breed at Flamborough. M. Bailey, the Flamborough taxidermist, could not however remember it, nor could several of the old residents, whose notes went as far back as 1837 in some cases.

Thomas Allis, in his report of 1844, stated that one had been killed by the gamekeeper of Mr Randall Gossip at Hatfield and the specimen went to Joseph Cook of Rotherham. F.O. Morris mentioned one, on the authority of Charles Dixon, which was killed near Sheffield in the spring of 1875 and preserved by H. Reid of Doncaster. It is strange that these two birds should have occurred at inland sites, and it may be well to bear in mind that collectors were anxious to add new specimens to their collections at that time, and the origin of some early records must remain in doubt.

Nelson considered a record at Masham in the winter of 1876 as authentic. The bird was seen by William Todd, a taxidermist, as it fed in the company of Rooks, when its red legs and bill showed plainly against the snow (*The Naturalist*, 1886, p. 234).

There is an ulna in the British Museum, attributed to this species, taken from Kirkdale Cave.

In April and May 1957, several people reported seeing a Chough on the Huntcliffe at Saltburn. It was first seen on 27th April by two schoolchildren, who reported seeing a Jackdaw-like bird with glossy black plumage and a red bill which flew along the cliff-edge. Some local people saw it on or about 22nd May and confirmed the story when interviewed by D.R. Seaward. In the absence of ornithological confirmation, such a record will always remain in some doubt, but the possibility remains.

The next authentic Chough to be seen in Yorkshire occurred on 30th July 1981 at Flamborough, when I. Armstrong and J. Crudass saw one suddenly appear above the clifftop and fly along the edge, affording close views.

Some Choughs are kept in captivity and there is always the possibility of an escaped bird, but the occurrence of these recent ones at very likely localities is somewhat encouraging.

Jackdaw
Corvus monedula

When Pennant travelled through Knaresborough in 1773, he wrote 'Near this place the vaste precipitous cliffs, darkened with ivy that spreads over their sides, exhibit a most magnificent scenery. Daws inhabit and caw far above on the face of [the rocks].' (*Tour from Alston Moor to Harrogate and Brimham Crags*, 1804, p. 104). Those high and ivy-clad limestone cliffs which tower above the River Nidd as it flows eastwards from the town still provide nesting sites for many Jackdaws.

The species is generally and commonly distributed over the whole county, and breeds in a large variety of habitats from the sea-cliffs to the high Pennine crags. Holes in trees or buildings, whether the latter be old or new, act as nesting places for this ubiquitous species. It is often common during the breeding season in the centre of large cities and towns, where it finds cavities to suit its needs under the eaves of buildings or in old chimneys. It is doubtful if there is a suitable piece of habitat in the whole county that is not utilised by Jackdaws.

On the sea-cliffs at Bempton and Flamborough, it was accused by the egg gatherers of rolling Guillemot's eggs off the ledges and then flying down to eat the contents, which no doubt it did; it was thus considered an enemy of the climbers, who sought to persecute it.

On 17th April 1945, R.M. Garnett and C.E.A. Burnham watched several pairs building nests in the top of spruce trees at Kirkdale, and a pair built an open Rook-like nest in the top of a 30-foot (9-m) spruce at Collingham in 1948 and hatched three eggs. A pair built a similar open nest in a Sitka spruce at Leighton in 1959, and five pairs did so in 1965.

Large concentrations gather at roosts, and some maxima in recent years are as follows. At Chevet, Wakefield, 4,000 left a roost at daybreak on 29th November 1953 and a further 10,000 birds left at 07.45 hours; even allowing for some exaggeration, these are the largest numbers ever recorded in the county. At Knotford Nook 4,000 left a roost on 25th December 1966 and again on 29th October 1970; 4,000 leaving Lower Wharfedale for Washburndale on 7th December 1974 were probably from the same roost; 3,500 were at the Hornsea corvid roost during December 1977, 1,900 in December 1978, 5,000 in December 1979 and 2,000 on 10th November 1981. For full details of a seven-year study of flight-lines in the Leeds area, organised by R.V. Jackson from 1955 to 1962, see *The Naturalist*, 1964, pp. 37-47.

Many Jackdaws come across the North Sea into Britain each autumn and watchers in Yorkshire record them every year. Most are impossible to tell apart from the British breeding birds, but some show the paler nape with a silvery-white patch at the sides, characteristic of the Scandinavian race *Corvus monedula monedula*. Single examples identified as belonging to this race occurred at Easington on 30th October 1887; found dead at Knaresborough on 10th March 1969 and brought to me for inspection; and at Knaresborough Ringing Station from 7th to 29th April 1980. P.A. Lassey and Miss I. Smith considered that 80 Jackdaws at Flamborough on 4th November 1979 included some Continental birds, one having particularly striking white patches on the neck sides. Flocks of 40 and 50 birds on 16th and 23rd October 1982 respectively were also considered to belong to this race.

A Jackdaw ringed at Spurn on 3rd April 1960 was recovered at Texel in the Netherlands on 15th April 1960, and a bird of the year ringed at the North Slob in

Wexford on 20th December 1975 was shot at Spennithorne on 1st July 1979.

Nelson was aware of immigration and mentioned a 'rush' on 17th October 1889 at Flamborough, and 'an extraordinary arrival' at Easington during the first week of November 1894 when flocks of 50 to 60 birds kept arriving for three or four days in succession.

A flock of 300 in fields near Kilnsea on 19th October 1968 was an unprecedented number for the Spurn Bird Observatory logbook at the time, and has not been approached since. Smaller numbers are seen arriving, often with Rooks, in most autumns.

Plumage variation is not uncommon and several pure white, pied and brown leucistic birds are on record. A bird with its entire plumage coloured French-grey was shot in Holderness in 1941.

Rook
Corvus frugilegus

According to Nelson in *The Birds of Yorkshire*, the earliest mention of the Rook in connection with the county dates back to about 1730 and concerns an incident which took place at Bilton, near Harrogate, when John Metcalfe, known as Blind Jack of Knaresborough, and a companion robbed a rookery at dead of night 'bringing away seven dozen and a half, excepting the heads which they left under the trees'. This so incensed the owner that he sent the bellman around, offering a reward of two guineas for the detection of the offenders (*Yorkshire Magazine*, 15th April 1875, iv, p. 71).

Nelson said that the Rook was 'without doubt the most abundant of our larger inland birds, and is not absent even from the desolate moorland tracts, for in the dales and on the high fells of the west and north-west it is met with in the most barren situations while on foraging expeditions'. The same applies today, but it is impossible to know whether or not it is any less numerous than formerly.

Widespread it most certainly is, and rookeries are a familiar sight over most of the county. Small stands of mature trees around upland farmsteads, and large tracts of lowland woodland are two extremes of habitat chosen by this species. It is not averse to building in conifers, especially Scots pines, but prefers large deciduous timber.

Several investigations into the Rook populations have been organised in Yorkshire by various societies and individuals. In 1942, J.P. Utley counted nests in the western half of the North Riding and visited 168 rookeries at altitudes up to 975 feet (297 m) above sea-level. Every rookery was near to a human dwelling, no doubt a reflection of the only available timber around the villages and farms.

In 1945, on an area of 575 square miles (1,489 km²) of the eastern part of the North Riding, C.E.A. Burnham estimated that 205 rookeries held 10,000 nests; W.G. Bramley counted 3,001 nests in an area of 65 square miles (168 km²) around Bolton Percy, near York; and pupils of the Malet Lambert High School counted over 4,000 nests between the River Hull and and the coast.

A census within 8 miles (12.8 km) of Huddersfield Town Hall in 1956 showed a total of 2,388 breeding birds. A count around Bradford in 1953, organised by C. Nelson, revealed 521 nests in 15 rookeries, an increase of 16 percent since 1947. The Doncaster and District Ornithological Society organised surveys in 1964, 1970, 1975 and 1980 within their recording area of 314 square miles (813 km²) formed within a 10-mile (16-km) radius of Doncaster city centre, the major part of which (274 square miles/710 km²) lies within Yorkshire. The basic results were as follows: 2,107 nests in 96 rookeries in 1964; 2,153 nests in 90 rookeries in 1970; and 1,986 nests in 81 rookeries in 1975 (the results for 1980 are not yet published). For full details see *The Lapwing*, No. 4, pp. 3-8; No. 6, pp. 2-9; No. 9, pp. 3-17, and No. 14, pp. 3-7.

Surveys were carried out within a 15-mile (24-km) radius of Leeds Town Hall in 1955 by R.V. Jackson and in 1973 by T.R. Birkhead. In the latter year, a total of 6,046 nests was counted in 187 rookeries and the general impression was that there had been little change in the population since 1955, in spite of much increase in urbanisation. For full details of the two studies see *The Naturalist*, 1959, pp. 85-90, and 1974, pp. 65-9.

The national census organised by the British Trust for Ornithology in 1975 showed a total within Yorkshire of 1,843 rookeries containing 63,039 nests. For full details of this survey, see *Bird Study*, 1978, pp. 64-86.

Details of successful breeding in a low bush by a flightless Rook were published in *The Naturalist*, 1976, p. 108.

Many Rooks arrive along the coastline every autumn from the Continent, and Nelson mentioned them 'coming in one steady stream, from early morning until late afternoon, and often in company with Hooded Crows, Lapwings, Starlings and Skylarks'. In the autumn of 1902, there were more migrant Rooks than he had previously known. On 28th October 1948, R. Chislett watched a large compact formation of some 500 Rooks come in from the sea at Spurn, with much cawing as they crossed the coast: 'The phalanx travelled at a great pace and behind them in a long procession straggled a similar number of Jackdaws, which seemed to find the great pace of the Rooks difficult to maintain.'

G.R. Bennett saw 200 flying in over the sea near Wilsthorpe at 17.00 hours on 7th October 1954 at an altitude of about 1,000 feet (305 m). Small numbers are recorded at Spurn every year and more in some, the largest numbers in recent years being 200 on 5th November 1975; and 260 on 1st November, 103 on 12th November and 153 on 13th November 1956. Spring movements are seldom so obvious, but small numbers are regularly seen along the coast during March and April.

Evidence of Continental origin comes from the recovery of three Dutch-ringed nestlings at Cawood, Selby and Pontefract. A bird caught on a lightship near Borkum Island in Germany on 31st October 1927 was recovered at North New-bald in the East Riding in December 1930. A juvenile ringed at Novgorod in the USSR on 8th June 1958 was found dead near Sheffield on 14th January 1959.

Further evidence is supplied by Rooks caught and ringed in Yorkshire during the winter months and subsequently recovered on the Continent, such birds being recovered in Sweden, Denmark, Holland, Belgium and Germany. There are several other recoveries of Yorkshire-ringed Rooks within the British Isles and Yorkshire. Large flocks of several hundred birds can be seen feeding on agricultural land during the winter months and no doubt contain many immigrants.

Roosting assemblies can be quite spectacular, especially during the pre-roost flight gatherings in the late afternoons when flocks may number several thousands. During the years 1955 to 1962, R.V. Jackson studied the roost flight-lines around Leeds and the main roost was located in Shire Oaks Wood, near Tadcaster, where many thousands of birds gathered nightly during the winter months. Full details of the study were published in *The Naturalist*, 1964, pp. 37-47. The corvid roost at Hornsea Mere held 4,000 Rooks on 1st February 1975 and 4,500 on 9th December 1978. The largest roosts in recent years have been at Mapple Yard, Doncaster, where 17,000 were counted in November 1976; Cookridge, near Leeds, where there were 10,000 on 8th January 1981; Bretton Park, where 10,000 gathered on 1st December 1981; and Frickley Park, where there were 15,000 during the autumn and winter months of 1980, 1981 and 1982.

Rooks with abnormal plumage are relatively common. There are several records of pied individuals and a few pale brown leucistic ones, including one at Thornton-le-Dale in 1942, one in the Lower Derwent Valley from 1976 to 1978 and one at Cawood in February 1980. Some pure white ones were recorded by Nelson and there have been four in more recent years: one at Lockington in the East Riding in 1947; one at Gargrave in 1949 and 1951; one at Horton-in-Craven in 1970; and one at North Rigton in October 1984.

This very familiar species has attracted much folklore, and in *The Birds of Yorkshire* Nelson recounts many interesting stories of the superstitions surrounding it.

Carrion Crow
Corvus corone

The Carrion Crow entered the Yorkshire ornithological literature in the sixteenth century when, in the accounts of the churchwarden in the Parish of Ecclesfield, near Sheffield, an item for the destruction of vermin reads '1590, Item for vj crowe heades, jd.'

At the beginning of the present century, Nelson summarised its status as 'Resident, generally but thinly distributed; scarce in the manufacturing districts, and decreasing generally. A few pairs nest on the sea-cliffs.' Today, Carrion Crows are probably more numerous and can be found breeding in the suburban areas of our large cities and towns where they are left unmolested. In some country districts they are rigorously persecuted, but manage to maintain themselves. They are distributed over the whole county and nest in many types of habitat. Stunted bushes along the coastline and the Humber foreshore, large trees in parks and gardens, isolated trees in agricultural areas, and gnarled trees on the high windswept moorlands may all hold nests.

This normally solitary species assembles in the evenings to roost communally and several large gatherings have been recorded. The earliest large number on record is 200 above Carlton-in-Cleveland in October 1952, and high counts in recent years probably reflect the success of the species in unkeepered districts. Up to 100 birds roosted at Adel Dam, Leeds, during March and April 1972; 150 were in Melton Wood on 13th July 1972; a roost in heather at Ogden Reservoir held 100 birds during the winter of 1972/73, 300 in January 1977 and 350 on 9th December 1977; 350 roosted near Settle on 2nd January 1975; 480 were in Haw Park on 7th September 1977; up to 150 near Ripon in 1980 during the winter months; 120 at Askham Bog on 10th May and 225 on 28th December 1982; 100 near Harrogate during January 1982; 480 in Deffer Wood on 30th January 1982; and flocks of up to 50 or more occur regularly in many widely scattered areas, both on the moors and close to suburbia. The largest numbers occur at Hornsea Mere, where a mixed corvid roost regularly holds up to 200 Carrion Crows, with larger counts of 550 in January 1975, about 1,000 in November 1976, 550 in December 1977, 500 in

January 1978 and 286 in February 1980. In 1977, 130 birds were at the roost on 23rd May, an unusual date for such a large number, and probably made up of failed breeders and non-breeders. A flock of 50 birds seen by J.K. Fenton on Pen-y-Ghent on 12th July 1959 was an unusual occurrence. A keeper's gibbet in the northwestern fells held 110 birds on 7th July 1951.

Nelson knew the Carrion Crow as an immigrant and published an interesting event concerning a bird shot at Flamborough. It had come in over the sea on 2nd October 1894, when it had, tied around its neck, a piece of board measuring 4 inches by 1¼ inches (10.2 × 3.2 cm) and bearing the inscription 'Leading Star. O.R.', indicating that it had been caught on that vessel somewhere at sea and liberated with the message (*The Naturalist*, 1894, p. 326).

H.O. Bunce watched 18 Carrion Crows circling high over Flamborough Head on 30th April 1955 and eight more on 15th April 1960. On 8th May 1976, 130 flew north at Flamborough Head, and 180 passed there on 9th April 1978, with smaller numbers to 1st May; 44 flew out to sea on 2nd May 1980. Similar movement is noted at Spurn in spring every year: 88 flew south between 04.30 hours and 07.30 hours on 19th April 1958 and smaller numbers, often up to 50 birds in a day, are evident every spring and autumn. W. Norman recorded 21 birds arriving from over the sea at South Gare on 29th January 1966. In the autumn of 1980, 100 were at Flamborough on 4th October and 150 on 22nd November.

Several pure white and leucistic birds have been recorded in the county and the species seems to be particularly prone to such aberration.

The Hooded Crow *Corvus corone cornix* is certainly less numerous as a visitor to Yorkshire than it apparently was during the first half of the present century and before. In *The Birds of Yorkshire*, Nelson mentioned that 'It sometimes begins to come from seaward at daylight and continues dropping in until noon. ...' A long straggling flock was once noted off Flamborough Head, 2 miles (3.2 km) offshore, passing over at a great height and descending on approaching the land, and Nelson himself, when in boats offshore, had seen parties coming in long, irregular lines. Nelson's statement that 'Most of these immigrants disperse over the county soon after arrival, although many remain in the neighbourhood of the coast' implies a much greater abundance than we experience today.

In *Yorkshire Birds*, Chislett said that up to 50 Hooded Crows roosting in Raincliffe Woods, near Scarborough, during February 1949 was an unusually large number, and a statement in the Yorkshire Naturalists' Union Ornithological Report for 1953 that 'The species was normal at Spurn with 17 on 17th February, two on 29th April and one on 12th July' gives some indication of the numerical status at that time. A. Credland counted 26 birds along the Humber bank between Patrington Haven and Kilnsea on 18th October 1959, and in the following year more occurred in the autumn than usual when A.F.G. Walker counted 21 at Flamborough and R.H. Appleby saw 32 at Filey Brigg on 29th October, with 55 at the latter place on 12th November and 60 on 3rd December. The moorland areas in the northeast also had several parties, with 35 on Stanghow on 13th November and 45 at Lockwood Beck on 25th December being the largest. In the early months of 1961, there were 70 at Winestead on 21st February and smaller numbers at many localities along the coast up to 13th May. The only subsequent flock of any size was 20 at Filey on 5th January 1967, but a relatively large influx occurred in 1976 with peak numbers as follows: 39 at Spurn on 31st October, 32 on 8th November, 42 on 13th November and 24 on 14th, most of which flew south; 11 at Flamborough on 8th May and 29 on 31st October, on which date 12 were at Ottringham. Smaller numbers were evident at several other coastal places. The only gathering of any note since that time was 26 on Scarborough tip during February 1977.

A 'Hoodie' may be seen anywhere inland during the winter months, often with its black relative, and usually singly, but two or three on occasions. On 13th October 1973, a party of four flew over Knaresborough Ringing Station.

The Hooded Crow arrives along our seaboard during October, with a few earlier records in late September, and most have departed by April and early May, a few odd birds lingering to the end of that month and into June.

Nelson cited several records of breeding by single pairs, at Flamborough in 1858 to 1871, 1876, and 1887 when a brood was reared near the lighthouse (*The Zoologist*, 1858, p. 6142); and also at Hornby Castle in 1865, Beverley in 1876 and Easington in 1896. A flock of 16 remained at Flamborough during the summer of 1891 (*The Naturalist*, 1891, p. 351). A female Hoodie paired with different Carrion Crows in three successive years at Hackness, the males being shot on each occasion, and produced young in the first two years before she was finally shot; the specimen went to the Scarborough Museum.

A Hooded Crow ringed in Denmark on 28th May 1925 was recovered near Eskrick, York, on 21st January 1926.

. This race of the Carrion Crow, which breeds in Ireland, northern Scotland, Scandinavia and from northern Italy to the Urals and lower Danube, is much scarcer in Yorkshire now than formerly.

Raven
Corvus corax

In 1907 when Nelson published *The Birds of Yorkshire* he could only say of the Raven's status 'Resident, but restricted now to one or two pairs in the north-western fells.' A century earlier, it was much more numerous, although never very common. Its prehistoric remains were found in Kirkdale Cave, and the old records showed that it not uncommonly built its nest in trees and woods of the West Riding.

The Reverend J.A. Haydyn of Dent Vicarage supplied Nelson with details from the churchwarden's account books relating to this species in the early part of the eighteenth century, showing that payments were made for the heads of Ravens: thus, in 1713 1s 4d was paid for eight heads, and another entry shows that ten-pence was paid for five heads; between 1713 and 1750, there were similar entries in every year, the price being around twopence per head, though in 1726 3s 0d was paid for eight heads, and in 1737 5s 10d for 35 heads.

The Raven bred in the gardens of Walton Hall, where the last one was destroyed in 1813, and the last nesting bird in the Aire Valley was killed in Trowler's Gill in 1837. A pair of young birds taken from the nest in Bishops Wood, Selby, around this time was kept alive for several years. It also bred in Nidderdale, at Ravensgill; near Pateley Bridge, where the last nesting bird was shot by an old local character who died in 1898 aged 92 years; at Hackfall; Gordale Scar; and Eavestone, near Ripon. A bird was trapped in Lower Nidderdale in 1860 and kept in captivity for some time, before it returned to the wild, found a mate and hatched young in a fir tree in Allerton Park.

In the North Riding, breeding places were on the Mausoleum at Castle Howard up to 1856; at White Mare Cliff near Helmsley and Peake's Scar near Rievaulx up to 1860; at Gowerdale; Rowlston Scar; Hood Hill; and in Bilsdale. A pair persisted up to 1875 in Newton Dale, where they bred on a crag known as Raven's Cliff. A pair bred near Guisborough up to 1866, either on Cass Rock or Highcliff near the Raven's Well (called Jackdaw's Well in Nelson's time). A few pairs bred in

Wensleydale and Swaledale up to the middle of the nineteenth century. In the year 1880, 11 Ravens were killed on Bowes Moor, and Nelson saw the remains of seven of these hanging on the walls of a keeper's cottage.

In the East Riding, a pair nested on a Scots pine in Scampston Park about the middle of the nineteenth century. A pair bred on Beverley Minster up to 1840 and the young were annually taken by an old mason named Gray; the nest was on the southernmost of the two west towers. The sea-cliffs at Flamborough and Speeton were breeding places; in 1837, the Flamborough site was near the King and Queen Rocks. A pair nested between Dane's Dyke and the 'Dor', and a man was killed when the rope snapped while he was descending to the nest of the last pair to breed there. The Raven nested also to the north of Filey Brigg before 1858; the Castle Cliff at Scarborough up to about 1855; on another cliff north of Scarborough and at Hawsker Bottoms, near Whitby, about 1865 and again in 1880. The high cliffs at Boulby also hosted an occasional pair around this time. About 1870, two birds were seen on the beach there feeding on the dead body of a sailor.

In 1915, W.H. St Quintin released some young birds onto the Bempton Cliffs, but they did not stay. During the present century, the few pairs that manage to survive the depredations of gamekeepers, egg collectors and youths do so in the extreme northwest, and no more than three or four pairs at the most have nested annually in recent years. I am unable to name the breeding sites for obvious reasons.

The largest parties seen along the Pennines in recent years have been 22 birds sporting together above Rawthey Valley on 19th August 1950; 11 attacking a Kestrel above Semerwater on 8th August 1960; 14 in Dentdale on 28th February

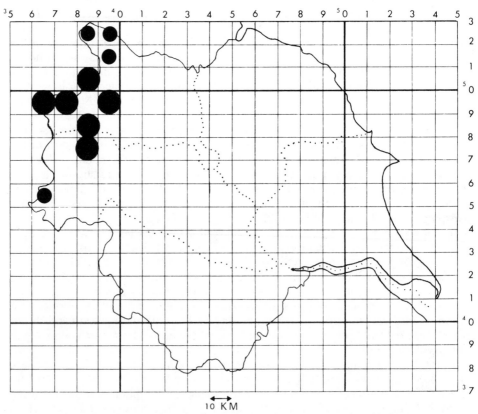

Raven. A declining species with a precarious foothold in the county. It is likely that no more than five pairs breed annually at the present time.

556

1965; and 12 at Arkengarthdale in July 1971.

During the winter months a solitary Raven may be seen wandering onto the Pennine foothill moors, but it is now a very scarce bird. Away from the high ground, they are most unusual but there have been a surprising number of sightings in recent years. Fairburn Ings has had more than its share, the first being seen on 22nd February 1958 and another on 15th November 1958; C. Winn saw one flying north there on 4th May 1974; another flying north on 16th June 1981; two flying northwest on 6th September 1982; and one flying north on 24th October 1982. L. Parkin and C. Winn saw two at Spurn with Carrion Crows on 8th October 1960; P.A. Lassey and Miss I. Smith saw one at Dane's Dyke, Flamborough, with other corvids on 4th September 1976 and two more at Flamborough on 26th May 1979, on which day D.I.M. Wallace saw one between Carnaby and Haisthorpe; Wallace also saw a juvenile at Flamborough on 4th June in that year. In 1980, W.F. Curtis saw two birds flying northwest between Driffield and Skerne on 23rd July 1980; D.I.M. Wallace saw one at Bessingby, near Bridlington, on 21st September 1980, and one was at Pugneys Gravel-pit, near Wakefield, on 5th May 1983. J. Lunn saw one in the Little Don Valley on 13th May 1984 and another at Winscar Reservoir on 31st May 1984.

It is difficult to imagine the origin of these birds, but it is not impossible that they have wandered down from farther north in Scotland as fairly large numbers, presumably non-breeders, move both south and north through Fair Isle during April and May each year; the records in May and June are thus interesting. The Scandinavian population is also increasing and immigration is possible.

The only recovery of which I have note concerns a nestling ringed in the northwest on 14th May 1939 and recovered on Malham Moor in the winter of 1940/41, while one ringed on the Cumberland side of the Pennines on 9th April 1949 was at Hawes on 1st May 1950. These perhaps provide a clue to the origin of some of the lowland wanderers in that month.

Starling
Sturnus vulgaris

This familiar species has been known in the literature in connection with Yorkshire since at least the early part of the seventeenth century, when it was referred to by Ralph Johnson of Greta Bridge. According to Nelson, it had increased enormously during the past 50 years (prior to 1907), particularly in the valleys of the Wharfe, Nidd and Washburn, and also in Swaledale and Arkengarthdale, where it was an 'abundant species even up to an elevation of 1,000 feet [305 m] above-sea-level and was known to nest at Malham'. A letter in *The Field* of 20th October 1888 said that a certain gentleman could recollect the first pair of Starlings that colonised Swaledale at a place called Low Row; a few years after which they made their way to Summerside, then to Muker, Keld and the head of the dale. It is hard to imagine someone from even the remotest part of the British Isles being unfamiliar with the species, and it is thus of interest to include a statement contained in a letter from the Duke of Argyll to Mr Harvie-Brown, as follows:

'Inverary, Jan. 19th 1894.
Dear Mr Harvie-Brown, I never saw a Starling till I went to England in 1836. I still recollect the great interest with which I saw the bird for the first time at the Posting Inn at Northallerton in Yorkshire. Argyll.'

Today it is distributed during the breeding season over every part of the county and is absent only where nest sites are non-existent; even the most remote stone building on the high Pennines will hold a pair, and the provision of nesting boxes in any locality will meet with immediate response.

The Yorkshire breeding birds may be in full bill colour and singing at their nest holes as early as January, when the winter visitors are still mostly black-billed and roaming in packs to feed on the pastureland.

During October, many thousands of immigrants arrive from the Continent and can be seen coming in over the sea in packs, low over the water. The large numbers of most migrant species quoted by Nelson suggest that more birds came then than now, even allowing for some exaggeration. 'On 4th November 1881, an enormous flight estimated to contain at least a million birds came off the sea at Redcar, extending in a dense mass for over two miles making a noise like thunder, and darkening the air.'

Winds from the eastern quarter are necessary to aid the arrival of such large numbers. In *Yorkshire Birds*, Chislett recalls that, in the autumn of 1950, he waited patiently at Spurn for a change of wind to one with some east in it. The change came on 21st October, and the next day Starlings arrived in packs. One flock dropped into the bushes adjacent to one of the Heligoland traps and 44 were caught at one drive. At Bridlington, many thousands arrived in the early morning and covered the harbour area, boats, ropes, masts and the jetties and adjoining houses, where some came down chimneys. In a couple of hours most birds had passed on, 'with a noise like that of several jet aeroplanes flying low' as one witness described the scene to a newspaper correspondent.

Such flights occur, in varying numbers, every year depending on the weather, and anywhere from the Tees to the Humber during October to December they are a common sight. On the days of heavy passage, numerous flocks of just a few to several hundreds or even thousands of birds are evident as they feed before dispersing inland. On 10th December 1977, 11,500 were gathered on the Spurn Peninsula, and on 28th December 1968 birds 'streaming' south all day totalled 20,000.

The exodus in early spring is never so obvious but there is some assembly along the coast at this time. Most Continental birds have left by early April.

Roosts of this species can be large and spectacular. They may shift from season to season or even within one winter period. The local breeding birds and their juveniles mass together from July onwards and form temporary roosts in a variety of habitats. Hawthorn thickets are a favourite, even those on the moorlands, as are conifer plantations in such areas. A roost at Middlesmoor in mid July 1956 held 100,000 birds, and one at Tosside in August 1978 held up to 50,000 birds, most of which were juveniles. Other large roosts involving Yorkshire Starlings and their young have been at Fairburn Ings, where 120,000 assembled in the reeds during early September 1960 after a gradual build-up from July; and at Elsecar Reservoir, where the roost peaked at 250,000 birds on 24th September 1972. Smaller roosts are common in many other areas at this time.

Once the immigrants are settled in their winter quarters, they form roosts, sometimes of immense proportions. It would be impossible and unnecessary to list all the places that have held such assemblies in recent years; even those with up to 50,000 birds are far too numerous to enumerate. Some of the most spectacular have been as follows: 100,000 at Hornsea Mere in November 1955; 250,000 at Sprotborough Flash in November 1972; up to 200,000 at Wentworth Woodhouse in the winters of 1972, 1974 and 1975; and 100,000 at Selby Railway Station in January and February 1978. During the early winter of 1980, 25,000 roosted on the sea-cliffs at Thornwick Bay.

The buildings in the centre of some of the larger cities and towns are popular roosting places for many birds, which cause problems in some. Town Halls and other large old buildings are particularly suitable because of the preponderance of ledges and ornamental stonework, and Leeds, Huddersfield and Bradford have large traditional roosts.

There are very many two-way recoveries of ringed Starlings which show them to visit us from western Europe, due east through Germany, Poland and the western USSR to Moscow, and from the north in Scandinavia. Yorkshire-born Starlings move within the British Isles with a southwesterly bias, and a few have been recovered on the adjacent Continent.

Aberration in plumage is relatively common in this species, and white or pale fawn leucistic birds are often seen; birds with just a few white feathers also occur. Bill abnormalities have also been recorded: Nelson illustrated one from Redcar in 1897 which had a very elongated bill, and I have the skin of a similar bird from Harrogate in October 1965.

The Starling has attracted many vernacular names in various parts of Yorkshire, and Nelson listed about 16 different ones of which Shepster is perhaps the best known today. He did not, however, include Stiggy, a name I have known since boyhood in Nidderdale, along with Gypo, although he mentioned Gypey from Cleveland.

Rose-coloured Starling
Sturnus roseus

This rare visitor from the Balkans and south Russia eastwards to Afghanistan has appeared in Yorkshire on some 31 occasions, 25 of which were listed by Nelson in *The Birds of Yorkshire* and occurred between 1829 and 1901. Only eight of these were credited with a month of occurrence: one in July, four in August and three in November, dates which fit into the modern pattern. All concerned single birds except for an unsatisfactory record of 'several' in 1862/63 at Skinningrove.

In *Yorkshire Birds,* Chislett could add only three others: two were seen by E.W. Wade at Roos on 20th January 1921; Chislett and his wife saw a male between Kilnsea and Spurn on 17th August 1937; and Dr S. Upton saw a bird on the York to Scarborough main road near Sandburn Wood on 20th September 1937.

There have since been six records. J.P. Utley was confident of the identification based on details supplied to him of a bird in a Northallerton garden with Starlings on 1st October 1954. An adult was seen by P. Gillet and his wife at Hutton Rudby, near Stokesley, on 31st August 1975, and another adult was seen by B. Shorrock and G. Tulloch at Malham Tarn on 30th June and 1st July 1979. A juvenile frequented the Warren area at Spurn, and also Kilnsea, on 26th August 1984; it was seen by several people, including J. Cudworth, R. Swales, Mrs J. Massingham and D. and S. Pogson. P.A. Lassey saw an adult with Starlings at Flamborough Head on 17th July 1984, and D.I.M. Wallace saw a juvenile with Starlings at the same place on 25th October 1984.

House Sparrow
Passer domesticus

The House Sparrow can be found breeding in every part of Yorkshire wherever human habitation exists, and the remote farms on the Pennine hills have their resident birds as do the busiest city centres.

Nesting sites are many and varied, but mainly in some cavity, whether it be in a stone wall, a wooden shed or any other man-made structure. Nesting boxes and natural holes in trees are readily used if these are close to man. Nelson recorded breeding pairs in the base of Rooks' nests and in Sand Martin burrows. Occasionally, an untidy nest is constructed in a thick bush or cypress tree.

In 1978, at Frickley Colliery, South Elmsall, a chick was hatched in the actual coal mine in late October and fledged successfully. A few birds have lived below ground here in recent years, but this was the first proof of successful breeding.

An exceptionally late nest was being built in York on 27th December 1944, which E.W. Taylor kept under observation. He reported that young were eventually hatched.

The species is particularly common during the autumn, when large numbers congregate to feed in the cornfields. Flocks may then reach up to 1,000 birds and include mainly juveniles.

Movements along the Spurn Peninsula have for many years posed questions as to their origins and destinations, but it is possible that these movements are of a relatively local nature and consist of birds breaking roost and flying to their feeding areas. Early-morning flights of birds moving south have been noted since the early 1950s and some very large counts have been made. The main months of activity are September and October, and in 1967 counts were as follows: 1,000 on 2nd, 8th and 12th October; 1,300 on 5th; 1,600 on 21st; 1,700 on 10th; 1,930 on 7th; and 2,000 on 16th. Some were flying fairly high and could be identified only as sparrows, being either this species or Tree Sparrows. In 1970, the largest daily counts were 1,650 on 27th September and 2,200 on 26th October. A total count of 5,000 mixed sparrows was made on 16th October 1976.

Ringing recoveries have shown that several birds cross the Humber into Lincolnshire and East Anglia. Three birds from Spurn have been recovered in Lincolnshire as follows: one ringed on 9th October 1974 was found dead at Chapel-St-Leonards on 30th May 1978; one ringed on 30th October 1980 was found dead at Boston on 24th July 1981; and one ringed on 12th October 1982 was retrapped at Gilbraltar Point on 19th October 1982. Three birds from Spurn have been recovered in Norfolk as follows: one ringed on 8th March 1961 was at Dersingham on 18th April 1962; one ringed on 9th June 1961 was at Wolferton on 18th May 1962; and one ringed on 29th October 1970 was at Kings Lynn on 6th May 1976. One ringed on 12th October 1960 was found dead in Peterborough in Nottinghamshire on 4th October 1962; and one ringed on 15th October 1965 had moved west to Worsley, near Manchester, where it was retrapped on 19th December 1965.

Evidence of northward movement of birds ringed in Lincolnshire came from two birds ringed at Gilbraltar Point: one on 18th October 1964 was shot at Leeds on 3rd February 1965; and one on 20th November 1964 was found dead at Cottingham, near Hull, on 25th April 1965.

An adult ringed at Knaresborough Ringing Station on 29th October 1961 was found dead at Bognor Regis in Sussex on 23rd August 1962. Several other recoveries of birds ringed at Spurn show relatively local movement, and two had moved to York and Ellerton.

Although Nelson considered that the House Sparrow crossed the North Sea and came to Yorkshire as an immigrant in the autumn, an impression based on information from the light stations and sightings of large flocks along the coastal strip, there is no evidence to support this view. The movements outlined above are undoubtedly connected with feeding and roosting flights, and in the main of a relatively local nature.

Plumage aberration is not uncommon in this species and there are many records of fawn, buff, cream, white and dark brown or black examples, the most recent ones of interest being a black individual at Foston, near York, in 1960 and a pure albino found dying at Yeadon on 9th August 1966. Several pale leucistic and pie-bald birds have occurred in recent years.

In March 1976, a female House Sparrow landed on the water at Adel Dam, Leeds, and after splashing about for some minutes was aggressively approached by a Little Grebe which eventually drowned it.

In the early nineteenth century, a price was put on the House Sparrow because of the damage to corn by feeding flocks, and in 1809 threepence per dozen was paid by the overseers at Falsgrave, now part of Scarborough, for all birds killed and brought to them. At Worsborough, one halfpenny each was paid for 488 sparrows, a fair price at that time. At Patrington, the prices paid were a halfpenny for two birds, a halfpenny for four nestlings and a halfpenny for six eggs.

The practice of paying for the extermination of sparrows continued in the parishes of Micklefield and Wakefield until 1872. It was the practice in some areas to shoot only the male of a nesting pair, whereupon the female would acquire a new mate which was then shot, and one particular female attracted no fewer than seven mates, all of which met the same fate before she deserted the site (*The Zoologist*, 1865, p. 9711).

Tree Sparrow
Passer montanus

The Tree Sparrow breeds in almost every district of Yorkshire, but it is by no means evenly distributed. There are large tracts of countryside with only a pair or two during the breeding season, but it is sometimes common where conditions suit it. It is rather choosy in its selection of habitat and prefers relatively open country with ageing timber, old buildings or quarries which provide nesting holes, and it will readily use nesting boxes. During the 1950s, I increased the size of a colony at Knaresborough Sewage-farm from just one or two pairs to around 20 pairs by the provision of boxes.

Two, and sometimes three broods are reared: in 1956 18 pairs at Knaresborough hatched 106 young; and in 1960 40 broods resulted in 167 young, all but three of which fledged.

It has been known to breed in the upper parts of the Flamborough Cliffs since Nelson's time, and in 1975 and 1976 about 30 pairs were nesting in the cliff faces at Bempton, with 40 pairs in 1978. It also uses Sand Martin burrows on the boulder-clay cliffs at Filey in some years.

The Annual Reports of the Yorkshire Naturalists' Union during the 1940s mention instances of Tree Sparrows visiting nesting boxes in March with the comment that this was 'unusually early', but boxes erected during the winter months at Knaresborough Sewage-farm in the 1950s were often occupied within a few days and lined for roosting. It is certainly not unusual for pairs to be in attendance at their nest sites during the early months of the year.

There is some evidence that the Tree Sparrow has increased in numbers during the present century. Nelson said that 'during the past 20 years (prior to 1907) it has greatly increased and multiplied in numbers. ...'; and during the 1940s and 1950s there were reports of colonisation in some of the dales, although the real picture is difficult to assess from the available records. There is no doubt that the largest autumn and winter flocks have been recorded since the 1950s, but that could be due solely to better observer coverage. The Yorkshire Naturalists' Union Ornithological Report for 1948 said 'seven birds were at Leathley on 17th March and on 4th July, near Leathley Hall, adults and young were noted. On 3rd April, at least three were included in a mixed flock at Esholt Sewage Works.' That is perhaps indicative of the lack of observers, rather than a true reflection of the status at that time.

During the autumn, Tree Sparrows collect in large flocks and feed with House Sparrows and finches in the cornfields, where gatherings of up to 300 birds are not uncommon in some localities from the coast westwards to the Pennine foothills. The largest flocks on record are as follows: 400 at Armthorpe in January 1962; 1,000 at Farnham in January 1967; 500 in the Went Valley in February 1972; 800 at Wintersett Reservoir in January 1975 and 400 in December 1975; 400 at Fairburn Ings on 26th August 1976; and 490 at Eastmoor, York, in December 1976.

Coastal movement occurs annually along the Spurn Peninsula during September and October (see last species), and daily counts of up to 500 birds flying south in the early mornings are not uncommon. In 1960, 900 occurred on 8th October and 800 were present on 12th and 13th. Exceptionally large counts were 1,000 on 8th and again on 16th October 1964; 1,000 on 21st October and 1,300 on 22nd October 1966; with 1,151 on 5th October 1976. Large numbers have been seen at Flamborough in recent years, with maximum counts in October 1976 of 300 on 4th, 500 on 16th and 600 on 22nd.

Unlike the House Sparrow, with which it moves south at Spurn during the autumn, only one Tree Sparrow ringed there has been recovered in Lincolnshire, 18 days after being ringed. Other Spurn-ringed birds have been recovered near York, at Boroughbridge and in Cheshire.

A bird ringed at Westleton in Suffolk on 16th November 1960 was retrapped at Spurn on 2nd May 1961; one ringed at Gilbraltar Point on 28th October 1961 was shot at Ellerton on 18th April 1962; and another ringed at Gilbraltar Point on 8th October 1967 was retrapped at Spurn 13 days later, showing a movement in the opposite direction from that one would expect at that season and perhaps illustrating that the movements of some birds are of a fairly local nature and related to feeding and roosting. One ringed in Zuid Holland on 26th October 1971 was retrapped at Spurn on 13th October 1972.

Other Yorkshire-ringed Tree Sparrows have travelled long distances: one ringed at Knaresborough Ringing Station in August 1965 was retrapped at Hornsea in November 1965; one ringed at Adwick-le-Street in April 1970 was retrapped at Inverness in July 1972; and a juvenile ringed at Knaresborough on 30th August 1976 was found dead at Yarmouth on the Isle of Wight on 12th January 1978.

Restless behaviour along the coast during the spring and autumn often indicates migratory activity. Such occurred at Redcar on 9th May 1958 when 100 dropped into bushes, 62 of which rose to a big height and flew northwest; parties were 'restless' in the area later in the year from 9th to 12th October.

Competition for nest sites between this species and Blue and Great Tits has been recorded on several occasions. There have been instances at Knaresborough Ringing Station of dual occupancy, with eggs laid by both species before one species became dominant and took over. Some nesting boxes around Doncaster in 1959 were similarly occupied. In one case, two young Tree Sparrows were successfully reared by a pair of Blue Tits, full details of which were published by J.B. Hague in *The Naturalist*, 1960, pp. 107-8. When ringing Sand Martins with J.A.S. Borrett in the 1950s, we often found a solitary pair of Tree Sparrows occupying a Sand Martin burrow, always at the edge of the colony. Nelson recorded nesting in Sand Martin burrows at Beverley and also commonly in chalk pits.

This handsome and engaging species has been called Rock Sparrow in the Halifax area, Red-headed Sparrow at Linton-on-Ouse, and Pennant referred to it as the Mountain Sparrow, a direct translation of its scientific name. The only other local name that I know of, and which is used frequently in the Knaresborough area, is Scodge.

Chaffinch
Fringilla coelebs

Perhaps one of the commonest songbirds in Yorkshire, the Chaffinch can be found breeding in every part of the county, even up to the fringes of the higher Pennine moors where it may sing from a solitary rowan. New plantations of conifers in the upland areas provided much suitable habitat, which it was quick to colonise.

During the autumn and winter months, Chaffinches flock together and feed with other finches in cornfields and on beech mast. Gatherings of up to 200-300 birds are not uncommon and may occur in any part of the county. Some larger flocks have been recorded in recent years, the largest being as follows: 1,000 at Dale Dyke Reservoir, west of Sheffield, on 24th December 1974 was the largest flock recorded in the county at the time; 1,000 were in Langdale on 30th November 1975; 450 roosted at Walshaw, Halifax, on 26th December 1976; 500 near Scarborough on 20th November 1977; 600 at Broomhead Hall on 4th December 1981; 500 in the Ewden Valley on 11th December 1982; and 1,000 in Thornton Dale on 28th December 1982.

In 1978, movement over Blackmoorfoot Reservoir in late autumn involved many Chaffinches, and a total of 900 flew west and south during the period 8th October to 5th November, the daily maxima being 200 on 12th October; 210 on 21st; 192 on 29th; and 112 on 5th November. Counts at Redmires Reservoir in 1981 showed a total of 4,000 birds moving west and southwest between mid July and mid November, including 334 on 15th October. Visible migration on a smaller scale can be noted at several inland localities during the autumn.

A statement by Nelson that males and females split into separate flocks during the non-breeding season, the males keeping to the high ground and the females and young ones keeping to the low country, has not been borne out in recent times.

Many immigrant Chaffinches arrive on the Yorkshire coast each autumn, and movement can be witnessed from mid September to early November, their numbers varying from year to year. Unlike most other migrant species, the heaviest passage at Spurn is noted during the spring period when birds fly south along the peninsula. The largest counts in recent years have been as follows: at least 3,000 in flocks of up to 100 on 23rd March 1951; 2,581 between 07.15 hours and 09.30 hours on 17th March 1957; 1,200 between 05.30 and 09.00 hours on 2nd April 1960, and 3,500 on 6th up to mid morning; 1,200 on 17th March and 1,100 on 18th March 1965; 1,000 on 17th March 1974; and 623 on 12th April 1979. The largest count on record is one of 3,451 birds flying south between dawn and 16.30 hours on 23rd October 1958: 'flock after flock of up to 100 birds were passing continuously during the morning'. Similar movements, usually involving up to 200 to 300 birds daily, can be seen anywhere along the coastline, but they are more obvious when concentrated into a narrow stream along the Spurn Peninsula.

Evidence of Continental origin comes from recoveries of birds ringed on their breeding grounds in western Europe and subsequently found in Yorkshire, and of birds ringed both inland and on the coast in Yorkshire during the winter months being recovered in Europe or en route. Chaffinches ringed here during March-April and October-November have been recovered in Finland, Norway, Sweden, Denmark, the Netherlands, Belgium and Germany, and one ringed at Pori, in Finland, in July 1960 was retrapped at Spurn in October 1960.

A juvenile ringed at Ilkley on 24th September 1956 was found dead in County Mayo on 7th February 1957, and one ringed near Pateley Bridge on 3rd November 1962 was in West Meath on 3rd February 1964. The first of these was doubtless a Yorkshire-bred bird spending the winter in Ireland, but the second could have been an immigrant en route for its winter quarters when caught and ringed. A bird ringed at Spurn on 14th October 1966 was retrapped in County Wicklow on 23rd February 1967, and another ringed on 9th October 1964 was in Bournemouth on 28th April 1968.

The darker, more vinous breasts and darker brown mantles of the Continental males are not difficult to detect among flocks of Chaffinches, and those along the coast in autumn usually exhibit these features. Bird-ringers at inland localities regularly trap individuals of this race.

A bird found dead at Spurn on 22nd March 1953 was sent to A. Hazelwood, who diagnosed it as belonging to the race *Fringilla coelebs hortensis* from Germany. This race was admitted to the British list in 1948, and is characterised by a paler breast and much whiter belly than the nominate race.

Plumage aberration is not common in this species, but Nelson mentioned a few white or pale-coloured specimens. Chislett listed a white bird seen at Silsden in January 1918 and another near Huddersfield in early 1950, and one such bird was at Ilkley in November 1953.

Brambling
Fringilla montifringilla

A 'regular winter visitor in varying numbers' has served to describe the Yorkshire status of the Brambling for 100 years. Every autumn, flocks come across the North Sea, mainly from Scandinavia, and spend the winter months in the county.

Nelson mentioned the winter of 1898/99 as a good one for Bramblings when 'thousands were seen in the beech woods ...'. On 18th October 1882, an immense flock, extending over 200 yards (183 m) in length, was seen at Spurn, and a considerable arrival had occurred on 12th and 15th at Teesmouth.

At any time from early October, flocks are assembled in the eastern part of the county after coming in along the coast, before they disperse westwards. Over the years, some very large flocks have been recorded, the first being one of 1,500 birds in Hookstone Woods at Harrogate on 8th April 1957 which quickly dispersed, none being seen three days later. In 1966, large numbers occurred at Spurn, with 770 on 6th October, 1,500 on 10th and 560 on 13th. Smaller numbers were seen all along the coast from the Tees to the Humber. Several good flocks of up to 200-300 were recorded at inland localities, the largest by far being 1,500 at Southfield Reservoir on 15th November which had reduced to 500 by 22nd.

Some big flocks occurred in 1967, the largest being 500 near North Newbold on 1st April with 800 there on 9th, and 500 on Thorne Moors on 2nd April. In 1968, a build-up in Bretton Park from early November reached a maximum of 1,250 birds on 21st December. The largest gathering in 1971 was 700 at Wroot on 21st November which fluctuated between 300 and 600 birds during the following winter months. Two flocks totalling 900 birds were at Midhope Reservoir on 1st December 1973. A spectacular flock of 2,000 birds was at Sherriff Hutton on 16th March 1974, and the majority of a mixed finch flock at East Ayton, near Scarborough, on 27th January 1974 were Bramblings. Large numbers were evident in the early months of 1975, the largest flock being 500 in Royd's Wood, Bradford, in mid January.

A massive arrival of immigrants occurred at Spurn on 10th October 1975, when 250 were at the Warren and 2,000 passed south over the Point. Inland flocks during the following winter were numerous and large, and included over 400 at Leighton Reservoir on 18th January, 600 on 14th March and 150 on 4th April. A flock of mixed finches at Sancton, in Holderness, on 1st January was mainly Bramblings.

Several large gatherings in 1977 included up to 600 birds at Underbank Reservoir on 27th November; 1,000 at Luddenden Head during January and February; 500 at Broomhead during January to mid April; and 500 at Strines in February and April. Many birds came in 1981, when flocks were scattered over much of the county, some being of quite spectacular proportions: 800 at Harrogate and 1,000 at Gott's Park, Leeds, on 17th January; 2,000 at Everton Carrs, Doncaster, on 28th January; 300 to 400 during January at Broomhead Hall, Porter Clough, Hook Moor and Bretton Park; and the same numbers at Hollingdale, Sheffield, in late March, when 500 were also at Beauchief, near Sheffield.

The Brambling is thus a common winter visitor, arriving along the coastline from mid September and departing during April, a few earlier and later birds occurring in some years.

Nelson considered 2nd October 1901 to be 'an exceptionally early date' for a Yorkshire arrival, but also mentioned one at Spurn on 26th September 1896, which Chislett published as having occurred at Teesmouth. One was at Spurn on 29th September 1945, and in more recent years there have been singles at Bempton on 30th August 1974 and Spurn on 1st September 1981.

Some birds linger late in the spring and are most often males in full breeding dress. One was seen at Luddenden Dean, Halifax, in June 1907 by T.A. Coward and W. Greaves (*The Naturalist*, 1907, p. 291). Nelson knew of no record after 10th April, but Chislett listed later birds in 1912, 1947, 1948 and 1949, the latest of which was seen by G. Bolam at Hornsea Mere on 8th May 1912 when a male was in full song, and one was at Spurn on 19th May 1949. Since that time there have been several birds in May, mainly along the coast, and especially at Spurn where single birds were also seen on 3rd June 1976 and 7th June 1980. A male sang at Seckar Wood in West Yorkshire on 25th June 1972; one was at Wath on 8th June 1977; and one was in song near Grimwith Reservoir on 26th June 1982.

Several Bramblings ringed at Spurn during the autumn have been recovered in subsequent autumns in Sweden (one), Belgium (seven), France (one) and Spain (one), the latter being shot in January 1973, three years after being ringed. Seven birds ringed inland at Nunthorpe and Skelton have been recovered in Germany (one), the Netherlands (three), Belgium (one) and France (two). Two birds ringed in Belgium have been recovered in Yorkshire: one ringed on 18th February 1958 was retrapped at Spurn on 14th January 1960, and the other ringed on 1st April 1961 was retrapped at Sand Hutton, near York, on 5th April 1962.

Plumage aberration is rare in this species and Nelson mentions only two examples: a white bird obtained at Masham in 1881 and a pied specimen from Harrogate. A male with white wing feathers occurred in a flock of birds at Knaresborough in late December 1955.

Serin
Serinus serinus

Nelson recorded an incident which G.C. Swailes of Beverley reported in *The Field* of 5th June 1897. Swailes had a small aviary and kept a pair of Serins which had produced young. On 26th May 1897, he noticed a strange male Serin near the aviary which stayed for some time and sang from the top of some nearby oaks. F. Boyes also saw and heard the bird, which as far as could be judged was a wild one. It is of course almost impossible to assess whether such a bird is of genuine wild origin or from captivity.

A flock of eight Siskin-sized birds with yellow on head and breast, conspicuous yellow rumps, no conspicuous wing markings and short thick bills was seen at North Ottrington on 8th December 1950, and again on 9th some 4 miles (6.4 km) farther south. They uttered a 'tiralee' note and, in Chislett's words, 'could only have been Serins'. If they were genuine Serins, the record is quite unprecedented, but it is difficult to believe that a mistake was not made. On 9th November in the same year, however, G.W. Temperley saw a Serin which spent two weeks in a South Shields garden in County Durham.

On 13th April 1961, a Serin was identified at Spurn, and half-an-hour later one was caught in the Point trap by P.J. Mountford. Spurn has produced all but one of the other Yorkshire Serins: single birds were seen on 8th May 1964, 22nd October 1966, 9th May 1971, one in song on 4th and 5th May 1976 with two birds on 23rd May 1976, one seen on 23rd April 1977, one caught on 14th February 1978, one seen on 19th April 1980 and another in song on 23rd April 1980, and one caught on 7th November 1982 (see plate 114). One was near Kilnsea on 7th May 1983 and P.A. Lassey saw one at Flamborough on 8th May 1983.

The Serin is a common bird in western and central Europe and has been extending its range northwards since about 1960, with breeding by one pair in southern England in recent years.

Greenfinch
Carduelis chloris

According to Nelson, the Greenfinch was first mentioned in connection with Yorkshire in the Tunstall Manuscript (1783, p. 66) thus: '*Loxia Chloris*, Green Grosbeak. Heard from pretty good authority, that there had been a mongrel between this bird and the canary.'

Wherever suitable habitat in the form of small trees, bushes, hedgerows and well-timbered gardens exists, the Greenfinch can be found during the summer in almost every part of Yorkshire. Only on the high and barren moors of the Pennines and the North York Moors is the species absent, but it will nest right up to the moorland edges along the valleys and gills if the necessary cover is present. The upland birds desert their breeding quarters in the winter months and flock together in the lowlands with other finches.

Autumn and winter flocks are frequent and often number up to 500 birds. More are seen not uncommonly, and as with all finches hard weather concentrates scattered flocks into often spectacular gatherings. The largest numbers on record are as follows: 1,000 at Dewsbury Sewage-farm in February 1953; 700 near Wakefield in February 1954; 1,000 at Airedale Sewage-farm in September 1961; 1,000 on Coatham Marsh, Redcar, in January 1971; 1,000 at Blackmoorfoot Reservoir in March 1971; 1,000 at Thrybergh Wood in October 1975; 1,000 at Wentworth in October and December 1976; 1,000 at Swinefleet Common in December 1980; and the majority of a large flock of 3,000 birds at Selby Brick Ponds in August and September 1981 were Greenfinches and Linnets.

At Spurn Point, some very large flocks have been recorded, and large numbers are seen flying south during the autumn, mainly during the early mornings. In October 1957, passage was noted between 7th October and 2nd November, with daily maxima of 900 on 20th October, 600 on 25th October, 883 on 27th October and 350 on 2nd November. Larger numbers were recorded in 1959, when the daily counts of birds flying south at the Narrow Neck included 1,300 on 24th October, 2,000 on 15th November and 1,500 on 28th November. In 1968, 1,200 flew south on 28th December and another 800 were feeding on the peninsula; 1,000 flew south the next day and a further 1,000 were down; no movement occurred on 31st, but 1,500 birds were feeding in the area. Winter flocks along the peninsula in 1970 were 2,000 from 6th to 8th January and 1,000 on 9th, numbers dropping rapidly thereafter with only 16 birds seen on 16th. Up to 1,000 birds in a day have flown south during October and November in several recent years, and smaller numbers on many days during the same period. In 1981, the total number of Greenfinches flying south between late September and mid November was 10,898.

Of the many Greenfinches ringed at Spurn, very few have been recovered other than locally. A male ringed on 17th April 1962 was retrapped in northern France on 1st May 1963. A female ringed on the isle of Heligoland on 7th January 1968 was retrapped at Spurn on 31st December 1968; and there are records of birds ringed farther north in England during the non-breeding season being retrapped in Yorkshire, providing the proof that many Greenfinches move south for the winter. A juvenile ringed at Skelton was retrapped in West Flanders, Belgium, on 22nd January 1968, and a juvenile male ringed in West Flanders on 29th July 1967 was killed by a car at Welwick on 1st May 1968. A male ringed in Kent on 10th March

1965 and probably on its way back from over the Channel was killed by a car between Bridlington and Scarborough on 18th July 1965; a male ringed near London on 12th March 1966 was found dead at Patrington on 19th July 1966; and a male ringed at Luton in Bedfordshire on 9th January 1966 was at Redcar on 11th March 1967.

There is ample proof of southerly movement of Yorkshire Greenfinches during the autumn, and those passing south at Spurn very likely include birds from farther north in Britain.

Nelson thought that vast numbers crossed the North Sea in autumn and came to Yorkshire where they resorted to the stubbles, and he also considered that the old males migrated separately from the females and young birds. There is no doubt that the presence of stubble in those days would have attracted many more birds than we get today, but there is no direct evidence of large numbers of immigrants arriving along our coastline, although a few probably do so. The coasting flocks of this and other finches with which we are familiar today were no doubt interpreted wrongly as direct immigrants at that time. Nelson spoke of flocks arriving from the east or northeast in foggy weather being so exhausted that they used to 'drop on the rocks, or the sands, directly they made the land'. In October 1901, 'a strong migration from the north took place at Redcar, accompanied by Linnets, Siskins and other small birds'. This was undoubtedly the same sort of coasting movement that is witnessed annually at the present time, and is unlikely to have originated in Continental Europe.

Greenfinches roost communally, mainly in evergreens, but sometimes in thick hawthorn bushes. Some large assemblies are on record, often in company with thrushes. During the winter of 1950/51, up to 1,000 spent the night with Redwings in fir trees at Catterick Camp; 630 entered a roost in Howell Wood on 3rd April 1965; at least 1,000 roosted in Cannon Hall Park in December 1966; 1,000 roosted on Thorne Moor in February 1974; and 1,000 did so at Allerton Park, near Knaresborough, during January 1981. On 25th November 1943, J.P. Utley was called to inspect a small bird that roosted nightly beside an electric light bulb in a porch; it proved to be a Greenfinch.

Plumage variants reported by Nelson were a white bird near Bradford in April 1890 (*The Naturalist*, 1890, p. 335) and 'specimens yellow as canaries' from Beverley.

The 'Green Linnet' is thus a common Yorkshire breeding species, whose numbers are augmented every autumn by birds from farther north in Britain.

Goldfinch
Carduelis carduelis

There are few places in Yorkshire where the Goldfinch cannot be found during the summer months, although in some districts it is rather thinly distributed. Only lack of suitable breeding habitat precludes its presence, and the barren uplands of the Pennines and North York Moors are thus devoid of breeding birds. Altitude does not affect it and nests may be found right up to the heather-line. It is fond of large gardens in suburbia, where it nests in orchards and ornamental trees. Six pairs nested in the centre of Leeds in 1980.

An apparent decrease in numbers around the turn of the century was attributed by Nelson to a destruction of food plants, the cessation of flax and linseed cultivation, and the attentions of bird-catchers. When Chislett published his *Yorkshire*

Birds in 1952, he considered that the Goldfinch was on the increase, an impression based on reports from several parts of the county at that time. In the Yorkshire Naturalists' Union Ornithological Report for 1951, he said 'With this species now again distributed in many areas not rarely, I can only mention parties', whereupon he listed seven flocks of 30, 20, 32, 50, 11, 15 and 20. It is certainly more numerous today.

Flocks of up to 50 birds were fairly regular during the 1950s, with 150 at Melton in September 1955, and larger parties became regular during the next decade. Watchers along the Spurn Peninsula and at Flamborough have found that small numbers coast southwards in spring and autumn, and such are a regular feature of the migration counts today.

The first large counts at Spurn were in the spring of 1968, when the daily maxima passing south were as follows: 150 on 30th April, 415 on 11th May and 238 on 18th May. In 1972 600 passed on 7th May, and there were unprecedented numbers in the spring of 1977 when a total of 11,873 birds flew south between late April and early June, the highest daily counts being as follows: 475 on 29th April, 342 on 30th April, 2,200 on 10th May, 2,100 on 11th May, and 1,300 on 15th May. Flamborough Head also had many birds, with 400 on 18th April as the largest number on any one day.

Passage along the coast during the autumn is more prolonged, but does not always involve high daily counts. Up to 200-300 may pass on some days, with larger numbers as follows: 686 on 20th September 1971; 929 on 4th October 1975; 946 on 7th October and 900 on 16th October 1976.

In addition to the birds recorded at Spurn, in 1977 there were several other large flocks, including 560 at the Humber Wildfowl Refuge on 9th September; 250 at Filey on 17th September; and 250 at Flamborough on 18th September.

Inland flocks during the autumn are often large and have certainly increased in size during the last 20 years. The largest numbers recorded are as follows: 160 at Gouthwaite Reservoir and 100 at Fairburn Ings on 23rd September 1972; 110 at Potteric Carr during September 1972 and an exceptional flock of 300 there during June 1975, an unusual time for such a large gathering; several flocks totalling 500 birds at Almholme on 1st October 1972; and 220 at Welton Water on 25th September 1975.

There were several big assemblies in 1976, the largest being 250 at Potteric Carr from August to October; 118 in Bretton Park on 27th October; 150 at Knostrop on 31st August; 200 near Harrogate on 12th September; 234 at Staveley Lagoon on 30th August; and 250 at Bishop Monkton on 17th September. The largest inland flocks in 1977, when there were several of up to 100 birds, were 400 at Potteric Carr on 24th August, 300 at Bishop Monkton on 18th September and 200 at Almholme on 25th September. Potteric Carr had 150 birds in September and 200 in October 1979; 150 were at Wath Ings on 5th October 1980; 200 at Redmires Reservoir and 150 at both Walmgate Stray, York, and Beighton, near Sheffield, on 25th September 1981, with 200 at the former locality in September 1982; 170 at Welwick on 6th September 1982; and 300 flying east on 29th September 1982 at Potteric Carr, where there was a flock of 200 on 2nd October. Large 'charms' are now a regular sight during the autumn months, and have become particularly so during the past ten years.

It is known that many British Goldfinches leave the country in autumn to spend the winter in southern France, Iberia and northwest Africa, and there are a few recoveries of ringed birds moving both to and from Yorkshire. An adult ringed on 1st May 1958 in Spain was found dead at Chapeltown, Leeds, on 1st June 1960, and a young bird ringed at Knaresborough Ringing Station on 26th August 1972 was shot in Spain on 30th March 1978. Two Yorkshire-ringed birds have travelled to Wales: a juvenile ringed at Knaresborough on 10th September 1967 was found dead in Flintshire on 23rd April 1968, and a juvenile ringed at Hackenthorpe on 18th August 1973 was retrapped in Caernarvon on 23rd April 1974.

Although the majority of breeding Goldfinches leave Yorkshire during the winter months, small flocks at that season are by no means uncommon, and there have been several of up to 100 birds in some recent winters. On 29th February 1975, 190 entered a roost near Hull.

The Goldfinch was at one time a favourite cagebird and received much attention from the professional bird-catchers. Nelson mentioned several instances of their activities. Said to be formerly numerous near Beverley, it was scarce there in Nelson's time and he recorded that 400 were once captured there in a few days by a famous bird-catcher called Greenhough, who caught large numbers in several years.

Of the several local names cited by Nelson, Goldie and Gold Spink are still in use today. He did not, however, mention Seven-coloured Linnet, a name used by some countrymen in the Knaresborough area.

To summarise, the Goldfinch has undoubtedly increased as a breeding species in Yorkshire since the beginning of the present century, having been numerous during the early part of the nineteenth. We now know it as a generally, but patchily distributed breeding species, whose numbers are swollen every autumn by birds from farther north, and most of which leave for the south in winter.

Siskin
Carduelis spinus

Nelson's opening comments on this species in 1907 were 'Although reported to have bred in Yorkshire, the alleged instances of the discovery of its nest are so few that the Siskin cannot accurately be described as a resident species, and must rank as a winter visitant, irregular in numbers and varying greatly in different years ... .' Apart from an increasing tendency for a few pairs to breed in recent years, that summary still applies. Many birds come across the North Sea from northern Europe in numbers varying from year to year, and, in addition to those that pass southwards along the coast to their wintering grounds on the Continent, many spread inland and spend the winter along the alder-lined rivers, streams and large sheets of water all over the county.

Nelson knew of no very large flocks, but Chislett listed a few, the largest being 100 at Castle Howard Park in December 1941. There have since been several flocks of up to 100 birds and some years have produced larger gatherings: 250 in Wykeham Forest on 30th March 1969; 200 roosting at Hornsea Mere on 26th March 1971; 200 near Scarborough in early March 1971; 200 near Harrogate on 12th December 1975; and 350 at Knaresborough Ringing Station on 9th November 1975.

Although the species feeds mainly on alder and birch seeds, some have taken to visiting suburban gardens in recent years to feed on peanuts and have learned to associate red plastic containers with this food source. On 6th February 1960, K. Dawson saw 100 birds feeding on compost at Beeston, Leeds; the flock built up to 300 by 21st February, but all had dispersed by 28th.

Passage along the coastline is evident every autumn, and daily counts of up to 100 birds occur during October and November in some years. Numbers vary annually, and in 1984 500 passed along the Spurn Peninsula on 16th September with 150 on 17th, 200 on 18th, 100 on 19th, 126 on 20th and smaller numbers to

30th. The first birds to arrive usually make their appearance from mid September, but earlier ones occur in some years. Single birds at Spurn on 3rd September 1965, 1st September 1968, 4th August 1978 and 9th August 1981 were exceptional.

Most wintering flocks have left Yorkshire by mid April, but a few stragglers appear along the coast up to early May in some years.

Nelson admitted a claim for breeding in Walton Park, details of which were given to A.G. More by Charles Waterton and published in *The Ibis*, 1865, p. 129. He dismissed a claim for nesting at Halifax about 1850, but said that 'one or two pairs have bred recently near Pickering'.

Chislett published details of an incident in 1939 when a man who had formerly kept Siskins in captivity watched a pair back to a nest with eggs near Goathland. The nest came to grief and F.C.R. Jourdain thought the eggs to be those of this species.

Before the winter flocks depart during March and April, several males may be in full song and such was being heard from a few birds during the 1950s. A pair was seen entering a spruce plantation on 9th June 1955 at Low Dalby, and breeding was strongly suspected near Ripley in 1956. Two birds were at Lastingham on 1st June 1957, on which date a male sang in Bastow Wood. A pair was feeding on the ground at Malham Tarn on 6th June 1966, and birds sang in two places on the North York Moors in May 1966 with one at a third locality on 27th July. In 1969, after 250 had been seen in Wykeham Forest on 30th March, a male was singing there on 4th May and another at Lastingham on 24th May. A female was picked up

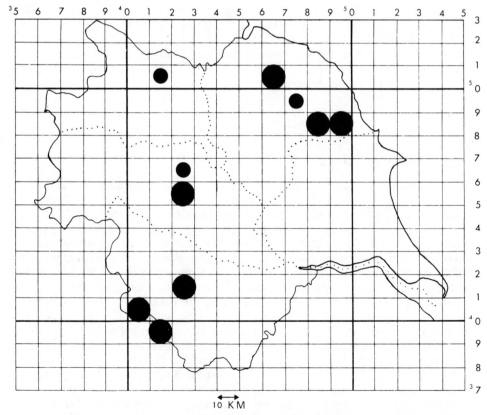

Siskin. A colonist of mature conifer plantations on the North York Moors, where it has bred since at least 1966; on the southwestern Pennines since 1974; and near Harrogate in more recent years. Further spread is to be expected coincident with maturing conifers.

dead on the road at Hutton-le-Hole on 26th May, and on examination was found to have a large and well-developed brood patch. A juvenile bird was killed in a strawberry net at Osbaldkirk on 27th June, and pairs were seen in the summer near Sproxton and Boltby.

In the following year, a nest with eggs was found in Gisburn Forest on 6th June. Single birds were seen there during the summer in 1973, with breeding suspected at two sites west of Sheffield and in the Harrogate pine woods, and a pair reared three young at another site near Harrogate. Two pairs bred successfully in the southwest in 1974 and a pair was seen building a nest near Birchall on the North York Moors. Birds were present at two breeding sites in the southwest in 1975, and at least three pairs bred in one locality there in 1976 and were seen attending up to 15 juveniles on 18th July.

In 1977, several pairs bred in conifers on the southwestern Pennines and singing males were at three localities on the North York Moors, and breeding has certainly occurred annually since then at these two localities. A pair bred in the Washburn Valley in 1978 and nesting has occurred annually to the present time.

Breeding birds will certainly increase as conifer plantations mature, and it is possible that many more than are known about are being successful in the large plantations on the North York Moors.

A bird ringed at Ilkley on 3rd March 1962 was found dead in the Netherlands on 28th January 1963. A male ringed in Cropton Forest on 16th February 1981 was unusually far south in the Bouches-du-Rhône area of France on 27th December 1981. A male ringed in Inverness-shire on 25th July 1977 was retrapped at Sheffield on 27th February 1978, indicating the origin of some of our winter birds. One ringed at Spurn on 13th September 1974 and retrapped in Germany on 15th March 1978 was also likely of British origin.

The only other name for the Siskin which was used by the old bird-catchers around Beverley at the turn of the century was 'Aberdevine', a generally used term for the 'Alder Finch' in that region.

Linnet
Carduelis cannabina

It is doubtful whether the status of the Linnet has changed since Nelson wrote 'Resident, common, and generally distributed. Large numbers of migrants arrive in autumn.' It is perhaps more thinly distributed than formerly owing to an increase in agricultural land and the generally more 'tidy' countryside, but wherever suitable scrubby ground exists, anywhere from the coast to the Pennine fringes, the species will occupy it during the breeding season; it is particularly fond of gorse.

Nelson reported a decrease in numbers during the early part of the present century, for which he blamed 'high Farming, the discontinuance of flax cultivation and the wiles of the bird-catchers . . .'. An interesting fact concerning its breeding in the Spurn area at that time was that 'the nests are sometimes lined with feathers of the Lesser Tern', a source of material that would be hard to find today. G.H. Ainsworth reported four nests among the marram grass on the Spurn Peninsula in 1944, but the nest is usually built a few feet from the ground in thick vegetation.

During the autumn, flocks of old and young Linnets gather together to feed on weed seeds, and any waste ground with *Persicaria*, *Chenopodium* or other plants typical of such areas will regularly attract flocks of up to 200 birds, with larger numbers of up to 500 on occasions. The largest flocks recorded have been as follows:

1,000 feeding on dock seeds at Swillington on 3rd September 1959; 1,000 at Horbury during late September 1970; 600 at Eastmoor, York, in September 1976; 1,000 at Hay-a-Park Gravel-pit during August 1976; 750 at Blacktoft Sands in late August 1976; and 1,000 at Cloughton Wyke on 2nd January 1978.

By the middle of October large flocks have usually disappeared as birds move south to spend the winter in southern France and Spain. Not all Linnets leave the county, however, and small numbers remain throughout the winter, especially if the weather is mild.

Some birds come to Yorkshire from northern Europe, but the majority of the autumn Linnets feeding in, or passing through, Yorkshire will have a British origin. Nelson mentioned large numbers along the coast in several years, and in the autumn of 1898 'thousands' were between Easington and Kilnsea. Coastal passage is noted annually in both spring and autumn, especially at Spurn where birds are funnelled along the peninsula. Passage may be to the south in both spring and autumn, and some large daily counts have been made. G.W. Follows counted 750 birds flying west at Saltburn on 16th April 1977, and G.R. Bennett counted 1,350 flying south at Hornsea on 1st October 1961 with 690 on 8th. Such large movements are now known to be an annual event at Spurn, where the highest daily counts of birds flying south in recent years have been: 4,000 on 23rd April 1966; 3,450 on 5th October 1968; 2,000 on 20th October 1971; 1,320 on 27th April 1973, with 1,063 on 28th, 1,800 on 5th May and 1,000 on 6th; 1,962 on 4th October 1975; and a phenomenal 7,000 on 29th April 1977, with 3,000 on 7th May.

These counts are the maxima only, and on any day from March to May and from September to early November Linnets passing along the peninsula may number up to 1,000 or more. The total number of birds passing south during the spring of 1977 was 59,398 between early March and mid May. During the years 1981 to 1983, the total numbers passing south during the autumn period were 11,697, 11,712 and 15,324 respectively, between early September and mid November, with maximum counts of up to 1,000-1,500 birds on some days.

Linnets flying south along the Yorkshire coast during the spring period are thought to be heading back for their breeding grounds farther south in England or in Europe, having corrected a migrational overshoot, but ringing recoveries to substantiate the theory are as yet lacking.

During very severe winter weather, some large numbers have been recorded flying south at Spurn. On 10th January 1959 700 were counted, and during the very hard winter of 1962/63 birds passed on two days: 3,000 on 12th January 1963 and 520 on 3rd February 1963; smaller numbers were seen along the coast farther north at Atwick. These could have been birds from either elsewhere in Yorkshire or farther north in Britain, having been forced out by the very severe cold.

As with most finches, Linnets roost communally and several large assemblies have been recorded in the county, for example: 500 on Thorne Moors on 16th October and 1,180 on 2nd December 1972, an exceptional number for the time of year, with 550 there on 26th January and 350 in December 1974; 600 at Wintersett Reservoir in early September 1974 and 520 on 6th August 1975; 500 at Wath Ings on 18th September and again on 20th October 1974; 400 at Blacktoft Sands in September and October 1974 and on 31st August 1978, with 600 on 7th September 1978; and 400 at Farnham Gravel-pit on 31st August 1980. The winter roost on Thorne Moors is very interesting and the largest concentration of Linnets at that time of year anywhere in the county.

Recoveries of ringed Linnets show that many Yorkshire-born birds spend the winter months in the known wintering areas of France and Spain, the majority having been recovered in France. Several birds ringed while on passage at Spurn, and therefore of unknown origin, have also been recovered in the same areas. One bird ringed at Ossett on 18th September 1968 was retrapped in Noord Holland on 27th October 1969, being only the third recovery of a British-ringed Linnet from that area. Evidence of immigration from northern Europe came from a nestling ringed at Stavanger in Norway on 4th June 1961 that was found dead in Sheffield in March 1962.

Nelson mentioned two leucistic examples, another with white wing and tail feathers, and one with a white head, and also an albino bird which was in the possession of William Morris of Sedbergh. Linnets with abnormal plumage have been scarce in recent years, and the only one of which I have note concerns a bird at Kilnsea in December 1969 that had the body and wings mainly white.

Twite

Carduelis flavirostris

The first published details of this species in connection with Yorkshire were contained in Willughby's *Ornithology* (1676), where there is a description of a bird obtained near Sheffield and sent to Willughby by F. Jessop.

According to T. Allis's report of 1844, the Twite bred in abundance on all the high moors about Halifax, where it still nests in good numbers; G.R. Edwards

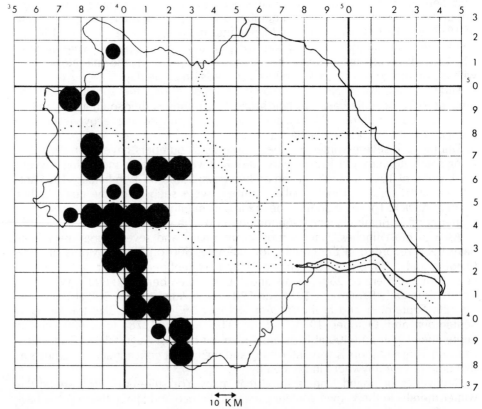

10 KM

Twite. Most commonly distributed on the southern part of the Pennines and in the upper dales of the northwest.

574

recorded 130 old and young birds sitting on wires in that region in late July 1944. A nest on Ilkley Moor in 1938 was the first that H.B. Booth had known there for 20 years; several were seen there in 1949. This area is on the eastern boundary of the Twite's breeding range in Yorkshire, although it nests regularly just to the north on the moors about Grassington. The main stronghold is along the southwestern Pennines, with a patchily distributed extension northwards.

On 25th June 1951, J.P. Utley watched a pair feeding fledged young at Osmotherley on the Hambleton Hills. Birds were seen there again in 1952 without breeding being proved, but none was seen on any of the northeastern moors thereafter and the British Trust for Ornithology survey during the years 1968-72 revealed no breeding evidence in that region and none nests there today.

Counts on Sutton Moor, near Keighley, have revealed the following figures: 22 pairs in 1973; 14 pairs in 1974; 18 pairs in 1975; and seven pairs in 1980. In 1979, 40 pairs were on Fountains Fell, near Malham Tarn, on 11th July. A pair bred for the first known time in Nidderdale in 1971, when a family party of five birds was seen on 25th June.

There is much apparently suitable moorland without breeding Twites, but where they do occur numbers are often large, as evidenced by the flocks recorded during the last 20 years. Gatherings of around 50 birds are fairly common, and there are much larger flocks on record: 200 at Denholme Clough on 29th August 1965 and 160 on 12th September 1967; 300 at Booth on 22nd April 1967; 200 at Gorple Reservoir in April 1972; 200 at Hardcastle Crags on 19th March 1972 increased to 600 by 16th April 1972, an exceptional number counted by D.J. Standring; 200 on Sutton Moor on 17th September 1973; 180 at Scammonden on 28th March 1974; 200 on Greenhow Hill on 23rd August 1975; 150 at Ringstone Edge in September 1973 and 200 in mid August 1975; 150 at High Trenhouse, near Settle, on 24th August 1976; 328 birds were caught and ringed during late July 1976 by M.L. Denton at Blackmoorfoot Reservoir, from a flock that never exceeded 200 birds at any one time; 200 at Malham Tarn on 27th September 1978; 200 at Horton-in-Ribblesdale on 28th August 1978 and 400 on 30th August 1980; 200 at Settle on 20th September 1978; 200 at Soyland, near Sowerby Bridge, on 7th October 1978; and 300 at Broadstones on 14th October 1979. Apart from 120 at Denholme in 1961, flocks of this size were not reported in Yorkshire prior to 1965, which may reflect, in part, a lack of observers rather than a marked increase in Twites, although the evidence suggests that there has been some increase.

Twites move to lower ground during the winter months and flocks are often seen well away from the breeding areas. Small numbers may occur almost anywhere, at gravel-pits, reservoirs and on any rough ground, and larger flocks gather along the coastline and along the Humber shore, where they spend the winter. The largest numbers on record are as follows: 50 on the saltings at Teesmouth during February and March 1950; 30 flying north at Spurn on 8th November 1960; 50 at Welwick Saltings on 15th January 1961; 50 at Patrington Haven in January 1962; 96 at Spurn on 7th November 1976; 159 at Spurn on 12th October 1967; 120 at Spurn in September 1974, in addition to which birds flew south along the peninsula on several dates, with 66 on 29th September, 120 on 5th October and 116 on 17th November as maxima; similar passage in 1975 had maxima of 161 on 4th October, 182 on 5th October and 144 on 6th October, and in 1978 the highest daily counts were 145 on 2nd October, 179 on 8th October, 162 on 11th October and 149 on 12th October. There were 28 birds at Flamborough on 28th September 1980 and 100 on 8th October 1982, and 60 were at Barmston on 12th October 1980. A flock of 47 at Broadstones, near Ingbirchworth, on 26th January 1980 was the first winter record of an upland flock since 1968.

Southerly passage occurs along the coast every autumn in varying numbers and is especially noticeable along the Spurn Peninsula. These coastal movements are not easy to understand and may consist of British birds or immigrant birds from the Continent on their way to wintering grounds farther south. That some birds come to Yorkshire from northwestern Europe at this season is certain (see details of specimens and sight record below), but ringing recoveries are as yet lacking. A bird ringed in the Netherlands on 16th November 1960 and found dead at Denholme on 6th May 1961 could have been a Yorkshire bird wintering in the Netherlands when ringed. Six birds ringed in Yorkshire have been recovered in the Netherlands, Belgium and France; all except one were ringed in breeding areas near Huddersfield in June and July and the other, ringed at Spurn on 12th October 1967, was recovered in France on 4th February 1968 and was the first British-ringed Twite to be recovered in that country.

A nestling ringed at Hebden Bridge on 20th June 1954 and retrapped at Colchester in Essex on 19th March 1955, and a Twite ringed at St Osyth in Essex on 7th February 1979 and found dead at Cleckheaton on 30th April 1981, illustrate migratory movement to and from southern England, perhaps while en route for the Continent.

The Continental race of the Twite *Carduelis flavirostris flavirostris*, which is distinguished by having a wholly yellow bill, has been recorded in Yorkshire. Three skins in the Backhouse Collection at the Yorkshire Museum, from Spurn Point in October 1899, Easington in July 1885 and Church Fenton on 9th December 1885, were identified by R. Wagstaffe as belonging to this race, which was confirmed by Colonel Meinertzhagen (*The Naturalist*, 1944, p. 92). July is an exceptionally early date for a Twite to be in Holderness, even one of Yorkshire origin. M. Limbert identified a bird of this race among a flock of 16 birds at Wroot on 26th January 1980.

There are records of this species being parasitised by the Cuckoo on Yorkshire moorlands.

Nelson recorded four white examples of Twites: two at Bewerley, near Pateley Bridge (*The Zoologist*, 1850, p. 2953); one at Bedale (*The Field*, 18th August 1977); and one near Huddersfield. A similar bird was seen by H.B. Booth and R. Butterfield on Haworth Moor in August 1932.

Redpoll
Carduelis flammea

In *The Birds of Yorkshire*, Nelson, in line with the practice of the period, gave specific rank to four redpoll species, two of which are today lumped under the title of *Carduelis flammea* with two recognised subspecies.

The first of these was the Mealy Redpoll *Linota linaria*; the second was the Northern Mealy Redpoll *Linota exilipes* (Coues's Redpoll), now considered to be a race of the Arctic Redpoll; the third was the Greenland Mealy Redpoll *Linota hornemanni*, now given specific rank as the Arctic Redpoll; and finally the Lesser Redpoll *Linota rufescens*.

The Redpoll *Carduelis flammea cabaret*, as in Nelson's time, is a fairly common, but patchily distributed resident over much of Yorkshire wherever suitable habitat exists in the form of sparsely wooded country, particularly where alder, birch or hawthorn is present. It is not averse to breeding in suburbia where trees and bushes predominate, and it also penetrates up the dales and cloughs of the Pennines as far as the heather-line. It is particularly numerous around the heathland areas in the south at Hatfield and Thorne, and 200 pairs bred on Hatfield Moor in 1977. Breeding numbers fluctuate annually, and there are occasional 'explosions' when large numbers nest and become obvious in areas which normally hold only a few pairs.

Redpolls visit Yorkshire every autumn from farther north in the British Isles and flocks of up to 100 to 200 feeding in alders along the rivers and by lakes and reservoirs are not uncommon. Larger flocks sometimes occur, and the maximum counts in recent years have been: 600 near Harrogate on 23rd September 1966; 400 in birch trees at Thorganby in the Lower Derwent Valley on 5th February 1972; a 'vast' influx during July 1974 in Melton Wood near Doncaster when W.G. Dye counted 480 birds on several dates from then up to the year end; another large influx in 1975, when 1,000 were in Selby Forest on 26th October where P. Reid caught 80 birds in ten minutes, and flocks of up to 300 were recorded at several other localities; several flocks of up to 200 birds at several places in 1976; 400 in Haw Park on 19th March 1977; 500 at Askham Bog during September to mid October 1977; and 439 on Hatfield Moor on 12th October 1980. More birds appear in some years than in others, and fluctuations no doubt reflect the varying breeding successes.

Many British Redpolls move south for the winter and birds can be seen flying south along the coast every autumn, especially along the Spurn Peninsula where daily counts from September to November may reach up to 100 birds and sometimes more. In 1967, for example, movement was noted daily from mid September and throughout October, with maximum daily counts of 360 on 30th September and 531 on 2nd October. A total of 1,554 birds flew south there during the autumn of 1981, with 624 on 10th October as the largest number in one day.

Ringing recoveries shed some light on their destinations: one ringed at Esholt on 25th January 1948 was in Belgium on 10th January 1950; an adult ringed at Wakefield on 23rd September 1961 was retrapped in northern France on 15th October 1961; an adult ringed at Newmillerdam on 10th October 1962 was retrapped in Belgium on 28th October 1962; one ringed at Wilton, near Redcar, on 13th May 1974 was retrapped at Beachy Head in Sussex on 4th November 1974; and a male ringed at Hackenthorpe on 2nd July 1981 was in France on 11th February 1982. Some of these birds may have been on passage from farther north when ringed in Yorkshire, as evidenced by one caught at Wintersett Reservoir on 27th September 1964 that had been ringed in Northumberland on 29th March 1963. Birds ringed in their winter quarters and subsequently recovered in Yorkshire have occurred as follows: two ringed at Christchurch in Hampshire (now in Dorset) on 21st February 1960 were at Scarborough in June 1960 and near Ingleton in July 1960 respectively; one ringed in Sussex on 21st March 1968 was retrapped at Follifoot, near Harrogate, on 23rd April 1968; and one ringed in France on 20th April 1974 was retrapped at Spurn on 25th August and on 12th September 1974.

The Mealy Redpoll *Carduelis flammea flammea*, which breeds across northern continental Eurasia (and also in North America), occurs annually as a winter visitor to the British Isles and is recorded in Yorkshire every year. It has been known as a visitor to the county since Nelson's time, and he mentioned October 1855, 1861, 1876 and 1881 as years when large numbers appeared. In the last of those years, a great flock occurred with Siskins on 24th October, and they were very numerous in the vicinity of Spurn, Kilnsea and Easington from 25th to 27th in small parties of 30 to 40 birds. 'An enormous flock' was at Flamborough during severe weather in January 1907.

In most years, only a few Mealy Redpolls are seen, with just a single record in some, but there are occasional invasions when large parties are recorded. A.F.G. Walker counted 150-200 near Harrogate on 14th October 1951.

Many were recorded in 1975 when several very pale birds were included. One such, at Ravenscar on 12th October, had snowy-white underparts and a very white rump which R.H. Appleby considered were not those of a classic Arctic Redpoll, although the bird was doubtless from the northern part of the range of *flammea*. Some 30 birds feeding on *Poinsettia* in a Selby garden on 9th November 1975 were stated by P. Reid to be paler than normal Mealies; 70 were at Plompton, near Knaresborough, on 27th December 1975 and one to ten at several other localities in that year including Spurn, where the highest count was 40 on 18th October.

There were good numbers in 1980, particularly in the East Riding, and D.I.M. Wallace had parties of 50 at Holme-on-Spalding-Moor on 21st and 23rd December, 35 at Market Weighton on 25th December and 55 at Hayton on 26th December.

The only other records of more than just a few Mealies are 20 at Flamborough on 1st November 1981 and 22 on 13th October 1982, and 40 at Spurn on 7th November 1984, 20 of which were caught and ringed.

The Redpoll was much prized as a cagebird up to the early part of the present century and the Mealy particularly so. Nelson said of the 'Lesser' Redpoll, that it 'holds its own in localities where it is secure from molestation by the professional bird-catchers'. A 'beautiful adult male' caught at Spurn on 25th October 1881 would have gone to grace someone's living room, first in the flesh then doubtless behind glass.

Nelson recorded two white examples of the 'Lesser' Redpoll, one from Horbury, near Wakefield, in 1872 and an undated bird from Kirkheaton.

Arctic Redpoll
Carduelis hornemanni

The taxonomy of this species, and some confusion with races of the previous species, is still in an undecided situation. Since old records of the two races at present referable to this species are somewhat confused owing to imprecise details being given, the records referred to below are listed in chronological order, whether they refer to the race *C.h. hornemanni* (previously known as Hornemann's or Arctic Redpoll) or *C.h. exilipes* (previously known as Coues's or Hoary Redpoll).

The first documented record is of a bird taken by Dr H.B. Hewetson in October 1883. The skin of this bird was seen by Lord Lilford and was used for the illustration by A. Thorburn in Lilford's *Birds of the British Islands*, 1891-7, vol. IV, plate 29. Lord Lilford quotes this bird as being taken at Easington, but Nelson in his *Birds of Yorkshire* quotes Spurn as the locality. This bird is accepted as the first record for Great Britain by Witherby in *The Handbook of British Birds*, and Nelson says that it went to the Royal Scottish Museum.

The next record concerned a bird seen by J. Cordeaux and Dr H.B. Hewetson on 25th February 1893 on Kilnsea Warren about which Cordeaux says '... a most beautifully-plumaged Redpoll, which appeared as large as a Linnet, clinging to a thistle, and from its size and light colour, and having had it for some time under observation at a distance of a few feet, I had at the time no doubt in referring it to *Linota hornemanni* of Greenland, Iceland, Spitzbergen and Eastern North America ...' (*The Naturalist*, 1893, p. 104, and 1894, p. 84).

Lord Lilford also refers to a bird, the skin of which was loaned to him by Dr H.B. Hewetson, as being taken at Easington in October 1893, and for which Nelson also gives Spurn as the locality. Nelson also implies, though does not say so specifically, that this bird belonged to the race *C.h. exilipes*, but there is considerable confusion in the records as to the date and locality of this example, as Nelson also mentions a bird of this race taken in the winter of 1893/94 by Dr Hewetson at Easington. There is, incidentally, no record of either of the birds taken by Hewetson in October 1883 or October 1893 in the annals of the Yorkshire Naturalists' Union.

Writing in *The Naturalist* on 9th February 1894, however, John Cordeaux says: 'In the present winter Mr Hewetson was fortunate in obtaining a very light-coloured Redpoll from near Easington, and this he obligingly sent me for examination. The cinereous markings are in this example more pronounced than in the bird seen by us in 1893 ...' This bird was also seen by Professor Newton and Mr H.E. Dresser, who both agreed that it belonged to the race *exilipes* (*The Naturalist*, 1894, p. 84). The above wording by J. Cordeaux implies that the bird was taken in January 1894, and he claimed it as the first record for Yorkshire and for Great Britain, which was accepted by Witherby in 1938 in volume I of *The Handbook of British Birds*.

Four years later, on 30th December 1898, Mr P. Loten shot two Redpolls at Skeffling, near Spurn, which he showed to J. Cordeaux, who had 'not the least hesitation in referring them to the Arctic and circumpolar *Linota exilipes* Coues's'. In reporting this record to the Yorkshire Naturalists' Union on 8th February 1899, Cordeaux goes on to say 'These Skeffling birds are identical in every respect with one from the same locality in 1894, which I sent to Mr H.E. Dresser.' Skeffling and Easington, where the 1894 bird was taken, are no more than 2 miles (3.2 km) apart, and his remarks confirm that the bird at Easington reported by Nelson as being taken in the winter of 1893/94 was in fact shot in 1894.

This leaves the bird shown to Lord Lilford by Dr H.B. Hewetson and taken either at Spurn (Nelson) or Easington (Lilford) in October 1893 without any other supporting evidence.

It is clear that the identification of this species in Yorkshire in the late nineteenth century depended entirely on the knowledge and expertise of John Cordeaux, who watched the Holderness area very diligently at that time, for it was to be 26 years before another example of this species was recorded in the county. On 18th December 1925, an injured bird picked up at Scarborough was identified by W.J. Clarke, R. Fortune, H.F. Witherby and E. Hartert as belonging to the race *exilipes* (*The Naturalist*, 1926, p. 11). There followed two records in 1946 and 1962, published in the Yorkshire Ornithological Report for each respective year, which are not acceptable in the absence of written evidence or otherwise.

There have been five acceptable birds in more recent years. The first was caught and ringed at Spurn Bird Observatory on 5th November 1972 by J. Cassidy, B.R. Spence and D. Woodward, and was identified as referable to the race *exilipes* (*Spurn Bird Observatory Report*, 1972, p. 46). Two birds were seen at Flamborough on 11th October 1975 as they flew in over the sea and landed, when they were examined in detail by P.A. Lassey and Miss I. Smith. A bird was caught at Spurn on 12th October 1975 which was, after much deliberation, considered to be a very pale *flammea*; after skins of both species had been examined, however, it was later identified as an Arctic Redpoll by J. Cudworth and B.R. Spence. One was identified at Spurn by D.I.M. Wallace on 21st October 1975 and was referred to in the Yorkshire Ornithological Report for that year, but was not, apparently, recorded in the Spurn Bird Observatory log. One found dead at Scarborough in February 1982 was sent to me for preservation and proved to be a young bird of the race *exilipes*.

Single birds which were ascribed to the race *exilipes* were seen at Flamborough by A.M. Allport, J.C. Lamplough and P.A. Lassey on 4th and 7th November 1984, and D.I.M. Wallace recorded two birds of the same race near Holme-on-Spalding Moor on 26th and 31st December 1984.

This species is clearly very variable, and perhaps no more than a very pale northern form of *Carduelis flammea* which some taxonomists consider it to be. There is certainly an area of overlap where the two populations meet, and very pale birds which are not typical of either *flammea* or *hornemanni* could come from these overlapping regions. It is worth quoting the comments of J. Cudworth in the Spurn Bird Observatory Report for 1975 following the three records in Yorkshire in the autumn of that year. He comments that the information on identification of Redpolls 'is a little misleading and lacks clarity. More observers now appreciate the difficulties of Redpoll identification but, doubtless, there will be no repeat of autumn 1975 for them to put their experience into practice.' Such has been the case in Yorkshire so far.

Two-barred Crossbill
Loxia leucoptera

A Two-barred Crossbill was shot at Plompton, near Knaresborough, in 1826 and was in the collection of J.C. Garth of the latter place until the sale of his effects in December 1904, when it was purchased by Riley Fortune of Harrogate.

On 27th December 1845, two males and two females were claimed to have been shot from a flock at Cowick, near Snaith, in south Yorkshire. The specimens went to Hugh Reid of Doncaster.

An immature male was obtained at Easington, near Spurn, on 12th August 1889 by the Reverend H.H. Slater (*The Naturalist*, 1889, p. 314).

Nelson inspected a male in the collection of Mr Forster of Bridlington which had been obtained at Flamborough about 1898.

The above records are listed by Nelson in *The Birds of Yorkshire*, and the following additional record was published by Chislett in *Yorkshire Birds*: 'On 3rd May 1931, in a pinewood near Goathland on the North York Moors, W.S. Medlicott saw a bird fly from the ground up into a pine, which at first glance he took for a Chaffinch. Through binoculars he saw that it was hanging back downwards, feeding on a pine cone. At 25 yards range, the two white wing-bars were conspicuous. It was a female, and the upperparts were a dull greyish-yellow with streaks, the underparts were lighter and the rump was pale and conspicuous. Medlicott had no doubt it was of this species.' Chislett agreed and I can see no reason to disagree.

There have been two other records A male frequented a Whitby garden from 3rd to 7th August 1972 where it spent most of the time among apple trees. Although it allowed fairly close approach, there were times when it would remain very still and was difficult to see. Many people saw it, including R.H. Appleby, R. Evison and A.J. Wallis. A male occurred in Hollingdale Plantation, near Howden Reservoir, on 30th October 1982 and between 9th January and 27th February 1983, when it was watched and described by D. Hursthouse, D. Herringshaw and several others.

The species breeds across northern Europe and America (where the race is smaller and darker) and has occurred almost annually in the British Isles since 1966, with an average of two each year. There are now about 60 records.

Crossbill
Loxia curvirostra

Nelson considered the Crossbill's appearance in Yorkshire to be 'so erratic and uncertain that the term "resident" or "annual visitant" cannot accurately be applied'. He listed several areas where they had occurred in varying numbers, and mentioned Upper Wharfedale in particular, where it sometimes occurred in large flocks, and the woods around Whitby and Grinkle, where it was once abundant with a flock of 200 birds being seen 'a few years ago' prior to 1907.

It bred in several years during the nineteenth and early twentieth centuries: at Fewston in 1902; Birstwith in Nidderdale; Pateley Bridge in 1876; Bramham Park in 1840 (several nests); Stockton-on-Forest, near York, in 1872, where 60 to 70 birds were seen and a nest with four eggs was found (*The Zoologist*, 1880, pp. 403 and 515); Market Weighton; Boynton Woods; and Sledmere.

In April 1939, R.M. Garnett and R. Chislett saw a nest in a Scots pine near Thornton-le-Dale which was successful and young fledged in early May. Two nests were found near the same place in 1943, one of which was successful. Two pairs nested in the North Riding in the same year.

In 1957, a female was seen carrying nesting material on 21st April at Bolton Abbey; a female was feeding fledged young on 14th April at Grass Woods, where three juveniles were later seen (*The Naturalist*, 1958, pp. 1-2); and a pair with four young was in the Barnsley area on 30th June. Three nests were unsuccessful near Ilkley in 1959, probably being robbed by Magpies, but a pair bred successfully near Lofthouse in Upper Nidderdale, five newly fledged young being seen by D.W. Swindells and A.F.G. Walker on 2nd May.

During the 1960s, there were a few records of breeding, but it is likely that many more pairs bred than were detected in the extensive forests of the North York Moors and the southern Pennines.

Many breeding records were forthcoming during the 1970s, and in 1973 it was suspected at several places along the southern Pennines but proved only at Strines Reservoir, and also in Gisburn Forest and the Harrogate pine woods. Breeding was proved again at Strines in 1977 and in the Washburn Valley in 1978. No fewer than 100 pairs nested in the coniferous woodlands west of Sheffield in 1981 and 50 pairs bred in one of these localities in 1982, with fewer pairs in several other nearby plantations.

Such large breeding numbers are just as likely to disappear as quickly as they came, but there is no doubt that the species breeds more regularly now than ever before. The annual total of breeding pairs in the extensive and inaccessible conifer plantations along the Pennines and the North York Moors may be very much higher than we know or even suspect at the present time.

As an immigrant, the species is much more obvious and some large flocks have been recorded, although the situation is usually one of many small and scattered parties in the years of plenty. The years 1962, 1963 and 1964 had more birds than usual, with flocks of 20 to 50 birds at many places. In 1966, up to 100 were seen at Ogden Reservoir from 4th to 6th July, after a marked influx at Spurn in late June which was followed by a second wave in late August and early September.

Several large flocks were seen in 1972, with 25 in Grass Woods on 1st July; 20 in Swinsty Park and 30 at Helmsley on 9th July; 40 to 50 at Wyming Brook during the month; and 40 at Bolton Abbey on 28th. Smaller numbers were seen at many localities in 1973 and in the years to 1980.

The Crossbill is thus a most erratic species, which comes to Yorkshire in varying numbers each year. In the good years, when many birds arrive, several pairs may stay on to breed. It is certainly a more regular breeding species now than formerly, and is likely to remain so coincident with maturing of the vast acreage of conifers on the upland areas in the west and northeast.

Parrot Crossbill
Loxia pytyopsittacus

In a footnote to Crossbill in *The Birds of Yorkshire*, Nelson states that 'in the woods of Scandinavia and North Russia, a large stout billed race is found, formerly known as the Parrot Crossbill *L. pityopsittacus*, now deemed to be unworthy of even sub-specific rank. A female of this form was procured by M. Bailey of Flamborough on 4th August 1806 and acquired by the late W.W. Boulton of Beverley' (*The Zoologist*, 1876, p. 543).

The Parrot Crossbill is now given specific status, but, owing to the early date and absence of the specimen, I do not consider this record admissible to the Yorkshire list.

On 12th October 1962, two crossbills were trapped and ringed at Spurn Bird Observatory, one of which was found dying on 13th. It was identified as a Parrot Crossbill by E. Gorton of the Bolton Museum, where the skin is now housed. I inspected it at Masham in 1963, during a meeting of the Yorkshire Naturalists' Union Records Committee, and the specimen exhibited the very large deep bill and general large body size, typical of the species. More than 50 birds were on Fair Isle from late September to late October in the same year, and others occurred in Shetland, the Outer Hebrides, Lincoln, Suffolk and Surrey.

Two birds occurred in 1975. The first, a male which was watched at Spurn Point on 22nd October as it perched, and also in flight, was fully described by I. Clarke and J.P. Guest. The second example was a female which was found stunned near a greenhouse at Tophill Low Reservoir on 23rd October and which later died; the corpse was examined by P.W. Izzard and D.E. Murray and exhibited at a meeting of the Beverley Naturalists', before being sent to me for preservation (see plate 116).

A remarkable influx occurred in 1982 and several birds were noted in Yorkshire, Lincolnshire, Derbyshire, Norfolk, Scotland and the Shetland Islands. The first Yorkshire bird was caught in the Warren trap at Spurn Bird Observatory on 11th October, but it was very weak and was found dead nearby on the following morning. The specimen, a young female, was sent to me for preservation (see plates 115 and 116). In the south of the county, near the border with Derbyshire, several Parrot Crossbills frequented the woodlands around Howden Reservoir, Langsett and Hollingdale Plantation near Strines Reservoir. The first bird was seen on 30th October and the majority remained in the general area until February 1983. There were maximum counts of 25 birds in the Howden area, 12 in Hollingdale Plantation and 11 at Langsett, where a few birds remained into May. Courtship feeding was seen by J.E. Dale, one pair had a completed nest, another pair was seen constructing a nest and newly fledged young were seen in early May.

D. Hursthouse took very detailed notes and made excellent sketches of the Howden birds which he submitted to the *British Birds* Rarities Committee for acceptance. Many other people watched these rare visitors during their stay. I am most grateful to J.E. Dale for supplying the breeding information.

Another flock was located in a spruce plantation at Winksley, near Ripon, by C. Slator and his colleagues on 29th January 1983. G.T. Foggitt and I saw 12 birds together there on 24th February.

Up to 14 birds which frequented the area of Wyming Brook in the Rivelin Valley from 31st October to 22nd December 1982 were reported by P.A. Ardron. For full details of the occurrences, see *British Birds*, 1983, pp. 522-3, and 1984, pp. 556-7.

Scarlet Rosefinch
Carpodacus erythrinus

This rare autumn visitor to the British Isles, which breeds from eastern Germany and south Finland eastwards through Russia and northwards to the Arctic Circle in Siberia and down to northern China in the east, and which winters from northern India to Vietnam, did not enter the Yorkshire list of birds until 1955. The next was in 1960, since when it has occurred in every year except six.

The first record for the county was a bird caught at the Spurn Bird Observatory by H.G. Brownlow and J.K. Fenton on 16th September 1955. It was seen by several other observers who were staying at the observatory, including C.E. Andrassy, E.W. Ellis, A. Frudd, M.M.B. Philpott and R.S. Pollard (*British Birds*, 1956, p. 46, and *The Naturalist*, 1956, p. 12).

On 1st October 1960, I drove the Spurn Bird Observatory Heligoland trap at Chalk Bank East, the site of which has long disappeared into the North Sea, and caught two birds. One was a Chiffchaff and the other a nondescript greenish-brown bird which I recognised as an immature Scarlet Grosbeak, as it was then called. R.C. Parkinson and G.R. Wilkinson were nearby and we took the bird back to the Warren Cottage and made detailed notes before ringing it. This second county record was to herald the almost annual appearances of the species, most of which have occurred at Spurn.

Since 1961, a total of 26 birds has been seen as follows: Spurn Point, three in May (one of which was in song), two in August, 11 in September, four in October and one on 9th November; Flamborough Head, one in May (in song) and two in September; Filey, one on 3rd June; and Scarborough Castle Hill, one in October.

An immature male was seen and heard singing at Gouthwaite Reservoir on 25th June 1977 by P.J. Carlton and A. O'Neill.

That the species was not recorded until 1955 is curious, and it is difficult to believe that it did not occur in Nelson's time and before.

Pine Grosbeak
Pinicola enucleator

There is only one authentic Yorkshire record of this rare bird. In 1896, G. Kitching shot five birds from a flock at Littlebeck, near Whitby. All were made into skins but only one was deposited in the Whitby Museum, the fate of the others being unrecorded. At the request of J.H. Gurney, the skin was compared with one from Sweden and pronounced to be of the same species but not in the same plumage. The Whitby bird was a dull carmine-red on the head, throat, breast and rump, with greyish feathers at the base of the bill and on the cheeks. There was an indistinct yellowish tinge on the flanks. The remiges were edged with a dirty-white colour, producing a barred effect on the closed wing. The length of the bird was about 7½ inches (19 cm).

Nelson also mentions two other records credited with a Yorkshire origin. These were in the sale catalogue of a Mr Sealey of Cambridge as 'Lot 59, Pine Grosbeaks, *three* in a case, one shot near Doncaster and one at Sheffield.' Either the *three* in a case should have read *two*, or the origin of the other specimen was not known. These birds are not admitted to the British list, and in the absence of any supporting evidence I do not suggest otherwise.

There are only seven accepted records for the British Isles of this species, which breeds across the whole of northern Europe.

Bullfinch
Pyrrhula pyrrhula

In Nelson's time, at the beginning of the present century, the Bullfinch was said to be 'resident and generally distributed where it can find situations such as gardens and woodland localities, containing food suitable for its habits, but it is becoming scarcer in most districts owing to the persecution of bird catchers and the animosity of gardeners who resent the damage done to fruit buds.' It had apparently been subjected to persecution for many centuries, as in the churchwarden's accounts for the Parish of Ecclesfield, near Sheffield is an entry stating '1590, Item for VIJ bulspynke heades, VJd.' and three acts, made during the reign of Elizabeth I, gave power to churchwardens to pay 'for the head of every bullfinsh or other bird that devoureth the blouth of fruit — 1d.'. As many as 300 were killed in the 1880s at Grinkle, and 50 were taken by one man in a week around that time near Harrogate.

Whether there are more Bullfinches now than at the turn of the century is doubtful. The loss of scrubby habitat under the plough will have likely replaced the depredations caused by the bird-catchers in the past. Although it is still generally distributed over much of the county, it is very thinly represented in many areas. Its very secretive habits during the breeding season render it most inconspicuous at that period, and breeding records are not easy to establish without much patience. It visits suburban gardens in the spring to feed on the buds of fruit trees and ornamental shrubs, but its presence at that time need not indicate breeding nearby.

In the winter of 1926, H.B. Booth estimated a flock at Harlow Hill, Harrogate, at about 130 birds, which Riley Fortune thought was an underestimate; nothing approaching that number has occurred since. The Bullfinch is not by nature a flocking species, but during the last 35 years there have been several autumn and winter gatherings which are worthy of note: 30 at Haxby in December 1949; 30 in Harrogate pine woods in November 1957; 30 at Chevet, near Wakefield, 30 at Hessle, 25 at Hampsthwaite, near Harrogate, and 27 at Fairburn Ings during October to December 1961; 40 in a small area of yew trees in Melton Wood on 1st November 1970; small parties totalling 50 birds on Thorne Moors on 18th February 1972 and again on 4th February 1973; 30 at Staveley on 18th December 1973; 30 at Eastmoor, York, in January and 36 in September 1976; 50 at Sprotborough Flash on 4th January 1977; 30 at Potteric Carr on 2nd February 1977; 50 at Denaby Ings on 20th November 1977; 40 near Leeds in December 1977; 40 at Wath Ings on 30th September 1979; 50 on Hatfield Moor in

November and December 1979, and flocks of 20 to 35 birds at six other places in that year; 50 at Potteric Carr on 25th December 1980; and 41 in Hall Dyke Valley, Huddersfield, in mid November 1982.

Roosts are seldom seen, but 25 birds entered one at Headingley during January to March 1981. In 1964, 68 birds were caught at Knaresborough Ringing Station from a flock that never exceeded 20 feeding on mugwort and meadowsweet during September and October; 96 were similarly caught in 1973.

A bird was near Ogden Reservoir at an elevation of 1,000 feet (305 m) on 25th May 1960, and a pair was seen by B. Shorrock amongst juniper bushes on Moughton Fell above Settle on 5th July 1975.

The Northern Bullfinch *Pyrrhula pyrrhula pyrrhula*, which breeds across northern Eurasia from Scandinavia to eastern Siberia, has occurred in Yorkshire on several occasions, mainly during the last 20 years.

The first British specimens came from Kilnsea and Hunmanby in November 1894, the first being shot by Craggs Clubley, brother of G.E. Clubley who shot the Houbara Bustard at Spurn in 1896. The second one was also shot and was acquired by J. Cordeaux from D. Brown of Filey. Both specimens were ultimately exhibited by Colonel L.H. Irby at a meeting of the Zoological Society in November 1895 (*Proceedings of The Zool. Soc.*, 1895, p. 681, and *The Naturalist*, 1896, p. 4). The Hunmanby bird was used for the painting by Thorburn in Lilford's *Birds of the British Islands* (vol. iv, pl. 34). Nelson reports that the Hunmanby specimen went to the Royal Scottish Museum, and that the Kilnsea bird went to the British Museum of Natural History at South Kensington.

Over the years, several sightings of apparently large, bright male Bullfinches have been claimed as probable Northerns, but not until the establishment of the Spurn Bird Observatory in 1945 did the opportunity arise to examine birds in the hand and take measurements. Even so, some are only seen in the field and assumed to be of this race; the following are on record, all from Spurn; a female on 23rd October 1964; a male from 10th to 24th April 1966; a male from 25th October to 1st November 1968; one caught on 11th November 1971 had a wing length of 94 mm; a male on 28th October 1973; a female caught on 1st May 1978 remained until 14th and two males were present on 17th December; a female caught on 27th October 1979, and different males on 27th October and on 28th-29th October, with another female from 31st October to 5th November; a female caught on 17th October 1980; and a female from 24th to 26th October 1981.

Birds have also occurred at Flamborough: a male on 15th October 1975; a male on 28th October 1976; one in late October 1979 (when another was at Grimston); two males and a female on 4th and 5th November 1980; a male and a female on 16th November 1980; and single birds on 24th March, 16th and 28th October and 13th November 1982.

Recoveries of Yorkshire-ringed Bullfinches have not shown movement other than local except for one ringed as a young male at Cantley, Doncaster, on 17th October 1965 which was retrapped at Theddlethorpe in Lincolnshire on 28th November 1965, and a juvenile ringed at Wintersett Reservoir on 9th August 1978 which was found dead at Farndon in Nottinghamshire on 27th March 1979.

The local names of Bullspink and Bully, listed by Nelson, are still used by countrymen and birdwatchers today.

Hawfinch
Coccothraustes coccothraustes

This large but secretive species was apparently far more numerous in Nelson's time than today, and he considered that it was still on the increase. He said that it had 'vastly increased of late years and extended its range northward' and listed Sheffield, Barnsley and Halifax as areas where it was breeding regularly. He also mentioned that it had greatly increased in the Aire Valley, where the first breeding was recorded in 1878, and also near Wakefield, Huddersfield, Selby and Askern. A nest found at Doncaster in 1863 was considered worthy of recording in *The Ibis* (1865), although Nelson said that it was resident in that area. It was relatively com-

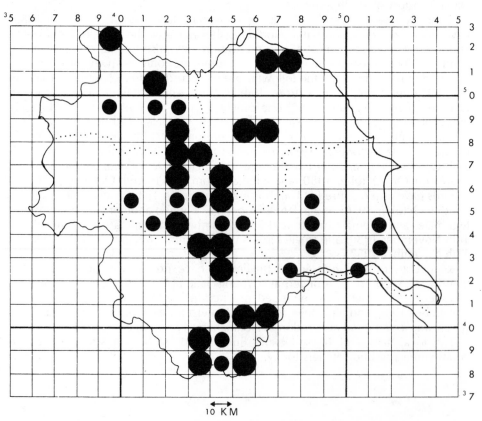

Hawfinch. The county stronghold of this very secretive species is in the area of Studley Park, near Ripon. Breeding will almost certainly take place in areas where it is not yet proven.

mon along the Pennine foothill country northwards to Bolton-by-Bowland, and was said to be fairly abundant in East Yorkshire near Patrington, Warter, Nunburnholme, Scampston and Beverley.

Colonisation as a breeding species in the North Riding, where the Hawfinch was formerly only a winter visitor, occurred at the end of the nineteenth century and Nelson said that the recent increase in Cleveland was 'very remarkable'.

The impression gained from the foregoing is one of much greater abundance than we know today and, although it is true to say that probably more Hawfinches breed in Yorkshire than we are aware of at the present time, it is certainly not common anywhere. As will be seen from the breeding distribution map compiled from the British Trust for Onithology survey during the years 1968 to 1972 and records since then, birds were present during the summer months in many areas but breeding was confirmed in only about half of these.

Hawfinches are particularly fond of yew trees, and wherever these exist they can usually be found. In 1947, Lord Bolton reported that about 20 birds stripped the yew trees of berries at Bolton Hall in Wensleydale. Studley Park, near Ripon, which is well stocked with yews, is perhaps the best place to see Hawfinches in the county and some large flocks have been found there, as follows: 20 in January 1965 and also in February 1969; 24 in December 1971; 70 in January 1973; 63 in December 1979; 64 in February 1980; and 65 in January 1982. No other locality in the county has attracted such large numbers. A few smaller flocks have been recorded: 16 fed on beech mast at Knaresborough in February and March 1971; 20 were near Leeds in the early months of 1978, with 13 in November 1980; 29 near Sheffield in 1981; and 14 at Sprotborough in March 1982. Elsewhere, flocks are small and usually of less than ten birds. A solitary Hawfinch, or small parties of two or three birds, may be seen or heard in any of the central and southern areas of the county. Oak woods are a favourite nesting habitat.

Nelson recorded 'a large colony in Cleveland' since 1897, and said that some 20 to 30 pairs bred there in comparative security. In 1902, although it was known that nearly 30 pairs were in the vicinity, only two nests were actually found, the remainder being hidden by the thick foliage; consequently, a 'swarm' of young birds eventually appeared in the local gardens and attacked the pea crops 'as soon as the pods began to fill'. The 'irate owners ... waged war on the plunderers, with the result that, up to the middle of September, no fewer than 35, young and old, were killed by means of traps, guns and bird-lime'.

The Hawfinch is a most interesting species and appears to be now well established as a breeding bird in Yorkshire, with some indication of increase and spread into new areas during more recent years.

Rufous-sided Towhee
Pipilo erythrophthalmus

On 5th September 1975, a male Rufous-sided Towhee was caught in the Warren area at Spurn Bird Observatory. It was retrapped on two occasions and remained in the area until 10th January 1976. Most of its time was spent in a large patch of buckthorn at the top of the beach behind the Warren Cottage, and many hundreds of birdwatchers were able to watch it as it fed out in the open at the top of the beach.

It had white spots on the scapulars and thus belonged to one of the western races of this common North American species. Birds showing these characters occur as far north as western Canada and a few have been recorded in the eastern states, so natural vagrancy is not impossible. The bird was, however, generally considered to have been an escaped cagebird, but there was nothing in either its condition or its behaviour to suggest such, and its true origin will never be known for certain.

The only other record for the British Isles was of one that occurred on the Isle of Lundy in June 1966, which was accepted as a genuine vagrant.

Song Sparrow
Zonotrichia melodia

The second record of this North American species in Britain and Europe, and the first for Yorkshire, came from Spurn Bird Observatory when, on 18th May 1964, G.R. Edwards heard an unfamiliar song outside the Warren Cottage. B.R. Spence was summoned and together they had good views of the bird which, from its boldly streaked plumage, they concluded was one of the American sparrows. After a short period of absence, it re-appeared at 14.00 hours near some wire traps which were baited with bread to catch Starlings. The sparrow was obviously interested in the bait and was soon caught (see plate 117).

It was weighed and ringed and a detailed description of its plumage and measurements taken before being photographed and released. It was also seen by J. Cudworth, Mr and Mrs J.H.I. Leach and Miss A. Leach among others, who all agreed as to its identity.

After its release, the sparrow spent some time in the vicinity of the Warren Heligoland trap and was retrapped there later in the day. It was not seen subsequently. Five days earlier, on 13th May, Spence had had brief views of a small reddish-brown bird in the same place, and on 17th Cudworth had obtained a similar brief view in the same general area. It is therefore likely that the bird was present from at least 13th. See *British Birds*, 1966, pp. 199-201, for full details.

White-crowned Sparrow
Zonotrichia leucophrys

This North American species was added to the Yorkshire list of birds on 22nd May 1977, only six days after the first for the British Isles had appeared on Fair Isle.

It was first seen by R.G. Hawley, I.G. Howard and D.P. Sharpe in a small poplar tree by the side of Hornsea Mere, as it preened before flying down onto the short grass, where it stayed briefly before returning to the tree. It eventually flew off through the bushes and out of sight. About half-an-hour later, it was seen again by G.C.M. Yates and R.J. Walker as it hopped about on the sloping trunk of a large willow tree at the edge of a nearby reedbed, after which it was not seen again.

White-throated Sparrow
Zonotrichia albicollis

At 10.25 hours on 12th May 1983, a cloudy day with rain and a light southeasterly wind, T.M. Clegg, M.E. Blunt and S. Hay saw a small bird fluttering in the holding area of the Warren trap at Spurn Bird Observatory. They immediately recognised it as a White-throated Sparrow and took it into the ringing laboratory, where it was examined in detail and ringed by B.R. Spence before being photographed (see plate 118).

This common North American species has been recorded in the British Isles on 12 previous occasions, all in spring.

At the beginning of the year 1893, an adult male was seen feeding with other small birds on the lawn of Holderness House in Hull. It was afterwards shot, on 13th February, and identified as this species by J. Cordeaux and confirmed by Professor Newton. Nelson concluded his remarks by saying that it 'was probably an escape from some ship while being conveyed to this country as a cage bird', a sentiment shared by H.F. Witherby in *The Handbook*. It can never be known for certain and the record is published here for completeness (see *The Zoologist*, 1893, p. 149, and *The Naturalist*, 1893, p. 113).

Dark-eyed Junco
Junco hyemalis

This common North American species, formerly known as the Slate-coloured Junco, made its appearance in Yorkshire on 3rd January 1977 when J. Hornbuckle saw one at close quarters near Rotherham.

Eight others had occurred in the British Isles up to the time of this one, and all had been seen during April and May.

Lapland Bunting
Calcarius lapponicus

Nelson considered that the paucity of records of this species in Yorkshire when compared with its wide distribution as a breeding species over the whole of northern Europe, and the fact that it frequently occurred on the island of Heligoland, was perhaps due to its being simply overlooked. It certainly is possible to overlook this small bunting, especially if one is not familiar with the call note.

Nelson could list only four instances of its occurrence in the county. One was caught at Ruswarp, near Whitby, in the spring of 1870 and the specimen went to the Whitby Museum; one was netted with Skylarks at Scarborough on 6th January 1893; and M. Bailey and J. Cordeaux saw a male close to the edge of Bempton Cliffs on 11th May 1893 and reported the occurrence in *The Zoologist*, 1893, p. 225. In November of the same year, 1893, Bailey sent word to Cordeaux that a large flock was near Flamborough village, and on going to investigate on 21st Cordeaux found the flock on barley stubble with Snow Buntings, Redpolls, Siskins and other small birds. It was estimated that there were 120 Lapland Buntings and the observers inspected them at close quarters, saying that they might easily pass over for Tree Sparrows, having similar habits of crowding on a hedge top and straggling down to feed, then flying up in a body when disturbed (*The Naturalist*, 1893, p. 356, and 1894, p. 39; *The Zoologist*, 1894, p. 4). This behaviour fits the Tree Sparrow very well and it is likely that some of the flock, if not most of it, were in fact that species. Some Lapland Buntings must surely have been present, thought, if one accepts that these two experienced observers 'inspected them at close quarters'.

Chislett could add only two further certain records when he published *Yorkshire Birds* in 1952: one seen by W.K. Richmond on the Yorkshire side of the Tees Estuary in mid winter 1936/37, and a small flock near Spennithorpe in January and February 1940 which was reported by J.P. Utley.

With regular watching at Spurn Point from the early 1950s, Lapland Buntings were detected annually, and they have occurred in the county in varying numbers each year since that time. The first records came in 1954, when one or two were seen at Gristhorpe Bay, Teesmouth and Spurn, with three on the moors between Richmond and Barnard Castle on 28th November which A. Anderson reported in *The Field* for 13th January 1955.

Counts of passing migrants along the Spurn Peninsula by J. Cudworth and others in 1956 revealed a hitherto unsuspected movement of this species when the following numbers were recorded flying south: 82 on 4th November; 230 on 15th November; 136 on 16th November; 105 on 17th November; and 80 on 1st December. That was an exceptional year and such large numbers have not been seen since.

Up to the end of the 1960s, birds were being identified at several coastal watchpoints, the largest parties being 30 at Filey, 21 at Atwick and 58 at Spurn in February 1963.

During the early part of the 1970s, numbers were generally small but were seen at several coastal localities from the Tees to the Humber. A flock of 30 was on the clifftop between Redcar and Marske during December 1973. Fraisthorpe and Barmston became known as a regular area for the species in 1975, when C.D.R. Heard and D.E. Murray located flocks of 17 on 18th February and ten on 3rd March. Up to 20 were at Filey in late October in that year, with 30 on 1st November.

More than usual appeared in 1977 when Spurn had its best autumn in recent years, with southerly movement on many October days, the maxima being as follows: 25 on 13th, 49 on 22nd and 39 on 29th; a total of 173 birds flew south on 16 days during the month. Numbers were high at other coastal places, with 14 at Atwick on 7th October, 13 at Flamborough on 13th October and 14 at Filey on 26th October.

Similar numbers occurred in 1978, with 30 at Filey on 14th January, increasing to 75 by 14th February during hard weather, and 60 on 19th. Flamborough had 30 birds on 22nd October, 51 on 11th November and 30 on 18th November.

In 1979, a large build-up in the Barmston/Fraisthorpe area during October and November peaked on 24th November when S.M. Lister counted 105 birds. I counted 60 there during the last week of December and smaller numbers were seen up to mid March 1980. There were also counts at Spurn in 1979 of 33 on 28th October; 37 on 31st; 54 on 2nd November; with a southerly movement in December when 34 passed on 8th, 27 on 15th, 17 on 22nd and 14 on 29th. Birds continued to be seen in the early months of 1980, and flocks of 20 to 40 were also seen at Flamborough, Kilnsea and Spurn up to March. A flock of 33 was at Kilnsea on 30th December 1980. Relatively few were seen during the years 1981 to 1983.

Clearly, this bird is an annual autumn immigrant, its numbers fluctuating from year to year, and must have been so in Nelson's time when it was doubtless over-looked. Birds fly south along the coast every autumn and one can confidently expect to flush a few birds from coastal stubbles, often in the company of Skylarks.

Away from the coast, Lapland Buntings are scarce. G.R. Naylor identified one at Eccup Reservoir on 9th October 1962, and the same observer saw another one there on 22nd December 1963. Single birds were on Rishworth Moor on 22nd January 1969 and on Slaithwaite Moor on 26th January 1969. J.E. Dale saw one on 6th January 1973 at Cupwith Reservoir, near Huddersfield, where he watched it on the ground at close range. Other single birds have been seen at Kexby, near York, on 19th October 1975; over Thorne Moor on 5th November 1978; on Broomhead Moor on 8th November 1981; at Fairburn Ings on 21st November 1981, where there were two birds on 29th October 1977; and one flew west over Sheffield on 13th October 1982. Single birds have also occurred at Blacktoft Sands in the Upper Humber Estuary in October and November 1974, October 1975, March 1976, October and November 1978, March, November and December 1979, February, October and November 1980 and December 1981.

P.J. Stead saw two Lapland Buntings being exhibited at a Scarborough cagebird show in the autumn of 1954 which behaved as if recently caught.

The first birds of the autumn usually appear in late September, the main influx often occurring during October. The earliest arrivals are on 5th September 1956 at Spurn; 7th September 1969 at Filey Brigg; and 30th August 1974 and 6th September 1976 at Spurn.

Most birds have departed by early April, but a few linger on to the end of the month and occasional birds have been seen in early May. A male stayed at Spurn from 31st May to 3rd June 1975.

Snow Bunting
Plectrophenax nivalis

The Snow Bunting breeds in Greenland, Iceland and Scandinavia and some visit Yorkshire every winter. As with several other species, the details given by Nelson in *The Birds of Yorkshire* indicate far greater numbers than we have records for today. He mentioned several years during the last part of the nineteenth century when large numbers occurred, and in 1881 (erroneously quoted as 1882 in *Yorkshire*

Birds, p. 61) there was 'an enormous rush extending from 14th November until the end of December.' At Teesmouth, the main arrival was during the period 23rd to 25th November and again from 6th to 10th December, many thousands of birds remaining to feed on the corn stubbles. In 1892, more than ever before were recorded at Spurn and Easington and an enormous flight also came in at Redcar on 24th November. On 31st October 1901, the sandhills at the Tees Breakwater were 'swarming with newcomers, mostly adults ...'.

In the winter of 1878/79, a large flock occurred near Leeds 'in one of the busiest parts', and in 1881 100 were killed near Huddersfield. The species occurred commonly on the Wolds, where it fed in the stubbles, and was also occasionally seen on the moors of the northwest.

The main autumn arrival usually takes place during October, but the first birds come in late September with a few earlier ones in some years. Nelson recorded one at Spurn on 26th August 1888, and the earliest in more recent years was also at Spurn, on 4th September 1976.

Flocks of up to 100 birds have been commonplace over the years from the Tees to the Humber, with larger gatherings on occasions. Coatham Sands attracted 250 birds on 21st November 1954 and 290 in January and February 1955. D.G. Bell reported a flock of up to 450 that wintered at Teesmouth in the early part of 1959. At Spurn, one of the best places for Snow Buntings in Yorkshire, 300 were present in January and 380 in December 1956; 300 on 3rd November 1957, with a count of 840 flying south between 11.40 hours and 12.45 hours on 27th December 1957 (900 were at Sunk Island on 29th December); 850 on 18th January and 700 on 10th March 1958. These high numbers during the 1950s were not repeated until the 1970s and subsequently.

The annual maxima in recent years have been as follows: 300 at Spurn on 19th November 1961; 300 at Filey on 16th November 1963; 400 at Spurn on 8th November 1962; 850 at Atwick on 8th and 9th December 1974, the first really large flock since the 1950s; up to 300 at Spurn in February 1975; 360 flew south at Spurn in the afternoon of 17th December 1977, a further 650 were in the area and a few other birds were scattered about the peninsula, giving a grand total of 1,016 birds in the general area during the day; and large numbers were again in the Spurn/Kilnsea area in December 1980, with maximum daily counts of 400 on 9th, 1,000 on 11th, 700 on 18th and 1,180 on 30th, with 500 in late January 1981.

The above figures are the maximum counts only, and several other areas had smaller numbers during the same periods and in other years. Places where flocks of around 250 birds have occurred during the last 25 years have been Patrington Haven, Withernsea, Atwick, Barmston, Bempton, Filey and South Gare.

Most birds have left the county before mid April, but a few have lingered into early May. A male sang for five minutes as it perched on a fence at Redcar on 14th March 1971.

During the early 1950s, bird-ringers at the Spurn Bird Observatory started to catch Snow Buntings in small wire traps baited with wheat and also by using small clap-nets. G.H. Ainsworth and G.R. Wilkinson played a large part in this operation, which proved very successful. In 1953, 100 were caught and ringed; 56 were trapped on 31st December 1955; 289 were caught in 1957; and in 1959, when birds did not start coming to the bait until Christmas Day, 97 had been caught by the year end.

Two males in a flock on 30th December 1952 were carrying yellow plastic rings in addition to the normal metal one, and had been so marked on Fair Isle in October and November 1950. Another Fair Isle bird was retrapped on 28th January 1956, having been ringed on 31st October 1955. A bird ringed on 30th December 1955 was retrapped in West Flanders, Belgium, on 28th November 1956, again on 11th December 1956 and eventually found dying in East Lothian,

Scotland, on 17th March 1957. A bird ringed on 5th February 1956 was found dead at Sandwick in the Orkney Islands on 25th March 1958; a young male ringed on 25th February 1956 was in Norway on 24th April 1958; a young male ringed on 26th December 1958 was in Iceland on 8th May 1959; and another young male ringed on 30th December 1959 was on Mainland, Orkney, on 14th March 1960. Several others were ringed in Lincolnshire during this period and subsequently retrapped at Spurn.

Although primarily a coastal species, occurrences inland are by no means unusual (see Nelson above) and some are recorded almost annually, their numbers often being linked to coastal abundance and activity, or being affected by the severity of the weather which forces birds to shift their feeding location.

Inland records come mainly from the high ground in the west and on the North York Moors, and small parties or single birds have occurred far too numerously to list in detail. The largest flocks, in excess of 20 birds, have been: 50 on Gorple Moors, above Hebden Bridge, from November 1942 to January 1943, with smaller numbers into February; 40 on Goathland Moor on 7th December 1947; 60 on Slaithwaite Moor on 19th November 1961; 25 at Cupwith Reservoir on 17th December 1961; 55 in two flocks at Scar House Reservoir in November and December 1962; 52 near Goodmanham on the Wolds on 2nd February 1964; 36 on Totley Moor in December 1965 and January 1966; 25 in Ribblesdale on 12th February 1966; 23 at Stagsfell, near Hawes, on 8th January 1970; 23 on Thorne Moors in two parties on 17th November 1974, on which date 15 were in the Lower Derwent Valley; 35 on Oxnup Scar above Askrigg on 18th November 1974; 20 at Malham Tarn on 7th December 1974; 40 at Redmires Reservoir on 7th January 1976; and 32 on Lofthouse Moor during heavy snow on 11th February 1978.

Some occur away from the high ground, and several single birds or small parties have been recorded at lowland gravel-pits and other similarly well-watched places. The largest flock in such a locality, apart from the Thorne Moors and Lower Derwent flocks mentioned above, was of 12 at Fairburn Ings on 3rd January 1975.

The Snow Bunting is thus a common winter visitor, chiefly along the coast, its numbers varying from year to year. Occurrences inland, mainly on the high ground, are not uncommon.

Yellowhammer
Emberiza citrinella

'One of the most abundant birds of our hedgerows and fields ...' is how Nelson described the Yellowhammer's status in 1907. He went on to say that it could be found anywhere from the cultivated parts of the extreme northwest to the coastal hedges. It is more thinly distributed in the northwestern dales than in the lowland agriculture on the plains, but occurs nonetheless right up to the heather-line.

In the autumn, Yellowhammers flock with finches and sparrows to feed in the stubbles and on wasteland, and such gatherings are often the only clue to the relative abundance of this otherwise thinly scattered breeding species. It is fond of flocking around cattle-feeding places where straw and hay cover the ground, especially during periods of snow, and also about farmyards where similar conditions exist. Flocks of 20 to 50 birds are regular during the winter months and may be encountered almost anywhere in the county. There have been flocks of up to 100 birds at many places during the last 30 years. Three places worthy of mention are Hatfield Moors, where large numbers occur in most years and have included maxima of 120 on 30th October 1965, 200 on 18th January 1975, 400 in February 1977, 300 in March 1979 and 215 in December 1981; Brotherton Ings, where there were 200 in February 1971, 550 on newly sown grass seed on 13th December 1975 with 670 on 18th, the largest assembly ever recorded in Yorkshire, 600 on 1st January 1976 with 400 on 17th, and 170 on 15th February; and near Healaugh, Tadcaster, where flocks of 200 occurred in November 1973, 370 on 24th December 1975, 240 on 1st January 1976 and 350 on 1st February 1976. Other flocks of 200 or more have occurred at the following localities: 200 at Fairburn Ings in January 1972; 200 near Harrogate in January 1973; 400 at Wintersett Reservoir from January to March 1975; 200 at High Bradfield in January 1978; 400 at Denaby Ings in February 1978; 220 at Flamborough in October 1982; and 200 in the Upper Moss Valley in October 1982. Up to 100 fed on the Humber shore at Spurn during the period 3rd to 5th January 1971.

Small numbers fly south along the Spurn Peninsula during both the spring and the autumn, mainly during the latter period, but never in numbers large enough to suggest immigration from abroad. Nelson considered it to be a 'common immigrant in the autumn during October and November', but most of the Yellowhammers along the coast at this time are doubtless moving southwards from places perhaps not too far north.

Numbers seen in the county each autumn and winter tend to fluctuate, and good years come in waves. Such periods of above-average flock sizes were in 1965, and again in 1975 and the years to the end of that decade.

Aberration of plumage is rare in this species. Nelson mentioned only two, one with white wingbars at Aldborough (*The Naturalist*, 1894, p. 284) and a pied bird at Scarborough in August 1905. On 20th June 1976, S.C. Madge, A.J. Wallis and myself watched a bird at Scalby which had all the yellow plumage replaced by pale bluish-grey, with no hint of yellow or olive; the bird resembled a Rock Bunting at times (*British Birds*, 1979, p. 80).

An immature male found dead at Hornsea on 29th September 1952 was sent by M.K. Taylor to A. Hazelwood at the Bolton Museum, who considered that it belonged to the nominate race *Emberiza citrinella citrinella*, which breeds in western, northern and some parts of central Europe. Dr J.M. Harrison agreed with the diagnosis and this was the first English record of this form at the time, although some must visit us annually and the birds breeding in southeastern England are now considered to belong to this race.

Local names for this typical country bird are numerous and Nelson listed no fewer than 20, some of which are still used in country districts. It was known as the Scribbling Lark in Nidderdale and that name is still used by the older countrymen today.

Cirl Bunting
Emberiza cirlus

The Cirl Bunting was described by Nelson in *The Birds of Yorkshire* as 'Resident; very limited both in number and distribution.' That assessment was just a little ambitious, for he was able to cite only a handful of records up to 1907. The first mention of it as a Yorkshire bird was by Neville Wood, who recorded a female shot at Campsall, near Doncaster, on 25th April 1837. In 1844, T. Allis wrote '... of the only two recorded Yorkshire specimens one was killed near Campsall Hall,

Doncaster, in 1837 ... and the other was shot near York.'

One was taken at Bolton-on-Dearne on 8th January 1881; a pair bred near Huddersfield in 1859; a nest with eggs was found near Wakefield in May 1882 and another in 1889; two were seen at Norland in 1864; it was also recorded at Wilstrop and Newton Kyme, and a nest with four eggs was found by Riley Fortune near Harrogate, a photograph of which appears in *The Birds of Yorkshire*. It was reported in 1840, 1850, 1870, 1883 and 1851 from the Richmond, Bedale, Carperby and Masham areas, and one was obtained at Fen Bog on 28th February 1882 which went to the Whitby Museum.

A Mr James Carter turned out a pair at Masham in 1886 which apparently nested and one was killed in the following year.

Some of the few subsequent records up to the publication of Chislett's *Yorkshire Birds* in 1952 are not very convincing. One near Whitby on 10th January 1918 (*The Naturalist*, 1918, p. 203) and one near Gillamoor on 3rd August 1941 (*British Birds*, 1944-45, p. 211) are perhaps acceptable.

Since 1952 there have been records claimed in seven years only, some of which are not satisfactory. The 'greenish head and dark bib of the male of a pair' near York in the spring of 1953 and published in the Yorkshire Naturalists' Union Report for that year cannot be accepted in the absence of supporting details. A record by a York schoolboy who also noted the dark chin of the male of a breeding pair near Overton in 1954 is also less than satisfactory. The record of a pair said to have bred at Beckwithshaw, near Harrogate, in 1955 is again without supporting details. The following three records are acceptable: D.R. Seaward watched a male in the Redcar Fox Covert on 17th September 1960; a male called and landed just a few feet from L.G. Dewdney and myself at Spurn on 26th April 1964 where it stayed until 30th, when it was caught and ringed; D.I.M. Wallace saw one at Seaton Ross, near Market Weighton, on 4th April 1983. The claim for a pair at Seamer Carr, near Scarborough, on 22nd October 1972 is not convincing.

The Cirl Bunting must now be termed a rare straggler to Yorkshire, either from southern England or the Continent. Close examination of bunting flocks in the autumn and winter months by experienced birdwatchers during recent years has not revealed their presence.

Rock Bunting
Emberiza cia

On 19th February 1965, an example of this south European species, which breeds in the mountain regions of Iberia and southern France eastwards into Asia, was seen at Spurn Point by J.R. Preston and shortly afterwards by B.R. Spence. It was eventually caught and ringed and stayed in the area until 10th March, giving very many observers the chance to see this very rare visitor to the British Isles.

Ortolan Bunting
Emberiza hortulana

The first Yorkshire example of this species, which breeds across Europe into Asia, was caught on board a collier off the coast in May 1822. The specimen went to the Newcastle Museum and was figured by Bewick in his *British Birds*.

One was reported near Guisborough on 16th August 1863 by Canon J.C. Atkinson (*The Zoologist*, 1863, p. 8768), who also claimed to have seen three in the same area 'fourteen or fifteen years ago'.

One was shot at Easington on 11th October 1889 (*The Naturalist*, 1890, p. 8), and a skin in the collection of S.L. Mosley of Huddersfield was labelled 'Bedale, Yorks. July 9th 1882' (*The Naturalist*, 1892, p. 3).

Chislett added four more records from Spurn which occurred singly in the years 1944 to 1947. Regular watching there from that time produced Ortolans in most subsequent years and annually since 1964. Of the 82 birds recorded from 1944 to the end of 1983, 58 have occurred in the Spurn area, 18 at Flamborough, two at Hornsea, with single birds near Scarborough, Cloughton, Guisborough and South Gare. One occurred at Tophill Low Reservoir in 1984 from 5th to 11th May. Most birds have been seen during the autumn from late August to mid October, in which period 61 have occurred, the maximum numbers in any one year being seven in 1976 and five in 1977 and 1981. The remaining 21 birds have occurred in spring during May, except for one at Flamborough on 12th April 1980 and singles at Kilnsea on 3rd June 1976 and 13th June 1982. The maximum spring numbers in any one year were three in 1969, 1980 and 1981.

Full plumage details of the first Ortolan to be caught and ringed in Yorkshire, at Spurn on 9th September 1955, are set out by R. Crossley in *The Naturalist*, 1956, p. 8.

The species can now be termed an annual passage migrant in very small numbers during both spring and autumn, being confined to the coastal region of the county.

Siberian Meadow Bunting
Emberiza cioides

This native of Siberia and Mongolia was included by Nelson in *The Birds of Yorkshire* on the strength of a generally accepted record from Flamborough Head, where one was said to have been caught in November 1886 at the foot of the cliffs, south of the Headland, during an easterly gale, by William Gibbon, a fisherman, who sold it to Matthew Bailey, the well-known naturalist and taxidermist.

In June 1888, R.W. Chase of Birmingham saw the mounted specimen at Bailey's shop in Bridlington and, when asked what it was, Bailey replied 'I don't know'. Chase purchased it from him and, on realising that it was not a known British bird, sent it to Canon H.B. Tristram who identified it as this species, which was new for Europe. He later exhibited it at a meeting of the Zoological Society on 15th January 1889, and the specimen was also examined by Professor Alfred Newton.

Seebohm remarked that it resembled the Chinese subspecies *Emberiza cioides castiniceps* more than the typical Siberian race. All the details of the occurrence were published in *The Naturalist*, 1889, pp. 79, 113, 334 and 356; in *Proceedings of the Zoological Society*, 1889, p. 6; and in *The Ibis*, 1889, pp. 293 and 295. The record was published in *The Handbook of British Birds* by H.F. Witherby.

In dismissing the record from the list of species in his *Yorkshire Birds*, Chislett gave information which had come to light over the years and he considered it unworthy of inclusion. There was certainly a desire on the part of some early naturalists and taxidermists to add new species to their lists, and it is likely that the specimen was brought in from the Far East as a cagebird. The specimen is housed in the Birmingham Museum and apparently has a bar across the forehead such as caged birds often acquire. Bailey was in the habit of publishing his annual records, but did not do so for this one until 20 months had elapsed. There was no gale meteorologically recorded for the time the bird was said to have been caught, and it is likely that the details were falsified. The record has since been deleted from the British list.

Rustic Bunting
Emberiza rustica

The Rustic Bunting breeds across northern Europe from Fenno-Scandia through Russia and Siberia, and winters in China and Japan. It has occurred in Yorkshire on nine occasions, the first of which was on 17th September 1881 at Easington. The bird was first observed on the beach close to the sea, where it was eventually captured and given to P.W. Loten of Easington who set it up for his collection. Not knowing the value of his acquisition, he did not note the sex and it remained unnamed until W. Eagle Clarke saw it on 7th October. Professor Alfred Newton confirmed the identification and exhibited the specimen at a meeting of the Zoological Society on 15th November 1881. It was an immature bird and probably a female, and the skin went to the Yorkshire Museum. (*The Naturalist*, 1881, p. 57, and 1888, p. 1; *The Zoologist*, 1881, p. 465; and *The Ibis*, 1882, p. 181)

The second record was unusual in that it was at an inland locality, at Blaxton Gravel-pits, near Doncaster, where on 14th September 1958 A.E. Platt and J. Burley noted a very light-coloured bird in a flock of Yellowhammers, Reed Buntings and House Sparrows gathered on a hawthorn hedge. The bird in question appeared to look like a white ball with a dark band running across it, and examination through a telescope revealed it to be fluffed out and preening with its head turned backwards. Full details were taken at fairly close range and the bird was identified as a male Rustic Bunting. Chislett agreed with the observers and published the record in the Yorkshire Naturalists' Union Report for that year.

The next was at Redcar on 9th and 10th May 1975, when it was seen by M.A. Blick, C.D.R. Heard and H. Mitchell. A first-year male was seen by P.A. Lassey, S. Rooke and others at Flamborough Head from 21st to 23rd May 1978; it was caught and ringed (see plate 119). P.A. Lassey saw single birds there on 4th June 1978, on

5th September 1982 and on 30th September 1983, the latter being an immature male. One was seen at Spurn from 20th to 22nd October 1982 by S.H. Holliday, S.T. Robinson, S.J. Roddis and several other observers, and G.W. Follows saw one at South Gare on 29th September 1984.

Little Bunting
Emberiza pusilla

This small bunting, which breeds from Lapland eastwards to Siberia and winters in tropical Asia, first made its appearance as a Yorkshire bird on 6th October 1913 when a male was captured at Airey Hill Farm, near Whitby. It was with a flock of Linnets and other small birds and the specimen was identified by W. Eagle Clarke (*The Naturalist*, 1913, p. 421).

One was watched in a hedge down the lane leading to New Marske Reservoir on 11th November 1967 by T. Bradbury and D.W. Wood (*The Naturalist*, 1968, p. 130).

Another was at South Gare from 3rd to 7th October 1972 which was trapped and ringed. It was examined in the hand by D.G. Bell, I. Boustead, M. Carter and others.

The fourth example was an immature bird at Spurn from 1st to 5th October 1976 which was caught and ringed on the first date by P. Flint, A. Goodman and B.R. Spence.

P.J. Dunn watched one at Filey Brigg on 30th September 1979; one was caught at Spurn Bird Observatory by J.W. Hartley and R. Spencer during a British Trust for Ornithology trainee-ringers' course on 15th October 1980; one was seen by P.A. Lassey at Flamborough on 18th May 1981; and A.M. Allport and D.G. Hobson had good views of one in a small wood on Flamborough Headland on 2nd June 1983.

That this rare bunting should have occurred in six years since 1967 is doubtless indicative of the better coverage by birdwatchers than prevailed up to the 1950s.

Yellow-breasted Bunting
Emberiza aureola

The Yellow-breasted Bunting has found its way to Yorkshire on three occasions. The first was at Spurn Point, where a male was seen on 14th and 15th June 1975 by J. Cudworth and Mr and Mrs C. Massingham.

The second was an immature bird seen at Flamborough on 5th September 1982 by P.A. Lassey and D.I.M. Wallace, and the third was also at Flamborough, where a male was seen by D.I.M. Wallace on 10th June 1984.

The species breeds from Finland eastwards through Russia and Siberia and spends the winter in tropical Asia. There are 120 accepted British records and the three from Flamborough have not, at the time of writing, been submitted to the *British Birds* Rarities Committee.

Reed Bunting
Emberiza schoeniclus

Fairly local in its distribution by virtue of its requirement of marshy areas and waterside vegetation, the Reed Bunting is nonetheless widely scattered during the breeding season in all suitable areas and is absent only on the higher moorlands of the Pennines and the North York Moors, although a few pairs may nest in these regions where marshy ground exists. Most breeding Reed Buntings leave their nesting areas in the autumn, after which they are often absent until the following spring. Nelson was of the opinion that their place was taken by immigrants, but there is no real proof of such birds arriving along our seaboard in any numbers. That many pass through Yorkshire from farther north in the British Isles is certain. A marked passage of bright 'black-headed' males can be seen during March and April in most years at sewage-farms, where they feed on the sprinkler beds, and also at gravel-pits and the like. These birds may be on their way to breeding grounds elsewhere in the county or farther north.

During the winter months, some birds attach to flocks of other buntings and finches to feed in the stubbles or on weed seeds, and during severe weather they are not averse to visiting suburban gardens, where they take advantage of the seed provided at bird tables.

Occurrences during the winter months at high altitudes among the heather on some moor-tops are most interesting and involve birds about whose origin we are not certain. A remarkable flock of 250 birds at the edge of Hawksworth Moor on 1st January 1958, when 12 inches (30 cm) of snow lay on the ground, was reported by J.C. Leedal; 60 Skylarks and 40 Snow Buntings were also present.

Other large gatherings have been as follows: 170 at Hornsea Mere in November 1960 and 150 in January 1963; 130 on Paull Holme Saltings in February 1970; 150 on Thorne Moor in October 1971; 100 at Wintersett Reservoir in December 1972; and 150 feeding on newly sown grass seed at Brotherton on 13th December 1975. Large numbers roost at Blacktoft Sands, where the highest counts have been 500 in January and February 1974; 500 during October 1974; 1,000 on 28th October 1975; 750 on 22nd December 1975; 700 on 7th January 1976 and again on 16th October 1976, with 850 on 7th November 1976; and 750 on 12th November 1978.

Other large roosting assemblies have been 200 at Wath Ings on 1st October 1975; 300 at Allerton Park during January to March 1978; 170 at Fulford Ings during January and 250 in February 1981; and 100 at Monkton on 20th January 1981.

Southerly passage along the Spurn Peninsula is recorded every autumn, and at any time from mid September to early November Reed Buntings can be seen moving. Maximum counts have been 350 on 11th October 1964 and 340 on 27th October 1964; 755 on 21st October 1966, with up to 100 on several other days; 600 on 21st October 1967, with 100 to 200 on several other days; 453 on 8th October 1973 and 335 on 24th October 1973, with 258 on 26th. Numbers have averaged fewer since that time, but up to 100 birds may pass on some days in most years. The total number of Reed Buntings passing in 1982 was 1,100 on 37 days between 11th September and early November, the most on any one day being 162 on 3rd October. Similar movement, but on a much smaller scale, is noted at other coastal watchpoints.

The few ringing recoveries showing other than local movement do not include any from outside the British Isles. A bird ringed at Bardney in Lincolnshire on 10th November 1963 was shot at Tockwith, near Wetherby, on 2nd December 1966; one ringed at Banbury in Oxfordshire on 4th November 1973 was retrapped at Wintersett Reservoir on 2nd March 1974, no doubt as a returning migrant; one ringed at Knaresborough Ringing Station on 28th January 1967 was found dead at Saxilby in Lincolnshire on 25th June 1967 (a reverse movement), and another ringed at the ringing station on 29th February 1976 was at Clifton in Nottinghamshire on 30th September 1981.

Plumage aberration is rare in this species and the only ones of which I have note are a pied bird with white crown, rump and wings seen in the reeds at Spurn by G.H. Ainsworth on 27th November 1943, and a leucistic bird seen by S. Worwood at Ripon on 8th October 1976.

Observations by R.F. Dickens at a Reed Bunting's nest at Spurn in July 1966 showed the female to have a head pattern similar to a moulting male, which it was first thought to be until the classic male bird arrived at the nest. Similar observations at a nest at Brotherton Ings in June 1954 were, at the time, construed as involving two males, as no normal female was seen. See *The Naturalist*, 1963, p. 134, for very full details.

Of its several local names, Reed Sparrow is perhaps the best known, and in general use in Nidderdale in Nelson's time and since.

Red-headed Bunting
Emberiza bruniceps

This native of the Far East has occurred in the county on several occasions since 1956. Formerly admitted to the British list, the species was deleted in 1968 after a review of the records, all of which were considered to have been escapes from captivity. It was a commonly imported cagebird up to the 1960s, and since, and most records have involved the brightly coloured males which were more popular with bird-fanciers.

All the Yorkshire records are published below for completeness and to aid future researchers in the event of a re-appraisal of the status of this large and conspicuous bunting.

The first occurred at Spurn in 1956, when one was seen from 9th to 11th September. Chislett commented in the Ornithological Report of the Yorkshire Naturalists' Union for that year that 'The bird was in perfect condition and carried no ring such as some aviculturalists use and behaved like a wild bird ...' Birds recently taken into captivity will always behave as if completely wild on regaining their freedom.

Another male, in perfect condition, was caught in the Spurn Warren trap on 19th May 1957; a male was seen at Pateley Bridge on 23rd May 1958; a male was at Knaresborough Ringing Station on 19th and 20th September 1961 which roosted with House Sparrows; another male was at Spurn from 25th to 27th May 1963; a male was at Sewerby, near Bridlington, during June 1970; and a male was at Spurn from 11th to 13th June 1976.

Once the species was taken off the British list, observers lost interest in recording any sightings and several other birds may have occurred without being reported. It seems, however, that occurrences are fewer now than during the 1950s and 1960s. The preponderance of records at Spurn is perhaps due to the likelihood of birds escaping from shipments into Hull, but it is equally likely that such wandering birds would find their way along this natural funnel, as do thousands of migrants.

It is strange that the seven reported birds have chosen to escape during the classic migration months of May-June and September.

Corn Bunting
Miliaria calandra

In his report to the British Association at York in 1844, T. Allis said of this large species 'Met with all over the county; common in most parts.' Nelson qualified this somewhat oversimplified assessment of its status by saying that some districts were much more favoured than others 'owing to its partiality to fields of high standing herbage, and particularly those in which grass, vetches, peas, beans or clover are grown'. It was scarce in the more wild and moorland tracts, but was 'not uncommon' in the cultivated districts of the northwest.

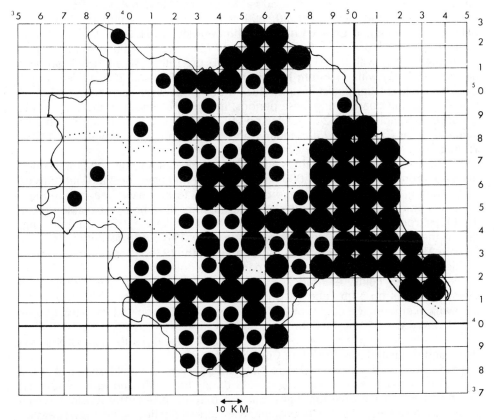

10 KM

Corn Bunting. Particularly common in the low-lying agricultural areas of the southeast and showing a tendency to spread into the foothills of the eastern Pennines.

Much the same situation applies today as the result of a spread into the eastern areas of the Pennine foothills since the middle of the present century. It is absent, or very scarce, on the high ground of the Pennines and North York Moors, but occurs on the chalk Wolds. A male singing at Scaling Dam in July 1973 was the first that D.G. Bell had heard there. It is most common in the East Riding, especially through the flat agricultural land of Holderness northwards to Scarborough, where it breeds right up to the clifftop fields.

Nelson considered that immigrants occurred along the coast during the autumn, an erroneous interpretation of the assemblies at that period which were probably no more than birds of fairly local origin flocking on suitable feeding grounds. Some Corn Buntings pass south along the coast each autumn, especially along the Spurn Peninsula, but only in very small numbers and such movement is now considered to be of a relatively local nature. A comment in the Yorkshire Naturalists' Union Annual Report for 1959, that 271 birds passing south along the Spurn Peninsula with other buntings and finches between 08.00 hours and 11.00 hours on 15th November was unique, still holds good today, for although many more than that may be seen feeding in the area very few actually pass southwards and counts of around 100 are scarce.

A flock of 50 birds at Spurn on 6th October 1949 was considered to be unusual by the editor of the county Annual Report for that year. Large flocks started to be reported during the 1970s, perhaps as the result of more intensive watching, and there have been flocks of quite spectacular proportions since that time: 900 at Spurn on 6th January 1970, with 400 next day; 200-300 on the Humber shore there from 3rd to 6th January 1971; 500 at Rosscarrs, Selby, in August 1976; 470 at Filey in January and February 1980; 600 at Kilnsea on 2nd February 1980; 350 between Welwick and Cherry Cobb on 14th February 1981; 400 at Filey on 17th January 1981, with 300 on 12th December and 650 on 25th; 400 at Spurn on 10th December 1981, with 1,000 on 14th and 800 on 19th; 250 at Atwick on 18th December 1981, with 350 from January to March 1982; and 200 at Filey on 6th January 1982. Smaller flocks of up to 150 to 200 birds were seen at several other places along the coast during these periods. In 1980, for instance, there were 120 at Kilnsea on 2nd January; 200 at Filey on 6th January; 120 at Stone Creek on 24th January; 80 at Cayton on 25th January; and 120 at Patrington Haven and 130 at Thorngumbald on 14th February.

Roosts often hold large numbers and some are used annually. The largest number away from the coast was 1,000 birds counted entering a roost at Wath Ings on 17th January 1974 by J. Hewitt, and counts of 300 to 800 have been made there since that time; in 1970, R.J. Rhodes considered 30 birds to be unusual at this locality. Other roosts have held maximum numbers as follows: 200 at Fairburn Ings during the 1970s; 300 at Denaby Ings in January 1978; 130 at Potteric Carr in January 1978; and 160 at Hornsea Mere in February 1978. There are many other smaller roosts in the south and eastern parts of the county.

On stubble fields at Tadcaster, S.M. Lister counted 240 birds with Yellowhammers on 14th February and 300 on 24th December 1975, and in the following year he made counts of 470 on 1st January, 550 on 15th January, 650 on 27th January and 850 on 1st February.

There are no ringing recoveries, other than of a local nature, to establish the origin and destinations of Yorkshire Corn Buntings.

From the records of the Yorkshire Naturalists' Union, it would appear that the Corn Bunting declined as a breeding species during the 1950s and early 1960s, and R. Chislett posed the question that pesticides may have been responsible, which doubtless they were. It is now flourishing, with spread continuing into new areas on the edges of its range, and is a common bird during the autumn and winter months, especially in the southeastern part of the county.

Nelson recorded an instance of two pure white eggs being found near Wakefield, and a nest in south Yorkshire in July 1941 contained four which were also pure white.

White, pied and cream-coloured specimens were recorded by Nelson and two aberrant birds have occurred since: a pale leucistic individual in the roost at Wath Ings in October 1976 and a white one at Filey in January 1980.

Bibliography

Allis, T. 1844. *Report on the Birds of Yorkshire*. Prepared for the British Association meeting at York in 1844, but never published. The manuscript is deposited at the Yorkshire Museum at York.

Almond, W.E., Nicholson, J.B., and Robinson, M.G. 1939. *The Birds of the Tees Valley*.

British Ornithologists' Union. 1971. *The Status of Birds in Britain and Ireland*. Blackwell Scientific Publications.

Brook, R.L. 1976. *The Aire Valley Wetlands*.

Chislett, R. 1940. Birds about a part of the southern county boundary. *The Naturalist,* 1940.

Chislett, R. 1952. *Yorkshire Birds*. A. Brown and Sons.

Chislett, R. 1958. *Birds on the Spurn Peninsula*, part 1. (Part 2 was never published.) A. Brown and Sons.

Chislett, R. 1961. A century of ornithology in Yorkshire. *The Naturalist,* 1961.

Cordeaux, J. 1872 and 1899. *Birds of the Humber District*. J. van Voorst.

Cramp, S., *et al.* 1974. *Seabirds of Britain and Ireland*. Collins.

Cramp, S., *et al.* 1977, 1980 and 1983. *The Birds of the Western Palearctic,* vols. 1, 2 and 3. Oxford University Press.

Dickens, R.F. 1960. A century of bird protection. *The Naturalist,* 1960.

Dickens, R.F., and Pickup, J.D. 1973. *Fairburn and its Nature Reserve*. Dalesman.

Dickens, R.F., and Mitchell, W.R. 1978. *Birdwatching in Yorkshire*. Dalesman.

Eagle Clarke, W. 1912. *Studies in Bird Migration*, 2 vols. Gurney and Jackson.

Fitter, A., and Smith, C.J. 1979. *A Wood in Askham: a study in wetland conservation*.

Harting, J.E. 1901. *Handbook of British Birds*, 2nd edition.

Hatfield Chronicles. 1966. *Historical Notes of Doncaster*.

Hazelwood, A. 1961. The first hundred years in brief survey. *The Naturalist,* 1961.

Hewitson, W.C. 1856. *Eggs of British Birds*. J. van Voorst.

James, H.T. 1970. The Seabirds Preservation Act 1869. *The Naturalist,* 1970.

Kendal, P.F., and Wroot, H.E. 1924. *The Geology of Yorkshire*.

Limbert, M. 1978. The old duck decoys of south-east Yorkshire. *The Naturalist,* 1978, pp. 95-103.

Limbert, M. 1982. The duck decoys of south-east Yorkshire, an addendum. *The Naturalist,* 1982, pp. 69-71.

Limbert, M., Mitchell, R.D., and Rhodes, R.J. In press. *Thorne Moors: birds and Man*.

Mead, C. 1984. *Robins*. Whittet Books Ltd.

Mitchell, W.R., and Robson, R.W. 1973. *Pennine Birds*. Dalesman.

Morris, F.O. 1879. *Letters to the Times about Birds etc*. Wm Poole.

Mosley, S.L. 1915. *The Birds of the Huddersfield District*.

Nelson, T.H. 1907. *The Birds of Yorkshire*. A. Brown and Sons.

Pashby, B.S. 1985. *John Cordeaux — Naturalist*. Spurn Bird Observatory Committee.

Rhodes, R.J. 1967. *Birds of the Doncaster District*.

Roebuck, W.D., and Eagle Clarke, W. 1881. *Handbook of the Vertebrate Fauna of Yorkshire*. Lovell Reeve and Co.

Saunders, H. 1889 and 1899. *Manual of British Birds*. Gurney and Jackson.

Seebohm, H. 1883. *British Birds*, 4 vols. R.H. Porter.

Sharrock, J.T.R. 1976. *The Atlas of Breeding Birds in Britain and Ireland*. T. and A.D. Poyser.

Sheppard, T. 1911. The Yorkshire Naturalists' Union and its work. *The Naturalist,* 1911.

Sheppard, T. 1938. W. Eagle Clarke, 1853-1938. *The Naturalist,* 1938.

Smith, S.H. 1912. *Snowden Slights, Wildfowler*.

Spencer, K.G. 1973. *Birds in Lancashire.*
Stanford, J.K. 1954. *A Bewilderment of Birds.* Rupert Hart-Davis.
Stead, P.J. 1964 and 1969. *The Birds of Teesmouth.*
Temperley, G.W. 1951. *A History of the Birds of Durham.*
Vaughan, R. 1974. *Birds of the Yorkshire Coast.*
Walker, A.F.G. 1976. *Birds in the Harrogate District.* Harrogate Naturalists' Society.
Wallis, A.J. 1956. *The Natural History of the Scarborough District,* vol. 2, pp. 372-407.
Waterton, C. 1871. *Essays on Natural History.* Warne and Co.
Witherby, H.F., *et al.* 1938-41. *The Handbook of British Birds.* Witherby.
Yarrell, W. 1843 and 1871-74. *British Birds.* J. van Voorst.
Yorkshire Naturalists' Union. 1971. *The Naturalists' Yorkshire.* Dalesman.

The following journals and magazines also contain many references to Yorkshire birds which are given in full in the text where applicable.

Annual Ornithological Reports of the Yorkshire Naturalists' Union 1940-1983.
Annual Reports of the Cleveland Bird Club.
Annual Reports of the Durham Bird Club.
Annual Reports of the Spurn Bird Observatory.
Bird Study (quarterly journal of the British Trust for Ornithology).
British Birds (monthly magazine).
The Ibis (quarterly journal of the British Ornithologists' Union).
The Naturalist (quarterly journal of the Yorkshire Naturalists' Union).
The North-Western Naturalist.
Ringing and Migration (journal of the British Trust for Ornithology Ringing Scheme).

Index of English names

Accentor, Alpine 455
Albatross, Black-browed 66
Auk, Little 376
Avocet 247

Bee-eater 412
— Blue-tailed 411
Bittern 92
— American 93
— Least 93
— Little 94
Blackbird 474
Blackcap 506
Bluethroat 459
Brambling 564
Bufflehead 172
Bullfinch 584
Bunting, Cirl 594
— Corn 601
— Lapland 589
— Little 598
— Ortolan 596
— Red-headed 600
— Reed 599
— Rock 595
— Rustic 597
— Siberian Meadow 596
— Snow 591
— Yellow-breasted 598
Bustard, Little 241
— Great 242
— Houbara 241
Buzzard 200
— Honey 181
— Rough-legged 202

Capercaillie 224
Chaffinch 563
Chiffchaff 514
Chough 549
Coot 236
Cormorant 85
Corncrake 234
Courser, Cream-coloured 251
Crake, Baillon's 233
— Little 233
— Spotted 231
Crane 238
— Demoiselle 240
Crossbill 581
— Parrot 582
— Two-barred 580
Crow, Carrion 553
Cuckoo 389
— Black-billed 390
— Great Spotted 388
— Yellow-billed 390
Curlew 299

Dipper 450
Diver, Black-throated 53

— Great Northern 54
— Red-throated 52
— White-billed 56
Dotterel 260
Dove, Collared 384
— Rock 380
— Rufous Turtle 387
— Stock 381
— Turtle 386
Dowitcher, Long-billed 292
Duck, Black 147
— Ferruginous 157
— Harlequin 166
— Long-tailed 167
— Ring-necked 156
— Ruddy 179
— Tufted 159
Dunlin 282
Dunnock 453

Eagle, American Bald 189
— Golden 203
— White-tailed 187
Egret, Cattle 98
— Great White 99
— Little 98
Eider 163
— King 165
— Steller's 166

Falcon, Eleonora's 214
— Gyr 214
— Red-footed 208
Fieldfare 476
Firecrest 519
Flycatcher, Pied 523
— Red-breasted 522
— Spotted 521
Fulmar 66

Gadwall 141
Gannet 83
Garganey 149
Godwit, Bar-tailed 296
— Black-tailed 294
— Hudsonian 296
Goldcrest 517
Goldeneye 173
Goldfinch 568
Goosander 177
Goose, Barnacle 126
— Bean 112
— Brent 129
— Canada 122
— Egyptian 130
— Greylag 119
— Lesser White-fronted 118
— Pink-footed 114
— Red-breasted 130
— Snow 120
— White-fronted 117
Goshawk 197

Grebe, Black-necked 64
— Great Crested 60
— Little 59
— Pied-billed 58
— Red-necked 62
— Slavonian 63
Greenfinch 567
Greenshank 304
Grosbeak, Pine 583
Grouse, Black 221
— Red 218
Guillemot 363
— Black 375
— Brünnich's 373
Gull, Black-headed 331
— Bonaparte's 331
— Common 334
— Glaucous 342
— Great Black-backed 343
— Great Black-headed 323
— Herring 338
— Iceland 341
— Ivory 350
— Laughing 326
— Lesser Black-backed 336
— Little 327
— Mediterranean 324
— Ring-billed 334
— Ross's 345
— Sabine's 329

Harrier, Hen 192
— Marsh 190
— Montagu's 194
— Pallid 193
Hawfinch 586
Heron, Green-backed 97
— Grey 100
— Night 95
— Purple 102
— Squacco 97
Hobby 212
Hoopoe 414

Ibis, Glossy 105

Jackdaw 550
Jay 544
Junco, Dark-eyed 589

Kestrel 207
— Lesser 206
Killdeer 258
Kingfisher 409
Kite, Black 184
— Red 184
— Swallow-tailed 186
Kittiwake 347
Knot 270

Lapwing 267

607

Index of Scientific names

Accipiter gentilis 197
— nisus 198
Acrocephalus arundinaceus 492
— dumetorum 488
— paludicola 486
— palustris 488
— schoenobaenus 487
— scirpaceus 490
Actitis hypoleucos 308
— macularia 310
Aegithalos caudatus 528
Aegolius funereus 402
Aix galericulata 135
Alauda arvensis 424
Alca torda 374
Alcedo atthis 409
Alectoris rufa 224
Alle alle 376
Alopochen aegyptiacus 130
Anas acuta 147
— americana 140
— clypeata 151
— crecca 143
— discors 150
— penelope 136
— platyrhynchos 145
— querquedula 149
— rubripes 147
— strepera 141
Anser albifrons 117
— anser 119
— brachyrhynchus 114
— caerulescens 120
— erythropus 118
— fabalis 112
Anthropoides virgo 240
Anthus campestris 434
— cervinus 438
— gustavi 436
— hodgsoni 435
— novaeseelandiae 433
— pratensis 437
— spinoletta 439
— trivialis 435
Apus apus 406
— melba 408
Aquila chrysaetos 203
Ardea cinerea 100
— purpurea 102
Ardeola ralloides 97
Arenaria interpres 311
Asio flammeus 400
— otus 398
Athene noctua 395
Aythya collaris 156
— ferina 154
— fuligula 159
— marila 161
— nyroca 157

Bartramia longicauda 301
Bombycilla garrulus 448
Botaurus lentiginosus 93
— stellaris 92
Branta bernicla 129
— canadensis 122
— leucopsis 126
— ruficollis 130
Bubo bubo 393
Bubulcus ibis 98
Bucephala albeola 172
— clangula 173
Bulweria bulwerii 70
Burhinus oedicnemus 249
Buteo buteo 200
— lagopus 202
Butorides striatus 97

Calandrella cinerea 420
— rufescens 421
Calcarius lapponicus 589
Calidris acuminata 279
— alba 273
— alpina 282
— bairdii 277
— canutus 270
— ferruginea 279
— fuscicollis 277
— maritima 280
— melanotos 278
— minuta 275
— pusilla 274
— temminckii 276
Calonectris diomedea 71
Caprimulgus europaeus 403
Carduelis cannabina 572
— carduelis 568
— chloris 567
— flammea 576
— flavirostris 574
— hornemanni 578
— spinus 570
Carpodacus erythrinus 583
Cepphus grylle 375
Cercotrichas galactotes 455
Certhia brachydactyla 538
— familiaris 537
Cettia cetti 483
Charadrius alexandrinus 259
— dubius 253
— hiaticula 256
— leschenaultii 260
— morinellus 260
— vociferus 258
Chlamydotis undulata 241
Chlidonias hybridus 360
— leucopterus 362
— niger 360
Chrysolophus pictus 230
Ciconia ciconia 104
— nigra 103

Cinclus cinclus 450
Circus aeruginosus 190
— cyaneus 192
— macrourus 193
— pygargus 194
Clamator glandarius 388
Clangula hyemalis 167
Coccothraustes coccothraustes 586
Coccyzus americana 390
— erythrophthalmus 390
Columba livia 380
— oenas 381
— palumbus 382
Coracias garrulus 413
Corvus corax 555
— corone 553
— frugilegus 551
— monedula 550
Coturnix coturnix 227
Crex crex 234
Cuculus canorus 389
Cursorius cursor 251
Cygnus columbianus 109
— cygnus 111
— olor 108

Delichon urbica 431
Dendrocopos major 417
— minor 419
Diomedea melanophris 66

Egretta alba 99
— garzetta 98
Elanoides forficatus 186
Emberiza aureola 598
— bruniceps 600
— cia 595
— cioides 596
— cirlus 594
— citrinella 593
— hortulana 596
— pusilla 598
— rustica 597
— schoeniclus 599
Eremophila alpestris 425
Erithacus rubecula 455

Falco columbarius 210
— eleonorae 214
— naumanni 206
— peregrinus 216
— rusticolus 214
— subbuteo 212
— tinnunculus 207
— vespertinus 208
Ficedula hypoleuca 523
— parva 522
Fratercula arctica 378
Fringilla coelebs 563
— montifringilla 564

Fulica atra 236
Fulmarus glacialis 66

Galerida cristata 422
Gallinago gallinago 289
— media 291
Gallinula chloropus 235
Garrulus glandarius 544
Gavia adamsii 56
— arctica 53
— immer 54
— stellata 52
Gelochelidon nilotica 352
Glareola nordmanni 253
— pratincola 252
Grus grus 238

Haematopus ostralegus 244
Haliaeetus albicilla 187
— leucocephalus 189
Himantopus himantopus 247
Hippolais calligata 493
— icterina 494
— pallida 493
— polyglotta 496
Hirundo daurica 431
— rustica 428
Histrionicus histrionicus 166
Hydrobates pelagicus 80

Ixobrychus exilis 93
— minutus 94

Junco hyemalis 589
Jynx torquilla 415

Lagopus lagopus 218
Lanius collurio 540
— excubitor 542
— isabellinus 539
— minor 541
— senator 543
Larus argentatus 338
— atricilla 326
— canus 334
— delawarensis 334
— fuscus 336
— glaucoides 341
— hyperboreus 342
— ichthyaetus 323
— marinus 343
— melanocephalus 324
— minutus 327
— philadelphia 331
— ridibundus 331
— sabini 329
Limicola falcinellus 285
Limnodromus scolopaceus 292
Limosa haemastica 296
— lapponica 296
— limosa 294
Locustella fluviatilis 485
— luscinioides 485
— naevia 484
Loxia curvirostra 581
— leucoptera 580

— pytyopsittacus 582
Lullula arborea 422
Luscinia luscinia 457
— megarhynchos 458
— svecica 459
Lymnocryptes minimus 288

Melanitta fusca 171
— nigra 168
— perspicillata 170
Mergus albellus 175
— cucullatus 174
— merganser 177
— serrator 176
Merops apiaster 412
— philippinus 411
Micropalama himantopus 285
Miliaria calandra 601
Milvus migrans 184
— milvus 184
Monticola saxatilis 471
Motacilla alba 445
— cinerea 444
— citreola 443
— flava 440
Muscicapa striata 521

Netta rufina 152
Nucifraga caryocatactes 547
Numenius arquata 299
— phaeopus 298
Nyctea scandiaca 394
Nycticorax nycticorax 95

Oceanites oceanicus 80
Oceanodroma leucorhoa 82
Oenanthe deserti 470
— hispanica 469
— oenanthe 467
Oriolus oriolus 539
Otis tarda 242
— tetrax 241
Otus scops 392
Oxyura jamaicensis 179

Pagophila eburnea 350
Pandion haliaetus 205
Panurus biarmicus 525
Parus ater 532
— caeruleus 533
— cristatus 531
— major 535
— montanus 530
— palustris 529
Passer domesticus 560
— montanus 561
Pelecanus onocrotalus 91
Perdix perdix 226
Pernis apivorus 181
Phalacrocorax aristotelis 89
— carbo 85
Phalaropus fulicarius 314
— lobatus 313
— tricolor 312
Phasianus colchicus 229
Philomachus pugnax 287

Phoenicurus ochruros 461
— phoenicurus 463
Phylloscopus bonelli 512
— borealis 508
— collybita 514
— fuscatus 511
— inornatus 510
— proregulus 508
— schwarzi 511
— sibilatrix 512
— trochiloides 507
— trochilus 515
Pica pica 546
Picus viridis 416
Pinicola enucleator 583
Pipilo erythrophthalmus 587
Platalea leucorodia 106
Plectrophenax nivalis 591
Plegadis falcinellus 105
Pluvialis apricaria 264
— dominica 263
— squatarola 266
Podiceps auritus 63
— cristatus 60
— grisegena 62
— nigricollis 64
Podilymbus podiceps 58
Polysticta stelleri 166
Porzana parva 233
— porzana 231
— pusilla 233
Prunella collaris 455
— modularis 453
Psittacula krameri 388
Pterodroma hasitata 70
Puffinus assimilis 79
— gravis 73
— griseus 75
— puffinus 76
Pyrrhocorax pyrrhocorax 549
Pyrrhula pyrrhula 584

Rallus aquaticus 230
Recurvirostra avosetta 247
Regulus ignicapillus 519
— regulus 517
Remiz pendulinus 538
Rhodostethia rosea 345
Riparia riparia 426
Rissa tridactyla 347

Saxicola rubetra 464
— torquata 465
Scolopax rusticola 293
Serinus serinus 566
Sitta europaea 536
Somateria mollissima 163
— spectabilis 165
Stercorarius longicaudus 320
— parasiticus 318
— pomarinus 315
— skua 322
Sterna albifrons 358
— bengalensis 353
— caspia 352
— dougallii 354

Yorkshire

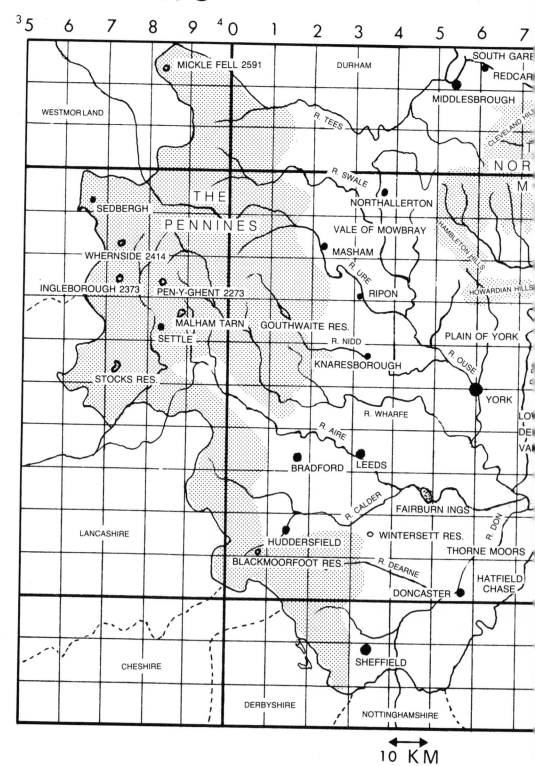

10 KM